# Scott Foresman – Addison Wesley

# ScienceInsights
## *Exploring Earth and Space*

## Teacher's Edition

## About the Authors

### *Michael DiSpezio, M.A.*
Michael DiSpezio is a science consultant who conducts workshops for educators throughout the United States. He taught and chaired the science departments of two independent schools in Cape Cod, Massachusetts. Mr. DiSpezio is a former marine biologist and a frequent contributor to NSTA journals. He currently resides in North Falmouth, Massachusetts.

### *Marilyn Linner-Luebe, M.S.*
Marilyn Linner-Luebe has been a science writer and editor since 1985. She taught physical science for fourteen years and chemistry for one year at Fulton High School in Fulton, Illinois. Ms. Linner-Luebe has a master's degree in journalism, specializing in science communication, from Boston University. She currently resides in Clinton, Iowa.

### *Marylin Lisowski, Ph.D.*
Marylin Lisowski is a professor of science education at Eastern Illinois University in Charleston, Illinois. She has taught biology, earth science, and elementary science. In addition to teaching, Dr. Lisowski leads international expeditions and field programs for high school students and teachers. Dr. Lisowski, who has been recognized as an Ohio Science Teacher of the Year, is also one of Florida's Honor Science Teachers.

### *Gerald Skoog, Ed.D.*
Gerald Skoog is a professor of science education and the supervisor of science teachers at Texas Tech University in Lubbock, Texas. Dr. Skoog has taught biology and chemistry and has been a director of several science curriculum and training projects. He served as president of the National Science Teachers Association in 1985 and 1986.

### *Bobbie Sparks, M.A.*
Bobbie Sparks is K–12 Science Consultant for the Harris County Schools in Houston, Texas. Ms. Sparks has taught science for sixteen years, including biology and middle school life and earth science. She has also supervised K–12 science teachers. Ms. Sparks is active in local, state, and national science organizations.

S F
A W

Scott Foresman
Addison Wesley

Editorial Offices: Menlo Park, California • Glenview, Illinois
Sales Offices: Reading, Massachusetts • Atlanta, Georgia • Glenview, Illinois
Carrollton, Texas • Menlo Park, California

http://www.sf.aw.com

Front cover photographs: Telegraph/FPG International (earth); Gareth Hopson for Addison-Wesley (geode); NASA/Dan McCoy/Rainbow (astronaut); Jeff Foott/Bruce Coleman Inc. (honeycomb); Telegraph/FPG International (integrated chip wafer).

Back cover photographs: Gareth Hopson for Addison-Wesley (geode); NASA/Dan McCoy/Rainbow (astronaut).

Printed in the United States of America.
Published simultaneously in Canada.

ISBN 0-201-33284-1
1 2 3 4 5 6 7 8 9 10 VH 02 01 00 99 98 97

# Teacher's Edition Contents

# Reviewers and Consultants

## Content Reviewers

**Steve Blume**
Science Teacher
St. Tammay Parish Schools
Slidell, Louisiana

**James Cole, Jr.**
Science Teacher
Clemente High School
Chicago, Illinois

**Kenneth Eiseman**
Supervisor of Science
West Chester Area School District
West Chester, Pennsylvania

**Jean Lake**
Eighth Grade Science Teacher
John Marshall Middle School
Wichita, Kansas

**Michele McCarthy**
Science Teacher
Fleming Junior High School
Los Angeles, California

**Kathie Poff**
Science Teacher
Parkhill Junior High School
Dallas, Texas

**Donna Stull**
Science Teacher
Western High School
Ft. Lauderdale, Florida

**Clive Tucceri**
Eighth Grade Science Teacher
East Hampton Middle School
East Hampton, Connecticut

## Multicultural Consultants

**Gloriane Hirata**
San Jose Unified School District
San Jose, California

**Joseph A. Jefferson**
Ronald McNair School
East Palo Alto, California

**Peggy P. Moore**
Garnet Robertson Intermediate
Daly City, California

**Modesto Tamez**
Exploratorium
San Francisco, California

# Participants

## Chapter Opener Participants

**Ellen Bonney**
Bingham Middle School
Kansas City, MO

**Francis Collins**
Neshaminy Junior High
Langhorne, PA

**Teri Dannenberg**
Thomas A. Edison Learning Center
Dallas, TX

**Martha Gilree**
Burney Harris Lyons Middle School
Athens, GA

**Barbara Hood**
Cimarron High School
Las Vegas, NV

**Rich Iwema**
Westwood Center for Health/Science
Grand Rapids, MI

**Bob Lewis**
Hanby Junior High
Wilmington, DE

**Virginia McBee**
Lyles Middle School
Garland, TX

**Michele McCarthy**
Fleming Junior High
Lomita, CA

**Debi Molina**
Park Junior High
Antioch, CA

**Jim Newman**
Carman Ainsworth Junior High
Flint, MI

**Melany Nussbaumer**
Riverside Middle School
Saluda, SC

**Nancy Paris**
Sequoyah Middle School
Edmond, OK

**Michael Petrosini**
McTigue Junior High
Toledo, OH

**Kathie Poff**
Parkhill Junior High
Dallas, TX

**Patti Pratt**
Snohomish Junior High
Snohomish, WA

**Theresa Reinke**
Richardson West Junior High
Richardson, TX

**Charles Ruble**
Rockwood South Junior High
Fenton, MO

**Linda Sciaroni**
Belvedere Junior High
Los Angeles, CA

**Marilyn Scott**
Stivers Middle School
Dayton, OH

**Vicki Taylor**
Mabelvale Junior High
Mabelvale, AR

**Bill Thorton**
Kesner Jr. High School
Salida, CO

**Pat Tobin**
St. Mary of the Annunciation School
Danvers, MA

**Clive Tucceri**
East Hampton Middle School
East Hampton, CT

**Cheryl Ulvestad**
Patrick Henry Middle School
Sioux Falls, SD

# Science Insights *Program Rationale and Goals*

**S**cience Insights *has been developed to meet the science learning needs of the early adolescent. To support the teacher in anticipating the special needs of this student, Science Insights contains a balance of features and teacher assistance that are geared to these needs.*

## *This middle school student...*

- ▶ Needs frequent **motivation** to focus attention in an increasingly distracting environment.

- ▶ Is beginning to see **integration** of ideas and processes but is still not able to generalize easily.

- ▶ Needs **activities** and hands-on experiences to channel energy and enrich learning.

- ▶ Requires special support to learn how to work with others **cooperatively**.

- ▶ Is **self-oriented** and wants to see how learning affects personal issues and the future.

- ▶ Needs special help in learning how to make **decisions** in a world that is beginning to provide more and more options.

- ▶ Students will be motivated by the dynamic and accurate **visual learning program**, the engaging writing, and the special features that speak to their interests.

- ▶ **Integration** of the sciences and of other subjects is used throughout the program.

- ▶ An active, hands-on approach to science within the student text and within other program materials is employed to involve all students and meet the needs of different learning styles.

- ▶ Teachers are provided with strategies to encourage students to work **cooperatively**.

- ▶ Emphasis on **Science, Technology, and Society** in every section shows students that science affects them and their future.

- ▶ Questioning format and activity strategies in every section encourage **decision-making** development.

Explore Visually

Themes

Cooperative Learning

Multicultural Perspectives

Portfolio

Connections

# Program Overview

**Science Insights Exploring Earth and Space**
*Student Edition*

**Science Insights Exploring Earth and Space**
*Teacher's Edition*

## Supplementary Materials
### Teacher's Resource Package

A resource of more than 700 blackline masters that can be used to review, reteach, reinforce, integrate, enrich, and assess.

▶ *Section Activities*
A comprehensive series of student worksheets that includes vocabulary and section reviews, and reteach and enrich worksheets that can be used to meet the needs of different student ability levels.

▶ *Skills Worksheets*
A series of student worksheets that stress science process skills, language arts and writing skills, and decision-making skills while reinforcing science content and concepts.

▶ *Integrated Resource Book*
Student worksheets that encourage students to explore the thematic, interdisciplinary, and intra-science connections of science concepts.

▶ *Spanish Supplement*
Spanish translations of the chapter summaries and the glossary.

▶ *Assessment Program—Chapter and Unit Tests*
Each chapter has two test versions. Chapter Test A has standard multiple-choice, true/false, and fill-in-the-blanks type questions. Each Chapter Test B is skill-based and has an extended answer format.

### Science Insights Exploring Earth and Space
### Laboratory Manual

*Student Edition*
*Annotated Teacher's Edition*

More than 30 hands-on exploratory and decision-making laboratory investigations and surveys.

### Overhead Transparency Package

Contains 96 color transparencies, 24 blackline transparencies, and the Overhead Transparency Teacher's Guide. The Teacher's Guide includes teaching strategies for using the color transparencies, overhead blackline master transparencies, and correlated student worksheets.

### Science Skills and Techniques Manual

*Student Edition*
*Annotated Teacher's Edition*

More than 50 worksheets and activities that stress basic science skills and laboratory techniques.

### Computer Software

SelecTest is a flexible test-generating computer program with a bank of more than 700 questions.

### Test File

A printed version of the test questions used in the SelecTest.

### Spaceship Earth Video

A 25-minute video that stresses connections between people, their environment, and technology. Relevant to students from its music to its message.

### Ancillary Options

Optional materials that can be used with *Science Insights Exploring Earth and Space* are:

▶ *Multiculturalism in Mathematics, Science, and Technology*

▶ *One-Minute Readings: Issues in Science, Technology, and Society*

▶ CEPUP Modules

▶ *Measuring Earthquakes*

▶ *Living Textbook:* Popular videodisc series, barcoded in the Teacher's Edition, available from Optical Data.

# See the Difference, Feel the

## From the beginning of each unit, Science Insights motivates and challenges students.

### Motivate

Dynamic color photography stimulates student interest right from the start.

### Creative ▶ Writing

Lots of opportunities for you to integrate creative writing throughout each unit.

---

UNIT

**4**

### Introducing the Unit

**Directed Inquiry**

Have students study the photograph and read the caption. Ask:

▶ How would you describe the rock formation in this picture? (Students might describe the archlike shape, the sun-baked coloration, and the smooth texture.)

▶ What is the surrounding landscape like? (Students might say that the landscape looks barren and filled with rock formations showing the same effects of wear.)

▶ What do you think the weather is like in this place? Why? (The rock formations suggest that the place is windy and has a lot of sun. The lichens and the sparse growth of leafy plants suggest lack of rain and cold temperatures.)

▶ Which of the following factors are most likely to have caused the formations in the picture: water, rain, ice, wind, people or animals, or chemical reactions. Explain why. (Wind erosion is the best candidate. Explanations will vary. Point out that the formations are above water, in an arid place, and quite massive.)

**Writing About the Photograph**

Suggest that students write what they think this area will look like in two thousand years. Remind them that the forces of wind erosion are constantly at work. Tell them to be very detailed in their descriptions.

236

## UNIT OVERVIEW

U nit 4 is an investigation of the forces of change in the earth's surface and how the changes relate to geological history. Chapter 11 presents weathering and soils. The chapter discusses weathering as the source of soil, then explains world soil characteristics and classification. Chapter 12 explores the forces of erosion, including discussion of river and stream deposition, wave erosion, ice erosion, and glaciation. Chapter 13 addresses the history of life on the earth, opening with a discussion of the theory of evolution and the classification of organisms. The chapter describes how fossils form and how to interpret fossils. The chapter closes with an examination of life through geologic time.

Unit **4**

## Changes on the Earth's Surface

*Chapters*

11  Weathering and Soils

12  Forces of Erosion

13  History of Life on Earth

# Excitement, Enjoy the Results

◄ **Data Analysis**

Develop students' science, reference, and research skills by using the Data Bank and its correlated skill-based unit and chapter questions.

**Challenge**

Challenge your students to agree or disagree with students' comments from around the country.

## Data Bank Answers

Have students search the Data Bank on pages 612 to 625 for the answers to the questions on this page.

**Interpreting a Diagram** The regolith reaches a depth of about 25 meters in the temperate climate. The answer is found on the diagram Climate and Weathering on page 613.

**Inferring** Answers will vary. Students should infer that many tributaries join with the Ganges. Also, the sloping terrain, the amount of rainfall, and the type of soil affect the amount of silt load that a river carries. Refer to the map Silt Loads of Major Rivers on page 612.

**Extension** Have students research why the Ganges has such a high silt load.

**Interpreting a Table** The Miocene epoch began about 24 million years ago. The most recent epoch is the Pleistocene. The answers are found in the table The Cenozoic Era on page 612.

**Reading a Map** The approximate silt load of the Amazon River is 1,200,000,000 tons (1200 ... The answer is found on ... Silt Loads of Major River... page 612.

**Extension** Have st... late the silt loads... shown on the ma...

**Answer to In-...**

Many years ... rainfall may ... erosion fro... on the ro...

## Data Bank

Use the information on pages 612 to 625 to answer the following questions about topics explored in this unit.

### Interpreting a Diagram

In which climate does the regolith reach a depth of about 25 meters?

### Inferring

Why do you think the Ganges River has the highest silt load shown?

### Interpreting a Table

How many years ago did the Miocene epoch begin? What is the most recent epoch?

### Reading a Map

What is the approximate silt load of the Amazon River?

The photograph to the left is of Arches National Park in Utah. How did this unusual rock structure form?

237

---

**CHAPTER 9**

### Introducing the Chapter

Have students read the description of the photograph. Ask if they agree or disagree with the description.

**Directed Inquiry**

Have students study the photograph. Ask:

► How would you describe the image in the picture? (Students may say that it looks like layers of crystals and rock around a cavity. They may also come up with more fanciful descriptions, such as a nest of precious gems.)

► What properties help you identify this object? (Students should mention such properties as color, shine, hardness, and heaviness.)

► How do you think this rock was formed? (Answers will vary. You might explain that the layers formed as water evaporated, in a way similar to the formation of stalactites.)

► What are some features that this formation has in common with all minerals? (Students may mention the crystals and the fact that it is naturally formed and not alive.)

## Chapter Vocabulary

cleavage
fracture
gem
luster
mineral

Mohs scale
ore
specific gravity
streak

184

### INTEGRATED LEARNING

**Writing Connection**

Ask students to imagine that the object in the photograph is a doorway into a special world of crystals. Have them write stories about what they see as they enter the doorway and explore. Students may wish to share their stories with the class.

## Chapter 9

### Minerals

**Chapter Sections**

9.1 Mineral Formation and Structure

9.2 Mineral Identification

9.3 Uses of Minerals

### What do you see?

"I see an amethyst cut crosswise. It was formed like all crystals, through many years. The colors are caused by different elements when it was being formed."

Eliza Bivins
Westwood Center for Health and Science
Grand Rapids, Michigan

To find out more about the photograph, look on page 206. As you read this chapter, you will learn about the composition and uses of minerals.

184

---

## Follow-Up

Questions in the Chapter Review encourage students to review or to expand their thinking about each chapter photograph.

# Integrate Learning in Every

## Science, Technology, and Society

Develop awareness of current technology and important issues in science as students learn concepts.

## Integrate Other Disciplines

Make the connections between science and other disciplines.

## Themes

Tie in themes as you integrate the sciences and various disciplines.

---

### TEACH ▪ Continued

**Directed Inquiry**

Have students study the illustrations and read the paragraphs on page 512. Then ask:

▶ How does an industrial society differ from an agricultural society in food production? (Agriculture produces food in both societies, but machines till, plant, weed, and harvest crops in an industrial society.)

▶ Which type of society uses the greatest amount of natural resources? (Industrial)

▶ How do industrial societies scar the land? (Examples include mining, clearing forests, and building factories and homes)

▶ How do food and products get to people in industrial societies? (They are shipped.)

**Critical Thinking**

**Compare and Contrast** How is an industrial society different from both a hunting-and-gathering society and an agricultural society? (Machines are used to transform natural resources into useful products. Industrial societies also use greater amounts of natural resources than the other societies.)

**Apply**

Ask students what the nearby natural habitat might be like if your school had not been constructed.

**Answers to In-Text Questions**

① Twenty years ago many of these products were not even available.

② Forested hills

**The Living Textbook:**
**Earth Science Sides 1-2**

Chapter 19          Frame 02706
Urbanization (4 Frames)
Search:                Step:

512

---

### INTEGRATED LEARNING

#### STS Connection

Ask students to name the machines that they use every day, and list these on the chalkboard. Discuss with students how their lives would change if the machines no longer existed. Have them rank the machines in order of those most often used. The students can then vote on what they think is the most useful machine on the list.

#### Math Connection

The United States makes up 4 percent of the world's population. However, it consumes 24 percent of all the world's energy. Have students make two circle graphs. One should compare the U.S. population to the world's population. The

▲ Industrial societies use far greater resources than any other type of so... are not reusable. The burning of fo... pollution. The collecting of natur... and the clearing of forests scars th... of factories and housing changes... the photograph of Hong Kong. Wh... be like if buildings had not been c...

512    Chapter 22    Humans and th...

---

### INTEGRATED LEARNING

**Class Activity**

Have students use references to find out how the evolution of marsupials was affected by geography during the Cenozoic Era. Have them prepare a bulletin-board display to illustrate where marsupials have flourished.

#### Explore Visually

Have students look at Figure 13.18, then ask:

▶ Where are the flowering plants in the picture? (On the ground; the trees)

▶ Which animals in the picture are plant-eaters? (The zebra-like, rhinoceros-like, and elephant-like animals)

▶ Where did meat-eating animals hunt? (On grassy plains)

▶ What is the biggest difference between this scene and the illustration in Figure 13.15? (Students should mention that the illustration of the Precambrian Era is made up entirely of sea life, while the organisms shown in Figure 13.18 all live on dry land.)

#### Integrating the Sciences

**Life Science** Have students do research to find out the common characteristics of mammals were better adapted to living in an era with repeated glaciation.

#### Themes in Scien...

**Scale and Structure** the structure of organisms they adapted to their enviro... organisms became smalle... became larger. The struct... isms also changed as the... evolved. For example, ce... evolved hooves.

---

**Cenozoic Era**

The era in which you now live, t... began 66 million years ago. If the M... be called the Age of Dinosaurs, the... is the Age of Mammals. The smal... in the Mesozoic Era evolved rapi... Cenozoic Era. Some became plant... and a larger body size. They gra... numbers of flowering plants. Oth... specializing in the hunting of pl...

By about 30 million years ag... the ancestors of most modern... On land, there were horses, rh... mastodons, camels, antelopes,... ocean, there were whales and...

The climate during most... been relatively cool and dry.... glaciers shaped the land. Ic... during the last 2... human spec... during... tion a...

**Figure 13.18**
**Life in the**
**Tertiary Period** ▼

Many plant-eating mammals grazed on the grassy plains that covered much of the land.

Flowering plants many different f...

**The Living Textbook:**
**Earth Science Sides 1-2**

Chapter 27          Frame 03840
Cenozoic Fossils (11 Frames)
Search:                Step:

306    Chapter 13    History of Life on Earth

# Lesson

*Integrate the Sciences*

Develop students' understanding of how the sciences are linked.
▼

## Integrating the Sciences

### Physical and Life Science
When people dive to great ocean depths, the air they breathe must have the same pressure as the surrounding water. If the pressure is less, the diver's body can be crushed by the high, surrounding water pressure. As a result of breathing high-pressure air, nitrogen becomes concentrated in the diver's blood and tissue fluids. If the pres- sure around the diver is lowered too quickly, the nitrogen can form gas bub- bles in the organs and bloodstream. This condition, known as the bends, can lead to death. To avoid the bends, deep-sea divers are raised to the surface in stages. By stopping at each stage, the body slow- ly adjusts to the lowering pressure.

## Physical Properties of Ocean Water

The physical properties of ocean water vary at different points in a water column. Look at Figure 15.3. A water column is a cross section reaching from the ocean floor to the surface at one location.

**Temperature** Only the top of the water column is directly warmed by the sun. Surface movements mix the warmed water, transferring heat downward to a depth of 100 to 400 m. Mixing makes the water about the same temperature throughout this zone. The actual surface water temperature varies. Summer sur- face temperatures are higher than those in winter.

The surface water temperature also varies from place to place. Solar energy heats ocean water the most near the earth's equator and the least at the poles. For example, summer surface zone tem- peratures range from 28°C near the equator to 2°C near the poles.

Just beneath the surface zone, the water temperature decreases rapidly. A zone of rapid temperature change is cal- led a **thermocline** (THUR moh KLYN). A thermocline forms because warm sur- face water floats on top of the colder water. The depth of the thermocline varies with location and season. Below a thermocline, the water temperature decreases only slightly.

**Density** Pure water has a density of 1 g/cm³. The density of ocean water ranges from 1.026 to 1.028 g/cm³. Salinity and temperature both affect the density of ocean water. High-salinity water is denser than low-salinity water, if the waters are the same temperature. Cold water is denser than warm water. The colder water becomes, the more closely its molecules pack together.

**Pressure** Imagine you have a bucket filled with berries. When you pour the berries out, you notice that the berries at the bottom of the bucket are squashed. Why did this happen? The combined weight of all the berries pressed down on the berries at the bottom.

A water column in the ocean behaves the same way. Deep in the water column, the combined weight of all the water above presses downward. Near the bot- tom, the pressure is much greater than near the surface. At a depth of 10 m, the pressure from the water above is about equal to the weight of a small car press- ing on an area of 1 square meter!

Warm, less dense, surface water

Thermocline

Cold, dense, deep water

Pressure increases with depth

Zone of light penetration

Ocean floor

**Figure 15.3** ▲
How do conditions change as you go deeper in a water column? ③

*Chapter 15 Ocean Water* **341**

### Skills Development

**Infer** Ask students: Why is high- salinity water more dense than low-salinity water at the same tem- perature? (There are more parti- cles, and more mass, in a given volume.)

### Class Activity

Have students work in small groups. Give each group two pieces of wood of the same kind, size, and weight; two clear con- tainers with equal amounts of water; and some salt. Have stu- dents dissolve the salt into one container of water. Have students place one piece of wood in the container of salt water and one in the container of fresh water. Have them note which piece of wood floats higher in the water. (The wood in the salt water floats higher.)

### Integrated Learning

Use Integrating Worksheet 15.1.

**Answer to In-Text Question**
③ Temperature decreases; densi- ty and pressure increase.

# Build Science and Decision-

## Activities

Laboratory activities promote hands-on science experiences.

## Cooperative Learning

Each activity is organized by task so that you can choose to use a traditional laboratory approach or assign cooperative learning groups.

## Teaching Options

Build students' understanding with a prelab discussion. Strategies and safety tips ensure safe and successful completion of each lab activity.

## SkillBuilder ▶

Enrich chapter concepts with additional skills practice and hands-on activities.

---

### TEACHING OPTIONS

**Prelab Discussion**

Have students read the entire activity. Discuss a few points before beginning:

▶ Ask students where condensation on windows and cold drink glasses comes from.

▶ Have students predict the relationship between dew point and temperature. Ask: Will a higher air temperature give a higher dew point?

---

### ACTIVITY 18

Time 20 minutes     Group pairs
Materials
15 small metal cans
15 thermometers
15 spoons
1 bag of crushed ice

**Analysis**

1. Class results will vary, depending on temperature and time of year, but students should have approximately the same values for indoor dew point.
2. Outdoor dew point values should be similar.
3. Answer will depend on time of year and indoor and outdoor temperatures. If the outdoor temperature is lower, the dew point is likely to be lower than the classroom dew point, given the same humidity indoors and outdoors.
4. Variables include: air temperature (indoor and outdoor), dew point (indoor and outdoor), temperature of the water, volume of water.
5. Accept any reasonable explanation.

**Conclusion**

Dew point is the temperature of the ice water at which condensation begins to form on the outside of the metal can.

**Everyday Application**

Answers will vary depending on time of year and temperature. When the temperature reaches the dew point, water vapor in the air will condense, forming droplets on cold surfaces.

---

### Activity 18   How can you determine the dew point?

**Skills** Measure; Observe; Compare

**Task 1   Prelab Prep**
Collect the following items: small or medium-sized metal can, warm water, crushed ice, spoon, thermometer.

**Task 2   Data Record**
1. On a separate sheet of paper, copy Table 18.2.
2. Record your observations from each location in the table.

**Table 18.2   Dew Points**

| Location | Dew Point |
|----------|-----------|
| Classroom | |
| Outdoors | |

**Task 3   Procedure**
1. Fill the can about half full with warm water.
2. Place the thermometer in the water. Position the thermometer so it doesn't touch the sides or bottom of the can, as shown in Figure 18.5.
3. Add a spoonful of ice. Watch the sides of the can for condensation as you stir the water. **CAUTION! Stir with the spoon, not the thermometer.**
4. Continue adding spoonfuls of ice, and continue stirring until condensation, or dew, forms on the outside of the can. Record this temperature as the dew point in the data table.
5. Remove the contents from the can.
6. Repeat steps 1 to 4 outdoors.

**Task 4   Analysis**
1. What is the dew point of the air in your classroom?
2. What is the dew point outdoors?
3. Compare the dew point of the air in your room to the [...]
4. List the varia[...]

5. List one reason why your dew point may not be the same as the dew point for other groups in your classroom.

**Task 5   Conclusion**
Write a short paragraph defining dew point, based on the activity you just completed.

**Everyday Application**
Find out the predicted low temperatures for your area over the next seven days. Will the temperature reach the dew point on each day? What will happen if it does? Make a line graph that plots the dew points for each day.

**Extension**
Set up a station outdoors on the school grounds to measure relative humidity and dew point. For measuring relative humidity, use wet and dry bulb thermometers. For dew point testing, set out a metal container. Check the container each morning to see if the dew point was reached the night before. Then test to find the relative humidity.

Figure 18.5 ▼

---

## SkillBuilder   Classifying

### Rock Groups

Copy the flowchart onto a sheet of paper. Use a hand lens to examine ten different rock samples that are identified with a number. Divide the ten rocks into three groups based on their texture. Record each sample number in the appropriate circle on the flowchart. Further divide the rocks in each texture group. Record the sample numbers and the characteristic you used for each new group. Compare your system of classification with the systems used by your classmates.

1. Which texture was the easiest to identify?
2. Which texture group had the most rocks?
3. What characteristics did you use for the additional groups? Why?
4. If you knew the minerals present in each rock, would you group them differently? Why?

Write a paragraph describing how a rock's physical characteristics help to identify it.

Rocks:
— Coarse-grain rocks:
  — Rocks:
  — Rocks:
— Fine-grain rocks:
  — Rocks:
  — Rocks:
— Glassy rocks:
  — Rocks:
  — Rocks:

# Making Skills

## ◀ *Consider This*

Decision-making skills are developed about issues related to science—encouraging students to write about them or debate them.

## *Consider This*

### Should Geothermal Power Plants Be Built?

Geothermal energy is another name for the earth's internal heat. Geothermal energy can be used to produce electricity for human use. In geothermal power plants, steam from water heated deep in the earth moves turbines connected to electric generators.

Geothermal power has some advantages. Unlike coal and oil, geothermal energy is constantly renewed. Compared to the cost of electricity made by burning coal or oil, geothermal power is inexpensive. Many possible geothermal sites could be developed.

There are limits to the usefulness of geothermal power. Only a few geothermal power plants have been built so far. But even if all geothermal sites were used, the power would only supply a small amount of our energy needs.

Also, geothermal power has some drawbacks. For example, the hot water contains and toxic met-

**Think About It** Is geothermal power a good alternative to burning coal and oil? Should geothermal energy be used more than it is now?

## *Career Corner* ▶

Open up a wide range of career opportunities for students.

## *Career Corner* Aerospace Worker

### Who Builds Spacecraft?

Space shuttles, satellites, and space probes gather valuable information about the solar system and the universe. Aerospace workers design, assemble, and repair these craft and the rocket boosters that launch them into space.

Aerospace employees may work on production lines, in machine shops, with engineering firms, or at space centers. Aerospace engineers design new spacecraft and the many machines that make them up. Inspectors check the quality of the crafts to make sure each

employs clerical workers, computer technicians, managers, and accountants.

The aerospace industry uses the latest technologies. Workers often specialize in a particular kind of machine. Most aerospace scientists and engineers have advanced college degrees in science or engineering. Aerospace machinists may train as apprentices or learn skills at trade schools. Mechanical drawing and blueprint reading are important skills for aero-

If you are interested in astronomy and space exploration, consider a career in the aerospace industry. Courses in science, mathematics, and shop will help you prepare for an aerospace career.

## *Historical Notebook*

### Ancient Agriculture

In prehistoric times, people hunted animals and gathered wild plants for food. But at least 18,000 years ago, people began farming. Ancient farmers poked holes in the ground with sticks and planted seeds they collected from wild grass. They farmed areas such as river deltas, where the ground was soft and easy to work. Wheat, barley, lentils, and chickpeas were grown in Africa 18,000 years ago. Corn was grown in North America 7,000 years ago. Rice began to be cultivated in Asia about 6,000 years ago.

As farming became a way of life, people developed farming technology. By 6,000 years ago, farmers were plowing their fields using animals dragging logs. About 4,800 years ago, the sickle was developed. The sickle, used for harvesting, had a curved handle made of wood or bone and a flint stone for a blade. About 3,500 years ago, metal plows began to be used.

1. Why did ancient people farm river deltas? What other areas might they have used as farm technology improved? Explain.

2. **Research** Many farmers still use sickles, plows, and other tools developed thousands of years ago. Do library research on farming techniques in other parts of the world. Write a one-page report.

## ◀ *Historical Notebook*

Focus students' attention on people in science, the evolution of scientific theories, and contributions from diverse cultures.

# **M**otivate with Features that

## *Unique page formats that draw in and engage students.*

### *Explore ▶ Visually*

Suggested teaching questions that encourage students to explore and to study the visual elements of their texts.

### *Visual Learning*

Carefully rendered and colorful illustrations work with the text to help sharpen students' understanding of science content and processes. Here, the visual helps students better understand one of the themes—Patterns of Change/Cycles.

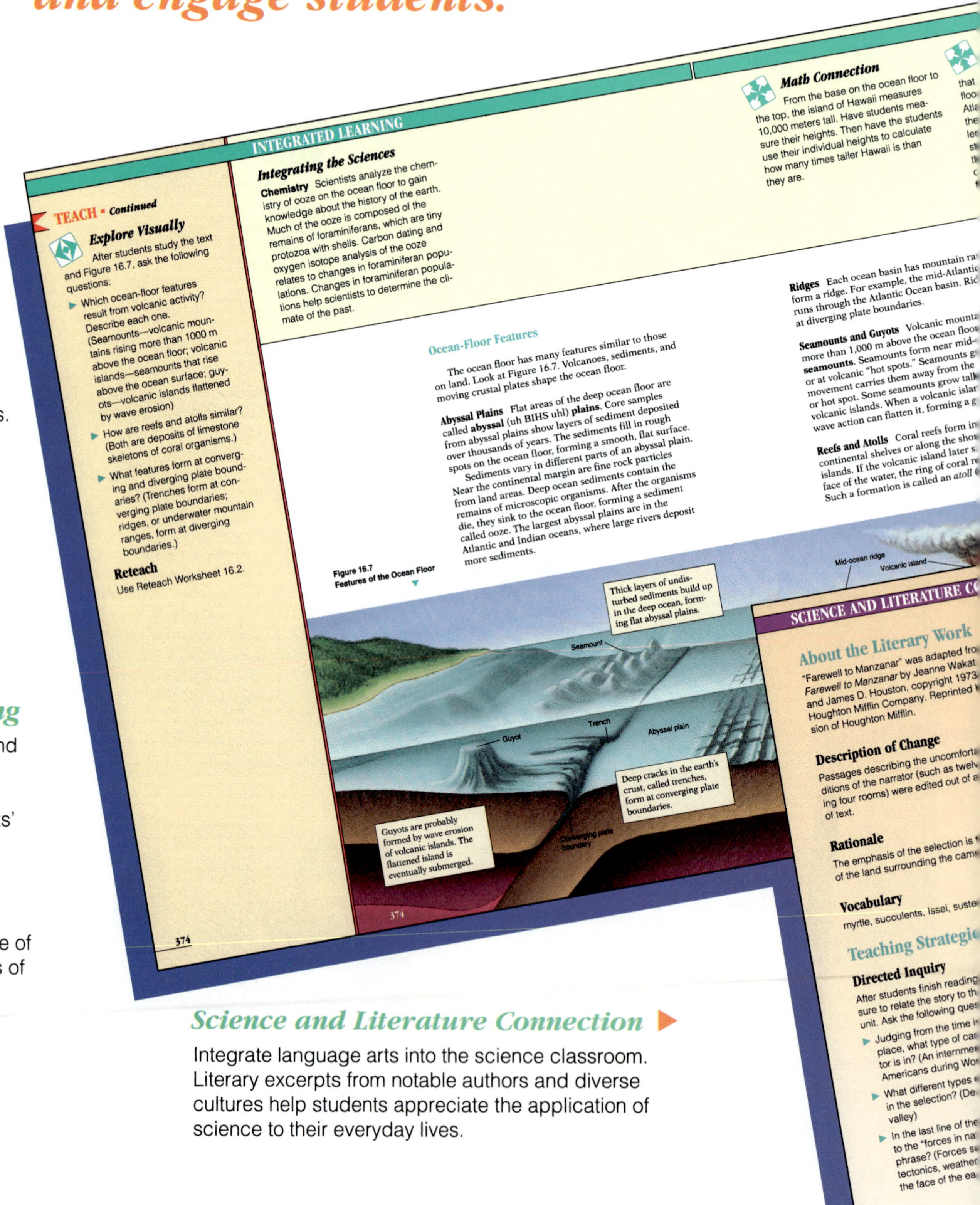

### *Science and Literature Connection ▶*

Integrate language arts into the science classroom. Literary excerpts from notable authors and diverse cultures help students appreciate the application of science to their everyday lives.

---

*[Reproduction of a teacher's edition textbook spread:]*

**INTEGRATED LEARNING**

**Integrating the Sciences**

**Chemistry** Scientists analyze the chemistry of ooze on the ocean floor to gain knowledge about the history of the earth. Much of the ooze is composed of the remains of foraminiferans, which are tiny protozoa with shells. Carbon dating and oxygen isotope analysis of the ooze relates to changes in foraminiferan populations. Changes in foraminiferan populations help scientists to determine the climate of the past.

**◀ TEACH ▪ Continued**

**Explore Visually**

After students study the text and Figure 16.7, ask the following questions:

▶ Which ocean-floor features result from volcanic activity? Describe each one. (Seamounts—volcanic mountains rising more than 1000 m above the ocean floor; volcanic islands—seamounts that rise above the ocean surface; guyots—volcanic islands flattened by wave erosion)

▶ How are reefs and atolls similar? (Both are deposits of limestone skeletons of coral organisms.)

▶ What features form at converging and diverging plate boundaries? (Trenches form at converging plate boundaries; ridges, or underwater mountain ranges, form at diverging boundaries.)

**Reteach**

Use Reteach Worksheet 16.2.

**Math Connection**

From the base on the ocean floor to the top, the island of Hawaii measures 10,000 meters tall. Have students measure their heights to calculate how many times taller Hawaii is than they are.

**Ocean-Floor Features**

The ocean floor has many features similar to those on land. Look at Figure 16.7. Volcanoes, sediments, and moving crustal plates shape the ocean floor.

**Abyssal Plains** Flat areas of the deep ocean floor are called **abyssal** (uh BIHS uhl) **plains**. Core samples from abyssal plains show layers of sediment deposited over thousands of years. The sediments fill in rough spots on the ocean floor, forming a smooth, flat surface.

Sediments vary in different parts of an abyssal plain. Near the continental margin are fine rock particles from land areas. Deep ocean sediments contain the remains of microscopic organisms. After the organisms die, they sink to the ocean floor, forming a sediment called ooze. The largest abyssal plains are in the Atlantic and Indian oceans, where large rivers deposit more sediments.

**Ridges** Each ocean basin has mountain ra[nges] form a ridge. For example, the mid-Atlanti[c] runs through the Atlantic Ocean basin. Ri[dges] at diverging plate boundaries.

**Seamounts and Guyots** Volcanic mounta[ins] more than 1,000 m above the ocean floor **seamounts**. Seamounts form near mid-[ocean ridges] or at volcanic "hot spots." Seamounts g[row] movement carries them away from the [ridge] or hot spot. Some seamounts grow tall[er. These] volcanic islands. When a volcanic islan[d] wave action can flatten it, forming a g[uyot].

**Reefs and Atolls** Coral reefs form in continental shelves or along the sho[re] islands. If the volcanic island later s[inks below the] face of the water, the ring of coral re[ef remains]. Such a formation is called an *atoll*.

**Figure 16.7**
**Features of the Ocean Floor**
▼

Thick layers of undisturbed sediments build up in the deep ocean, forming flat abyssal plains.

Mid-ocean ridge

Volcanic island

Seamount

Trench

Abyssal plain

Guyot

Deep cracks in the earth's crust, called trenches, form at converging plate boundaries.

Guyots are probably formed by wave erosion of volcanic islands. The flattened island is eventually submerged.

Converging plate boundary

374

**SCIENCE AND LITERATURE CO[NNECTION]**

**About the Literary Work**

"Farewell to Manzanar" was adapted fro[m] *Farewell to Manzanar* by Jeanne Wakat[suki] and James D. Houston, copyright 1973[, by] Houghton Mifflin Company. Reprinted [by permis]sion of Houghton Mifflin.

**Description of Change**

Passages describing the uncomforta[ble con]ditions of the narrator (such as twel[ve people shar]ing four rooms) were edited out of a [portion] of text.

**Rationale**

The emphasis of the selection is [on the beauty] of the land surrounding the cam[p.]

**Vocabulary**

myrtle, succulents, Issei, suste[nance]

**Teaching Strategie[s]**

**Directed Inquiry**

After students finish reading [, be] sure to relate the story to th[e] unit. Ask the following ques[tions:]

▶ Judging from the time [and] place, what type of ca[mp the narra]tor is in? (An internme[nt camp for Japanese] Americans during Wo[rld War II])

▶ What different types [of plants grow] in the selection? (De[sert plants in a] valley)

▶ In the last line of the [selection, what does] to the "forces in na[ture" refer to in the] phrase? (Forces su[ch as plate] tectonics, weather[ing, that change] the face of the ea[rth])

T 14

# Students Have Asked for...

## Skills Development

Reading skills and writing skills help enforce comprehension of the scientific basis in literary works.

## Activities

Additional activities further connect the science concepts and content of the literary works.

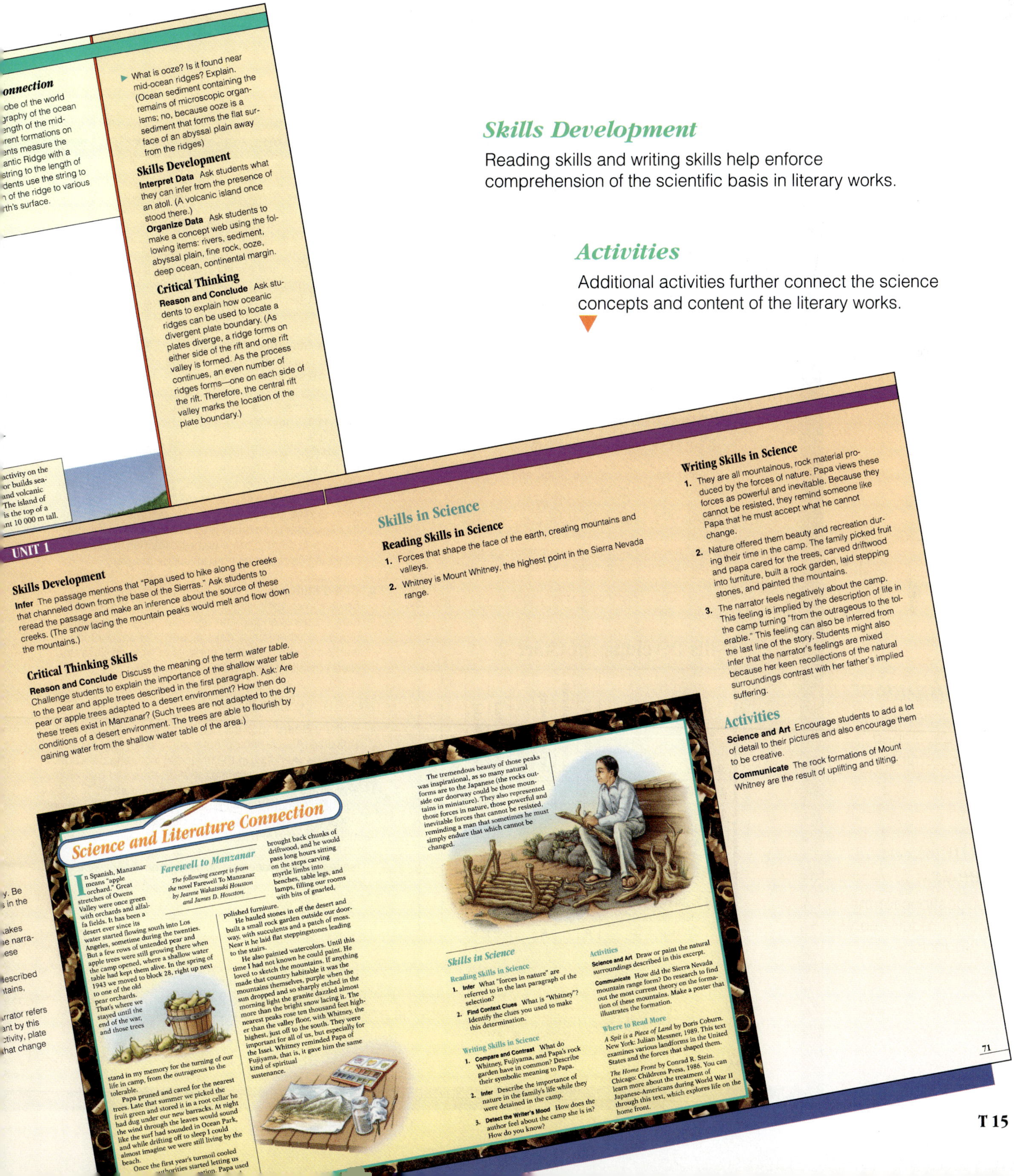

▼

---

(Inset sample page 1)

What is ooze? Is it found near mid-ocean ridges? Explain. (Ocean sediment containing the remains of microscopic organisms; no, because ooze is a sediment that forms the flat surface of an abyssal plain away from the ridges)

### Skills Development

**Interpret Data** Ask students what they can infer from the presence of an atoll. (A volcanic island once stood there.)

**Organize Data** Ask students to make a concept web using the following items: rivers, sediment, abyssal plain, fine rock, ooze, deep ocean, continental margin.

### Critical Thinking

**Reason and Conclude** Ask students to explain how oceanic ridges can be used to locate a divergent plate boundary. (As plates diverge, a ridge forms on either side of the rift and one rift valley is formed. As the process continues, an even number of ridges forms—one on each side of the rift. Therefore, the central rift valley marks the location of the plate boundary.)

---

(Inset sample page — UNIT 1)

**UNIT 1**

### Skills Development

**Infer** The passage mentions that "Papa used to hike along the creeks that channeled down from the base of the Sierras." Ask students to reread the passage and make an inference about the source of these creeks. (The snow lacing the mountain peaks would melt and flow down the mountains.)

### Critical Thinking Skills

**Reason and Conclude** Discuss the meaning of the term *water table.* Challenge students to explain the importance of the shallow water table described in the first paragraph. Ask: Are the pear and apple trees described in the first paragraph? How then do these trees exist in Manzanar? (Such trees are not adapted to the dry conditions of a desert environment. The trees are able to flourish by gaining water from the shallow water table of the area.)

---

(Inset sample page — right column)

### Skills in Science

#### Reading Skills in Science

1. Forces that shape the face of the earth, creating mountains and valleys.
2. Whitney is Mount Whitney, the highest point in the Sierra Nevada range.

#### Writing Skills in Science

1. They are all mountainous, rock material produced by the forces of nature. Papa views these forces as powerful and inevitable. Because they cannot be resisted, they remind someone like Papa that he must accept what he cannot change.
2. Nature offered them beauty and recreation during their time in the camp. The family picked fruit and papa cared for the trees, carved driftwood into furniture, built a rock garden, laid stepping stones, and painted the mountains.
3. The narrator feels negatively about the camp. This feeling is implied by the description of life in the camp turning "from the outrageous to the tolerable." This feeling can also be inferred from the last line of the story. Students might also infer that the narrator's feelings are mixed because her keen recollections of the natural surroundings contrast with her father's implied suffering.

#### Activities

**Science and Art** Encourage students to add a lot of detail to their pictures and also encourage them to be creative.

**Communicate** The rock formations of Mount Whitney are the result of uplifting and tilting.

---

(Sample student page)

## Science and Literature Connection

### Farewell to Manzanar

*The following excerpt is from the novel Farewell To Manzanar by Jeanne Wakatsuki Houston and James D. Houston.*

In Spanish, Manzanar means "apple orchard." Great stretches of Owens Valley were once green with orchards and alfalfa fields. It has been a desert ever since its water started flowing south into Los Angeles, sometime during the twenties. But a few rows of untended pear and apple trees were still growing there when the camp opened, where a shallow water table had kept them alive. In the spring of 1943 we moved to block 28, right up next to one of the old pear orchards. That's where we stayed until the end of the war, and those trees stand in my memory for the turning of our life in camp, from the outrageous to the tolerable.

Papa pruned and cared for the nearest trees. Late that summer we picked the fruit green and stored it in a root cellar he had dug under our new barracks. At night the wind through the leaves would sound like the wind through the leaves in Ocean Park, and while drifting off to sleep I could almost imagine we were still living by the beach.

Once the first year's turmoil cooled and authorities started letting us out for hikes, Papa used to hike along the creeks... brought back chunks of driftwood, and he would pass long hours sitting on the steps carving myrtle limbs into benches, table legs, and lamps, filling our rooms with bits of gnarled, polished furniture.

He hauled stones in off the desert and built a small rock garden outside our doorway, with succulents and a patch of moss. Near it he laid flat steppingstones leading to the stairs.

He also painted watercolors. Until this time I had not known he could paint. He loved to sketch the mountains. If anything made that country habitable it was the mountains themselves, purple when the sun dropped and so sharply etched in the morning light the granite dazzled almost more than the bright snow lacing it. The nearest peaks rose ten thousand feet higher than the valley floor, with Whitney, the highest, just off to the south. They were important for all of us, but especially for the Issei. Whitney reminded Papa of Fujiyama, that is, it gave him the same kind of spiritual sustenance.

The tremendous beauty of those peaks was inspirational, as so many natural forms are to the Japanese (the rocks outside our doorway could be those mountains in miniature). They also represented those forces in nature, those powerful and inevitable forces that cannot be resisted, reminding a man that sometimes he must simply endure that which cannot be changed.

### Skills in Science

#### Reading Skills in Science

1. **Infer** What "forces in nature" are referred to in the last paragraph of the selection?
2. **Find Context Clues** What is "Whitney"? Identify the clues you used to make this determination.

#### Writing Skills in Science

1. **Compare and Contrast** What do Whitney, Fujiyama, and Papa's rock garden have in common? Describe their symbolic meaning to Papa.
2. **Infer** Describe the importance of nature in the family's life while they were detained in the camp.
3. **Detect the Writer's Mood** How does the author feel about the camp she is in? How do you know?

### Activities

**Science and Art** Draw or paint the natural surroundings described in this excerpt.

**Communicate** How did the Sierra Nevada mountain range form? Do research to find out the most current theory on the formation of these mountains. Make a poster that illustrates the formation.

### Where to Read More

*A Spit is a Piece of Land* by Doris Coburn. New York: Julian Messner, 1989. This text examines various landforms in the United States and the forces that shaped them.

*The Home Front* by Conrad R. Stein. Chicago: Childrens Press, 1986. You can learn more about the treatment of Japanese-Americans during World War II through this text, which explores life on the home front.

71

# Organize Lessons at a Glance

## Two-page interleaf section with everything

### Adance Planner

Reminders about special preparations for the chapter—keyed to the page where you'll need them.

### Skills ▶ Development

An overview of the skills developed in each chapter.

### Individual Needs

Suggestions for the special requirements of students.

**CHAPTER**
**25**

### Overview

Chapter 25 discusses the characteristics, life cycles, and groupings of stars. The first section introduces the equipment used by astronomers through history. The second section explains how stars are classified, and the third section explores the life cycles of stars. The final section discusses galaxies, star clusters, and constellations.

### Advance Planner

▶ Obtain a prism and a box for TE page 588.

▶ Collect metric rulers, pencils, chalk, and masking tape for Activity 25, SE page 595.

▶ Provide thick rubber bands for SE page 602.

▶ Gather black construction paper, cardboard, pins, and glow-in-the-dark paint for TE page 603.

▶ Provide a box, black construction paper, and a flashlight for TE page 606.

### Skills Development Chart

| Sections | Communicate | Compare/Contrast | Decison-Making | Infer | Interpret Data | Make a Model | Observe | Predict |
|---|---|---|---|---|---|---|---|---|
| **25.1** Skills WarmUp | | | | | | | ● | |
| **25.2** Skills WarmUp | | | | ● | | | | |
| SkillBuilder | | | | | ● | | ● | |
| Activity 25 | ● | | | | ● | | ● | ● |
| **25.3** Skills WarmUp | | ● | | | | | | |
| Skills WorkOut | ● | | | | | | | |
| **25.4** Skills WarmUp | | | | | | | ● | |
| Skills WorkOut | | | | | | ● | | |
| Consider This | ● | | ● | | | | | |

### Individual Needs

▶ **Limited English Proficiency Students** Ask students to copy each concept in the Chapter 25 Concept Summary in their science portfolios. Have them leave space after each concept and explain it in two or three sentences. Where appropriate, students may also give examples and draw diagrams. Encourage them to use their summary when they review the chapter.

▶ **At-Risk Students** Have students work in small groups to make a constellation map. Arrange to meet on a night when the sky is clear. Have them face North and pick out a few easy-to-recognize constellations such as the Big Dipper, Cassiopeia, and the Pleiades. Have them sketch the constellations they see on a circular piece of paper starting with those right above them (in the center of the paper) and working toward the northern horizon (toward the top edge of the circle). Have them add stars they see that are not in the constellations. They should continue until they have filled in the circle. Inside the edges have them draw any obstructions such as trees and houses that kept them from seeing all the way to the horizons. Encourage them to transfer their sketches to blue or black construction paper using light ink for the stars.

▶ **Gifted Students** Invite students to learn about the objects in space that astronomers call *quasars* and *pulsars*. Students should find out what they are, how they are related to other space objects, and how astronomers learned about them. Ask students to write an illustrated report detailing their findings.

### Resource Bank

▶ **Bulletin Board** Title the bulletin board *Distances in the Universe*. Attach photographs and pictures of various objects and entities in the universe, including the earth, moon, sun, solar system, as well as stars and galaxies. Add labels to identify each. Then invite students to find out the distances from the earth to these objects and entities and their sizes. Have students make labels showing this information and add them to the bulletin board. You might want to also display a scale that correlates distances in light-seconds, -minutes, and -hours with kilometers.

584A

## CHAPTER 25 PLANNING GUIDE

| Section | Core | Standard | Enriched |
|---|:---:|:---:|:---:|
| **25.1 The Study of Stars** pp. 585–589 | | | |
| **Section Features** Skills WarmUp, p. 585 | ● | ● | ● |
| **Blackline Masters** Review Worksheet 25.1 | ● | ● | ● |
| Skills Worksheet 25.1 | ● | ● | ● |
| Integrating Worksheet 25.1 | | ● | ● |
| **Ancillary Options** One-Minute Readings, p. 108 | ● | ● | ● |
| **Color Transparencies** Transparencies 77, 78 | ● | ● | ● |
| **25.2 Characteristics of Stars** pp. 590–595 | | | |
| **Section Features** Skills WarmUp, p. 590 | ● | ● | ● |
| SkillBuilder, p. 592 | | | ● |
| Activity, p. 595 | ● | ● | ● |
| **Blackline Masters** Review Worksheet 25.2 | ● | ● | ● |
| Skills Worksheet 25.2 | ● | ● | ● |
| **Color Transparencies** Transparencies 79, 80 | ● | ● | ● |

| Section | Core | Standard | Enriched |
|---|:---:|:---:|:---:|
| **25.3 Life Cycles of Stars** pp. 596–600 | | | |
| **Section Features** Skills WarmUp, p. 596 | ● | ● | ● |
| Skills WorkOut, p. 597 | ● | ● | ● |
| **Blackline Masters** Review Worksheet 25.3 | ● | ● | ● |
| Reteach Worksheet 25.3 | ● | ● | ● |
| Skills Worksheet 25.3 | ● | ● | ● |
| **Laboratory Program** Investigation 38 | ● | ● | |
| **Color Transparencies** Transparencies 81a, 81b | ● | ● | ● |
| **25.4 Galaxies and Star Groups** pp. 601–606 | | | |
| **Section Features** Skills WarmUp, p. 601 | ● | ● | ● |
| Skills WorkOut, p. 604 | ● | ● | ● |
| Consider This, p. 605 | ● | ● | ● |
| **Blackline Masters** Review Worksheet 25.4 | ● | ● | ● |
| Integrating Worksheet 25.4 | ● | ● | ● |
| Vocabulary Worksheet 25.4 | ● | | ● |
| **Overhead Blackline Transparencies** Overhead Blackline Master 25.4 and Student Worksheet | ● | ● | |

◀ *Chapter Planning Guide*

Teaching options at a glance. Program resource materials keyed directly to section content and concepts.

Student ability recommendations help you make decisions about what materials to use to meet students' abilities and needs.

## Bibliography

The following resources can be used for teaching the chapter. See page T–46 for supplier codes.

**Library Resources**

Dickinson, Terence. *Exploring the Night Sky: The Equinox Astronomy Guide for Beginners.* Camden East, Ont.: Camden East, 1987.

Schatz, Dennis. *Astronomy Activity Book.* New York: Simon and Schuster, 1991.

Sneider, Cary I. *Earth, Moon and Stars.* Berkeley, CA: Laurence Hall of Science, 1986.

**Technology Resources**

*Internet*

**PLANETDIARY** at *http://www.planetdiary.com*
• Explore astronomy and recent events in *Astronomy/Space* (click on *Phenomena Backgrounders*) and *Current Phenomena.*

*Software*

Discover Astronomy. Win. LS.
Encyclopedia of Space and the Universe. Win. LS.
Universe. Mac, Dos, Win. LS.

*CD-ROMs*

Interactive Earth. SFAW.
An Odyssey of Discovery for Science Insights: Have students try the activity *Shadow Watch* on the Earth and Space Disk. SFAW.

*Videos*

Discovering Our Universe. 30 min. MMI.
Universe. 60 min. CABISCO.

584B

# Plan Lessons with Ease

## Science Insights works for you by organizing each section into a three-step lesson: Motivate, Teach, and Evaluate.

### Integrated Learning

Bring themes, science and subject connections, and multicultural perspectives into each lesson.

▼

### Motivate

Choose the strategy that works best for students—from skills development activities to directed-inquiry questions.

◀ ### Skills Development

Skills WarmUp and Skills WorkOut activities focus students on science skills and methods.

◀ ### Prior Knowledge

Find out how much science knowledge students bring to each chapter.

---

*Integrating the Sciences*

**Astronomy** For many years, meteorologists have researched how sunspots influence the weather. From 1987 to 1990, German meteorologist Karin Labitzke used graphs to show that the rise and fall of polar air temperature matched the increase and decrease in the number of sunspots. Scientists are continuing to investigate the connection between sunspots and weather.

*Themes in Science*

**Patterns of Change/Cycles** Air masses are in a constant state of change. The properties of air masses are determined by the part of the earth's surface over which they form. For example, a cold air mass forms over cold land areas.

**SECTION**

**19.1**

**Section Objectives**
For a list of section objectives, see the Student Edition page.

**Skills Objectives**
Students should be able to:

**Define Operationally** weather factors.

**Infer** barometric pressure differences.

**Observe** how air pressure changes affect the wind.

**Vocabulary**
air mass, cold front, warm front, stationary front, occluded front, isobar, cyclonic wind pattern, anticyclonic wind pattern

### 19.1 Air in Motion

**Objectives**

▶ **Identify** the six types of air masses.

▶ **Explain** how winds occur.

▶ **Compare** and **contrast** the four kinds of fronts that occur when air masses meet.

▶ **Infer** about the differences in barometric pressure.

▼ **ACTIVITY**

**Defining Operationally**

*Bring an Umbrella*

Imagine that a friend from out of town is coming to visit you. Your friend calls to ask about the weather in your town. What do you tell your friend? Based on your answer, make a list of the variables that make up the weather.

**SKILLS WARMUP**

▼ **MOTIVATE**

**Skills WarmUp**
To help students define the term *weather*, have them do the Skills WarmUp.

**Answer** Answers will depend on local weather conditions. Students should list several of the following variables: temperature, precipitation, humidity, air pressure, wind, sunshine, cloud cover.

**Prior Knowledge**
To gauge how much students know about the weather, ask the following questions:

▶ Why does the weather differ from one location to another?

▶ What causes rain?

▶ What causes the wind to blow?

Every time you go out, you are exposed to the outside air. Is the outside air the same every day, or different? Conditions in the outside air change often. The air may be warm or cold. It may be moving or still. It may be moist, dry, or wet with rain. The general condition of the outside air at a given time and place is called the weather. Weather includes air temperature, cloud cover, precipitation, humidity, air pressure, and air movement.

**Air Masses**

Why does the weather around you change? You are always in an **air mass** that extends into the atmosphere above you. The air mass around you changes several times during a typical month. The characteristics of an air mass, where it came from, and how it moves all affect the weather.

All weather occurs in the layer of air directly above the earth's surface. This layer, the *troposphere*, is warmed or cooled by direct contact with the earth and by convection. Look at Figure 19.1. As the sun heats the earth's surface, the heat energy warms the air above it.

When a very large amount of air sits over one location for several days, an air mass with certain characteristics forms. The air mass takes on the location's temperature and humidity. For example, a cold air mass forms over cold land areas. A moist air mass forms where water is able to evaporate into the air. A dry air mass forms over a surface without much water.

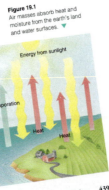

**Figure 19.1**
Air masses absorb heat and moisture from the earth's land and water surfaces.

Energy from sunlight

Evaporation

Heat    Heat

Chapter 19  Weather    **439**

439

### TEACH

#### Explore Visually

Have students study Figure 8.19. Ask:

▶ What does the number in each square represent? (The element's atomic number)

▶ What other information can you find in each square? (The element's symbol and name)

▶ What are the vertical columns in the table called? (Groups)

▶ What are the horizontal rows called? (Periods)

▶ How many groups does the table have? (18)

▶ How many periods does the table have? (7)

▶ How are the elements within a group similar? Why? (They have similar properties because their atoms have similar arrangements of electrons.)

▶ Why don't the elements 104–109 have symbols or names? (Their names are not officially assigned.)

#### Enrich

Use Enrich Worksheet 8.3.

### TEACHING OPTIONS

#### Cooperative Learning

Reproduce a periodic table and cut it apart by elements. Challenge cooperative groups to put the table back together like a puzzle. When they finish, ask them to explain the process they used to reassemble the table.

#### Portfolio

Tell students to make a list of elements, then go on an element hunt. Each time they can name a substance or product containing an element, they can put a check mark next to the element. Have students search the labels on daily vitamins, food products, plant fertilizers, and cleaning products to find elements. Tell students to keep their checklists in their portfolios.

### The Periodic Table

On these pages, you will tour the periodic table. During the tour, you will learn more about how the table is put together and learn more about how the ful. The periodic table is an important tool of earth science.

**Figure 8.19**
**Periodic Table of the Elements** ▶

**Groups**  Vertical columns are called groups. Elements within a group can have many similar properties. Their properties are similar because their similar ...

176

### STS Connection

The Keck telescope in Mauna Kea, Hawaii, is considered one of the most sophisticated telescopes in use today. However, telescope technology is advancing rapidly. The major advances are in mirror technology. The Keck telescope and others like it are considered ground-based optical infrared telescopes. There are a number of telescope projects around the world that are in various stages of implementing mirror technology. Examples include the Very Large Telescope (or VLT) project, sponsored by the European Southern Observatory, the Japanese National Large Telescope, sponsored by the National Astronomy Observatory of Japan, and the Columbus Project, sponsored by Italy, Ohio State University, and the University of Arizona.

#### Discuss

Ask students to identify the advantages of multiple-mirror telescopes over single-mirror telescopes. (They can produce larger, clearer images of distant objects; small mirrors adjust more quickly to changing temperatures; small mirrors weigh less and are easier to support.) Why must the mirrors adjust quickly to changing temperatures? (Materials shrink or expand as temperatures change.)

### EVALUATE

#### WrapUp

**Reinforce**  Have students make a chart in which they list the tools scientists use to study the stars, how each one works, and what information each one provides. Use Review Worksheet 25.1.

#### Check and Explain

1. Students should list the forms of radiant energy identified in Figure 25.2.

2. Light rays enter the telescope and are collected, focused, and reflected by the concave mirror to a flat mirror and into the eyepiece lens.

3. Similarities: Both collect visible light; both provide information on stars. Differences: Spectroscopes break up visible light into its spectrum; optical telescopes simply focus visible light.

4. As frequency increases, wavelengths decrease.

### Science and Technology
#### The Keck Telescope

For many years, the reflecting telescope at the Hale Observatory was thought to be the biggest telescope that could be built. A telescope with a mirror larger than the Hale's 5-m mirror could not be built because it would bend from its own weight. Then scientists thought of making telescopes with many separate mirrors, called multiple-mirror telescopes.

The largest multiple-mirror telescope now in use is the Keck telescope. It is located on top of Mauna Kea, an extinct volcano in Hawaii. Together, its 36 six-sided mirrors equal a single mirror 10 m across.

The small mirrors of the Keck telescope adjust to changing temperatures more quickly than a big mirror. And the lightness of the mirrors makes them easy to support. If one massive mirror was used, it would crush the mount holding it up.

The use of so many small mirrors does have some drawbacks. It is difficult to keep each one aligned so that all the mirrors work together. To solve this problem, the mirrors on the Keck telescope have computer-controlled pistons that adjust twice a second. This adjustment keeps the mirrors perfectly aligned.

With the Keck telescope, astronomers see more objects in the universe. They form clearer images of distant objects. Scientists using the telescope hope to learn more about how the first stars formed. Other powerful multiple-mirror telescopes are now being built.

**Figure 25.7** ▲
If you look closely you can see the separate six-sided mirrors of the Keck telescope.

#### Check and Explain

1. What types of radiant energy make up the electromagnetic spectrum?

2. Trace the path of light from a star through the parts of a reflecting telescope to the eye of an observer. What happens to the light at each part?

**Compare and Contrast**  How are optical telescopes ... similar? How do they differ?

**The Living Textbook:**
**Earth Science Sides 3-4**

Chapter 9                    Frame 07738
Mauna Kea Telescopes    (13 Frames)
Search:                         Step:

# Themes in Science

*Themes are like trellises—they provide support and structure. By using a thematic approach to teaching, you can help students relate science concepts to their lives, both in and out of the classroom. The goal of using themes to teach science is to help students understand the important ideas in science and the connections between those ideas.*

## Defining Themes

Using a thematic approach to teaching is not new, but different teachers may have different definitions of the word *theme*. Themes are sometimes defined as topics, such as when someone explains that the theme of a lesson is *plate tectonics*. This topical approach can be very useful to students and teachers. In this text, however, themes are defined as links between the major concepts or ideas in science. Since there are many ways to link ideas, there is no one official list of themes in science. See the chart on page T-21 for a list and descriptions of the themes used in *Science Insights*.

## Using a Thematic Approach

The volume of scientific information has grown so large that it is impossible to teach students every fact that has been discovered. Too often, though, science curricula present science as a long string of unconnected facts and activities. A thematic approach to science allows students to derive a sense of how the big ideas in science relate to one another. You may wish to use themes to help students integrate different branches of science, connect science concepts with other disciplines, or relate science to their lives and society.

While it is not necessary for students to memorize themes, it is useful to pose questions that encourage students to analyze concepts in the light of specific themes. The following is a list of some questions that can be used in classroom discussions for each of the themes used in *Science Insights*:

- ▶ **Diversity and Unity**  How are the processes that shape the earth alike? How are they different?
- ▶ **Energy**  What role does energy play in these processes? How has energy flowed through these processes?
- ▶ **Evolution**  How has the earth changed over time? How have these changes affected the living things on the earth?
- ▶ **Patterns of Change/Cycles**  How do natural cycles keep the earth's biosphere in balance? What happens when these cycles are disrupted?
- ▶ **Scale and Structure**  What are the levels of organization in the earth's internal structure? In its atmosphere?
- ▶ **Stability and Equilibrium**  What is and isn't changing in the process we are studying? What keeps the process from changing?
- ▶ **Systems and Interactions**  How do the parts of this system work together? How would changing one part of this system affect the other parts?

## Themes and *Science Insights*

Themes are often used to enhance the presentation of concepts in *Science Insights*. Material in the student text is presented thematically, with various themes weaving in and out of the prose. For example, the chapters describing plate tectonics, the forces of folding and faulting, earthquakes, and volcanoes all incorporate the theme of Energy. Teacher's Edition margin notes provide strategies for using themes that are appropriate for a particular chapter. These include references to theme that unify an entire chapter. For example, Chapter 8, which describes the structure of matter, begins with a reference to the theme Scale and Structure. Themes also relate specific concepts, as in Chapter 10 when the theme Patterns of Change/Cycles helps link ideas about different rock structures and how they change due to forces within the earth.

# *Themes in* Science Insights

Addison-Wesley's *Science Insights* series focuses on seven themes. They do not represent all possibilities.

| | |
|---|---|
| **Diversity and Unity** | Throughout the sciences, diverse kinds of structures—living and nonliving—are described. Yet, despite great diversity—such as of geological formations, diversity of life, and of chemical structures—there is unity. For example, coal, graphite, and diamond are all pure forms of carbon, yet each differs in crystal structure. |
| **Energy** | The theme of energy is the central concept to all of science. Physical and chemical changes, life processes, interactions, and the forces that change the earth's features and cause natural cycles all involve energy. |
| **Evolution** | In the most general sense, evolution can be defined as change through time. Both living and nonliving things evolve, or change over time. |
| **Patterns of Change/Cycles** | Patterns of change are an essential feature of the natural world. It is useful to understand that changes occur as trends or as cycles, and that not all changes are predictable. Trends are relatively steady patterns, such as soil forming as weathering occurs. Cycles, such as the oxygen–carbon dioxide cycle, are repeating patterns. |
| **Scale and Structure** | Scientists study the natural world at both microscopic and macroscopic levels. While much is learned by observing the smallest parts of objects, often it is necessary to observe structures as parts of systems. For example, particle size affects the amount of moisture a soil will hold, but mixtures of soils make up the seven world soil types. |
| **Stability and Equilibrium** | Stability and equilibrium refer to the ways that things do not change. All forces are balanced in a system at equilibrium. The flow of ocean currents, mineral crystal systems, and the conservation of mass in a chemical reaction are examples of stability and equilibrium. |
| **Systems and Interactions** | In science, natural systems range from the weather systems, to ecosystems, to the solar system. Within every system, there are many kinds of interactions. For example, the moon's gravity causes changes to ocean tides on the earth. |

# Thematic Matrices in Science Insights

| Theme | Chapter 1 | Chapter 2 |
|---|---|---|
| *Diversity and Unity* | All scientists, regardless of their field of study, search for knowledge about the natural world using the same basic science skills. | Topographic maps are used to map landforms on the ocean floor as well as on land. |
| *Energy* | | |
| *Evolution* | Scientific ideas about the natural world have changed over time. | Living things have adapted to conditions in the earth's diverse biomes. Certain factors, such as rainfall and temperature, determine where an organism can live. |
| *Patterns of Change/ Cycles* | Often computer models predict what may occur if current trends continue. For example, computer models have predicted population size based on the current pattern of growth. | The appearance of a surface feature on a topographic map depends on variations in elevation. |
| *Scale and Structure* | Scientists often observe the smallest parts of the earth in order to learn about the whole earth system. | The mapping of the earth begins, at the largest scale, by setting reference points on a huge sphere. All other frames of reference from which maps are produced are based on this original scale. |
| *Stability and Equilibrium* | The density of material does not change unless a phase change takes place. The smallest piece of granite has the same density as a giant granite boulder. | |
| *Systems and Interactions* | The living and nonliving substances on the earth all affect one another. Air, water, and wind change the surface features of the earth. Organisms interact with and affect the nonliving parts of the earth. | The overall view from space and the close-up view of landforms from the ground are important in understanding and mapping the earth's surface. |

| Chapter 3 | Chapter 4 | Chapter 5 |
|---|---|---|
| The similarity in composition between the earth's core and many meteorites demonstrates that matter elsewhere in the universe is made of many of the same elements that exist on earth. | The sun and the earth both formed from a spinning cloud of matter in space. | Similarities in rock types and glacial erosion of rocks are evidence of the movement of continents. |
| • The energy produced by earthquakes passes through the earth in the form of waves.<br>• Heat from the earth's core causes the asthenosphere to flow in convection cells. | | The kinetic energy of the earth's tectonic plates is a product of the earth's inner heat energy. When this inner heat energy is transferred to the asthenosphere, it flows in convection cells. |
| | The ancient earth was very different from the current earth. Most of the changes have occurred over a very long period of time. The earth is continuing to evolve. | Alfred Wegener's theory of continental drift fundamentally changed the way scientists have studied the earth's crust. |
| The circulation of convection cells in the asthenosphere affects the earth's surface. | Many changes on the earth's surface occur as part of a continuous cycle of deposition and erosion. | Patterns of change on the earth's surface are the result of the structure of the earth's crust and its dynamic processes. |
| The division of the earth into layers defines its most basic internal structure. The earth's overall structure is dependent upon each of its individual layers. | Earth scientists must consider a very long time scale in their study of the earth. The geologic time scale is different from the time scale that humans experience. | Evidence of the movement of very large landmasses is seen in the observations of smaller structures in the land. |
| The balance between temperature and pressure within the earth determines the varying states of matter that exist. | | |
| Scientists study the movement of seismic waves in order to learn more about the earth's interior, such as the physical properties of layers. | Living things interact with the physical environment, affecting the earth. Living things are responsible for many major changes that have occurred on the earth, such as the addition of oxygen to the atmosphere. | The earth's crust is composed of a system of different plates that float upon the surface and interact. Different types of interactions result in different surface formations. |

# *Thematic Matrices in Science Insights* continued

| Theme | Chapter 6 | Chapter 7 |
|---|---|---|
| *Diversity and Unity* | Different landforms can be created by similar stresses in the earth's crust. | Earthquakes, tsunamis, and volcanic eruptions are all events at the earth's surface that are triggered by stresses within the earth. |
| *Energy* | The energy of moving tectonic plates is the underlying force causing deformation of the crust. | The potential energy that is stored in the earth's crust is changed into kinetic energy during an earthquake. The energy is transferred to the surface, and can cause major changes on the landscape. |
| *Evolution* | The earth's crust has changed over time. | |
| *Patterns of Change/ Cycles* | • Patterns formed in the earth's crust by deformation help scientists learn more about the crust.<br>• When a mountain loses mass through erosion, it may uplift slightly because of increased buoyancy. | |
| *Scale and Structure* | • Younger rock layers are usually found above older rock layers.<br>• Folds in rocks range in size from microscopic to as large as a mountain. A group of small folds can become part of a much larger fold. | The strength of an earthquake is usually given in terms of its Richter magnitude. |
| *Stability and Equilibrium* | | Some parts of the earth's crust are relatively stable and earthquake-free, while other regions are under enormous stress and have many earthquakes. |
| *Systems and Interactions* | | • Scientists study evidence from the structures on the earth's surface to infer what is occurring to plates deep within the earth.<br>• Tsunamis are ocean waves that are triggered by earthquakes on the ocean floor. |

| Chapter 8 | Chapter 9 | Chapter 10 |
|---|---|---|
| All elements have different properties, but they share a basic atomic structure in which a nucleus is surrounded by one or more electrons. | Minerals are diverse in color, streak, luster, cleavage, density, and hardness, but all have a crystalline structure and a definite chemical composition. | Rocks are classified as igneous, sedimentary, or metamorphic according to their composition and how they are formed. |
| • Many chemical reactions give off some form of energy.<br>• Phase changes and changes in chemical composition both result from energy changes. | Extracting a metal from its ore requires heating the ore to a high enough temperature to separate atoms of metal from the rest of the mineral. | • Within the earth, pressure and heat may cause changes in rock.<br>• Igneous rock forms as a result of cooling molten rock. |
| | Mineral use has changed through time. People have improved the processes of mining and smelting, and have learned how to combine metals with other materials in order to make them more useful. | • Fossils are found in sedimentary rock.<br>• Rocks change over time during the rock cycle. |
| Chemical reactions cause substances to change in predictable ways. Elements combine and separate in chemical reactions according to certain patterns. | | The rock cycle is a continuous series of processes that changes one type of rock into another type of rock. |
| Matter can be broken down into increasingly smaller parts. Atoms, the smallest units of matter, are made up of subatomic particles. | • Minerals are made of elements.<br>• The properties of a mineral are determined by its crystal structure and the compounds it contains. | Sediments are small particles of rock, minerals, or remains of organisms. Sediments compact and cement together to form large sedimentary rock structures. |
| In all chemical reactions, energy is conserved. | The crystal structure of a particular mineral is always the same. Crystal structure is one of many stable patterns in the natural world. | |
| Interactions of matter form new substances during chemical reactions. | | The rock-forming process determines the rock type. Whether extrusive or intrusive rock forms depends on the rate at which magma cools, for example. |

# Thematic Matrices in Science Insights *continued*

| Theme | Chapter 11 | Chapter 12 |
|---|---|---|
| *Diversity and Unity* | There are seven different world soil types. All soils are formed from weathering and contain rock fragments, decayed organic matter, air, and water. | Deposition and erosion produce a wide variety of formations on the surface of the earth. Certain factors influence the types and rates of erosion and deposition. |
| *Energy* | Soil helps maintain the flow of energy between plants, animals, and the atmosphere. | The energy of gravity, running water, waves, moving glaciers, and wind moves sediments from place to place. |
| *Evolution* | • Thousands of years ago, people began to farm the soil and to develop farming technology.<br>• The use of soil in ceramics has become important to people's everyday lives. | The surface of the earth changes over time through the erosion and deposition of weathered rock on the earth's surface. |
| *Patterns of Change/ Cycles* | Soil bacteria are part of the global nitrogen and phosphorus cycles. | Erosion and deposition cycle materials on the earth's surface, causing changes in landforms. |
| *Scale and Structure* | | • All rivers begin with many short, steep streams that gradually merge into one long, sloping river.<br>• The movement of individual, tiny grains of sand shapes giant sand dunes. |
| *Stability and Equilibrium* | Mature soils have reached equilibrium. In a mature soil there are three horizons, each with a stable structure and a specific location in the soil profile. | The movement of material on the earth is constant due to the forces of erosion. |
| *Systems and Interactions* | Overgrazing can change grasslands into deserts by destroying plant cover, which protects soil from erosion by wind and water. | • Erosion removes weathered material from its point of origin; deposition causes the material to be laid down in new places.<br>• The energy of wind erosion begins with the sun. Wind is a form of solar energy. |

| Chapter 13 | Chapter 14 | Chapter 15 |
|---|---|---|
| During evolutionary history, living things became diverse in body structure, diet, and behavior. Yet all organisms evolved from a common ancestor. | All living things need water to survive. | The oceans and seas of the earth form one world ocean. |
| Disruptions of the rock layers at the earth's surface are caused by tectonic plate movements. These movements are caused by heat energy in the earth's interior. | • The driving force of the water cycle is heat energy from the sun.<br>• In a geyser, the earth's heat increases the temperature and pressure of groundwater, forcing it out of an opening. | • Two waves can combine to form one large wave with greater energy. Two waves can also combine to form a much smaller wave with much lower energy. |
| Both the earth's surface and the organisms living on it have undergone continuous change for billions of years. The fossil record provides evidence for how living things have changed over time. | | The world ocean has changed continuously through time in size and chemical composition. |
| • Natural selection is the process by which the traits of a species as a whole change over time.<br>• Changes in the earth's environment and movement of tectonic plates affects the evolution of living things. | • The water cycle is a closed system that moves water continuously from one place to another on the earth.<br>• During the water cycle, heat energy from the sun causes water to change phases. | • Wind direction determines the direction of surface currents.<br>• The orbit of the moon around the earth influences the patterns of the tides. This pattern is cyclic and predictable. |
| The size and the structure of organisms change as they adapt to their environments. Some organisms become smaller, while others become larger. | • The structure of the water molecule is important to water's unique properties.<br>• Rivers, streams, and runoff are narrow structures that flow into broad, low areas to create lakes or ponds. | |
| If an organism is protected from decay when it dies, it may become a fossil. | Water gains and loses heat slowly, a property that makes the water cycle possible. | • The difference in density between surface water and deep-ocean water has formed an independent stable system.<br>• The flow of ocean currents has a predictable pattern that can be mapped. |
| Radiometric dating of rocks and fossils is based on the constant rate of decay of radioactive isotopes. | Streams and rivers form drainage systems. A complex drainage system has many tributaries. Watersheds supply runoff to the streams of drainage systems. | • The pull of the moon's gravity causes the ocean waters on the earth to rise and fall against the landmasses.<br>• The Coriolis force bends winds and ocean currents. |

# *Thematic Matrices in Science Insights continued*

| Theme | Chapter 16 | Chapter 17 |
|---|---|---|
| *Diversity and Unity* | The land formations on the ocean floor are as diverse as those on the earth's surface. Many of the structures present on the earth's surface can be observed on the ocean floor. | Each layer of the atmosphere influences the conditions of the entire atmosphere. |
| *Energy* | • The amount of energy in a habitat determines the types of organisms that can live there. <br> • A food chain transfers energy throughout an ecosystem. | The energy contained in the gas molecules in air determines the pressure and temperature of air. |
| *Evolution* | The varied conditions in the world ocean produce many different habitats for ocean organisms. Some organisms have adapted to extreme conditions in the ocean. | The earth's current atmosphere is very different from the ancient atmosphere. The earth's atmosphere continues to evolve. |
| *Patterns of Change/ Cycles* | | Atmospheric gases continuously pass through the oxygen–carbon dioxide cycle and the nitrogen cycle. |
| *Scale and Structure* | | The atmosphere is divided into layers, each defined by composition, height from the surface, and temperature. |
| *Stability and Equilibrium* | • Vessels used in deep-ocean locations must maintain stable internal conditions despite tremendous pressure changes. <br> • Subduction balances the plate-spreading that occurs at the mid-ocean ridges. | The oxygen–carbon dioxide cycle keeps carbon levels constant. Nitrogen fixation and deposition in the nitrogen cycle keep nitrogen levels constant. |
| *Systems and Interactions* | The interactions at plate boundaries form subduction zones. Subduction zones create deep ocean trenches and volcanoes. | A change in one part of the atmosphere affects all other parts. |

| Chapter 18 | Chapter 19 | Chapter 20 |
|---|---|---|
| Precipitation has a variety of forms, all of which are types of moisture that fall to the ground from the atmosphere. | Six different types of air masses interact at four different kinds of fronts. | Although separated by great geographical distance, some areas of the world have similar climates. Their plant and animal life also share similar characteristics. |
| Evaporation requires energy, which is generally absorbed from the surrounding air. | Every type of weather occurs because the sun's energy keeps the atmosphere in constant motion. | The changing distribution of energy from the sun is related to changes in the climate on the earth. |
| Organisms have adaptations that enable them to survive in regions that are either extremely humid or extremely dry. | | • Over time, organisms adapt to the climate in which they live in order to survive.<br>• The world's climate has changed gradually over time. |
| | • Air masses are in a constant state of change.<br>• Winds move from an area of high pressure to an area of low pressure. | • A change in an ocean current can cause climatic changes on a global scale.<br>• Scientists hypothesize that ice ages occur in cycles. |
| Clouds are made up of microscopic water vapor molecules that condense to tiny droplets. A great number of droplets may collide and collect as precipitation. | Large-scale and small-scale atmospheric changes are caused by the interaction of air masses. | |
| | The world's winds are part of a global system of air circulation that keeps world temperatures in balance. | The stability of climates has enabled scientists to classify the regions of the world into climate zones. Each climate zone has a relatively consistent temperature range and amount of precipitation. |
| The technology of water-delivery systems influences where people settle. | The differences in air pressure that cause winds are in turn caused by differences in air temperature. Temperature differences exist because the sun heats the earth unevenly. | • Temperature and precipitation are two major factors that determine a region's climate.<br>• Topography and prevailing winds interact to dictate the amount of precipitation an area receives. |

# *Thematic Matrices in Science Insights* continued

| Theme | Chapter 21 | Chapter 22 |
|---|---|---|
| *Diversity and Unity* | Energy resources as diverse as hydro-electricity, nuclear fission, windmills, and geothermal wells all produce electricity by driving turbines. | |
| *Energy* | The primary energy source is the sun. Energy from the sun produced the organic compounds in once-living organisms. The stored energy of these organisms may become fossil fuels. | • Agricultural societies can stay in one place because of a constant food supply.<br>• Industrial societies use the greatest amounts of natural resources for their energy needs. |
| *Evolution* | | The oldest way of living on the earth has been practiced by people in hunting-and-gathering societies for thousands of years. Few hunting-and-gathering societies exist today. |
| *Patterns of Change/ Cycles* | • Areas where underground coal deposits exist today were swampy and warm millions of years ago.<br>• Petroleum formed from the remains of plants and animals that lived hundreds of years ago in the oceans. | The way humans use technology to meet their needs can cause changes in the earth's natural cycles. |
| *Scale and Structure* | | |
| *Stability and Equilibrium* | Reclamation is the process of returning a site to its former condition. | • Organisms are linked together in food webs. The loss of even one species affects other organisms.<br>• Human activities affect the stability of the earth's land, water, and air. |
| *Systems and Interactions* | Power sources are energy-changing systems. Nuclear fission converts energy from uranium atoms to heat, or kinetic energy. Steam turbines in generators convert the kinetic energy to electricity. | Humans depend upon systems in the environment for survival. The interaction of humans with the environment affects the flow of materials and energy through the environment. |

| Chapter 23 | Chapter 24 | Chapter 25 |
|---|---|---|
| | Each of the structures in the solar system has unique features. All of the bodies in the solar system were created from the original gas and dust that produced the sun. | • All stars come into being in nebulae, and are classified into four groups.<br>• Stars vary greatly in size and mass. |
| Sunlight reflects off the surface of the moon, creating lunar phases. | • The sun's energy is produced by nuclear fusion reactions and is necessary to maintain life on Earth.<br>• The sun is the original source of most energy used on Earth. | • Stars produce many different types of electromagnetic wave energy.<br>• Over the course of a star's life, the transfer of energy occurs through conduction, convection, and radiation. |
| Some scientists theorize that the moon evolved from material knocked from Earth during a powerful impact. Earth's gravity then captured and collected the material. | The universe has changed throughout its history. Gases clumped together to form stars and planets. The stars and planets evolved to form solar systems. | Stellar evolution occurs over millions of years. Ideas about the process of stellar evolution continue to change. |
| • The number of hours of daylight is determined by the solstice and the equinox.<br>• The cycle of Earth orbiting the sun corresponds to life-cycle changes in organisms. | Daily cycles in living things correspond to cycles of available sunlight. | • Observation of the light spectrums of other galaxies has shown that the universe is expanding.<br>• Stars have life cycles, during which they go through many changes. |
| The study of Earth is carried out at many different scales. One way that space scientists study the planet Earth is by comparing it to other large bodies in the solar system. | The smaller bodies of the solar system follow the same laws of motion as the larger bodies. | Scientists must use a special unit of measurement called a light-year to measure the great distances between stars. |
| The gravitational interaction between Earth and the moon produced the relatively stable Earth-Moon system. | The planets follow regular elliptical orbits around the sun that are stable and predictable. | |
| • The tilt of Earth's axis causes seasons.<br>• An eclipse occurs when one planet passes between the sun and another body. | | |

# Skills in Science

*The study of science involves more than the absorption of information. Inquiry, investigation, and discovery are also part of a scientist's work. Educators have observed that students need to develop process skills and critical thinking skills as they study science. By developing skills as well as concepts, students will be prepared for life both in and out of the classroom.*

As students use process skills, they will also use particular critical thinking skills and a pattern may emerge linking these two types of skills.

**Observe** Observing is a skill that is fundamental to all learning. As students study science, they need to extend their senses using tools such as microscopes or hand lenses.

**Classify** Classifying is the grouping of objects or events according to an established scheme. When classifying, students should be able to perceive similarities and differences among objects. Classifying is both a critical thinking skill and a process skill.

**Infer** When students infer, they make evaluations and judgements based on past experiences. The skill of inferring may involve identifying cause-and-effect relationships from events observed, identifying the limits of inferences, and testing the validity of inferences. Inferring also relates to the critical thinking skills Find Causes and Reason and Conclude.

**Predict** When students predict, they formulate an expected result based on past experience. Students learn that it takes repeated observations of an event to predict the next occurrence of that event. Predicting is a critical thinking skill and a process skill.

**Measure** Measuring involves direct or indirect comparison of an object with arbitrary units. In science classrooms, the SI system of units is generally used. Measure is also related to the critical thinking skill Compare and Contrast.

**Communicate** Communicating involves an exchange of information. The exchange can involve speaking, listening, writing, reading, or creating a visual display. Communication is a common thread that runs through all critical thinking skills.

**Define Operationally** An operational definition is a statement about an object or phenomenon based on one's experience with it. Define Operationally is related to the critical thinking skill Generalize.

**Hypothesize** When students hypothesize, they formulate a statement that can be tested by experiment. Hypothesizing relates to the critical thinking skills Generalize and If . . . Then Arguments.

**Make Models** Models can be physical or mental representations that explain an idea, object, or event. Making models is related to the critical thinking skill Reason by Analogy.

**Estimate** The skill of estimating generally involves an indirect means of measuring. Estimating requires students to make mental comparisons between physical objects or lengths of time. Estimating is related to the critical thinking skill Compare and Contrast.

**Control Variables** As part of designing experiments, students need to identify factors that may affect the outcome of an event. They must then decide how to manipulate one factor while holding other factors constant. Controlling variables relates to the critical thinking skill Find Causes.

**Collect Data** The skill of collecting data includes gathering information in a systematic way and recording it.

**Interpret Data** Three skills are included in this category—Read a Graph, Read a Table, and Read a Diagram. When students read a graph, table, or diagram, they must explain the information presented in that graphic form and/or use it to answer questions.

# Applying Skills in *Science Insights*

In *Science Insights Exploring Earth and Space,* process skills and critical thinking skills are emphasized and integrated throughout the text. Students are given many opportunities to develop their skills. These opportunities range from informal to formal activities and investigations that use process and critical thinking skills. In Chapter 1, students learn how to apply eleven key process skills as they study science. The following features in *Science Insights* also stress the use and application of various skills.

## Process Skills and Critical Thinking Skills

### Skills WarmUp

A Skills WarmUp activity appears in the margin of every section. It focuses students' attention on specific skills. The Skills WarmUp is usually a simple pencil and paper activity or discussion that leads students into the main topic of the section. For example:

▶ *Skills WarmUp, Chapter 10, page 209* Students infer about the formation of a rock by its texture and appearance. The WarmUp reinforces the skills of observing and reasoning.

### Skills WorkOut

Skills WorkOut activities appear in the margins throughout the text. Students mainly do hands-on activities and research, extending the process skills they have learned. For example:

▶ *Skills WorkOut, Chapter 16, page 377* Students make models that demonstrate the collision of two plate boundaries. The WorkOut reinforces the skills of observing and communicating.

### Check and Explain

Each section ends with four Check and Explain questions. The third and fourth questions require that students apply critical thinking or process skills. The questions are tied to the objectives.

### Chapter Review

Two sections of the Chapter Review require students to use both process and critical thinking skills. They include Check Your Understanding and Develop Your Skills. All skills are in boldface.

### SkillBuilders

There are 23 SkillBuilders in *Science Insights.* The SkillBuilder focuses on a specific process skill, but other skills are required as well. For example:

▶ *SkillBuilder, Chapter 2, page 43* Students practice their map-reading skills by answering questions about a map that is shown on the page. The SkillBuilder reinforces the skills of interpreting data, measuring, and observing.

### Activities

There are 25 activities in *Science Insights,* one for each chapter. All activities emphasize the process skills that students use while doing the activity.

## Decision-Making Skills

### Consider This

After reading about the two sides of an issue related to science in a Consider This feature, students must decide where they stand on the issue. They then communicate their opinions orally by debating the issue with classmates. Students also express their opinions in essays or editorials.

## Research Skills

### Historical Notebook

In the Historical Notebook feature, students read about a historical technological development in science or prominent people in science history. Students answer questions about the feature, then research a related topic or find out more about the subject of the feature.

### Data Bank

Data Bank questions are presented in both the Chapter Review and Unit Opener pages. As students research answers to data bank questions, they use a variety of process skills, including predicting, inferring, classifying, and reading a diagram or table.

# Skills Matrix

| Chapters | Observe | Compare and Contrast | Classify | Infer | Predict | Measure/ Calculate | Communicate | Decision Making | Hypothesize | Make a Model | Make a Graph | Collect/ Organize Data | Interpret Data | Generalize | Find Causes | Reason/ Conclude | Research |
|---|---|---|---|---|---|---|---|---|---|---|---|---|---|---|---|---|---|
| Chapter 1 | | ■ | ▲■ | ■ | ▲■ | ▲■ | ▲■ | | ■ | ▲ | ■ | ▲ | | | | | |
| Chapter 2 | ▲ | ▲ | | | | ■ | | | ▲ | | | | ■ | ■ | | ■ | ▲■ |
| Chapter 3 | ▲ | ■ | ▲ | ▲■ | ▲■ | | | | ▲■ | ▲■ | ■ | | ■ | ▲ | | ■ | ▲ |
| Chapter 4 | ▲ | | | ▲■ | ■ | ▲ | ▲■ | | ▲■ | ▲ | ▲■ | | ■ | | | | |
| Chapter 5 | ▲ | ■ | | ■ | ■ | | | ▲■ | | ▲■ | | | ▲■ | ▲ | | | ▲■ |
| Chapter 6 | ▲ | ■ | ■ | ▲■ | | ▲ | | | | ▲■ | | | | | | | ■ |
| Chapter 7 | | ■ | | ▲■ | ■ | | ▲ | | | ▲■ | ▲ | | | ▲ | | | ▲ |
| Chapter 8 | ▲ | ■ | ▲■ | | | | ▲■ | | | | | ▲ | ▲■ | ■ | | | |
| Chapter 9 | ▲ | ■ | ▲■ | ■ | ▲ | ▲■ | ▲ | | | ■ | | | ■ | | | ■ | ▲■ |
| Chapter 10 | ▲■ | ▲■ | ▲■ | ▲■ | ■ | | | | ▲ | ▲■ | | | ■ | | | ■ | ▲ |
| Chapter 11 | ▲ | ■ | ▲■ | ▲■ | ▲■ | | ▲ | ▲■ | | ■ | | | ▲■ | ■ | | | ▲■ |
| Chapter 12 | ▲ | ■ | ▲■ | ▲■ | ▲■ | | ▲ | | | ▲■ | | | ▲■ | | ■ | | |
| Chapter 13 | ▲■ | ■ | ▲■ | ▲■ | | ▲■ | | | | ▲■ | | ▲■ | ■ | | ■ | | |
| Chapter 14 | ▲ | | ▲■ | ■ | ▲■ | ▲ | ▲ | ▲■ | | ▲■ | | | ■ | ■ | ▲■ | | |
| Chapter 15 | ▲ | ■ | | ■ | ■ | | | | ▲■ | ▲■ | | | ▲■ | ■ | | ■ | ▲ |
| Chapter 16 | ■ | ▲■ | | ▲■ | ■ | | | | ▲ | ▲■ | ▲ | | ■ | | ■ | ▲ | |
| Chapter 17 | ▲ | ▲■ | | ■ | ▲■ | | ▲ | | ▲ | | | ▲ | | | ▲ | ■ | ▲ |
| Chapter 18 | ▲ | ▲■ | ■ | ▲ | ▲■ | ▲■ | | ▲■ | | ▲ | ▲ | | ■ | ▲ | | ■ | |
| Chapter 19 | ▲ | ■ | ■ | ▲■ | | ▲ | | | ■ | | | | ▲■ | ▲ | | | |
| Chapter 20 | ▲ | ■ | ■ | ▲■ | ▲■ | | ▲■ | ▲■ | | ▲ | | | ■ | | ▲■ | | ▲ |
| Chapter 21 | | ▲■ | ▲ | ▲■ | ▲■ | ▲ | ▲■ | ▲■ | | | ▲■ | ■ | ▲■ | | | ■ | |
| Chapter 22 | ▲■ | | ▲■ | ▲■ | | ■ | ▲■ | | | | | | ■ | | ■ | | ▲■ |
| Chapter 23 | | ■ | ■ | ▲■ | ▲■ | ▲ | ▲ | | | ▲■ | | | ▲■ | | | ■ | ▲ |
| Chapter 24 | ▲■ | ■ | | ▲■ | ■ | ▲ | ▲ | | ■ | ▲■ | | | ▲■ | | | ■ | ■ |
| Chapter 25 | ▲ | ▲■ | | ▲■ | ▲■ | ▲ | ▲ | ▲■ | | ▲ | | | ▲■ | | | ■ | |

**Key**   ▲ Apply   ■ Assess

# Integrated Learning

*Integrated learning not only makes teaching and learning more fun, it helps students synthesize concepts and integrate skills.*

Most middle schools and junior high schools are structured in such a way that fragmentation of the curriculum is obvious. Students have several teachers—each of whom specializes in teaching a particular subject in isolation of other subject areas. Teachers have observed that this approach may not be the best way to serve the early adolescent's educational needs. Instead, presenting an integrated approach to learning can help students synthesize concepts and coordinate experiences. In an integrated approach, teams of teachers work together to integrate the subjects that they teach. Integrated learning can often answer the age-old student question, "Why do I have to learn this?"

## Integrating the Curriculum

A commitment to integrate the curriculum requires planning—sometimes months in advance. For integrated learning to be successful, all teachers must be involved and informed. While it may not be practical to integrate all lessons in a given school, some lessons can be integrated or individual teachers can implement integration into individual lessons within their classrooms. Ideally, integrated learning in science should occur at three levels:

▶ Integrating other sciences

▶ Connecting science to other disciplines

▶ Integrating science, technology, and society

## Integrating the Sciences

Within *Science Insights Exploring Earth and Space,* several strategies are used to help teachers integrate and make connections. For example:

*Section 20.2  Climate Classification*  Within this section, **earth science** and **life science** are integrated.

Students learn about a common system that meteorologists use to classify world climates. They then learn about common plants and animals that live in the climate zones.

*Section 5.3  Physics of Plate Movement*  Within this section, **physics** and **earth science** are integrated. Students learn how scientists model plate movements by showing how convection occurs inside the earth.

Margin notes throughout the **Teacher's Edition** provide numerous strategies and suggestions for integrating the sciences. For example, in Chapter 12, page 268, a life science integration describes some of the organisms that have adapted to the unique conditions in a delta ecosystem.

## Integrated Resource Book

This unique resource provides science integration worksheets that are correlated to the student text, covering topics from chemistry to physics to environmental science.

## An Interdisciplinary Approach

Various components in *Science Insights* have been developed to help teachers make connections across curricula. In the **Student Edition,** features such as Skills WorkOut, Consider This, Historical Notebook, SkillBuilder, and Science and Literature connect science content, events, and concepts to language arts skills, literature, and mathematics.

Margin notes throughout the **Teacher's Edition** include strategies for making interdisciplinary connections.

## Science, Technology, and Society

Within the Student Edition of *Science Insights,* each section concludes with a Science, Technology, and Society subsection.

In the Teacher's Edition, margin notes also stress STS Connections, providing additional resources for integration and relevancy.

# Multicultural Perspectives

*The demographics of the United States are changing rapidly. The school-age population of the nation's largest cities is becoming more and more ethnically diverse. A multicultural perspective has become essential in education as students prepare for membership in these diverse communities.*

## Building Multicultural Awareness

Multicultural education is a process through which students learn to respect ethnic and cultural diversity. Through this process, students can gain a global perspective on the universal role of science in the world. Multicultural education includes the history and accomplishments of people of all heritages, particularly those who have been underrepresented in the past, such as people of African, Asian, Native-American, Pacific-Island, and Hispanic backgrounds.

Many of the techniques that you use in your classroom already are well-suited to a program that includes multicultural perspectives. In particular, cooperative learning, hands-on activities, and cross-curricular strategies are effective approaches to content that combine science concepts and multicultural understanding.

Here are some suggestions to help you incorporate multiculturalism into your science curriculum:

▶ Tell students about the contribution to science and technology of people from diverse ethnic and cultural backgrounds.

▶ Invite members of the community who are scientists to speak to students about careers in science and technology.

▶ Provide opportunities for students to work in cooperative groups that are balanced with respect to gender, race, and ethnic background.

▶ Provide examples to students of how science applies to the daily lives of all people.

▶ Allow students to develop projects based on their own cultural experiences.

## Multiculturalism in *Science Insights*

You will find that multiculturalism is infused throughout the *Science Insights* program.

**Student Edition** The Student Edition includes many text references and visuals that stress cultural diversity. In addition, Asian, African, Native-American, Pacific-Island, and Hispanic people are represented in illustrations and photographs. For example:

*Chapter 22, page 514* In a Science and Society feature, students learn about the ancient city of Mohenjo-daro, which existed in India in about 2300 B.C. The feature is accompanied by a photograph of the ruins of the city and a sculpture from the ruins.

**Teacher's Edition** You will also find specific strategies for teaching multiculturalism in the Teacher's Edition margin notes, under the head Multicultural Perspectives. For example:

*Chapter 9, page 200* Information about the technology used by the African people of Tanzania to produce steel nearly 2,000 years ago is included for discussion.

*Chapter 13, page 292* Teachers learn how the Inuits have developed their own classification system to describe snow. They are then encouraged to find examples of classification systems used by non-industrial societies and share the examples with students.

**Ancillaries** References to Addison-Wesley's *Multiculturalism in Mathematics, Science, and Technology: Readings and Activities* are provided in the Teacher's Edition. This book offers a variety of multicultural readings and activities appropriate for grades 7 to 12 in a blackline master format. The lesson topics, covering a diverse multicultural spectrum, combine the vision and experiences of 12 multicultural educators throughout the United States.

# Cooperative Learning in the Science Classroom

## When people cooperate on a task, they often achieve surprising results.

Cooperative learning is an approach to teaching that involves building a cooperative climate in the classroom as well as structuring specific group activities. To accomplish a cooperative task, students work in small learning groups. Often students find that in sharing information with team members, they come to a better understanding of the science concepts they are studying. Process and critical thinking skills are extended as students become aware of the methods teammates use to solve a problem.

## Cooperative Learning Groups

Cooperative learning groups should range in number from two to six. The ideal group size for a cooperative learning activity, however, is four. Once a cooperative learning group has been established, the cooperative group should remain together until the assigned activity has been completed. If a cooperative learning group is having difficulty working together socially or keeping on task, do not dissolve the group. It is important to keep the group intact so that students within the group will learn the social interaction skills necessary to solve problems or to complete tasks effectively through cooperation and collaboration.

## Suggested Roles in Cooperative Groups

Here are some suggested roles.

**Principal Investigator** The Principal Investigator is responsible for managing the tasks within the activity and ensuring that all members understand the goals and content of the activity. The Principal Investigator should read instructions, check results, and ask questions of the teacher. Also, the Principal Investigator should facilitate group discussions.

**Materials Manager** The Materials Manager is responsible for assembling and distributing the materials and equipment needed. As an activity progresses, the Materials Manager is responsible for assembling and operating equipment, as well as checking the results of the activity. The Materials Manager is also responsible for ensuring that all equipment is cleaned and returned.

**Data Collector** The Data Collector is responsible for gathering, recording, and organizing the data. The Data Collector also is responsible for coordinating the certification of the data among all group members and reporting the results of an activity either in writing or orally to the class or to the teacher. If information is being gathered on a master table on the chalkboard, the Data Collector is responsible for recording the data on the chalkboard.

**Timekeeper** The Timekeeper is responsible for keeping track of time, for safety, and for monitoring noise level. The Timekeeper must also observe and record the group's social interactions and encourage group members to discuss the activity as well as check the results.

## Collaborative/Social Skills

Social skills are basic to the cooperative learning process. You should assign a specific social skill for each cooperative learning task. For example, if the activity requires students to hold a debate, the social skill for the activity can be *listening carefully*. Other cooperative group skills include the following:

▶ Taking turns
▶ Sharing resources
▶ Encouraging participation
▶ Treating others with respect
▶ Providing constructive feedback
▶ Resolving conflict
▶ Explaining and helping without simply giving answers

## Self-Evaluation

Encourage students to become actively involved in the evaluation process by providing time for them to reflect on the activity.

# Exploring Science Visually

*In the science classroom, visual learning strategies have become just as important as the written word. No longer are visuals just pretty pictures. They convey and expand information in a way that helps students learn.*

Visual learning is the pedagogical strategy for the 1990s. The strategy employs a distinct correlation between the prose of a text and the illustrations—both photography and art. The integration of prose and visuals enables the graphics to be conveyors of content and concepts. By using visual learning in textbooks and in classroom experiences, the learning process can be enhanced. Visual learning motivates students and makes the content more relevant to them. It also helps students zero in on concepts. Besides its motivational and relevancy aspects, visual learning also helps to promote a number of skills that are essential in the educational environment and in daily life.

## Visual Learning and Skills Development

The following is a list of skills that can be developed and strengthened by using visual learning strategies.

▶ Recognizing color cues that signal important information

▶ Understanding symbols and their uses

▶ Recognizing color cues that indicate connections between ideas

▶ Analyzing and interpreting observations

▶ Reading graphs, charts, and maps

▶ Comparing and contrasting

▶ Identifying and labeling

▶ Comprehending difficult concepts

## Visuals in the Diverse Classroom

Think about the opportunities that visual learning offers the diverse student population in today's classrooms. In a single classroom, you may be teaching students with limited proficiency in English, as well as students who are at-risk or gifted. How do you meet the diverse needs of all these students? Visual learning is part of the answer. Because visuals are a universal language, visual learning provides opportunities for all learners. Integrated prose, diagrams, photographs, art, and maps provide students with broader educational materials, empowering students to approach the content in a way that best suits their individual needs.

## Visual Learning in *Science Insights*

**Color Cues** In Chapter 8, Earth Chemistry, the symbols for every element are color cued; for example, the symbol for oxygen is always represented in red. This color scheme is consistent throughout the text.

**Understanding Symbols and Their Uses** Many symbols are used throughout the *Science Insights* text, including safety symbols and symbols in everyday life.

## Analyzing and Interpreting Observations

Explore Visually is a teaching strategy used throughout the Teacher's Edition that can encourage students to explore the text graphics.

**Integration of Prose and Visuals** Here are examples of the various ways in which visual learning is employed in *Science Insights*:

*pages 102–103  Plate Geography*
The earth's tectonic plates are presented as a two-page spread that integrates art, photos, and prose.

*pages 330–331  The Effects of Groundwater*
The zones created by groundwater in the earth and the effects of moving groundwater are presented in a dynamic two-page visual spread that includes content blocks directly correlated to the illustration.

# Concept Mapping

*Concept mapping offers a visual representation of relationships, linking concepts in a way that is highly effective in helping students synthesize new information.*

Each student connects concepts differently. Therefore, constructing a concept map with a partner or a team gives students valuable experience in comprehending and communicating the meanings of scientific concepts and terms. Whether used to interpret textbook passages or as a problem-solving tool, concept mapping when paired with cooperative learning leads to lively classroom discussion.

## Using Concept Maps in Your Classroom

Here are some strategies for introducing students to concept mapping and making concept maps part of the learning environment:

▶ Create a large concept map of the year's lessons for the bulletin board.

▶ List familiar and unfamiliar words from a new lesson and ask students if they can connect the words based on what they already know.
▶ Have students show their concept maps on the chalkboard and explain how the concepts link.
▶ Before testing, have students review and revise concept maps they have already made.
▶ Use concept mapping as a way to let students assist in planning the year's course of study.

## Concept Mapping in *Science Insights*

Addison-Wesley's *Science Insights* provides concept mapping opportunities in the Make Connections section of each Chapter Review. In each of the first chapters in a unit, students copy a concept map on a separate sheet of paper, then complete the map by writing the correct term in the empty spaces. With each successive chapter in a unit, the concept maps become more challenging. In the last chapter of each unit, students create their own concept maps using terms listed in the Make Connections section.

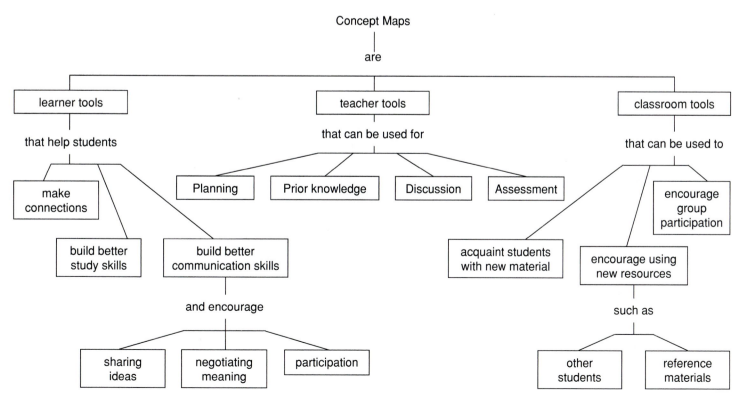

# Portfolio Assessment

*Portfolio assessment can be an exciting, experimental, and evolving tool for both the student and the teacher.*

Portfolio assessment derives its name and approach from the collection of work and achievements usually assembled by artists, designers, and architects. A portfolio is meant to illustrate the true scope of the talents of the professional. In the educational forum, portfolio assessment enables the student and teacher to work together to assemble and to complete the student's best work during a given period of time, usually for a marking period.

With portfolio assessment, the emphasis is placed on overall achievement rather than numerical test scores. Portfolio assessment stresses what students can do rather than what they cannot do. Also, portfolio assessment allows students to remove materials from their portfolios and revise them.

## Benefits for Students, Teachers, and Parents

Portfolios motivate students to gauge their own growth. By comparing drafts and finished work, students can see a graphic record of their progress—which can only enhance their self-esteem and make them receptive to further challenges. Instead of measuring themselves against their classmates, they learn to take pride in their own strengths and weaknesses and in personal improvement.

Teachers can use portfolios to communicate more effectively with parents. A portfolio allows parents to browse through a representative collection of their child's work during conferences. Instead of a mere summary of test results, the portfolio reveals an actual legacy of the student's learning experiences.

## Contents of the Portfolio

Portfolios can contain any items that students have negotiated with teachers to include. Students should date each piece of work they place in their portfolios and provide a brief description of the assignment and an explanation of the choice.

Students should be encouraged to include various drafts and preliminary stages, as well as finished products, to demonstrate progress. Interesting or humorous mistakes are also appropriate items for a portfolio—particularly if the student adds an analysis or revision of the error. Some suggested materials for portfolios are:

▶ Photographs of any work too large to fit in a portfolio

▶ Diagrams, tables, graphs, or charts

▶ Audiotapes/videotapes

▶ Projects, laboratory investigations, and activities

▶ Computer printouts

▶ Science journal excerpts

▶ Statements about goals

## Portfolios in the Classroom

It will help you to give some thought as to where portfolios will be kept. Both teachers and students will need easy access to the portfolios, and of course the portfolios will take up a good deal of space. Students will also be curious about your system for assessing portfolios. You may wish to get students to help you address both questions.

## Portfolios and *Science Insights*

Throughout the Teacher's Edition, suggestions are provided for materials, projects, and so on that students may wish to place in a portfolio. These suggestions can be presented to students. Encourage students to plan ahead and suggest ways to revise their work if necessary.

Portfolio suggestions are a frequent feature of the Teacher's Edition. Here is an example: Have students keep a cloud diary. They can record the date, time of day, weather conditions, types of clouds, their description, and a drawing for each diary entry. After several weeks, have students tally the number of different types of clouds they observed.

# Individual Needs

*Every day, classroom teachers face the challenge of a diverse student population with individual students bringing to the educational forum unique sets of abilities, needs, and learning styles.*

## A Positive Learning Environment

In an effort to provide all students with a positive educational environment with optimum opportunities for success, the following strategies may help teachers structure learning for diverse student populations, especially for those students with different ability levels and those students with limited English proficiency (LEP):

▶ Provide tools, such as picture dictionaries and other visual learning resources.

▶ Encourage a variety of responses during discussions, including speaking, drawing, demonstrating, and writing.

▶ Use hands-on activities and demonstrations to reinforce concepts.

▶ Speak clearly and slowly using body language and gestures.

▶ Relate and incorporate various cultural content into discussions. Stress relevant examples.

▶ Check for understanding and comprehension frequently.

▶ Use cooperative learning groups for activities and investigations, and actively encourage individuals to participate within their groups.

▶ Use a variety of combination visual/verbal aids to create a language-rich classroom environment.

▶ Approach concepts in several different ways and provide relevant, common examples.

## Ability Levels

In *Science Insights,* the various components of each chapter and the supplements have been designated for use by core, standard, and enriched students. The leveling of the components and supplements is presented in suggestions. Based upon individual students, classroom management, and teaching styles, the components and supplements may be used in different levels, as deemed necessary by the teacher.

## Limited English Proficiency Students

Science presents a challenge to LEP students at three levels—overcoming a language barrier, achieving mastery in science, and addressing social concerns as students interact with their peers and teachers. The following teaching strategies are designed to help teachers create a positive and rewarding educational environment for LEP students:

▶ Create audiocassettes for each chapter that model language patterns.

▶ Use newspapers, magazines, and library research to provide connections between school and the larger world.

▶ Use illustrations with labeling exercises to build vocabulary.

▶ Have students keep a "dictionary" of key terms and words that includes the term in English, the term in their native language, and the definition. Attaching drawings or photographs next to the terms or words is also helpful.

▶ Encourage LEP students to use an English–primary language dictionary.

▶ Use remedial or average vocabulary and skills worksheets.

▶ Provide opportunities for LEP students to communicate nonverbally.

# Master Materials List

Most of the activities in *Science Insights Exploring Earth and Space* have been designed for use with commonly available materials. The quantities shown are based on a class of 30 students with the recommended student grouping found in the Teacher's Edition. When ordering, adjust quantities for your class size and activity groupings. Quantities shown for nonconsumable equipment used in more than one activity reflect the largest quantity needed for any of the activities.

All activities are optional. Your equipment needs will vary, depending on the activities you elect to do. To help you determine your specific needs, each item is referenced by activity number to the activity or activities in which it is required. Readily available materials such as tap water and notebook paper are not listed.

Addresses of science materials suppliers follow the materials list.

| Item | Quantity | Chapter Activities | SkillBuilders |
|---|---|---|---|
| alum | 0.5 kg | 9 | |
| bags, garbage | 15 | 22 | |
| baking soda (sodium bicarbonate) | 30 g | 8 | |
| balloons | 30 | | 17.1 |
| balls, table-tennis | 1 | | 23.3 |
| barometers | 8 | 19 | |
| beakers (250-mL or larger) | 10 | 3 | |
| beakers, small | 30 | 9 | |
| books | 15 | 4 | |
| bottles, plastic soda | 15 empty 473-mL | 17 | |
| boxes, shoe | 15 | 5 | |
| butcher paper | about 5 m | 13 | |
| calcium chloride | 30 g | 8 | |
| cans, small or medium, metal | 15 | 18 | |
| cans, small, metal | 12 | 20 | |
| cardboard, corrugated | 30 sheets | 6, 7, 24 | |
| chalk | 1 piece | 25 | |
| clay soil | 0.5 kg | 17 | |
| clay, modeling | 30 blocks | 2 | |
| clay, modeling (3 different colors) | 10 balls of each color | 16 | |
| clay, powdered | 1 kg | 10 | |
| coffee filters or filter paper | 30 | 11 | |
| compasses | 30 | 19, 24 | |
| copper pennies | 30 | | 9.2 |
| cotton gauze | 30 strips | | 18.1 |

| Item | Quantity | Chapter Activities | SkillBuilders |
|------|----------|-------------------|---------------|
| cups, paper | 30 | 11 | |
| cups, plastic or foam | 30 | 8, 10 | |
| cylinders, graduated | 15 | 8, 10 | |
| drinking glasses | 30 | 15 | 14.1 |
| drinking glasses, large | 20 | 15 | |
| drinking straws | 30 | 16 | |
| drinking straws, clear | 15 | 17 | |
| droppers | 30 | 3, 15, 17 | 14.1 |
| flashlights | 1 | | 23.3 |
| flexible plastic sheets | 7 of each color | 21 | |
| food coloring, blue | 1 bottle | 3, 15, 17 | |
| funnels | 15 | 17 | |
| glass pieces | 30 | | 9.2 |
| gloves, plastic | 30 pairs | 22 | |
| gravel | 1 kg | 10 | |
| hammers | 6 | 20 | |
| hole punch | 30 | 23 | |
| hot plates | 10 | 3, 9 | |
| ice, crushed | 1 bag | 18 | |
| ice, large pieces | 15 | 12 | |
| jars | 20 | 14 | |
| jars with lids, large | 12 | 20 | |
| jars, medium-size | 15 | 10 | |
| knives, butter | 30 | 2, 16 | |
| knives, kitchen | 30 | | 9.2 |
| map, world | 1 | | 20.1 |
| markers | 30 | 5, 14 | |
| marking pens | 15 | 17 | |
| measuring cups | 10 | 11 | |
| measuring tapes | 30 | | 17.1 |
| mineral samples | 150 | | 9.2 |
| nails | 6 | 20 | |
| needles, sewing | 30 | | 14.1 |
| note cards | 30 | | 18.1 |
| nuts and washers, assorted | about 300 pieces | 13 | |

| Item | Quantity | Chapter Activities | SkillBuilders |
|---|---|---|---|
| paper towels | 1 roll | 8, 12, 22 | |
| paper, plain white | 120 sheets | 2, 4, 5 | |
| paper, construction | 30 sheets | 23 | |
| paper, color construction | 15 sheets of each color | 1 | |
| paper, graph | 30 sheets | 1, 8, 21 | |
| paper, plain white | 15 sheets | 5 | |
| paper, tracing | 30 sheets | | 15.2 |
| paper, wax | 30 sheets | 2, 16 | |
| pencils | 30 | 2, 4, 8, 9, 23, 25 | |
| pencils, assorted colors | 32 (3 colors) | 2, 8, 21 | |
| pie tins | 35 | 21 | |
| pipe cleaners | 30 | 9 | |
| plants, small | 40–50 | 20 | |
| plastic sheets | 15 large | 22 | |
| plastic squares | 15 hard | 12 | |
| protractors | 30 | 24 | |
| rock samples | 300 | | 10.1 |
| rocks or pebbles | 300 | | 1.2 |
| rolled oats cereal | 1 box | 3 | |
| rubber bands | 30 | 2 | |
| rulers, metric | 15 | 1, 5, 6, 11, 17, 23, 25 | 23.3 |
| safety goggles | 30 | 9 | |
| salt | 1 kg | 9, 15 | |
| sand | 1 kg | 10, 11, 12, 20 | |
| saucers | 10 | 11 | |
| scissors | 30 pairs | 1, 5, 6, 11, 16, 21, 23, 24 | |
| softball | 1 | | 23.3 |
| soil | 1 kg | 11, 20 | |
| spoons | 20 | 3, 8, 9, 10, 15, 18, 20 | |
| sticks | 8, about 1 meter long | 19 | |
| stiff wire pieces | 15 | 12 | |
| stir sticks | 20 | 15 | |
| streak plates | 30 | | 9.2 |

| Item | Quantity | Chapter Activities | SkillBuilders |
| --- | --- | --- | --- |
| string | 1 ball | 19 | |
| tape | 30 rolls | 23, 24 | |
| tape, masking | 15 rolls | 7, 9, 14, 25 | |
| thermometers | 30 | 8, 18, 21 | 18.1 |
| thermometers, Celsius | 15 | 1 | |
| timers or clock with second hand | 15 | 1, 8, 10 | |
| toothpicks | 1 box | 10 | |
| tubing, clear plastic | 10, 50–75 cm each | 14 | |
| white glue solution | 1 L diluted | 10 | |
| wood blocks 1 x 1 x 1 cm | 15 | 7 | |
| wood blocks 1 x 1 x 5 cm | 15 | 7 | |
| wood blocks 1 x 1 x 9 cm | 15 | 7 | |
| wood blocks or rocks | 30 small | 11 | |

# Science Suppliers

## Equipment Suppliers

**Analytical Scientific**
11049 Bandera Rd.
San Antonio, TX 78250

**Arbor Scientific**
P.O. Box 2750
Ann Arbor, MI 48106-2750

**Carolina Biological Supply Co.
(CABISCO)**
5100 W. Henrietta Rd.
Charlotte, NC 20391

**Central Scientific Co.**
3300 CENCO Parkway
Franklin Park, IL 60131

**Cuisenaire Co. of America**
10 Bank St.
White Plains, NY 10606

**Fisher Scientific Co.**
4901 W. LeMoyne Ave.
Chicago, IL 60651

**Learning Alternatives, Inc.**
2305 Elm Rd., NE
Cortland, OH 44410

**Learning Things, Inc.**
68A Broadway
P.O. Box 436
Arlington, MA 02174

**Nasco**
901 Janesville Ave.
Fort Atkinson, WI 53538

**Northwest Scientific Supply Co., Inc.**
4311 Anthony Ct., #700
P.O. Box 305
Rocklin, CA 95677

**Sargent-Welch Scientific Co.**
7300 N. Linder Ave.
Skokie, IL 60077

## Audiovisual Distributors

**AIMS Media**
6901 Woodley Ave.
Van Nuys, CA 91405-4878

**Churchill Films (CF)**
662 N. Robertson Blvd.
Los Angeles, CA 90069

**Coronet Films & Video (C/MTI)**
108 Wilmot Rd.
Deerfield, IL 60015

**Encyclopaedia Britannica
Educational Corp. (EB)**
425 N. Michigan Ave.
Chicago, IL 60611

**Films Incorporated (FI)**
5547 N. Ravenswood Ave.
Chicago, IL 60640-1199

**Guidance Associates (GA)**
P.O. Box 3000
Mt. Kisco, NY 10549

**Human Relations Media (HRM)**
175 Tomkins Ave.
Pleasantville, NY 10570

**Media Center**
2175 Shattuck Ave.
Berkeley, CA 94704

**The Media Guild**
11722 Sorrento Valley Rd., Suite E
San Diego, CA 92121

**National Film Board of Canada**
1251 Avenue of the Americas, 16th Floor
New York, NY 10029

**National Geographic Society
Educational Services (NGSES)**
17th and M Sts., NW
Washington, DC 20036

**Optical Data**
30 Technology Dr.
Warren, NJ 07059

**TVO Video**
1443 W. Franklin St., Suite 206
Chapel Hill, NC 27516

**Videodiscovery, Inc. (VID)**
1700 Westlake Ave. N., Suite 600
Seattle, WA 98109-3012

**WINGS for Learning**
P.O. Box 66002
Scotts Valley, CA 95066

## Software Distributors

**Educational Software Institute (ESI)**
4213 South 94th St.
Omaha, NE 68127

**Learning Services (LS)**
P.O. Box 10636
Eugene, OR 97440

**Educational Resources (ER)**
1550 Executive Dr., P.O. Box 1900
Elgin, IL 60121

## Chapter Bibliography Supplier Codes

**AIMS** = Activities that Integrate Math & Science, Fresno, CA.
**AVNA** = Audio Visual Narr. Arts, Pleasantville, NY.
**A-W** = Addison-Wesley Pub. Co., Reading MA.
**BFA** = BFA Educational Media, New York, NY.
**C/MTI** = Coronet/MTI Film & Video, Deerfield, IL.
**CES** = Cross Educational Software, Rustin, LA.
**CM** = Cabisco Mathematics, Burlington, NC.
**COM** = COMPress, Fairfield, CT.
**CSWS** = The Council for Solid Waste Solutions, Washington, D.C.

**EI** = Estes Industries, Penrose, CO.
**EQ** = EduQuest/IBM, Atlanta, GA.
**FA** = Falcon, Wentworth, NH.
**IBM** = IBM, Atlanta, GA.
**J & S** = J & S Software, Port Washington, NY.
**JF** = Journal Films, Evanston, IL.
**JWW** = J. Weston Walch, Portland, ME.
**LCA** = Learning Corp. of America, New York, NY.
**LHS** = Lawrence Hall of Science, University of California, Berkeley, CA.
**MF** = Macmillan Films, Mount Vernon, NY.

**MMI** = MMI Corp., Baltimore, MD.
**PBS** = PBS Video, Alexandria, VA.
**PF** = Pyramid Films & Video, Santa Monica, CA.
**QE** = Queue, Fairfield, CT.
**SC** = Sunburst Communications, Pleasantville, NY.
**SVE** = Society for Visual Education, Chicago, IL.
**T-L** = Time-Life Video, New York, NY.
**UL** = United Learning, Niles, IL.
**V** = Vernier, Portland, OR.
**WN** = Ward's Natural Science Establishment, Inc., Rochester, NY.

# Scott Foresman - Addison Wesley

# Science Insights
## *Exploring Earth and Space*

## *Authors*

***Michael DiSpezio, M.A.***
Science Consultant
North Falmouth, Massachusetts

***Marilyn Linner-Luebe, M.S.***
Former Science Teacher
Fulton High School
Fulton, Illinois

***Marylin Lisowski, Ph.D.***
Professor of Education
Eastern Illinois University
Charleston, Illinois

***Bobbie Sparks, M.A.***
K–12 Science Consultant
Harris County Department
  of Education
Houston, Texas

***Gerald Skoog, Ed.D.***
Professor and Chairperson
Curriculum and Instruction
Texas Tech University
Lubbock, Texas

 Scott Foresman
Addison Wesley

Editorial Offices: Menlo Park, California • Glenview, Illinois
Sales Offices: Reading, Massachusetts • Atlanta, Georgia • Glenview, Illinois
Carrollton, Texas • Menlo Park, California

http://www.sf.aw.com

## Content Reviewers

**Steve Blume**
Science Teacher
St. Tammay Parish Schools
Slidell, Louisiana

**James Cole, Jr.**
Science Teacher
Clemente High School
Chicago, Illinois

**Kenneth Eiseman**
Supervisor of Science
West Chester Area School
  District
West Chester, Pennsylvania

**Jean Lake**
Eighth Grade Science Teacher
John Marshall Middle School
Wichita, Kansas

**Michele McCarthy**
Science Teacher
Fleming Junior High School
Los Angeles, California

**Kathie Poff**
Science Teacher
Parkhill Junior High School
Dallas, Texas

**Dr. Tim Cooney**
Professor of Earth Science
University of Northern Iowa
Cedar Falls, Iowa

**Donna Stull**
Science Teacher
Western High School
Ft. Lauderdale, Florida

**Clive Tucceri**
Eighth Grade Science Teacher
East Hampton Middle School
East Hampton, Connecticut

**Dr. James Walters**
Professor of Earth Science
University of Northern Iowa
Cedar Falls, Iowa

**Dr. Thomas Hockey**
Associate Professor of
  Astronomy
University of Northern Iowa
Cedar Falls, Iowa

## Multicultural Reviewers

**Gloriane Hirata**
San Jose Unified School
  District
San Jose, California

**Joseph A. Jefferson**
Ronald McNair School
East Palo Alto, California

**Peggy P. Moore**
Garnet Robertson
  Intermediate
Daly City, California

**Modesto Tamez**
Exploratorium
San Francisco, California

**About the Cover:** One of the most interesting sights that an astronaut sees from space is the earth. As you explore the earth, you will discover why it is such a unique planet. You will learn about the earth's many different processes, including the formation of beautiful gemstones.

Front cover photographs: Telegraph/FPG International (earth); Gareth Hopson for Addison-Wesley (geode); NASA/Dan McCoy/Rainbow (astronaut); Jeff Foott/Bruce Coleman Inc. (honeycomb); Telegraph/FPG International (integrated chip wafer).

Back cover photographs: Gareth Hopson for Addison-Wesley (geode); NASA/Dan McCoy/Rainbow (astronaut).

# Contents

## Unit 1
## Exploring the Sciences

page 1

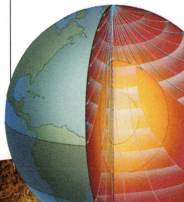

## Unit 3 Composition of the Earth

page 156

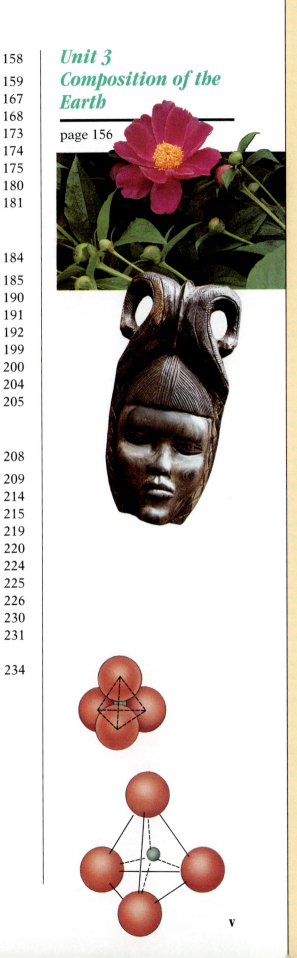

## Unit 5
## Earth's Waters

page 314

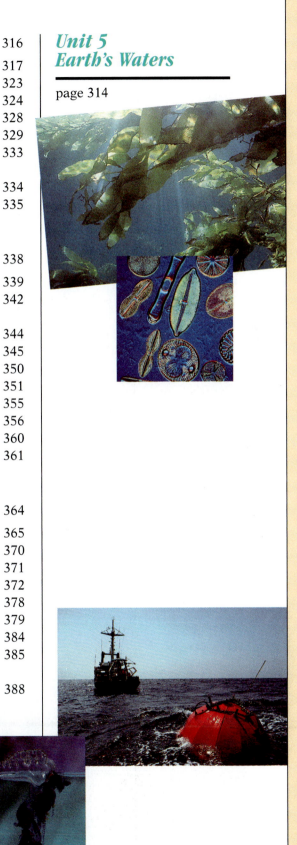

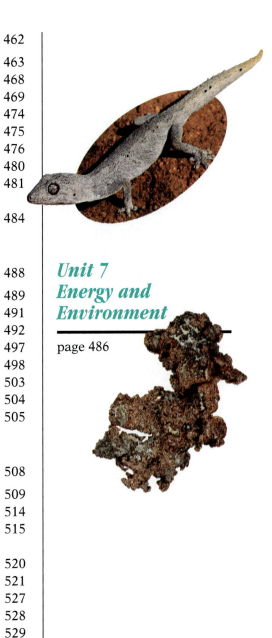

**Unit 7
Energy and
Environment**

page 486

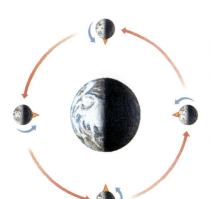

# Features

# Hands-On Science

## Activities

## SkillBuilder Activities

**Problem Solving/Process Skills**

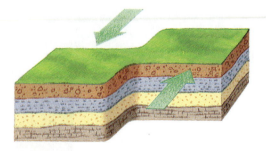

## Skills WarmUp Activities

## Skills WorkOut Activities

# Concept Mapping...

Reading a science textbook is not like reading a magazine or a story. You usually don't have to work hard to understand a story. You probably won't remember it for a long time, either. But when you read science, you are reading to learn something new. You will need to think about what you read. You will also need to remember as much as you can. You may just *read* a story, but you will need to *study* your textbook.

## Build a Concept Map

One way to help you study and remember what you have learned is to organize the information in the chapter visually. You can do this by making concept maps. In a concept map, the main ideas are identified by a word or phrase enclosed in a box. When these boxes are linked together, you can better understand the meanings of the ideas by seeing how the concepts are connected to one another. To build a concept map, follow the steps below.

## Identify

1. Identify the concepts to be mapped. They may come from a short section of your book, directions from an activity, or a vocabulary list. List the concepts on a separate sheet of paper or on small cards.

## Decide

2. Decide which concept is the main idea. Look for ways to classify the remaining concepts. You may want to list or rank the concepts from the most general to the most specific. For example, look at the concept map shown above. Notice that "solar system" is general, and then "meteoroids," "planets," "asteroids," and "comets" are more specific concepts.

## Organize

3. Place the most general concept at the top of your map. Link that concept to the other concepts. Draw a circle or square around each concept.

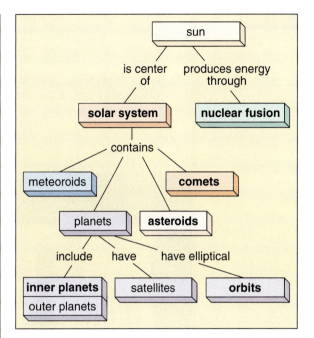

## Choose

4. Pick linking words for your map that identify relationships between the concepts. Linking words should not be the concepts themselves. Label all lines with linking words that explain how each pair of concepts relate to each other.

## Create

5. Start making your map by branching one or two general concepts from your main concept. Add other, more specific, concepts to the general ones as you progress. Try to branch out. Add two or more concepts to each concept already on the map.

## Connect

6. Make cross-links between two concepts that are already on the map. Label all cross-links with words that explain how the concepts are related. Use arrows to show the direction of the relationship.

As you build a concept map, you are doing two things. First, you are automatically reviewing what you already know. Second, you are learning more. Once you have a completed map, you can use it to study and test yourself. You will often find that several different maps can be made from the same group of concepts.

**U**nit 1 presents many of the tools that scientists use to study the earth. Chapter 1 opens by describing scientific method, then explains scientific units and graphing. The chapter concludes with an overview of the earth's biosphere and a discussion of the importance of studying geography. Chapter 2 discusses topography and geography, and characterizes the biomes of the earth. The chapter also presents and compares different methods for mapping the earth's surface. Students learn how to read topographical maps. Chapter 3 outlines the structure of the earth, and what may be learned about the earth's interior by studying seismic waves.

## Introducing the Unit

### Directed Inquiry

Have students study the photograph and read the caption. Ask:

► How big is 50 meters? What are some visual clues to the size of this dome? (Students might compare the dome to a gymnasium in size; some clues are the flagposts in the foreground and in the surrounding snow.)

► What is the environment like in Antarctica? How did people build a base at the South Pole? (Frigid; The construction required time, a great deal of planning, and sophisticated technology for keeping workers warm.)

► Why has so much planning time, work, and money gone into building this base in Antarctica? Would you want to work there? (Antarctica is one of the earth's frontiers. Scientists go there for many reasons, including the study of the earth's history, and world climate changes. Students' responses will vary.)

► What are some other places on the earth that scientists have a lot to learn about? (Similar frontiers include the deep ocean, outer space, and the earth's interior.)

### Writing About the Photograph

Have students imagine that they are scientists stationed at this base in Antarctica. Have them write two or three journal entries describing their living conditions, the project they've been assigned, and how they feel about living in Antarctica. Have volunteers read their entries.

# Unit 1

# Exploring the Sciences

## Chapters

**1** Studying Science

**2** Topography and Geography

**3** Structure of the Earth

# Data Bank

Use the information on pages 620 to 621 to answer the following questions about topics explored in this unit.

## Measuring

Approximately how many kilometers long is the Rio Grande River?

## Interpreting a Map

What areas of the United States have the highest elevation? What areas have the lowest elevation?

## Reading a Map

What state is located between 25° and 30°N latitude and 80° and 85°W longitude?

The photograph to the left is of a 50-meter dome that covers a United States base in the South Pole, Antarctica. Why do you think research is being conducted in Antarctica?

## Overview

This chapter introduces the study of science. The first section describes science skills, safety skills, and methods for designing experiments. The second section discusses base units of the SI system with everyday applications. The chapter also describes various kinds and specific uses of graphs. The final section identifies the areas of the earth studied by earth scientists.

## Advance Planner

▶ Obtain jars and seeds, marbles, or similar objects for TE page 4.

▶ Collect nails, staples, screws, bolts, washers, and nuts for TE page 5.

▶ Prepare scissors, metric rulers, construction paper: red, white, blue, and black, Celsius thermometers, timers or clocks, and graph paper for SE Activity 1, page 12.

▶ Gather containers labeled by volume, including containers with pint, quart, and half-gallon designations, as well as SI volumes for TE page 15.

▶ Collect 20 small rocks or pebbles per student for SE page 17.

▶ Provide an example of an EKG, EEC, or seismograph output for TE page 21.

## Skills Development Chart

| Sections | Analyze | Classify | Communicate | Gather Data | Make a Model | Measure | Predict |
|---|---|---|---|---|---|---|---|
| **1.1** Skills WarmUp | | | ● | | | | |
| Skills WorkOut | ● | | | | ● | | ● |
| Activity 1 | | | ● | ● | | ● | ● |
| **1.2** Skills WarmUp | | | | | | ● | |
| Skills WorkOut | | ● | | | | | |
| SkillBuilder | | | | | | ● | |
| **1.3** Skills WarmUp | | | | ● | | | |
| Skills WorkOut | | | | | ● | | |
| **1.4** Skills WarmUp | | ● | | | | | |

## Individual Needs

▶ **Limited English Proficiency Students** Have students turn to Figure 1.18 and list the six parts of the earth studied by earth scientists. Ask students to leave extra space after each term. Then have students choose a process skill from pages 3 to 5 to show how they might study each of the six parts. First, students can define the skill using their own words. Then they should give an example of how someone might use a skill. For example, for *predict* they might list predicting changes in the atmosphere (forecasting weather) and predicting earthquakes.

▶ **At-Risk Students** Ask students to divide the pages of their science portfolios in half vertically. Have them write journal entries for the next two days in their lives on one half of the page. Beside the entries, have them write a process skill from pages 3 to 5 that they used in each activity. They may find it helpful to work with a partner and share suggestions about the skills they used.

▶ **Gifted Students** Encourage students to research historical contributions by famous scientists. Here are a few examples: Marie Curie's discovery of radium; William Herschel's discovery of binary stars; Maria Mitchell's discovery of a new comet; Benjamin Franklin's work with electricity. Have each student pick a contribution that interests him or her and analyze it according to the description of experiments given on page 7. If possible, they should show how the scientist's work followed the steps given in Figure 1.6. Have them make a poster describing and analyzing the experiment.

## Resource Bank

▶ **Bulletin Board** On one part of the bulletin board hang pictures showing familiar objects or scenes that could represent a metric measurement. Write the measurement for each picture on a card. The card for a picture of the earth might say *40,000 kilometers in circumference;* one for a photograph of melting snow would say *0° Celsius.* Place the cards on a separate section of the board. Invite students to add more pictures and cards to the display. Have them make a list matching the pictures and measurement cards. When the lists are complete, have the class discuss which cards go with which pictures. Attach the cards to the appropriate pictures.

# CHAPTER 1 PLANNING GUIDE

| Section | Core | Standard | Enriched | Section | Core | Standard | Enriched |
|---|:---:|:---:|:---:|---|:---:|:---:|:---:|
| **1.1 Science Skills and Methods** pp. 3–12 | | | | **1.3 Graphing** pp. 19–21 | | | |
| **Section Features** Skills WarmUp, p. 3 | ● | ● | ● | **Section Features** Skills WarmUp, p. 19 | ● | ● | ● |
| Skills WorkOut, p. 5 | ● | ● | ● | Skills WorkOut, p. 21 | | ● | ● |
| Skills WorkOut, p. 10 | ● | ● | ● | **Blackline Masters** Review Worksheet 1.3 | ● | ● | ● |
| Skills WorkOut, p. 11 | ● | ● | ● | Skills Worksheet 1.3a | ● | ● | ● |
| Activity, p.12 | ● | ● | ● | Skills Worksheet 1.3b | ● | ● | ● |
| **Blackline Masters** Review Worksheet 1.1 | ● | ● | ● | Integrating Worksheet 1.3 | | ● | ● |
| Reteach Worksheet 1.1 | ● | ● | ● | **Ancillary Options** *Multiculturalism in Mathematics, Science, and Technology, pp. 109–110* | | ● | ● |
| **Ancillary Options** *CEPUP,* Determining Threshold Limits | | ● | ● | **Laboratory Program** Investigation 2 | ● | ● | ● |
| **Laboratory Program** Investigation 1 | ● | ● | ● | **1.4 Studying the Earth** pp. 22–26 | | | |
| **Color Transparencies** Transparency 1 | ● | ● | ● | **Section Features** Skills WarmUp, p. 22 | ● | ● | ● |
| **1.2 Measuring with Scientific Units** pp. 13–18 | | | | Career Corner, p. 24 | ● | ● | ● |
| **Section Features** Skills WarmUp, p. 13 | ● | ● | ● | **Blackline Masters** Review Worksheet 1.4 | ● | ● | ● |
| Skills WorkOut, p. 14 | ● | ● | ● | Skills Worksheet 1.4 | ● | ● | ● |
| SkillBuilder, p. 17 | | ● | ● | Integrating Worksheet 1.4 | ● | ● | ● |
| **Blackline Masters** Review Worksheet 1.2 | ● | ● | ● | Vocabulary Worksheet 1.4 | ● | ● | ● |
| Skills Worksheet 1.2 | ● | ● | ● | | | | |

## Bibliography

The following resources can be used for teaching the chapter. See page T–46 for supplier codes.

### Library Resources

Farndon, John. *How the Earth Works.* Pleasantville, NY: The Reader's Digest Association, Inc., 1992.

Kramer, Stephen P. *How To Think Like a Scientist: Answering Questions by the Scientific Method.* New York: Crowell, 1987.

Oosterman, M. A. and M. T. Schmidt. *Earth Science Investigations.* Alexandria, VA: American Geological Institute, 1990.

Swertka, Eve and Albert. *Make it Graphic! Drawing Graphs for Science and Social Studies Projects.* New York: Messner, 1985.

VanCleave, Janice Pratt. *Earth Science for Every Kid.* New York: Wiley, 1991.

### Technology Resources

#### Internet

**PLANETDIARY** at *http://www.planetdiary.com*
- Learn more about animals and plants in *Fauna* and *Flora* by clicking on *Phenomena Backgrounders.*

#### Software

*Big Science Ideas. Mac, Win. LS.*
*Earth. Mac, Dos, Win. ER.*
*Graph Power. Mac. LS.*

#### CD-ROMs

*Interactive Earth. SFAW.*

*An Odyssey of Discovery for Science Insights:* Let students explore the activities *Shadow Watch, Data From Space,* and *Dig It* on the Earth and Space Disk. Let them try *Paramecia, Aquarium,* and *Nerve Express* on the Living Science Disk. SFAW.

*Small Blue Planet: The Real Picture World Atlas. Mac, Dos. ESI.*

#### Laserdiscs

*Living Textbook.* (See barcodes on pages in this chapter.) Optical Data.

#### Videos

*Inferring in Science. 15 min. 1983. AIT.*
*Laboratory Safety. 17 min. 1987. SFAW.*
*The Rock Cycle: Understanding the Processes and Products of an Ever-Changing Earth. 30 min. 1992. MMI.*

#### Audio-Visual Resources

*Exploring the Scientific Method. Filmstrip. NGSES.*

### Writing Connection

Have students write a short story about what it would be like to be an astronaut aboard a spaceship that is circling the sun at a safe distance. Have students describe what they think that scientists might learn about the sun and Earth from studies done in space.

## Introducing the Chapter

Have students read the description of the photograph. Ask if they agree or disagree with the description.

### Directed Inquiry

Have students study the photograph. Ask:

▶ What colors, shapes, and textures do you see in this photograph of the sun? (Students may mention blue, red, black, and purple, the perfectly rounded black shape, the flare, the corona, and the light concentric semicircles around the sun.)

▶ What information does this kind of photograph give a scientist? (Scientists can measure and record several characteristics of the sun with such photographs. This image of the sun's corona gives data about the heat, duration, and area of a solar flare.)

▶ Why does it take special technology to study the sun? (Direct sunlight harms the eyes. Any solar photography requires at least special film and/or strong filters, even during an eclipse.)

▶ What does this photograph have to do with the topic of the chapter? (Science often requires making observations with special instruments.)

## Chapter Vocabulary

| | |
|---|---|
| biosphere | liter |
| control | kilogram |
| data | mass |
| density | meter |
| dependent variable | volume |
| independent variable | |

**Chapter 1** **Studying Science**

### Chapter Sections

**1.1** Science Skills and Methods

**1.2** Measuring with Scientific Units

**1.3** Graphing

**1.4** Studying the Earth

### What do you see?

❝I see a picture of the sun and the fire around it. I think it is very large. I really can't estimate how large, because it's probably bigger than I think. The picture was made by a satellite up in space— many miles up. Scientists could use this to learn what the sun is made of. They could also learn what temperatures the sun has in the core and the outer surfaces of the sun.❞

*Frank Dahlquist*
*Snohomish Junior High*
*Snohomish, Washington*

To find out more about the photograph, look on page 28. As you read this chapter, you will discover some of the methods scientists use to learn about your world.

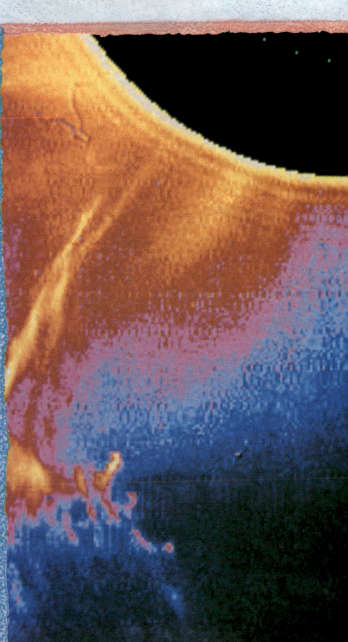

### Cooperative Learning

Have students work in groups of four. Ask them to list the different ways in which they gather knowledge. Combine the lists of the different groups on the chalkboard. Discuss with students how scientists gather information. Have the cooperative groups compare how science is different from other ways of gathering knowledge.

## 1.1 Science Skills and Methods

### Objectives

▶ **Identify** and **use** science skills.

▶ **Explain** what an experiment is.

▶ **Describe** the scientific method.

▶ **Distinguish** between fact and theory.

▶ **Apply** science and safety skills to everyday life.

H ow do you gain knowledge about the world around you? Much of your knowledge comes from personal experiences, books, television, and other sources. You also learn a lot from people. Which kind of knowledge do you trust the most?

The desire to gain the most trustworthy, accurate knowledge is the main motivation behind science. Science is a particular way of gathering and organizing information about the natural world. Science involves observing, experimenting, and studying information in an orderly and objective way.

### Science Skills

When scientists study, observe, and experiment, they gather information, or **data**. While they work, scientists use many skills. Sometimes these skills are called science process skills. As you read about these skills, you will discover a kind of secret. These skills are not some mysterious or hard way to do something. You may not realize it, but you use many of these skills every day.

**Observe**  The most direct way of gaining knowledge about something in nature is to observe it. When you observe, you use one or more of your senses to get information about your surroundings. Your senses are sight, touch, taste, smell, and hearing. Your ability to observe can be extended through the use of tools, such as telescopes, thermometers, and rulers. Look at the object in Figure 1.1. Write as many observations as you can about it. Which sense did you use? ①

▼ **ACTIVITY**

**Communicating**

*Five Senses*

Choose an object in your classroom. Write down what you would see, feel, taste, hear, and smell if you picked the object up and examined it. Exchange your description with a partner, and see if you can guess what each other's object is.

**SKILLS WARMUP**

**Figure 1.1** ▲
You can make observations about the color, shape, and size of this crystal.

**Section Objectives**
For a list of section objectives, see the Student Edition page.

**Skills Objectives**
Students should be able to:

**Communicate** observations about objects in the classroom.

**Interpret Data** by examining how an index is organized.

**Make a Model** of the classroom.

**Predict** what they will have for dinner.

**Apply** previous information to predict weather.

**Classify** clothing according to similar characteristics.

**Measure** how color affects the absorption of heat from sunlight.

**Vocabulary**
data, independent variable, dependent variable, control

**MOTIVATE**

### Skills WarmUp

To give students practice in using science process skills to communicate about the world, have them do the Skills WarmUp.
**Answer**  Answers will depend on the object chosen. Students should be able to explain how a correct guess matches a description .

### Misconceptions

Students may think that all observations involve the sense of sight. Explain that not only are many observations made by using senses other than sight, but also many of the most important observations are made indirectly.

**Answer to In-Text Question**

① **Students will probably report that they used their sense of sight.**

## Class Activity

Adjust the classroom environment before students arrive: play an audiotape of birds chirping, light a scented candle, turn off lights, or make other adjustments. As students arrive, let them observe and discuss with each other the changes they sense. Write senses and observations they mention on the chalkboard.

## Discuss

Have students list several everyday activities, such as dressing for school, making coffee, meeting the bus, and watching a basketball game. Ask students to tell which of the science skills they rely on most when they do these activities. For instance, on a cloudy day, they may predict it will rain, so they take an umbrella.

## Skills Development

**Communicate** Ask students to write the boldface science skills terms on these two pages in a notebook or science journal. Suggest that they write only one or two terms per page, leaving room to fill in their observations and experiences. Ask them to record, during a week, any instances where they used the skills listed. Have students compare their records and work in cooperative groups to write sentences describing how they used each skill.

### Answers to In-Text Questions

① The floating ice looks as if it has broken off from the larger piece of ice.

② Students may predict that it is going to rain.

 *Math Connection*

Fill jars with a known number of seeds, marbles, or similar objects. Ask students to estimate how many objects are in each jar. Have several of the closest guessers share their methods of estimating with the rest of the class.

 *Themes in Science*

**Scale and Structure** Scientists often observe the smallest parts of the earth that are part of the whole earth system. For example, in studying a lake, scientists may study its temperature, the composition of the water, and the types of plants and animals surrounding the lake to learn about the lake as a freshwater system.

**Figure 1.2** ▲
① What can you infer about where the chunks of ice came from?

**Infer** When you infer, or make an inference, you make a logical deduction from something you know or observe. You can often make more than one inference from an observation. Look at Figure 1.2. Where do you think the big pieces of floating ice came from? If you notice that the white wall in the background is a huge wall of ice, or glacier, you might infer that the floating pieces broke off of the glacier. Closer observation of the glacier and the ice chunks may support this inference.

**Estimate** When you estimate, you make careful guesses. Estimating skills are used to gather information when exact measurements are not needed or when they would be impossible or too time-consuming to get. You learn to make estimates about many things. You estimate speed, distance, size, time, and so on.

**Measure** When you need exact and careful information about an observation, you measure. Measurements describe the amount of something. Measurements include both a number and a unit. The volume of water in a lake, the number of fish living in the lake, and the temperature at the lake's surface—all these are forms of measurement.

**Predict** When you predict, you state what you think might happen in the future. Predictions are based on past experiences and observations. With this knowledge, you can state both how something might occur and why it might occur. One way to check a prediction is by doing an experiment.

**Figure 1.3** ▶
How will the weather change?
② What is your prediction?

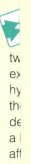

### Cooperative Learning

Assign students to cooperative groups of four. Give each group a collection of nails, staples, screws, bolts, washers, and nuts. Ask them to classify the collection according to any number of categories and to name each category based on the characteristics shared by the objects. Have each group report on its classification system. For an extra challenge, ask each group to classify the objects into two categories, each of which should be broken down into two more categories, and so on. Have each group show its classification system with a tree diagram.

◀ **Figure 1.4**
What are some different ways in which you could classify these rocks? ③

**Classify** When you classify, you group things based on how they are alike. You may be able to group things in many different ways. Some ways to group things are by size, color, shape, texture, or any other characteristic. For example, an area of land may be classified by its location, climate, vegetation, height, type of soil, or even by the number of people living on it.

**Hypothesize** When you state a hypothesis (hy PAHTH uh sihs), you state one possible explanation for some event that happened. Your hypothesis is based on the information you already know. Think of a hypothesis as an explanation or an idea that states why something may always occur. Once you state a hypothesis, you can test your hypothesis by observing, studying, or experimenting. Your observations, research, or the results of experiments should support your hypothesis. If not, you need to think about your hypothesis again and then state a new one.

**Record and Organize** Scientists must keep careful records of their observations. During activities and investigations, you, too, will record observations, measurements, predictions, and so on. Often you will want to organize the data you collect in some way. There are a number of ways you can record and organize data. Some ways are tables or charts, graphs, and diagrams.

**Analyze** Once data have been recorded and organized, you need to analyze the data. When you analyze data, you study the data to look for trends or patterns. You are looking to see if your data support your hypothesis, prediction, or inference.

▼ **ACTIVITY**

**Interpreting Data**

*Cover to Cover*

Look through the index in the back of this book. How is the information in the index organized? How is the organization related to the use of the index?

**SKILLS WORKOUT**

To familiarize students with metric units of length, have students run or walk measured distances of 100 meters and 1 kilometer. Also, have students work in pairs. They can measure with a meter stick how far each student can jump from a still starting position and with a running start.

▼ **ACTIVITY**

### Sequencing

*A Matter of Meters*

Arrange the following lengths in the correct order from shortest to longest.
**a.** 5,000 mm
**b.** 9 km
**c.** 7.3 dm
**d.** 72 cm
**e.** 1.1 m

**SKILLS WORKOUT**

**Figure 1.9** ▲
You will measure many distances that are less than 1 meter. The numbers on this metric ruler represent millimeters.

Multiples of ten make conversion between units very simple. You simply move the decimal point. For instance, 130 centimeters equals 1.3 meters. Think of it in terms of U.S. money: $1.00 = 100 pennies or 10 dimes. These are base = 10 measurements. A centimeter is 1/100 of a meter, and a kilogram is 1,000 grams.

### Length

The basic SI unit of length is the **meter**. A meter is about the distance from the floor to the knob of a door. Chances are that the SI measuring tool that you'll be using in class is a metric ruler, which shows centimeters.

A metric ruler, a tape measure, or any other measuring device with a scale marked in equal divisions makes it possible for you to make exact measurements. A scale helps you find out how many units there are as you measure, without having to count them one by one.

The SI units of length are the kilometer (km), the meter (m), the centimeter (cm), and the millimeter (mm). Use whichever unit is most appropriate for the length you are measuring. The metric ruler is marked in units called centimeters. A centimeter is 1/100 of a meter. Your little finger is about 1 centimeter across. Each centimeter is divided into ten smaller units called millimeters. A dime is about 1 millimeter thick. How long is the rock in Figure 1.9? ①

**Figure 1.10** ▶
A tape measure works best for larger measurements outdoors.

## Integrating the Sciences

**Astronomy** Because there is negligible gravity in space, astronauts and other objects are weightless there. This is why objects aboard a spaceship float. However, since the amount of matter in the object does not change, its mass remains the same. For the mass of an astronaut to change, matter would need to be added or removed from the astronaut. Ask students if an astronaut's mass would change after eating a meal or getting a haircut. (Yes)

## Volume

Take a deep breath. As your lungs fill with air, you can feel your chest expand. The change in lung size can be measured in terms of **volume**. Volume is the amount of space that something occupies. As your lungs expand, they occupy more space. A greater amount of air will fit inside them.

Because the SI base unit of length is the meter, the unit of volume is the cubic meter, or m³. A cubic meter is the space occupied by a cube that is 1 m × 1 m × 1 m. This unit of volume is used to measure large quantities, such as the volume of concrete in a building.

In your science activities, you are more likely to use the cubic centimeter (cm³). How big is a cubic centimeter? ② How many cubic centimeters do you think will fit in a teaspoon? ③

**Figure 1.11** ▲
To read the volume of liquid in a graduated cylinder, keep your line of sight level with the liquid, and read the bottom of the meniscus.

You are probably most familiar with the basic SI unit of volume, the **liter** (L). Soft drinks often come in 1-liter or 2-liter containers. A smaller unit of volume is the milliliter (mL). There are about 20 drops of water in each milliliter.

In your science class, you will probably use a graduated cylinder to measure liquid volumes. As you can see in Figure 1.11, the cylinder is marked in milliliters. Notice that liquids in a graduated cylinder have a curved surface. The liquid rises slightly up the sides of the container and dips slightly in the center. That dip in the surface of the liquid is called the *meniscus* (meh NIHS kuhs). To measure the volume of liquid accurately, you read the level of the liquid at the *lowest point* of the meniscus. The best way to do this is to look at the surface of the liquid at eye level.

## Mass and Weight

Did you know that things are slightly lighter when weighed at the equator than at the poles? The reason is because an object's weight depends on the force of gravity. At the equator, gravity is measurably less, so things are lighter.

Because weight measurements depend on where they are taken, weight can be unreliable for scientific use. That is why scientists use a measurement called **mass**. Mass depends on the number and kinds of atoms that make up an object. Because it does not depend on gravity, an object's mass always remains the same, no matter where the measurement is taken.

The basic SI unit of mass is the **kilogram** (kg). Your mass is probably between 35 and 75 kg. In the laboratory, however, scientists often use a much smaller unit called the gram (g). A paper

Chapter 1  Studying Science  **15**

## Skills Development

**Measure** Bring in some common containers labeled by volume to class. Include containers with pint, quart, and half-gallon designations, as well as SI unit volumes. Remove the volume labels from some of the containers. Have students compare and estimate the volumes of each. Then have them use water to test their estimates and comparisons. Finally have them measure, label, and display the unlabeled items.

**Collect Data** Allow students to find the mass of various volumes of water. Have them make a table listing each volume and its mass.

## Class Activity

Have students calculate the volume of the classroom.

### Answers to In-Text Questions

② **A little smaller than a sugar cube**

③ **4 to 5 cm³**

## TEACH ▪ Continued

## TEACH ▪ Continued

### Skills Development

**Communicate** Have students work in groups to find the density of several items. Remind them to record the data they gather in a table. Then ask students to write a problem or riddle about each item. Have them include some observable characteristics or measurements but not the name of the item. They can exchange problems with other groups and solve one another's problems.

### Answers to In-Text Questions

① **131.8 g**

② **Air and Styrofoam are possible answers.**

③ **It will be suspended, under water, without bobbing above the surface.**

④ **Float**

⑤ **Answers will vary. Although it depends on the type of water, the student's body composition, and whether he or she has inhaled or exhaled, a student will normally float in water.**

⑥ **Overall, students' densities are close to, but less than, that of water.**

### Integrating the Sciences

**Chemistry** Ask students if they think air has density. Explain that air is matter in the form of gas, and is made up of particles that are much farther apart from each other than the particles that make up liquids and solids. The density of gases is therefore much less than that of liquids and solids.

### Themes in Science

**Stability and Equilibrium** The density of a solid or liquid material does not change appreciably unless a phase change takes place. For example, the density of a rock would remain the same no matter how many times the rock is cut. The smallest piece of granite would have the same density as a giant granite boulder.

---

clip has a mass of about 1 gram. For even smaller measurements, scientists use a milligram (mg).

You will use a balance to determine an object's mass. A balance lets you compare an unknown mass with a known mass. Look at the triple-beam balance in Figure 1.12. The known masses are the riders on the three beams. You move the riders to make the pointer of the balance read zero. Then you add together the numbers under each rider to determine the object's mass.

### Density

Imagine you have a plastic spoon in one hand and a metal spoon in the other. They are both the same size. Which feels heavier? The metal spoon has a greater mass because metal has a greater **density**

**Figure 1.12**
What is the mass of the rock? ▼ ①

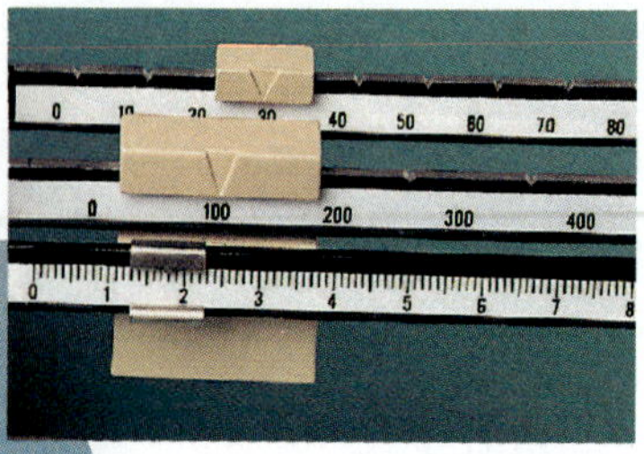

than plastic. Density is the measure of how much matter is packed into a given volume. In mathematical terms:

$$\text{density} = \frac{\text{mass}}{\text{volume}}$$

Every substance has its own characteristic density. Scientists often measure density in grams of matter per cubic centimeter ($g/cm^3$). Pure water has a density of 1 $g/cm^3$. This means that for every cubic centimeter of water, there is 1 gram of matter. In contrast, lead has a density of about 11 $g/cm^3$. On the less-dense side, balsa wood has a density of only about 0.1 $g/cm^3$. What is a substance that is even less dense than balsa wood? ②

In addition to helping identify a substance, an object's density determines whether the material will float or sink. The density of everything is compared to the density of pure water. Materials with densities greater than that of pure water (1 $g/cm^3$) always sink. Materials with densities less than that of water always float. How will an object with the same density as water behave? If you put ③ some balsa wood in water, will it float or ④ sink? What happens to you in water? ⑤ What's your density compared to water? ⑥

## Integrating the Sciences

**Life Science** Discuss the importance of temperature in determining the kinds of organisms that can live in a certain place. What kinds of organisms can withstand temperatures below the freezing point of water? What characteristics enable them to adapt to this kind of environment?

## Temperature

You've probably had your temperature taken when you were sick. Chances are that your body temperature was 98.6 degrees Fahrenheit (F), which is what it is when you are healthy. Scientists, however, do not use Fahrenheit temperature readings. Instead, they measure temperature using the Celsius scale. In fact, most of the countries of the world use Celsius as their temperature scale. On this scale, your body temperature is about 37 degrees Celsius, or 37°C.

In your classroom, you probably will use a Celsius thermometer to measure temperature. A thermometer is a thin glass tube filled with a colored liquid. As the liquid heats up, it expands and moves up the tube. As the liquid cools, it moves down the tube. The sides of this tube are marked in degrees Celsius. Two important reference marks on the Celsius scale are the freezing point (0°C) and the boiling point (100°C) of water.

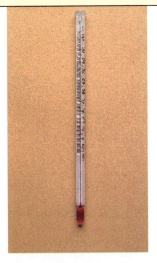

**Figure 1.13** ▲
On the Celsius scale, water freezes at 0°C and boils at 100°C.

## SkillBuilder *Measuring*

### Average Mass

You want to compare the soil in two different places. You dig a hole at each place and find that one of the main differences is the size of the rocks in the soil. What is the best way to describe this difference with numbers? You would probably want to determine the *average* mass of the rocks in both places.

Earth scientists often want to find the average mass of a group of similar objects. Practice this skill by finding the average mass of a group of rocks.

1. Collect 20 small rocks or pebbles of similar size.

2. On a separate sheet of paper, copy the data table shown.

3. From your group of rocks, choose one that seems average. Measure its mass and record it in the table.

| Number of Rocks | Mass | Average Mass |
|---|---|---|
| 1 | | |
| 5 | | |
| 10 | | |
| 20 | | |

4. Count out 5 rocks and measure their mass together. Divide this number by 5. Record this measurement in your table as the average mass of 5 rocks.

5. Repeat step 4 using 10 rocks, then 20 rocks.

How "average" was the first rock you chose? Did the average masses vary as your sampling size increased? Does a larger sample of rocks give you a more accurate average? Explain.

## Discuss

Ask students to provide examples of other common temperatures in SI units. For instance, room temperature is about 20°C. Remind students that many outdoor temperature signs give the temperature in both Fahrenheit and Celsius degrees. Ask them to identify other ways they could improve their familiarity with SI temperature units.

## SkillBuilder

**Define Operationally** Encourage students to form a definition of *average* in their own words.
**Answers**
**3–6.** Answers will vary. Some students will find that the rock they chose as average was a little above or below the average they calculated for each group of rocks. They should recognize that the most accurate average is obtained by measuring all the rocks in the group. From these observations, students should be able to conclude that a larger sample of rocks gives a more accurate average.

## Enrich

Have students form a hypothesis about the relationship between the accuracy of an average and the size of the sample used to calculate it. Have them predict how the average mass will change if they add a very large rock to their sample. Ask them to infer how the average would change if they added five large rocks to the sample. Ask: Will the new average be as descriptive as the other averages you found? Why or why not?

### Skills Development

**Infer** Ask students to describe the difficulty of buying shoes if the unit of size measurement varied from store to store. Then have them explain why researchers around the world use the same system of measurement.

### Enrich

Olives were once sold by sizes such as jumbo, colossal, super colossal, medium, large, and extra large. Have students arrange these sizes in order of largest to smallest. Then have them use package labels or information from the FDA to check their lists. Ask them to look for other confusing or nonstandard measurements in advertisements and newspapers. Have them propose a standard unit in each case that would make comparing the sizes easier.

### EVALUATE

### WrapUp

**Portfolio** Students may make a list of common items that have standard SI measurements. For instance, a dime is about a millimeter thick and has a mass of about 10 grams. Have them work in groups to find an item for each of the SI units in this section.

Use Review Worksheet 1.2.

### Check and Explain

1. Kilogram, meter, and liter

2. Weight varies because gravitational force varies. Mass depends only on the number and kinds of atoms in a sample and does not change from place to place.

3. Float; its density is less than the density of water.

4. Answers will vary. Examples, width of a pencil, piece of chalk, aquarium

### *Math Connection*

Point out to students that a year is 365.25 days long, the time it takes Earth to orbit once around the sun. Ask them what happens to the extra fraction of a day. When they make the connection with a leap year, ask how often a leap year occurs and how they know. (Leap years occur every four years; February 29th makes up for the time lost annually.)

### *Integrating the Sciences*

**Physical Science** Einstein developed the Theory of Relativity, which describes how time is affected by motion in space at constant speed. According to the theory, if a person were to travel through space at the speed of light, time would stand still.

### Time

The basic SI unit of time is the second. In your classroom, you will use a watch with a second hand to measure time. As you know, other units such as the minute, hour, day, and year are not based on the number ten. There are 60 seconds in a minute, 60 minutes in an hour, 24 hours in a day, and 365.25 days in a year. This system of measuring time is used everywhere in the world. In science, the prefix *milli-* is used with the unit second for some short time measurements.

### Science and Society
*Measurement Standards*

You've just bought a tape deck made in Japan. The box says it is 30 cm long, so you trust it will be 30 cm according to your metric ruler. Centimeters, like other SI units, are the same throughout the world. They are standard units. However, a standard, universal system of measurement did not always exist.

You may be surprised to know that early systems of measurement were often based on the human body. The Egyptians defined a cubit as the distance between the elbow and the tip of the middle finger, a distance that varied for each person. In order to be more useful, units such as this one had to be defined according to an unchanging standard.

In SI, each unit is precisely defined. A meter is equal to 1 650 763.73 wavelengths of red-orange light given off by the element krypton. A kilogram is the mass of the cylinder stored at the National Institute of Standards and Technology in Maryland.

**Figure 1.14** ▲
This photograph shows the cylinder that defines a kilogram of mass in the United States. The cylinder is at the far right of the turntable.

### Check and Explain

1. List the SI units for mass, length, and volume.

2. Why do scientists use mass instead of weight?

3. **Predict** A certain material has a density of 0.95 $g/cm^3$. Will a block of it sink or float?

4. **Measure** In your classroom, find objects with the following measurements: less than 1 cm long, about 20 g in mass, more than 1 L in volume.

## Geography Connection

Have students use an atlas to make bar graphs of the highest mountains on each continent and the depth of the world's largest oceans and seas. Have students compare their graphs to the bar graphs of these features shown on pages 618 and 622 of the Data Bank.

# 1.3 Graphing

## Objectives

▶ **Identify** the types of graphs.

▶ **Explain** how data are plotted on a line graph.

▶ **Make a graph** showing the number of people in a group with blue, brown, and green eyes.

---

▼ **ACTIVITY**

**Gathering Data**

*Hands on the Table*

Count and record the number of left-handed and right-handed people in your class.

Display this information in a table, a bar graph, and a circle graph. Which organizer seems best for showing the information?

**SKILLS WARMUP**

How would you present the data from an experiment in which you measured changes in temperature over time? You might choose to make a graph. A graph is a picture or diagram of data. You've probably seen many different graphs in newspapers and magazines, and on television news reports. Graphs are useful tools for presenting lots of information in a small space.

## Kinds of Graphs

There are three kinds of graphs: circle, bar, and line graphs. No matter which kind of graph you look at, all graphs let you compare numerical data. Each kind of graph, however, shows the data in a different way.

**Circle Graphs** Think about a pie cut into pieces, and you have a mental model of a circle graph. A circle graph is a divided circle. It shows how a part or share of something relates to the whole. You can see what fraction, percentage, or share each part represents.

Look at the circle graph in Figure 1.15. The circle represents the amount of water used during one year in the United States. Each "slice" of the circle shows the percentage of that amount used for a particular kind of purpose.

**Bar Graphs** Just as its name describes, a bar graph has bars. The bars help you compare things. You can compare measurements, amounts, and changes.

Look at the bar graph in Figure 1.16 on page 20. It shows the lengths of the four longest rivers on the earth. You can see very easily which river is the longest and how its length compares to the others.

**Use of Water in the United States**

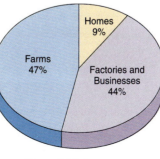

**Figure 1.15** ▲
What type of water use is the largest? ①

**Section Objectives**
For a list of section objectives, see the Student Edition page.

**Skills Objectives**
Students should be able to:

**Gather Data** about classmates and organize it.

**Make a Graph** that best shows the information presented.

**Analyze** the average rainfall to show what bar-graph scale should be used.

**Make a Graph** of student eye colors.

**MOTIVATE**

### Skills WarmUp

To give students practice in gathering and graphing data, have them do the Skills WarmUp.
**Answer** Students will probably choose the circle graph, which is best for showing at a glance how each number relates to the class as a whole. Bar graphs, however, are more useful in numerical comparisons or for adding new data, such as the number of people who are both right-handed and left-handed.

### Prior Knowledge

To gauge how much students know about graphs, ask the following questions:

▶ Where have you seen graphs before?

▶ What kinds of information besides numbers can be shown with graphs?

**Answer to In-Text Question**

① **The largest percentage of water is used for farming.**

## TEACH

### Critical Thinking

**Compare and Contrast** Ask students to collect several circle and bar graphs from newspapers or magazines. Have them choose one circle graph and make a bar graph showing the same information. Ask: Which was easier to read and understand? Why?

### Directed Inquiry

After students study the text and Figure 1.17, ask the following questions:

▶ How much water will be in the control setup on the 7th day from the start of the experiment? Explain. (Between 125 and 150 mL. The volume hasn't decreased more than 25 mL in any one day.)

▶ What kind of graph would be useful for predicting what percent of the water in the experimental setup would have evaporated on the 7th day? (Answers will vary. The line graph itself is useful. A bar graph showing the amount of water evaporated each day or showing the amount of water evaporated as a percent of the starting volume would also be helpful.)

▶ Which type of graph would be most useful for predicting the average rainfall in August? Why? (A bar graph showing August rainfall for the last few years)

### Ancillary Options

If you are using the blackline masters from *Muticulturalism in Mathematics, Science, and Technology,* have students read about Jan Matzeliger and complete pages 109 to 110.

### Answers to In-Text Questions

① Nile

② About 170 mL

③ Changes that occur in related variables

20

### Math Connection

Using a simple example such as $x = 2y$, show how an equation can be shown as a line on a graph. Give students other simple equations to plot on graphs.
**Use Integrating Worksheet 1.3.**

**Figure 1.16**
① Which river is the longest? ▼

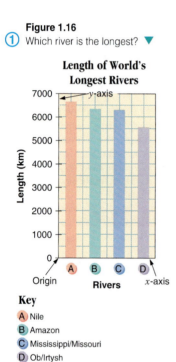

Length of World's Longest Rivers

**Key**
Ⓐ Nile
Ⓑ Amazon
Ⓒ Mississippi/Missouri
Ⓓ Ob/Irtysh

Notice that on the left side of the bar graph is a scale showing length in kilometers. The data on river length are plotted according to this vertical line, called the *y*-axis. Each bar is labeled on the horizontal line, called the *x*-axis. On this graph, the labels are letters keyed to the names of the rivers.

When you make a bar graph, you need to choose the scale by looking at the highest and lowest numbers in your data. On this graph, the scale ranges from 0 to 7,000 km. Notice that the scale is higher than the longest river. Also, the scale is divided into 1,000-km segments. All bar graphs have a scale and equal divisions.

**Line Graphs** Line graphs are made from pairs of numbers. Each pair expresses a relationship between two factors, or variables. For this reason, line graphs are useful for showing changes that occur in related variables. Line graphs can help you answer if-then questions. They also help you see patterns or trends in data. Unlike bar graphs and circle graphs, line graphs let you plot several different sets of data on one graph. In this way, you can make comparisons between the sets of data.

Look at the line graph in Figure 1.17. Do the data look familiar? The data it shows are from the evaporation experiment on page 7. Notice that the graph includes two sets of data, one from the control setup and one from the experimental setup. For each day of the experiment, the volume of each beaker is plotted as a dot according to the scale on the *y*-axis. For example, above day 1 on the *x*-axis is a dot showing 180 mL for the experimental setup. What is the volume of the beaker in the control setup on day 4? ②

**Figure 1.17** ▶
What kind of data can be shown on a line graph? ③

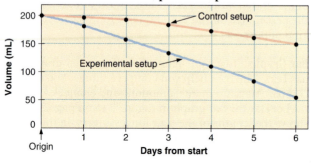

Data from Evaporation Experiment

The dots for each beaker are connected with a line. The lines, as you can see, vary in steepness. This difference indicates that the water in the experimental setup evaporated at a faster rate than the water in the control setup. You can see that line graphs are very useful for both showing and analyzing data from experiments. Line graphs are also good for showing any kind of change over time.

### Science and Technology  *Graph Uses*

You will see many graphs in this book. All of these graphs were produced by computers. As you may know, graphs are not just used in textbooks. In the business world, graphs are often used for important presentations. For example, a manager may need to present statistics that show his or her department's financial gains for the year. The manager may use a bar, circle, or line graph to show the information.

In the field of medicine, graphs are used to interpret information in a number of ways. An electrocardiograph, or EKG, is an instrument that picks up and records electrical currents produced by the human heart. The currents are picked up by metal strips, or electrodes, attached to the patient's body. The EKG records the currents on paper as wavy lines. The graph that is produced is used by physicians to diagnose heart damage. The damage may have been caused by blood pressure or other factors. The EKG also helps determine irregular heartbeats and the amount of injury caused by heart attacks.

### Check and Explain

1. What are three kinds of graphs?

2. What does a dot or point represent on a line graph?

3. **Analyze** The average rainfall in five cities is given in centimeters: 25, 35, 43, 45, and 68. What scale would you use to show these data on a bar graph? What would be the equal divisions?

4. **Make a Graph** Count the number of students in your class with blue eyes, brown eyes, and green eyes. Display these data in a graph.

# 1.4

## Section Objectives

For a list of section objectives, see the Student Edition page.

## Skills Objectives

Students should be able to:

**Classify** materials that make up the earth.

**Communicate** an earth science adventure.

## Vocabulary

biosphere

## MOTIVATE

### Skills WarmUp

To help students become familiar with the earth's different materials, have them do the Skills WarmUp.

**Answer** Students should list various materials that make up each of the six parts of the earth shown on pages 22 to 23. These may include rocks, soil, water, sand, plants, and air.

### Misconceptions

Students may not think of organisms as being a part of the earth. Explain that bacteria and plant and animal matter make up more than 20 percent of some soils. Also, the actions of living things change the rocks, water, and atmosphere of the earth. These relationships exist as a part of the earth, and they are crucial to the earth's survival.

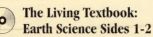

**The Living Textbook: Earth Science Sides 1-2**

Chapter 23        Frame 02841
Rocky Mountains (1 Frame)
Search:

## Portfolio

Have students write a story about where they would choose to go if they had the power to go anywhere on the earth. If students need ideas, refer them to the introduction of this section. Have the students share their stories with the class, or post some of the stories on a bulletin board. They can keep the stories in their portfolios. As students learn more about the earth throughout the year, they may want to revise or write new stories.

### ▼ ACTIVITY

#### Classifying

**What on Earth?**

List the different materials that make up the following:
- ◆ the earth
- ◆ the earth's surface
- ◆ the earth's atmosphere

How many different kinds of materials can you find?

Classify the materials into a few groups. What basis do you use for your classification?

**SKILLS WARMUP**

**Figure 1.18**
**Parts of the Earth** ▼

## 1.4 Studying the Earth

### Objectives

▶ **Identify** six parts of the earth studied by earth scientists.

▶ **Explain** what the biosphere is.

▶ **Infer** how living things are dependent on the nonliving parts of the earth.

▶ **Communicate** what it might be like to be an earth scientist.

Imagine you have the power to go anywhere on the earth. You can sail across the ocean or dive to the ocean floor. You can climb the highest mountains, trek across deserts, or tromp through tropical jungles. You can explore caverns deep in the earth or climb down into a volcano. You can even fly high above the clouds.

This power to go anywhere in the world may only take place in your imagination, but in a way, the pages of this book can also give you that power. Within this book, you will take many different journeys of exploration. You will discover that your home planet is amazingly varied and very beautiful.

**Ocean**
Most of the earth's surface is covered by huge bodies of salt water called oceans. The oceans are home to a great variety of living things.

### Themes in Science

**Systems and Interactions** The living and nonliving substances on the earth affect one another. Air, water, and wind change the surface features of the earth. Organisms depend on these substances for survival. Organisms themselves interact with and affect the nonliving substances of the earth.

There are many places to go on Earth if you want to understand it as a whole planet. Earth is a massive, rocky sphere moving in space. On its surface are oceans and landmasses. Above the surface is an envelope of air. The air and water on the earth are always moving and changing, affecting the landmasses in different ways.

All over the earth's surface are living things, or *organisms*. They depend on nonliving substances such as air and water to stay alive. Organisms, in turn, affect the nonliving parts of the earth. Look at Figure 1.18 to learn about the parts of the earth you will be studying.

**Atmosphere**
Between the earth's surface and outer space is an envelope of air and water vapor called the atmosphere. In the atmosphere, certain changes occur that produce wind, rain, snow, and changes in temperature.

**Rocks**
Much of the earth is made of different kinds of rocky material. The upper layer of the rocky earth, called the crust, moves and changes, forming mountains and other features.

**Fresh Water**
Water flows on the earth's surface in rivers and streams. It fills lakes and ponds. Fresh water is also found under the surface and in frozen masses called glaciers.

**Organisms**
The earth's atmosphere, fresh water, oceans, and soil are homes for the billions of organisms that live on earth. Scientists classify the organisms into five large kingdoms: plants, animals, fungi (FUHN jeye), monerans, and protists.

**Soil**
The breakdown of rocks and the decay of dead organisms produce soil. Soil nourishes plants. It also contains many living things.

### Explore Visually

After students study the text and Figure 1.18, ask the following questions:

▶ In what kinds of locations can fresh water be found? (Rivers, streams, lakes, ponds, underground, and in glaciers)

▶ What is the earth's crust? What kind of landscape features does it make? (The crust is the earth's upper layer of rocky material. It moves and as it moves it forms mountains and other features.)

▶ Where is the atmosphere, and what is it made of? (The atmosphere is an envelope around the earth between the earth's surface and outer space. It is made of water and air.)

▶ How are rocks and soil related? (Soil is produced by the breaking apart of rocks and the decay of dead organisms.)

### Reteach
Use Reteach Worksheet 1.1.

**The Living Textbook: Earth Science Sides 1-2**

Chapter 23          Frame 02933
Soil Development (1 Frame)
Search:

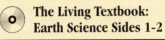

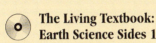

**The Living Textbook: Earth Science Sides 1-2**

Chapter 9          Frame 02093
Waterfalls (4 Frames)
Search:          Step:

TEACH ▪ *Continued*

## *Career Corner*

**Classify** After students study the text and the table, ask them to make a concept map, including the branches of science listed in the text and the following terms: *ocean currents, volcanoes, planets, hurricanes,* and *mountains.*

## Class Activity

Have students prepare a poster or bulletin board that represents the biosphere. Have them add pictures of the kinds of plant and animal life that can be found in different areas of the biosphere. Ask students how they know which organisms live in which section of the biosphere.

## Integrated Learning

Use Integrated Worksheet 1.4.

### *Themes in Science*

**Diversity and Unity** Many different types of organisms exist on the surface of the earth. The organisms live in almost every location. Each type of organism has adapted to living on the surface in different ways. However, all organisms have certain characteristics in common, such as taking in energy, getting rid of wastes, and reproduction.

### *Integrating the Sciences*

**Environmental Science** Many of the habitats in which organisms live are being destroyed by human beings. For example, people cause water pollution and are responsible for deforestation. Have students make a list of the different ways that the biosphere is being affected by human beings.

## Biosphere

Where do organisms live on the earth? Most organisms you're familiar with live right at the surface, just as you do. You know that many organisms also live in the ocean. Crabs, clams, and other organisms even live on the ocean floor.

On land, some organisms live below the surface. Insects and worms live in the soil. Some organisms live in caves. Others live in the tiny, water-filled spaces between rocks that lie underneath riverbeds.

Organisms also live well above the earth's surface. Birds and insects make their homes in trees. Some birds soar so high you can't see them from the ground. Some spiders have been found floating on webs several kilometers above the surface. All the places where life exists make up the biosphere (BY uhs feer). The **biosphere** is a zone of life that extends from the ocean floor to high in the atmosphere.

## *Career Corner*

### *What Careers Use Scientific Skills and Knowledge?*

Careers that use scientific skills or knowledge are many and varied. In some of these careers, you mostly do scientific research. However, there are many careers that require some science study, but involve nonscientific work, including underwater photographer, weather forecaster, or air traffic controller.

Each branch of earth science is different from the others. Each prepares you for certain opportunities. Look at the table to the right to get an idea of what kinds of careers are related to each branch of science.

| Careers in Science | | |
|---|---|---|
| **Branch** | **Study** | **Careers** |
| Geology | The structure and makeup of the earth | Geologist, land use planner, geophysicist |
| Biology | All living things | Park ranger, public health educator, medical illustrator |
| Oceanography | The earth's oceans and the organisms living in them | Oceanographer, fisheries biologist, underwater photographer |
| Chemistry | Makeup of substances and the changes that substances undergo | Environmental technician, chef, food scientist |
| Meteorology | Weather and the earth's atmosphere | Air pollution technician, air traffic controller, weather forecaster |
| Space Science | The solar system, galaxy, and universe | Planetarium technician, astronomer, astronaut |
| Geography | Earth's surface features, both natural and human-made | Cartographer, surveyor, urban planner |

## Geography

How much of the earth's surface does the town or city you live in cover? What is the name of the tallest mountain in Africa? How deep is the Grand Canyon? What's the average summer temperature in Mexico City? To answer these questions and others like them, you would look up information provided by geographers. Geographers study the earth. They look at the size, shape, and features of the earth. They also study what is beneath the earth's surface. Geography is often considered an earth science.

In addition to the earth's natural features, geographers look at features made by humans. They study what humans do to the earth's surface, what they build, and where they live. Geographers collect data on human populations and their growth and movement over time. They look for patterns in how humans use the earth's surface and relate these patterns to factors such as rainfall. They also study how humans interact with their environments. Geographers want to know how humans use the earth and how they change it as they use it.

Geographers provide much of the information used to make maps. In fact, maps are often a geographer's most important tools. Because maps can represent large parts of the earth's surface, they are useful for providing a variety of information. In this book, you will see many kinds of maps. As you study these maps, remember that many would probably not even exist for you if it weren't for the important work of geographers.

**Figure 1.19** ▲
How does geography help you learn more about the earth? ①

### Life Science
**L I N K**

Maps can show many different kinds of information, including the diversity of animals that live on the earth.

On a separate sheet of paper, trace the map on pages 32–33. Research the kinds of animals that live on each of the seven continents. Look in magazines for photographs of at least three animals for each continent. Cut out the photographs and paste them in the correct location on your map. Do any of your animals live on more than one continent? What animals are unique to the continent they live on?

**A C T I V I T Y**

## Science and Technology *Telescopes*

Earth is one of nine planets in the solar system. The nearby star called the sun is one of many billions of stars in the Milky Way. The Milky Way is a huge collection of stars called a galaxy. It is one of many galaxies in the universe. What is Earth's place in the vast space of the universe? This, too, is a concern of earth scientists. The study of planets, stars, and other bodies in space is called astronomy (uh STRAHN uh mee).

Astronomers depend on special tools for studying distant objects in space. The most important of these tools are several kinds of telescopes. Telescopes that focus light from stars and planets to form a magnified image are *optical telescopes.* A *reflecting telescope,* shown

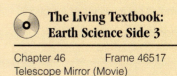

## Skills Development

**Organize Data** Ask students to make a table describing the different kinds of telescopes. Make sure students include what the telescopes are used for and what forms of energy they collect. (*Reflecting:* mirror and lenses focus light to form an image *refracting:* lenses focus light to form an image *radio:* antenna and computer convert radio waves into an image)

## EVALUATE

## WrapUp

**Portfolio** Have students make a diagram of a cross section of the biosphere and label the areas in which they would find the oceans, fresh water, fossils, rocks, soil, and atmosphere. They can add the diagrams to their portfolios.

Use Review Worksheet 1.4.

## Check and Explain

1. Atmosphere; water and air

2. The biosphere is all places were life exists. It extends from the ocean floor to high in the atmosphere.

3. Organisms need space, water, nutrients, warmth, and air. The space provides a place to live, either on land or in the water. Water for organisms can come from rain or streams. Nutrients are provided by soil. Warmth comes from the land, atmosphere, and water which store heat from the sun. The air comes from the atmosphere, and provides the gases organisms need in order to function.

4. Short stories will vary.

## STS Connection

Several radio telescopes are currently scanning the skies to detect any radio signals that might be transmitted from planets with intelligent life. This project is called SETI, or the search for extraterrestrial intelligence. Discuss with students how people might react if any of the SETI radio telescopes pick up an alien message.

**Figure 1.20** ▲
A reflecting telescope at Mt. Hamilton in California (left). The radio telescopes (right) are located in New Mexico.

in Figure 1.20, is a kind of optical telescope that uses both mirrors and lenses to focus light. A *refracting telescope* focuses light using only lenses.

Visible light is only one of the many forms of energy given off by stars and other objects in space. Other forms of energy include invisible radiation called radio waves. Radio waves can be collected and focused just like visible light. The telescope that collects radio waves is called a *radio telescope*. You can see an example of a radio telescope in Figure 1.20. This telescope is a large dish that collects the radio waves and focuses them on an antenna. The antenna transmits the waves to a computer that converts the electrical signals into an image.

### Check and Explain

1. What is the envelope of air above the earth's surface? What does it contain?

2. Describe the biosphere. What are the boundaries of the biosphere?

3. **Infer** Name at least five ways that organisms are dependent on the nonliving parts of the world. Explain.

4. **Communicate** Choose a part of the earth you would like to study. Write a short story about an adventure you have as an earth scientist studying that part of the earth.

## Chapter 1 Review

### Concept Summary

**1.1 Science Skills and Methods**
▶ In their study of nature, scientists observe, infer, estimate, measure, predict, classify, hypothesize, record, organize, and analyze.
▶ Scientists perform experiments to gather data and test hypotheses.
▶ Scientific theories may change to explain new facts and discoveries.
▶ Scientists use models to represent the parts of nature they study.

**1.2 Measuring with Scientific Units**
▶ Scientists measure length, volume, mass, density, temperature, and time with standard SI units.
▶ Mass is the amount of matter an object contains; it is not the same as weight.

▶ Density is the measure of how much mass is in a certain volume of matter.

**1.3 Graphing**
▶ Circle graphs show percentages of the different parts that make up a whole.
▶ Bar graphs compare one characteristic of several different things.
▶ Line graphs show data defined by two variables.

**1.4 Studying the Earth**
▶ The earth is made up of oceans, an atmosphere, and a rocky crust. Its landmasses contain soil, bodies of fresh water, and fossils.
▶ The biosphere extends from the ocean bottoms into the atmosphere.

### Chapter Vocabulary

| | | | |
|---|---|---|---|
| data (1.1) | control (1.1) | liter (1.2) | density (1.2) |
| independent variable (1.1) | meter (1.2) | mass (1.2) | biosphere (1.4) |
| dependent variable (1.1) | volume (1.2) | kilogram (1.2) | |

### Check Your Vocabulary

Use the vocabulary words above to complete the following sentences correctly.

1. When you measure ____ , you determine how much matter an object contains.

2. You use the SI unit called the ____ to measure length.

3. When you study nature, you gather information called ____ .

4. The variable in an experiment that causes a change in another variable is the ____ .

5. The liter is a unit of ____ .

6. The zone of the earth in which organisms live is the ____ .

7. Matter's ____ is measured in g/cm³.

8. The variable in an experiment that changes in response to changes in the independent variable is the ____ .

9. Experiments often have an experimental setup and a ____ setup.

10. The mass of your body is best measured in ____ .

11. In the science laboratory, you will measure volumes using the unit called the ____ .

### Write Your Vocabulary

Write sentences using the vocabulary words above. Show that you know what each word means.

### Check Your Vocabulary

1. mass
2. meter
3. data
4. independent variable
5. volume
6. biosphere
7. density
8. dependent variable
9. control
10. kilograms
11. liter

### Write Your Vocabulary

Students' sentences should show that they know the meaning of each word as well as how to use it in a sentence.

Use Vocabulary Worksheet for Chapter 1.

## Check Your Knowledge

1. All measurements must include a number and the appropriate units.
2. Wear safety goggles and a laboratory apron when using heat, chemicals, and harmful materials.
3. Experiments are carried out to test hypotheses.
4. Organisms require many nonliving substances in order to live.
5. Answers will vary, but may include: terrariums, aquariums, maps, diagrams.
6. Liters and cubic centimeters are SI units of volume measurement.
7. Mass is the amount of matter that makes up an object. Weight is a measure of the force of gravity on an object.
8. An inference is a logical deduction from something that is known or observed. A prediction is a statement of what you think might happen in the future.
9. You should use the emergency eyewash station to flush the chemicals out of your eyes.
10. False; sometimes
11. False; 10
12. True
13. False; grams per cubic centimeter
14. False; line
15. False; radio

## Check Your Understanding

1. a. bar
   b. circle
   c. line
   d. line
2. A hypothesis is a possible explanation for the cause of something. A prediction is a statement of what might happen in the future. A prediction may be stated as the logical consequence of a certain hypothesis, but a prediction does not explain a cause.

3. The energy for all living things on earth comes initially from the sun. The sun is responsible for warming the earth and providing the energy to drive the weather.
4. 0.5 km = 500 m, which is greater than 50 m; 2 $m^3$ is larger.
5. Answers will vary.
6. A reflecting telescope uses mirrors to enlarge the image of the object being viewed, while a refracting telescope uses lenses.
7. a. liters; $m^3$ are also acceptable
   b. $g/cm^3$
   c. °C

---

# Chapter 1 Review

## Check Your Knowledge

Answer the following in complete sentences.

1. All measurements must include what two parts?
2. When you work in the laboratory, what should you wear?
3. How are experiments related to hypotheses?
4. How are organisms related to nonliving substances such as air and water?
5. Give two examples of a scientific model.
6. What are two SI units used to measure volume?
7. What is the difference between mass and weight?
8. What is an inference? How does an inference differ from a prediction?
9. What should you do if you get a chemical in your eyes during a laboratory activity?

Determine whether each statement is true or false. Write *true* if it is true. If it is false, change the underlined word(s) to make the statement true.

10. Scientific theories <u>never</u> change.
11. SI units are based on multiples of <u>1,000.</u>
12. You read the level of the <u>lowest point</u> of the meniscus to measure the volume in a graduated cylinder.
13. Density is measured in <u>kilograms</u>.
14. <u>Circle</u> graphs have an *x*-axis and a *y*-axis.
15. <u>Optical</u> telescopes capture and focus radio waves.

## Check Your Understanding

Apply the concepts you have learned to answer each question.

1. **Application** What kind of graph—circle, bar, or line—would you use to show each of the following kinds of data?
   a. The heights of four different mountains.
   b. The amount of time you spend each day sleeping, eating, working, studying, being with friends, and watching television.
   c. The increase in the number of sit-ups you can do through a six-week exercise program.
   d. The world population from 1800 to the present.
2. **Critical Thinking** How does a prediction differ from a hypothesis?
3. **Mystery Photo** The photograph on page 2 is a false-color image of solar flares coming off the surface of the sun. What is the importance of the sun to the earth and its life?
4. Which is the greater length, 0.5 km or 50 m? Which is the larger volume, 2 $m^3$ or 2 L?
5. **Application** Measure and record your height in meters. If possible, also measure your mass in kilograms.
6. **Compare and Contrast** What is the difference between a reflecting telescope and a refracting telescope?
7. What SI unit or units would you use to measure each of the following?
   a. The volume of water in a swimming pool.
   b. The density of pure gold.
   c. The temperature of a pond.

## Develop Your Skills

**1.** a. About 7°C

    b. The temperature rose slowly from October 13 to 15, then increased sharply, from 7°C to 15°C on the 16th.

    c. October 16

**2.** a. 142 796 km; 130 040 km larger

    b. Earth, Mercury, Venus

**3.** Check students' line graphs for accuracy.

**4.** a. 1 m

    b. 500 g

    c. 1 L

## Make Connections

**1.**

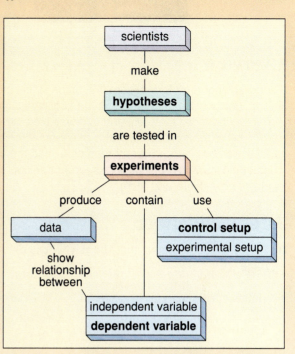

**2.** Student reports will vary. Make sure students describe obstacles the scientist faced, and how she overcame them.

**3.** Students' answers will vary. Examples include: Good observational skills can help you be a safe cyclist or driver. Estimation can help when making purchases. Prediction can help you plan for the future. Measurement skills are important for anyone who builds or uses blueprints or plans.

---

### Develop Your Skills

Use the skills you have developed in this chapter to complete each activity.

**1. Interpret Data** The line graph below shows the highest temperature reached each day for four days in two different cities.

    a. What was the highest temperature in Pineville on October 15?

    b. Describe the change in temperature in Pineville over the four-day period.

    c. On which day did Pineville have a higher maximum temperature than Central City?

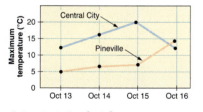

**2. Data Bank** Use the information on page 612 to answer the following questions.

    a. What is the diameter of Jupiter? How much larger than Earth is Jupiter?

    b. Which three planets have the greatest average density?

**3. Graph** Use the following data about a pet snake to construct a line graph: 1990, 1.4 m long; 1991, 1.7 m long; 1992, 2.1 m long; 1993, 2.3 m long.

**4. Calculate** Make the following conversions.

    a. 100 cm = _____ m

    b. 0.5 kg = _____ g

    c. 1,000 mL = _____ L

### Make Connections

**1. Link the Concepts** Below is a concept map showing how some of the main concepts in this chapter link together. Only parts of the map are filled in. Copy the map. Using words and ideas from the chapter, complete the map.

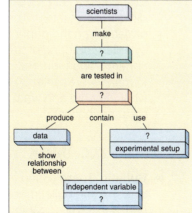

**2. Science and Society** Throughout history, most scientists have been men. What is it like to be a woman scientist? Research the life and work of a well-known female scientist. Choices include Marie Curie, Rachel Carson, Barbara McClintock, and Mary Leakey. Write a report about the person you choose. Describe the obstacles she faced and how she overcame them.

**3. Science and Living** Choose one of the science process skills. Describe how improving that skill could benefit your daily life. Give several examples.

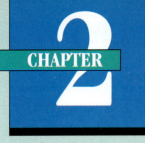
## Overview

Topography and geography are the topics of this chapter. The first section shows the locations of the continents and oceans and describes their features, and explores the biomes of the earth. The second section explains mapping of the earth's surface, while comparing different map types and methods. The chapter closes with a discussion of topographical maps and explains how to interpret them.

## Advance Planner

▶ Provide a globe or map that shows your city or town for SE page 31.

▶ Obtain a relief map for TE page 34.

▶ Supply protractors for SE page 38.

▶ Copy a local map for TE page 43.

▶ Supply a newspaper weather map for TE page 44.

▶ Gather blocks of modeling clay; wax paper; rubber bands; pencils; metric rulers; paper; brown and blue colored pencils; and a butter knife for SE Activity 2, page 50.

## Skills Development Chart

| Sections | Estimate | Locate | Make a Model | Observe | Read a Map |
|---|---|---|---|---|---|
| **2.1** Skills WarmUp | | ● | | | |
| Skills WorkOut | ● | | | | |
| **2.2** Skills WarmUp | | | ● | | |
| SkillBuilder | | | | | ● |
| **2.3** Skills WarmUp | | | | ● | |
| Activity 2 | | | ● | ● | ● |

## Individual Needs

▶ **Limited English Proficiency Students** Ask students to list the chapter vocabulary and the landforms shown in Figure 2.3 in their science portfolios. Have them define each term using their own words. Then have students draw or trace outline maps of the countries from which they or their families originally came. Ask them to draw symbols representing different landforms on their maps and to make a key to the symbols. Have them add the name of the country, its continent, data about its latitude and longitude, and any oceans that may border it. Make a display of their maps.

▶ **At-Risk Students** Have students work in groups of three or four and provide each group with a copy of the contour map in Figure 2.16 or another simple one. Ask them to make a three-dimensional model of land represented by the map. Have them trace the closed loops and transfer these drawings to thick cardboard or sheets of plastic foam. After cutting out the flat shapes, they should glue them in a pile, positioning each as shown on the map. Students may want to paint their models realistically when they are finished.

▶ **Gifted Students** Have students work in pairs to make map projections. Have them cut the hemisphere of clear plastic from the top of a two-liter soft-drink bottle. Ask them to draw lines resembling longitude and latitude lines on their hemisphere. They might want to add island or continent shapes. Have them place the hemisphere open side up on a flat piece of paper and shine a flashlight directly down into it. Then have them draw over the image projected on the paper. Have them repeat by wrapping a cylinder and cone of tracing paper around the hemisphere using Figures 2.9 and 2.10 as a guide. Ask them to make a presentation to the rest of the class showing what they did and what kind of map would result from each projection.

## Resource Bank

▶ **Bulletin Board** Bring in examples of maps of different kinds for the bulletin board. Invite students to contribute unusual maps or copies of them that they come across. Do not label the maps, but encourage students to try to figure out what they represent and their uses. Hold a class discussion sharing information about the maps. Afterward have students make labels explaining each one.

# CHAPTER 2 PLANNING GUIDE

| Section | Core | Standard | Enriched | Section | Core | Standard | Enriched |
|---|:---:|:---:|:---:|---|:---:|:---:|:---:|
| **2.1 Earth's Surfaces** pp. 31–37 | | | | **Laboratory Program** Investigation 3 | | ● | ● |
| **Section Features** Skills WarmUp, p. 31 | ● | ● | ● | **Color Transparencies** Transparency 4 | ● | ● | ● |
| Skills WorkOut, p. 32 | | ● | ● | **2.3 Topographical Maps** pp. 45–50 | | | |
| **Blackline Masters** Review Worksheet 2.1 | ● | ● | ● | **Section Features** Skills WarmUp, p. 45 | ● | ● | ● |
| Enrich Worksheet 2.1 | | ● | ● | Career Corner, p. 47 | ● | ● | ● |
| Skills Worksheet 2.1 | ● | ● | ● | Activity, p. 50 | ● | ● | ● |
| Integrating Worksheet 2.1a | | ● | ● | **Blackline Masters** Review Worksheet 2.3 | ● | ● | ● |
| Integrating Worksheet 2.1b | | ● | ● | Skills Worksheet 2.3 | ● | ● | ● |
| **Color Transparencies** Transparencies 2a, 2b, 3a, 3b | ● | ● | ● | Vocabulary Worksheet 2.3 | ● | ● | ● |
| **2.2 Mapping the Earth** pp. 38–44 | | | | **Overhead Blackline Transparencies** Overhead Blackline Master 2.3 and Student Worksheet | ● | ● | ● |
| **Section Features** Skills WarmUp, p. 38 | ● | ● | ● | **Laboratory Program** Investigation 4 | | | ● |
| SkillBuilder, p. 43 | ● | ● | ● | **Color Transparencies** Transparency 5 | ● | ● | ● |
| **Blackline Masters** Review Worksheet 2.2 | ● | ● | ● | | | | |
| Skills Worksheet 2.2 | ● | ● | ● | | | | |
| Integrating Worksheet 2.2 | ● | ● | ● | | | | |

# Bibliography

The following resources can be used for teaching the chapter. See page T–46 for supplier codes.

**Library Resources**

Collinson, Alan. *Mountains.* New York: Dillon, 1992.

Farndon, John. *How the Earth Works.* Pleasantville, NY: The Reader's Digest Association, Inc., 1992.

Lauber, Patricia. *Seeing Earth from Space.* New York: Orchard, 1990.

**Technology Resources**

*Internet*

**PLANETDIARY** at *http://www.planetdiary.com*
- Discover more about animals and plants in *Fauna* and *Flora* by clicking on *Phenomena Backgrounders.*
- Find information on mapping by clicking on *Universal Measurements.*

*Software*

*The Earth.* Mac, Win. LS.
*Earth Science.* Mac, Win. ER.

*CD-ROMs*

*Interactive Earth.* SFAW.
*Small Blue Planet: The Real Picture World Atlas.* Mac, Dos. ESI.

*Laserdiscs*

*Living Textbook.* (See barcodes on pages in this chapter.) Optical Data.
*The United States: A Geographic Overview.* 1992. SVE.

*Videos*

*The Geography Tutor.* 6 videos. 15 min. each. 1991. INT/MS.
*Geomorphology—A Study of the Shape of the Land.* 28 min. MMI.
*Map Reading.* Five single concept videos. MMI.

**Audio-Visual Resources**

*Latitude/Longitude and Time Zones.* Film. C/MTI.

 *Writing Connection*

Have students imagine they are piloting a plane that is traveling across one of the earth's landmasses. Encourage them to write a short story about their travels, describing where they went and what special land features they saw. Students can share their stories with the class.

## Introducing the Chapter

Have students read the description of the photograph. Ask if they agree or disagree with the description.

### Directed Inquiry

Have students study the photograph. Ask:

▶ What does this photograph show? (Students will recognize farm fields, roads, and streams.)

▶ Which features are natural and which are made by humans? (Farm fields—natural but laid out and cultivated by humans; roads—humans; streams—natural)

▶ From what point of view was this picture taken? How do you know? (From overhead—probably from an airplane or helicopter. Students will say that it looks like a map, or like what they have seen from an airplane.)

▶ How could you use such a photograph? (To help in mapping an area)

▶ Why is this photograph a good way to begin a chapter on topography and geography? (Because it clearly shows features of a land area's surface in a way that resembles a map)

## Chapter Vocabulary

| | |
|---|---|
| biome | latitude |
| continent | longitude |
| contour line | prime |
| equator | meridian |
| hemisphere | scale |
| international date line | topography |

Chapter **2**

# Topography and Geography

### Chapter Sections

**2.1** Earth's Surface

**2.2** Mapping the Earth

**2.3** Topographic Maps

### What do you see?

❝I see patches of farmland with streams in the foreground and background. If I was making a map of this area, I would include the individual patches and what's growing in each one. I would also include the streams. The roads in between the patches and the buildings will also be put into my map. I would show the road with a black line and the buildings with boxes. The streams would be big blue lines.❞

*Frank Sturniolo*
*McTigue Junior High*
*    School*
*Toledo, Ohio*

To find out more about the photograph, look on page 52. As you read this chapter, you will learn about the surface of the earth and different methods of mapping it.

**Section Objectives**
For a list of section objectives, see the Student Edition page.

**Skills Objectives**
Students should be able to:

**Locate** their city or town on a map.

**Estimate** the percentage of the earth's surface covered by the Pacific Ocean.

**Make a Map** of a sailing route crossing all four oceans.

**Vocabulary**
continent, biome

## 2.1 Earth's Surface

### Objectives

▶ **Locate** the seven continents and the four oceans.

▶ **Name** and **describe** four major landforms.

▶ **Explain** how biomes can be used to describe the distribution of living things on the earth's surface.

▶ **Map** a route through all four oceans.

▼ **ACTIVITY**

| Locating |
| --- |

*Where Am I?*

Using a globe or a world map, locate your city or town. Was it easy for you to find your location? How could you locate it more easily next time?

**SKILLS WARMUP**

A thousand years ago, most people lived in small villages. Almost everything they knew about the world around them was based on what they could see with their own eyes. Imagine you're one of those ancient people. Your village is near a river, below a tall, forested mountain. In the other direction stretches a wide, grassy plain.

To find out what lies beyond this familiar landscape, you climb to the top of the mountain. You see more mountains in the distance. The plain goes on as far as you can see. The world is much bigger than you thought!

Now imagine you're suddenly transported into the future. You're a passenger on a spaceship blasting off the surface of the earth. What do you see as you look out the window? As you climb higher, you realize that what you see below is all part of a huge sphere.

### Earth from Space

The sphere is the planet Earth. Viewed from space, Earth is a watery globe partly hidden by clouds. It rotates slowly around an axis, like a spinning top. How is this view from space different from the view of a person standing on the surface?

People have viewed the earth from space, and they have studied and explored its surface features. Both ways of looking at the earth have contributed to their knowledge of it. As a result, people have a very complete picture of their planet.

**Figure 2.1** ▲
What can you observe about the earth's surface from this point of view? ①

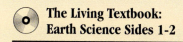

## Skills WorkOut

To help students practice their skill at estimating, have them do the Skills WorkOut.

**Answer** The percentage of the earth's surface taken up by the Pacific Ocean is 34 percent. The answer can be checked by adding up all the areas of the oceans and land and finding the percentage for the Pacific Ocean.

## Directed Inquiry

Have students study Figure 2.2. Ask:

▶ What three continents border the Indian Ocean? (Africa, Asia, Australia)

▶ What two oceans are separated by North America and South America? (Atlantic Ocean and Pacific Ocean)

▶ Which continents are actually connected? (North and South America; Asia, Africa, and Europe)

▶ Where does the Atlantic Ocean connect with the Indian Ocean? (At the southernmost tip of Africa)

▶ Why are the divisions of the world's continents and oceans given separate names? (Students may suggest that it is convenient for people to think of them as separate entities, or that the oceans and continents are so large that people have historically assumed that they are entirely separate from each other.)

## Discuss

Have students study this illustration and other maps or illustrations of Asia and Europe, or Eurasia. Ask: What divides the Eurasian landmass so that it may be thought of as two continents? (The Ural Mountains in the north and large bodies of water in the south help divide the landmass physically.)

**32**

### Social Studies Connection

Have students use a world map or library references to identify nations on each continent. They can then work in cooperative groups, listing important statistics about specific nations. Tell students to research information, such as type of government, economy, climate, major cities, the people who live there, the population, and land features. Be sure that nations from around the world are represented. You may wish to either assign the nations or have students choose the nations they want to research. Have groups present their findings to the class.

**Table 2.1**
**Area of the Continents**

| Continent | Area (thousands of km²) |
|---|---|
| Africa | 30,340 |
| Antarctica | 14,000 |
| Asia | 45,120 |
| Australia | 8,550 |
| Europe | 9,850 |
| North America | 24,370 |
| South America | 17,890 |

**Figure 2.2  Earth's Continents and Oceans** ▶

### ▼ ACTIVITY

**Estimating**

*Ocean Size*

What percentage of the earth's surface is covered by the Pacific Ocean? How can you check your estimate using the data in Tables 2.1 and 2.2?

**SKILLS WORKOUT**

## Continents

From space, the earth's land appears as large green and brown shapes surrounded by the blue of the oceans. These large landmasses are the earth's **continents**. Most people say there are seven continents, but others think there should be six. Look at Figure 2.2. How many continents do you count?

The largest landmass you see is usually divided into two continents, Europe and Asia. When this landmass is counted as one continent, it is named Eurasia. Directly below Europe, find the continent of Africa. Now look to the right of Africa and find Australia.

On this page you can see North America and South America. Below South America you can see another continent, Antarctica. Antarctica lies over the South Pole, so parts of it are also visible below Africa and Australia.

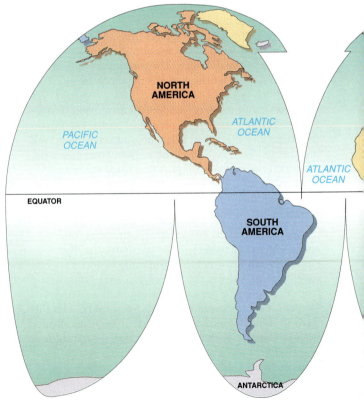

## Integrating the Sciences

**Oceanography** Tell students that the oceans vary in temperature and life forms by latitude (defined as nearness to the top, bottom, or middle of a map). Have groups of students research some of the ocean organisms that live in both the Northern and Southern hemispheres. Have them report some of the differences and similarities among the organisms.

## Multicultural Perspectives

Discuss the everyday lives and cultures of people who live on small islands and depend on the ocean for their food and livelihood. Have a few volunteers research what life is like for many of the people living on the Pacific Islands. Students can discuss how their lives are similar and different from Pacific Islanders.

## Class Activity

Have students work in small groups with world maps or globes to locate some of the world's seas in addition to the Caribbean Sea and the Mediterranean Sea. They may enjoy also looking at Landsat maps taken from actual photographs. For example, have them locate the Arabian Sea, the Barents Sea, the Bering Sea, the Black Sea, the Caspian Sea, the Coral Sea, the Japan Sea, and the Red Sea. Ask: Which of these seas are not connected to oceans? (Black Sea and Caspian Sea)

## Enrich

Use Enrich Worksheet 2.1.

### Answers to In-Text Questions
① **Between Europe and Africa on one side and North and South America on the other side**

② **Between Asia and Australia on one side and North and South America on the other side**

## The World Ocean

The continents are only about 28 percent of the earth's surface. The other 72 percent is one large body of water. This body of water is the world ocean.

The world ocean is usually divided into four oceans with different names. Look at Figure 2.2 and find the Arctic Ocean, which surrounds the North Pole. Most of the Arctic Ocean is permanently covered by an ice cap. Now find the Indian Ocean, located south of Asia between Africa and Australia. Where is the Atlantic ① Ocean? Where is the Pacific Ocean? ②

You may notice that small parts of the oceans are mostly surrounded by land. These bodies of salt water, much smaller than a whole ocean, are called seas. One of the largest seas on the earth is the Caribbean Sea, located between North and South America.

**Table 2.2**
**Area of the Oceans**

| Ocean | Area (thousands of km²) |
|---|---|
| Arctic Ocean | 13,240 |
| Atlantic Ocean | 86,660 |
| Indian Ocean | 73,500 |
| Pacific Ocean | 166,440 |

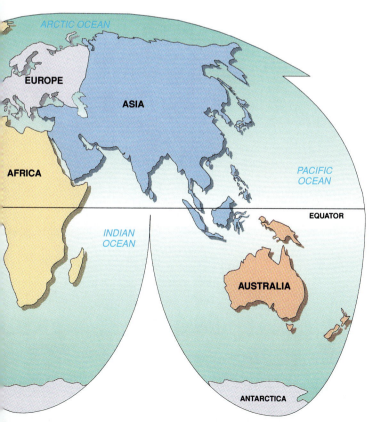

## TEACH ▪ Continued

### Explore Visually

Have students read the paragraph and study Figure 2.3. Then ask:

▶ What are the earth's major landforms? (Mountains, valleys, canyons, plateaus, and plains)

▶ What is the name given to a large, flat area of land that is usually without trees? (Plain)

▶ What is the main difference between a plain and a plateau? (A plateau is higher than its surroundings, but a plain is not.)

▶ What is a valley with very steep walls called? (Canyon)

▶ What landforms are often between mountains? (Valleys)

▶ What distinguishes a mountain from a plateau? (A mountain has sloping sides, but a plateau is relatively flat.)

### The Living Textbook: Earth Science Sides 1-2

Chapter 23          Frame 02833
Mountain and Valley (1 Frame)
Search:

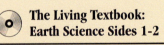

### The Living Textbook: Earth Science Sides 1-2

Chapter 20          Frame 02717
Plains (2 Frames)
Search:               Step:

### The Living Textbook: Earth Science Sides 1-2

Chapter 23          Frame 02961
Grand Canyon (25 Frames)
Search:               Step:

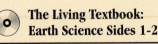

### Art Connection

After students study Figure 2.3, have them draw pictures of what the view looks like from various places in the illustration. You may wish to show some of the drawings to the class and have students guess where the views were drawn from.

### Geography Connection

Show students a relief map and have them find and name examples of the landforms shown in Figure 2.3. Be sure that students can differentiate between a bay, a lagoon, and a strait.

## Landforms

Features of the earth's surface smaller than continents and oceans are best seen from a closer, bird's-eye view. Have you ever climbed a mountain or crossed a valley? Mountains and valleys are landforms, the main features of the earth's varied landscape. Landforms are defined by their shape, size, and elevation. Elevation is the distance above sea level. Look below to see examples of the earth's major landforms.

**Figure 2.3  Features of the Earth's Surface ▼**

**Valley**
An area of land lower in elevation than its surroundings.

**Mountain**
An elevated area of land, higher than a hill, with sloping sides.

**Canyon**
A valley with very steep walls.

**Plateau**
A fairly flat area above surrounding land.

**Plain**
A large, flat area of land, usually without trees.

## Writing Connection

Have students write a story about exploring the area in Figure 2.3 by sailing ship, starting with their discovery of the strait. Have students share their stories with the class.

### Ocean and Coastal Features

Where land and water meet, pieces of land and bodies of water take on a variety of sizes and shapes. The land defines bodies of water such as bays and straits. Areas of land such as islands and peninsulas are defined by the water around them. Have you ever been on an island? What makes an island different from a peninsula? Look below to see examples of these and other coastal features.

**Strait**
A narrow passage of ocean water joining two larger bodies of water.

**Bay**
A body of ocean water mostly surrounded by land and smaller than a sea or ocean.

**Island**
Land completely surrounded by water.

**Peninsula**
A fingerlike projection of land surrounded on three sides by water.

**Lagoon**
A shallow body of salt water mostly or completely surrounded by land.

**Archipelago**
A group or chain of islands.

▶ What are the ocean and coastal features found on this page? (Bay, strait, island, peninsula, lagoon, and archipelago)

▶ What is the name given to a narrow passage of ocean water that joins two larger bodies of water? (Strait)

▶ What is the difference between a bay and a lagoon? (A lagoon is a shallow body of water that may be completely surrounded by land, but a bay is larger than a lagoon and is never completely surrounded by land.)

▶ What is a group or chain of islands called? (Archipelago)

## Skills Development

**Infer**  Ask students to make inferences from the following questions:

▶ Which type of landform would be best to use for growing crops? (Plain)

▶ Which of the features described would most likely be associated with a series of volcanoes in the ocean? (Archipelago)

**Answer to In-Text Question**

① **An island is completely surrounded by water, but a peninsula is a projection of land that is surrounded by water only on three sides.**

**The Living Textbook: Earth Science Sides 1-2**

Chapter 30        Frame 04290
Bay and Peninsula (1 Frame)
Search:

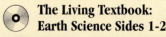

**The Living Textbook: Earth Science Sides 1-2**

Chapter 30        Frame 05733
Lagoon (1 Frame)
Search:

## TEACH ▪ Continued

### Critical Thinking

**Compare and Contrast** Ask students to compare the six biomes in terms of their vegetation. Ask:

▶ What are the differences between the three forest biomes? (The rain forest is thick with diverse vegetation. The coniferous forest has cone-bearing, needle-leaf trees, and the deciduous forest has trees that lose their leaves in winter.)

▶ How are the desert and tundra alike? (Both have no trees and are harsh environments.)

▶ How do grasslands differ from forests? (Grasslands have few or no trees.)

### Directed Inquiry

Have students study Figure 2.4. Ask:

▶ Which continent has the largest desert? (Africa)

▶ Where is the tundra biome? (In far northern areas of North America, Europe, and Asia)

▶ Where are rain forests located on the earth? (In areas near the equator)

▶ Where, in general, are coniferous forests located with respect to tundra? (In broad areas south of the tundra)

▶ Where, in general, are deciduous forests located with respect to coniferous forests? (South of the coniferous forests)

### Critical Thinking

**Generalize** If you were to divide the world's life zones into only two biomes, what would they be? (Answers will vary. An example would be forest and plain.)

### Answers to In-Text Questions

① **In northernmost lands**

② **Central and South America, Africa, Asia**

③ **Answers depend on location.**

---

### *Integrating the Sciences*

**Life Science** Discuss the kinds of organisms found in each biome, and how the physical environment of a biome affects the shape, size, diet, and lifestyle of each kind of organism. You may wish to use life science textbooks, biology textbooks, or other references to show students examples of organisms that live in each biome.

**Use Integrating Worksheet 2.1b.**

### *Multicultural Perspectives*

Discuss how a culture might be influenced by the biome in which its people live. For example, point out the desert biome in Figure 2.4. Ask students to discuss what life is like for people living in the desert, such as the Bedouins, who live in the deserts of the Middle East. Have students discuss how people adapt to life in the desert.

---

**Table 2.3**
**Characteristics of the Major Land Biomes** ▼

| Biome | Characteristics |
|---|---|
| Rain forest | Thick forest; high rainfall |
| Grassland | Tall grasses and few or no trees |
| Desert | Sparse vegetation; very low rainfall |
| Tundra | Low plants covered by ice and snow most of the year |
| Coniferous forest | Cone-bearing needle-leafed trees |
| Deciduous forest | Broadleaf trees that lose leaves in winter |

### Life on Earth's Surface

Do you have polar bears in your backyard? Does cactus grow around your school? Can you visit a nearby forest? Will you see monkeys in the trees? You probably can't answer yes to more than one of these questions. That's because different parts of the earth's land surface have different organisms living on them.

The major factors that determine where an organism can live are temperature and rainfall. These factors vary depending on location. Average temperature is highest near the earth's middle and lowest near its two ends, or poles. Rainfall depends on many factors, such as surrounding landforms and nearness to an ocean.

Variations in rainfall and temperature across the land surface can be seen in the differences in vegetation, the kinds of plants that grow on the landscape. Based on vegetation patterns, scientists have defined six different major life zones, or **biomes**. Each biome is described in Table 2.3. The map in Figure 2.4 shows where each biome is located on the earth. Where is the tundra biome? Where on the earth are rain forests ① located? What biome do you live in? ② ③

**Figure 2.4  Earth's Major Land Biomes** ▼

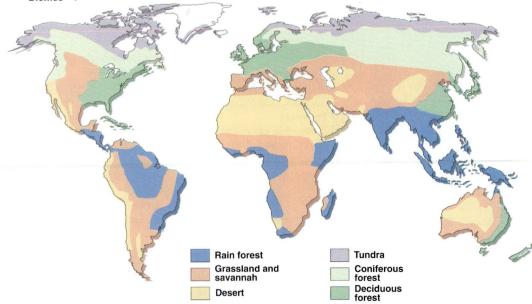

| | | | |
|---|---|---|---|
| ■ Rain forest | | ■ Tundra | |
| ■ Grassland and savannah | | ■ Coniferous forest | |
| ■ Desert | | ■ Deciduous forest | |

## Integrating the Sciences

**Environmental Science** Discuss how humans may affect the populations of marine life in the oceans. For example, for many years the United States tuna industry used fishing methods to catch tuna that also killed and injuried many dolphins. However, in 1988, biologist Samual F. La Budde released a videotape, showing dolphins trapped in tuna nets, hurt and drowning. Since that time, the United States and other countries have taken steps to protect the dolphins. New nets and fishing techniques have been designed to help alleviate this problem.

### Science and Society  *Sharing the Oceans*

For every person on the earth, the oceans are an important resource. For centuries, the oceans have connected the nations of the world like a watery highway. Ocean trade routes have allowed the people of the world to share goods and to experience each other's cultures.

The oceans also provide much of the world's food. Over 70 million metric tons of fish are harvested by fishing nations every year. Other sea animals such as crabs, shrimps, lobsters, and oysters are also caught. Ocean plants are harvested as well. Seaweed is eaten as food, and it is used to make ice cream and salad dressing. Some ocean plants are collected for use in medicines and vitamins.

Even countries without an ocean coastline depend on the oceans. Tiny algae floating near the ocean's surface, among the plankton organisms, produce some of the oxygen that land animals and humans breathe. The clouds that drop life-giving rain on land develop mainly from water that evaporates from the oceans.

The ocean is such an important resource that the nations of the world have had to agree on how it is used. Under an agreement called the Law of the Sea, each nation has rights to ocean waters near its coast. The rest of the ocean, however, is free for all to use. Under this and other agreements, nations try to keep any one nation from damaging the shared parts of the ocean and its limited resources.

**Figure 2.5** ▲
People from many nations harvest food from the oceans.

### Check and Explain

1. List the seven continents, and tell which oceans border each one.

2. What's the difference between a mountain, a plateau, and a plain?

3. **Generalize** Where is the rain forest biome located? Where is the deciduous forest located?

4. **Make a Map** Copy the map of the world on pages 32–33. Select a starting point on the coast of one continent, and draw a sailing route that would take you through all four oceans and back to your starting point.

### Life Science
**L I N K**

Study the map on page 36 to determine which biome you live in. Research your biome's characteristic vegetation. Outside your home or school, collect a few samples of vegetation that represent your biome. Display and label these samples on a sheet of posterboard.

**A C T I V I T Y**

Chapter 2 Topography and Geography **37**

---

EVALUATE ◄

## WrapUp

**Reinforce** Have students trace the outline of each of the seven continents, cut them out, mix them up, and take turns identifying them.

Use Review Worksheet 2.1.

## Check and Explain

1. North America—Atlantic Ocean, Pacific Ocean, and Arctic Ocean; South America—Atlantic Ocean and Pacific Ocean; Africa—Atlantic Ocean and Indian Ocean; Europe—Arctic Ocean and Atlantic Ocean; Asia—Arctic Ocean, Pacific Ocean, and Indian Ocean; Australia—Indian Ocean and Pacific Ocean; Antarctica—Indian Ocean, Pacific Ocean, and Atlantic Ocean

2. A mountain is an elevated area that is higher than a hill and that has sloping sides. A plateau is an elevated area that is relatively flat, and a plain is a flat area that is not elevated above its surroundings.

3. Rain forest is located in warm parts of the world near the equator. Deciduous forest is located in mild parts of the world.

4. Sailing routes will vary, but each route should go through the Atlantic Ocean, the Pacific Ocean, the Indian Ocean, and the Arctic Ocean.

### Answer to Link

Caution students about harmful vegetation and picking plants from cultivated gardens. Displays may vary but characteristic vegetation should be similar.

## Themes in Science

**Scale and Structure** The mapping of the earth begins, at the largest scale, by setting reference points on a huge sphere. All other frames of reference from which maps are produced are based on this original scale.

## Integrating the Sciences

**Physical Science** Point out to students that showing the earth with the Northern Hemisphere facing "up" is only a matter of convention. The earth doesn't really have a top and bottom. Anywhere on the earth, "up" is simply the direction directly opposite the center of the earth and thus the pull of the earth's gravity.

---

### Section Objectives
For a list of section objectives, see the Student Edition page.

### Skills Objectives
Students should be able to:

**Make a Model** of the earth with degree measurements.

**Read a Map** using a scale and legend.

**Locate** a continent using latitude and longitude.

### Vocabulary
equator, hemisphere, latitude, longitude, prime meridian, international date line, scale

---

## ◀ MOTIVATE

### Skills WarmUp
To give students practice in mapping the earth, have them do the Skills WarmUp.
**Answer** Students might suggest that parallel lines could be drawn between matching degree measurement points on both sides of the circle to represent parallels of latitude.

### Misconceptions
Students may think that maps can show any or all parts of the earth's surface accurately to scale. Explain that, for centuries, mapmakers have been trying with limited success to represent the earth's surface on flat maps. Mapmakers are still only partially successful at representing the earth's topography in two-dimensional form. One part of the map is always distorted in order for other map features to be accurate.

### Answer to In-Text Question
**① Any location in North America that is below the 45th parallel is closer to the equator than to either of the poles.**

---

## ▼ ACTIVITY

### Making a Model

**Degree of Accuracy**

Collect a piece of paper, a protractor, and a pencil.
**1.** Draw a half circle on the piece of paper by tracing around the protractor.
**2.** Make marks on the half circle at 10° intervals. Label the marks.
**3.** Complete the circle by turning the protractor over and tracing around it.
Study the circle. How might degree measurements be used in mapping the earth?

**SKILLS WARMUP**

---

# 2.2 Mapping the Earth

## Objectives

▶ **Explain** how longitude and latitude are used to map the earth's surface.

▶ **Compare** two different map projections.

▶ **Interpret** the symbols on a map legend.

▶ **Locate** a position on a map.

---

**Y**ou want to invite people to your birthday party who don't know where you live. How do you help them find your house? You might draw them a map. They can use the map to see where your house is located in relation to landmarks they know, such as streets and buildings.

You've probably used maps many times in your life. They show, on a piece of paper, the space relationships among real objects. Maps can represent any size area, from your classroom to the entire surface of the earth.

## Earth's Reference Points

If you had to draw a map of your room, you could do it without having to learn how. But what about making a map of the whole earth? Mapping the earth poses special problems because it is a huge sphere.

The first step in mapping the earth is to set up reference points on the earth itself. Recall that the earth's rotation gives it two fixed points through which an imaginary line called an axis passes. These fixed points are the North Pole and the South Pole. Locations on the earth can be described in terms of their distance from one of these poles.

An imaginary line can be drawn around the center of the earth that is equidistant from the two poles. This imaginary line is the **equator**. Look at Figure 2.6. Notice that the earth can be divided into two equal halves. The equator is the dividing line between the halves. Each half is called a **hemisphere**. These reference points and lines on the earth are the basis for all maps made of the earth's surface.

Axis of rotation
North Pole
Equator
Northern hemisphere
Southern hemisphere
South Pole

**Figure 2.6 ▲**
Do you live closer to the equator, the North Pole, or the South Pole? **①**

**Math Connection**

To help students grasp latitude and longitude lines, have cooperative groups figure out ways of drawing lines of longitude and latitude on a sphere such as a table-tennis ball.

 **Geography Connection**

Ask students to speculate about why the prime meridian passes through Great Britain and not some other country. Does it make a difference where the prime meridian is placed?

## Latitude and Longitude

When you place a point on a line graph, you need to know two numbers. One is for the *x*-axis and one for the *y*-axis. Locating a point on the earth also requires two measurements.

The first measurement of location on the earth is provided by imaginary lines telling the distance away from the equator. These are lines of **latitude**. Look at Figure 2.7. It shows lines of latitude drawn around the earth. Notice that all the lines are parallel and that each forms a circle of a different size.

Each line of latitude is numbered in units called degrees. They range from 0° for the equator to 90° for each of the poles. Latitude lines in the Northern Hemisphere are labeled with an N for north. In the Southern Hemisphere they are labeled S for south. A point halfway between the equator and the North Pole, therefore, is at 45°N latitude.

The other measure of location on the earth is provided by lines of **longitude**

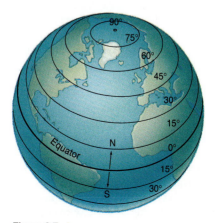

**Figure 2.7** ▲
Latitude lines form concentric circles around the earth. What is another name for 90°N latitude? ②

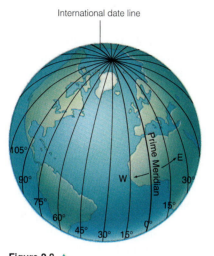

**Figure 2.8** ▲
At what points do all longitude lines meet? ③

(LAHN jih tood). Longitude lines run from pole to pole and are also called meridians. They are shown in Figure 2.8.

Unlike lines of latitude, longitude lines have no natural reference points from which to measure distance. Therefore, people have defined a line of reference—the meridian passing through Greenwich, England. This longitude line is called the prime meridian and is labeled 0°. Locations west of the **prime meridian** are measured in degrees west. Locations east of the prime meridian are measured in degrees east.

Lines of longitude range from 0° to 180° in both directions. The line of longitude that measures 180° is directly opposite the prime meridian. The **international date line** closely follows the 180° longitude but does not cross any land mass.

Together, latitude and longitude locate any place on the earth. For example, Mexico City is located near 20°N latitude and 100°W longitude. What is the latitude and longitude of your hometown? ④

**TEACH**

### Skills Development

**Classify**  Have students use the diagrams to help them distinguish between latitude and longitude. Then ask:

▶ Which lines are parallel, the lines of latitude or the lines of longitude? (Lines of latitude)

▶ Which kind of line is the prime meridian? (A longitude line)

### Discuss

Remind students that the international date line is 180° from the prime meridian from either side of the prime meridian. Then tell them that there are 12 time zones on either side of the prime meridian. Explain what it means to cross the international date line. (It is the transition line for calendar days. If you travel east across this line, you gain one day. If you travel west across it, you lose one day.)

### Class Activity

Have students work in small groups. Have them use maps and globes to identify the location of several major cities by using the following coordinates:

1. 30°N, 31°E (Cairo, Egypt)
2. 52°N, 13°E (Berlin, Germany)
3. 34°N, 84°W (Atlanta, Georgia)
4. 23°S, 43°W (Rio de Janeiro, Brazil)

You may wish to add to this list.

### Answers to In-Text Questions

② **North Pole**
③ **At the poles**
④ **Coordinates will vary.**

🔘 **The Living Textbook: Earth Science Sides 1-2**

Chapter 28        Frame 03905
Longitude/Latitude (2 Frames)
Search:                Step:

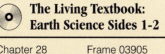

## Directed Inquiry

Have students study Figure 2.9 or a large world map that has been made by means of a cylindrical projection. Ask:

▶ How does the size of Greenland compare to the size of South America on this map? (Greenland looks larger than South America.)

▶ Because Greenland is actually one-ninth the size of South America, what does this tell you about the projection? (It distorts the sizes of landmasses.)

▶ Where on the map are landmasses distorted least? (At the equator)

## Critical Thinking

**Reason and Conclude** Point out that a conic projection of part of the Northern Hemisphere is shown in Figure 2.10. Then ask: How would a conic projection of the Southern Hemisphere look if north is kept on top? (The "fan" of the projection would be small at the bottom and wide at the top where the equator is.)

## Class Activity

Have students attempt to make a cylindrical projection and a conic projection of the seams of a baseball or tennis ball. Have students explain what makes the job difficult.

## Integrated Learning

Use Integrating Worksheet 2.2.

**Answer to In-Text Question**

① **It distorts the sizes of landmasses less.**

### Math Connection

Demonstrate the difficulty of representing the spherical earth on a flat surface by having students remove the skin of an easily peeled orange in one piece and then try to press it flat. Have students discuss what happens. (The peel won't lay completely flat and looks distorted.)

### Math Connection

Point out to students the similarities between the grid formed by lines of latitude and longitude on a cylindrical projection map and the grid formed by the *x*- and *y*-axes of a graph. Have students make maps of the classroom or school grounds using both methods of forming a grid. Ask them how the two methods are similar.

## Map Projections

A globe represents the spherical earth very accurately. But a globe is difficult to carry around and can't show much detail. To solve these problems, the curved surface of the earth must be shown on a flat map. How is this done?

Look at Figure 2.9 below. Imagine a light at the very center of the globe. The globe is marked with latitude and longitude lines and the continents. The light will cause an image of the latitude lines, longitude lines, and continents to appear on the cylinder wrapped around the globe. If the images are traced and the cylinder unrolled, a map results! This map is an example of a *projection*. A projection is a way of transferring the features of the earth onto a flat surface.

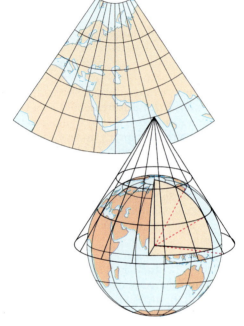

**Figure 2.10** ▲
What advantage does a conic projection have over a cylindrical projection? ①

There are many different kinds of map projections. The projection in Figure 2.9 is a cylindrical projection. It shows the shapes of continents accurately, but it distorts their size. Landmasses away from the equator look much larger than they really are.

The conic projection in Figure 2.10 is another common type of projection, produced by projecting the globe's features onto a cone. A conic projection does not distort the sizes of the continents very much. However, it can only show one hemisphere.

Each type of map projection is best for a certain kind of use. A cylindrical projection, for example, is ideal for navigating on the ocean. All distances can be calculated as straight lines.

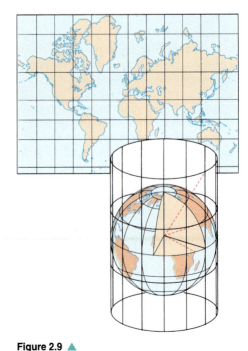

**Figure 2.9** ▲
Most maps of the world are cylindrical projections.

## *Multicultural Perspectives*

Discuss how maps may vary in their representations of a continent's size. Some maps show the United States to be just as large as Africa. Some European maps show Europe to be larger than South America. Ask students how these kinds of representations show bias. Have them discuss the importance of representing the true sizes of the continents on maps.

## *Writing Connection*

Have students draw a treasure map based on actual locations and write directions for how to reach the treasure from a specific point on the map. Then students can test their directions by having another student attempt to reach the treasure by following the directions.

## Critical Thinking

**Compare and Contrast** Have students compare the size of Greenland and South America on the equal-area projection with their sizes on the cylindrical projection on page 40. Ask: Which projection gives a less distorted picture of the size of landmasses? Why? (The equal-area projection; the sizes are not distorted with the equal-area projection because this projection more nearly represents the spherical earth on a flat map.)

## *Portfolio*

Have students work in small groups. Have them read the paragraphs in the text on the different types of maps and then see if they can list 15 or more other types of maps. Fifteen types are given on this page, but students may be able to think of more. On their lists, have them briefly state what each kind of map does. Have students take turns stating and describing one type of map. They can keep their lists in their portfolios.

**Answer to In-Text Question**

② **Areas are accurate; shapes are distorted.**

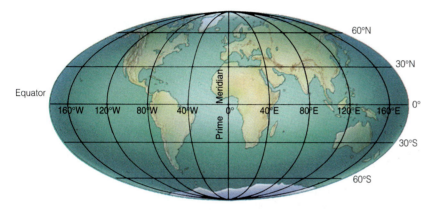

**Figure 2.11** ▲
This equal-area projection shows the sizes of the continents accurately. In what way are the continents distorted? ②

You are probably used to seeing the countries of the world shown on maps made by cylindrical projection. Therefore, you probably think of countries away from the equator, such as the United States, as being large compared to others. But the United States is not really as large as it appears on a cylindrical projection map.

Maps made by cylindrical projection may cause people to have a false view of the size of some land areas. For instance, on a cylindrical projection, Greenland appears to be as large as Africa. Actually Africa is about 14 times larger than Greenland. To avoid this problem, mapmakers have learned how to make maps in which the areas of the continents are very accurate and the edges are only slightly distorted. These maps are called equal-area projections.

An equal-area projection of the world is shown in Figure 2.11. Compare the sizes of its continents to those on the cylindrical projection in Figure 2.9. Where is the difference in size greatest?

## Types of Maps

Maps are made for many purposes. A world map, for example, can show the earth's physical features, or it can show the borders of different countries. A map showing national borders is called a political map. Road maps show people how to travel from place to place. Transit maps help you find the shortest bus route. Mall maps locate your favorite stores.

Many maps show a particular kind of information. A weather map, for example, shows weather patterns for a certain area. A population map can use color-coding to show the number of people per square kilometer. A geologic map shows rock types.

In a similar way, maps can show rainfall, temperature, vegetation, land use, minerals, average income of people, or many other things. Maps can even be used to record history by showing the locations of old cities or important events such as battles.

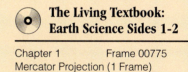

**The Living Textbook:**
**Earth Science Sides 1-2**

Chapter 1       Frame 00775
Mercator Projection (1 Frame)
Search:

**The Living Textbook:**
**Earth Science Sides 1-2**

Chapter 28      Frame 04081
Types of Maps (11 Frames)
Search:       Step:

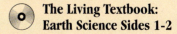

## TEACH ▪ *Continued*

### Critical Thinking

**Compare and Contrast** Have students suggest both the advantages and disadvantages of field mapping as compared to satellite mapping. (Field mapping advantages: firsthand information; great detail possible; highlights and place names can be collected. Satellite advantages: large areas can be mapped with accuracy; special types of photographs can be taken; information can be processed by computers.)

**Reason and Conclude** Have students answer this question in their own words: Why is it that maps that cover small areas can be made with less distortion than maps that cover large areas? (Longitude lines seem nearly parallel over small areas. The greater the area covered by a map, the greater will be the distortion because the lines are parallel on the flat surface of the map.)

### Answers to In-Text Questions

① **Airplane silhouette in a circle**
② **Line crossed by hash marks**

**The Living Textbook:**
**Earth Science Sides 1-2**

Chapter 1          Frame 00747
Computer Generated Maps (25 Frames)
Search:          Step:

 **STS Connection**

**Research** Have students find out more about how satellites and computers are used to map the earth. Then they can use diagrams and illustrations to present their findings to the class.

 **Art Connection**

Have students create maps of their own neighborhoods and draw symbols to represent familiar objects and locations. Have them exchange maps and see if they can correctly read one another's maps. Ask them what makes a symbol a good symbol.

## Mapping Methods

Maps are made by cartographers. For thousands of years, cartographers or surveyors went to the area to be mapped. They used relatively simple instruments to measure the land and then draw it on maps. This mapping method is called field mapping. Much of the earth's land was accurately mapped this way.

With advances in technology, mapmaking has changed. Satellites with remote-sensing devices pass high over the earth's surface gathering information useful for mapping. The satellites take photographs that show differences in the amount of heat given off by the surface. Because different kinds of objects give off different amounts of heat, these photographs can be used to distinguish among forests, cities, and water. A computer interprets this photographic data and makes accurate, detailed maps.

**Figure 2.12 ▲**
Photographs like this one are valuable for making maps. The red color indicates land, which is warmer than the dark blue water.

## Reading a Map

Through lines, shapes, colors, numbers, and symbols, maps carry a great deal of information. To get the most out of a map, you need to be able to interpret and read it. Just like reading a book, reading a map requires certain skills.

**Symbols** Every map uses a certain set of symbols to represent different features. Freeways, highways, and streets, for example, may be shown by lines of different thickness. The sizes of cities can be indicated by dots and circles of varying size. Important buildings, such as schools and hospitals, may each have their own symbol.

The symbols used in a map are collected together in a legend. The legend explains the meaning of each symbol. Look at the legend of the map in Figure 2.13. What is the symbol for an airport? ① What is the symbol for a railroad? ②

**Direction** Where on a map is north? If you answer that north is up, you're correct for most maps, but not all. Most maps of small areas of the earth are drawn so that the sides are parallel to lines of longitude and the top and bottom are parallel to lines of latitude. On these maps, an arrow labeled *North* may point straight up. West is then to the left, and east is to the right.

Longitude lines, however, are not exactly parallel to each other on the earth's surface. This begins to make a difference on maps of larger areas. On these maps, longitude lines are not shown parallel, except for maps with certain projections. When longitude lines aren't parallel, north-south direction will vary depending on which part of the map you're looking at!

### Cooperative Learning

If possible, make copies of a local map for the entire class. Be sure that the map clearly shows a scale. Have students find the school's location on the map. Then list specific local places on the chalkboard, such as a public library, the airport, the post office, and so on. Have students work in groups, using the maps to find out how far these places are from the school.

### Class Activity

Have students choose their own scale and use graph paper to draw a map of the room and various objects of their choice in the room. Then have students compare drawings to see if they can read their classmates' maps. Ask students if the scale that was used makes a difference in identifying objects and features.

### *SkillBuilder*

**Answers**

1. 1 cm/100,000 cm
2. 3 km; 4 km
3. 3 km; 2 km
4. San Juan; it has a bigger symbol and it is at the intersection of two state routes.
5. West, or west-northwest
6. State route 2, state route 64, state route 15; also, 6, 13, 64, 15
7. Copper City
8. Big River
9. Take state route 6 to state route 13 and state route 13 to Madison Lake; about 9 km

Paragraphs will vary. Students may choose San Juan because it is near the lake and has a hospital, or Copper City because it is near the river and has an airport.

---

**Scale** Every map is drawn so that a certain distance on the map represents a certain distance on land. The relationship between these two distances is called a map's **scale**. For example, a centimeter on a map may be equal to one kilometer on the earth's surface.

Scale can be expressed in different ways. Some maps have a graphic scale. On a graphic scale, a line divided into equal parts is labeled with the actual distances each segment on the line represents. Scale can also be expressed as a ratio. The scale 1:25,000, for example, means that 1 unit on the map equals 25,000 of the same units on the ground. A third way to state a map's scale is shown in Figure 2.13.

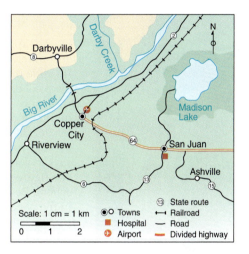

**Figure 2.13** ▲

This map shows roads, towns, and bodies of water.

## *SkillBuilder*   *Reading a Map*

### Find Your Way

How good are your map-reading skills? Study the map in Figure 2.13 above. Then answer the following questions.

1. What is the scale of the map? State the scale as a ratio. Remember that both parts of the ratio must be the same unit.

2. What is the approximate distance between the hospital and the airport? Between the hospital and Big River?

3. What is the driving distance between Riverview and Copper City? What is the straight-line distance between the two cities?

4. Which city has a larger population, San Juan or Ashville? How do you know?

5. Which direction do you travel when you ride a bicycle from San Juan to Copper City?

6. What highways do you travel on to get from Riverview to Ashville?

7. Which city is most likely to have a railroad station?

8. What physical feature lies between Copper City and Darbyville?

9. Using a separate sheet of paper, trace the roads and cities that appear on the map. With a different color pen or pencil, show a route you can take between Riverview and Madison Lake that does not involve traveling on Highway 64. How far will you travel if you take this route?

Choose a place on the map where you'd like to live. In a paragraph or two, describe the natural and human-made features around that place.

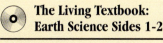

**The Living Textbook: Earth Science Sides 1-2**

Chapter 28        Frame 04077
Map Scale (1 Frame)
Search:

TEACH ▪ *Continued*

## Reteach

Most students use maps on a regular basis. Ask students to draw a map of the route from their home to a local store, library, or movie theater. Ask them to write a description of the route that would help another person use the map.

## EVALUATE

### WrapUp

**Reinforce** Have students do a survey of their homes and school to find examples of as many different types of maps as they can. Have them make a list of the maps and, if possible, make a bulletin-board display of the types of maps.
Use Review Worksheet 2.2

### Check and Explain

1. A latitude measurement tells how many degrees north or south of the equator a place is. A longitude measurement tells how many degrees east or west of the prime meridian a place is.

2. Cartographers obtain data by making measurements of the land and then drawing maps according to the measurements.

3. An equal-area projection is a more realistic map because it is not as distorted as a map made by a cylindrical projection. The areas of the landmasses are accurate, although the shapes are slightly distorted. This makes it better than a cylindrical projection map for comparing the sizes of continents and countries.

4. South America

## *Integrating the Sciences*

**Meteorology** Bring in a weather map from a newspaper. Have students infer the meaning of the symbols commonly used on such a map. Point out that weather maps symbols may vary.

**Figure 2.14** ▲
You often need maps to find your way around a big city.

### Science and You   *A Map or More a Day*

You may not even realize it, but you may encounter many different maps in the course of a day. Imagine the following sequence of events. Could this be a typical day in your life?

You go into the kitchen for breakfast and find your mother looking at a road map. "The radio reported a big accident on the freeway," she says. "I need to find another route to work." Then your father comes in. He says to you, "I left the transit map on the table, so you can figure out which bus to take to the library after school. Be sure to take your umbrella. The weather map in the paper shows a storm heading our way."

You eat, grab the transit map, and catch the bus to school. In social studies class, you study a map of Africa as your teacher talks about the people of Nigeria. In science class, you read this chapter about maps. Finally, when school's over for the day, you check your transit map and see that you need to catch a bus on Route 53 to get to the library.

When you get to the library, you use the map on the wall to locate the reference section. You copy information you need for your report on maps, and then leaf through an atlas, a big book full of maps of everywhere in the world.

You decide to head for the mall to get a present for your mother's birthday. The mall map tells you the location of the store that will have what you want. When you get home, you finish your report on maps. You've had a day full of maps!

### Check and Explain

1. What does a latitude measurement tell you about a location? What does a longitude measurement tell you about the same place?

2. What is one important way cartographers obtain data for making maps?

3. **Evaluate** What advantages does an equal-area projection have over a cylindrical projection?

4. **Locate** Which continent is located at 15°S latitude and 50°W longitude? Use the map on page 41.

***Themes in Science***

**Scale and Structure** Topographic maps represent the three-dimensional details of the earth's surface. Reading topographic maps requires the ability to interpret contour lines.

## 2.3 Topographic Maps

### Objectives

▶ **Describe** what topographic maps show about the earth's surface.

▶ **Explain** how contour lines show topography.

▶ **Interpret** contour lines on a topographic map.

▶ **Calculate** average slope.

**Y**ou and a group of friends are going to hike to the top of a mountain in a local park. When you meet, you find there are three different trails leading to the summit. Which one should you take? "I have a topographic map," says one of your friends. "That will help us decide."

Why will the topographic map help? Unlike regular maps, a topographic map shows **topography**, the variations in elevation over the landscape. By looking at the trails on the topographic map, you can tell the steepness of each trail. Topographic maps are useful not just for hikers, but for earth scientists and other people, too.

### Contour Lines

How can a flat map show the very uneven surface of the earth? Some maps give an impression of topography with shading. Topographic maps, however, show topography very precisely with **contour lines**. A contour line connects points that have the same elevation. If you've ever walked along a trail on the side of a mountain that went neither down nor up, you have followed a contour line.

A topographic map shows contour lines for only certain elevations. Lines may be drawn, for example, at 50 m, 100 m, 150 m, and so on. The elevation of any location can be estimated by finding the elevation of the nearest contour line. Contour lines show topography with their shape and spacing. A set of contour lines forming smaller and smaller loops, for example, indicates a mountain or hill. The closer the spacing of the lines, the steeper the slope of the mountain.

▼ **ACTIVITY**

**Observing**

*Mapping for Apples*

Imagine an apple sitting in a deep bowl. This special apple will not float. You add a little water and draw a line around the apple at the water level. You add a little more water and draw another line. You continue adding water and drawing lines until the apple is covered with water. When you remove the apple, what does it look like? How have the lines defined its shape?

**SKILLS WARMUP**

**Figure 2.15** ▲
As long as this trail stays horizontal, it follows a contour line.

**Section Objectives**
For a list of section objectives, see the Student Edition page.

**Skills Objectives**
Skills should be able to:

**Observe** how a shape can be represented by contour lines.

**Calculate** the average slope of a hillside.

**Model** a topographic map.

**Vocabulary**
topography, contour line

**MOTIVATE**

### *Skills WarmUp*

To give students practice in interpreting topographic maps, have them do the Skills WarmUp.
**Answer** Students should see that the apple would be striped with horizontal parallel lines from top to bottom. The lines define the apple's shape by giving evenly spaced samples of the shape of its outside surface.

### Prior Knowledge

To gauge how much students know about topographic maps, ask the following questions:

▶ How can maps and globes show the heights of landforms?

▶ How would you describe a slope?

▶ How would a map that shows the shape and steepness of the land be useful?

**The Living Textbook: Earth Science Sides 1-2**

Chapter 28      Frame 04080
Contour Lines (1 Frame)
Search:

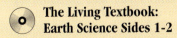

## TEACH

### Directed Inquiry

Have students study Figure 2.16. Then ask:

▶ From what level is elevation measured on an island? Why? (From sea level; it is the lowest level of the land.)

▶ What do the heaviest contour lines represent? How often do they occur on this map? (They are index contour lines. They occur every 100 meters.)

▶ Why do contour lines almost never cross? (Only nearest points of equal elevation are connected by a contour line. Rarely, contour lines may intersect or cross at an overhanging cliff.)

▶ What do the short marks called *hachures* inside a closed loop indicate? Why are they necessary? (They indicate a depression or crater; if they were not there, a person might assume that there was a hill in that place.)

▶ What is the difference in elevation between two successive contour lines called? What does it indicate? (It is called the contour interval; it gives an idea of the steepness of the terrain.)

### Skills Development

**Infer** How can the elevation of an unlabeled contour line be determined? (With the contour interval and the elevation of the index contour lines on either side of the unlabeled line)

### Answer to In-Text Question

① **They never cross; they connect points that have the same elevation, and they show steepness.**

### Cooperative Learning

To help students read countour lines on topographic maps, have them work in pairs. Using Figure 2.16, have one student mark a point on the map, using a tiny bead or seed. The other student must then try to determine as precisely as possible the elevation. Have students reverse roles.

**Figure 2.16  Topographic Map of an Island ▼**

Look at Figure 2.16. In the upper left, it shows how the topography of a three-dimensional structure such as a mountainous island can be projected onto a two-dimensional map. Study the map that results. What can you learn about contour lines? ①

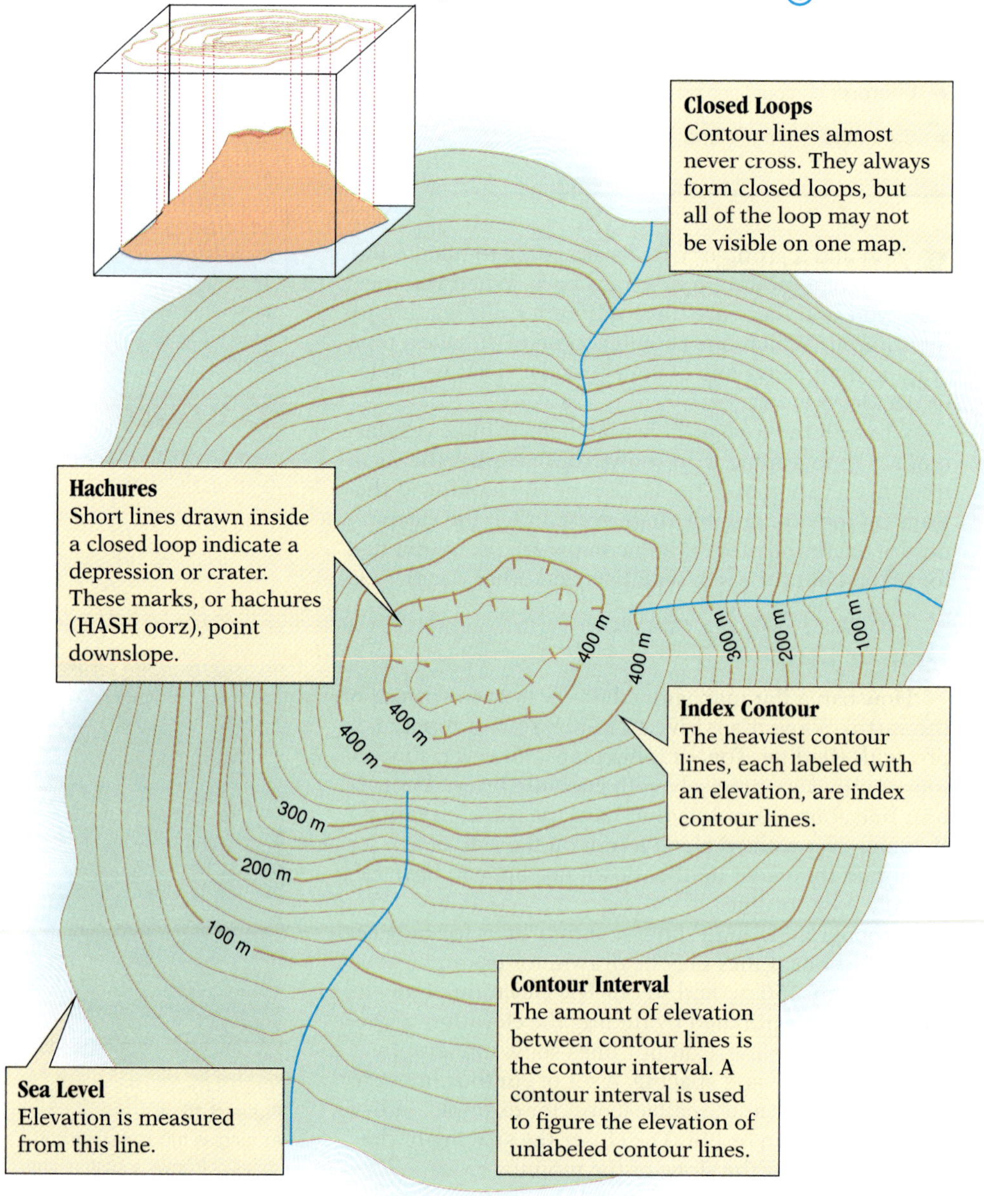

**Closed Loops**
Contour lines almost never cross. They always form closed loops, but all of the loop may not be visible on one map.

**Hachures**
Short lines drawn inside a closed loop indicate a depression or crater. These marks, or hachures (HASH oorz), point downslope.

**Index Contour**
The heaviest contour lines, each labeled with an elevation, are index contour lines.

**Contour Interval**
The amount of elevation between contour lines is the contour interval. A contour interval is used to figure the elevation of unlabeled contour lines.

**Sea Level**
Elevation is measured from this line.

400 m  400 m  400 m  400 m  300 m  200 m  100 m  300 m  200 m  100 m

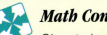

### Math Connection

Give students practice in calculating average slope. Ask them to figure out how to show average slope as a line on a slope profile. If appropriate, this can be used as an introduction to the more abstract mathematical concepts of the slope of a line on a graph and the slope of the equation that represents that line.

### Class Activity

Have students make a profile of one slope of the island in Figure 2.16. They can lay a ruler across the figure to determine a profile line. Have students pick the vertical scale that they will use. Also have them indicate the vertical scale (For example, 1 cm = 50 m) below the profile.

### Career Corner

**Reason and Conclude** Ask students: If a cartographer were assigned the task of making a new map of Yellowstone National Park, should he or she use existing maps to help make the new ones? Why or why not? (Yes, existing maps may be used to verify the features that are there.) What information is needed before the map can be made? Why? (Collecting information from satellites, airplanes, helicopters, trucks, on horseback, and/or on foot needs to be done. Some changes may have occurred as a result of erosion, fires, landslides, or new structures made by people.)

## Slope

The slope, or steepness, of the land is important to hikers, skiers, geologists, and builders. Topographic maps provide the information needed to create an accurate picture of any slope. Look at Figure 2.17. It shows a cross section, or profile, of the slope represented by the contour lines above it. The cross section is like a graph, with elevations plotted by horizontal distance. The cross section is made along a profile line drawn between two points on a topographic map, usually at right angles to contour lines.

You can also use a topographic map to figure the average slope of any hill or mountainside. Average slope is calculated as the change in elevation divided by the horizontal distance in which this change occurs. If the elevation rises from 10 m to 60 m in a distance of 100 m, for example, the average slope is

$$\frac{60-10}{100} = \frac{1}{2} = 50 \text{ percent.}$$

**Figure 2.17  Profile of a Slope** ▲

## Career Corner *Cartographer*

### Who Designs and Makes Maps?

Cartographers have been making maps for thousands of years. The ancient Greeks had road maps. The Romans used maps for military purposes.

Today cartographers are still in demand. Maps are constantly revised. New maps are always being made to show information to scientists, governments, employees, business owners, motorists, and many others.

Mapmaking is more than just drawing maps. Cartographers plan and design maps, and they collect information. Some cartographers work mainly indoors

drawing maps. Others work in the field. They collect information from airplanes, helicopters, trucks, or on foot.

A cartographer must have mathematical ability, as well as knowledge of drafting and computer science. Experience in photography and an eye for detail are also important.

A college degree in cartography, geography, or civil engineering is often desirable. However, a college degree is

not required for all jobs in cartography. If you are interested in mapping the land, you can prepare by taking math, art, and computer science classes in high school.

## Discuss

Have students read and study the guidelines carefully. Then ask:

▶ If there are many contour lines that seem to come together in an area on the map, what can be inferred about that area? (It is a very steep area, such as a cliff.)

▶ If there are widely spaced contour lines in an area, what can be inferred about that area? (It is a fairly flat area.)

▶ Which way do the Vs of a stream or river point? Why? (They point upstream because the stream erodes into the earth in a V-shape. The elevation in the stream is then upstream of the same elevation on the bank.)

▶ What does a series of closed loops within a broad loop indicate? Why? (The series of closed loops indicates a hill or mountain because, as the elevation increases, the hill or mountain occupies less area and the points of equal elevation will form smaller loops.)

### Answers to In-Text Questions

① **North of Dunderberg Peak and Castle Peak in the right half of the red square marked 25**

② **Easiest route is around Gray Butte toward Summit Lake; north of Summit Lake to below Epidote Peak toward Gilman Lake, then north to East Lake.**

③ **East Lake**

④ **About 1,339 m; Camiaca Peak is at 11,739 m, Summit Lake is at 10,400 m.**

⑤ **Castle Peak (12,374)**

## Writing Connection

Ask students to choose a point on the topographic map in Figure 2.18 and to imagine viewing the surrounding landscape from that point. Have them write descriptions of what they would see. They can then share their descriptions with the class.

| Topographic Map Symbols | |
|---|---|
| 4-lane highway | |
| 2-lane highway | |
| Unpaved road | |
| Trail | |
| Railroad | |
| Buildings | |
| School | |
| Church | |
| Index contour | |
| Depression contour | |
| Stream | |
| Lake | |
| Swamp | |

**Figure 2.18**
Most topographic maps use the same symbols (above). Can you read the topographic map below? ▼

## Using Topographic Maps

Using a topographic map requires all the skills you use in reading any map, plus some others. The main skill to learn is how to interpret contour lines. This means learning to see in your mind three-dimensional landforms when you look at contour lines. The guidelines below will help you interpret contour lines:

1. The closer the spacing of the contour lines, the steeper the slope. Flat places have widely spaced lines, and cliffs have very closely spaced lines.

2. Contour lines that cross a valley are V-shaped. If a stream or river flows in the valley, the Vs point upstream.

3. A series of increasingly smaller closed loops indicates a hill or mountain.

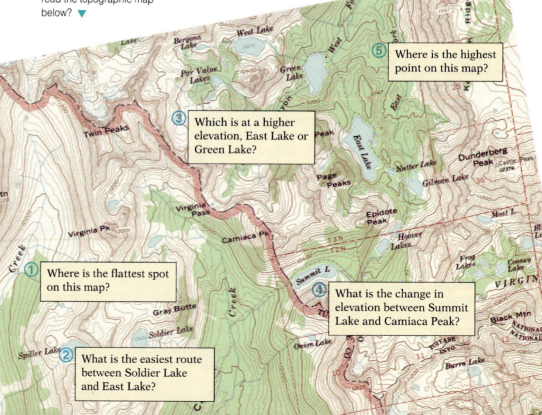

Where is the highest point on this map?

Which is at a higher elevation, East Lake or Green Lake?

Where is the flattest spot on this map?

What is the change in elevation between Summit Lake and Camiaca Peak?

What is the easiest route between Soldier Lake and East Lake?

## Science and Technology
### Topographic Mapping by Satellite

The date is 1882. A group of men and horses are working their way up a steep, rocky slope. Each horse carries a load of heavy equipment. The men walk beside them, coaxing the animals up the slope. The party sets up camp at a small flat spot. Before the sun sets, several men take out long chains and place them across the land, making measurements. Others peer at compasses and make marks on paper. Another uses an altimeter to take a reading that will help to determine elevation.

The group was part of the United States Geological Survey (USGS), established in 1879. Its goal was to map the topography, geology, mineralogy, and biology of the western territories. The instruments were crude, but the results were relatively accurate.

Topographic maps produced by the USGS today look much the same as they did in the 1880s. However, the detail, accuracy, and amount of information has greatly changed. The USGS now uses data from Landsat satellites traveling almost 1,000 km above the earth's surface. Through Landsat technology, every spot on the earth's surface is photographed every 16 days. More than 90 percent of the United States has been mapped using information from Landsat satellites.

It may sound like the new technology for mapping will soon put itself out of a job. Once a place is mapped, does it have to be mapped again? Very often it does, because the land is always changing. Roads are built, forests cut down, slopes eroded. Landsat data are always needed for updating of maps.

**Figure 2.19** ▲
Map makers need computers to process the information provided by satellites.

### Check and Explain

1. How are topographic maps different from other maps?

2. Describe how a mountain looks on a topographic map. Make a drawing to go with your answer.

3. **Reason and Conclude**   Why do contour lines almost never cross?

4. **Calculate**   What is the average slope of a hillside that rises 25 m over a horizontal distance of 75 m?

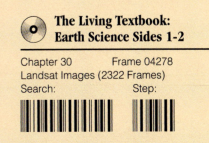

**Time** 40 minutes **Group** one

**Materials**

30 blocks of modeling clay

wax paper

rubber bands

30 blue colored pencils

30 brown colored pencils

30 butter knives

### Prelab Discussion

Have students read the entire activity. Discuss a few points before beginning:

▶ Review the details of topographic maps in Section 2.3.

▶ Go over the activity procedure, especially steps 6 and 7. Make sure students understand that they are to cut horizontal slices.

## Analysis

1. The map should be an accurate representation of the mountain.

2. Answers will vary.

3. Average slope will depend on each student's design. Check maps for accuracy.

## Conclusion

Students' conclusions will vary, but should accurately reflect the topographic map.

## Extension

Results will vary. Most will come close to making the mountains look the same.

---

## Activity 2 *How can you make a topographic map?*

**Skills** Measure; Interpret Data; Model

### Task 1 Prelab Prep

1. Collect the following items: block of modeling clay, piece of wax paper, rubber band, pencil, metric ruler, paper, brown and blue colored pencils, butter knife.

2. Using the modeling clay, mold a small mountain a little over 10 cm high. Include gullies or valleys where streams would be. Place the mountain on the wax paper.

3. Use the rubber band to attach the pencil 2 cm from the end of the ruler, as shown in Figure 2.20.

### Task 2 Procedure

1. Hold the ruler upright, with the pencil point touching the clay model.

2. Mark a line completely around the mountain by moving the ruler assembly.

3. Move the pencil to the 4-cm mark on the ruler. Repeat step 2.

4. Mark a contour line every 2 cm until you reach the top.

5. Peel the wax paper off, and place the mountain on a sheet of blank paper. Trace around the outside edge with the brown pencil. Take the mountain off the paper, and put it back on the wax paper.

6. Using the butter knife, carefully cut your mountain at the 2-cm elevation contour line. Move the knife all around the mountain, and make the cut as flat as possible. Be careful not to change the shape of the mountain.

7. Remove the wax paper and the bottom slice. Set the slice aside. Place the remainder of the mountain in the center of the contour line loop you drew on the paper. Trace the edge as before, and put the mountain back on the wax paper.

8. Repeat the procedure for all the remaining contour lines to complete the topographic map of your mountain.

9. Label the first contour line 0 cm, the next 2 cm, and so on, to the top of the mountain. Using the blue pencil, draw streams in the gullies or valleys.

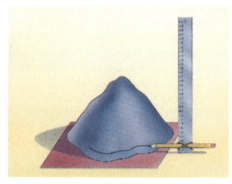

**Figure 2.20** ▲

### Task 3 Analysis

1. Look at your mountain and your topographic map. Is the topographic map an accurate representation of the mountain?

2. What is your mountain's elevation?

3. Draw a straight line down one side from the top of your mountain to the bottom. Calculate the average slope along this line.

### Task 4 Conclusion

Imagine your mountain is real. Describe what you would see during a hike to the top.

### Extension

Trade topographic maps with a classmate. Don't look at each other's mountains. Get more modeling clay, and mold a mountain to look like the one in the topographic map you borrowed. When you are done, compare your mountain to the original mountain. How close did you come to making the mountains look the same?

## Chapter 2 Review

### Concept Summary

**2.1 Earth's Surface**

▶ The surface of the earth has land-masses called continents and bodies of salt water called seas and oceans.

▶ Types of landforms include mountains, plateaus, valleys, canyons, and plains.

▶ Ocean and coastal features include bays, straits, lagoons, islands, peninsulas, and archipelagos.

▶ Major life zones, or biomes, differ in their temperature and rainfall patterns.

**2.2 Mapping the Earth**

▶ The equator, an imaginary line drawn exactly between the two poles, divides the earth into two halves called hemispheres.

▶ Latitude lines and longitude lines locate points on the earth.

▶ A map projection is a way of showing the surface of the earth on a flat map.

▶ Features such as roads and buildings are shown on a map with different symbols. A map scale tells the relationship between the distance on the map and the distance on the land.

**2.3 Topographic Maps**

▶ Topographic maps show variations in elevation over a landscape.

▶ A contour line on a topographic map connects points with the same elevation. Contour lines form closed loops and never cross.

▶ Contour lines show slope, or steepness. Contour lines can be used together with the map scale to calculate average slope.

### Chapter Vocabulary

| | | | |
|---|---|---|---|
| continent (2.1) | hemisphere (2.2) | prime meridian (2.2) | topography (2.3) |
| biome (2.1) | latitude (2.2) | international date line (2.2) | contour line (2.3) |
| equator (2.2) | longitude (2.2) | scale (2.2) | |

### Check Your Vocabulary

Use the vocabulary words above to complete the following sentences correctly.

1. The lines that show land elevations on a topographic map are called _____ .

2. The Northern and Southern Hemispheres are divided by the _____ .

3. The earth's land surface can be divided into six major life zones, or _____ .

4. The variation in elevation over a landscape is called _____ .

5. The large landmasses on the surface of the earth are _____ .

6. Lines on a map that tell the distance in degrees from the equator are called lines of _____ .

7. On a map the relationship between distances on the map and distances on land is shown by the _____ .

8. The longitude line that passes through Greenwich, England, is the _____ .

9. The earth can be divided into two _____ .

10. The lines on a map drawn from pole to pole are meridians, or lines of _____ .

11. The meridian that measures 180° is called the _____ .

### Write Your Vocabulary

Write sentences using the vocabulary words above. Show that you know what each word means.

### Check Your Vocabulary

1. contour lines
2. equator
3. biomes
4. topography
5. continents
6. latitude
7. scale
8. prime meridian
9. hemispheres
10. longitude
11. international date line

### Write Your Vocabulary

Students' sentences should show that they know the meaning of each word as well as how to use it in a sentence.

Use Vocabulary Worksheet for Chapter 2.

## Check Your Knowledge

1. Elevation is the height of the land above sea level at a given place. Topography relates to variations in elevation over the landscape.

2. Answers will vary, but may include descriptions of: straits, bays, islands, peninsulas, lagoons, and archipelagos.

3. Latitude and longitude provide reference points for locating any place on earth.

4. Types of projections include: cylindrical, conical, and equal area. A cylindrical projection distorts the sizes of continents; a conical projection can only show one hemisphere; and an equal area projection slightly distorts the shapes of the continents to represent areas accurately.

5. Maps contain symbols to represent different features of the area. Examples include roads, railroads, and buildings.

6. An index contour is a contour line that is heavier than the others and is marked with the elevation.

7. Average slope can be calculated by dividing the change in elevation by the horizontal distance. If the elevation changes from 50 m to 150 m over a distance of 500 meters, the average slope is $(150 - 50) \div 500 = 0.20$, or 20%.

8. The four oceans of the earth are the Atlantic, Arctic, Indian, and Pacific.

9. Rain forest, grassland, desert, tundra, coniferous forest, and deciduous forest

10. plateau

11. North and South poles

12. hachures

13. upstream

14. island

## Check Your Understanding

1. Cylindrical projections are made by transferring the features of the earth onto a cylinder. This results in an accurate depiction of the shape of the continents, but distorts the size. A conical projection puts the features of a single hemisphere onto a cone. This results in fairly accurate sizes, but can only show one hemisphere.

2. Accept any logical, supported answer.

3. Lines of latitude run parallel to the equator and measure distances north and south; longitude lines run perpendicular to the equator and measure distances east and west. They are similar because both are measured in degrees and are used to find locations on the earth.

4. Cartographers make maps either by actually measuring the terrain they are mapping, called field mapping, or by using satellites to take measurements that can be turned into a map.

5. Tundra is found near the poles; coniferous forests are found at higher elevations and northern latitudes; deciduous forests are found in middle latitudes in North America, Australia, Europe, and Asia; grasslands and deserts are found on all continents except Antarctica; rain forests are found along the equator.

6. Students' answers may vary. Examples include: Topographic maps can help hikers find their way through unfamiliar terrain; engineers can use them to help plan the building of roads, bridges, and other structures.

7. $(25 - 5) \div 80 = 0.25$, or 25%

8. Northern: Africa, Asia, Europe, North America, South America; southern: Africa, Antarctica, Australia, Asia, South America; both: Africa, Asia, South America

---

## Chapter 2 Review

### Check Your Knowledge

Answer the following in complete sentences.

1. What is elevation? How is elevation related to topography?

2. Describe four major coastal features.

3. What is the purpose of latitude and longitude lines?

4. List two types of map projections and describe how they differ.

5. Why do maps contain symbols? Give examples of two map symbols.

6. What is an index contour?

7. How do you calculate the average slope of a hill? Give an example.

8. Name the four oceans of the earth.

9. List the earth's six biomes.

Choose the answer that best completes each sentence.

10. A flat, raised area of land is a (mountain, plateau, plain, valley).

11. The two fixed points through which the axis of the earth pass are (the North and South Poles, the equator and the poles, the equator and the prime meridian, the poles and the prime meridian).

12. The short lines that indicate depressions on a topographic map are called (slopes, contour intervals, meridians, hachures).

13. When contour lines form V-shapes, the Vs always point (upstream, downstream, north, toward a mountain).

14. Land completely surrounded by water is a(n) (archipelago, peninsula, strait, island).

### Check Your Understanding

Apply the concepts you have learned to answer each question.

1. Compare cylindrical map projections to conical map projections.

2. **Critical Thinking** Decide whether you think the earth has six or seven continents. Explain why.

3. What are the differences between lines of latitude and lines of longitude? How are they similar?

4. Describe the methods cartographers use for mapping the earth.

5. Describe where on the earth's surface each of the six major biomes is located.

6. Name a use for topographic maps.

7. Determine the average slope of a hill if the elevation rises from 5 to 25 m in a distance of 80 m.

8. List the continents that have land in the northern hemisphere. List the continents that have land in the southern hemisphere. Which continents appear on both lists?

9. **Extension** Using graph paper divided into squares, make a map of your classroom. Label the $x$-axis and $y$-axis of your map as you would a line graph. Name the points on your grid that would identify where you sit. What points correspond to the door?

10. **Application** Discuss the different types of maps you have used. Tell why you used each type of map.

11. **Mystery Photo** The photograph on page 30 shows the view of a rural area taken from an airplane. Make a map of the area shown in the photograph. Write a legend for the symbols used in your map.

9. Students' graphs will vary.

10. Students' answers will vary, but may include road maps, building maps, weather maps, trail maps.

11. Students' maps will vary. Make sure each student includes the important features of the terrain, including streams and roads.

## Develop Your Skills

1. a. About 17%
   b. From 0 to 100 m and from 300 to 400 m

2. a. Brooks range
   b. Between 700 and 1500 m
   c. Florida Everglades and at the Mississippi delta in Louisiana

3. a. New York City
   b. New Orleans
   c. Yellowstone National Park

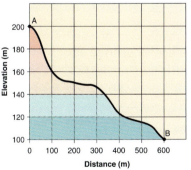

## Develop Your Skills

Use the skills you have developed in this chapter to complete each activity.

1. **Interpret Data** The graph below shows a slope profile for a hill.

   a. What is the average slope from point A to point B?
   b. Name a section of the hill where the slope is steeper than the average slope.

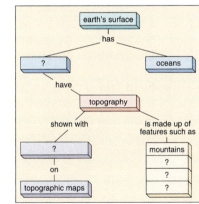

2. **Data Bank** Use the information on pages 620–621 to answer the following questions.

   a. What mountain range is located in northern Alaska?
   b. What is the elevation of most of the Central Plains?
   c. What are the locations of two major swamps in the United States?

3. **Read a Map** Using a map of the United States, find and name each location.

   a. 41°N, 74°W
   b. 30°N, 90°W
   c. 45°N, 109°W

## Make Connections

1. **Link the Concepts** Below is a concept map showing how some of the major concepts in this chapter link together. Only part of the map is filled in. Finish the map, using words and ideas from the chapter.

2. **Science and You** Write down directions from your home to school. Now draw a map from your home to school. Which is easier to understand, the written directions or the map? Explain.

3. **Science and Social Studies** Find a copy of a map of North or South America made by early European explorers. Compare this map to a modern map of the same place. How accurate were the early explorers?

4. **Science and Art** Drawing to scale is not limited to mapmaking. Artists often draw objects to scale to create a realistic picture. Draw a piece of fruit using a 1:10 scale.

## Make Connections

1.

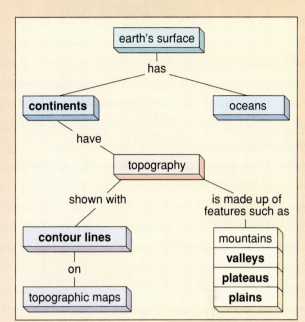

2. Student maps and instructions will vary. Most will probably say that the map is easier to understand than the written directions.

3. Student answers will vary. Early explorers were fairly accurate in some places, not as accurate in others.

4. Student drawings will vary. Make sure they have correctly scaled their drawings.

**CHAPTER 3**

## Overview

This chapter presents the structure of the earth. The first section identifies the chemical and physical properties of the layers of the earth, including the lithosphere and asthenosphere. The second and final section explores the earth's interior, concentrating on seismic waves and what can be inferred by studying them. This section concludes with an explanation of ways to detect seismic waves.

## Advance Planner

▶ Provide cornstarch and water for TE page 57.

▶ Gather water, glass, and pencils for TE page 62.

▶ Supply a coiled spring toy for TE page 62.

▶ Supply hot plates, 250-mL beakers, water, food coloring, droppers, spoons, and rolled oats cereal for SE Activity 3, page 66.

## Skills Development Chart

| Sections | Classify | Generalize | Graph | Infer | Model | Observe | Predict |
|---|---|---|---|---|---|---|---|
| **3.1** Skills WarmUp | ● | | | | | | |
| Skills WorkOut | | ● | | | | | |
| SkillBuilder | | | ● | | | | |
| **3.2** Skills WarmUp | | | | ● | | | |
| Skills WorkOut | | | | | | ● | |
| Historical Notebook | | | | | | ● | ● |
| Activity 3 | | | | ● | ● | ● | |

## Individual Needs

▶ **Limited English Proficiency Students** Have students make two diagrams of the earth's interior, one showing the chemical makeup of the layers and the other the physical properties of the layers. Have students use labels appropriate to each way of classifying the earth's layers. Each label should include a brief definition of the layer in the student's own words.

▶ **At-Risk Students** Invite students to work in groups to present their own version of a journey to the center of the earth based on the material in this chapter. Encourage each group to design a vehicle for taking the journey. Then ask groups to present their journeys to the class as if they were experts leading a tour of the earth's interior. Each group member should play a different role, such as captain of the earth vehicle, chemist, or physicist, and take turns presenting a commentary on each part of the journey.

▶ **Gifted Students** Ask students to learn more about the continental crust. Encourage them to find out about its known physical and chemical features and what is not yet known about it. Have them make a three-dimensional model showing a cross-section of continental crust.

## Resource Bank

▶ **Bulletin Board** Make a time line to illustrate various theories and discoveries relating to what lies below the earth's surface. Include such things as Aristotle's belief that the earth was a solid ball and the discovery of the Moho. Ask students to contribute photos and drawings to illustrate the events on the time line.

▶ **Field Trip** If there is a seismographic station nearby, make arrangements to visit it. Encourage students to ask questions about how seismographs record seismic waves, what the records of different waves look like, and the various ways the data from these devices is used.

| Section | Core | Standard | Enriched | Section | Core | Standard | Enriched |
|---|:---:|:---:|:---:|---|:---:|:---:|:---:|
| **3.1 Layers of the Earth**<br>pp. 55–60 | | | | **Color Transparencies**<br>Transparencies 6a, 6b | ● | ● | ● |
| **Section Features**<br>Skills WarmUp, p. 55<br>Skills WorkOut, p. 58<br>SkillBuilder, p. 59 | ●<br>●<br> | ●<br>●<br> | ●<br>●<br>● | **3.2 Studying the Earth's Interior**<br>pp. 61–66 | | | |
| **Blackline Masters**<br>Review Worksheet 3.1<br>Skills Worksheet 3.1a<br>Skills Worksheet 3.1b<br>Integrating Worksheet 3.1a<br>Integrating Worksheet 3.1b | ●<br>●<br>●<br><br>● | ●<br>●<br>●<br>●<br>● | ●<br>●<br>●<br>●<br>● | **Section Features**<br>Skills WarmUp, p. 61<br>Skills WorkOut, p. 64<br>Historical Notebook, p. 64<br>Activity, p. 66 | ●<br>●<br><br>● | ●<br>●<br>●<br>● | ●<br>●<br>●<br>● |
| **Overhead Blackline Transparencies**<br>Overhead Blackline Master 3.1 and Student Worksheet | ● | ● | ● | **Blackline Masters**<br>Review Worksheet 3.2<br>Reteach Worksheet 3.2<br>Vocabulary Worksheet 3.2 | ●<br>●<br>● | ●<br>●<br>● | ●<br>●<br>● |
| **Laboratory Program**<br>Investigation 5 | | | ● | **Color Transparencies**<br>Transparency 7 | ● | ● | ● |

# Bibliography

The following resources can be used for teaching the chapter. See page T–46 for supplier codes.

## Library Resources

Farndon, John. *How the Earth Works.* Pleasantville, NY: The Reader's Digest Association, Inc., 1992.

Markle, Sandra. *Digging Deeper: Investigations into Rocks, Shocks, Quakes, and Other Earthly Matters.* New York: Lothrop, Lee, and Shepard Books, 1987.

Van Rose, S. *Volcano & Earthquake.* Eyewitness Series. New York: Alfred A. Knopf, Inc., 1992.

## Technology Resources

### *Internet*
**PLANETDIARY** at *http://www.planetdiary.com*
- Find geological news by exploring *Current Phenomena.*
- Learn about earthquakes and volcanoes by clicking on *Phenomena Backgrounders.*

### *Software*
*CampOS Science: Structure-Function Relationships. Mac. LS.*

### *CD-ROMs*
*Interactive Earth. SFAW.*

### *Laserdiscs*
*Living Textbook. (See barcodes on pages in this chapter.) Optical Data.*

## Audio-Visual Resources
*Earth: The Geology of an Ever-Changing Planet. Filmstrips. UL. The Interior of the Earth. Film. CRM Films.*

**Writing Connection**

Have students imagine that the photograph is a motion picture with a sound track. Have students write paragraphs describing the sounds that they hear and colors that they see in the motion picture.

## Introducing the Chapter

Have students read the description of the photograph. Ask if they agree or disagree with the description.

### Directed Inquiry

Have students study the photograph. Ask:

▶ What is this a photograph of? (Students will probably recognize it as a body of water.)

▶ What can you tell about the temperature of this water from the photograph? Explain. (Students may recognize that the white clouds above the surface are produced by water at a high temperature.)

▶ What could make this body of water hot enough to produce clouds of steam? (Students should suggest hot rocks or hot gases from inside the earth.)

▶ Do you think anything could live in this water? Why or why not? (There is life in this water. The yellow ring around the edge—not the green—is algae.)

▶ How is the photograph related to the subject of the chapter? (The structure of the earth includes what is below its surface. Hot rocks and gases are part of that structure.)

## Chapter Vocabulary

asthenosphere
convection
core
crust
lithosphere

mantle
Moho
seismic wave
shadow zone

**Chapter** **3**

**Structure of the Earth**

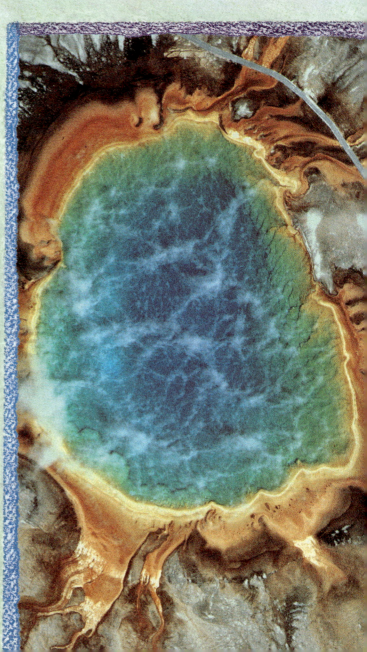

### Chapter Sections

**3.1** Layers of the Earth

**3.2** Studying the Earth's Interior

### What do you see?

❝I think it is a body of very hot liquid or water. I think it is hotter than we can imagine. The white matter could be clouds or foam from the water. I think the water could be from inside the earth and shows how hot it is there.❞

*Colleen Kenna
Neshaminy Junior High
School
Langhorne, Pennsylvania*

To find out more about the photograph, look on page 68. As you read this chapter, you will learn about the composition of the earth.

## Themes in Science

**Scale and Structure** The division of the earth into layers defines its most basic internal structure. By examining its individual layers, scientists can study the earth as a whole but on a smaller, more manageable scale. The earth's overall structure is dependent upon each of its individual layers.

## 3.1 Layers of the Earth

### Objectives

▶ **Describe** and **compare** the crust, mantle, and core.

▶ **Describe** the structure of the lithosphere.

▶ **Explain** why matter within the asthenosphere moves.

▶ **Make a model** of the earth and its layers.

---

**ACTIVITY**

**Classifying**

*Layer by Layer*

Make a list of different objects that are made up of layers. Classify the objects into groups based on the number, type, or thickness of their layers. Do most of the objects contain soft or hard centers?

**SKILLS WARMUP**

---

The rocks, soil, and water you can see on the earth's surface make up only a tiny fraction of the total mass and volume of the earth. What is the earth like below its surface? What makes up the interior of our planet?

At one time, some people thought the earth might be hollow. They imagined a person could find cracks in the surface that would lead them into enormous underground caverns. In 1864, French writer Jules Verne wrote about just such an adventure in *Journey to the Center of the Earth*. In this book, three explorers go deep into the earth and encounter a huge sea, prehistoric animals, and monster mushrooms. Today, scientists know there are no open, hollow spaces deep in the earth. But they also know that it is not all solid rock.

### Earth's Interior

What would you find if you could bore a hole down deeper and deeper into the earth until you reached its center? First, you would find that the chemical makeup of the materials changes as you go deeper. Second, you would discover that the materials increase in density. Third, you would observe that temperature and pressure increase with depth, but at different rates.

Because of the way these factors interact, the materials of the earth's interior form *layers*. The layers contain different chemical substances and have quite different physical properties. Earth scientists classify three main layers according to their location from the outside to the center of the earth. You will read more about those layers on the next pages.

**Figure 3.1** ▲
Even the deepest caverns are nowhere near the earth's interior.

**SECTION**

For a list of section objectives, see the Student Edition page.

**Skills Objectives**
Students should be able to:

**Classify** objects made up of layers.

**Generalize** about objects besides the earth that have a crust.

**Graph** temperature changes in the earth.

**Make a Model** of the earth's layers.

**Vocabulary**
crust, mantle, core, lithosphere, asthenosphere, convection

**Section Objectives**

---

**MOTIVATE**

### Skills WarmUp

To help students understand the concept of layers, have them do the Skills WarmUp.
**Answer** Answers will depend on the objects chosen. Students should be consistent in classifying by number, type, or thickness of layers.

### Prior Knowledge

To gauge how much students know about the layers of the earth, ask the following questions:

▶ If you went on a trip straight through the earth, what would you need to take with you?

▶ What are some differences between the surface of the earth and the center of the earth?

▶ What do you think is between the earth's surface and the center?

### Integrated Learning

Use Integrating Worksheet 3.1a.

**TEACH**

## Skills Development

**Calculate** Find the thickness of the mantle and core in Figure 3.2. Express the thickness of the mantle as a percentage of the earth's total thickness.
$(2900 \div (2900 + 3500) = 45\%)$

### Explore Visually

Have students study Figure 3.2 on pages 56 and 57. Explain that a *silicate* is a substance containing the elements silicon and oxygen. Ask:

▶ How thick is the crust, and what does it contain? (The crust varies from 5 to 40 kilometers in thickness; it contains much aluminum silicate material.)

▶ What materials does the mantle contain? (Dense silicates of iron and magnesium)

▶ How much of the earth's volume does the mantle make up? How much of the earth's mass? (82 percent of the earth's volume and 68 percent of the mass)

▶ Which layer is more dense, the mantle or the core? How do you know? (The core is more dense because it accounts for 32 percent of the earth's mass but only 16 percent of its volume; the mantle takes up five times as much volume but only twice as much mass. Remind students that scientists use a strict definition for *density*. The density of a substance is the relationship of its mass to a unit of volume.)

▶ What materials account for the density of the earth's core? (The metals iron and nickel, which make up most of the core)

### Integrating the Sciences

**Chemistry** Explain what an element is and how elements differ in their properties. Have students locate the major elements of the crust, mantle, and core in the periodic table on pages 176 and 177.

###  Math Connection

Have students examine carefully the numbers that describe the percentage of the earth's volume and mass each layer makes up. Ask: Which layer contains the largest percentage of the earth's mass? The largest percentage of its volume? What does this tell you about the relative densities of the two layers? (Remind students that density is calculated by dividing mass by volume.)
**Use Integrating Worksheet 3.1b.**

## Chemical Makeup of Layers

From Earth's outside to its center, the three main layers are the crust, mantle, and core. The **crust** is the outermost layer of the earth. The **mantle** is the middle layer of Earth. The center layer of the earth is the **core**.

The three layers are made of different chemicals. Rocky materials called silicates are the main substances of the crust and the mantle. Silicates are compounds of silicon and oxygen combined with other elements. The silicates of the crust are rich in aluminum, iron, and magnesium. In contrast, the silicates of the mantle contain mostly iron and magnesium. Unlike the other layers, the core is made up primarily of two metals: iron and nickel.

**Figure 3.2**
**Layers of the Earth** ▼

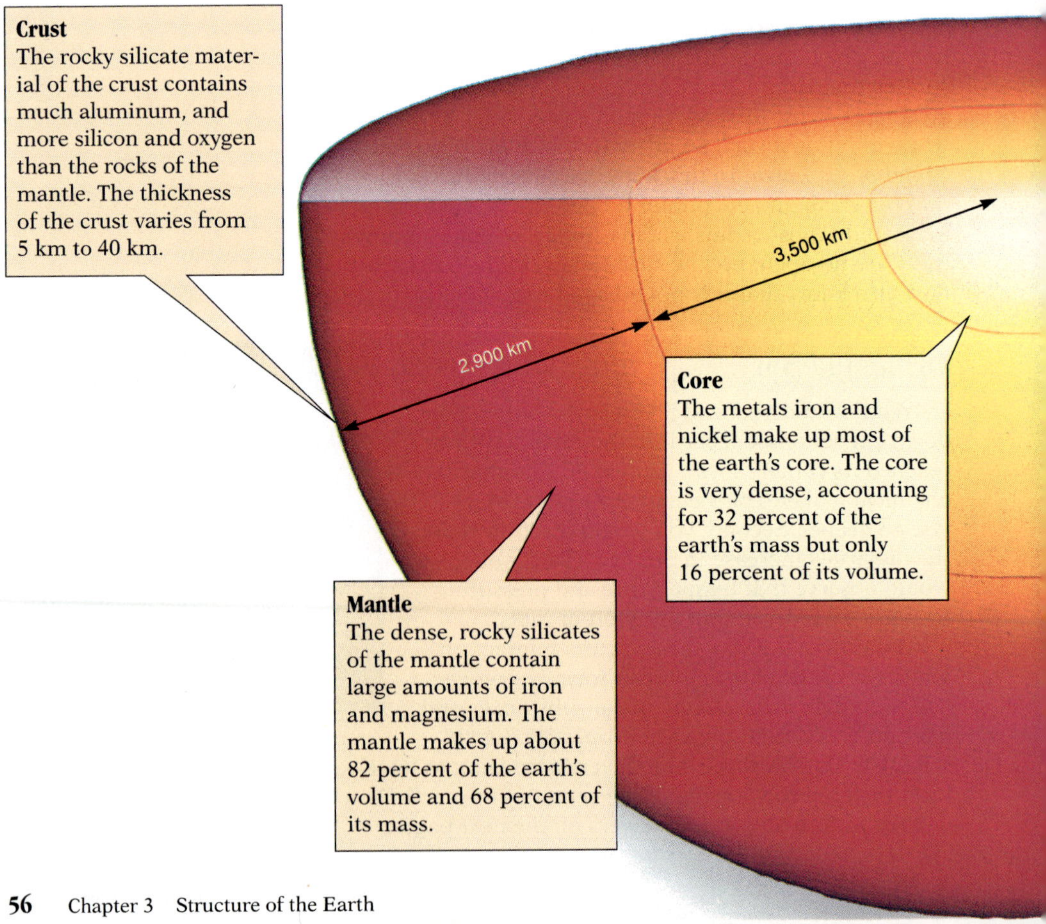

**Crust**
The rocky silicate material of the crust contains much aluminum, and more silicon and oxygen than the rocks of the mantle. The thickness of the crust varies from 5 km to 40 km.

**Core**
The metals iron and nickel make up most of the earth's core. The core is very dense, accounting for 32 percent of the earth's mass but only 16 percent of its volume.

**Mantle**
The dense, rocky silicates of the mantle contain large amounts of iron and magnesium. The mantle makes up about 82 percent of the earth's volume and 68 percent of its mass.

2,900 km

3,500 km

## Integrating the Sciences

**Physical Science** Show students how pressure can make matter in the asthenosphere flow without being liquified. Add just enough water to cornstarch to make a thick, flowing substance. When students handle the substance and squeeze, press, or move it, the mixture stops flowing and acts like a solid. Discuss how the consistency of this material is similar to the asthenosphere's plasticity.

## Physical Properties of Layers

The temperatures deep inside the earth are high enough to melt the silicates and other substances that make it up. Yet most of the earth's interior is not liquid. Why? The enormous pressures inside the earth offset the high temperatures. In much of the earth's interior, high pressures will not allow the matter to melt.

The balance between temperature and pressure in the earth varies with depth. Depending on this balance, the matter can be solid, liquid, or in-between. Note the differences among the zones in the diagram below. The outer zone, the **lithosphere** (LITH uhs FEER), is cool and rigid. Below it, the **asthenosphere** (as THEHN uhs FEER), is hot and semiliquid. The lithosphere includes the crust and upper mantle. The asthenosphere is in the mantle.

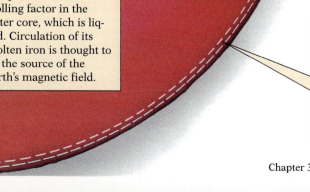

4,000°C-4,500°C  3,200°C-4,000°C   1,600C°-3,200°C  1,300C°-1,600°C

**Lithosphere**
The cool, solid lithosphere "floats" on top of the asthenosphere. The lithosphere includes the crust and the uppermost part of the mantle.

**Inner Core**
The very high pressure in the inner core is a more important factor than the very high temperature. As a result, the inner core is solid.

**Mantle**
This layer is solid and rigid compared to the asthenosphere because the temperature is not high enough to overcome the high pressure.

**Outer Core**
Temperature is the controlling factor in the outer core, which is liquid. Circulation of its molten iron is thought to be the source of the earth's magnetic field.

**Asthenosphere**
The right balance of pressure and temperature in the asthenosphere makes its rocky material soft and flowing but not completely liquid. This condition is called *plasticity*.

▶ Based on their characteristic physical properties, what are the five zones of Earth? (Inner core, outer core, mantle, asthenosphere, and lithosphere.)

▶ What does the lithosphere include? (The crust and the uppermost part of the mantle)

▶ What is the hot, soft, and flowing condition of the asthenosphere called? (Plasticity)

▶ What is the physical condition of the outer core? Why? (The outer core is liquid because temperature is the controlling factor and pressure is not high enough to keep it solid.)

▶ What is the physical condition of the inner core? Why? (The inner core is solid because pressure is the controlling factor.)

## Critical Thinking

**Reason and Conclude** Have students consider the balance between temperature and pressure in the earth. Ask: How does depth affect pressure and temperature? (The greater the depth, the higher the pressure from the material above, and the higher the temperature.)

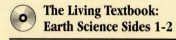

**The Living Textbook: Earth Science Sides 1-2**

Chapter 1                    Frame 00741
Litho- and Asthenosphere (1 Frame)
Search:

## TEACH ▪ Continued

### Skills WorkOut

To help students understand the structure of the earth's crust, have them do the Skills WorkOut.

**Answer** Answers may vary, but most students would mention the crust of a pie or of a loaf of bread or other bakery product. The skin of a fruit or shell of a nut can also be compared to a crust. Of course, the earth's crust is much harder than piecrust or bread crust. Dictionaries generally define *crust* as a hard external coat or covering. The earth's cool, rigid crust compares with its inner layers much like piecrust compares with a pie's filling.

### Critical Thinking

**Compare and Contrast** Have students think about the layers of the crust. Ask: How are tall mountains like icebergs? (Both have deep "roots." Most of the iceberg is below the water, and most of the mountain is below sea level.)

**Answer to In-Text Question**
① The two kinds of crust touch each other where the edges of the continents meet the oceans.

### Language Arts Connection

Have students look up the Greek origin of the words lithosphere and asthenosphere. Ask them whether the words' origins accurately describe these layers of the earth. (*Litho* comes from the Greek word for "rock" and *astheno* comes from the Greek word for "weak.")

▼ **ACTIVITY**

**Generalizing**

**Crust**

What objects besides the earth have a crust? How are their crusts similar to and different from the earth's crust? Look up the word *crust* in the dictionary. How does crust apply to the earth's outermost layer?

**SKILLS WORKOUT**

## Structure of the Lithosphere

The crust is the only layer of the earth that people have direct contact with. Together with the upper mantle, it forms a cool, rigid layer, the lithosphere, which undergoes slow but important changes. These changes, which you will learn about in later chapters, affect the earth's surface and its living things.

The lithosphere, like the rest of the earth, has a layered structure. You already know that it includes the crust and upper mantle. But the crust itself is made up of two distinct parts called continental crust and oceanic crust. Look at Figure 3.3 below. It is a cross section of the lithosphere showing these two kinds of crust. Notice that continental crust lies underneath continents and oceanic crust is underneath the oceans. Both kinds of crust are on the top of the lithosphere.

How are these two kinds of crust different? Continental crust is less dense than oceanic crust. Compared to oceanic crust, it is made up of a higher percentage of silicon and oxygen, and contains more aluminum. The rocks that make up continental crust are mostly granite and rhyolite. Denser, darker rocks called basalt and gabbro make up oceanic crust.

Continental crust, as you can see in Figure 3.3, varies in thickness. Tall mountains have deep "roots." You can stand on top of a tall mountain and have over 40 km of continental crust below you. At a continent's edge, in contrast, the thickness of continental crust thins to zero.

**Figure 3.3** ▶
Two kinds of crust float on top of the lithosphere. Where do these two kinds of crust touch each other? ①

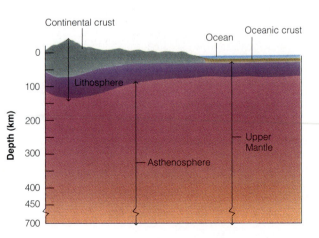

## Themes in Science

**Energy** Heat energy released from the earth's core creates the movement of material in the asthenosphere. The energy causes the asthenosphere to flow in convection cells. In turn the energy from the movement of the convection cells affects the surface of the earth.

## Movement in the Asthenosphere

The material of the asthenosphere is like thick liquid or hot tar. As intense heat from the earth's core moves toward the surface through the mantle, it causes the material of the asthenosphere to circulate. Matter rises through certain parts of the asthenosphere. Then it cools and slowly sinks in other places. The result is a circular flow of matter called **convection** (kuhn VEHKT shuhn).

Convection in the asthenosphere is shown in Figure 3.4. This circulation is so slow that a piece of rock may take millions of years to rise through the asthenosphere. Yet this movement has a very important effect on the lithosphere above, as you will find out in Chapter 5.

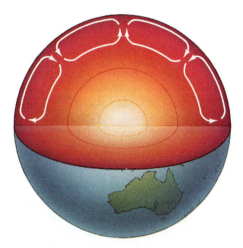

**Figure 3.4** ▲
Matter in the asthenosphere moves slowly by convection.

## SkillBuilder *Graphing*

### Temperature Changes in the Earth

Most of the earth's surface and its underlying crust are cool. Below the crust, however, the temperature begins to increase. At the earth's center, the temperature is estimated to be over 4,000°C!

How does the temperature of the earth's interior increase with depth? This is an important question, because the temperature and pressure at a particular depth determine whether the material there will be solid, liquid, or plastic.

Use the table of data at the right to make a graph showing how temperature increases with depth. Then answer the questions below.

1. On which axis did you put depth? Why? What would your graph look like if you put depth on the other axis?

2. What is the shape of the curve on your graph?

| Depth | Estimated Temperature |
|-------|----------------------|
| 25 km | 20°C |
| 50 km | 500°C |
| 100 km | 900°C |
| 150 km | 1,350°C |
| 200 km | 1,550°C |
| 300 km | 1,600°C |
| 400 km | 1,800°C |

3. Where on the curve does temperature increase at the fastest rate? The slowest?

4. Your graph goes to 400 km in depth. Where in the earth is this? Through which layers do you pass to get there?

In a short paragraph, describe what the graph tells you about the earth's interior.

## SkillBuilder

**Answers**

1. Answers will vary. Depth can be placed on either axis. Whichever axis is chosen, the other choice will result in a curve that bends in the opposite direction.

2. Answers will vary. If depth is on the x-axis, the curve moves rapidly upward until the depths are greater, where it levels out.

3. The temperature increases at the fastest rate at the beginning of the curve. It increases at the slowest rate between 200 km and 300 km.

4. The depth of 400 km is probably in the asthenosphere of the mantle. It is necessary to pass through the continental crust and the oceanic crust of the lithosphere to get there.

The graph tells us that the temperature increases rapidly at first with depth, then increases more slowly as a new layer is reached, and finally increases more rapidly again.

**The Living Textbook: Earth Science Sides 1-2**

Chapter 1    Frame 00724
Convection (1 Frame)
Search:

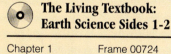

**The Living Textbook: Earth Science Side 2**

Chapter 47    Frame 25860
Earth's Interior (Movie)
Search:    Play:

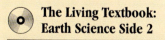

**TEACH ▪ Continued**

### Discuss

Students may ask why the composition of soil from oceanic crust differs from the soil of continental crust. Ask students to list what they know about the differences between oceanic crust and continental crust. (They differ in chemical composition, in density, and in the type of rocks that make them up.) Point out that because soils are formed from surface rocks, the type of crust at the surface affects the characteristics of the soil that forms there.

### EVALUATE

### WrapUp

**Reteach** Have students state why the physical properties of the earth's layers differ. (A layer may be solid, semisolid, or liquid depending on the balance between temperature and pressure. Solid layers are more influenced by pressure. Liquid layers are more influenced by temperature.)
  Use Review Worksheet 3.1.

### Check and Explain

1. The mantle contains silicates of iron and magnesium, but the core contains the metals iron and nickel. The mantle is less dense than the core.

2. The lithosphere is made up of the continental crust, the oceanic crust, and a part of the upper mantle.

3. The properties of the earth's layers are determined by both chemical changes and physical changes.

4. Models will probably not represent pressures and temperatures.

## Integrating the Sciences

**Chemistry** Tell students what elements plants need to grow and what elements are contained in granitic rock. Have students compare the elements in granitic rock to those found in basalt. Based on the comparison, have students infer why plants grow better in soils formed from granitic rock, rather than in soils formed from basalt.

 **Science and You** *Living on Oceanic Crust*

Most oceanic crust is covered with ocean water. Yet it is possible that oceanic crust lies right under your feet. Many islands are made of oceanic crust. In addition, at the surface of some parts of continents there are thick sheets of basalt, the same rock that makes up oceanic crust.

Regions with oceanic crust at the surface include the Hawaiian Islands and parts of Alaska. Iceland is another region of the world made up of oceanic crust. It is part of an area in the Atlantic Ocean where the ocean floor rises above the ocean's surface. The Columbia Plateau is a sheet of basalt almost 2 km thick covering parts of Idaho, Washington, and Oregon. Formed by a volcanic flow, the Plateau is very similar to oceanic crust but was never under water.

Living on land made of oceanic crust or basalt can be different from living on continental crust. For example, the soils formed from basalt and similar rocks are different from those formed from the granitic rock of continental crust. Soil formed from basalt contains large amounts of the elements iron and magnesium. It contains relatively small amounts of many of the elements plants need to grow. As a result, this type of soil is usually not very fertile. It is often used to grow crops such as wheat, barley, and sugarcane, or for grazing animals such as sheep and cattle.

**Figure 3.5** ▲
People living in Iceland build their houses directly on rocks of the oceanic crust.

### Check and Explain

1. How does the mantle differ from the core?

2. What makes up the earth's lithosphere?

3. **Reason and Conclude** Why do earth scientists use two different ways of classifying the earth's layers?

4. **Make a Model** Choose a way to make a model of the earth and its layers. After the model is complete, answer these questions: What does your model show about the earth? What doesn't it show? What kind of model would you need to make it show these other characteristics?

### Cooperative Learning

Working in cooperative groups of three or four, have students infer the general characteristics of waves based on what they already know about waves in bodies of water. Have each group share their inferences with the class. Use the characteristics listed by the groups to make an operational definition for *wave*.

## 3.2 Studying the Earth's Interior

### Objectives

▶ **Identify** two types of seismic waves.

▶ **Describe** the movement of seismic waves.

▶ **Explain** how earth scientists make inferences about the earth's core.

▶ **Infer** the characteristics of an object through indirect observation.

H ow have earth scientists found out about the structure and composition of the earth's interior? The interior cannot be observed directly. The deepest mine is less than 4 km deep. On land, the deepest hole ever bored into the crust went down only 15 km—still far from the mantle.

The earth's surface does provide some clues to what lies below. For example, the molten rock, or magma, that flows from volcanoes is evidence for high temperatures inside the earth. However, to gain most of their knowledge of the earth's interior, earth scientists have relied on one kind of indirect observation. They have made inferences based on how shock waves from earthquakes travel through the earth.

### Seismic Waves

When you hit a softball with a bat, you feel vibrations from the impact in your hands. The vibrations, or shock waves, travel through the bat to your hands. In a similar way, shock waves travel through the earth.

Earthquakes—sudden movements of the crust—are a cause of shock waves in the earth. Shock waves from an earthquake are called **seismic** (SYZ mihk) **waves**. Seismic waves can pass all the way from one side of the earth to the other. Earth scientists use tools called seismographs to detect seismic waves. Seismographs are located all over the earth's surface. By comparing the strength and arrival time of waves at different locations, scientists gain valuable information about the earth's interior.

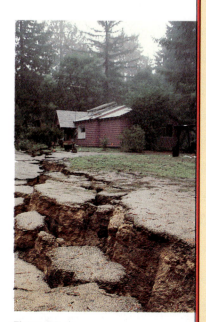

**Figure 3.6** ▲
The same earthquake that caused these cracks in the surface sent seismic waves throughout the earth.

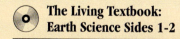
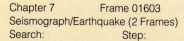

## Class Activity

Have students work in small groups with a coiled spring toy. Have two group members stretch the toy on the floor between them. Then have one student cause a wave to travel in the toy by compressing several coils together at one end of the toy and then releasing them. Tell students that this demonstrates the way P waves travel in the earth. If one person moves one end of the toy quickly sideways, waves travel through the toy differently. Students should be able to tell you that this is the way S waves move in the earth.

## Discuss

Ask students: How have earthquakes increased our knowledge of the inside of the earth? (Earthquakes cause S and P waves, which are used to determine which rocks of different densities are at different depths.)

## Skills Development

**Interpret Data** Have students study the graph in Figure 3.7 carefully. At about what depth and P-wave velocity does the Moho begin in this case? (It begins at about 33 km deep and at a velocity of 7.5 km/s.)

## Reteach

Use Reteach Worksheet 3.2.

**Answer to In-Text Question**

① **There is an abrupt increase in density.**

**Answer to Link**

Waves reflect, or bounce, off the gelatin edge. Some waves travel through the gelatin, but appear different from the waves in water. As waves travel through different media, they may change speed and direction, depending on the density and structure of the media.

## *Integrating the Sciences*

**Physical Science** Demonstrate the principle of refraction of light through different mediums by having students observe how objects look that are half submerged in water. Place a pencil in a clear glass that is half filled with water. Have students observe the pencil by looking at the boundary between the water and air. Explain to the students that light waves slow down or bend when they pass through water. The bending rays make the pencil appear bent.

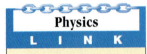

### Physics
### L I N K

Collect the following items: a shallow pan, water, gelatin mix, a small flat board, and a pencil. Prepare the gelatin mix in the shallow pan. Place in refrigerator to solidify.

**1.** When the gelatin is stiff, remove half of it from the pan, leaving a flat-sided edge to the remaining gelatin.

**2.** Add water to the pan level with the gelatin.

**3.** Hold the board upright, at water end of pan, parallel to gelatin edge. Tap the back of the board with the pencil to make small waves at regular intervals.

**4.** Hold the board at different angles and repeat step 3.

What happens to the waves as they meet the gelatin edge? How might the behavior of these waves be similar to wave behavior on the earth?

**A C T I V I T Y**

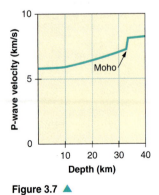

**Figure 3.7** ▲
What happens at the Moho to
① change the velocity of P waves?

**Types of Seismic Waves** An earthquake produces several kinds of seismic waves. The two types most useful for studying the earth's interior are called P waves and S waves. P waves travel by a back-and-forth movement of rock particles. The particles are squeezed together and pulled apart as the wave passes through. S waves, in contrast, travel by an up-and-down movement of rock particles. P waves and S waves behave differently as they pass through the earth. S waves, for example, cannot travel through liquids.

**Bending of Waves** The speed at which both kinds of seismic waves travel is determined in part by the density of rock; the higher the density, the faster the speed. As a seismic wave passes through the earth, it encounters rock of different densities. Its speed changes. If it passes through rock layers at even a slight angle, its change in speed results in a change of direction, too. Most seismic waves travel in curved lines through the earth. This curving of direction is called *refraction*. When a wave passes from rock of one density into rock of very different density, its path may bend sharply.

### Inferring From Seismic Waves

With knowledge of how seismic waves travel, scientists have developed a good picture of the earth's interior. They have determined the location of boundaries between layers. They have also inferred the composition and physical properties of the layers.

**The Moho** In 1909, the Croatian scientist Andrija Mohorovičić (MOH huh ROH vuh chihch) discovered the boundary between the crust and the mantle. He found that at a depth of between 30 and 35 km below the surface, seismic waves suddenly speeded up. He inferred that at this depth the rocks became much more dense and were therefore probably different in chemical makeup.

Figure 3.7 shows how the speed, or velocity, of P waves varies with depth. Notice that the velocity rises gradually until 30 km deep, where a sudden increase in velocity marks the Moho. In honor of Mohorovičić, the boundary between the crust and mantle was named the Mohorovičić discontinuity, or **Moho**, for short.

## Themes in Science

**Energy** The energy produced by earthquakes passes through the earth in the form of waves. Many other forms of energy, such as sound and light, move as waves.

**The Core** When an earthquake occurs in the crust, it sends seismic waves in all directions. Over a large part of the earth's surface, both S and P waves from the quake can be detected by seismographs. At a certain distance away from the earthquake, however, a zone in which no waves can be detected at all begins. Earth scientists have inferred that this **shadow zone** is caused by the earth's core. Look at Figure 3.8 below to see why the core creates a shadow zone. Directly across the earth from the earthquake, only P waves are detected. What does this suggest about the core? ②

**Figure 3.8**
**The Core's Effect on Seismic Waves** ▼

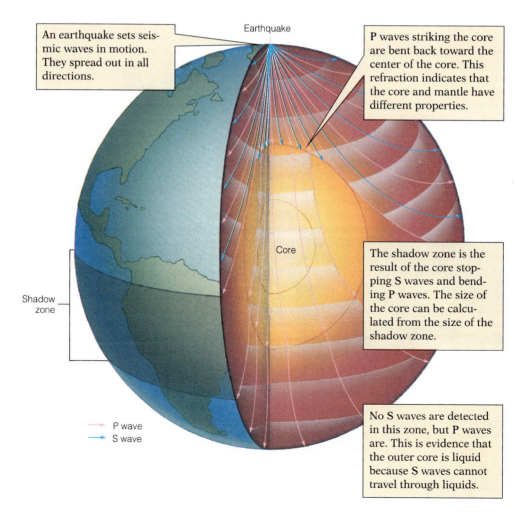

An earthquake sets seismic waves in motion. They spread out in all directions.

Earthquake

P waves striking the core are bent back toward the center of the core. This refraction indicates that the core and mantle have different properties.

Core

The shadow zone is the result of the core stopping S waves and bending P waves. The size of the core can be calculated from the size of the shadow zone.

Shadow zone

No S waves are detected in this zone, but P waves are. This is evidence that the outer core is liquid because S waves cannot travel through liquids.

→ P wave
→ S wave

## Explore Visually

Have students study Figure 3.8 on this page and the descriptions provided. Then ask:

▶ Where do the seismic waves from an earthquake go? (In all directions throughout the inside of the earth)

▶ What happens as P waves strike the core? Why? (P waves are bent toward the center of the core because the core and mantle have different properties.)

▶ Which waves cross the core? (P waves)

▶ Which waves are detected at the shadow zone? (Neither)

▶ What can be used to calculate the size of the core? (The size of the shadow zone can be used to calculate the core's size.)

## Skills Development

**Infer** Ask students: Why does the location of the shadow zone change from one earthquake to the next? (The shadow zone changes in location because the seismic waves begin at a different place on the earth's crust. This changes where the waves travel.)

**Answer to In-Text Question**

② If only P waves are detected across from the earthquake, it suggests that at least part of the core is liquid because S waves cannot travel through liquid.

Chapter 3   Structure of the Earth   **63**

**63**

## TEACH ▪ Continued

### Skills WorkOut

To help students understand indirect observations, have them do the Skills WorkOut.

**Answer** You could smell the gases that escape from under the cover of the pot.

### Historical Notebook

**Answers**

1. Scientists would want to take samples of rocks at the Moho to test their ideas about how the rocks in the earth change at the Moho boundary.

2. Drilling sites beneath the ocean would have a thinner crust than sites on land. Therefore, it would be cheaper and take less time to drill in the crust under the ocean.

**Answer to In-Text Question**

① The density of the core must be about 10 g/cm³. (0.68 X 3.5 g/cm³ + 0.32 × = 5.5 g/cm³. Solving for × yields 9.8 g/cm³.)

 **The Living Textbook: Earth Science Sides 1-2**

Chapter 34          Frame 07710
Meteorite (1 Frame)
Search:

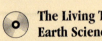

 **The Living Textbook: Earth Science Sides 1-2**

Chapter 12          Frame 02367
Meteorites (5 Frames)
Search:          Step:

---

 **Themes in Science**

**Diversity and Unity** The similarity in composition between the earth's core and many meteorites demonstrates that matter elsewhere in the universe is made of many of the same elements that exist on earth, and that matter everywhere is subject to the same physical laws.

 **Multicultural Perspectives**

Ancient Chinese writings describe the five elements of the earth, which were given as wood, fire, earth, metal, and water. Have students research the work of the early Chinese alchemists in applying these basic elements to chemistry, medicine, and philosophy.

▼ **ACTIVITY**

**Observing**

*Boiling Over*

Without removing the cover from a pot cooking on the stove, how could you determine what was cooking inside? How might your method of determining the pot's contents be similar to the way scientists determine what is inside the earth?

**SKILLS WORKOUT**

### Inferring the Chemical Makeup

Earth scientists cannot drill deep into the earth. So they make inferences about the chemical makeup of the earth's layers. Meteorites, pieces of rock or metal from space that strike the earth, are one important source of data. Some meteorites are made of iron and nickel. Scientists hypothesize that meteorites are the remains of the cores of planets that have broken apart. If this is true, then meteorites are further evidence that the earth's core is also made of iron and nickel.

Scientists also use measurements to infer the earth's chemical makeup. By dividing the earth's mass by its volume, they get an average density of about 5.5 g/cm³. Scientists hypothesize that if the earth's mantle has a density of 3.5 g/cm³, the core must be made up of very dense materials to bring the average density up to 5.5 g/cm³. Based on these figures, what is the core's density? ①

## Historical Notebook

### The Mohole Project

The Moho is an important part of the earth's structure. Since Mohorovičić discovered it in 1909, earth scientists have dreamed of observing the Moho directly. In the 1950s, a group of scientists and engineers set out to achieve this goal. With money from the United States government, they set up the Mohole Project.

The goal of the project was to drill into the earth to sample all layers of the crust and reach the mantle. The first step was to decide where to drill the holes. Seismic studies indicated that the crust was thinnest under the ocean.

In 1961, the first drilling took place off the California coast. The purpose of this part of the study was not to reach the Moho, but to see if it was possible to collect crust samples located under thousands of meters of water.

The next stage was to build ocean drilling equipment that could actually drill deep enough to reach the Moho. It took four years to develop the technology for deep drilling. However, in 1966 the program was cancelled because of the high cost of the research. The Moho has never been observed directly.

1. Why would scientists want to directly observe the Moho?

2. What was the reason for choosing drilling sites that were beneath the ocean?

## Science and Technology   *Seismic Arrays*

Mohorovičić and other earth scientists who made the first major discoveries about the earth's interior used very simple seismographs to obtain their data. Since that time, the accuracy and sensitivity of seismographs have greatly increased. In addition, more seismographs have been placed all over the earth. As a result, earth scientists have been able to gain more and more detailed knowledge of the earth's interior.

One important advance in the detection of seismic waves has been the development of seismic arrays. A seismic array is a cluster of interconnected seismographs. For example, one seismic array in Montana is made up of 525 seismographs. They are linked together in 21 clusters. The clusters are arranged in a circle about 200 km in diameter.

With the help of computers, a seismic array can make very precise comparisons among the seismic data received by individual seismographs. Why is this interconnection important? It lets earth scientists filter out seismic "noise." Seismic noise is created by constant small movements of the crust. These movements are detected by seismographs and hide weak seismic waves from distant earthquakes. When the seismic noise is filtered out, seismographs in the array can better detect these faint seismic waves.

**Figure 3.9** ▲
Comparison of data from different seismographs helps earth scientists interpret seismic waves.

## Check and Explain

1. What are two types of seismic waves?

2. What is the shadow zone? What does the shadow zone tell scientists about the earth's core?

3. **Predict**  A seismic wave passes at an angle from a dense rock layer into a denser rock layer. What will happen to the wave?

4. **Infer**  Suppose you are given a sealed shoe box containing an object. What kinds of indirect observation can you use to learn about the object in the box?

**Time** 30 minutes    **Group** 3

**Materials**

10 hot plates

10 beakers (250-mL or larger)

food coloring

10 droppers

10 spoons

10 tbs. rolled oats cereal

## Analysis

1. Students may have seen the food coloring sinking to the bottom of the beaker then swirling back up to the top. They may have observed somewhat circular patterns in its movement.

2. It represents the mantle, or asthenosphere.

3. The oats should float on the water's surface and follow the direction of the food coloring at the surface of the water.

4. The rolled oats represent the crust, because they drift on convection currents as the crust does in one of the models of plate movement.

5. The water is similar to the mantle in that it is fluid and can carry convection currents. It is different in that it is much less dense, moves more rapidly, and is cooler.

6. Once the water is completely heated, it may begin to boil. Also, if the water is evenly heated, the currents will stop.

## Conclusion

Accept reasonable conclusions.

## Everyday Application

Examples will vary, but may include: boiling water for cooking, heating a room in the winter, dust particles over a lamp.

## Extension

Students should find that thicker materials flow more slowly, if they observe movement at all.

### Prelab Discussion

Have students read the entire activity. Before beginning, review the structure and characteristics of the mantle and crust of the earth.

## Activity 3  *How does matter move in the mantle?*

**Skills**  Observe; Infer; Model

### Task 1  Prelab Prep

1. Collect the following items: hot plate, 250-mL or larger beaker, water, food coloring, dropper, spoon, rolled oats cereal.

2. Turn the hot plate on to medium heat.

### Task 2  Data Record

1. On a separate sheet of paper, draw the outlines of two beakers, as shown below. Label one beaker A and the other B.

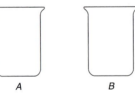

2. You will use the drawings to record your observations about the movement of two different substances in the beaker.

### Task 3  Procedure

1. Fill beaker about two-thirds full of water. Place it on the hot plate. **CAUTION! Keep hair and loose clothing away from the hot plate.**

2. Wait about two minutes. Using the dropper, carefully add one drop of food coloring to the surface of the water near the side of the beaker. Try not to disturb the water.

3. Observe the path of the food coloring for as long as possible. Draw your observations of the movement of the food coloring in the beaker labeled A on your paper.

4. Repeat steps 2 and 3 if you have any difficulty observing the movement of the drop of food coloring.

5. Sprinkle one spoonful of the rolled oats evenly across the surface of the water in the same beaker. Observe the path of the rolled oats on the water.

6. Draw your observations of the movement of the rolled oats in the beaker labeled B on your paper.

7. Turn off the hot plate. Once the beaker has cooled, remove it from the hot plate and dispose of the contents.

### Task 4  Analysis

1. Describe the path taken by the food coloring. What pattern did you see in its movement?

2. What part of the earth does the water represent?

3. Describe the path taken by the rolled oats. How does the movement of the rolled oats compare with the movement of the food coloring?

4. What part of the earth could the rolled oats represent? Why?

5. How is the water similar to the mantle? How is it different?

6. Once the water is completely heated, it no longer serves as an accurate model of the mantle. Why?

### Task 5  Conclusion

Write a short paragraph explaining how the beakers of water model the movement of material in the earth's mantle.

### *Everyday Application*

Convection is a common process of heat transfer in substances. You experience convection currents every day. Give three examples of convection that you have experienced. What type of matter is moving in each case?

### *Extension*

The material in the mantle is much thicker and denser than water. Try heating a thick but flowing substance, such as cooked cereal or flour and water. Record your observations.

# Chapter 3 Review

## Concept Summary

### 3.1 Layers of the Earth

▶ The layers of the earth are classified into the crust, mantle, and core. They are made of different chemicals.

▶ Temperature and pressure differences cause the lithosphere, asthenosphere, mantle, inner core, and outer core to be solid, liquid, or in-between.

▶ The crust is composed of a dense layer called oceanic crust and a less dense layer called continental crust.

▶ Convection in the asthenosphere causes a circular flow of matter.

### 3.2 Studying the Earth's Interior

▶ Scientists use indirect observations from earthquake vibrations to study the interior of the earth.

▶ Earthquakes produce several kinds of seismic waves. P and S waves are the most useful to study Earth's interior.

▶ Seismic waves change speed when they encounter materials with different densities. They are refracted, or bent, if they pass at an angle through materials of different density.

▶ The boundary between the mantle and the crust, the Moho, was discovered by studying the speed of seismic waves.

▶ The shadow zone is an area of the earth's surface where no seismic waves are detected after an earthquake. The size of the core was determined from the size of the shadow zone.

## Chapter Vocabulary

| | | | |
|---|---|---|---|
| crust (3.1) | lithosphere (3.1) | convection (3.1) | Moho (3.2) |
| mantle (3.1) | asthenosphere (3.1) | seismic wave (3.2) | shadow zone (3.2) |
| core (3.1) | | | |

## Check Your Vocabulary

Use the vocabulary words above to complete the following sentences correctly.

1. The semiliquid layer of the earth between the lithosphere and deep mantle is the _____ .

2. The circular flow of matter in the mantle is called _____ .

3. The layer of the earth that lies above the mantle is the _____ .

4. The dense, metallic, innermost layer of the earth is the _____ .

5. A boundary called the _____ separates the crust and the mantle.

6. The cool, solid part of the earth that includes the crust and the upper part of the mantle is the _____ .

7. Geologists study the _____ produced by earthquakes to make inferences about the earth's structure.

8. Between the crust and the core is the _____ .

9. The earth's core produces a _____ on the other side of the earth from an earthquake.

Explain the difference between the words in each pair.

10. mantle, asthenosphere

11. P waves, S waves

12. lithosphere, crust

13. seismic wave, seismograph

## Check Your Vocabulary

1. asthenosphere

2. convection

3. crust

4. core

5. Moho

6. lithosphere

7. seismic waves

8. mantle

9. shadow zone

10. *Mantle* is an identification based on chemical properties; *asthenosphere* is an identification based on physical properties.

11. P waves travel by back-and-forth movement of rock particles and can travel through the core; S waves travel by up-and-down movement of rock particles and cannot travel through the core.

12. *Crust* is the outer layer of Earth. The *lithosphere* is the solid outer zone of the earth's structure that includes the crust and upper part of the mantle.

13. Seismic waves are movements in the earth's crust caused by earthquakes. A seismograph is a device that records seismic waves.

Use Vocabulary Worksheet for Chapter 3.

## Check Your Knowledge

1. The three main layers of the earth are the crust, mantle, and core.

2. The lithosphere is the rigid zone that includes the crust and the upper mantle.

3. Convection takes place within the asthenosphere.

4. Earthquakes produce seismic waves.

5. A Croatian scientist noticed that seismic waves speeded up at a particular depth below the earth. He reasoned that there must be a layer of rocks denser than those at other depths.

6. The shadow zone suggests both the size and the liquid composition of the core.

7. Refraction is a change in direction of a wave as it moves through rock layers of different densities.

8. Scientists study seismic waves with seismographs to make inferences about the interior of the earth.

9. Continental crust is formed from granitic rock, is less dense, and has a higher percentage of oxygen, silicon, and aluminum; the oceanic crust is formed from basalt and is denser.

10. Lithosphere, asthenosphere, mantle, outer core, inner core.

11. False; crust

12. False; lithosphere

13. True

14. True

15. False; nickel

16. True

3. Direct observation is the actual observation of an object or phenomenon by the senses or with instruments that extend the senses, while indirect observation is the observation of the effects an object or phenomenon has on its environment.

4. The core contributes more to the earth's mass than to its volume because it is very dense.

5. Scientists can create seismic waves by applying strong forces to the crust—for example, by setting off explosions.

6. Meteorites are thought to be pieces of planets that have broken apart. Meteorites made of iron and nickel may be remnants of the cores of these planets. If other planets have iron-nickel cores, the earth may also.

7. The size of the core was determined by studying the shadow zone that results from the bending of P waves and the stopping of S waves.

## Check Your Understanding

1. In the lithosphere, both temperature and pressure are low. In the asthenosphere, high temperature is most important in determining the physical characteristics. In the solid parts of the mantle, high pressure is more important than the high temperature. In the outer core, high temperature is the controlling factor. In the inner core, high pressure dominates.

2. The lithosphere floats on the asthenosphere; students may infer that convection currents in the asthenosphere move the lithosphere.

---

# Chapter 3 Review

## Check Your Knowledge

Answer the following in complete sentences.

1. What are the three main layers of the earth?

2. What is the lithosphere?

3. Where does convection take place within the earth?

4. What produces seismic waves?

5. How was the Moho discovered?

6. What information does the shadow zone suggest about the core?

7. What is refraction?

8. What tool have scientists used to help them make inferences about the interior of the earth?

9. How does continental crust differ from oceanic crust?

10. List the five zones of the earth that differ in their physical properties.

Determine whether each statement is true or false. Write *true* if it is true. If it is false, change the underlined word(s) to make the statement true.

11. Scientists have drilled holes into the <u>core</u>.

12. The <u>core</u> floats on top of the asthenosphere.

13. The material in the asthenosphere flows by <u>convection</u>.

14. <u>Seismic waves</u> can pass from one side of the earth to the other.

15. Scientists think that the core is composed of iron and <u>magnesium</u>.

16. The continental crust is <u>less</u> dense than the oceanic crust.

## Check Your Understanding

Apply the concepts you have learned to answer each question.

1. For each of the five zones of the earth, explain the relationship between temperature and pressure in that layer.

2. **Infer** How does convection in the asthenosphere affect the lithosphere above?

3. **Compare** Explain the difference between a direct observation and an indirect observation.

4. Explain why the core can make up 32 percent of the earth's mass but only 16 percent of its volume.

5. Instead of waiting for an earthquake to happen, how might earth scientists create seismic waves?

6. Why is the existence of iron-nickel meteorites evidence that the earth's core is made of iron and nickel?

7. Explain how the size of the core was determined.

8. **Extension** In a dictionary, look up the rocks granite and rhyolite, which make up the continental crust. Also look up the rocks basalt and gabbro, which make up the oceanic crust. Describe and compare each of the rocks.

9. **Mystery Photo** The photograph on page 54 shows a mineral hot spring. The water is heated by hot underground rock. The rock is heated by gases released from molten rock within the earth. Describe other ways in which the high temperatures in the mantle affect the surface of the earth.

**8.** Granite is a course-grained, light-colored, hard igneous rock. Rhyolite is a fine-grained volcanic rock. Basalt is a hard, dark, dense volcanic rock having a glassy appearance. Gabbro is a course-grained igneous rock.

**9.** Student responses may vary, but might include: high temperatures in the mantle can contribute to volcanic activity, geysers.

## Develop Your Skills

**1.** a. About 0.9 million atmospheres
   b. Between 3000 km and 4000 km
   c. The pressure stops changing because you reach the center of the earth.

**2.** a. 12 km
   b. 4 km; students should note that the inner core is more than 6000 km deeper than both the deepest mine or well.

**3.** Check students' tables for accuracy.

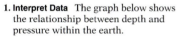

### Develop Your Skills

Use the skills you have developed in this chapter to complete each activity.

**1. Interpret Data** The graph below shows the relationship between depth and pressure within the earth.

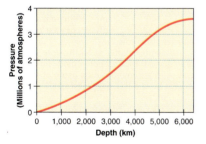

a. What is the pressure at 2,000 km?
b. Between what two depths is the rate of pressure change the greatest?
c. What happens to the change in pressure at depths greater than 6,000 km?

**2. Data Bank** Use the information on page 613 to answer the following questions.

a. How deep was the deepest well drilled into the earth?
b. How deep was the deepest mine drilled into the earth? How much deeper is the inner core than the deepest mine? The deepest well?

**3. Organize Data** Make a table comparing the core, mantle, and crust. Include columns listing percentages of the earth's mass and chemical makeup. What other columns will you include?

### Make Connections

**1. Link the Concepts** Draw a concept map showing how the concepts below link together. Add terms to connect, or link, the concepts. Use the following words to construct your concept map:

| | |
|---|---|
| crust | mantle |
| core | continental crust |
| convection | nickel |
| iron | oceanic crust |

**2. Science and You** Study a world map. Do you live on continental or oceanic crust? How does the type of crust you live on affect your life?

**3. Science and Literature** Read the book *Journey to the Center of the Earth*, by Jules Verne. Based on what you have learned in this chapter, is the story scientifically accurate? Choose four or five excerpts from the book that are related to concepts from the chapter. Write about the scientific accuracy of these excerpts. Explain why this book is classified as a science fiction novel.

**4. Science and Math** Make a bar graph that shows the average temperature for the lithosphere, asthenosphere, mesosphere, outer core, and inner core. Be sure to label the *x*-axis and the *y*-axis.

**5. Science and Physical Education** Find a worn-out or torn baseball or golf ball. Determine its structure by removing the cover and taking the rest of it apart. How is its structure similar to and different from that of the earth?

## Make Connections

**1.** Concept maps will vary. The map below shows a possible organization of the concepts listed.

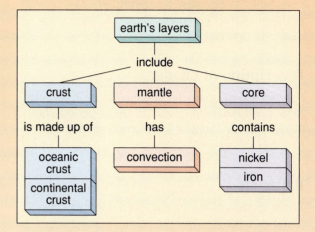

**2.** Student answers will vary by region. The type of crust influences the types of plants and animals in the region.

**3.** Student reports will vary. Make sure the excerpts chosen are related to this chapter.

**4.** Check students' graphs for accuracy. Use Figure 3.2 on page 57.

**5.** A baseball or an old golf ball will have an outer covering, like the earth's crust, an interior of wound string or rubber band, corresponding to the mantle, and a solid core of rubber, corresponding to the earth's core. The balls do not have any liquid or semiliquid layers; the temperature of the balls is constant throughout. (Note: many golf balls have only an outer covering and a solid, uniform filling.)

## About the Literary Work

"Farewell to Manzanar" was adapted from the text *Farewell to Manzanar* by Jeanne Wakatsuki Houston and James D. Houston, copyright 1973 by Houghton Mifflin Company. Reprinted by permission of Houghton Mifflin.

## Description of Change

Passages describing the uncomfortable living conditions of the narrator (such as twelve people sharing four rooms) were edited out of a short section of text.

## Rationale

The emphasis of the selection is the topography of the land surrounding the camp.

## Vocabulary

myrtle, succulents, Issei, sustenance

## Teaching Strategies

### Directed Inquiry

After students finish reading, discuss the story. Be sure to relate the story to the science lessons in the unit. Ask the following questions:

▶ Judging from the time in which the story takes place, what type of camp do you think the narrator is in? (An internment camp for Japanese Americans during World War II)

▶ What different types of landforms are described in the selection? (Desert, beach, mountains, valley)

▶ In the last line of the selection, the narrator refers to the "forces in nature." What is meant by this phrase? (Forces such as volcanic activity, plate tectonics, weathering, and erosion that change the face of the earth)

## Skills Development

**Infer**  The passage mentions that "Papa used to hike along the creeks that channeled down from the base of the Sierras." Ask students to reread the passage and make an inference about the source of these creeks. (The snow lacing the mountain peaks would melt and flow down the mountains.)

## Critical Thinking Skills

**Reason and Conclude**  Discuss the meaning of the term *water table*. Challenge students to explain the importance of the shallow water table to the pear and apple trees described in the first paragraph. Ask: Are pear or apple trees adapted to a desert environment? How then do these trees exist in Manzanar? (Such trees are not adapted to the dry conditions of a desert environment. The trees are able to flourish by gaining water from the shallow water table of the area.)

# Science and Literature Connection

## Farewell to Manzanar

*The following excerpt is from the novel* Farewell To Manzanar *by Jeanne Wakatsuki Houston and James D. Houston.*

In Spanish, Manzanar means "apple orchard." Great stretches of Owens Valley were once green with orchards and alfalfa fields. It has been a desert ever since its water started flowing south into Los Angeles, sometime during the twenties. But a few rows of untended pear and apple trees were still growing there when the camp opened, where a shallow water table had kept them alive. In the spring of 1943 we moved to block 28, right up next to one of the old pear orchards. That's where we stayed until the end of the war, and those trees stand in my memory for the turning of our life in camp, from the outrageous to the tolerable.

Papa pruned and cared for the nearest trees. Late that summer we picked the fruit green and stored it in a root cellar he had dug under our new barracks. At night the wind through the leaves would sound like the surf had sounded in Ocean Park, and while drifting off to sleep I could almost imagine we were still living by the beach.

Once the first year's turmoil cooled down, the authorities started letting us outside the wire for recreation. Papa used to hike along the creeks that channeled down from the base of the Sierras. He

brought back chunks of driftwood, and he would pass long hours sitting on the steps carving myrtle limbs into benches, table legs, and lamps, filling our rooms with bits of gnarled, polished furniture.

He hauled stones in off the desert and built a small rock garden outside our doorway, with succulents and a patch of moss. Near it he laid flat steppingstones leading to the stairs.

He also painted watercolors. Until this time I had not known he could paint. He loved to sketch the mountains. If anything made that country habitable it was the mountains themselves, purple when the sun dropped and so sharply etched in the morning light the granite dazzled almost more than the bright snow lacing the nearest peaks rose ten thousand feet higher than the valley floor, with Whitney, the highest, just off to the south. They were important for all of us, but especially for the Issei. Whitney reminded Papa of Fujiyama, that is, it gave him the same kind of spiritual sustenance.

# Skills in Science

## Reading Skills in Science

1. Forces that shape the face of the earth, creating mountains and valleys.

2. Whitney is Mount Whitney, the highest point in the Sierra Nevada range.

## Writing Skills in Science

1. They are all mountainous, rock material produced by the forces of nature. Papa views these forces as powerful and inevitable. Because they cannot be resisted, they remind someone like Papa that he must accept what he cannot change.

2. Nature offered them beauty and recreation during their time in the camp. The family picked fruit and papa cared for the trees, carved driftwood into furniture, built a rock garden, laid stepping stones, and painted the mountains.

3. The narrator feels negatively about the camp. This feeling is implied by the description of life in the camp turning "from the outrageous to the tolerable." This feeling can also be inferred from the last line of the story. Students might also infer that the narrator's feelings are mixed because her keen recollections of the natural surroundings contrast with her father's implied suffering.

## Activities

**Science and Art** Encourage students to add a lot of detail to their pictures and also encourage them to be creative.

**Communicate** The rock formations of Mount Whitney are the result of uplifting, tilting, and glacial activity.

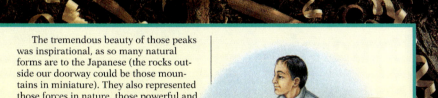

The tremendous beauty of those peaks was inspirational, as so many natural forms are to the Japanese (the rocks outside our doorway could be those mountains in miniature). They also represented those forces in nature, those powerful and inevitable forces that cannot be resisted, reminding a man that sometimes he must simply endure that which cannot be changed.

### Skills in Science

#### Reading Skills in Science

1. **Infer** What "forces in nature" are referred to in the last paragraph of the selection?

2. **Find Context Clues** What is "Whitney"? Identify the clues you used to make this determination.

#### Writing Skills in Science

1. **Compare and Contrast** What do Whitney, Fujiyama, and Papa's rock garden have in common? Describe their symbolic meaning to Papa.

2. **Infer** Describe the importance of nature in the family's life while they were detained in the camp.

3. **Detect the Writer's Mood** How does the author feel about the camp she is in? How do you know?

#### Activities

**Science and Art** Draw or paint the natural surroundings described in this excerpt.

**Communicate** How did the Sierra Nevada mountain range form? Do research to find out the most current theory on the formation of these mountains. Make a poster that illustrates the formation.

#### Where to Read More

*A Spit is a Piece of Land* by Doris Coburn. New York: Julian Messner, 1989. This text examines various landforms in the United States and the forces that shaped them.

*The Home Front* by Conrad R. Stein. Chicago: Childrens Press, 1986. You can learn more about the treatment of Japanese-Americans during World War II through this text, which explores life on the home front.

Unit 2 explores the forces behind the changing earth. Chapter 4 examines the surface, climate, and organisms of the earth's distant past. The chapter goes on to discuss the concept of geologic time. Chapter 5 discusses plate tectonics. The theory of continental drift, the existence of Pangaea, and the structure, boundaries, geography, and movement of the plates are all explored. Chapter 6 discusses changes within the earth's crust as a result of folding, fault-

ing, and isostasy. Chapter 7 explores earthquakes and volcanoes. The chapter illustrates the energy and physics of earthquakes, with an examination of seismic waves, magnitude, epicenters, tsunamis, and the damage that earthquakes cause. The chapter also describes the formation and eruption of volcanoes, including types of volcanoes, and outlines developments in predicting and monitoring eruptions.

## Introducing the Unit

### Directed Inquiry

Have students study the photograph and read the caption. Ask:

▶ What made this cloud of smoke and ash? Could anything else create such a cloud? Explain why or why not. (Volcano; Students might mention forest fires, or other major fires; they may say that this cloud is much larger than any other kind of smoke cloud they can imagine.)

▶ What does this cloud tell you about the eruption that caused it? Explain. (The eruption had to have tremendous energy, because of the huge quantity of material that was expelled.)

▶ Do you think the truck is moving quickly or slowly? Why? (Quickly; The nearby eruption indicates that there is great underground heat and pressure in the area; further eruptions are possible.)

### Writing About the Photograph

Have students imagine they are with a group of people in the truck in the photograph. Have them write a page or two of dialogue that tells the reader what the group is doing there, what they know about the volcano, and what their feelings are in the moments following the eruption.

Unit **2**
## The Dynamic Earth

### *Chapters*

**4** Time and Change

**5** Plate Tectonics

**6** Movement of the Crust

**7** Earthquakes and Volcanoes

# Data Bank

Use the information on pages 612 to 625 to answer the following questions about topics explored in this unit.

## Calculating

How much taller is Mt. Everest than Mt. McKinley?

## Reading a Table

What was the magnitude of the earthquake that struck northwestern Argentina? When did it happen?

## Organizing Data

List in order how long the epochs of the Cenozoic Era lasted. Begin with the epoch that was the longest.

## Interpreting Data

What is the elevation of Mt. Kilimanjaro in Africa?

The photograph to the left shows an explosion of volcanic ash after the eruption of Mt. Pinatubo in the Philippines in 1991. What do you think caused the eruption?

## Overview

Chapter 4 describes time and the processes of change on the earth. The first section explores the origin and early history. The concept of change is examined in relation to the planet's surface, its climate, and its organisms. The second section examines geologic time and its divisions, and closes the chapter with a discussion of how time is calculated.

## Advance Planner

▶ Provide oatmeal, water, spoons, and bowls for TE page 76.

▶ Collect rocks, hand lenses, cloth, and hammers for TE page 77.

▶ Supply large, plastic, clear jars with covers; soil; sand; and fine gravel for TE page 78.

▶ Obtain books, pencils, and pieces of paper for SE Activity 4, page 81.

## Skills Development Chart

| Sections | Communicate | Hypothesize | Infer | Make a Graph | Make a Model | Measure | Observe |
|---|---|---|---|---|---|---|---|
| **4.1** Skills WarmUp | ● | | | | | | |
| Historical Notebook | | | ● | | | | |
| Skills WorkOut | ● | ● | | | | | |
| Activity 4 | ● | | | | ● | ● | |
| **4.2** Skills WarmUp | | | | | ● | | |
| SkillBuilder | | | | ● | | | |
| Skills WorkOut | | | | | | | ● |

## Individual Needs

▶ **Limited English Proficiency Students** Have students divide a page from their science portfolio into three columns. As they study, students can list boldface, italic, and unfamiliar words in the first column. Have students use the glossary or dictionary to find the definition for each term. Ask them to write these definitions in the second column. As students read each section, have them draw a picture or diagram in the third column that represents the words.

▶ **At-Risk Students** Invite students to choose one of these concepts: weathering, erosion, deposition, formation of sedimentary rock, uplift, fossils, rock layering. Have the students work in pairs or small groups to make a model to illustrate or demonstrate their concept.

▶ **Gifted Students** Encourage students to research and construct a display comparing fossils of Coelacanth (SEE luh kanth) with pictures of actual specimens caught off the coast of Africa. Have students include a brief account of the discovery of this "living fossil" from the Paleozoic Era.

## Resource Bank

▶ **Bulletin Board** Attach pictures illustrating several people working in occupations that use information about the earth presented in this chapter. Add labels that name the occupation and tell something about it. Ask volunteers to find out what chapter information is relevant to each occupation and why. For example, petroleum engineers need to know the age of rocks in order to learn where petroleum deposits are likely to occur.

| Section | Core | Standard | Enriched |
|---|:---:|:---:|:---:|
| **4.1 Earth's History** pp. 75–81 | | | |
| **Section Features** | | | |
| Skills WarmUp, p. 75 | ● | ● | ● |
| Historical Notebook, p. 79 | ● | ● | ● |
| Skills WorkOut, p. 80 | | ● | ● |
| Activity, p. 81 | ● | ● | ● |
| **Blackline Masters** | | | |
| Review Worksheet 4.1 | ● | ● | ● |
| Integrating Worksheet 4.1 | ● | ● | ● |
| **4.2 Geologic Time Scale** pp. 82–86 | | | |
| **Section Features** | | | |
| Skills WarmUp, p. 82 | ● | ● | ● |
| SkillBuilder, p. 84 | ● | ● | |
| Skills WorkOut, p. 86 | ● | ● | ● |

| Section | Core | Standard | Enriched |
|---|:---:|:---:|:---:|
| **Blackline Masters** | | | |
| Review Worksheet 4.2 | ● | ● | ● |
| Reteach Worksheet 4.2 | ● | ● | ● |
| Skills Worksheet 4.2a | ● | ● | ● |
| Skills Worksheet 4.2b | ● | ● | ● |
| Integrating Worksheet 4.2 | ● | ● | ● |
| Vocabulary Worksheet 4.2 | ● | ● | ● |
| **Overhead Blackline Transparencies** Overhead Blackline Master 4.2 and Student Worksheet | ● | ● | ● |
| **Laboratory Program** Investigation 6 / Investigation 7 | ● | ● ● | ● ● |
| **Color Transparencies** Transparency 8 | ● | ● | ● |

# Bibliography

The following resources can be used for teaching the chapter. See page T–46 for supplier codes.

## Library Resources

Farndon, John. *How the Earth Works.* Pleasantville, NY: The Reader's Digest Association, Inc., 1992.

Parker, Steve, with Raymond L. Bernor, editor. *The Practical Paleontologist.* New York: Simon and Schuster, 1990.

Rydell, Wendy. *Discovering Fossils.* Mahwah, NJ: Troll, 1984.

Taylor, Paul D. *Fossil.* New York: Alfred A. Knopf, Inc., 1990.

U.S. Geological Survey. *Geologic Time.* Washington, D.C.: U.S. Department of the Interior.

## Technology Resources

### Internet

**PLANETDIARY** at *http://www.planetdiary.com*
• Learn more about volcanoes in *Volcano* by clicking on *Phenomena Backgrounders.*
• Find geological news by exploring *Current Phenomena.*

### Software

*Earth.* Mac, Dos, Win. ER.
*The Earth.* Mac, Win. LS.
*Earth Science.* Mac, Win. ER.
*Rocks and Volcanoes.* Mac, Win. ER.
*Sim Earth Classic.* Mac, Dos, Win. ER.

### CD-ROMs

*Interactive Earth.* SFAW.
*An Odyssey of Discovery for Science Insights:* Have students explore the activity *Dig It* on the Earth and Space Disk. SFAW.

### Laserdiscs

*Living Textbook.* (See barcodes on pages in this chapter.) Optical Data.

### Videos

*Fossils: Clues to the Past.* 23 min. 1983. NGSES.

### Audio-Visual Resources

*The Drifting of the Continents.* Film. T-L.
*The Earth: Discovering Its History.* Film. C/MTI.
*Evolution: The Four Billion Year Legacy.* Film. FI.

## Introducing the Chapter

Have students read the description of the photograph. Ask if they agree or disagree with the description.

### Directed Inquiry

Have students study the photograph. Ask:

▶ What does this photograph show? (It shows a fossil of a bird.)

▶ What features make you think it is a bird? (Students should mention the beak, the long curved neck, and the two legs.)

▶ How do you know it's a fossil? (Students may say because a skeleton is all that is left and it appears embedded in rock, like other fossils they may have seen.)

▶ How do you think this fossil was formed? (After the bird died, sand or mud covered its body. The soft parts decayed, leaving the skeleton, which was itself gradually replaced by rock. The sand or mud surrounding it became rock.)

▶ What does the picture have to do with the subject of this chapter? (Fossils reflect *change* in matter from living tissue and soil to rock over a huge span of geologic *time*.)

## Chapter Vocabulary

| | |
|---|---|
| deposition | geologic time |
| era | period |
| erosion | weathering |
| fossil | |

 *Writing Connection*

Have students study the photograph of the bird fossil. Ask them to infer from the fossil what the bird might have been like when it was alive: What might it have eaten, how might it have moved, and where might it have lived? Then have students write a paragraph about the bird's life based on their inferences.

Chapter **4**    **Time and Change**

### Chapter Sections

**4.1** Earth's History

**4.2** Geologic Time Scale

### What Do You See?

❝I see a fossil of a bird that looks like it might have been a flightless bird. It looks like it might have run to catch insects, small lizards, and small reptiles. It looks like it was an early form of the ostrich. I would say it is probably one to two million years old.❞

*Cliff Thompson*
*Kesner Junior High School*
*Salida, Colorado*

To find out more about the photograph, look on page 88. As you read this chapter, you will learn about the earth's history.

### Themes in Science

**Evolution** The features of the earth have undergone many changes over its long history. The ancient earth was very different from the current earth. Most of the changes have occurred over a very long period of time. The earth is continually evolving.

## 4.1 Earth's History

### Objectives

▶ **Describe** the origin and early history of the earth.

▶ **Describe** processes of change on the earth's surface.

▶ **Infer** how different sedimentary rock forms.

▶ **Communicate** in a diagram how processes of surface change are related.

### ▼ ACTIVITY

**Communicating**

*Time to Change*

Look around your classroom. Then look outside your classroom. Now make a list of ten objects or conditions inside and outside your classroom that don't seem to change from day to day. For example, do the walls change? If so, how? For each item, write down one way that it could change, and how long it would take.

**SKILLS WARMUP**

**Section Objectives**
For a list of section objectives, see the Student Edition page.

**Skills Objectives**
Students should be able to:

**Communicate** changes that take place over long periods of time.

**Hypothesize** how ice ages affected the earth's oceans and shores.

**Infer** how rock layers formed from mud differ from rock layers formed from sand.

**Communicate** with a diagram how earth-changing forces are related.

**Measure** time using different scales.

**Vocabulary**
geologic time, weathering, erosion, deposition, fossil

### MOTIVATE

**Skills WarmUp**
To help students understand change on the earth over time, have them do the Skills WarmUp.
**Answer** Lists will depend on the objects chosen. Students' descriptions should indicate both the type of change and the span of time necessary for the change to occur.

### Misconceptions

Students may think that all of the changes on the earth happened long ago and that the earth is no longer changing. Have students discuss how much they've changed since they were born. Students should agree that they have changed a great deal during their lives. Students should also agree that they expect to change more in the future, even though such change is not noticeable at the moment. Tell them that the earth's changes are similar—they are not always obvious.

H ow much will you change during the next year? You will probably grow several inches. You'll make new friends and learn new skills. In just ten years, you will change a great deal. Much about your family and community will change, too.

During those same ten years, will the earth change? Will its mountain ranges change in elevation? Will the oceans shrink in volume? Compared to changes in the human world, changes in mountains and oceans are small and unmeasurable. For this reason, you are used to thinking of the earth and its features as permanent and unchanging. And yet they are not.

The earth, oceans, atmosphere, and climate all undergo changes. The difference between change in your life and change in the earth is a matter of scale. Many important changes in and on the planet Earth take place very slowly, over enormous periods of time. Studying earth science, therefore, means adjusting the way you think about time.

### Age of the Earth

How old are you? Most people can answer this question with a one- or two-digit number. How old is the earth? This question requires an answer with ten digits: 4,600,000,000 years.

Compare the age of the earth to a 24-hour day. Based on this time scale, how old are you? The correct answer is not hours, minutes, or even seconds. Even if you were 100 years old, your lifetime would be measured in only *fractions* of a second.

**Figure 4.1** ▲
The human environment of a city changes much more rapidly than the natural earth on which it is built.

## Skills Development

**Calculate** Another way to have students think of the length of geologic time is to have them calculate how a million years compares to a person's lifetime. Ask: If a person can live 100 years, how much longer is a million years? (It is 10,000 times as much as a person lives.) Then ask: How long is 4.6 billion years, or the age of the earth, compared to a million years? (The age of the earth is 4,600 times more than a million years.)

## Research

Explain that scientists have proposed many hypotheses about the origin of the earth. Have students use references to find out about one or more of the following:

▶ Planetesimal hypothesis of Moulton and Chamberlin

▶ Tidal hypothesis of Jeans and Jeffries

▶ Double-star hypothesis of Lyttleton

▶ Nova-explosion hypothesis of Hoyle

▶ Nebular hypothesis of Laplace

▶ Dust-cloud hypothesis of Whipple

▶ Cosmic-cloud hypothesis of Kuiper

Have students work in groups to present illustrated reports on these hypotheses. Allow for discussion time after each presentation.

**Answer to In-Text Question**
① **Less than a millimeter**

**Answer to Link**
Answers will vary. An adult mayfly will see time passing extremely quickly, an elephant more slowly, and a redwood much more slowly. Humans should perceive time passing at about the same rate as an elephant which has nearly the same lifespan.

### Math Connection

Have students imagine that the entire history of the earth could be compressed into one day. Have students calculate the number of years in a second, minute, and hour if 24 hours were defined as 4.6 billion years. (One hour would equal 192 million years, one minute would equal 3 million years, and one second would equal 50,000 years.)

### Integrating the Sciences

**Astronomy** Have students model the formation of the sun by floating oatmeal in a bowl of water. They should observe what happens to the oatmeal after it is stirred with a spoon. Ask students what the oatmeal represents. The water? (The oatmeal is the huge cloud of matter that is gradually coming together in a mass. The water is space.)

**Figure 4.2 ▶**
If the length of this soccer field stands for the age of the earth, how much of the field equals your lifetime? ①

**Life Science**
**L I N K**

Find out the lifespans of the following organisms:
◆ mayfly
◆ African elephant
◆ redwood tree

Write a short paragraph for each organism describing its major life stages. Now, imagine yourself as each of these organisms and write how you would perceive the passage of time. How does your perception of time as another organism compare to your perception of time as a human?

**A C T I V I T Y**

For another comparison, look at Figure 4.2. It shows a soccer field, 100 m long. Imagine that this length represents the age of the earth. How "long" is your life in comparison? It would be much less than the thickness of one blade of grass.

As you can see, the earth's history is very long. This amount of time is so much longer than anything humans experience that scientists have given it a special name: **geologic time.** If the passage of geologic time were recorded in books so that each year was condensed into one letter, your life would be the length of an average sentence. The earth's history, in contrast, would fill not only this whole book, but a good-sized library *full* of books!

## Origin of the Earth

Old as it is, the earth has not always existed. About 5,000 million years ago, a huge cloud of matter spinning in space began to collapse. Matter was drawn toward the center of the cloud by an ever-increasing gravitational pull. As the center increased in mass, it grew hotter and denser.

Eventually, the center of the cloud became so hot and dense that individual atoms began to join, or fuse. This fusion of atoms released large amounts of heat and light. The sun was born.

The matter that still spun around the newly formed sun began to clump. Each clump drew the surrounding matter toward it. Over time, each clump became a planet. Earth is one of the nine clumps that became a planet.

**Figure 4.3 ▲**
The earth began as a clump of matter spinning around a hot cloud of matter that would become the sun.

## Themes in Science

**Systems and Interactions** Living things interact with the physical environment, and, in so doing, they affect the earth. Living things are responsible for many changes that have occurred on the earth, such as the addition of oxygen to the atmosphere.

**Patterns of Change/Cycles** Changes on the earth's surface occur as part of a continuous cycle of building up, or deposition, and wearing down, or erosion.

### Earth's Early History

During its first billion years or so, the earth was very different than it is now. At first, the hot surface had no oceans or continents. There was probably no atmosphere. Volcanoes erupted constantly, spewing gases. An atmosphere slowly formed, and some of the gases in the atmosphere began to condense, or turn to liquid. Much of this liquid was water, and it fell to the earth as rain. An ocean eventually covered the surface.

By about 3,800 million years ago, the first small landmasses had formed as a result of volcanic eruptions. Around the same time, the first living things came into being in the oceans. Some of these organisms began to produce oxygen as a by-product of their life processes.

By about 2,000 million years ago, the earth was much like it is today. Organisms did not yet live on land, but there were mountains and rivers on the continents. The atmosphere contained oxygen, and energy from the sun created weather patterns.

### Changes on the Surface

Over the last 2,000 million years, the earth has continued to change. But unlike the changes that occurred in the earth's early history, these changes have followed regular patterns. The same patterns continue today.

**Weathering and Erosion** One basic process that has shaped the earth's surface is the wearing away of rock. Rock wears down in two related steps. First, rock undergoes **weathering**, during which it is broken down into smaller particles. Second, these smaller particles are carried away by **erosion** (ee ROH zhuhn). Wind, waves, ice, flowing water, and gravity can all erode weathered rock particles. Particles carried away by erosion are called *sediment*.

Weathering and erosion work very slowly. Over long periods of time, however, weathering and erosion together cause major changes in the surface. They can make mountains disappear or carve canyons over 1 km deep.

**Figure 4.4** ▲
The first landmasses on the earth may have formed in the way you see here.

**Figure 4.5** ▲
Can you see the sediment that has eroded from this hillside? ②

## TEACH ▪ Continued

### Class Activity

Have students work in small groups. Each group should have a large, clear, plastic jar with a cover, and soil, sand, and fine gravel. Place equal amounts of soil, sand, and gravel in the container so that it is about one-third full. Add water until the jar is half full. Close the jar tightly and shake the jar for 30 seconds. Then allow the sediments to settle. Have students note the order in which the sediments settle and how long settling takes.

### Skills Development

**Infer** Ask students to give examples of uplift. (Students may suggest earthquakes or mountain-forming.)

### Answers to In-Text Questions

① Rock deposited in the riverbed came from mountain erosion.

② Layers

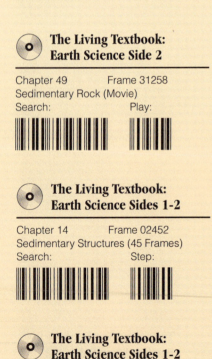

**The Living Textbook:
Earth Science Side 2**

| Chapter 49 | Frame 31258 |
| --- | --- |
Sedimentary Rock (Movie)
Search:        Play:

**The Living Textbook:
Earth Science Sides 1-2**

| Chapter 14 | Frame 02452 |
| --- | --- |
Sedimentary Structures (45 Frames)
Search:        Step:

**The Living Textbook:
Earth Science Sides 1-2**

| Chapter 14 | Frame 02409 |
| --- | --- |
Sedimentation (1 Frame)
Search:

## Integrating the Sciences

**Environmental Science** People have a great effect on the deposition of sediment. Often harbors and rivers are dredged to rid the bottom of collected sediment. People create a kind of deposition when they fill in wetlands for construction, or make landfills.

**Deposition** Because of gravity, particles of rock are carried by erosion to low places. These places include the bottoms of lakes and valleys, and the ocean floor. There, rock particles stop moving and collect. The buildup of eroded particles, or sediment, is called **deposition** (DEHP uh ZIH shuhn).

In contrast to the wearing-down processes of weathering and erosion, deposition is a building-up process. Deposition happens slowly all the time. It is another major cause of change on the earth's surface. At any one time, most parts of the earth's surface are either being eroded or having sediment deposited on them.

**Figure 4.6** ▲
Eroded pieces of rock were deposited in this riverbed. Where did they come from? ①

### Formation of Sedimentary Rock

Sediment builds up over long periods of time, forming horizontal layers. Newer layers form on top of older layers. The growing mass of the upper layers puts more pressure on the sediments in the lower layers. As pressure compacts the sediment particles and minerals cement them together, sediments become rock.

Rock that forms from sediment is called *sedimentary rock*. Sedimentary rock has formed on the earth for such a long time that in some places it is very thick. The Grand Canyon, for example, cuts through sedimentary rock over 1 km thick. Because of the way sedimentary rock forms, its layers vary in age. Like the bricks in the wall of a building, the lowest layers are laid down first. Therefore, the deeper a layer of sedimentary rock, the older it is.

**Figure 4.7** ▲
What evidence of its formation does this sedimentary rock contain? ②

**Uplift** What would happen if weathering, erosion, deposition, and the formation of rock from sediment were the only processes shaping the earth's surface? High places would wear down, and low places would fill up. Erosion and deposition would then stop. What prevents this from happening?

In a number of different ways, parts of the crust are raised above others in a process called *uplift*. Through uplift, mountains and plateaus form. Because uplift, like weathering and erosion, has been going on constantly over at least the last 2,000 million years, there are always new, elevated landforms to be worn away.

## Integrating the Sciences

**Life Science** Present the concept of adaptation to students and discuss how changes in the earth's physical environment might lead to changes in organisms. Specific examples of environmental change include warming or cooling of the climate, formation of mountain ranges, drying of swamps, flooding of coastlines, and dying out of organisms used as food.

**Paleontology** Explain to students that most fossils are made of rock. The original bones or shells of the organisms no longer exist. Discuss how original matter could be replaced slowly by particles of matter from the surrounding rock.

## Changes in Life

Organisms have lived on the earth's surface millions of years. They are, therefore, an important part of the earth's history. Organisms that lived in the past have left evidence of their existence in the rocks of the crust. These traces of past life are called **fossils**.

Most fossils formed when an organism was buried in sediment. Over time, the remains of the organism became part of a layer of sedimentary rock. A fossil, therefore, is as old as the rock of which it is a part.

By studying fossils, scientists found that living things changed greatly over time. Most of the kinds of organisms, or species, that left fossils no longer exist today. They became extinct.

Over time, living things evolved. Through the process of evolution, the inherited traits of a species change, and new species arise. Therefore, as the earth's surface changed over time, so have the organisms living on it.

**Figure 4.8** ▲
The organisms that left these fossils lived over 150 million years ago. They are now extinct.

# Historical Notebook

## The Discovery of Earth's Old Age

If you had lived 200 years ago, you would probably have learned in school that the earth was 6,000 years old. In fact, the accepted view of history was that humans had lived on the earth nearly all that time. Therefore, human history and the earth's history were the same.

In the late 1700s, however, this view was challenged by a group of Scottish scientists led by James Hutton. Hutton made observations of rocks that made sense only if the earth was far older than anyone had imagined. He observed that rocks were made of particles eroded from even older rocks.

Hutton saw that the earth's surface had changed gradually over a very long period of

time. He based his ideas on the principle of uniformitarianism (YOO nih FORM uh TAIR ee uhn izm). According to this principle, the laws of nature do not change over time. Thus, the same processes that shaped the earth in the past are still at work today.

The idea that the earth was very, very old gave birth to the modern science of geology. It changed the way life scientists viewed organisms. And it changed forever the human concept of time.

1.  What made Hutton believe the earth was very old?

2.  What is the principle of uniformitarianism?

---

## Enrich

Tell students that some fossils are the hard parts of organisms that once lived. These hard parts could be bones, shells, wood, teeth, or seeds. Other fossils are remains that have been replaced by the minerals in groundwater. Still other fossils are molds and casts in the shape of a fish's bone, a leaf, or a shell. Footprints can become fossils called *impressions*. Have students who are interested do some research on these different kinds of fossils. Ask students what kind of fossil is shown in Figure 4.8. (Cast)

## Historical Notebook

**Answers**

1.  Hutton observed that rocks were made of particles from even older rocks.

2.  The principle of uniformitarianism states that the laws of nature do not change over time. Therefore, the same processes that shaped the earth in the past are still at work today.

## Discuss

Ask students to suggest how Hutton's theory could give rise to a new science. (Suggestions might include: Realizing the possibility that the earth and types of living things may actually change and that what has changed before may be changing now. So, studying the past may give clues to what will happen in the future.)

## Integrated Learning

Use Integrating Worksheet 4.1.

**The Living Textbook:
Earth Science Sides 1-2**

Chapter 27          Frame 03851
Fossils (45 Frames)
Search:                    Step:

## Skills WorkOut

To help students hypothesize about ice age effects, have them do the Skills WorkOut.

**Answers** Possible hypothesis: As more of the earth's water becomes "locked up," the ocean level goes down because some of the water that would have become a part of the ocean is trapped in the ice. This causes the lowering of shorelines, so erosion would take place lower on the edges of continents.

## EVALUATE

## WrapUp

**Reteach** Have students take turns adding to a timeline of the earth. Ask volunteers to add the following: When life appeared, weathering and erosion, how sedimentary rock forms, uplift, and formation of the evidence for past life.

Use Review Worksheet 4.1.

## Check and Explain

1. The earth formed from one of the clumps of matter that spun around a newly formed sun.

2. Erosion changes the earth's surface by carrying away weathered particles from mountains, hills, and canyons.

3. The layer formed from mud would have finer grains and might be darker in color.

4. Students' diagrams should show that the processes are all part of a cycle.

---

## Integrating the Sciences

**Environmental Science** Discuss with students how global warming might affect the polar ice caps, the climates of different areas on the earth, and the vegetation in various locations. Discuss how these changes might affect human beings and other living things on the earth.

▼ **ACTIVITY**

**Hypothesizing**

*On Ice*

When sheets of ice expand and advance from the poles, much of Earth's water is frozen in ice. What do you think might happen to the ocean levels? How might this affect shoreline erosion? State a hypothesis to explain your reasoning.

**SKILLS WORKOUT**

### Changes in Climate

Throughout the earth's history, the climate of the planet as a whole varied considerably. At certain times, most of the planet was warm and wet. At other times, it was much drier and colder. During the dry, cold times, the polar ice caps increased in size. Huge sheets of ice spread from the poles into the middle latitudes. These periods are called *ice ages*.

### Science and Technology
*Are Humans Changing the Climate?*

For most of the earth's history, natural processes caused slow changes in climate. However, scientists have evidence showing that human technology is changing the climate today. These changes may be both local and global.

On a local scale, cities cause changes in temperature. The average temperature in a large city is often slightly higher than in the surrounding countryside. Scientists also determined that cutting down large areas of forest in tropical regions changes rainfall patterns. The deforested areas hold less moisture, so more rainwater drains to the oceans, instead of evaporating slowly to form clouds. As a result, rainfall in these areas may decrease.

Scientists are also worried about global warming. The burning of fossil fuels for energy increased the amount of carbon dioxide in the atmosphere. This caused small increases in the average temperature of the earth.

### Check and Explain

1. From what did the earth form?

2. What does erosion do to the earth's surface?

3. **Infer** How would a layer of sedimentary rock formed from mud be different from one formed from sand?

4. **Communicate** Using words and arrows, draw a diagram to show how weathering, erosion, deposition, sedimentary rock formation, and uplift are related.

### Prelab Discussion

Have students read the entire activity. Discuss these points before beginning:

▶ Discuss various actual units of time from very small (milliseconds, nanoseconds) to very large (eras, periods, epochs, ages, millenia). Give examples of situations in which each one is appropriate.

▶ Discuss misconceptions that students might have, such as thinking that a light-year measures time, or that time scales are not arbitrary.

**Time** 30 minutes    **Group** pairs

**Materials**

15 books

## Analysis

1. Answers will vary depending on how fast they carry out each procedure. Make sure answers agree with data table.

2. Answers will vary. Students may suggest that title years are the best because they are the longest.

3. Answers will vary. Students might say that book years was the most difficult scale to use because the speed of opening and closing a book varies.

4. Students need to time each "year." They then have to multiply their age by 31,536,000 (the number of seconds in a year) to find out how many seconds they have been alive, then divide by the number of seconds in each made-up "year" to find out their age in "years." Answers will be in the hundreds of millions.

5. None of these time scales would be useful for measuring the age of the earth because the unit of time is too small—on the order of a few seconds.

## Conclusion

Accept any logical conclusions. Long time scales are useful in natural history for measuring events and phenomena that occur over long spans of time (eras, periods, ages, millenia, for example). Small time scales (milliseconds, nanoseconds) are useful for events that occur quickly, such as chemical reactions or subatomic particle collisions.

## Extension

Measuring systems and measurements will vary.

## Activity 4  How can you measure time differently?

**Skills**  Measure; Collect Data

### Task 1  Prelab Prep
Collect the following items: a book, a pencil, a piece of paper.

### Task 2  Data Record
Copy the data table below on a separate piece of paper and use it to record your measurements.

**Table 4.1   Time in Different Scales**

| Type of year | Number of years to walk across the room | Number of years to write my name |
|---|---|---|
| book years | | |
| step years | | |
| title years | | |
| ??? years | | |

### Task 3  Procedure

1. You will investigate some different ways that you can measure time. You'll begin by measuring in "book years." A book year equals the time it takes to open and close a book. Walk across the room opening and closing a book. Count the number of book years it takes to cross the room. Record this number in your data table.

2. Measure the number of book years it takes to write your name by having one partner count book years, while the other partner writes. Record this measurement in the table.

3. Count the number of steps it takes you to cross the room. Each step counts as one year. Record the "step years" in the table.

4. Measure the number of step years it takes to write your name by having one partner walk across the room while the other writes your name. Count the step years as

your name is written. Record this number in the data table.

5. A "title year" is the amount of time it takes to read the title of this activity. Count how many times you say the title as you walk across the room. Record this number in the table.

6. Measure the number of title years it takes to write your name by having one partner count title years, while the other partner writes your name. Record this number in the table.

7. Make up a scale for a type of year. Record the name of your type of year in Table 4.1. Use your new time scale to measure the number of years it takes to walk across the room and to write your name. Record these numbers in the data table.

### Task 4  Analysis

1. Compare each of the new time scales to the real time scale. Which time scale has the shortest year? The longest?

2. Which time scale do you think would be the best to use? Why?

3. Which time scale was the most difficult to use? Why?

4. Calculate your age using one of the time scales from the data table.

5. **Infer**  Would any of the time scales in this activity be useful in measuring the age of the earth? Explain.

### Task 5  Conclusion
Write a paragraph explaining the possible uses for different time scales. Include the advantages and disadvantages of each scale.

### Extension

Use easily obtainable items to define several different scales for measuring length. Measure the length of your book, your height, and the length of an eraser using each of the measuring systems that you defined.

**Skills Objectives**
Students should be able to:

**Make a Model** of major life stages by using a timeline.

**Make a Graph** showing how long the earth's eras lasted.

**Observe** characteristics of a 100-year-old object.

**Predict** where to find Paleozoic rocks in the Grand Canyon.

**Infer** how sedimentary rock layers and the geologic time scale are related.

**Vocabulary**
era, period

---

### MOTIVATE

#### Skills WarmUp
To help students understand stages in geologic history, have them do the Skills WarmUp.
**Answer** Student timelines will vary. Students should give a criterion for the life stages they identify. For example, some may base their stages on chronological age and some on events in their lives.

#### Misconceptions
Students may think that, by identifying the material in a layer of rock sediment, the exact age of the layer can be determined. Explain to students that when geologists examine sedimentary material, they discover only whether a layer is younger or older than another. They cannot pinpoint a layer's precise age using this method.

---

### Themes in Science
**Scale and Structure** Differences of scale are important in both space and time. Earth scientists must consider a very long time scale—5,000 million years—in their study of the earth.

### STS Connection
Discuss with students how the layering of trash in a garbage dump over time would reveal the history of a city or town to a "garbage archaeologist." Ask them where they might expect to find antique bottles. A current newspaper?

---

### ▼ ACTIVITY

#### Making a Model

*The Time of Your Life*
Make a timeline showing the major events in your life. Divide the timeline into stages based on these events. How many stages did you make? How did you decide what a stage was?

#### SKILLS WARMUP

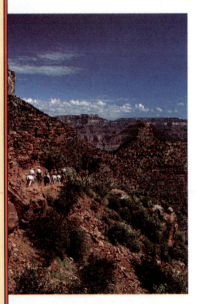

**Figure 4.9** ▲
As these people move down into the canyon, they will pass by older and older rocks.

---

## 4.2 Geologic Time Scale

### Objectives

▶ **Explain** how scientists determine the relative age of sedimentary rocks.

▶ **List** the order of events that may result in an unconformity being formed.

▶ **Describe** the major divisions of the geologic time scale.

▶ **Infer** the relationship between the layering of sedimentary rock and the geologic time scale.

---

What stages have you gone through in your life? First you were an infant. Then you learned to walk and talk to become a toddler. After a few more years, you went to elementary school. Now you're a teenager or about to become one.

The earth, too, has gone through stages. Like the stages in your life, each one began with some important event or change. But the stages in the earth's history took place in geologic time. Each stage stretched over enormously long periods of time.

### Time Record in the Rocks

How have scientists learned enough about the earth's history to divide it into stages? How do they find out about events that took place millions or even billions of years ago? The rocks of the earth's crust hold all the evidence. Scientists simply learned how to "read" the record of time preserved in the rocks.

**Rock Layering** Layers of sedimentary rock provide scientists with important evidence of past events. As you learned, layers of sedimentary rock form one after another. They are stacked according to age, like a pile of old magazines. Older rocks are found under younger rocks. Therefore, going down into deeper layers of rock is like going back in time. This principle holds true as long as the rock layers were not turned upside down by intense folding. What do you think scientists can learn by studying the layering of rock?

**Relative Age** The layering by age of sedimentary rock allows earth scientists to determine the *relative age* of these rocks. They can say a certain layer is older or younger than other layers by comparing its position to other layers. The relative positions of layers also helps in the ordering of past events. For example, suppose a certain layer of sedimentary rock formed from volcanic ash. Above it is a layer formed by sediment deposited in a shallow sea. What can you infer from this evidence? ①

◀ **Figure 4.10**
How are these rock layers an example of an unconformity? ②

**Unconformities** A break in the layering of rock can also be informative. Look at the photograph in Figure 4.10. Layers of rock tilted at an angle are covered by horizontal layers. An earth scientist knows that the tilted rock layers are much older than the horizontal layers. The line between them, called an *unconformity* (UHN kuhn FORM uh tee), represents a break in time.

Look at Figure 4.11 to see how an unconformity forms. Many different changes occurring over a long time period produce an unconformity. Geologists can infer what these changes were and when they occurred.

**Absolute Age** Geologists also have methods to determine the approximate age of rocks in years. These methods tell them the *absolute age* of rocks. The main method of determining absolute age is through radiometric dating. You will learn more about radiometric dating when you study fossils in Chapter 13. Through methods of absolute and relative dating, earth scientists have pieced together the earth's history.

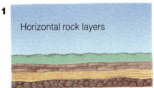

1 Horizontal rock layers

2 Layers are tilted by folding

3 Surface is eroded

4 New sediments are deposited

**Figure 4.11** ▲
An unconformity forms over a long period of time.

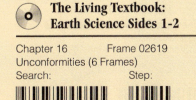

## Enrich

Inform students that some earth scientists divide the Precambrian Era into two eras: the Archeozoic Era and the Proterozoic Era. The Archeozoic Era starts at the formation of the earth and it is the longest era of the earth's history. A great deal of volcanic activity took place during this era. Mountain-building activity was common during the Proterozoic era. Fossils of algae and worm trails have been found in rocks from this era.

## SkillBuilder

### Answers

Answers for table: Precambrian—4055 million years/88%; Paleozoic—300 million years/7%; Mesozoic—179 million years/4%; Cenozoic—66 million years/1%

1. Cenozoic Era; Precambrian Era

2. The circle graph would not change much proportionally by adding 10 million years. The 10 million years would probably add to the 66 million years in the Cenozoic Era. That would make the Cenozoic Era a little larger and the other eras would be adjusted to be just a little smaller.

 **The Living Textbook: Earth Science Sides 1-2**

Chapter 1          Frame 00706
Geologic Time Scale (19 Frames)
Search:                    Step:

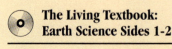

**The Living Textbook: Earth Science Sides 1-2**

Chapter 27         Frame 03820
Paleozoic Fossils (20 Frames)
Search:                    Step:

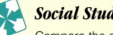

## Social Studies Connection

Compare the division of the earth's geologic history into eras with the division of a nation's history into periods. Ask students how it is decided when one stage ends and another begins.

## Integrating the Sciences

**Life Science** Discuss with students how sea-dwelling life forms changed as they began to live on land. How is a land environment different from an ocean environment? What problems had to be solved in terms of evolution before organisms began living on land?

## Divisions of Geologic Time

Scientists have divided geologic time into four large units. These units are called **eras** (AIR uhz). Each era covers one major stage in the earth's history. Look at Figure 4.12. It is a timeline showing the length of each era. Notice how the eras vary greatly in length.

**Precambrian Era** The first era of the earth's history is the longest. It includes all the events from the earth's formation to a time about 640 million years ago. The Precambrian (pree KAYM bree uhn) Era ended when many new and different life forms began to appear.

**Paleozoic Era** The 400 million years following the end of the Precambrian Era make up the Paleozoic (PAY lee UH ZOH ihk) Era. During this era, plants and animals began to live on land. The Paleozoic Era ended when many kinds of organisms became extinct.

## SkillBuilder  *Making a Graph*

### Earth History Pie

A circle graph helps you to compare different amounts. You will make a circle graph that shows approximately how long each of the earth's eras lasted. Copy the table below.

| Geologic Time Scale | | |
|---|---|---|
| **Era** | **Length (millions of years)** | **Percentage of Earth's History** |
| Precambrian | | |
| Paleozoic | | |
| Mesozoic | | |
| Cenozoic | | |

Using Figure 4.12 on page 85, determine how long each era lasted. Record the length for each era in the table.

Calculate the percentage of the total earth history that each era lasted. To do this, divide the era length by the age of the earth, then multiply by 100. The formula is

$$\frac{\text{era length}}{4,600} \times 100$$

Record the percentage for each era in the table.
Using the percentages you recorded, draw and label a circle graph of the earth's history in geologic time. Then answer the questions.

1. Which era occupies the smallest section of the circle graph? The largest?

2. How might your circle graph change in ten million years? Work with a partner to construct a circle graph that represents the eras ten million years from now.

## Language Arts Connection

Provide students with the following terms derived from ancient Greek and their meanings: *zoic*—"animal," *pale*—"ancient," *mes*—"middle," and *cene*—"recent." Have students find the literal meanings of the earth's eras from these roots.

**Mesozoic Era**  This era was the time of the dinosaurs. Most of the earth had a warm, wet climate. The Mesozoic (MEHZ uh ZOH ihk) Era ended when most of the dinosaurs and many other life forms died out. Many scientists hypothesize that mass extinctions occurred after a large asteroid, or rock from space, struck the earth.

**Cenozoic Era**  Since the end of the Mesozoic Era, the earth has been in the Cenozoic (SEE nuh ZOH ihk) Era. During this time, the earth's climate became cooler and drier. Several ice ages have come and gone. Humans lived on the earth for only a small part of this era.

**Periods and Epochs**  The Paleozoic, Mesozoic, and Cenozoic Eras are divided into smaller units called **periods**. Look at Figure 4.12. It shows these divisions of time on a small part of the geologic timeline. The periods of the Cenozoic Era, in turn, are divided into epochs (EHP uhks).

Periods and epochs help scientists locate more exactly the changes and events in the earth's history. When a scientist says a fossil is from the Devonian period, for example, other scientists know how long ago the organism lived.

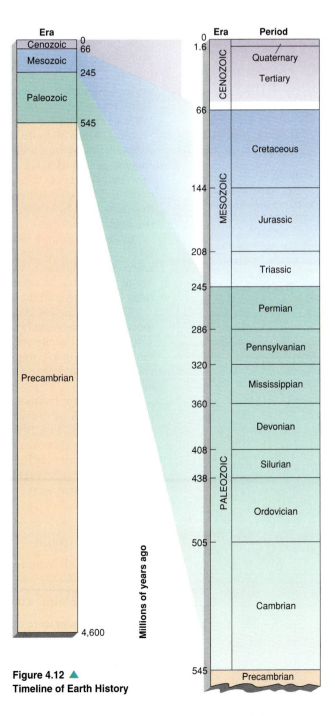

**Figure 4.12** ▲
**Timeline of Earth History**

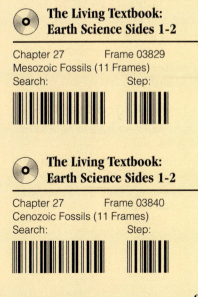

### *Skills WorkOut*

To help students make observations about age, have them do the Skills WorkOut.

**Answer** Answers will vary, but there may be several indications that an object is old depending on the kind of object chosen. In general, newer objects show less wear.

## EVALUATE

### WrapUp

**Reteach** Using references, draw a geologic column on the chalkboard. Explain to the class what the geologic column represents, how sedimentary rocks are indicated, and how unconformities are shown.

Use Review Worksheet 4.2.

### Check and Explain

1. They look at the positions of the layers in relation to one another.

2. Layers of sedimentary rock are folded and partially eroded, then new sediments are deposited on top of the original layers.

3. Rocks from the Paleozoic Era would be found near the bottom of the canyon, just above the Precambrian layer.

4. The layers are arranged vertically in the same relative positions as the parts of the scale. Students' diagrams should correspond to the geologic time scale.

### Answers to In-Text Questions

① All measure time in hours and minutes.

② Seasons would be shorter; you would be twice as old in years.

③ Seasons would be longer; you would be half your age in years.

## *Multicultural Perspectives*

The sundial is the oldest known instrument used to measure time. It is believed to have been used by the Egyptians as early as 4000 years ago. A sundial tells time by measuring the angle of a shadow cast by the sun. When the sun hits the *gnomon*, a flat piece of metal at the center, the shadow it casts tells the time. Since the gnomon is useful only during the day, the water clock, or *clepsy-drae*, was developed by the Egyptians about 3500 years ago. The water clock used water entering or leaving a container at a regular flow to measure time.

▼ **ACTIVITY**

**Observing**

*Something Old, . . .*

Find something living or nonliving that is over 100 years old. You may find something in your home or outside. You may also look for pictures of objects in books or magazines. What evidence do you have that the object is old? How does it differ from a similar object that is much newer?

**SKILLS WORKOUT**

### Science and Society *Telling Time*

How do you tell time? Usually, you probably look at a clock. A clock is a mechanical or electronic device designed to measure units, or intervals, of time. Think about the different kinds of clocks you've seen. What do they have in common? ①

Most clocks measure time in hours, minutes, and seconds. But where do these units of time come from? An hour is 1/24 of a day. A day is defined by the earth's movement. A day is the amount of time it takes the earth to rotate once on its axis. You can get an idea of the time of day by looking at where the sun appears in the sky.

In a similar way, a year is the amount of time it takes for the earth to revolve around the sun. You know where the earth is in its revolution by the season. The age of the earth is equal to the total number of revolutions it made around the sun.

The earth, then, is the ultimate clock. The earth's movements determine how people experience and measure time. How would your life be different if the earth took half as long to complete one journey around the sun? What would change if one rotation took twice as long? ③ ②

An important characteristic of a clock is that the intervals of time it measures stay the same. You trust that each day will be 24 hours and each year 365.25 days. You have this trust because the earth's rate of movement doesn't change. It would be more difficult to measure the earth's age if its revolving speed steadily increased or decreased.

### Check and Explain

1. How do earth scientists determine the relative age of rock layers?

2. What are the steps in the formation of an unconformity?

3. **Predict** If you were exploring the Grand Canyon, where would you find rocks from the Paleozoic Era?

4. **Infer** How are sedimentary rock layers and the geologic time scale related? Draw a diagram as part of your answer.

## Chapter 4 Review

### Concept Summary

**4.1 Earth's History**

▶ Geologic changes occur on a different time scale than the changes humans experience.

▶ The earth is about 4,600 million years old. This length of time is called geologic time.

▶ The sun and the earth formed from a spinning cloud of matter in space.

▶ It took over 1 billion years for the earth to form oceans, continents, and an atmosphere containing oxygen.

▶ For about the last 2 billion years, the processes of weathering, erosion, deposition, formation of sedimentary rock, and uplift have caused regular patterns of change on the earth's surface.

▶ Organisms living on the earth's surface have evolved over time. Their fossil remains have been left in layers of sedimentary rock.

**4.2 Geologic Time Scale**

▶ Sedimentary rocks form so that the oldest layers are below younger layers. The position of rock layers in relation to each other enables scientists to determine their relative ages.

▶ Unconformities form as a result of repeated cycles of sedimentation, sedimentary rock formation, and uplift.

▶ Geologic time is divided into four eras: the Precambrian, Paleozoic, Mesozoic, and Cenozoic.

### Chapter Vocabulary

| | | | |
|---|---|---|---|
| geologic time (4.1) | erosion (4.1) | fossil (4.1) | period (4.2) |
| weathering (4.1) | deposition (4.1) | era (4.2) | |

### Check Your Vocabulary

Use the vocabulary words above to complete the following sentences correctly.

1. Weathered particles of rock are carried away by ____.

2. Geologic time is divided into four large units called ____.

3. You can find the remains of ancient organisms, or ____, in layers of sedimentary rock.

4. The buildup of sand on the bottom of a lake is an example of ____.

5. The age of the earth is the length of time called ____.

6. An era is divided into smaller units of time called ____.

7. Rocks are broken down through the process of ____ and the particles are carried away by erosion.

Explain the difference between the words in each pair.

8. period, epoch

9. weathering, erosion

10. deposition, sediments

11. geologic time, relative age

### Write Your Vocabulary

Write sentences using the vocabulary words above. Show that you know what each word means.

### Check Your Vocabulary

1. erosion
2. eras
3. fossils
4. deposition
5. geologic time
6. periods
7. weathering
8. *Epochs* are subdivisions of *periods.*
9. *Weathering* breaks down rocks into smaller and smaller pieces, while *erosion* is the carrying away of these smaller particles by wind, water, ice or gravity.
10. *Deposition* is the process by which *sediments* are built up.
11. Geologic *time* refers to the total history of the earth, while *relative age* refers to the fact that older rock layers are deeper than more recent ones.

### Write Your Vocabulary

Students' sentences should show that they know the meaning of each word as well as how to use it in a sentence.

Use Vocabulary Worksheet for Chapter 4.

## Check Your Knowledge

1. The first oceans formed as the earth cooled and water vapor in the atmosphere condensed and fell as rain.

2. Fossils show some of the physical features of organisms.

3. Sedimentary rock is formed as lower layers of sediment are compressed by the pressure of the layers above and their particles are cemented together by minerals.

4. Inferences can be made about the relative ages of the rocks and about the age of fossils found in the rocks.

5. Wind, flowing water, ice, waves, and gravity can cause erosion.

6. The process of uplift creates elevated landforms.

7. Sediments are commonly deposited on the bottoms of lakes and rivers, and on the ocean floor.

8. erosion

9. younger than

10. fractions of a second

11. Precambrian

12. Cenozoic

13. the same age as

## Check Your Understanding

1. At various times in the earth's early history, a time traveler would find either a very hot surface and no atmosphere, many volcanic eruptions and an atmosphere with no oxygen, or oceans with no land.

2. Unconformities tell geologists when and where the process of deposition and formation of sedimentary rock was interrupted by a period of erosion. Unconformities represent a break in time and help show that geologic time is very long.

3. Geologic time differs from normal time in its length, or scale.

4. Papers from the beginning of the school year will be close to the bottom. Her locker is a model of sedimentary rock layers and their relative ages.

5. Student answers will vary. More is known about events in the Cenozoic Era, so scientists date these events more precisely.

6. The sea organism died and its shell sank to the ocean floor. Over time, sediment was deposited. After more time, the ocean disappeared and a portion of the former sea floor was uplifted, resulting in a fossil sea shell near the top of a mountain.

7. The sediment will accumulate behind the dam.

8. The early earth had no oceans, continents, atmosphere, or life, as the moon is now.

9. The range that is lower and more rounded is probably older. Over time, erosion lowers the elevation of a mountain and rounds its features, so the lower and more rounded a mountain range, the longer it has existed.

10. Students' answers will vary. This fossil, like any other, can give information about the structure of a specific type of organism, about other types of plant and animal life of the time, and about the climate of the area at the time.

## Chapter 4 Review

### Check Your Knowledge

Answer the following in complete sentences.

1. How did oceans form in the early part of the earth's history?

2. What do fossils show about the organisms that lived long ago?

3. How do layers of sediment become rock?

4. What kinds of inferences can earth scientists make by observing layers of sedimentary rock?

5. Name four forces that cause erosion.

6. What geologic process creates elevated landforms that can be eroded?

7. Where on the earth are sediments commonly deposited?

Choose the answer that best completes each sentence.

8. Wearing-down processes include (deposition, uplift, formation of sedimentary rock, erosion).

9. The uppermost layer of sedimentary rock is (younger than, older than, the same age as, denser than) the layers of rock below it.

10. If geologic time were compressed into 24 hours, a human life span would be measured in (minutes, seconds, fractions of a second, hours).

11. Life has existed on the earth since the (Mesozoic, Cenozoic, Paleozoic, Precambrian) Era.

12. You live in the (Paleozoic, Mesozoic, Cenozoic, Precambrian) Era.

13. A fossil is (older than, the same age as, younger than, not related to) the rock layer in which it is found.

### Check Your Understanding

Apply the concepts you have learned to answer each question.

1. If you could travel back in time, why would you not want to go back too far into the earth's past?

2. What do unconformities tell earth scientists about the earth's history?

3. How is geologic time different from time as you normally experience it?

4. **Application** Anne hasn't cleaned out her locker all year. Where will she find papers from the beginning of school? What is her locker modeling?

5. **Critical Thinking** Why are epochs used to measure geologic time in the Cenozoic Era but not in the other eras?

6. You find fossils of sea shells in rocks near the top of a mountain. Explain all the geologic processes that resulted in the fossils ending up in this location.

7. **Predict** Rivers carry large amounts of eroded sediments into the oceans. Predict what will happen to a river's sediments when a dam is built on the river.

8. The early earth has been compared to the moon as it is now. Explain the similarities on which this comparison is based.

9. **Application** You explore two mountain ranges. One has tall, jagged peaks. The other is lower and more rounded. Which mountain range is likely to be the older one? Why?

10. **Mystery Photo** The photograph on page 74 shows a bird fossil from the Tertiary period. It was discovered in Wyoming. What kinds of information might this fossil provide to scientists studying the earth's history?

# Develop Your Skills

1. a. About 10 million years; about 20 million years

   b. The rate of erosion decreases over time.

   c. As a mountain range gets older, there are fewer structures left that are easily eroded.

2. a. Eocene; 21.2 million years

   b. 58

3. Students' hypotheses will vary. The Paleozoic Era is defined by the appearance of new forms of life. Prior to this time, there were fewer organisms likely to become fossilized. Also, Precambrian life forms were mostly soft bodied, so they did not fossilize easily.

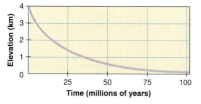

## Develop Your Skills

Use the skills you have developed in this chapter to complete each activity.

1. **Interpret Data** Study the graph below, which shows the decrease in the elevation of a mountain range over time due to erosion.

   a. How many million years does it take for the elevation to change from 3 km to 2 km? How long does it take to change from 2 km to 1 km?

   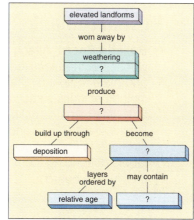

   b. Describe how the rate of erosion of the mountain range changes over time.

   c. Explain why a mountain range would erode more slowly the older it became.

2. **Data Bank** Use the information on page 612 to answer the following questions.

   a. Which epoch lasted the longest in the Cenozoic Era? How long did it last?

   b. How many millions of years ago did the Eocene epoch begin?

3. **Hypothesize** Fossils from the Precambrian Era are rare. In comparison, Paleozoic fossils are common. Suggest several explanations.

## Make Connections

1. **Link the Concepts** Below is a concept map showing how some of the main concepts in this chapter link together. Only part of the map is filled in. Complete the map, using words and ideas from the chapter.

2. **Science and Technology** Do library research on the greenhouse effect. Write a report describing how global warming may affect the environment and human society over the next 50 years.

3. **Science and Geography** Go to places where you can see the landforms around your community. Then write a description of how you think the area looked 10 million years ago.

4. **Science and Social Studies** Find out how time is thought of in the traditions of Native Americans. How do Native-American concepts of time differ from yours?

# Make Connections

1.

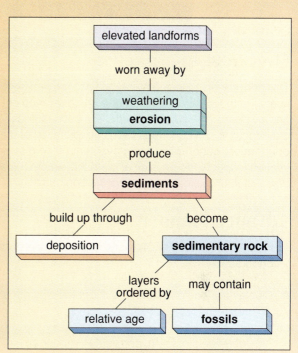

2. Students' reports will vary. Some predicted effects include: an increase in global average temperatures; an increase in desertification; increased melting of polar ice caps leading to rising sea levels; shifts in the location of agricultural regions.

3. Students' descriptions will vary. Make sure descriptions are reasonable for your area during the Cenozoic Era.

4. Students' responses will vary. Students may report on the Aztec ages of the sun, for example, or focus on the Northern Americans' concept of cyclical time, or time as a circle instead of a straight line.

# Overview

This chapter discusses plate tectonics. The first section presents the theory of continental drift, the existence of Pangaea, and evidence that supports both. The second section explains plate tectonics. It continues with an exploration of the structure, boundaries, geography, and movement of the plates. The final section inspects the physics of plate movement, closing with a discussion of the formation of convection currents.

# Advance Planner

▶ Mount a large map of the world on posterboard for TE page 92.

▶ Display a globe or map that distinguishes continents for SE page 94.

▶ Provide sheets of foam, corrugated cardboard, clay, or similar materials for SE page 99.

▶ Provide foam or blocks of wood for TE page 100.

▶ Prepare shoe boxes, white paper, different-colored wide-tipped markers, metric rulers, and scissors for SE Activity 5, page 105.

▶ Gather a heatable container, water, and food coloring for TE page 108.

# Skills Development Chart

| Sections | Define Operationally | Evaluate | Generalize | Interpret Data | Make a Model | Observe |
|---|---|---|---|---|---|---|
| **5.1** Skills WarmUp | | | | | | ● |
| Skills WorkOut | | ● | | | | |
| **5.2** Skills WarmUp | ● | | | | | |
| SkillBuilder | | | | ● | | |
| Skills WorkOut | | | | | ● | |
| Activity 5 | | | | | ● | ● |
| **5.3** Skills WarmUp | | | ● | | | |
| Consider This | | ● | | | | |

# Individual Needs

▶ **Limited English Proficiency Students** Photocopy and distribute a map of the earth's tectonic plates. Ask students to write each of the following terms on a 3 x 5 card: *continental plate, oceanic plate, divergent boundary, transform boundary, oceanic-oceanic convergent boundary, oceanic-continental-oceanic boundary,* and *continental-continental boundary.* Have students write a description of the term and a number on the card. Then have them write the number for each term in appropriate places on the map. For example, if the *transform boundary* card is number 4, a student might write that number on the San Andreas Fault.

▶ **At-Risk Students** Encourage students to find out more about the San Andreas Fault and the Great Rift Valley by researching the following questions: What is each area like today? What aspects of plate tectonics does each represent? Why is the San Andreas Fault of major concern to those who live near it? What might these areas be like in 50 million years? Ask students to use blank pages of their science portfolios to answer the questions with written descriptions, drawings, and magazine pictures.

▶ **Gifted Students** Invite students to consider why the theory of plate tectonics is important to science. How did it help the work of different kinds of earth scientists? What geological facts did the theory help explain? Have them use research and inference to prepare an oral presentation of their views on this subject.

# Resource Bank

▶ **Bulletin Board** Attach the names of several scientists whose contributions led to the theories of continental drift and plate tectonics. Start with Alfred Wegener and include scientists such as David Griggs, A. L. Du Toit, S. K. Runcorn, Harry H. Hess, D. P. McKenzie, Bryan Isacks, Jack Oliver, and Lynn R. Sykes. Ask interested students to find out about their contributions and add labels describing them, as well as appropriate pictures, to the bulletin board.

| Section | Core | Standard | Enriched | Section | Core | Standard | Enriched |
|---|:---:|:---:|:---:|---|:---:|:---:|:---:|
| **5.1 Drifting Continents** pp. 91–95 | | | | **Blackline Masters** Review Worksheet 5.2 Skills Worksheet 5.2 Integrating Worksheet 5.2 | ● ● ● | ● ● ● | ● ● ● |
| **Section Features** Skills WarmUp, p. 91 Skills WorkOut, p. 95 | ● | ● ● | ● ● | **Ancillary Options** *Measuring Earthquakes* | | ● | ● |
| **Blackline Masters** Review Worksheet 5.1 Integrating Worksheet 5.1 | ● | ● ● | ● ● | **Color Transparencies** Transparencies 9, 10, 11a, 11b | ● | ● | ● |
| **Overhead Blackline Transparencies** Overhead Blackline Master 5.1 and Student Worksheet | ● | ● | ● | **5.3 Physics of Plate Tectonics** pp. 106–108 | | | |
| **Laboratory Program** Investigation 8 | ● | ● | | **Section Features** Skills WarmUp, p. 106 Consider This, p. 107 | ● | ● ● | ● ● |
| **5.2 Theory of Plate Tectonics** pp. 96–105 | | | | **Blackline Masters** Review Worksheet 5.3 Reteach Worksheet 5.3 Skills Worksheet 5.3 Vocabulary Worksheet 5.3 | ● ● ● ● | ● ● ● ● | ● ● ● ● |
| **Section Features** Skills WarmUp, p. 96 SkillBuilder, p. 98 Skills WorkOut, p. 99 Activity, p. 105 | ● ● | ● ● ● | ● ● ● ● | | | | |

# Bibliography

The following resources can be used for teaching the chapter. See page T–46 for supplier codes.

**Library Resources**

Aylesworth, T. G. *Moving Continents: Our Changing Earth.* Hillside, NJ: Enslow, 1990.

Condie, Kent C. *Plate Tectonics and Crustal Evolution.* Elmsford, NY: Pergamon Press, 1989.

Farndon, John. *How the Earth Works.* Pleasantville, NY: The Reader's Digest Association, Inc., 1992.

Van Rose, S. *Volcano & Earthquake.* Eyewitness Series. New York: Alfred A. Knopf, Inc., 1992.

**Technology Resources**

*Internet*

**PLANETDIARY** at *http://www.planetdiary.com*
• Find geological news by exploring *Current Phenomena.*
• Learn more about earthquakes and volcanoes by clicking on *Phenomena Backgrounders.*

*Software*

*Big Science Ideas.* Mac, Win. LS.
*Earth Science.* Mac, Win. ER.
*The Oceans.* Mac, Win. LS.

*CD-ROMs*

*Interactive Earth.* SFAW.

*Laserdiscs*

*Living Textbook.* (See barcodes on pages in this chapter.) Optical Data.
*Plate Tectonics.* MMI.

*Videos*

*Folding, Flooding, and Faulting: How the Earth is Shaped.* 60 min. Blue Sky Associates.
*Plate Tectonics: The Puzzle of the Continents.* 15 min. 1992, MMI.

**Audio-Visual Resources**

*The Drifting of the Continents.* Film. T-L.

### Cooperative Learning

Have students work in cooperative groups to make a list of words that describe volcanoes and earthquakes. Have each group share the list with the class. Encourage students to use their knowledge of volcanoes and earthquakes to make inferences about movement and energy beneath the earth's surface.

## Introducing the Chapter

Have students read the description of the photograph. Ask if they agree or disagree with the description.

### Directed Inquiry

Have students study the photograph. Ask:

▶ What features of the earth do you see in this picture? What is happening to them? (Students will mention land and ocean, and burning rock moving into the water from a volcanic eruption.)

▶ What is the burning rock called? Where does it come from? (Students will say that it is molten lava pouring into the sea from inside the earth.)

▶ What might cause such an eruption of lava from the earth? (Students will mention increased heat or pressure on rocks or movements in the earth's crust.)

▶ From this image showing lava flowing from dry land into the ocean, what do you think the subject of this chapter might be? (Students may suggest volcanic eruptions at the places where parts of the earth's crust meet. Many of these plate boundaries are under water.)

## Chapter Vocabulary

convergent boundary
divergent boundary
Pangaea
plate tectonics
sea-floor spreading
subduction
transform boundary
trench

## Chapter 5    Plate Tectonics

### Chapter Sections

**5.1** Drifting Continents

**5.2** Theory of Plate Tectonics

**5.3** Physics of Plate Movement

### What do you see?

"I see a volcano eruption with lava flowing into the water and cooling off rapidly. A volcano must have erupted nearby because of the lava. Pressure and underground heat make it erupt. Volcanoes usually occur on or around plate boundaries."

*Julie Lehman*
*Sequoyah Middle School*
*Edmond, Oklahoma*

To find out more about the photograph, look on page 110. As you read this chapter, you will learn about the plates that make up the earth's crust.

## Language Arts Connection

Have students look up the origins of the prefix *pan-* and the suffix *-gaea* in the dictionary. Based on the origin of both, have students determine what is meant by the name *Pangaea.* Ask if they think that the word *Pangaea* is a good description for the ancient continent and have them explain their answers. (*Pan-* means "all"; *-gaea* means "earth"; both are from ancient Greek.)

**Section Objectives**
For a list of section objectives, see the Student Edition page.

**Skills Objectives**
Students should be able to:

**Observe** the shapes of continents.

**Reason by Analogy** how scientists criticized Wegener's theory.

**Predict** how the Atlantic Ocean will change in size in 50 million years.

**Make a Model** of Pangaea.

**Vocabulary**
Pangaea

## 5.1 Drifting Continents

### Objectives

▶ **Describe** how the continents moved over the past 250 million years.

▶ **Explain** the evidence supporting continental drift.

▶ **Make a model** of the supercontinent Pangaea.

▼ **ACTIVITY**

**Observing**

*A Puzzling World*

Look at a globe or map of the world. Study the shapes of the continents closely. What do you notice about the shapes of the continents on opposite sides of the Atlantic Ocean?

**SKILLS WARMUP**

**MOTIVATE**

### Skills WarmUp

To help students understand continental drift, have them do the Skills WarmUp.

**Answer** Students should see that facing coastlines on opposite sides of the Atlantic Ocean have contours that roughly match up like puzzle pieces.

Hundreds of years ago, the first accurate maps were made of the continents on both sides of the Atlantic Ocean. Many people who looked at the maps noticed something interesting about the shapes of the continents. It seemed as if Africa and South America could fit together like pieces of a jigsaw puzzle. The coastlines of Europe and North America made a good match, too, if Greenland filled a gap between them.

This observation suggested that the continents on either side of the Atlantic Ocean were once joined. Few people, however, took the idea seriously. How could the continents have moved? They were solid rock! Yet a few scientists dared to suggest that this movement, or continental drift, had actually happened.

### Prior Knowledge

To gauge how much students know about continental drift, ask the following questions:

▶ What kinds of movement occur in the earth's crust?

▶ Why are the continents shaped the way they are?

▶ Why are so many of the same animals found on both sides of the Atlantic Ocean?

**Answer to In-Text Question**

① **Judging from their shapes, the landmasses look like they were once joined.**

### Theory of Continental Drift

During the 1800s, scientists studying rocks and fossils found bits of evidence that seemed to support the idea of moving continents. In the early 1900s, Alfred Wegener, a German meteorologist, collected all this evidence and made observations of his own. In 1912, he proposed the first complete, scientific theory of continental drift. He claimed that all the world's landmasses had once been joined in a giant supercontinent he called **Pangaea** (pan JEE uh).

For many years, most scientists rejected Wegener's theory. But in the 1950s, scientific ideas about the structure of the earth's crust began to change completely. Because of new discoveries, continental drift began to seem possible. Scientists soon agreed that the continents had moved as Wegener proposed.

**Figure 5.1** ▲
Do you think that the two landmasses shown here were connected at one time? ①

## TEACH

### Class Activity

Glue or mount a large map of the world on posterboard. Have students cut out individual continents. Then have volunteers move the pieces to model the process of continental drift. Ask students what type of information might help to determine if they placed the continents correctly.

### Explore Visually

Have students read the text and study Figure 5.2. Ask the following questions:

▶ What two landmasses formed during the break up of Pangaea? (Gondwanaland and Laurasia)

▶ What landmass did India belong to? What happened to this landmass? (Gondwanaland; it drifted into Laurasia.)

▶ Which of the continents present today were once part of Laurasia? (North America, Europe, and Asia)

**Answers to In-Text Questions**

① The continents have continued to drift to their current locations.

② Yes. Continental drift continues at a very gradual pace.

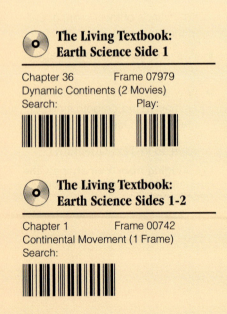

**The Living Textbook: Earth Science Side 1**

Chapter 36          Frame 07979
Dynamic Continents (2 Movies)
Search:               Play:

**The Living Textbook: Earth Science Sides 1-2**

Chapter 1          Frame 00742
Continental Movement (1 Frame)
Search:

### Integrating the Sciences

**Life Science** Ask students for ideas about how the breakup of Pangaea into separate continents might have affected organisms living on land. You may wish to record these ideas on the chalkboard, and students can add them to their portfolios for later reference.

### Geography Connection

Point out that, when the landmasses we call India and Asia met, the earth's tallest mountains, the Himalayas, were created. Show their location on the map on page 103. Ask students why the coming together of two continents might produce mountains. (The forces produced by the meeting of landmasses is tremendous.)

**Use Integrating Worksheet 5.1.**

### The Breakup of Pangaea

From years of study, scientists collected large amounts of data on how the continents moved. From this information, they pieced together a history of the continents. They now have a good idea of how Pangaea split up and how the parts became the present-day continents. The maps you see in Figure 5.2 show how the earth's landmasses changed over the last 250 million years.

Pangaea began to break apart across its middle during the Mesozoic Era, about 200 million years ago. Two major continents formed: a southern continent called Gondwanaland (gahnd WAH nuh LAND) and a northern continent called Laurasia (lawr AY zhuh).

About 135 million years ago, Gondwanaland began to break up into smaller pieces that would become Africa, South America, Antarctica, India, and Australia. By about 40 million years ago, Laurasia had broken apart, forming landmasses that would become North America, Europe, and most of Asia. A little later, India, which was drifting north for 100 million years, finally collided with Asia. How have the earth's continents changed since then? Do you think they will change ① in the future? ②

**Figure 5.2 Stages in Continental Drift** ▼

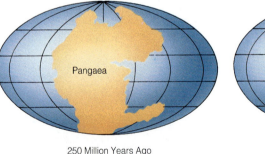

250 Million Years Ago

Laurasia

Gondwanaland

200 Million Years Ago

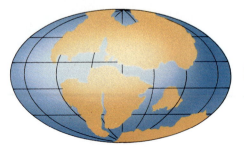

135 Million Years Ago

40 Million Years Ago

## Integrating the Sciences

**Physical Science** To perceive an object in motion, a stationary object serves as a reference point. Have students discuss how scientists can know that continents moved on the earth's surface if movement is measured in relation to an object that doesn't move.

**Life Science** Discuss the different ways that organisms are dispersed, or spread, over a large area of land or water. Ask students for examples. (Some animals migrate; seeds are dispersed by wind, water, and animals.)

## Evidence for Continental Drift

Why are scientists now sure that the continents moved over time? They collected much evidence supporting two related conclusions:

▶ Continents now separated by wide oceans were once joined.

▶ Since the Mesozoic Era, each continent's location on the earth's surface changed.

**Fossil Evidence** Scientists know that a new kind of organism, or species, appears on the earth only in one area and then spreads outward. Animals that swim and plants with windblown seeds can spread across an ocean. Many other living things, however, can only spread across land.

Paleontologists found fossils of an ancient fernlike plant called *Glossopteris* in South America, Africa, India, Australia, and Antarctica. The seeds of *Glossopteris* are too heavy to have blown across oceans by wind. Scientists infer from this evidence that all these continents were connected at one time.

Fossils of several other species have the same pattern, as you can see in Figure 5.3. None of these organisms could spread across an ocean. So how did the organisms end up on different continents? They must have lived on one large continent that later broke up.

Fossil evidence also shows that the continents moved over the earth's surface. Antarctica now lies at the South Pole, covered with ice. But fossils found there show that it once supported vast green swamps and forests full of plant and animal life. This evidence suggests that Antarctica was once much closer to the equator.

**Figure 5.3  Fossil Evidence for Continental Drift** ▼

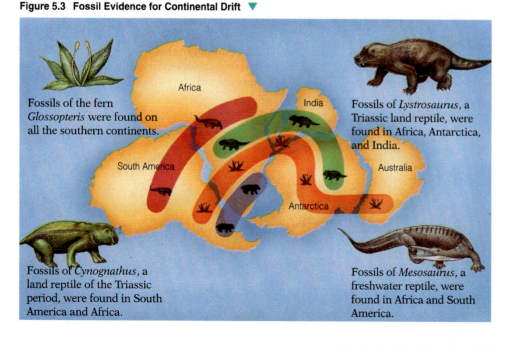

Fossils of the fern *Glossopteris* were found on all the southern continents.

Fossils of *Lystrosaurus*, a Triassic land reptile, were found in Africa, Antarctica, and India.

Fossils of *Cynognathus*, a land reptile of the Triassic period, were found in South America and Africa.

Fossils of *Mesosaurus*, a freshwater reptile, were found in Africa and South America.

## Critical Thinking

**If . . . Then Statements** Have students make an *If . . . Then* chart of the information contained in the text and in Figure 5.3. Help them recognize that the best *If . . . Then* statements are those for which there is scientific evidence. Have them supply any evidence needed for their *If . . . Then* statements. To get them started, you may wish to supply one or two entries such as:

▶ If *Mesosaurus* fossils are in South America and Africa, *then Mesosaurus* must have lived in these places.

▶ If *Mesosaurus* is a freshwater reptile, *then* it probably could not have migrated across an ocean.

After they complete the chart, have students supply the *If . . . Then* statement for the following: *. . . then the continents were joined.*

## Discuss

Have students use a map and the fossil evidence of *Glossopteris* locations to explore the idea that Antarctica was once closer to the equator. Ask them to explain how the movement of this landmass can support the argument that all the continents were once joined. (The living plant required an equatorial climate, and Antarctica's shape provides potential tectonic junctures for India, Africa, Australia, and South America.)

## Critical Thinking

**Reason and Conclude** Have students list the rock evidence that scientists use to support the hypothesis that South America and Africa were once a single continent. Ask them to discuss whether the evidence can support the idea that all the continents were once joined. Have them explain their reasoning.

## Directed Inquiry

Have students read the text and study Figure 5.4. Ask the following questions:

▶ In what kind of climate would you expect to find glaciers? (Cold)

▶ If you found evidence of glaciers in areas that have warm climates, what would you conclude? (That the climate was colder at some time in the past)

▶ How does evidence of glacier movement support the idea of a single landmass? (Glaciers move toward oceans. With the continents in their present positions, the glaciers would have moved away from oceans. For the ancient glaciers to have moved toward oceans, the continents must have fit together into a single landmass.)

**Answer to Link**

Students should be able to explain how they determined dispersal methods.

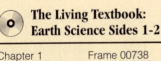
**The Living Textbook:
Earth Science Sides 1-2**

Chapter 1          Frame 00738
Rock/Glacial Evidence (2 Frames)
Search:          Step:

## *Themes in Science*

**Scale and Structure** Some of the evidence used to determine the movement of very large landmasses came from the observations of smaller structures in the land. Similarities in rock types and glacial erosion of rocks are evidence of the movement of continents.

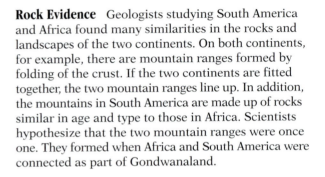
### Life Science
### L I N K

Plant seeds can be dispersed to different areas by the wind or by animals. Some seeds float on water.

Collect samples of five different types of seeds, such as dandelion, maple, cocklebur, annual bluegrass, and acorns.

For each of your seed samples, try different methods of seed dispersal. Determine which method best disperses each seed sample.

In a data table, list the seeds you used and their methods of dispersal.

### A C T I V I T Y

**Figure 5.4**
Present-day evidence for glacial movement is shown on the left. The hypothesized position of the continents during the time of glaciation is shown on the right. ▼

**Rock Evidence** Geologists studying South America and Africa found many similarities in the rocks and landscapes of the two continents. On both continents, for example, there are mountain ranges formed by folding of the crust. If the two continents are fitted together, the two mountain ranges line up. In addition, the mountains in South America are made up of rocks similar in age and type to those in Africa. Scientists hypothesize that the two mountain ranges were once one. They formed when Africa and South America were connected as part of Gondwanaland.

**Evidence from Ancient Glaciers** Glaciers are huge masses of ice that move slowly over land. During the ice ages, glaciers spread outward from the poles. Rocks found in parts of South America, Africa, India, and Australia all show evidence of glaciers at the end of the Paleozoic Era. For these places to have glaciers, they had to be closer to the South Pole.

The rocks also show the direction in which the glaciers traveled. These directions are shown by arrows in Figure 5.4. You can see that in most cases the ice-age glaciers moved away from present-day oceans. This doesn't make sense because glaciers always move toward oceans. The movement of the ice-age glaciers could be explained, however, if Africa, South America, India, Australia, and Antarctica were all part of the same landmass when the glaciers existed. Figure 5.4 shows how the glaciers spread outward on Gondwanaland.

## STS Connection

Have students discuss why a new scientific theory might cause controversy among more than just scientists. Some examples for discussion include biological evolution, the Gaia principle, the probability of life on other planets (SETI), and the theory of relativity.

### Science and Society  *Accepting New Ideas*

In 1923, Alfred Wegener traveled to the United States to present his theory of continental drift to other scientists. Most of the people who heard his talks refused to accept his ideas. In fact, many scientists thought he was crazy! One earth scientist exclaimed, "Wegener. . . is blind to every fact and argument."

Why did scientists react this way? It was probably because Wegener's ideas were not only new, they were upsetting. At that time, the idea that the continents were solidly anchored in the earth's crust was very important. Much of the knowledge scientists had about the earth was understood in terms of this idea. If the continents had drifted, it meant that many facts had to be questioned and many theories thrown out. Accepting the idea of continental drift was something like believing that space aliens control the earth!

Most scientists, therefore, did not look at Wegener's evidence objectively. They had already decided that the continents could not move. They rejected any evidence that suggested otherwise.

Many other scientists have had experiences similar to Wegener's. The astronomer Copernicus, for example, proposed in 1543 that the sun was the center of the solar system. Scientists at that time believed the planets and sun revolved around the earth. They refused to consider the evidence and reasoning behind Copernicus' theory. The theory contradicted much of what they believed to be true about the universe. Only with time was Copernicus proved correct.

### Check and Explain

1. Which present-day continents or pieces of continents were once part of Gondwanaland?

2. List two types of evidence that support the idea of continental drift.

3. **Predict**  What will happen to the size of the Atlantic Ocean during the next 50 million years?

4. **Make a Model**  Paste a map of the world on heavy paper. Cut out the landmasses and fit them together to form the supercontinent Pangaea.

## ▼ ACTIVITY

### Reasoning by Analogy

*Is It True?*

Recall a time when someone told you that something you believed to be true, wasn't really true. How did you react? How was your reaction similar to the way scientists reacted to Wegener's theory?

**SKILLS WORKOUT**

### Enrich

Have students make a list of once hard-to-prove claims that are now accepted as scientific facts, such as the shape of the earth. Have the class compile a list of these facts. You may wish to post the list on newsprint or the chalkboard.

### Skills WorkOut

To help students understand the acceptance of new scientific theories, have them do the Skills WorkOut.
**Answer**  Answers will vary. Students may offer examples of a favorite team losing a game. Some may indicate that they checked the news reports or asked other fans if the reports were true.

## EVALUATE

### WrapUp

**Portfolio**  Ask students to draw two outline maps. One should show the continents joined in a single landmass shaped like Pangaea; the second, the continents as they were 40 million years ago. Have students choose three pieces of evidence and place them in position on the Pangaea outline and then on the multicontinent outline. Have them write a caption explaining how the evidence supports Wegener's continental drift theory. Students can keep the maps in their portfolios.
Use Review Worksheet 5.1.

### Check and Explain

1. Africa, South America, Antarctica, India, and Australia

2. Answers will vary but should include two of the following: fossils, rocks, mountain ranges, glaciers.

3. It will increase.

4. Check students' models for accuracy.

## Section Objectives
For a list of section objectives, see the Student Edition page.

## Skills Objectives
Students should be able to:

**Define Operationally** the meaning of *plate tectonics*.

**Interpret Data** of magnetic patterns on the ocean floor.

**Make a Model** of an oceanic plate and a continental plate.

**Infer** the kind of plate boundary located near Japan.

**Make a Model** of a divergent plate boundary.

## Vocabulary
divergent boundary, subduction, sea-floor spreading, convergent boundary, trench, plate tectonics, transform boundary

---

## MOTIVATE

### Skills WarmUp
To help students understand the theory of plate tectonics, have them do the Skills WarmUp.
**Answer** Answers will vary slightly based on the definitions found. Students might suggest, "Having to do with how pieces of the earth's crust deform," based on the definitions "flat, thin piece of material" (plate) and "relating to the deformation of a geologic crust" (tectonic).

## Misconceptions
Students may think that the crustal plates are under landmasses only and that they are the same shape as the continents. Explain that the earth's entire crust is divided into plates. Both the continents and oceans "ride" on tectonic plates.

96

---

### *Themes in Science*
**Patterns of Change/Cycles**
Patterns of change on the earth's surface are the result of the overall structure of the earth's crust and its dynamic processes.

### *STS Connection*
Sonar was originally developed during World War II to detect enemy submarines. Use this as an example to show students how technological innovations are important spinoffs for solving problems. You may also wish to discuss how technological advances, such as ultrasound, have benefitted the field of medicine.

---

▼ **ACTIVITY**

**Defining Operationally**

*Moving Plates*

Use a dictionary to find the meaning of the words *plate* and *tectonic*. Based on the definitions, explain what you think the two words mean together. What do you think the theory of plate tectonics is about? Do you think using a dictionary is enough to get a good idea about the theory of plate tectonics?

**SKILLS WARMUP**

---

# 5.2 Theory of Plate Tectonics

## Objectives

▶ **Describe** the process of sea-floor spreading.

▶ **Identify** different types of plate boundaries.

▶ **Explain** what happens where plates come together.

▶ **Infer** from observation of a large surface feature what kind of plate boundary process produced it.

---

Have you ever wondered what lies at the bottom of the ocean? Imagine what you would see if you could travel into the cold, dark depths of the ocean in a submarine and shine lights on the bottom. Would it be flat? Or would it have valleys and mountains like the continents?

Until the 1950s, scientists could only guess about the deep ocean bottom. It was impossible to explore and map this large part of the earth's crust. To understand the crust's structure, they had to rely on their knowledge of continents. They didn't know that the key to understanding continental drift lay on the ocean floor.

## Ocean-Floor Discoveries

In the 1950s, scientists finally had the tools they needed to learn about the ocean floor. One of the most important tools was sonar. Sonar devices bounced sound waves off the ocean bottom, providing scientists with data about its topography.

Scientists used sonar and other tools to make the first reliable maps of the ocean floor. They discovered long underwater mountain ranges. These ranges formed one long ridge snaking through all the oceans like the seams of a baseball. This mid-ocean ridge had one remarkable feature: a deep valley running the length of its crest.

Scientists found that the rocks of the ocean bottom were very young compared to rocks in the continents. They also discovered that the rocks were youngest near the mid-ocean ridge. Scientists puzzled over this new information.

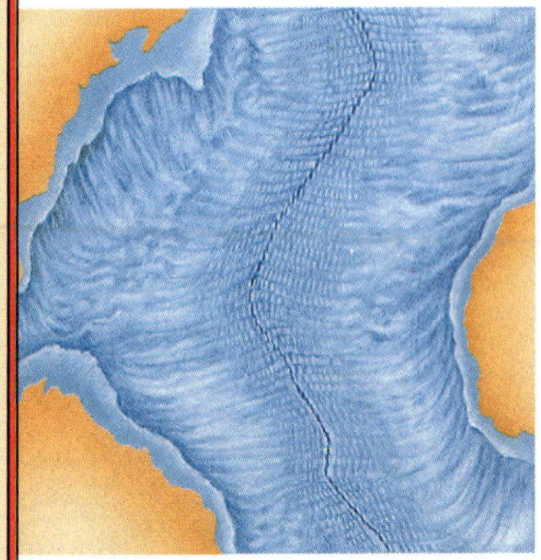

**Figure 5.5** ▲
Discovery of the mid-ocean ridge helped scientists understand continental drift.

## Integrating the Sciences

**Physical Science** In certain material, such as iron, cobalt, and nickel, the magnetic field of each individual atom causes the atoms in the materials to group together. The poles of the individual atoms line up and group together in magnetic regions called *magnetic domains*. When all of the magnetic domains are lined up in an iron bar, the bar becomes a permanent magnet.
    **Use Integrating Worksheet 5.2.**

### Sea-Floor Spreading

In 1960, American geologist Harry Hess proposed the theory of **sea-floor spreading** to explain these discoveries about the ocean floor. He claimed that the mid-ocean ridge was a huge crack in the crust where the hot mantle pushed upward. The pieces of crust on each side of the crack were moving slowly away from each other. As they moved, molten rock from the mantle welled up between them, forming new ocean crust. This spreading process is shown in Figure 5.6.

At the same time, old ocean crust was being swallowed up in deep ocean trenches. In this way, the total amount of oceanic crust stayed the same. The ocean bottoms were remade every 300 million years or so.

Other scientists soon provided convincing evidence for Hess' theory. They sampled rocks on both sides of the mid-ocean ridge. They found a pattern of parallel magnetic "stripes" that was identical on each side. This striping pattern is shown in Figure 5.7. The stripes were formed when the earth's magnetic field caused mineral crystals in rocks to line up in a certain way when the rock was still young and not yet solid. The stripes were different because the earth's magnetic field reversed itself many times in the past. The stripes showed that new ocean crust was being added to both sides of the mid-ocean ridge at the same rate.

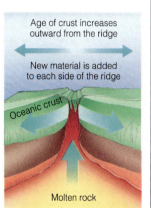

**Figure 5.6 ▲**
New crust is produced at the mid-ocean ridge.

**Figure 5.7**
When new rock is formed at the mid-ocean ridge, it is affected by the polarity of the earth's magnetic field at that time. The resulting patterns are evidence for sea-floor spreading. ▼

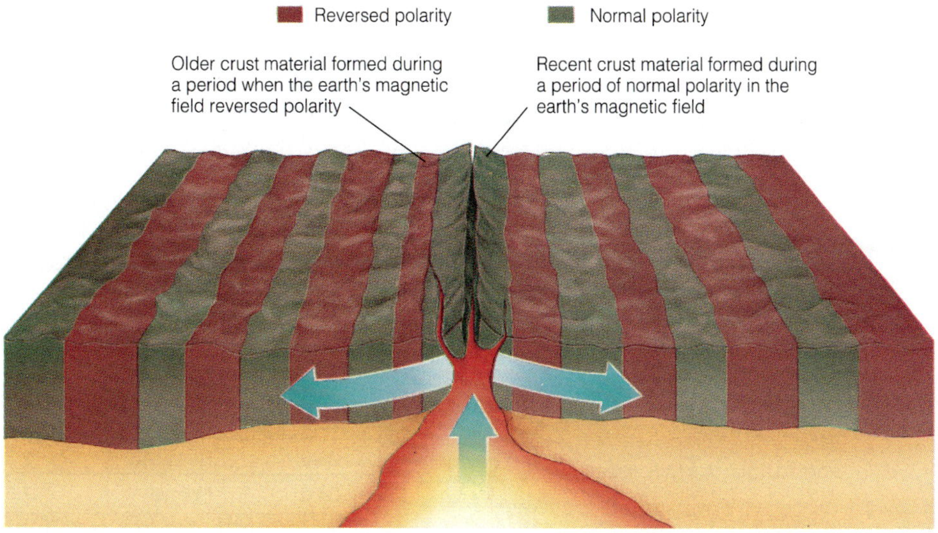

■ Reversed polarity     ■ Normal polarity

Older crust material formed during a period when the earth's magnetic field reversed polarity

Recent crust material formed during a period of normal polarity in the earth's magnetic field

### Direct Inquiry

Have students study the text and Figures 5.6 and 5.7. Ask the following questions:

▶ Where are the youngest rocks of oceanic crust? (Nearest the mid-ocean ridges)

▶ Why are there magnetic "stripes" on the ocean floor? (The stripes are a result of mineral crystals in rocks being affected by the earth's magnetic field as the rock cooled and hardened. Because the direction of the earth's magnetic field changes periodically, the direction of the crystals changes as well.)

### Critical Thinking

**Reason and Conclude** Point out that new ocean crust is continuously forming, yet the total amount of oceanic crust does not change. Ask students to explain how the amount of crust remains constant. (Older ocean crust is consumed in ocean trenches.)

**The Living Textbook:
Earth Science Sides 1-2**

Chapter 1          Frame 00744
Sea-Floor Spreading (2 Frames)
Search:            Step:

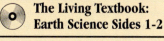

## TEACH ▪ *Continued*

### Directed Inquiry

Ask students to describe how sea-floor spreading and the theory of continental drift are related. Use the following questions:

▶ How did the theory of sea-floor spreading change researchers' model of the continental crust? (The theory allowed for new crust to be created and old crust to be recycled, which meant that the crust had to move constantly. Scientists developed the theory of plate tectonics from this new data about the crust's movement.)

▶ How do the two theories support each other? (Plate tectonics provides a model for the structure and movement of crustal plates. Sea-floor spreading explains how the plates move.)

### *SkillBuilder*

**Interpret Data** Students' scale models may vary but should resemble Figure 5.7.

1. The average should be about 13 km per million years.

2. 1.3 cm/year

3. 2,500 km ÷ (13 km) × $10^6$ year = about 190 million years.
   Reports should point out that the crystals in cooling rocks align with the earth's magnetic field. The sea-floor rocks have regular bands of reversed polarity showing that new material was added to the sea floor, which implies movement and supports plate tectonic theory.

**The Living Textbook: Earth Science Side 1**

Chapter 38         Frame 21568
Plate Tectonics (Movie)
Search:              Play:

---

### *Language Arts Connection*

The word *tectonics* is derived from the Greek word *tektonikos*, which means "a carpenter or builder." Share the original meaning of this word with your students. Discuss with your students how this word may have become used as a geologic term.

### Tectonic Plates

Sea-floor spreading was the missing piece of information scientists needed to accept the theory of continental drift. It provided a way for pieces of the crust to move. With this new knowledge, scientists had to develop a new model of the structure of the earth's crust.

The new model that arose came to be known as the theory of **plate tectonics** (tehk TAHN iks). According to the theory, the entire lithosphere of the earth is divided into pieces called plates. The plates are constantly moving, each at a different rate and direction. Because the plates are parts of the lithosphere, they are often called lithospheric plates.

Recall that the earth's lithosphere is a cool, rigid layer about 100 km thick on average. It sits atop the asthenosphere, a hot layer of partially molten rock. A lithospheric plate moves as a unit, "floating" on top of the asthenosphere like a flat rock on wet cement.

### *SkillBuilder* *Interpreting Data*

#### *Magnetic Patterns on the Ocean Floor*

Using the data in the table, make a scale map of magnetic striping on the ocean floor. Place the mid-ocean ridge in the center of the map at distance zero. On each side of the ridge, make a scale in kilometers. Then color in areas where you think the rocks will show normal magnetic alignment and reversed magnetic alignment. Remember that each side of the ridge has the same pattern.

Now use the data to calculate the rate at which the ocean floor spreads. The formula for this is

$$rate = \frac{distance}{time}$$

From the table, choose four measurements. Calculate the rate of spread in km/million years for each. Record each number. Average these four values.

1. What is the average rate of ocean-floor spreading at this mid-ocean ridge?

2. Convert your average rate to cm/year.

3. The distance from a point on the coast of Africa to the mid-ocean ridge is 2,500 km. How long ago was that point at the ridge?

Write a report explaining how magnetic polarity on the ocean floor supports the plate tectonic theory.

| Distance from Ridge (km) | Magnetic Polarity | Age (millions of years) |
|---|---|---|
| 6.5 | Normal | 0.5 |
| 7.7 | Normal | 0.6 |
| 10.0 | Reversed | 0.8 |
| 20.5 | Reversed | 1.6 |
| 24.5 | Normal | 1.9 |
| 28.5 | Reversed | 2.2 |
| 29.6 | Reversed | 2.3 |
| 34.0 | Normal | 2.6 |

## Integrating the Sciences

**Physical Science** Have students explore flotation. The principle of flotation states that floating objects displace the weight of fluid equal to their own weight. Have students try to float a ball of clay. Ask students how they might make the ball of clay float. Students should discover that the clay will float if it is flattened, because the flattened clay displaces a greater volume of water than the ball of clay. When the weight of the displaced water equals the weight of the object, the object will no longer sink into the water. It will float.

## The Structure of Plates

Each lithospheric plate is made up of both crust and mantle. However, there are two different kinds of crust: oceanic and continental. Oceanic crust material is mainly made up of two types of rock: basalt and gabbro. Continental crust is less dense, made up mainly of granite and rhyolite. The earth's lithospheric plates can be classified according to the kinds of crust they contain.

**Continental Plates** The earth has seven major plates, six of which are continental plates. Continental plates carry mostly continental crust material and consist of one continent and a large section of oceanic crust. In the bottom part of Figure 5.8 you can see a diagram of a typical continental plate.

The continental crust material of a continental plate can be in the center of a plate or at one side. Some continental plate edges, therefore, have both oceanic and continental crust. This kind of edge interacts with other plates differently than an edge made up of oceanic crust alone.

**Oceanic Plates** One major plate and several smaller ones are oceanic plates. They contain little or no continental crust material. They are made up entirely of oceanic crust, as you can see in Figure 5.8.

▼ **ACTIVITY**

### Making a Model

*A Mountain of Plates*

Use sheets of foam, corrugated cardboard, clay, or other materials to make models of an oceanic plate and a continental plate. How does your model distinguish among the different layers making up each plate? If you use a combination of materials, explain why your materials are appropriate for the layers they represent.

**SKILLS WORKOUT**

Oceanic crust

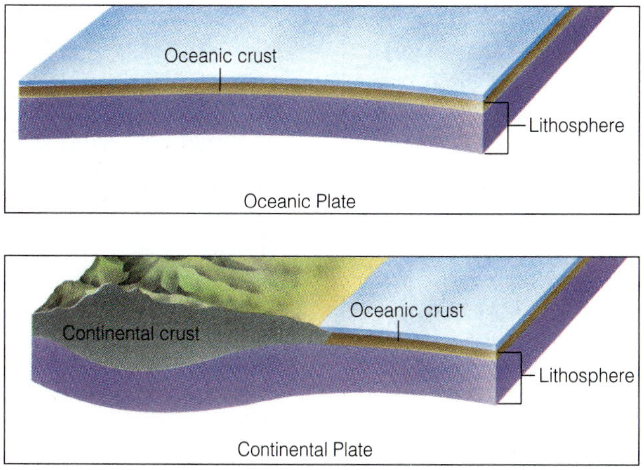

Lithosphere

Oceanic Plate

Continental crust

Oceanic crust

Lithosphere

Continental Plate

◀ **Figure 5.8**
What is the difference between the two types of tectonic plates? ①

## Skills WorkOut

To help students understand the structure of the oceanic and continental plates, have them do the Skills WorkOut.

**Answer** Models will vary. However, there should be little or no continental plate materials in the model representing the oceanic plate.

## Skills Development

**Organize Data** Have students study the text and Figure 5.8. On the chalkboard, have the class make a table showing the differences between the two kinds of plates. (*Oceanic plate:* oceanic crust; edges of oceanic crust; one large plate, several smaller. *Continental plate:* continental and oceanic crust; edges of both; six major plates) Remind them that the type and amount of crust materials, and type of boundary or edge may distinguish one type of plate from another.

### Answer to In-Text Question

① **Oceanic plates carry oceanic crust made of basalt and gabbro and contain little to no continental crust materials. Continental plates carry the less dense continental crust made of granite and rhyolite.**

**The Living Textbook: Earth Science Sides 1-2**

Chapter 1        Frame 00725
Major Plates (1 Frame)
Search:

## TEACH ▪ *Continued*

### Class Activity

Have students study the text and illustrations on the page. Then ask them to slide two large books, such as telephone books, along a table. Ask them to move the books past each other on the table. Ask the class to tell which motion is being modeled. (Transform boundary) Have student volunteers suggest how to move the books to model convergent and divergent boundaries as well.

### *Portfolio*

Have students make drawings of divergent, convergent, and transform boundaries. Have them list characteristics of each under the appropriate drawing. Students might also add memory cues to help them remember the characteristics of these boundaries. For instance, they might take a *mid-ocean dive*. Students can keep the drawings in their portfolios.

### *Cooperative Learning*

Have students work in cooperative groups of three or four to model the different types of plate boundaries. Use pieces of foam cut into rectangles or blocks of wood to represent the two lithospheric plates.

**The Living Textbook:**
**Earth Science Sides 1-2**

Chapter 1          Frame 00726
Plate Margins (1 Frame)
Search:

---

## Plate Boundaries

What happens where plates meet? Three kinds of interactions are possible at plate boundaries. Plates can move away from each other, they can collide, and they can slide past each other. To picture the interaction of plates, imagine yourself riding in a bumper car at the amusement park. You may collide with other cars in front and move away from cars behind you. And you may slide past or be bumped by cars on the side. What actually happens is determined not just by how you move, but by how all the other cars move too. The earth's lithospheric plates interact in a similar way, except that each plate is always in contact with other plates on all of its sides. Most plates have all three types of boundaries around them.

### Divergent Boundaries

Any boundary where plates move away from each other is called a **divergent boundary**. These are places where new crust is being created. The mid-ocean ridges are all divergent boundaries. Divergent boundaries also occur in continents, where they signal the beginning of the continent's breakup. ▼

### Convergent Boundaries ▲

A boundary where two plates come together, or collide, is called a **convergent boundary**. At most convergent boundaries, one plate moves under another, and crust material is destroyed. Convergent boundaries produce many different kinds of features on the surface of the earth.

### Transform Boundaries

At the third type of boundary, two plates slide in opposite directions beside each other. Such a boundary is called a **transform boundary**. Crustal material is not created or destroyed along a transform boundary. The break or crack along which movement occurs is called a transform fault. ▼

## Themes in Science

**Systems and Interactions** The earth's crust is composed of a system of different plates that float upon the surface. The types of interaction at these plates varies. Different types of interactions result in different formations on the earth's surface.

## Convergent Boundaries

The collision of two plates releases huge amounts of energy. This energy causes many important geologic processes to take place at and near convergent boundaries. These processes include volcanic activity and mountain building. What occurs at a particular convergent boundary is determined by the kinds of plates that meet there. Three kinds of convergent boundaries exist.

**Oceanic-Oceanic** Where two oceanic plates meet, one plate is pushed down under the other. This process of one plate moving under another is called **subduction** (suhb DUHK shuhn). It takes place in what is called a subduction zone.

As you can see in Figure 5.9, the lower, or subducting plate, descends into the asthenosphere. There it melts and is absorbed into the mantle. The melting of the subducting plate causes molten rock to rise up through the other plate. Volcanoes form on the ocean bottom and build a chain, or arc, of volcanic islands. As the subducting plate sinks into the earth, it also creates a deep ocean valley, or **trench**. Trenches are the deepest parts of the ocean.

**Oceanic-Continental** Subduction also occurs where an oceanic plate meets a plate with continental crust material. Because the oceanic plate is denser, it is always subducted under the continental plate. The oceanic plate melts in the asthenosphere, causing molten rock to rise up through the continental plate. A mountain range forms, usually containing volcanoes.

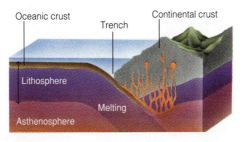

**Figure 5.10** ▲
An oceanic plate is subducted under a less-dense continental plate.

**Continental-Continental** A third and very different process occurs where two continental plates collide. Because both are thick and have similar densities, neither can move under the other. Instead, they compress and buckle each other, forming tall mountains. The plates become joined in a single continental block.

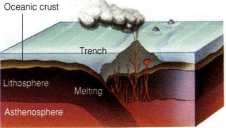

**Figure 5.9** ▲
Where two oceanic plates converge, one is subducted under the other.

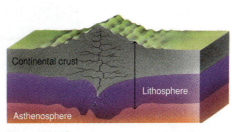

**Figure 5.11** ▲
Where two continental plates converge, both buckle, producing a mountain range.

## Explore Visually

Have students study the text and Figures 5.9, 5.10, and 5.11 and answer the following questions:

► Where does a trench form? What kind of boundaries are involved? (At a subduction zone, an oceanic plate moves under another oceanic plate or continental plate, melts, and is absorbed into the mantle. As the plate sinks, a trench forms.)

► How do volcanoes form at an oceanic-continental boundary? (A dense oceanic plate subducts under a continental plate; the materials in the oceanic plate melt, then rise up through the continental plate and form volcanoes.)

► What happens at a continental-continental plate boundary? (Tall mountains are formed by colliding continental plates. Neither one can move under the other because both are thick and have similar densities. Instead they push against each other and buckle upward.)

## Skills Development

**Classify** List the three kinds of convergent boundaries on the chalkboard. Ask students to classify the following characteristics as either oceanic-oceanic, oceanic-continental, or continental-continental:

► mountains and volcanoes made by subduction (O-C, O-O)

► trench formed by subduction (O-O, O-C)

► mountains formed by compression and buckling (C-C)

**The Living Textbook:
Earth Science Sides 1-2**

Chapter 1          Frame 00728
Convergent Boundaries (4 Frames)
Search:                    Step:

102

## TEACH ▪ Continued

### Explore Visually

Ask students to study Figure 5.12 and its captions. Ask the following questions:

▶ Where is the longest continuous divergent boundary? What takes place at that boundary? (Along the middle of the Atlantic ocean; new crust is being created and the sea floor is spreading.)

▶ At what type of boundary do the Nazca and South American plates meet? (Convergent boundary)

▶ What new divergent boundary is gradually splitting Africa in two? (Great Rift Valley)

▶ Which plate is entirely under water? (Nazca plate)

▶ What two plates collided to form the Himalayas? (Eurasian plate and the Indian-Australian plate)

▶ What transform boundary is on land? What events does it cause? (San Andreas Fault; earthquakes)

### Ancillary Options

If you are using the blackline masters from *Measuring Earthquakes,* have students do Activity 5, *Damaging Earthquakes in the Pacific Northwest,* pages 55–67.

### Writing Connection

Have each student write a paragraph describing one of the places shown on these two pages. Ask them to focus on creating a word picture for someone who cannot see the photograph. Have student volunteers read their descriptions to see if the class can choose the photograph being described.

## Plate Geography

The movement and location of plates helps explain many of the earth's features. Movement at plate boundaries creates mountain ranges, forms ocean basins, makes continents grow, and splits them apart. It causes earthquakes and volcanoes. The earth's tectonic plates and the boundaries between them are shown below.

**Figure 5.12 ▶**
**Tectonic Plates of the Earth**

The volcanic activity at the convergent boundary of a continental plate and an oceanic plate produced the Aleutian Islands of Alaska.

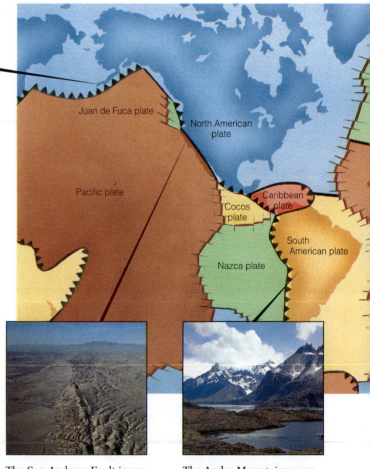

**Key**

Divergent plate boundaries

Convergent plate boundaries

Transform plate boundaries

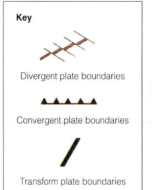

The San Andreas Fault is one of the few transform boundaries on land. Its movement causes severe earthquakes.

The Andes Mountains were built as a result of the Nazca plate subducting under the South American plate.

## Plate Movement

The very slow movements of the plates are detected and measured by certain instruments. Scientists have determined the speed and direction of most of the earth's plates. They used this information to reconstruct the locations of the plates in the past and to predict their locations in the future.

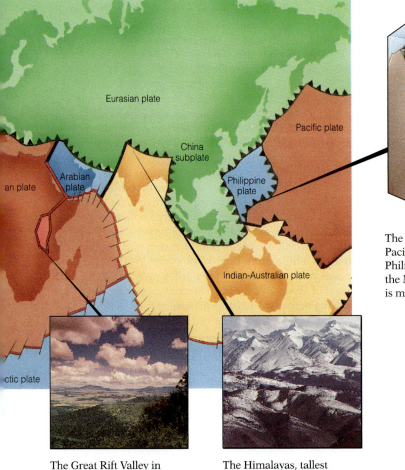

The subduction of the Pacific plate under the Philippine plate created the Mariana Trench, which is more than 11 km deep.

The Great Rift Valley in Africa is a fairly new divergent boundary beginning to split Africa in two.

The Himalayas, tallest mountains on earth, are the result of two continental plates colliding.

TEACH ▪ Continued

## Discuss

Have students explain how stars are helping scientists measure continental drift. (VLBI measurements rely on signals from distant stars. By timing signals reaching two distant earth stations, researchers can determine precisely how far apart the stations are at different times, and, therefore, how fast the plates beneath the stations are moving.)

## EVALUATE

### WrapUp

**Reteach**  Have students prepare a table of terms and definitions that are important to plate tectonics. They should include the following: *convergent boundary, transform boundary, divergent boundary; earthquakes, mountains, volcanoes; subduction; oceanic plate, continental plate.*
Use Review Worksheet 5.2.

### Check and Explain

1. Oceanic plates move apart; molten rock flows in between them and forms new crust.

2. Divergent: spread apart, new crust forms, any mid-ocean ridge; transform: slide past, cause earthquakes, San Andreas Fault; convergent: plates collide and buckle, the Himalayas.

3. Both are at plate boundaries and are hidden under the ocean. Mid-ocean ridges are divergent and are places where new crust is formed; subduction zones are convergent and are places where old crust is consumed.

4. Convergent; one plate subducts the other, it melts, and rising molten rock forms a chain of volcanic islands.

### Math Connection

Encourage students to do several rate problems in order to give them a better idea of the time scale involved in plate movement. Example: At the rate of 1 cm/year, how many years would it take for North America and Europe to move 1 km farther apart? (About 100,000 years)

**Figure 5.13** ▲
Radio telescopes collect data that are used to measure plate movement.

### Science and Technology
*Measuring Plate Movement*

From the time that Alfred Wegener proposed his theory of continental drift, scientists have searched for new and better ways to find out about movement of the earth's crust. You may be surprised to know that some of the most useful data about this movement was collected with the help of signals from deep in space.

Today scientists can use a technique known as VLBI to make very precise measurements of the earth's shape and the motion of its plates. VLBI stands for very long baseline interferometry. This technique uses radio signals from distant stars, known as quasars, to help scientists make their measurements.

To make VLBI measurements, two stations far apart on the earth's surface receive signals from the same quasar. Using very precise atomic clocks, scientists compare the signals. The tiny differences from when the signals are received are converted into a precise measurement of the distance between the stations. By making these measurements at different times, very small changes in the distance can be determined.

VLBI measurements helped confirm plate tectonics theory. Using VLBI, scientists observed plate motion of 11 cm a year between Hawaii and Japan. They found that the North American and Eurasian plates move apart at a little more than 1 cm a year. While these distances may seem insignificant, they provide the final proof of Wegener's theory. The continents are, indeed, drifting across the earth's surface.

### Check and Explain

1. What happens during sea-floor spreading?

2. Describe the three types of plate boundaries, and give an example of each.

3. **Compare and Contrast**  Explain how mid-ocean ridges and subduction zones are similar. How are they different?

4. **Infer**  Japan is made up of a long chain of islands formed from volcanoes. What kind of plate boundary do you think is nearby? Why?

### Prelab Discussion

Have students read the entire activity. Discuss these points before beginning:

▶ Discuss the use of models by scientists and the fact that all models have limitations.

▶ Review the details of sea-floor spreading.

▶ Review the different types of plate boundaries.

**Time** 45 minutes    **Group** pairs

**Materials**

15 shoe boxes

15 sheets of white paper

15 different-colored wide-tip markers

15 metric rulers

15 pairs of scissors

## Activity 5    *What happens at a divergent boundary?*

*Skills*  Model; Observe; Infer

### Task 1    Prelab Prep

1. Collect the following items: shoe box, metric ruler, scissors, white paper, two wide-tip markers in different colors.
2. Cut two identical strips of white paper, each 7 cm wide by 30 cm long.
3. Cut an 8 cm-long slit in the bottom of the shoe box. Look at Figure 5.14 to see how it should look.

### Task 2    Data Record

1. Title a separate sheet of paper *Model of a Divergent Plate Boundary.*
2. Use this data sheet to record all your observations about the model you create.

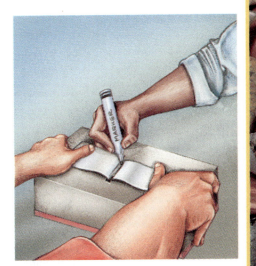

**Figure 5.14** ▲

### Task 3    Procedure

1. Put the two strips of paper together and push one end through the slit in the box.
2. Place the shoe box bottom-up as shown in Figure 5.14. Let about 5 cm of the paper strips stick out of the slit.
3. Separate the strips and hold each one down against the surface of the box as shown.
4. Take one of the markers and mark across the paper strips where they come out of the box. Make sure each strip gets colored with a stripe about 1 cm wide.
5. Pull the strips evenly so that another 1 cm comes out of the slit on each side.
6. Use the second marker to color all the new white paper now visible above the slit. On your data sheet, describe what is happening in the model.
7. Repeat steps 5 and 6 until both strips of paper are pulled out of the box. Use a different color marker each time.
8. When you're done, draw on your data sheet a picture of how the strips appear.

### Task 4    Analysis

1. What part of the earth do the construction paper strips represent?
2. What do the markers represent? What do the different colored stripes on the paper strips represent?
3. What part of the earth does the slit in the box represent?
4. What type of plate boundary did you model?
5. How does your model differ from the actual movement of plates at this type of boundary?

### Task 5    Conclusion

Write a short report explaining how your model shows that oceanic crust is created. Discuss how it models the creation of magnetic patterns in the rock of the ocean floor. Describe how the actual earth differs from the model that you built.

### Extension

Create models for the different kinds of convergent plate boundaries. Use different materials if you think they will work better.

## Analysis

1. The strips represent the earth's crust.
2. The markers represent the magnetization of the rocks in the crust. The stripes are the parallel magnetic "stripes" on either side of the mid-ocean ridge.
3. The slit represents the divergent boundary.
4. A divergent boundary
5. Students' answers may vary. The model moves much more quickly than the actual movements.

## Conclusion

Reports will vary. The limitations of the model include: the actual process is much slower, the materials are different, and the stripes are much more uniform than on the actual sea floor, where unequal terrain would alter the conformity of the stripes.

## Extension

Materials for models will vary, but might include cardboard, clay, foam rubber strips, blocks of packing material, and carpet remnants.

**The Living Textbook: Earth Science Sides 1-2**

Chapter 1            Frame 00732
Divergent Boundaries (1 Frame)
Search:

**Section Objectives**
For a list of section objectives, see the Student Edition page.

**Skills Objectives**
Students should be able to:

**Generalize** how a conveyor belt works.

**Evaluate** models of convection-based plate movement.

## MOTIVATE

### Skills WarmUp

To help students better understand the physics of plate movement, have them do the Skills WarmUp.
**Answer** Descriptions and lists will vary. Some conveyer belts are simply stretched around motor-driven rollers. Objects placed on the belt move along with the belt as the rollers turn. Another conveyer-beltlike system is simply a series of rollers all turning in the same direction. Objects are carried directly on top of the rollers and move in the direction in which they are rolling.

### Prior Knowledge

To gauge how much students know about the physics of plate movement, ask the following questions:

▶ What are some clues to the movement of the earth's plates?

▶ What is under the plates?

▶ What are some forces that act on the earth's plates?

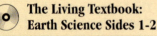

**The Living Textbook:
Earth Science Sides 1-2**

Chapter 1          Frame 00724
Convection (1 Frame)
Search:

### *Themes in Science*

**Energy** The kinetic energy of the earth's tectonic plates is a product of the earth's inner heat energy. When the inner heat energy is transferred to the partially melted zone of the mantle, heat energy changes to movement energy, or kinetic energy.

▼ **ACTIVITY**

**Generalizing**

*Convey the Concept*
Describe how a conveyor belt works. Make a list of where conveyor belts are used. What happens to objects placed on a conveyor belt?

**SKILLS WARMUP**

## 5.3   Physics of Plate Movement

### Objectives

▶ **Describe** two models of how convection occurs in the earth's mantle.

▶ **Explain** how a tectonic plate may move as part of a convection cell.

▶ **Evaluate** models explaining plate movement by convection.

▶ **Compare** and **contrast** two models for how convection results in the movement of the plates.

F ifty years after Alfred Wegener presented his theory, the scientific community came to accept the idea of moving continents in the form of plate tectonic theory. Since then, earth scientists collected more and more information about plates. They know how fast plates move, which directions they move in, and how they interact at boundaries. However, even today, one question remains only partly answered: What is the driving force that moves the plates?

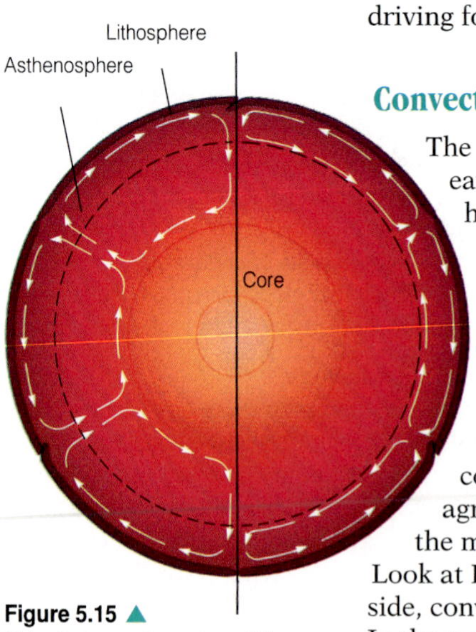

### Convection in the Mantle

The question is partly answered because earth scientists do know that the driving force has something to do with movement within the mantle. Recall that heating of rock material within the partially melted zone of the mantle causes the material to move in a circular motion, the movement called convection. It occurs in circular units of movement called convection cells.

Although most earth scientists agree that convection causes plate movement, there is no agreement on exactly how convection occurs in the mantle. Earth scientists have two basic models. Look at Figure 5.15. In the model shown on the right side, convection occurs mainly in the asthenosphere. In the model shown on the left, the convection cells are much larger. They include the entire mantle. There is strong evidence for both models.

Lithosphere
Asthenosphere
Core

**Figure 5.15** ▲
This diagram shows two different models describing how convection occurs inside the earth.

## Multicultural Perspectives

In Iceland, 80 percent of the homes are heated using geothermal steam and hot water. The growing season is very short. However, greenhouses warmed by geothermal energy produce nearly all of the tomatoes, lettuce, and cucumber for Iceland. Ask students how the use of this energy source might affect the way Icelanders live.

## Models for Plate Movement

Earth scientists also disagree about how convection moves the plates. In one model proposed, the plates are carried along by the movement of convection. In other words, the plates are like passengers on giant conveyor belts. Where convection pushes material upward, divergent boundaries form. Where convection goes downward back into the mantle, convergent boundaries form. Many earth scientists still think this is the best model for explaining plate movement.

According to a newer model, the plates themselves have an active role in convection. Each plate is thought to be part of a convection cell. Because a plate is cooler and more dense than the hot asthenosphere below, it tends to sink. Its sinking in a subduction zone "pulls" the rest of the plate down, helping create the circular movement of convection. Scientists observed a similar process in pools of molten lava.

## Consider This

### Should Geothermal Power Plants Be Built?

Geothermal energy is another name for the earth's internal heat. Geothermal energy can be used to produce electricity for human use. In geothermal power plants, steam from water heated deep in the earth moves turbines connected to electric generators.

Geothermal power has some advantages. Unlike coal and oil, geothermal energy is constantly renewed. Compared to the cost of electricity made by burning coal or oil, geothermal power is inexpensive. Many possible geothermal sites could be developed.

There are limits to the usefulness of geothermal power. Only a few geothermal power plants have been built so far. But even if all geothermal sites were used, the power would only supply a small amount of our energy needs.

Also, geothermal power has some drawbacks. For example, the hot water contains minerals and toxic metals that must be disposed of. Toxic hydrogen sulfide gas, which smells like rotten eggs, is also released in the steam.

**Think About It** Is geothermal power a good alternative to burning coal and oil? Should geothermal energy be used more than it is now?

**Write About It** Write a paper stating your position for or against building geothermal power plants.

## Skills Development

**Interpret Data** Have students study the text and Figure 5.15. Have students form two groups, each representing one of the models for plate movement. Write two headings on the chalkboard: *Asthenosphere Convection Model* and *Plate Convection Model*. Have students from each group list data and observations that support their model. (*Asthenosphere Convection:* Convection currents in asthenosphere carry plates, where convection pushes materials upward, divergent boundaries form; convergent boundaries form where convection pushes materials downward, plates are like luggage on a conveyer belt. *Plate Convection:* plates are part of convection, plates are cooler and more dense than asthenosphere and so they sink pulling rest of the plate down, similar process observed in pools of cooling molten lava.)

**Communicate** After data are listed, have students work together to write a few sentences, describing the group's model or theory.

## Consider This

**Think About It** Answers will vary. Students should evaluate risks and benefits, such as cheap fuel, renewable resource; by-products include minerals and toxic chemicals. Plant needs to be near geothermal source.

**Write About It** Students should give the reasons why they have chosen their points of view.

## Skills Development

**Infer** Encourage students to make diagrams of convection cells that form in their daily lives. Examples include convection cells formed in the shower by a room heater, or in a pan of soup. Students can keep their diagrams in their portfolios.

## EVALUATE

## WrapUp

**Reteach** Have students prepare a concept map that includes the following terms: *convection cells, molten rock, asthenosphere, lithosphere, and plates.*

Use Review Worksheet 5.3.

## Check and Explain

1. Convection currents in the asthenosphere carry plates; plates are part of convection cells.

2. The items being conveyed, or passengers

3. Answers will vary. Accept any reasonable answer that students can justify.

4. Both models require convection in the earth's mantle. In one, plates "ride" the currents. In the other, plates themselves are part of the currents.

## Reteach

Use Reteach Worksheet 5.3.

**Answer to In-Text Question**

① Students should be able to supply examples: hot water heating on a stove, hot water heater, dishwasher, air furnaces, air conditioning.

## *Integrating the Sciences*

**Physical Science** Convection is the transfer of heat energy by the movement of a liquid or a gas. The heat energy flows in a pattern called a *convection current*. Demonstrate the formation of a convection current. Fill a Pyrex® container half full of water. Begin to heat the water. Add a drop of food coloring to the edge of the water. The food coloring should move through the water outlining a convection current.

**Figure 5.16** ▲
Next time you heat water on the stove, watch for convection.

 **Science and You** *Convection at Home*

You have probably had direct experience with convection without even knowing it. For example, when you take a shower, cold air blows into your warm environment under the bottom of the shower curtain. The invasion of the cold air is caused by a convection current. The hot water heats the surrounding air in the shower. The hot air rises and escapes through the opening above the shower curtain. Denser, colder air replaces the warm air by entering under the shower curtain. A convection cell is created.

Rooms in your home may be heated by convection, too. Warm air enters the room through a heating vent or a radiator. The warm air rises. Colder air moves in to take its place and is heated by the radiator or heating vent. A convection current forms that moves heat throughout the room.

As in the mantle, convection also moves matter in liquids. For example, if you place a pan of water on the stove, convection heats the water. Look at Figure 5.16. The heat from the stove burner transfers to the bottom of the pan. Water at the bottom of the pan becomes hot and decreases in density. The hot water moves upward. Cold, denser water moves downward. The convection cell created in the pan spreads heat throughout the water, until all the water is heated equally.

Convection moves heated matter in both liquids and gases. In your home, there are many places where liquids and gases become heated. Where are some places where convection cells may form in your home? ①

## Check and Explain

1. What are two models for convection in the mantle?

2. If convection cells in the mantle are like conveyer belts, what are plates like?

3. **Evaluate** Which model do you think best explains how convection moves the plates? Explain the reasons for your choice.

4. **Compare and Contrast** What are the similarities and differences between the two major models explaining how convection causes plate movement?

# Chapter 5 Review

## Concept Summary

### 5.1 Drifting Continents
▶ Alfred Wegener proposed the first scientific theory of continental drift.
▶ 250 million years ago, the continents were joined in the supercontinent Pangaea and have since drifted apart.
▶ The theory of continental drift is supported by evidence from fossils, land formations, and glacial movement.

### 5.2 Theory of Plate Tectonics
▶ Sea-floor spreading occurs at the mid-ocean ridge, where molten material from the mantle forms new crust.
▶ The theory of plate tectonics states that the entire lithosphere is divided into moving pieces called plates.

▶ The earth has seven major plates and several smaller plates. The plates are classified as continental plates or oceanic plates.
▶ Plates meet at divergent, convergent, and transform boundaries.
▶ Different kinds of convergent boundaries create ocean trenches, volcanic islands, and mountain ranges.

### 5.3 Physics of Plate Movement
▶ Convection in the mantle causes plate movement.
▶ According to two different models, plates are either carried along by convection, or they are parts of convection cells.

## Chapter Vocabulary

| | | |
|---|---|---|
| Pangaea (5.1) | sea-floor spreading (5.2) | plate tectonics (5.2) |
| divergent boundary (5.2) | convergent boundary (5.2) | transform boundary (5.2) |
| subduction (5.2) | trench (5.2) | |

## Check Your Vocabulary

Use the vocabulary words above to complete the following sentences correctly.

1. At the mid-ocean ridge, _____ occurs because of the welling up of molten material from the mantle.

2. The process of one plate moving under another is _____ .

3. Any plate boundary where the plates move away from each other is called a _____ .

4. All of the earth's landmasses were once joined in the supercontinent _____ .

5. A plate boundary where two plates slide past each other is a _____ .

6. The theory of _____ states that the lithosphere of the earth is divided into moving pieces.

7. When a plate is subducted, a deep ocean valley, or _____ , is formed.

8. A plate boundary where two plates come together is called a _____ .

Explain the difference between the words in each pair.

9. convergent boundary, divergent boundary

10. subduction zone, trench

11. lithosphere, tectonic plate

## Write Your Vocabulary

Write sentences using the vocabulary words above. Show that you know what each word means.

## Check Your Vocabulary

1. sea-floor spreading
2. subduction
3. divergent boundary
4. Pangaea
5. transform boundary
6. plate tectonics
7. trench
8. convergent boundary
9. Two plates come together at a *convergent boundary*; two plates move away from each other at a *divergent boundary*.
10. A *subduction zone* is the place where one plate is pushed down under another. A *trench* is an ocean valley that forms in a subduction zone.
11. A *tectonic plate* is one of the pieces that make up the *lithosphere*.

## Write Your Vocabulary

Students' sentences should show that they know the meaning of each word as well as how to use it in a sentence.

Use Vocabulary Worksheet for Chapter 5.

## TEACH ▪ Continued

### Skills WorkOut

To help students understand folded topography, have them do the Skills WorkOut.

**Answer** Compressing from both sides should produce a variety of folds. Have students compare their models.

### Discuss

Ask students to describe how domes and basins can change over time. Then ask: What kinds of erosion could move materials from a dome to a basin? (Answers can include erosion by rain, melting snow, gravity, and wind.)

### Critical Thinking

**Reason and Conclude** Ask students to explain how fossils in a layer of rock could help researchers determine that the rock had folded. (Answers will vary. For example, if the fossils were dated, then researchers would know that the sections of rock were the same age even though they were different distances from the surface.)

### Answers to In-Text Questions

① **The higher part of the folded surface is eroded away; the lower parts are filled in.**

② **Ridges exist as the edges of upward-tilting rock layers.**

③ **The rock layers appear folded, and ridges suggest that material from the center of the anticline has been eroded, leaving the upward-tilting rock layers exposed.**

**The Living Textbook: Earth Science Sides 1-2**

Chapter 16        Frame 02557
Folds (12 Frames)
Search:                Step:

## Cooperative Learning

Have students work in cooperative groups to find magazine photographs of landscapes produced by folding. Have the groups share what they find. Ask the class to choose the photographs that best illustrate folded topography and display them on a bulletin board.

### ▼ ACTIVITY

**Modeling**

*Folded Sheets*

Collect newspaper, water, and soil for a model you will construct outdoors.

**1.** Cut the newspaper into several 25 by 35 cm sheets.

**2.** Use the water to moisten the soil and the newspaper.

**3.** Construct a layer cake, alternating layers of wet newspaper with 1 to 2 cm-thick layers of moistened soil.

**4.** Compress these layers from two sides.

What happens? Can you form both anticlines and synclines?

**SKILLS WORKOUT**

**Figure 6.3** ▶
Erosion changes folds in characteristic ways (right). How can you tell this landscape (bottom) was produced by folding? ▼ ③

### Folded Topography

Much of the earth's crust has been folded at one time or another, often in complex ways. Synclines and anticlines may be combined together. Folds can be pushed on top of other folds, and a group of small folds can become part of a much larger fold.

Folds, however, are not always visible at the surface. They may be eroded or covered by newer layers of rock or sediment. Together, folding and erosion produce a great variety of landforms and features, including mountains, valleys, jagged ridges, and rounded hills. Look at Figure 6.3. How is the folded surface changed by erosion? What evidence is left of the original folding? ②

Many parts of the crust have been gently folded into a rolling landscape of anticlines and synclines. Anticlines form long hills or ridges. Synclines form low areas called basins. Over time, anticlines erode to reveal the upward-tilting rock layers.

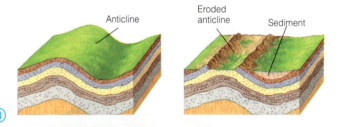

Anticline

Eroded anticline

Sediment

### Social Studies Connection

Have each student draw a cross-section showing a fault that bisects a horizontal mining shaft. Have them show how the hanging wall "hangs" above the head of a miner in the shaft, and how the footwall lies beneath the miner's feet. Tell students that miners named the blocks of crust on each side of a fault.

### Integrating the Sciences

**Physical Science** Have students use physical science textbooks to find examples of pulleys or other simple machines that change the direction of a force. Have them compare the action of each machine to the movement of the earth's crust along faults.

### Explore Visually

Have students study the illustration of types of faults. Then ask the following questions:

▶ What kind of movement does compression along a fault cause? What kind of fault results? (Compression can cause a hanging wall to move upward in relation to the footwall; reverse fault)

▶ Which way does the hanging wall move if the stress in the rocks is from tension? What kind of fault results? (Downward in relation to the footwall; normal fault)

▶ What kind of fault is associated with shear stress? How do the rocks around the fault move? (Lateral fault; rocks in a lateral fault slide past one another.)

### Class Activity

Ask volunteers to complete a fault chart on the chalkboard. Under the name of each kind of fault, students should describe the fault plane, the type of stress involved, and the motion of the hanging wall. (*Normal:* steeply inclined, tension, downward; *Reverse:* inclined, compression, upward; *Lateral:* vertical, shear stress, side-to-side)

## Faulting

Stress can cause rocks to break, or fracture. Fracturing occurs as a result of tension or shear. Fracturing also happens under certain conditions when the stress is compressional. A fracture becomes a **fault** when the rocks on either side of the fracture move in relation to each other. Much deformation of the crust occurs through the process of faulting. Faulting can transform horizontal stress into vertical movement.

Faults vary in many ways. To make them easier to classify, earth scientists named their parts. The fracture line of a fault is called the *fault plane*. The fault plane may slope at any angle from horizontal to vertical. Look at the fault in Figure 6.4, and find the fault plane. When the fault plane is inclined, or at any angle other than vertical, there is rock above it and below it. The rocks above the fault plane form the *hanging wall*. The rocks below the fault plane form the *footwall*. Two of the main types of faults are distinguished by the direction the hanging wall moves in relation to the footwall.

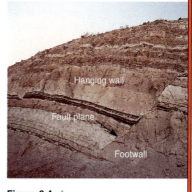

**Figure 6.4** ▲
The hanging wall is on the upper side of the fault plane, and the footwall on the lower side.

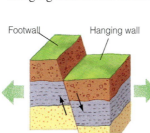

**Normal Fault** ▲
When the hanging wall moves downward in relation to the footwall, the fault is a **normal fault**. Normal faults occur when the stress is from tension. The fault plane in a normal fault is usually steeply inclined.

**Reverse Fault**
When the stress is from compression, the hanging wall moves upward in relation to the footwall. The result is a **reverse fault**. If the hanging wall rides up and over the footwall, it is called a *thrust fault*. ▼

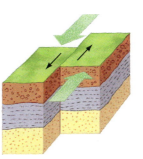

**Lateral Fault** ▲
Shear stress causes side-to-side movement, resulting in a **lateral fault**. Unlike normal and reverse faults, there is little or no up-and-down movement along a lateral fault. In addition, the fault plane of a lateral fault is usually vertical.

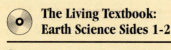

### The Living Textbook:
### Earth Science Sides 1-2

Chapter 16        Frame 02570
Normal and Reverse Faults (2 Frames)
Search:              Step:

**117**

## TEACH ▪ Continued

### SkillBuilder

**Answers**

1. A–F; B–G; C–H; D–I

2. Along the lower boundary of layer D; layers of rock above it are tilted and the layers below it are horizontal.

3. ABCD are the hanging wall, EFGHI are the footwall.

4. The hanging wall is moving up and over the footwall; downward in relation to the fault plane.

5. Thrust fault or reverse fault

6. D; A, unless rocks have been overturned

7. Material that was the same as layer E was originally present on top of layer A, but was evidently removed by erosion.

8. Folding: Layers FGHI bend near the fault plane. Also, layers ABCD have been tilted.

Paragraphs will vary but should suggest that the rock sample had four layers and that erosion has occurred in layers ABCD.

**The Living Textbook:**
**Earth Science Sides 1-2**

Chapter 16          Frame 02576
Faults (15 Frames)
Search:                    Step:

118

### Art Connection

Have students draw cross-sections of folded and faulted rock layers. Ask students to describe the forces and movements that produced the structures in their drawings.

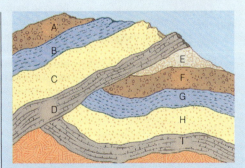

**Figure 6.5** ▲
The structures produced by fault movement are not always easy to interpret.

### Studying Faults

Earth scientists are very interested in faults because they help form some of the earth's most important surface features. In many areas, faulting is the major force shaping the crust and the surface topography. By studying faults, earth scientists can learn how blocks of the crust moved in the past. The main principle earth scientists follow in studying faults is that a fault is always younger than the rock it passes through.

Often, upward-moving blocks are no higher in elevation than downward-moving blocks because of erosion. In addition, the blocks on each side of the fault may be tilted in such a way that past movement is hard to determine by looking at the surface. In such cases, earth scientists must rely on the relative positions of the rock layers on each side of a fault to infer how the fault has moved.

### SkillBuilder  Inferring

### Interpreting Faults

Faults are geologic puzzles. The relative positions of rock layers on each side of a fault provide clues for inferring how the rocks have moved. Study the diagram at the right, and then answer the following questions:

1. Which layers in the diagram match up?

2. Where is the fault plane? How can you tell?

3. Which layers make up the hanging wall? The footwall?

4. Which direction is the hanging wall moving? Which direction is the footwall moving?

5. What kind of fault is this?

6. Which layer above the fault plane is the oldest? The most recent?

7. Why doesn't layer E match up with any other layer shown?

8. What kind of deformation occurred here besides faulting?

In one or two paragraphs, explain what happened to the rock layers in the diagram. Include a description of what the rock layers looked like before the faulting occurred.

## History Connection

Have students reread the Historical Notebook about James Hutton in Chapter 4 on page 79. Hutton's principle of uniformitarianism was the basis of *Principles of Geology*, written by Sir Charles Lyell in 1830. Charles Darwin read Lyell's book and applied the principle of uniformitarianism to his theory of the origin of species.

### Science and Society   *Faulty Theories*

Faults in the crust and the stress caused by plate movement create much of the earth's varied topography, such as hills, mountains, and valleys. Today this idea is logical and easy to understand. However, it has been accepted for less than 100 years. Before then, many other theories were proposed to explain the formation of different landforms.

In the 1600s, most people believed that the earth's landforms were created in one terrible event, or catastrophe. Thomas Burnet, a clergyman, suggested that mountains were the result of a giant flood. He believed that the earth was a smooth shell before the flood. When the shell cracked apart, it released water that covered the surface. Mountains were the pieces left from the cracks in the shell.

In the 1800s, the shrinking earth theory became popular. The shrinking earth theory was proposed by James Dwight Dana, a geology professor at Yale University. Dana thought the earth had once been a hot ball of semimolten rock. As the earth cooled, it shrank and created wrinkles on the surface. The wrinkles were the earth's mountains. His idea was easily demonstrated by observing the wrinkles formed on the skin of an apple as it dried.

These two theories remained popular for many years. After earth scientists better understood the structure and age of the earth, these theories were discarded. Faulty theories may remain popular only until new theories are backed by a great amount of evidence.

### Check and Explain

1. Describe the three types of stress that can deform rocks in the crust.

2. What is an anticline? How does it differ from a syncline?

3. **Compare and Contrast**   How are normal, reverse, and lateral faults similar? How are they different?

4. **Make a Model**   Find a substance that will fold when you apply compression. Use layers of it to make a model of folding in the earth's crust.

---

▼ **ACTIVITY**

**Inferring**

*A One Time Deal*

What observations and evidence might have convinced people that the earth's landforms were all formed during one catastrophic event? Explain.

**SKILLS WORKOUT**

---

**Time** 30 minutes **Group** pairs

**Materials**

15 sheets of corrugated cardboard (25 cm × 6 cm)

15 scissors

15 metric rulers

### Analysis

1. Modeling normal fault movement should have resulted in an
increase in the overall length.
This type of change would
result from tension.

2. Modeling reverse fault movement should have resulted in a
decrease in length. This type
of change is caused by compression.

3. Square pieces of cardboard
could move up and down without changing the overall length.

### Conclusion

Students' conclusions will vary.
Tension will increase the total
length of a section of crust, resulting in blocks of crust made of
hanging walls sinking to fill up the
space. Compression will squeeze
the crust, causing the same blocks
of crust to rise. Students may infer
that up-and-down movements of
blocks of crust can occur only if
fault planes are tilted, and that
there is a relationship between the
angle of fault planes and both vertical and horizontal movements in a
section of crust.

### Extension

Results of students' experiments
will vary, depending on the shapes
they choose.

## Prelab Discussion

Have students read the entire activity.
Discuss these points before beginning:

▶ Review the difference between tension
and compression.

▶ Give some actual examples of the
types of faults being modeled.

▶ Have students explain what each of the
following is modeling: cardboard
pieces, boundaries between pieces,
the student (blocks of crust, faults,
stress forces).

## *Activity 6* *How does stress cause movement along faults?*

***Skills*** Model; Observe; Measure; Interpret
Data; Infer

### Task 1 Prelab Prep
1. Collect the following items: sheet of corrugated cardboard, scissors, pencil, paper,
metric ruler.
2. Cut out pieces of cardboard to match the
five shapes in Figure 6.6. Each piece should
be about 6 cm tall. Together they should
form a straight line about 25 cm long.
3. Label the shapes with letters as shown in
Figure 6.6.

### Task 2 Data Record
On a separate sheet of paper, copy Table 6.1.
Use your copy of the table to record your obser-
vations and measurements in this activity.

**Table 6.1 Models of Movement Along Faults**

| Type of Faulting | Length at Start | Length after Movement |
|---|---|---|
| Normal faulting | | |
| Reverse faulting | | |

### Task 3 Procedure
1. On a flat surface, fit the cardboard pieces
together as shown in Figure 6.6. Move the
pieces together to remove all gaps.
2. Measure the total length of the assembled
pieces, from the left edge of the first *A* piece
to the right edge of the last *A* piece. Record
this measurement in both boxes of the first
column of your data table.
3. Model normal fault movement by sliding all
three *A* pieces down about 1 cm in relation
to the *B* pieces.
4. Measure the total length of the assembled
pieces, and record this measurement in your
data table.

5. Model reverse fault movement by sliding all
three *A* pieces up about 1 cm in relation to
the *B* pieces.
6. Measure the total length of the assembled
pieces, and record this measurement in your
data table.

**Figure 6.6** ▼

### Task 4 Analysis
1. How did the length of the assembled pieces
change when you modeled normal fault
movement? What kind of stress would produce this change in length?
2. How did the length of the assembled pieces
change when you modeled reverse fault
movement? What kind of stress would produce this change in length?
3. What results would you get using cardboard
pieces shaped as squares?

### Task 5 Conclusion
Write a short paragraph explaining how tension
and compression can produce up-and-down
movement in blocks of the earth's crust. Include
an explanation of the importance of the angle of
the fault planes.

### *Extension*

Experiment with differently shaped blocks of
crust. Try making cardboard pieces that increase
and decrease the angle of the fault planes. Can
you model thrust faulting?

### Literature Connection

Find and read a story or myth in which mountains play a key role. Have students discuss why the mountains were so important to people's lives.

### Writing Connection

Have students write a story about hiking, driving, or camping in the mountains. The stories may be fictional or nonfictional experiences as told by the students themselves. Some students may wish to share their stories with the class.

**Section Objectives**
For a list of section objectives, see the Student Edition page.

**Skills Objectives**
Students should be able to:

**Observe** patterns in mountain formation.

**Infer** how mountains form at a convergent boundary between two oceanic plates.

## 6.2 Mountains and Plateaus

### Objectives

▶ **Identify** four mountain-building processes.

▶ **Distinguish** between folded and fault-block mountains.

▶ **Relate** mountain-building processes to different kinds of plate boundaries.

▶ **Classify** types of mountains according to how and where they formed.

▼ **ACTIVITY**

**Observing**

*Mountain Building*

Look at a globe or a map of the world. Locate mountain ranges on all seven continents. Can you detect any patterns in their shape or location? What inferences can you make about how mountains are formed?

**SKILLS WARMUP**

You feel like you can't take another step. The trail is steep and crumbly. You're breathing hard, and your heart is pounding. But you look up and see you're near the top. You make your legs work again and trudge on up. Finally you reach the rocky summit. You climb atop the highest rock and gaze at the world stretched out at your feet.

If you've ever climbed a tall mountain, you know the feeling of awe you get viewing the earth from such a high perch. Mountains have always had a special meaning to people. Many cultures consider mountains to be sacred places. Mountains have also been a source of valuable metal and mineral resources.

### Mountain Building

Mountains are evidence that incredibly powerful forces are at work shaping the crust. What produces these forces? Forces powerful enough to raise huge blocks of rock kilometers above sea level are the result of the movement of tectonic plates. Recall that the places where tectonic plates collide are called convergent boundaries. Most active mountain building occurs at or near convergent plate boundaries. Mountains can also be produced at divergent plate boundaries.

Because it is related to plate boundaries, most mountain building happens on a huge scale. Whole mountain belts, made of many mountain ranges, are produced. If you look at a globe, for example, you can see that a mountain belt stretches all along the western edge of both North and South America.

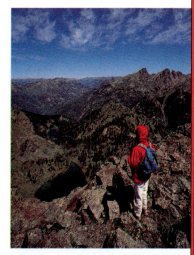

**Figure 6.7 ▲**
Have you ever wondered how mountains are built?

**MOTIVATE**

### Skills WarmUp

To help students observe patterns in the location of mountain ranges, have them do the Skills WarmUp.
**Answer** Students should observe that mountain ranges occur in belts, and that each range consists of a series of peaks. Mountains on globes or maps look and sometimes feel like wrinkles. Students might infer that mountains are formed by forces that "wrinkle" the crust. Students may also relate mountain building to the movement of tectonic plates.

### Prior Knowledge

Gauge how much students know about mountains by asking the following questions:

▶ How are all mountains alike?

▶ Why are some mountains higher than others?

▶ What is underneath a mountain range?

⊙ **The Living Textbook: Earth Science Sides 1-2**

Chapter 23          Frame 02823
Mountains (19 Frames)
Search:                    Step:

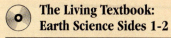

121

### Skills Development

**Infer** Have students examine a plate boundary map, such as Figure 5.12 on pages 102 and 103 in Chapter 5. Then have them compare it to a world relief map. Ask them what they can infer about the location of mountains by comparing the two maps. (Most mountain systems are at plate boundaries.)

### Directed Inquiry

After students have read the text and studied the photograph, ask:

▶ What type of stress can form a folded mountain? Where does this kind of stress occur? (Compression; where rocks are pushed together, such as where continental plates collide)

▶ What kind of fault results from this kind of stress? (Reverse)

### Enrich

Use Enrich Worksheet 6.2.

### Art Connection

To help students understand the forces that produce folding, have them place tracing paper over the photograph in Figure 6.9 and lightly trace the lines that show folding.

### Geography Connection

Show students a physical map of North America and have them find the Appalachian Mountains. Then have students infer the location of the now-vanished convergent plate boundary that produced these mountains.

**Figure 6.8** ▲
From high up, the Appalachian Mountains look like folds in the earth's crust. This photograph was taken with special equipment sensitive to infrared light.

## Folded Mountains

You just learned that folding of the crust is the result of compression. When the compressive force is very powerful, the folding is great enough to produce mountains. At what type of convergent boundary do you think this type of mountain building occurs? It happens where two continental plates collide.

Two of the world's tallest mountain ranges—the Alps and the Himalayas—were built up as a result of two continental plates colliding. Another folded mountain range is the Appalachians in North America. Notice the folds in the Appalachians shown in Figure 6.8. The Appalachians were uplifted long ago, during the Paleozoic Era, and have undergone much erosion. They are no longer at a convergent plate boundary.

Thrust faults are common in folded mountain ranges. This makes sense if you remember that both folding and thrust faulting are the result of compressional stress. Because thrust faulting pushes rocks on top of other rock layers, it helps in the mountain-building process.

**Figure 6.9** ▶
In parts of the Canadian Rocky Mountains, folded rock layers are clearly visible.

## Fault-Block Mountains

Tensional stress, or the stretching out of the crust, can also create mountains. This may seem impossible unless you remember that tensional stress causes up-and-down movement along a normal fault. The footwall moves upward as the hanging wall moves downward.

Look at Figure 6.11. As you can see, a block of crust may have normal faults on either side and be the footwall of both sides. This block will therefore move upward, while the two blocks of crust on either side move downward. As a result of these movements, the block of crust becomes a fault-block mountain.

In the eastern part of Africa, the crust is stretching in a somewhat narrow area along a divergent plate boundary. The result is a long *rift valley*. It is surrounded on both sides by fault-block mountains.

In the Great Basin of western North America, a wider zone of crust has stretched from east to west. Over time, the area has become wider. In fact, it is now 50 percent wider than it was 30 million years ago. As a result of this tensional stress, a series of long fault-block mountain ranges was created. Can you infer which direction these fault-block mountain ranges run? ①

**Figure 6.10** ▲
The Grand Tetons of Wyoming are fault-block mountains.

**Figure 6.11**
Movement along normal faults makes some blocks of crust rise in relation to others. ▼

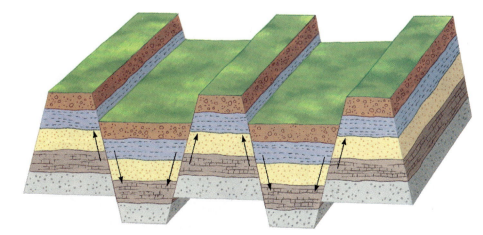

## Discuss

Ask students to explain how fault-block mountains and folded mountains could be considered opposites. Ask:

▶ How are tension stresses the opposite of compression stresses? (One pulls objects apart, the other pushes them together.)

▶ How do normal faults differ from reverse faults? (In normal faults, tension causes the hanging wall to move downward in relation to the footwall. In reverse faults, the hanging wall moves upward in relation to the footwall.)

▶ What kinds of mountains would you find around divergent plate boundaries? (Fault-block)

▶ What kinds of mountains would you find around convergent plates? (Folded)

**Answer to In-Text Question**
① **North-South**

## Skills Development

**Organize Data** Write the following phrases on the chalkboard. Ask students to arrange them in the proper sequence:

▶ pool of magma forms under the earth's surface (4)

▶ oceanic crust subducts at boundary with continental plate (1)

▶ magma solidifies, forming a *pluton* (5)

▶ oceanic crust melts (2)

▶ magma rises through the earth's crust (3)

**Make a Model** Have students describe how they could make a model of plutonic mountain building with wet newspaper, moist soil or sand, and a balloon. (Students should say that as the balloon inflates it can raise layers of soil and newspaper.)

## Discuss

Ask students to describe the relationship between magma, a pluton, and a batholith. (Magma may push the earth's surface upward, and it solidifies to form a pluton. A pluton exposed by erosion is a batholith.)

### Language Arts Connection

Tell students the word *batholith* comes from the Greek roots *bath*, which means "deep," and *lith*, which means "rock." Ask: Why is *batholith* a good name for a pluton exposed at the surface?

### Literature Connection

Explain that the words *pluton* and *plutonic* come from Pluto, the Roman god of the underworld. Ask students to explain why plutons are named for this mythological figure.

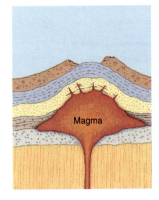

**Figure 6.12** ▲
When a pool of magma collects under the surface, rock layers above are lifted. When it solidifies, the magma becomes a pluton.

**Figure 6.13**
Batholiths form large areas of mountain ranges in western North America (left). The Sierra Nevada batholith (right) includes many mountains rising above 3,300 m. ▼

### Plutonic Mountains

Fault-block mountains and folded mountains differ in that they are caused by different types of stress. Both compression and tension, however, are horizontal forces. Another type of mountain-building process, in contrast, involves a direct vertical force. This force is the upward movement of molten material from the mantle.

Recall that one place where molten material rises through the crust is near the boundary between an oceanic and a continental plate. At this type of plate boundary, oceanic crust subducts and melts deep in the earth. This molten material then rises through the crust of the continental plate. In some places, the magma breaks the surface to form volcanoes. But much of the time, a large pool of molten rock builds up under the surface. It raises the surface above it and then solidifies, forming a *pluton*. This process is shown in Figure 6.12. Large plutons exposed at the surface by erosion are called *batholiths*.

Many mountain ranges in western North America are made up of batholiths. These include the Sierra Nevada and the Coast Ranges of British Columbia and Baja California. Locate these batholiths on the map in Figure 6.13. Uplift from plutonic activity often occurs before, during, or after other forms of mountain building. For example, a rising pool of magma may raise a folded mountain range even higher.

## Volcanic Mountains

Magma reaching the surface can form another type of mountain called a volcano. Volcanoes occur at the convergent boundary formed by two oceanic plates or an oceanic and a continental plate. At both kinds of plate boundaries, entire mountain ranges are formed by volcanic activity. Because they are made by the vertical force of rising magma, volcanic mountains are similar to plutonic mountains. In fact, volcanoes are often found in mountain ranges uplifted by plutonic activity.

Volcanic mountains are often cone-shaped. Some of the world's best-known mountains, such as Mt. Fuji in Japan and Mt. Kilimanjaro in Tanzania, are volcanoes. The mountains on the Hawaiian Islands and the Aleutian Islands of Alaska are all volcanic in origin. Many earth scientists think that volcanoes created the first continents early in the earth's history. You will learn more about volcanoes in the next chapter.

**Figure 6.14** ▲
Japan's Mt. Fuji is a volcanic mountain.

## Career Corner  *Field Geologist*

### Who Infers the History of the Landscape?

Your mission is to map the geology of a remote mountain range in the desert of Nevada. You have four months to cover 100 km². You load camping supplies, shovels, picks, and hammers onto your horses and head out. You'll live in a tent most of the time, leaving your study site only a few times for supplies.

Many field geologists spend their summers this way. Their job is to observe, infer, and collect all sorts of data in the field. Their findings are then used for locating valuable resources, or simply for understanding how the varied geo-

logic processes have shaped the crust.

Most field geologists also work in laboratories some of the time. There they analyze rock samples and other data, draw up maps, and write reports. But the focus of their work is outdoors.

Field geologists may work for oil or mining companies, government agencies, or universities. Most have advanced degrees in geology, but there are some job opportunities for people with four-year college degrees.

If you might be interested in being a field geologist, high

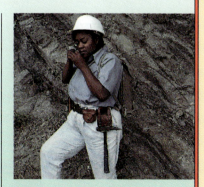

school courses in mathematics, physics, geology, and chemistry are good preparation. You should also practice outdoor skills such as rock climbing, camping, and map reading.

## TEACH ▪ *Continued*

### Discuss

Ask students to describe the two kinds of plateaus and give an example of each. (Formed near a mountain range by same forces, Colorado Plateau; molten rock pours through surface cracks and fractures, basalt plateau, Columbia Plateau.) Ask which is most common and why this might be so. (The plateau formed near a mountain range; answers may suggest that mountains and associated structures are more plentiful than volcanoes.)

### Critical Thinking

**If . . . Then Arguments**  Ask students to imagine that they are surrounded by a large expanse of relatively flat land. Have them form If . . . then statements that could help them decide whether or not they are on a plateau. (Answers will vary. For example, if the area rises above the land surrounding it, then it is a plateau. If the surface is eroded to form deep canyons, then it is a plateau.)

### Answer to In-Text Question

① **They are dark and jumbled-up, suggesting volcanic origin.**

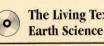

**The Living Textbook: Earth Science Sides 1-2**

Chapter 23          Frame 02875
Plateaus (9 Frames)
Search:                    Step:

**126**

---

### *Language Arts Connection*

Have students construct sentences using the words *plateau, mountain,* and *peak* figuratively. Example: "Her level of skill on piano reached a plateau."

### *Geography Connection*

Have students locate the Grand Canyon and the Colorado Plateau on a topographic map of North America or the United States. If you have a world topographic map, you may wish to have them find the Deccan Plateau and Tibetan Plateau in Asia, and the Andean Altiplano in South America.

---

### Plateaus

In many parts of the world, areas of the crust have been uplifted without forming mountains. Instead, the land has stayed relatively flat. Recall that this kind of elevated, level area is called a plateau.

There are two basic types of plateaus. The most common type of plateau is formed next to a mountain range by the same forces that produced the mountains. The largest of these plateaus include the Andean Altiplano in South America, the Tibetan Plateau in Asia, and the Colorado Plateau in North America.

The other type of plateau is formed by a flood of molten rock pouring through cracks or fractures in the earth's surface. This type of plateau is called a basalt plateau. Two of the world's largest basalt plateaus are the Deccan Plateau in India and the Columbia Plateau in the western United States.

**Figure 6.16 ▲**
What do you notice about the rocks in this part of the Columbia Plateau? ①

Because plateaus are usually made up of flat rock layers and are high above neighboring regions, they tend to erode in characteristic patterns. Streams carry away the softer material and leave the harder materials exposed as cliffs. Streams and rivers carve deep canyons.

**Figure 6.15 ▲**
Rivers have cut deep canyons into the Colorado Plateau.

## Floating Crust

Mountains don't last forever. After their uplift stops, weathering and erosion slowly reduce their elevation. However, after erosion wears away much of a mountain range, it may be slightly uplifted again. This upward movement is the result of *isostasy* (eye SAHS teh see).

Isostasy is the balancing of two basic forces. Because the crust has mass, gravity pulls it down into the mantle. But the crust is also less dense than the mantle, giving it buoyancy. So, while gravity pulls the crust down, the force of buoyancy pushes it up. These forces balance at different points depending on the mass of the crust.

Because mountains have great mass, they sink deeper into the mantle than other parts of the crust. However, as a mountain range erodes, it loses mass. The upward force of buoyancy becomes greater, making the crust "spring back." The springing back, or rebounding, of the crust makes the mountain regain some elevation. This process is shown in Figure 6.17.

◀ **Figure 6.17 Isostasy at Work**

A newly uplifted mountain range sinks deeply into the mantle because of its great mass. Erosion begins to slowly wear it away.

After many years, erosion greatly reduces the elevation and mass of the mountain range. The upward force of buoyancy now increases.

The mountain range rises upward, once again gaining some elevation. The downward force of gravity and the upward force of buoyancy come back into balance.

### TEACH ▪ *Continued*

## Research

Have the class work in five groups. Have each group research how athletes in a particular sport prepared for the 1992 Olympics held in the alpine location of Albertville, France. Ask each group to make a brief report. As a class, discuss similarities and differences among the training routines.

### EVALUATE

## WrapUp

**Reteach** Draw diagrams of folded, fault-block, plutonic, and volcanic mountains on the chalkboard. Have students work together to list information about each type of mountain. Be sure they include the types of plates and the direction of stress or force.

Use Review Worksheet 6.2.

## Check and Explain

1. Compression or folded; tension or fault-block; upward movement of molten rock beneath surface, plutonic; upward movement of molten rock through surface, volcanic

2. *Differ: folded*—Compression forces, continental plates colliding, hanging wall moves upward and perhaps over footwall where faults occur; *faultblock*—tension forces, hanging wall moves downward in relation to footwall; *Common:* vertical crust movement; both are results of stress in the crust.

3. Volcanic

4. *Folded:* compression, two continental plates
   *Fault-block:* tension, two continental plates
   *Plutonic:* compression, oceanic and continental plates
   *Volcanic:* compression, two oceanic plates or oceanic and continental plates

## Integrating the Sciences

**Health** People who aren't adjusted to high elevations often get altitude sickness when they travel in the mountains. Until they become acclimated, or adjusted, to the reduced amount of oxygen, even light exertion can cause headaches, nausea, fatigue, and dizziness. Ask students what they would do if they got altitude sickness.

**Figure 6.18** ▲
Tibetans are adapted to living where the air contains much less oxygen than it does at sea level.

### Science and You *Into Thin Air*

If you travel to the top of a mountain, you may notice changes occurring in your body. Maybe your ears pop. When you try to run or walk, you may have difficulty breathing. Although these changes may seem strange, they are your body's normal response to changes in altitude. At high altitudes, air pressure is lower and the amount of oxygen in the air is less than at low altitudes.

When you go from low to high elevation, your body must adjust. Some adjustments occur quickly. Others take days or weeks. Your ears adjust quickly. There must be equal pressure on both sides of the eardrum for it to move freely. The sensation of popping ears is the ear balancing the pressures by letting some air out of the inner ear through the auditory tube.

Your body adjusts to the reduced amount of oxygen in several different ways. The first response is rapid: an increase in the rate and depth of breathing. When you breathe more quickly and more heavily, your oxygen intake increases.

A slower adjustment is the creation of more red blood cells. Since red blood cells carry oxygen, an increase in their numbers helps your other cells get the oxygen they need. Your body releases some extra red blood cells from storage areas, such as the spleen. But it also produces red blood cells at a more rapid rate. If you try to exercise at high elevation before your body is fully adjusted, you'll tire easily, and you may get dizzy.

### Check and Explain

1. What are four ways in which mountains can be formed?

2. How do folded and fault-block mountains differ? What do they have in common?

3. **Infer** What type of mountain is produced at a convergent boundary between two oceanic plates?

4. **Classify** In a table, classify each type of mountain by the kind of stress or force that produces it, and by the kind of plate boundary at which it is produced.

## Check Your Vocabulary

1. monocline
2. tension
3. reverse fault
4. anticline
5. lateral fault
6. deformation
7. compression
8. shear
9. syncline
10. fault
11. normal fault

## Write Your Vocabulary

Students' sentences should show that they know the meaning of each word as well as how to use it in a sentence.

Use Vocabulary Worksheet for Chapter 6.

# Chapter 6 Review

## Concept Summary

### 6.1 Folding and Faulting
▶ Compression, tension, and shear are three types of stress that deform the rocks of the crust.
▶ The crust responds to stress by folding and by faulting.
▶ Folding produces monoclines, anticlines, and synclines.
▶ Faulting is a result of the fracturing and movement of pieces of crust. Depending on the type of movement that occurs along a fault, it is classified as normal, reverse, or lateral.

### 6.2 Mountains and Plateaus
▶ Most mountain building is related to the movement of the earth's tectonic plates.

▶ Powerful stress in the form of compression produces folded mountains.
▶ Stress in the form of tension creates fault-block mountains.
▶ Plutonic mountains are formed by the upward movement of molten rock from the mantle.
▶ Volcanic mountains are built up by molten material reaching the surface and solidifying.
▶ Plateaus can be formed by some of the same processes that produce mountains and mountain ranges.
▶ Once a mountain range loses much of its mass from erosion, it may uplift slightly because its smaller mass gives it increased buoyancy.

### Chapter Vocabulary

| | | | |
|---|---|---|---|
| deformation (6.1) | compression (6.1) | tension (6.1) | shear (6.1) |
| monocline (6.1) | anticline (6.1) | syncline (6.1) | fault (6.1) |
| normal fault (6.1) | reverse fault (6.1) | lateral fault (6.1) | |

## Check Your Vocabulary

Use the vocabulary words above to complete the following sentences correctly.

1. The simplest kind of fold is a(n) ____ .
2. The force that pulls or stretches rock is ____ .
3. In a ____ , the footwall moves down in relation to the hanging wall.
4. A fold with an upward bulge is a(n) ____ .
5. Two pieces of crust move in opposite horizontal directions along a ____ .
6. Two kinds of ____ are folding and faulting.
7. When rock is stressed by ____ , folding or reverse faulting occurs.

8. The type of stress that causes movement along a lateral fault is ____ .
9. A fold with a downward bulge is a(n) ____ .
10. When rocks on either side of a fracture move in relation to each other, a ____ results.
11. In a ____ , the footwall moves up in relation to the hanging wall.

## Write Your Vocabulary

Write sentences using the vocabulary words above. Show that you know what each word means.

## Check Your Knowledge

1. A fault-block mountain is a mountain created by a block of crust that has been forced upward by tension in relation to surrounding blocks.

2. Compression can either cause folding or fracture of the crust.

3. Folded mountains form at convergent boundaries.

4. Rocks become more ductile under high temperatures and pressures.

5. A plateau is formed when the uplifted crust stays relatively flat.

6. Mountains can be formed by the faulting or folding of the crust, by the upward movement of molten rock from the mantle, and by magma that reaches the surface.

7. A monocline has only one bend; rocks on one side are higher than those on the other side. An anticline is an upward bulge, with the center part higher than either side.

8. If the rocks on either side do not move in relation to each other, a fracture is not a fault.

9. Both are formed by the action of molten rock from the mantle.

10. reverse

11. volcanic activity

12. reverse

13. tension

14. mass

## Check Your Understanding

1. Because they are both compressional features. Two synclines next to each other have an anticline in between; or, two anticlines next to each other have a syncline in between.

2. Transform boundary

3. Folded mountains are formed by compression forces. If the rock breaks in response to these forces, a thrust fault can be formed.

4. As a mountain range erodes, its mass decreases, and the buoyant force increases, causing it to float higher on the mantle.

5. The forces between adjoining tectonic plates are strongest near the boundary. Mountain ranges are long because plate boundaries are lines that stretch long distances. For a mountain range to be very wide, the forces creating it would have to be transmitted through the crust a long distance from where they are applied.

6. Tensional stress causes blocks of crust separated by tilted fault planes to move up and down in relation to each other in order to compensate for the spreading-out of the crust.

7. The enormous mass of the glaciers pushed down on the crust below, making it sink into the mantle; when the glaciers melted, the added mass was removed, allowing the land to "rebound" to its previous height due to buoyant forces.

8. Folds would show up as a gently rolling landscape, or as upward-tilting layers of rock that are from an eroded anticline. A fault would have evidence of side-to-side or up-and-down displacement of surface features.

9. The folded layers were probably formed by compression.

## Chapter 6 Review

### Check Your Knowledge

Answer the following in complete sentences.

1. What is a fault-block mountain? How does it form?

2. In what two ways can compression deform the crust?

3. At what type of plate boundary are folded mountains produced?

4. What conditions make rock more ductile?

5. How does a plateau differ from a mountain?

6. List four types of mountain-building processes.

7. What is the difference between a monocline and an anticline?

8. When is a fracture not a fault?

9. How are plutonic and volcanic mountains similar?

Choose the answer that best completes each sentence.

10. If you're standing on a footwall, and the hanging wall in front of you has moved up, you're at a (normal, reverse, lateral, transform) fault.

11. One way mountains are built up by a direct upward force is through (folding, volcanic activity, faulting, erosion).

12. A thrust fault is a type of (normal, transform, lateral, reverse) fault.

13. A rift valley is produced as a result of (tension, compression, folding, movement of lateral faults).

14. A mountain range sinks deep into the mantle because of its (mass, size, elevation, buoyancy).

### Check Your Understanding

Apply the concepts you have learned to answer each question.

1. Why do anticlines and synclines occur together?

2. What kind of plate boundary would you expect to produce a lateral fault?

3. Why do thrust faults occur in folded mountain ranges? Suggest a way in which a fold could become a thrust fault.

4. Explain why a mountain range may be uplifted slightly after much of its mass has been eroded.

5. **Critical Thinking** Why does mountain building usually occur at the edge of a continent? Why are most mountain ranges much longer than they are wide?

6. Explain how tensional stress can cause up-and-down movement of the crust.

7. **Critical Thinking** Some areas of land that were covered by thick glaciers during the last ice age are now slowly rising in elevation. Explain why this may occur.

8. **Application** What kinds of evidence would you look for to determine if the crust where you live had been folded at some time in the past? What kinds of evidence would you look for to find a fault?

9. **Mystery Photo** The photograph on page 112 shows folded layers of rock in Death Valley, California. What type of stress produced these folds?

## Develop Your Skills

**1.** a. Normal; reverse; same as A

b. Because 2 is located in a zone of tension, it will either rise or fall in relation to blocks 1 and 3. Accept either answer.

c. Students' diagrams will vary depending on how they visualize the direction of tilt in the fault planes of faults A, B, and C. Check the diagrams for logical correspondence between fault plane tilt, type of stress, and vertical movement of crust blocks.

**2.** a. Mt. Everest; about 8800 m; Himalayas

b. Mt. McKinley; its height is about 2600 m less than Mt. Everest.

## Make Connections

**1.**

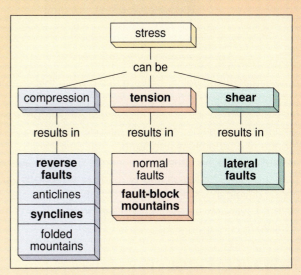

**2.** Students' reports will vary. People living high in the Andes have physically and culturally adapted to the conditions commonly found at high altitudes.

**3.** Students' answers should accurately reflect your geographical area.

**4.** Students' stories will vary. Check the use of vocabulary words.

---

## Develop Your Skills

Use the skills you have developed in this chapter to complete each activity.

**1. Read a Map** The map below is a view from above of three faults separating four blocks of crust. The direction of stress on each block is shown by the arrows.

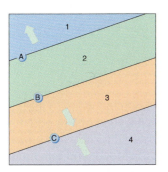

a. What type of fault is A? What type is C? Is fault B the same type as A or C?

b. How does the elevation of block 2 compare to that of block 3? Explain your reasoning.

c. How would these faults appear viewed from the side, in cross section? Draw a diagram that illustrates the information on the map.

**2. Data Bank** Use the information on page 618 to answer the following questions.

a. What is the world's tallest mountain? What is its elevation? In what mountain range is it found?

b. What is the tallest mountain in North America? How does its elevation compare to that of the tallest mountain in the world?

## Make Connections

**1. Link the Concepts** Below is a concept map showing how some of the main concepts in this chapter link together. Only part of the map is filled in. Finish the map, using words and ideas from the chapter.

**2. Science and Social Studies** Do library research to find out about the people who live high in the Andes Mountains of Ecuador or Peru. How does the high elevation affect their lifestyle, culture, and food crops?

**3. Science and Geography** Is there a mountain range near where you live? If so, observe its shape and relationship to the surrounding land. Infer how it formed. Then do research to find out which mountain-building processes contributed to its formation.

**4. Science and Writing** Write a short story about a long trip during which you explore new places with different landscapes. Use as many vocabulary words from this chapter as you can to describe the landscape and how it was formed.

## Overview

Earthquakes and volcanoes are explored in this chapter. It begins with the energy and physics of earthquakes, and follows with an examination of seismic waves, magnitude, epicenters, and the three major zones. The second section explores evidence of earthquakes and factors that determine damage. Also discussed are the causes of tsunamis. The third section describes the formation and eruption of volcanoes, including types of volcanoes and areas of activity. The chapter concludes with an overview of developments in predicting and monitoring eruptions.

## Advance Planner

▶ Obtain rope for TE page 135.

▶ Prepare adding-machine tape, felt tip pens, and paper for TE page 135.

▶ Collect wood, cardboard, and masking tape for SE Activity 7, page 139.

▶ Supply rubber bands, empty cardboard tubes, paper towels, and sand or rice to overfill the tubes for SE page 140.

▶ Provide baking soda, balloons, and vinegar for TE page 145.

▶ Supply colored modeling clay for TE page 147.

▶ Gather string for TE page 149.

## Skills Development Chart

| Sections | Generalize | Infer | Make a Graph | Make a Model | Make Analogies | Read a Table |
|---|---|---|---|---|---|---|
| **7.1** Skills WarmUp | | ● | | | | |
| Skills WorkOut | | | ● | | ● | |
| SkillBuilder | | | | | | ● |
| Activity 7 | | | | ● | | |
| **7.2** Skills WarmUp | | | | ● | | |
| **7.3** Skills WarmUp | ● | | | | | |
| Historical Notebook | ● | | | | | |

## Individual Needs

▶ **Limited English Proficiency Students** As students read the chapter, have them make a list of the boldface terms. Then encourage them to study the chapter summary on page 151 and use it as a guide in preparing a "newscast" reporting either an earthquake or volcanic eruption. Their newscast should include definitions of the boldface terms—in their own words—as well as summaries of the chapter's concepts. They may want to use diagrams to illustrate the terms and concepts. Have them make audio-tapes of their newscasts, and use them as part of the chapter review.

▶ **At-Risk Students** Have students work in groups to make a model that shows what happens to the land in an earthquake. Have them cut a rectangular foil baking pan in half cross-ways. Then have them put the two halves of the pan together and line them with a piece of foil. They should fill the pan with moist soil. If they want to, they may add buildings and roads to their model. Then ask them to simulate different forms of crustal stress by moving the halves of the pan apart (tension), together (compression), or past one another (shear). They should observe what happens to the soil each time. They may want to experiment with different kinds of soil, such as hard clay or sand.

▶ **Gifted Students** Encourage students to learn more about the history of seismology, including an early Chinese device featuring metal balls and dragons used to register earthquakes, as well as more modern seismographs and other earthquake-detecting apparatus. Have them make an exhibit that shows how these devices work and what they tell us.

## Resource Bank

▶ **Bulletin Board** Attach a large map of the world to the bulletin board. On it lightly sketch the Ring of Fire and other areas of earthquake and volcanic activity as shown in Figures 7.6 and 7.12. Have each student find out about a historic earthquake or volcanic eruption and add a symbol for it to the map, along with its name and date. When the map is complete, each student should give a short report about the seismic event to the rest of the class.

| Section | Core | Standard | Enriched | Section | Core | Standard | Enriched |
|---|:---:|:---:|:---:|---|:---:|:---:|:---:|
| **7.1 Earthquakes** pp. 133–139 | | | | **Blackline Masters** Review Worksheet 7.2 Skills Worksheet 7.2 | • • | • • | • • |
| **Section Features** Skills WarmUp, p. 133 Skills WorkOut, p. 134 SkillBuilder, p. 136 Skills WorkOut, p. 138 Activity, p. 139 | • • | • • • • • | • • • • • | **Ancillary Options** *One-Minute Readings,* p. 104 | | • | • |
| **Blackline Masters** Review Worksheet 7.1 Enrich Worksheet 7.1 Integrating Worksheet 7.1 | • | • • • | • • • | **7.3 Volcanoes** pp. 144–150 | | | |
| **Ancillary Options** *Measuring Earthquakes* | | • | • | **Section Features** Skills WarmUp, p. 144 Historical Notebook, p. 149 | • • | • • | • • |
| **Laboratory Program** Investigation 10 | | • | | **Blackline Masters** Review Worksheet 7.3 Skills Worksheet 7.3 Integrating Worksheet 7.3 Vocabulary Worksheet 7.3 | • • • | • • • | • • • |
| **Color Transparencies** Transparencies 13, 14 | • | • | • | **Overhead Blackline Transparencies** Overhead Blackline Master 7.3 and Student Worksheet | • | • | • |
| **7.2 Earthquake Evidence** pp. 140–143 | | | | **Laboratory Program** Investigation 11 Investigation 12 | • | • | • |
| **Section Features** Skills WarmUp, p. 140 | • | • | • | **Color Tranparencies** Transparency 15 | • | • | • |

# Bibliography

The following resources can be used for teaching the chapter. See page T–46 for supplier codes.

## Library Resources

Booth, Basil. *Volcanoes and Earthquakes.* Englewood Cliffs, NJ: Enslow, 1991.

Lasky, Kathryn. *Surtsey: The Newest Place on Earth.* Illustrated by Christopher Knight. New York: Hyperion, 1992.

Lauber, Patricia. *Volcano: The Eruption and Healing of Mount St. Helens.* New York: Bradbury Press, 1986.

Markle, Sandra. *Digging Deeper: Investigations into Rocks, Shocks, Quakes, and Other Earthly Matters.* New York: Lothrop, Lee, and Shepard Books, 1987.

Poynter, Margaret. *Looking for Answers.* Hillside, NJ: Enslow, 1990.

Van Rose, S. *Volcano & Earthquake.* Eyewitness Series. New York: Alfred A. Knopf, Inc., 1992.

## Technology Resources

### Internet
**PLANETDIARY** at *http://www.planetdiary.com*
- Learn more about volcanoes and earthquakes in *Volcano* and *Earthquake* by clicking on *Phenomena Backgrounders.*
- Find geological news by exploring *Current Phenomena.*

### Software
Earthquake. Mac, Win. ESI.
Rocks and Volcanoes. Mac, Win. ER.
Violent Earth. Mac, Win. ESI.

### CD-ROMs
Interactive Earth. SFAW.

### Laserdiscs
Living Textbook. (See barcodes on pages in this chapter.) Optical Data.
Volcanoes. EB.
STV: Restless Earth. SC.

### Videos
Earthquakes. 20 min. MMI.
Mount St. Helens: What Geologists Learned. 40 min. MMI.
Volcanoes of the United States. 20 min. MMI.

## Introducing the Chapter

Have students read the description of the photograph. Ask if they agree or disagree with the description.

### Directed Inquiry

Have students study the photograph. Ask:

▶ What is happening in this photograph? (Red-hot lava is flowing from a volcano.)

▶ What do volcanic eruptions reveal about the earth's interior? (There are temperatures and pressures that can melt solid rock, as well as forces moving the earth's crust from below.)

▶ What do you think the darker material floating on the molten lava is? Is it like anything you know of? (Students may say that it is cooling patches of lava formed by exposure to the air above it like the "skin" on hot milk or soup.)

▶ Why is this picture appropriate to the subject of earthquakes and volcanoes? (Earthquakes are produced by some of the same forces that cause eruptions: the buildup and release of pressure beneath the earth and movement of the earth's plates.)

## Chapter Vocabulary

| | |
|---|---|
| cinder cone volcano | lava |
| composite volcano | seismic wave |
| crater | shield volcano |
| earthquake | tsunami |
| epicenter | vent |
| focus | volcano |

### Writing Connection

Have students list the five senses. Then have them write words to describe how the material in the photograph would feel, look, sound, smell, and taste. Encourage students to write a paragraph about the photograph based on the list of words.

**Chapter 7**

# Earthquakes and Volcanoes

### Chapter Sections

**7.1** Earthquakes

**7.2** Earthquake Evidence

**7.3** Volcanoes

### What do you see?

“This picture is lava flowing from a nearby volcano or volcano spout. The tremendous heat and pressure under the volcano force this lava out onto the earth's surface. The lava or magma (as it is called when it is underground) can cause vast changes in the earth's appearance. The Hawaiian Islands were all formed by lava like this. The next day this place probably looked like a mass of black rock, just like the Hawaiian Islands.”

*Derek Smiley*
*Patrick Henry Middle School*
*Sioux Falls, South Dakota*

To find out more about the photograph, look on page 152. As you read this chapter, you will learn about volcanoes and earthquakes.

*Themes in Science*

**Energy** The potential energy that is stored in the earth's crust is changed into kinetic energy when it is released during an earthquake. The energy of an earthquake is transferred through the crust of the earth, to the surface and the objects resting there. This energy can cause major changes on the landscape.

## 7.1 Earthquakes

### Objectives

▶ **Describe** what happens during an earthquake.

▶ **Explain** the difference between an earthquake's focus and epicenter.

▶ **Compare** and **contrast** the three types of waves produced by earthquakes.

▶ **Infer** the number of seismograph stations needed to locate an earthquake's epicenter.

▼ **ACTIVITY**

**Inferring**

*This Just In . . .*

Imagine you are listening to the radio when the announcer says that a 5.8 earthquake has occurred in Alaska. What are your first thoughts? How did it happen? What does the "5.8" mean?

**SKILLS WARMUP**

I magine you and a friend are standing on a sidewalk. Suddenly the pavement seems to move under your feet. You grab your friend to avoid falling. In front of you, a streetlight sways wildly. You feel dizzy and scared. Neither of you has experienced this before, but you both yell, "Earthquake!"

In less than a minute, the shaking stops. You and your friend look at each other with relief. You feel a small earthquake later that day, but it passes almost before you notice it. As the days go by, you begin to forget the terrifying feeling of the earth moving. Yet you often find yourself wondering when the next earthquake will strike. You also find yourself curious to know why earthquakes occur.

### Energy of Earthquakes

Movements of the earth's crust that occur when plates shift and release stored, or potential, energy are called **earthquakes**. The energy quickly travels outward in waves from the point of breakage. The energy of an earthquake can break and move rock and soil. Most earthquakes occur at depths less than 100 km, where rocks are brittle.

Earthquakes can be dramatic events, or they can be so small that most people don't notice them. Most earthquakes result from movements of the earth's crust along faults. As you learned in Chapter 6, a fault is a fracture in the earth's crust. The two sides of a fault move in different directions. These opposing movements set the stage for earthquakes to occur.

**Figure 7.1** ▲
In 1989, the Loma Prieta earthquake in California caused the collapse of this building in San Francisco.

## TEACH

### Skills WorkOut

To help students understand the movement of waves, have them do the Skills WorkOut.

**Answer** Answers may vary.

1. Students may suggest that the water molecules move up and down at the surface, while the wave spreads outward from the source. This movement is like an L wave.

2. Students should recognize that the motion of the string is at right angles to the motion of the wave. The movement is most like an S wave.

3. Students should describe the motion as stretching and compressing, the spring and the wave move in the same direction. These waves are most like P waves.

### Discuss

Have students explain in their own words the difference between the focus and the epicenter of an earthquake and how each relate to a fault. (Focus is the location beneath the earth where rocks break apart, epicenter is the surface location above the focus; both are likely to be along a fault, crack, or fracture in the earth's surface.)

### Directed Inquiry

Have students study Figure 7.2. Ask the following questions:

▶ What form of energy do seismic waves carry, potential or kinetic? (Kinetic)

▶ During an earthquake, where is potential energy transformed into kinetic energy? (At the focus)

▶ What happens to the amount of kinetic energy carried by the wave as the wave moves away from the focus? (It decreases. As the wave moves, kinetic energy is transferred to the earth and to objects on the earth in the path of the wave.)

### Themes in Science

**Systems and Interactions** The force from an earthquake builds up in the earth's crust and is released as energy waves. The energy waves interact with the surrounding rock to produce vibrations.

### Integrating the Sciences

**Physical Science** Remind students that if an elastic material is stretched or compressed beyond a certain limit, it will remain distorted. The elastic limit is the point at which this distortion occurs. Have students describe experiences they have had with materials and elastic limits. (Examples include breaking the ribbon around a gift box or snapping a twig in half.)

▼ **ACTIVITY**

**Making Analogies**

*Making Waves*

Briefly describe the movement of the waves in the following situations:

**1.** A pebble drops into a puddle.

**2.** A string is pulled on one end and the other end is loose.

**3.** A spring scale is held and a heavy object is attached to the bottom of the spring. Which situation is most like a P wave? S wave? L wave?

**SKILLS WORKOUT**

**Figure 7.2**
**Earthquake Epicenter** ▼

### Physics of Earthquakes

In Chapter 6, you learned about the types of force, or stress, in the earth's crust. These forces are at work along faults. They cause the two sides of a fault to move past each other. Sometimes the rocks along the two sides of a fault may snag and remain locked. Tremendous stress builds in these areas as the two sides of the fault attempt to move past each other.

The limit to how much stress a material can absorb is called its *elastic limit*. For example, if you stretch a rubber band too far, it will break and snap back. When rocks are strained beyond their elastic limit, the rocks break and grind past each other, releasing huge amounts of energy.

Look at Figure 7.2. As the rocks break and move, potential energy is transformed into kinetic energy in the form of **seismic waves**. Recall that seismic waves are the vibrations produced by earthquakes. Earthquakes produce three main types of seismic waves: primary, secondary, and surface.

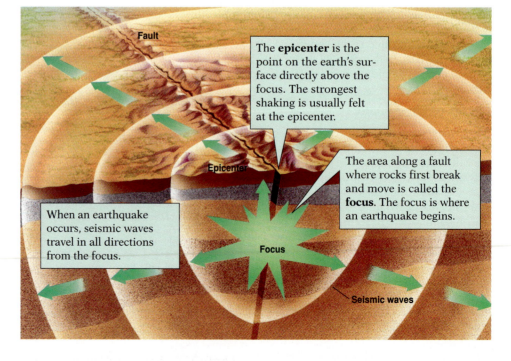

The **epicenter** is the point on the earth's surface directly above the focus. The strongest shaking is usually felt at the epicenter.

The area along a fault where rocks first break and move is called the **focus**. The focus is where an earthquake begins.

When an earthquake occurs, seismic waves travel in all directions from the focus.

Fault

Epicenter

Focus

Seismic waves

## Integrating the Sciences

**Physical Science** Demonstrate the difference between transverse and longitudinal waves. To show a transverse wave, attach one end of a rope to a stationary object. Shake the rope up and down so waves begin to form. Have students describe the shape of the transverse wave. To show a longitudinal wave, obtain a large coiled spring. Place the spring on a level surface and squeeze several of the loops together. Release the coils. Have students describe the shape of the longitudinal wave.

Primary waves, or P waves, are the fastest seismic waves. P waves are *longitudinal waves*. Figure 7.3 shows the movement of a longitudinal wave. In a longitudinal wave, the material through which the wave is traveling moves in the same direction as the wave. P waves compress and stretch the earth in the direction of the wave.

The second waves to arrive at a given point are secondary waves, or S waves. S waves are *transverse waves*. You can see how a transverse wave moves in Figure 7.3. It is similar to the up and down movement of a rope wave. In a transverse wave, the material moves at right angles to the wave direction.

When P waves and S waves arrive at the earth's surface, their energy is changed into surface waves, or L waves. L waves cause the most damage during an earthquake because they cause the earth's surface to move up and down or side to side.

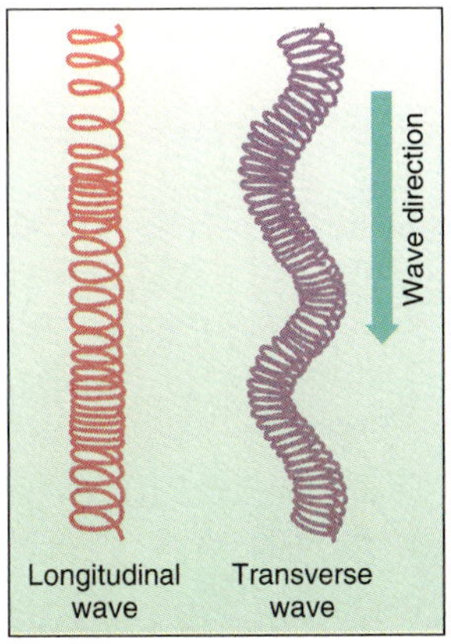

### Detecting Seismic Waves

You have learned that seismographs are used to detect and record seismic waves. The seismograph, shown in Figure 7.4, has a pen attached to a weight and a sheet of paper on a revolving drum. Seismic waves from earthquakes cause the pen to vibrate and record a wavy line on the paper as the drum revolves. The height of the peaks of the wavy line indicates the strength of the earthquake. Notice the pattern in the seismograph's record below.

### Locating an Epicenter

Because P, S, and L waves travel at different rates, they reach a seismograph at different times. The difference between the arrival times of the waves enables scientists to find the epicenter's distance from the seismograph.

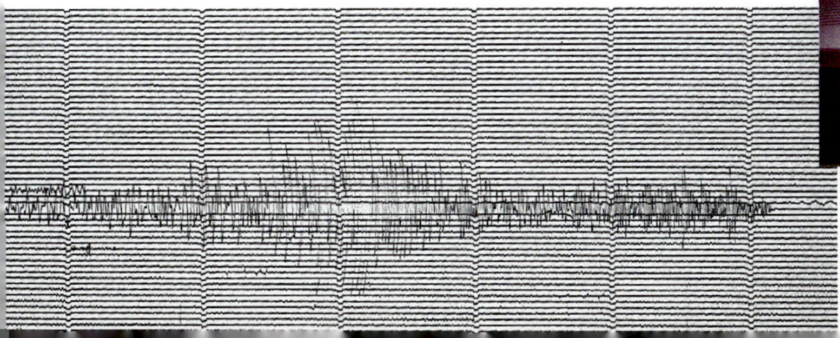

**Figure 7.3** ▲
Which wave represents the movement of a P wave? An S wave? ①

**Figure 7.4**
Study the printout at left. It shows seismic wave activity from the Landers earthquake in southern California. The earthquake was recorded on June 2, 1992. ▼

## Class Activity

Demonstrate the principle of a seismograph using a strip of adding-machine tape. Ask two students to guide the strip slowly across a long table. A third student should hold a felt tip pen just above the paper so that a straight line forms as the paper moves. When a fourth student shakes the table back and forth, wavy lines will form on the paper strip.

### ◆ Explore Visually

Have students study Figure 7.4. Ask the following questions:

▶ What does the printout tell you about the movement of the earth on June 2, 1992? (The taller lines at the center of the printout probably indicate an earthquake.)

▶ Which area of the printout shows waves that probably cause the most damage? What kind of waves are shown? (The tall waves in the center; surface or L waves)

▶ What part of the printout probably shows secondary waves reaching the seismograph? (The area to the left of the large wavy lines showing smaller wavy lines)

### Enrich

Use Enrich Worksheet 7.1.

### Integrated Learning

Use Integrating Worksheet 7.1.

### Answer to In-Text Question

① **The longitudinal wave represents a P wave. The transverse wave represents an S wave.**

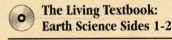
**The Living Textbook:
Earth Science Sides 1-2**

Chapter 7          Frame 01593
Locating Epicenter (1 Frame)
Search:

## TEACH · *Continued*

### Critical Thinking

**Reason and Conclude** Ask students to explain why the information from three seismographs, rather than one or two, is used to locate the epicenter of an earthquake. (One seismograph gives the location as anywhere on the perimeter of a circle; two seismographs give two circles, which may intersect at two points. Plots from three seismographs intersect at only one point, locating the epicenter with increased accuracy.)

### *SkillBuilder*

**Answers**

1. Similar: each measures earthquake intensity. Different: Richter measures energy released, Mercalli uses personal observations of intensity.

2. A very destructive earthquake during which some structures are destroyed; XI and greater

3. Richter 5, Mercalli VI to VII

4. Answers may vary, but students should suggest that strong earthquakes in undeveloped areas cause less structural damage than mild quakes in heavily populated areas. Two scales offer a method for describing all quakes.

### Enrich

The Richter scale is based on measurements of the *amplitude* of ground motion. For each magnitude increase of 1 on the scale, 32 times as much *energy* is released.

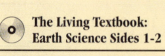

**The Living Textbook:
Earth Science Sides 1-2**

| Chapter 16 | Frame 02574 |
| Locating Epicenter (2 Frames) |
| Search: | Step: |

---

### *Integrating the Sciences*

**Astronomy** Tell students that seismographs have been placed on the moon to detect moonquakes and meteorite impacts. Data are then sent back to the earth, enabling scientists to learn more about the moon's interior. Have students discuss other ways that seismographs might be useful in space exploration. (To study the interiors of other planets)

 **Math Connection**

Point out to students that the Richter scale is a base 10 logarithmic scale. Richter scale measurements can be shown using scientific notation. Show how exponents can be added or subtracted. Ask students how much more ground motion an earthquake of magnitude 8 has compared to one with a magnitude of 4. Use scientific notation and the rules of exponents to solve the problem. ($10^8 \div 10^4 = 10^4$ or 10,000 times stronger)

**Figure 7.5** ▲
The epicenter is the point at which the three circles intersect.

The calculated distance to the epicenter becomes the radius of a circle that is then plotted on a map. The epicenter lies somewhere on the circle. As shown in Figure 7.5, plotting circles from three different seismograph stations pinpoints the epicenter.

### Rating Earthquakes

The strength of an earthquake, or its magnitude, is often described in terms of numbers on the Richter scale. The *Richter magnitude* is based on the amount of shaking caused by an earthquake. On the scale, each increase of 1 magnitude number equals an increase of 10 in ground motion caused by seismic waves. A magnitude 7 earthquake causes 10 times more ground motion than a magnitude 6 and 100 times more than magnitude 5.

Earthquakes are also rated on the Mercalli intensity scale. This scale is based on earthquake intensity, which includes ground motion and damage.

### *SkillBuilder* *Reading a Table*

#### *Comparing Earthquake Scales*

The Mercalli scale and the Richter scale for rating earthquakes are based on different factors. The Richter scale is based on energy released by an earthquake, whereas the Mercalli scale is based on personal observations of earthquake intensity.

The table shows a rough relationship between the two scales. Study the table, then answer the following questions:

1. How are the two scales similar? How are they different?

2. What occurs during a Richter magnitude 8.0 earthquake? What is the measurement for the same quake on the Mercalli scale?

3. At which measurement on each scale does damage to buildings begin?

4. Why are two different scales used for measuring earthquakes?

| Measurement | | |
|---|---|---|
| **Richter Scale** | **Mercalli Scale** | **Earthquake Effects** |
| 3 | III | Felt slightly in areas near epicenter, no damage |
| 4 | V | Felt by most people up to several miles from earthquake, some objects upset |
| 5 | VI–VII | Strongly felt, some damage to weak buildings |
| 6 | VII–VIII | Moderately destructive, some severe damage to weak buildings |
| 7 | IX–X | Major earthquake, destructive to many buildings |
| 8 | XI–? | Very destructive, some structures destroyed |

## Geography Connection

Show students a map of the United States that includes Hawaii and Alaska. Using the map of major earthquake zones in Figure 7.6 and the United States map, have students locate states where earthquakes are most likely to occur. (For example, California, Oregon, Hawaii, Alaska, Washington)

## Portfolio

Have students collect newspaper and magazine reports, including photographs, of worldwide earthquake activity. Have students add the articles to their portfolios for later reference.

### Skills Development

**Collect Data** Students can form "earthquake watch" groups, one for each of the major zones shown in Figure 7.6. They can plot the information they collect on a class map similar to Figure 7.6. Students may use different colored pins or paper flags to indicate the intensity of the earthquakes they report. Allow students to add information to this map as they study both earthquakes and volcanoes.

### Critical Thinking

**Compare and Contrast** Ask students to trace the continents and earthquake zones shown in Figure 7.6. Then have them trace the major plates of the earth using Figure 5.12 on pages 102 and 103. Ask them to identify at least three areas where the plate boundaries and the earthquake zones overlap.

## Earthquake Zones

Some parts of the earth's crust are more stable than others and have few, if any, earthquakes. Other regions are under enormous stress and have many quakes. Figure 7.6 shows that most of the world's earthquakes occur along or near the edges of plate boundaries, where stress is greatest.

The earth has three major earthquake zones. The most active of these zones is the Ring of Fire, shown in Figure 7.6. It accounts for 80 percent of the world's seismic activity. The Ring of Fire extends nearly all the way around the Pacific Ocean and includes the eastern coast of Asia, and the western coasts of North America and South America. Along the ring, some plates are being subducted. In a subduction zone, one plate is forced under another plate. Some plates along the ring are scraping past each other. In the United States, the most active earthquake region is in Alaska along the volcanoes of the Aleutian Islands. Another very active earthquake region is California.

The other main earthquake zones are the mid-Atlantic ridge and the Mediterranean-Asiatic belt. Scientists hypothesize that new ocean crust is being created along the mid-Atlantic ridge, causing the region's many earthquakes. Along the Mediterranean-Asiatic belt, continental plates are colliding, often causing very destructive earthquakes.

A small number of the world's earthquakes occur far from plate boundaries. For example, some of North America's strongest quakes have struck the eastern United States. These include the New Madrid, Missouri, quakes of 1811 and 1812 and the Charleston, South Carolina, quake of 1886. The activity in Missouri and South Carolina shows that even quiet parts of the earth's crust may conceal large amounts of stress.

**Figure 7.6**
**Major Earthquake Zones** ▼

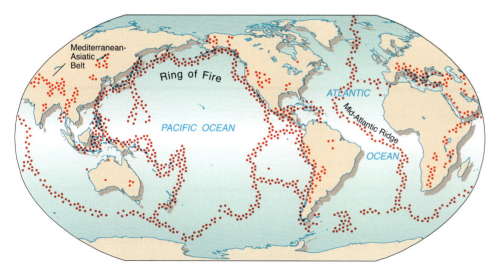

The Living Textbook:
Earth Science Sides 1-2

Chapter 7          Frame 01588
Faults (4 Frames)
Search:                    Step:

## Skills WorkOut

To help students discover powerful earthquakes in history, have them do the Skills WorkOut.

**Answers** Answers and graphs will vary. Have students use references. Students should recognize that most earthquakes occurred along the Ring of Fire, and one occurred along the boundary of the Arabian plate.

## EVALUATE

## WrapUp

**Review** At the chalkboard, make a chart of earthquake information. Include L, S, and P waves. Have students describe the wave motion, the evidence of energy transfer, and the damage or destruction the energy can cause. Ask students to relate the terms *fault*, *epicenter*, and *focus*.

Use Review Worksheet 7.1.

## Check and Explain

1. Earthquakes are caused by sudden movements of the earth's crust that occur when plates move along faults and release stored potential energy.

2. The focus is the area along a fault where the rocks first break and move. The epicenter is the point on the earth's surface directly above the focus.

3. In P waves, the medium and the energy wave move in the same direction. In S waves, the medium moves at right angles to the energy wave. In L waves, the wave moves outward from the epicenter in many directions.

4. No, three stations are all that is needed to locate an epicenter. The circles plotted from three seismographs intersect at only one point.

### STS Connection

Remind students that in areas with a high risk of earthquakes, seismic networks are often set up to monitor movements in the earth. These networks may help predict earthquakes. Other changes studied by Chinese scientists have concluded that the concentration of radon, a radioactive gas, increases in groundwater before earthquakes. Chinese scientists have also studied changes in animal behavior that may be used to predict earthquakes. Reports of farm animals and pets acting agitated, not eating, and making odd noises were recorded nine hours before an earthquake in January 1975.

### ▼ ACTIVITY

**Making a Graph**

*Shaky Ground*

Use resources at your school's library to research historically strong earthquakes. Make a line graph to illustrate the magnitudes of the ten most powerful earthquakes of the twentieth century. Identify the earthquakes by their epicenter. How many of these earthquakes occurred in the earth's major earthquake zones?

**SKILLS WORKOUT**

**Physical Science**
**L I N K**

As fault blocks slide past each other, they may lock or stick together due to friction along the fault. Collect the following items: 2 shoe boxes, 10 wide rubberbands, glue, and scissors.

**1.** Cut the rubberbands into 2 to 5 cm pieces. Glue the pieces to the bottoms of the shoe boxes. Allow glue to dry.

**2.** With a partner, press the bottoms of the shoe boxes together, sliding the boxes past each other with differing amounts of effort.

How much effort was needed to move the "blocks" past each other? How strong was the force of friction along your "fault"?

**A C T I V I T Y**

### Science and Technology
*What Fault Is This?*

In 1983, a Richter magnitude 6.7 earthquake struck Coalinga, California. Coalinga is midway between Los Angeles and San Francisco. The earthquake surprised seismologists for three reasons. First, though the area's geology had been studied as a result of oil drilling, no active faults had been mapped. Second, there was no recorded history of any large quakes in the area. Third, studies showed no sign of hidden faults capable of large quakes. Yet a large quake struck Coalinga. In fact, the damage from the quake was so great that it was easier to tear down many buildings than to repair them.

How could the Coalinga earthquake have happened? Should residents expect future tremors? Many scientists studied damage to buildings. They examined the oil wells in the area. They also searched the town's historical records. They hoped to find evidence of previous earthquakes in the area.

The work of seismologists, geophysicists, and others finally revealed the truth. Several faults exist 6 to 10 km beneath Coalinga. The faults had not been detected because they are deeper than the deepest oil wells. Also, the faults are hidden by folds. Many geologists were surprised that active faults could be hidden in folds.

In the end, the scientists' investigations found that the Coalinga faults are not very active. They concluded that future earthquakes are more likely to occur on more active faults, such as the San Andreas. But the events in Coalinga are a reminder that unknown faults can surprise residents and scientists alike.

### Check and Explain

1. Explain what causes earthquakes.

2. What is the difference between an earthquake's focus and its epicenter?

3. **Compare and Contrast** How do the three types of seismic waves differ? How are they similar?

4. **Infer** Would using four seismograph stations to locate the epicenter of an earthquake be any more accurate than using three? Explain.

### Prelab Discussion

Have students read the entire activity. Discuss these points before beginning:

► Review Richter magnitude and the Richter scale.

► Have students predict which block will be easiest to knock down.

► Discuss the different types of seismic waves and determine which type will be simulated in the model.

### Answer to Link

Likely responses are that high effort was required to move the blocks past each other, depending on the amount of rubberband strips and how hard the partner pressed boxes together. The force of friction involved should be almost the same as that required to push the boxes past each other.

**Time** 30 minutes   **Group** pairs

**Materials**

15 blocks of wood (3 × 3 × 3 cm)

15 blocks of wood (3 × 3 × 15 cm)

15 blocks of wood (3 × 3 × 25 cm)

15 strips of cardboard

masking tape

## Activity 7   *How can you model the Richter scale?*

**Skills** Model; Infer

### Task 1  Prelab Prep

1. Collect the following items: three blocks of wood with the following relative sizes: 3 × 3 × 3 cm, 3 × 3 × 15 cm, 3 × 3 × 25 cm; piece of cardboard large enough to hold the blocks; masking tape; pencil.
2. Place the cardboard on a desk or table. Be sure the desk is level.
3. With the tape, label the longest block *1*, the medium-sized block *5*, and the smallest block *9*.
4. Place the three blocks on the cardboard with the long side facing up.

### Task 2  Data Record

1. On a separate sheet of paper, copy Table 7.1.
2. In the data table, record all your observations and measurements about the movement of the blocks.

### Task 3  Procedure

1. Move the cardboard to create a gentle shaking for 5 seconds.
2. Record any observations about the blocks.
3. Repeat the gentle shaking for about 65 seconds. Record your observations.

4. Repeat steps 1 through 3 and carefully use moderate force and violent force to shake the blocks.

### Task 4  Analysis

1. Identify the variables in this activity.
2. Which block was the hardest to knock down? The easiest?
3. Which had a greater impact on the blocks, the length of the shaking or the strength of the shaking? Why?
4. The label on each of the blocks corresponds to a reading on the Richter scale. The energy it takes to knock over each block relates to an earthquake of that size on the Richter scale. Which block was the hardest to knock down? What is the Richter scale number for an earthquake of that size?

### Task 5  Conclusion

How does your model compare to the Richter scale? Write a short paragraph comparing the earthquake energy that relates to the different numbers on the Richter scale.

### *Extension*

Calculate the size of the blocks needed to represent earthquake energies for the rest of the Richter scale. Make enough blocks to complete an entire Richter scale set. Test the set that you make.

### Analysis

1. Size of block, force of shaking, pattern of cardboard movement, length of shaking

2. The tallest block should have been the easiest to knock down; the shortest block, the hardest.

3. Students' answers may vary; however, students probably found that the strength of shaking had a greater impact because of initial damage.

4. The small block was the hardest to knock down. Nine was the Richter number corresponding to the block that was hardest to knock down.

### Conclusion

Accept reasonable conclusions. The model corresponds to the Richter scale in that the scale rates earthquakes based on energy released and the model involved the energy needed to knock down the blocks.

### Extension

The entire scale could be represented by blocks ranging from 3 × 3 × 3 cm to 3 × 3 × 25 cm. Answers should be related to actual test results.

**Table 7.1  Earthquake Energy Table**

| Type of Shaking | | Movement | | |
|---|---|---|---|---|
| Strength | Length (sec) | Block 1 | Block 5 | Block 9 |
| Gentle | 5 | | | |
| | 65 | | | |
| Moderate | 5 | | | |
| | 65 | | | |
| Violent | 5 | | | |
| | 65 | | | |

### Section Objectives

For a list of section objectives, see the Student Edition page.

### Skills Objectives

Students should be able to:

**Make a Model** of seismic wave movement in soft materials.

**Predict** hazards caused by earthquakes.

**Infer** ways to reinforce structures for surviving earthquakes.

### Vocabulary

tsunami

## MOTIVATE

### Skills WarmUp

To help students understand seismic-wave activity in soft materials, have them do the Skills WarmUp.

**Answer** Students will find that it is more difficult than they expected to push the sand or rice through the paper towel. They should infer that seismic waves move more slowly through sand.

### Answer to In-Text Question

① **The road damage looks as if one segment of ground had suddenly lifted, and the other had fallen.**

**The Living Textbook:
Earth Science Sides 1-2**

| | |
|---|---|
| Chapter 7 | Frame 01604 |
| Alaskan Earthquake (4 Frames) | |
| Search: | Step: |

### Themes in Science

**Scale and Structure** The movement of plates deep in the earth's crust affects much smaller structures, such as roads and trees, on the surface of the earth. Scientists study evidence from the structures on the surface to infer what is occurring to plates deep within the earth.

## ▼ ACTIVITY

### Making a Model

*Traveling Waves*

Collect the following items: rubber band, cardboard tube, paper towel, and sand or rice.

**1.** Using the rubber band, cover one end of the cardboard tube with a paper towel.

**2.** Fill the tube with sand or rice.

**3.** Push down on the sand with your finger. Try to push the sand out through the paper towel.

What happens? Infer how you think seismic waves move through soft materials, such as sand.

**SKILLS WARMUP**

# 7.2 Earthquake Evidence

## Objectives

▶ **Describe** some features produced by earthquakes.

▶ **Discuss** factors that determine earthquake damage.

▶ **Explain** what causes tsunamis.

▶ **Make inferences** about ways to build structures that could withstand major damage from earthquakes.

---

Look at Figure 7.7. How do you think the road became separated? What powerful forces can cause the earth's surface to separate in this way? You can probably easily guess that an earthquake caused the separation.

Evidence of the powerful force of earthquakes occurs in many forms. Some of these forms may be permanent, such as ground movement. Others are temporary, such as damage caused to a road that is quickly repaired. Scientists learn a lot about earthquakes by studying the evidence the quakes leave behind.

### Ground-Level Evidence

Evidence from earthquakes is sometimes preserved in vertical or horizontal changes in ground level near a fault. The road in Figure 7.7 was separated by movement along the San Andreas fault in California. Strong, abrupt earthquakes generally leave more dramatic evidence than small earthquakes.

Along some active faults, ground-level changes occur slowly but nearly continuously whether or not an earthquake occurs. This type of slow, steady motion is called *creep*. Even at the creep rate of only 1 cm per year, ground levels on either side of a fault would be displaced by 1 m after about 100 years. If a house or fence sat on the fault, the creep would become evident within a decade or two. The reason is that the ground displacement caused by creeps eventually breaks buildings and other structures located on the fault.

**Figure 7.7** ▲
What kind of evidence was left behind after an earthquake struck this area? ①

## Social Studies Connection

Tell students that coastlines are often heavily populated. These areas also tend to be active earthquake zones. Earthquakes along coastal areas may create scarps that are subject to erosion. Have students locate coastal cities or towns that are in earthquake zones. Discuss whether communities should prohibit or regulate building along these coastlines.

## Landscape Evidence

Powerful earthquakes can cause permanent changes in an area's landscape. One of the most dramatic examples occurred in Alaska in 1964. The 8.4 magnitude of this earthquake caused the upheaval of over 260 000 sq km of ground. The city of Anchorage was actually moved sideways!

Earthquake movements especially affect poorly compacted sediments, such as sands, silts, and clays. When seismic wave energy is more powerful than the compacted sediments, the sediments may fracture or slide. You can see examples of sudden movements that uplift parts of the earth's crust below.

### Slides ▲

Earthquakes often trigger slides, or rapid downslope movements of soil, debris, and rock. A 1985 earthquake in Mexico caused the slide shown above. Slides can occur on a fault or a long distance away. Large sections of mountains may fracture and race downward, coming to rest where the slope ends. Some slides continue for many kilometers, often destroying everything in their path, including houses and roads.

### Scarps

Sudden earth movements along a fault may create a scarp, or cliff. A scarp's height depends on the type of materials uplifted and the amount and frequency of uplift. Some scarps may be as high as 1,500 m. Scarps, like most steep hillsides, are subject to erosion. Over time, a scarp may become so eroded that its origin is difficult to recognize. The scarp shown below occurred along the San Andreas fault in California. ▼

### Fissures ▲

Earthquakes can produce fissures, or long cracks, in soil or rock. In rocky areas, these cracks may extend for many kilometers. Massive landslides may result if the fissures occur on a hill or mountainside. The fissures in the photograph above are located near the San Andreas fault in California.

---

## Directed Inquiry

After students study the page, ask them to tell how landscape features can provide evidence of an earthquake. Then ask the following questions:

▶ How is a slide formed? How is it different from a scarp? (A slide is a downward movement of rock, soil, and debris. A scarp is a clifflike feature caused by uplift.)

▶ What are fissures? (Long cracks in soil or rock)

▶ How are fissures and landslides related? (If a fissure is produced on a hill or mountainside, a landslide may result.)

▶ What kinds of landscape are most affected by earthquake movements? (Sand, silt, clay, and other loosely compacted sediments)

## Skills Development

**Classify** Have students study the photographs of earthquake damage that they added to their portfolios in Section 7.1 on page 137. Have them classify the damage shown as either a fissure, slide, or scarp. Remind students that they may need to look for clues to help them interpret the photographs.

⊙ **The Living Textbook:**
**Earth Science Sides 1-2**

Chapter 7            Frame 01606
Slide and Scarp (2 Frames)
Search:                    Step:

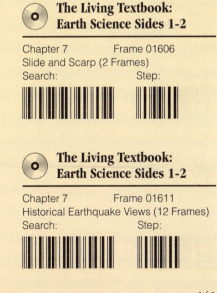

⊙ **The Living Textbook:**
**Earth Science Sides 1-2**

Chapter 7            Frame 01611
Historical Earthquake Views (12 Frames)
Search:                    Step:

**TEACH ▪ Continued**

### Class Activity

Draw a vertical line on the chalkboard. At the bottom, write the label *Least Earthquake Damage*, at the top, write the label *Most Earthquake Damage*. Ask volunteers to come to the chalkboard and put the following phrases in the correct position:

▶ building anchored in bedrock

▶ wood-frame buildings

▶ buildings built on loose soil

▶ unreinforced brick buildings

▶ seashore dwellings

▶ epicenter close to populated area

### Enrich

Encourage students to find out how much power is in a wall of water 10 or 15 meters high. They may base estimates on figures from proposed wave-energy projects. A one-meter-high wave one kilometer long contains about 20,000 kW of power. Ask: What could you do with the harnessed energy of a tsunami?

### Answer to In-Text Question

① **Materials with spacing or "shock absorbers" are more likely to withstand an earthquake than rigid, unyielding materials.**

---

**The Living Textbook:
Earth Science Sides 1-2**

Chapter 7      Frame 01596
Structural Damage (2 Frames)
Search:        Step:

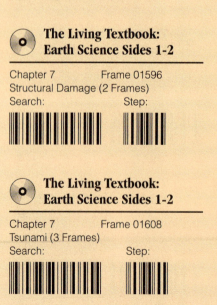

**The Living Textbook:
Earth Science Sides 1-2**

Chapter 7      Frame 01608
Tsunami (3 Frames)
Search:        Step:

142

## Multicultural Perspectives

Point out to students that the word *tsunami* is Japanese for "large waves in harbors." Tsunamis are most common in the Pacific Ocean. Japan has suffered from many tsunamis that have accompanied earthquakes. One of the most destructive earthquakes of this century occurred in Japan on September 1, 1923. About 143,000 people died, and the tsunami that followed caused the water in a Japanese harbor to sink 30 meters.

### Earthquake Damage

The enormous forces that cause landslides and uplift scarps can seriously damage human-built structures. In fact, earthquakes can level entire towns. What determines how much damage a quake causes?

Perhaps the most important factor that determines earthquake damage is how close an earthquake epicenter is to a populated area. In fact, a moderate quake that occurs in a crowded city is more likely to cause damage than a large quake in a desert.

The type of ground on which structures are built also influences damage. Soft, wet, loose soils can increase seismic waves several fold. In 1985, an earthquake that occurred in Mexico City caused major destruction and many deaths. Most of the buildings in Mexico City were built on loose soil. Buildings on loose soils have less of a chance of surviving earthquakes than buildings on solid ground.

**Figure 7.9** ▲
The 1964 earthquake that struck Alaska unleashed a series of tsunamis. Waves crossed the Pacific Ocean and damaged areas as far away as California, Japan, and Hawaii. Here you can see some of the damage that occurred.

**Figure 7.8** ▲
The earthquake that caused the collapse of the middle building occurred in Managua, Nicaragua, in 1972. How do the materials used in a building's construction affect its ability to withstand an earthquake? ①

Damage also depends on building design and materials. Wood-frame structures may be able to move with and withstand ground motion. Unreinforced brick and cement structures are likely to sway and collapse during large quakes. An earthquake in Peru in 1970 destroyed most buildings made of adobe (uh DOH bee), a soil-clay mixture from which bricks are formed. The adobe structures could not withstand the earthquake vibrations.

People who live near the seashore face another threat from quakes. An offshore earthquake can cause movements in the ocean floor that create a **tsunami** (soo NAHM ee). A tsunami is an ocean wave caused by earthquakes.

In deep water, tsunamis are low and fast-moving. In shallow water, they begin to slow down and increase in height, to as much as 30 m. When the wave breaks, the tsunami releases tremendous energy. Few structures can survive a large tsunami. Figure 7.9 shows the damage caused by a tsunami.

### Cooperative Learning

Have students work in cooperative groups of three to devise an earthquake preparedness plan. In their plan, they should note necessary supplies, a school evacuation plan, and a crowd management system. Have each group present its plan to the class.

**Answer to Link**

Drawings will vary, but designs should be testable.

## Discuss

Have students study Table 7.2. Then have them work in groups to form a plan they might use if an earthquake damaged the school. Encourage students to find out if the school has a disaster plan.

## Skills Development

**Communicate** Have students write a letter to a class in a school that has been damaged by a natural disaster. They can list information they would like to receive and prepare a specific list of questions they would like answered.

## EVALUATE

### WrapUp

**Review** Have groups of students compare their portfolio pictures of earthquake damage. Ask them to decide which pictures show the most destruction and offer explanations for that damage.

Use Review Worksheet 7.2.

### Check and Explain

1. The landscape near a fault or affected by an earthquake may lift up, form fissures, or slide downhill.

2. Factors such as closeness to epicenter, amount and density of population, compactness of soil, and building structure and materials

3. Answers will vary. Answers might include fire; being struck by falling objects; tsunami; avalanche.

4. Answers will vary. Answers should take into account that the building should be able to move with the movement of the earth during an earthquake.

### Decision Making

If you have classroom sets of *One-Minute Readings*, have students read Issue 61, "Earthquakes," on page 104. Discuss the questions.

---

## Earthquake Prediction

For centuries, people have tried to predict earthquakes by observing changes in animal behavior and well levels, among other things. Today, seismologists use more sophisticated prediction techniques. They look at evidence of former quakes to predict future ones. Changes in creep rates and lower water levels in wells may also tell of future quakes.

In 1981, seismologists predicted that a quake was likely in the Santa Cruz Mountain area of the San Andreas fault within 15 years. When moderate earthquakes rocked this area in 1988 and 1989, scientists identified these as foreshocks. The devastating Loma Prieta quake in October of 1989 proved them correct.

### Science and Society  *Earthquake Safety*

If you live near an active fault, you and your family may already know about the importance of preparing for possible earthquakes. In some earthquake-prone areas, such as California, city officals are encouraging families and communities to develop earthquake disaster plans. These plans include what to do during an earthquake, where to meet after one, and how to communicate if telephones don't work. Table 7.2 lists some ways in which people can prepare for earthquakes.

In a number of earthquake-prone areas, strict building and zoning laws are enforced to reduce seismic risks. Many public facilities are built to survive the largest earthquakes expected.

### Check and Explain

1. What are some changes caused by earthquakes?

2. What factors determine the amount of damage caused by an earthquake?

3. **Predict** Describe the hazards you might face if an earthquake struck while you were asleep in bed; standing next to a tall building; at the beach; skiing.

4. **Infer** If you were an architect in an earthquake-prone area, what could you do to reinforce structures to reduce hazards?

---

### Physical Science
### L I N K

Design a structure that is capable of withstanding an earthquake jolt. Collect two boxes of dominoes and a 0.5 x 0.5 m piece of cardboard.

**1.** Place the cardboard so that one edge hangs over the side of a table by 1 cm.

**2.** Using the dominoes, build a structure as tall as possible on the cardboard.

**3.** Slap the cardboard edge with your hand.

Draw a simple top view and side view sketch of your structure to show your earthquake–resistant design.

### A C T I V I T Y

---

**Table 7.2  Earthquake Safety**

| Outside the Home | Inside the Home |
|---|---|
| Add internal or external braces to weak structures. | Anchor hot water heaters and bookshelves to walls. |
| Anchor house or building to its foundation. | Use flexible connectors on gas appliances. |
| Know where the main gas valve is and have tools to turn it off. | Store emergency supplies in a safe location. |
| Make plans to meet at a specific location outdoors if your home is destroyed. | Install latches on cabinets to protect dishes and other valuables. |

## Section Objectives
For a list of section objectives, see the Student Edition page.

## Skills Objectives
Students should be able to:

**Generalize** about the effects of pressure on closed systems.

**Infer** how volcanic activity can trigger tsunamis.

**Make a Model** of a volcano.

## Vocabulary
volcano, lava, vent, crater, cinder cone volcano, shield volcano, composite volcano

## Integrating the Sciences

**Chemistry** Share with students that when a volcano erupts, it emits several gases that include water vapor, carbon dioxide, and nitrogen and sulfur compounds. The sulfur dioxide released from a volcano changes to sulfuric acid in the atmosphere. The sulfuric acid travels along wind currents and is distributed on ice sheets. By drilling into the ice sheets and examining the sulfuric acid that they find there, scientists can better understand the history of volcanic activity on the earth. Using this method, scientists have found sulfuric acid deposits dating back 100,000 years.

## MOTIVATE

### Skills WarmUp

To help students understand how heat and pressure build up in volcanoes, have them do the Skills WarmUp.
**Answer** Both the balloon and the inner tube burst when overinflated. Students should generalize that built-up pressure in any closed system can lead to an explosion. Pressure released suddenly is accompanied by an eruption.

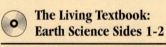

**The Living Textbook:
Earth Science Sides 1-2**

Chapter 4          Frame 00994
Mt. Saint Helen's (3 Frames)
Search:              Step:

**The Living Textbook:
Earth Science Sides 1-2**

Chapter 3          Frame 01380
Lava (5 Frames)
Search:              Step:

▼ **ACTIVITY**

**Generalizing**

*The Pressure is Mounting*

What happens when you blow up a balloon or inflate a tire and put in too much air? What happens when heat and pressure build up in a closed space and the pressure is suddenly released? How might these pressure situations be similar to a volcano that is about to erupt? Explain.

**SKILLS WARMUP**

**Figure 7.10** ▲
This active volcano is located in the Lake District of southern Chile.

# 7.3 Volcanoes

## Objectives

▶ **Describe** how volcanoes form.

▶ **Explain** why volcanoes erupt.

▶ **Compare** the three main types of volcanoes.

▶ **Make a model** of the structure of a volcano.

**D**o you think you know what a volcano looks like? You can probably easily identify the conical, snow-covered peak in Figure 7.10 as a volcano. Some of the world's most beautiful mountains, such as Mt. Fuji in Japan, Mt. Rainier in Washington state, and Mt. Etna in Sicily, are volcanoes. Any opening in the earth's crust that has released molten rock is a **volcano**. The mountain that builds up from volcanic eruptions is also referred to as a volcano.

## Formation of a Volcano

Magma, or molten rock, is under tremendous pressure deep inside the earth. Magma forms deep pockets called magma chambers in some places. Sometimes the magma cools and hardens deep within the crust. However, if the pressure and heat are great, magma tends to force its way upward through the earth's crust.

The more heat and pressure acting on magma, the more potential energy it contains. The higher the potential energy, the more likely the magma will force its way to the earth's surface. Magma that reaches the earth's surface is called **lava**. When lava or other volcanic materials reach the earth's surface, the event is called an eruption.

Volcanoes that have erupted in the past century are considered to be active. Those that haven't erupted in hundreds of years are considered to be dormant, or inactive. Volcanoes that haven't erupted in thousands of years are considered extinct. The eruptive life of a volcano may span hundreds of thousands of years, including periods of dormancy. Study Figure 7.11, which shows the major parts of an active volcano.

## Integrating the Sciences

**Physical Science**  Tell students that when pressure is increased in a closed volume, an explosion might occur. Demonstrate this to the class by adding several teaspoons of baking soda to a balloon. Pour in several tablespoons of vinegar. Quickly tie the balloon. Set the balloon in a trash can or a large bucket. Observe to see what happens to the balloon. Ask students why this occurs. (Because the pressure builds up in a closed volume, leading to an explosion)

**Figure 7.11
Parts of a Volcano ▼**

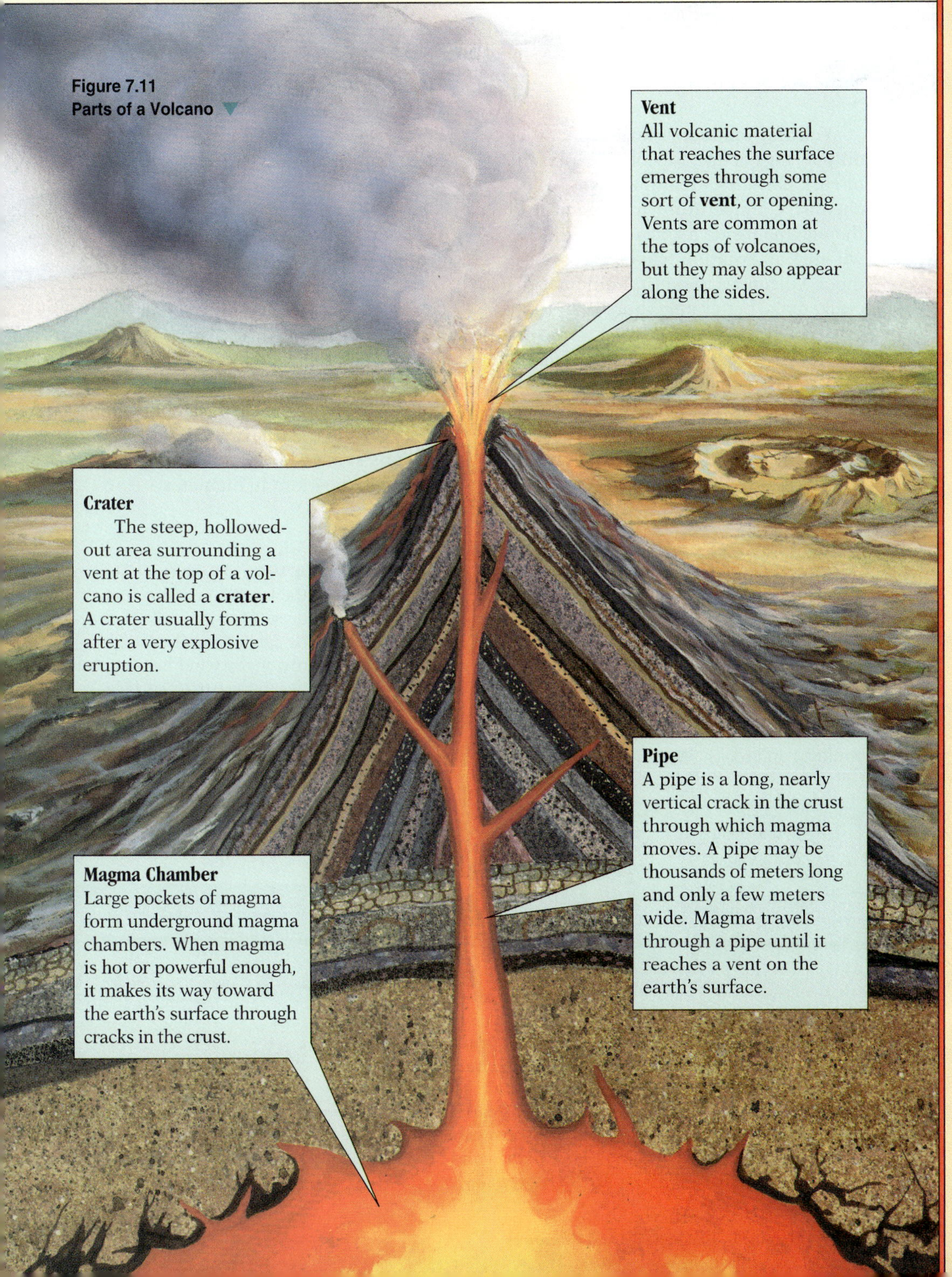

**Vent**
All volcanic material that reaches the surface emerges through some sort of **vent**, or opening. Vents are common at the tops of volcanoes, but they may also appear along the sides.

**Crater**
   The steep, hollowed-out area surrounding a vent at the top of a volcano is called a **crater**. A crater usually forms after a very explosive eruption.

**Pipe**
A pipe is a long, nearly vertical crack in the crust through which magma moves. A pipe may be thousands of meters long and only a few meters wide. Magma travels through a pipe until it reaches a vent on the earth's surface.

**Magma Chamber**
Large pockets of magma form underground magma chambers. When magma is hot or powerful enough, it makes its way toward the earth's surface through cracks in the crust.

## Explore Visually

Have students study Figure 7.11. Ask the following questions:

▶ Is the volcano in the figure active or dormant? How do you know? (Active; it is erupting.)

▶ Where is magma located? (In an underground magma chamber and in the pipe)

▶ At what point does magma become lava? (When it reaches the surface)

▶ What causes magma to move through a pipe? (Pressure and heat)

▶ What is a pipe? Where is it located and what happens in a pipe? (A pipe, along a nearly vertical crack in the earth's crust, connects the magma chamber with the earth's surface. This allows magma to escape from the underground chamber to the earth's surface.)

▶ How is a vent related to a crater? (A crater is a bowl-shaped depression around a vent.)

▶ How many vents are shown in the figure? (Two)

▶ What happens at a vent in the earth's surface? (Volcanic material that reaches the earth's surface emerges.)

**The Living Textbook:
Earth Science Sides 1-2**

Chapter 5          Frame 01415
Kilauea Vent (2 Frames)
Search:                    Step:

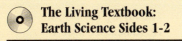

**The Living Textbook:
Earth Science Sides 1-2**

Chapter 5          Frame 01204
Diamond Head Crater (1 Frame)
Search:

145

### ◀ TEACH ▪ Continued

## Discuss

Have students discuss the destruction that can be caused by lava flows and volcanic eruptions. Help them recognize that both can destroy trees, plants, animals, and structures in their paths.

## Skills Development

**Measure** Ask students what measurements a volcanologist may take to learn about a volcano. (Students may state that the mass, volume, temperature, distance traveled, and rate of flow all would provide valuable data for a volcanologist.)

### Portfolio

Invite students to gather pictures of each kind of volcanic eruption from magazines or newspapers of recent or ancient volcanic activity. Have them identify any lava flows, volcanic ash, or bombs that may appear in the photographs. Have students add these to the articles they collected earlier about earthquakes.

### The Living Textbook: Earth Science Side 1

Chapter 52     Frame 43273
Volcanic Bombs (1 Movie)
Search:          Play:

### The Living Textbook: Earth Science Side 1

Chapter 47     Frame 36940
Lava Flow/Ash (2 Movies)
Search:          Play:

### Social Studies Connection

In Washington, on May 18, 1980, Mount St. Helens erupted. The mountain blew off its summit. Large amounts of ash and dust were released into the air; however, very little lava was emitted. Obtain pictures of Mount St. Helens from before and after May 18, 1980. Have students compare the size of the mountain before and after the eruption.

### Multicultural Perspectives

Share with students that the Hawaiian native language distinguishes between two types of lava. *Aa* is a viscous lava that resists flowing. *Aa* tends to form very rough boulders. *Pahoehoe* refers to fluid, flowing lava. When *pahoehoe* cools, its surface is smooth or ropey. Ask students to think about why the Hawaiians would make this distinction in lava types.

## Volcanic Eruptions

Volcanic eruptions range from quiet outpourings of lava to violent explosions of rock particles, steam, and gas. The chemistry, temperature, and pressure of the magma inside a volcano determine whether an eruption will be explosive or quiet. Volcanoes that erupt quietly generally make better neighbors than those that explode. However, even slow-moving lava flows can destroy towns and villages.

**Lava Flows** A common type of eruption for some volcanoes, especially those in Hawaii, is a lava flow. A lava flow is a stream of lava that flows from a vent.

The stream may be narrow, or it may spread out. On steep slopes, some lava flows can reach speeds as high as 30 to 40 km per hour. As the lava moves, it cools and hardens.

**Volcanic Explosions** When volcanoes erupt explosively, they mainly give off rock particles. These particles, called volcanic debris, contain a range of airborne materials including dust, ash, cinders, and bombs. The kinds of volcanic debris are identified by the size of their particles. With an average particle the size of a flour grain, dust is the finest volcanic debris. The largest are called bombs, which measure at least 64 mm in diameter.

### River of Lava

This lava flow comes from Mauna Loa (MOW nuh LOH uh), an active volcano on the island of Hawaii. This stream of lava is traveling at about 10 km per hour. When it hardens, it will form an uneven surface of very rough boulders and rocks. ▼

### Bombs ▶

Hurled from the vent as molten or semimolten masses, volcanic bombs cool as they sail through the air. Some bombs are as large as cars. This bomb is from a volcano on the Hawaiian island of Maui (MOW ee).

### Ash

◀ Volcanic ash can cover the landscape many meters deep. Fine-grained ash may be carried hundreds of kilometers by wind before it settles to the earth's surface. If hot enough, ash will ignite trees, plants, and animals. This ash is erupting from the small volcanic island of Krakatoa (KRAH kuh TOH uh) in Indonesia.

## Language Arts Connection

Have students describe the shape of a cone and a shield. Have them apply their descriptions to the shape of cinder cone and shield volcanoes. Ask students if they think that the names are accurate for these two types of volcanoes.

## Integrating the Sciences

**Environmental Science**  Tell students that when Mt. Pinatubo in the Philippines erupted in June 1991, it released large amounts of sulphur dioxide. The sulphur dioxide reacted with moisture to form aerosols. These aerosols remain in the atmosphere for several years. During this time, chemical reactions may produce ozone-depleting molecules from the aerosols.

## Directed Inquiry

Have students study the text and illustrations shown on the page. Ask the following questions:

▶ Which type of volcano is likely to be tallest and steepest? How is the shape formed? (Composite volcano built up of alternating layers of debris and lava is usually the result of many cycles of eruptions. The tops are steep but they generally have gently sloping bases.)

▶ What kind of shape does an explosive volcano form? What kind of magma forms these volcanoes? (Cinder cone; the steeply sloping sides are generally formed by wet, silica-rich magma.)

▶ How would you describe a shield volcano? (Less steep and tall than other types of volcanoes; shield volcanoes are formed from runny lava that flows away from the vent.)

## Class Activity

Using modeling clay, have students make models of the different types of volcanoes. Students may use modeling clay of different colors to show a cutaway model of each type of volcano.

## Types of Volcanoes

The different types of volcanic eruptions and explosions produce different types of volcanoes. Each type is named for its shape or structure.

### Cinder Cone Volcanoes

Volcanoes that form from the products of explosive eruptions are called **cinder cone volcanoes.** Ash, cinders, and other volcanic debris mound up around the vent, forming a cone. Cinder cones have steeply sloping upper slopes, but their bases usually slope gently. They generally form from wet, silica-rich magmas. These cinder cone volcanoes are located on Java, an island in Indonesia. ▼

### Shield Volcanoes ▲

Volcanoes that have flat-top, shieldlike shapes are called **shield volcanoes.** The lava that forms shield volcanoes is runny and flows easily when it reaches the surface. As a result, most lava flows away from the vent. As the lava cools, it becomes thicker, then slows down and collects. One of the largest shield volcanoes in Hawaii, Mauna Loa, is shown above. Many ocean islands are the tops of large shield volcanoes.

### Composite Volcanoes

Volcanoes that contain alternating layers of volcanic debris and lava are called **composite volcanoes.** Usually, composite cones are formed from many cycles of eruptions. Most have steep tops but gently sloping bases. Mt. Rainier, shown below, and Mt. Fuji are composite volcanoes. ▼

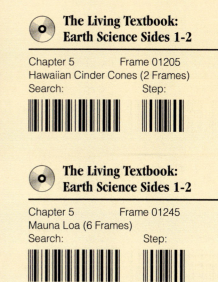

**The Living Textbook:
Earth Science Sides 1-2**

Chapter 5          Frame 01205
Hawaiian Cinder Cones (2 Frames)
Search:               Step:

**The Living Textbook:
Earth Science Sides 1-2**

Chapter 5          Frame 01245
Mauna Loa (6 Frames)
Search:               Step:

## TEACH · *Continued*

### Portfolio

Students can form "volcanic watch" groups that plot the information they collect on a class map similar to Figure 7.12. Allow students to compare this information with the information they gathered on earthquakes (Figure 7.6, page 137).

## Skills Development

**Classify** Have students devise three different systems for classifying volcanoes. Ask them to base one system on time, one on location, and one on shape. (Classification headings should include extinct, dormant, active; Ring of Fire, oceanic ridge, hot spot; and cinder cone, shield, and composite.)

## Discuss

Help students recognize that some volcanic activity occurs away from plate boundaries. Ask them to identify a land formation, such as Iceland, located at a plate boundary and one, such as the Hawaiian Islands, formed over a hot spot.

### Answer to In-Text Question

① **One major chain runs along the eastern coast of Asia and south along the Pacific Plate.**

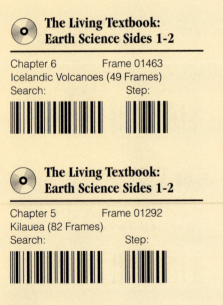

**The Living Textbook:**
**Earth Science Sides 1-2**

Chapter 6          Frame 01463
Icelandic Volcanoes (49 Frames)
Search:          Step:

**The Living Textbook:**
**Earth Science Sides 1-2**

Chapter 5          Frame 01292
Kilauea (82 Frames)
Search:          Step:

**148**

### *Integrating the Sciences*

**Astronomy** Point out to students that through space exploration, scientists have discovered volcanoes on Mars, Venus, and Jupiter's moon Io. Mars has a large shield volcano named Olympus Mons that is more than twice as high as Mt. Everest. Venus also has both active and inactive volcanoes. Volcanoes erupting from Io were recorded by the Voyager I spacecraft.

## Areas of Volcanic Activity

You know that most earthquakes occur along plate boundaries. Most of the earth's volcanic activity also occurs in the same regions. In fact, volcanic activity can often produce earthquakes. As magma moves upward, it may fracture rocks or buckle the overlying crust. The resulting earthquakes often serve as warnings to scientists that volcanic eruptions may occur.

**Ring of Fire** Look at Figure 7.12. Like earthquakes, the major zone of active volcanoes is along the Ring of Fire that encircles the Pacific Ocean. As you know, oceanic plates along the Ring of Fire are subducting. In this area, volcanoes occur in long chains that stretch for hundreds of kilometers. One major chain runs along the western coasts of North and South America. Where is another major chain located? ①

**Oceanic Ridge Systems** The oceanic ridge systems are the earth's longest volcanic zones. Here, plates are moving apart along ocean ridges, forming cracks called rifts. As magma rises from the rifts, the ocean water cools it. Lava builds up from the ocean bottom, forming volcanoes. Most volcanic eruptions along the ridge systems happen deep beneath the ocean's surface. However, along the mid-Atlantic ridge, volcanoes have risen above sea level, forming the island of Iceland. Iceland has many active volcanoes.

**Hot Spots** In Figure 7.12, you can see that volcanic activity called *hot spots* occurs in some areas. Notice that many of the hot spots are located far from plate boundaries. Scientists hypothesize that hot spots develop in parts of the earth's mantle that are especially hot. As the hot spots melt the surrounding rock, the rock changes into magma and rises to the surface. The Hawaiian Islands are an example of a volcanic island chain formed over a hot spot.

**Figure 7.12**
**Map of Volcanic Activity** ▼

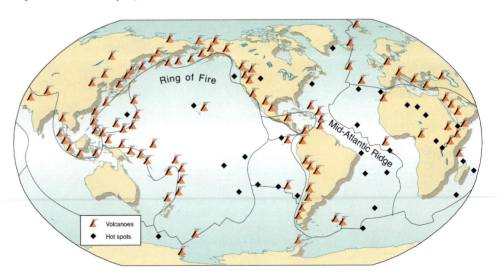

## Integrating the Sciences

**Life Science** Share with students that within three years after the eruption of Mount St. Helens, almost all of the plant species that had lived on the mountain had reappeared. Volcanic soil is very rich in minerals that support plant life. The growth of plants attracts animal species.

## Literature Connection

The first section of James Michener's book *Hawaii* describes the formation of the volcanic island, Hawaii, and the introduction of life to the island. Read this section of *Hawaii* to the class. Discuss with students whether the description accurately depicts the formative stages of a volcanic island.

# Historical Notebook

## The Great Vesuvian Eruption

On August 24, AD.79, none of the residents of Pompeii and Herculaneum in what is now Italy imagined that nearby Mt. Vesuvius would erupt. The volcano had been peaceful for over 300 years. Most people who lived in the area probably didn't suspect that the mountain was a volcano. They also didn't know about the relationship between earthquakes and volcanoes. If they had, they would have realized that a nearby earthquake 17 years earlier was a warning of the renewed activity in the volcano.

The great eruption rained hot ash, mud, and stones upon the residents of Pompeii and Herculaneum. As the ash piled deeper, many people tried to save themselves by climbing to the second stories of buildings. Many did not escape. Some accounts of the event claim that 80 percent of the population perished. The two towns completely disappeared under about 20 m

of ash and stone. About 1,500 years later, the forgotten towns were discovered.

1. What warning did residents of the two towns have of a volcanic eruption?

2. **Research** Find out about the discovery of Pompeii and Herculaneum. Who discovered the ruins? What did they find?

## Life on a Volcanic Island

Organisms cannot survive on molten rock, where temperatures are sometimes above 1,000°C. Yet many of the world's volcanic islands are filled with life. How does a volcanic island, which was once covered with life-destroying lava, become a home for organisms?

The slow process begins as moisture from rain and fog reacts chemically with the exposed lava. Over time, soil develops. Wind, waves, and birds scatter microbes, plant spores, and pollen. Lichens and mosses appear and break down rock. Ocean currents deliver marine organisms, including algae, seaweed, kelp, corals, mollusks, insects, fish, and marine mammals.

Although new volcanic eruptions may wipe out this progress, the process begins again when the new layer of lava cools. Eventually, most volcanic islands will have a community of plants and animals.

**Figure 7.13** ▲
Surtsey, Iceland, is a volcanic island that was built by a series of eruptions that began in 1963. Just a few weeks after its first eruption, Surtsey showed signs of life.

## Historical Notebook

Outdoors or in a hallway, have students use a string to mark off a length of 20 m. Then ask them to estimate how tall a 20 m column of ash might be. (A 6- to 7-story building). Encourage student volunteers to make a presentation about the life and culture that existed in Pompeii and Herculaneum at the time of the disaster.

1. Seventeen years earlier there had been an earthquake nearby.

2. A peasant working in his fields in 1748 first discovered the ruins. Reports will vary.

## Critical Thinking

**Reason and Conclude** Have students suggest how a volcanic island can be used to understand the natural history of life and organisms. (Newly created land, like a vacant lot, provides an opportunity for the naturalist to study succession from its earliest stage.)

## Integrated Learning

Use Integrating Worksheet 7.3.

**The Living Textbook: Earth Science Side 1**

Chapter 49     Frame 39466
Surtesy Island (Movie)
Search:        Play:

**The Living Textbook: Earth Science Side 1**

Chapter 50     Frame 40651
Vesuvius and Pompeii (Movie)
Search:        Play:

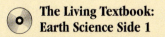

## Social Studies Connection

Tell students that in 1883, the eruption of three volcanoes on the island of Krakatoa in the Indian Ocean completely destroyed the island. The noise of Krakatoa could be heard on an island that was almost 5,000 kilometers away. The tsunamis caused by the explosion were as high as 35 meters, and the expelled ash circled the world for almost two years. Have students research other famous volcanic explosions and their effects. (For example, Mont Pelée, 1902; Paricutín, Mexico, 1943)

---

# TEACH · Continued

## Discuss

Have students identify changes in Mt. Pinatubo that helped warn people in the Philippines of the 1991 eruption. Then have students discuss how infrared photography can help monitor volcanic activity.

# EVALUATE

## WrapUp

**Reinforce** Have students relate the following pairs of terms:

▶ *Pipe, vent* (Magma travels from beneath the earth through a *pipe* and escapes at a *vent* in the earth's surface.)

▶ *Lava, magma* (*Magma* that reaches the earth's surface is called *lava*.)

▶ *Cinder cone volcano, shield volcano* (Explosive eruptions form *cinder cone volcanoes*; *shield volcanoes* are formed by lava that flows easily at the surface.)

Use Review Worksheet 7.3.

## Check and Explain

1. An opening in the earth's crust that has released molten rock; A volcano forms when molten rock is forced up through a weakened area of the earth's surface.

2. Student comparisons should follow those given on page 147. Answers should include differences in shape, structure, and formation.

3. Eruption causes an abrupt ocean floor movement; energy from the movement pushes against the water and forms a wave that travels to the surface. This wave is similar to the wave generated by an earthquake.

4. Check students' models for accuracy.

## Science and Technology
### Predicting and Monitoring Eruptions

In the past, volcanic eruptions often took people by surprise, sometimes at the cost of many lives. Today, advances in technology can give people warnings about eruptions. For example, when seismic activity, surface temperatures, and gas venting increased on Mt. Pinatubo in May 1991, Philippine authorities began to evacuate neighboring areas. Their actions probably saved many lives.

Fifty years ago, few instruments existed to detect volcanic activity. Those that did were inaccurate, heavy, and inefficient. Most required a person to operate them from potentially dangerous locations. Today, sophisticated devices can monitor volcanoes from safer distances. They also detect changes, such as when magma accumulates underground, increased seismic activity, changes in temperature, and gas emissions.

Advances in photography and satellite imaging also help monitor volcanic activity. They enable volcanologists to study eruptions in remote parts of the world. Infrared photography reveals minor differences in surface temperatures, even through thick cloud layers. This makes it possible to track volcanic activity in any type of weather.

With these developments in predicting and monitoring volcanic activity, scientists hope to save lives and protect property. In addition, scientists are gathering valuable information about the powerful processes that take place within the earth.

**Figure 7.14** ▲
A scientist from the Hawaii Volcano Observatory dips hot lava out of a lava flow for research purposes.

## Check and Explain

1. What is a volcano? How does it form?

2. Explain the differences between shield volcanoes, cinder cones, and composite volcanoes.

3. **Infer** Volcanic activity has been known to trigger tsunamis. Explain how this is possible.

4. **Make a Model** Use a large sheet of paper to draw a diagram of a volcano. Be sure to label its parts.

## Chapter 7 Review

### Concept Summary

**7.1 Earthquakes**

▶ Earthquakes are movements of the earth's crust that occur when rocks break and release energy in the form of seismic waves.

▶ An earthquake's focus is the point in the earth's crust where rock first breaks. The epicenter is the point on the surface above the focus.

▶ The strength of an earthquake is usually given in terms of its Richter magnitude.

**7.2 Earthquake Evidence**

▶ Earthquakes can cause changes in ground level near a fault. Ground-level changes can be vertical or horizontal.

▶ Earthquakes can trigger slides, create scarps, and cause fracturing.

▶ Tsunamis are ocean waves that are caused by earthquakes on the ocean floor.

**7.3 Volcanoes**

▶ Volcanoes are vents in the earth's crust that have released molten rock. The mountain that builds up is also called a volcano.

▶ Volcanic eruptions can be quiet or explosive. Volcanoes may give off lava, gas, steam, and other volcanic debris.

▶ The three main types of volcanoes are cinder cones, shield volcanoes, and composite volcanoes.

### Chapter Vocabulary

| | | | |
|---|---|---|---|
| earthquake (7.1) | seismic wave (7.1) | lava (7.3) | cinder cone volcano (7.3) |
| epicenter (7.1) | tsunami (7.2) | vent (7.3) | shield volcano (7.3) |
| focus (7.1) | volcano (7.3) | crater (7.3) | composite volcano (7.3) |

### Check Your Vocabulary

Use the vocabulary words above to complete the following sentences correctly.

1. Any opening on the earth's surface that has emitted lava is a _____ .

2. A volcano that forms from layers of slow-moving lava is a _____ .

3. A volcano that forms from alternating layers of lava and volcanic debris is a _____ .

4. The point on the earth's surface where an earthquake's shaking is generally the strongest is the _____ .

5. The _____ of an earthquake is the point within the crust where breakage occurs.

6. A volcano with steeply sloping sides that forms from explosive eruptions is a _____ .

7. Magma that has reached the earth's surface is called _____ .

8. The vibrations produced by an earthquake are _____ .

9. Earthquakes can trigger huge ocean waves called _____ .

10. A hollowed-out area at the top of a volcano is called a _____ .

11. Lava usually emerges from a _____ at the top of a volcano.

12. An _____ releases energy in the form of seismic waves.

### Write Your Vocabulary

Write sentences using the vocabulary words above. Show that you know what each word means.

### Check Your Vocabulary

1. volcano
2. shield volcano
3. composite volcano
4. epicenter
5. focus
6. cinder cone volcano
7. lava
8. seismic waves
9. tsunamis
10. crater
11. vent
12. earthquake

### Write Your Vocabulary

Students' sentences should show that they know the meaning of each word as well as how to use it in a sentence.

Use Vocabulary Worksheet for Chapter 7.

## Check Your Knowledge

1. During an earthquake, rock in the crust shifts and releases stored energy that travels outward in the form of seismic waves.

2. The focus is the actual point where the earthquake begins. The epicenter is the point on the surface of the earth directly above the focus, where the strongest shaking usually occurs.

3. Three types of seismic waves are primary (P), secondary (S), and surface (L). Primary waves are fastest; surface waves are slowest.

4. Surface waves cause the most damage because they cause the earth's surface to move up and down.

5. Three seismographs are needed to locate the epicenter because the plots from three seismographs only intersect at one point.

6. Earthquakes can produce slides, scarps, and fissures.

7. Factors that influence the amount of damage done by an earthquake include: distance to a populated area from the epicenter, type of soil, design of buildings, proximity to an ocean.

8. Seismic activity on or near the ocean floor often generates tsunamis.

9. A magma chamber is a large pocket of molten rock that can create a volcano.

10. Cinder cone volcanoes form from explosive eruptions that throw large amounts of cinders and debris into the air. Shield volcanoes are formed from lava that spreads out over the area surrounding the vent. A composite volcano forms when alternating layers of lava and debris build up to form a cone.

11. magma
12. P waves
13. scarp
14. potential energy

## Check Your Understanding

1. The chemistry, temperature, and pressure of the magma inside a volcano determine how it erupts.

2. Loose soil may magnify seismic waves, while firmer soils may absorb some of the energy of the quake.

3. Seismic waves cause a large, rotating, paper-covered drum to vibrate beneath a stationary pen, producing a wavy line that graphs the strength of the earthquake.

4. The Richter scale rates earthquakes in terms of the ground motion, while the Mercalli scale rates the intensity of and damage done by an earthquake. Because the Mercalli scale rates both the intensity and the damage done, it is possible for a given quake to have several ratings, depending on the location.

5. Lava is molten rock that has reached the surface of the earth. When it cools, it solidifies into rock.

6. Minerals are released into the surrounding area by the volcanic eruptions.

7. Volcanoes can produce earthquakes as magma moving toward the surface fractures rocks in the overlying crust.

8. The eruption sent large quantities of ash and gases into the air.

9. A slide is a rapid movement of soil, debris, and rock down a slope. An earthquake can trigger a slide by shaking loose poorly compacted particles.

10. Organisms can migrate, or be carried by the wind, ocean currents, or other organisms, to a newly created volcanic island.

---

## Chapter 7 Review

### Check Your Knowledge

Answer the following in complete sentences.

1. Describe what happens during an earthquake.
2. Explain the difference between an earthquake's focus and its epicenter.
3. List the three types of seismic waves. Which type is the fastest moving? Which is the slowest moving?
4. Which type of seismic wave causes the most damage? Why?
5. How many seismograph readings are needed before an earthquake's epicenter can be located? Why?
6. Name some different types of surface changes that an earthquake can cause.
7. List factors that influence how much damage an earthquake causes.
8. What is the relationship between tsunamis and seismic activity?
9. Describe a magma chamber and its relationship to a volcano.
10. What are the different types of volcanoes? How does each form?

Choose the answer that best completes each sentence.

11. Molten rock within the earth is called (magma, lava, volcanic debris).
12. The fastest moving seismic waves are (S waves, P waves, L waves).
13. A cliff created by an earthquake is a (slide, scarp, fracture).
14. Rocks in the earth's crust can store a great deal of (elastic limit, stress, potential energy, seismic waves) before they fracture.

### Check Your Understanding

Apply the concepts you have learned to answer each question.

1. **Compare and Contrast** Why do some volcanoes erupt explosively whereas others erupt quietly?
2. Why does soil type have an effect on how much damage a building sustains during an earthquake?
3. Explain how a seismograph works.
4. **Application** Describe the methods used to rate earthquakes. Explain why a single earthquake can have many ratings on the Mercalli intensity scale.
5. **Mystery Photo** The photograph on page 132 shows a volcanic eruption and lava flow. The red material is the lava. What is lava? What do you think happens to lava when it cools?
6. **Extension** The soils of volcanic islands are often very rich in minerals. Explain why this is so.
7. Explain how volcanoes can cause earthquakes.
8. **Infer** Many people in Pompeii and Herculaneum died as a result of suffocation during the eruption of Mt. Vesuvius. What might have caused their suffocation?
9. What is a slide? Explain how an earthquake can trigger a slide.
10. **Application** How is it possible that a volcanic island, such as Surtsey, is now home to many organisms? Explain.

## Develop Your Skills

1. a. 6000 km

   b. About 7500 km

   c. About 2 minutes faster

2. a. 7.5

   b. Japan

   c. Answers may include distance from epicenter to a populated area, types of building materials used, time of day during the earthquake.

## Make Connections

1. Concept maps will vary. The map below shows a possible organization of the concepts listed.

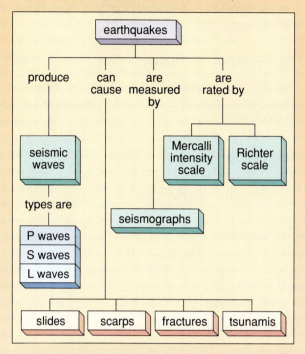

2. The most recent eruption was Mount St. Helens in Washington.

3. Students' reports will vary.

4. Students' reports will vary. Geothermal energy can be used directly for heat, or it can be used to create steam that is used to turn electric generators. The main advantage is that geothermal energy is a free, limitless source. The disadvantages include the fact that it is limited to certain geographical areas and that the areas where geothermal sources are located tend to be very active geologically. Geothermal plants are still relatively rare in the United States.

## Develop Your Skills

Use the skills you have developed in this chapter to complete each activity.

1. **Interpret Data**  The graph below shows the time and distance that seismic waves travelled from the focus of an earthquake. Study the graph, then answer the questions that follow.

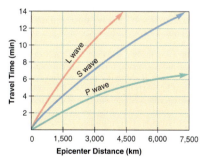

a. How far did the P wave travel in 6 minutes?

b. How far did the S wave travel in 14 minutes?

c. At 2,000 km, approximately how much faster was the P wave than the S wave?

2. **Data Bank**  Use the information on page 619 to answer the following questions.

a. What was the magnitude of the quake that occurred in Guatemala?

b. In what country did the earthquake with the highest magnitude occur?

c. **Infer**  Some earthquakes with high magnitude ratings caused many deaths. Others didn't. List two or three reasons why the statistics differ.

## Make Connections

1. **Link the Concepts**  Draw a concept map showing how the concepts below link together. Add terms to connect, or link, the concepts.

| | |
|---|---|
| seismic waves | seismograph |
| earthquakes | P waves |
| scarps | Mercalli scale |
| L waves | Richter scale |
| fractures | S waves |
| | tsunamis |

2. **Science and Social Studies**  Find out about the last major volcanic eruption in the United States excluding Alaska and Hawaii. When and where did it occur? Did scientists gather data that suggested an eruption would occur? How has the area recovered from the eruption?

3. **Science and Literature**  Do some research at your school library to find out about Pele, the Hawaiian goddess of volcanoes. How do the legends about Pele describe her? What purpose do these legends serve? Make up your own legend that explains the origin of volcanoes.

4. **Science and Society**  Iceland is home to tremendous volcanic activity and geothermal energy, or heat, trapped within the earth's crust. In fact, over half the homes on Iceland are heated by geothermal energy. Find out about the practical applications of geothermal energy. How can it be used? What are its advantages and disadvantages? Is geothermal energy used in the United States?

## About the Literary Work

"Legend Days" was adapted from the novel *Legend Days* by Jamake Highwater, copyright 1984 by Harper and Row, Publishers. Reprinted by permission of Harper and Row.

## Description of Change

This is a short passage from the novel that details an eleven-year-old Native-American girl's wilderness experiences.

## Rationale

In keeping with the theme of this unit, the excerpt selected describes the topography of the setting.

## Vocabulary

travois, pemmican, umber

## Teaching Strategies

### Directed Inquiry

After students finish reading, discuss the story. Be sure to relate the story to the science lessons in this unit. Ask the following questions:

▶ What is meant by the *Cold-Maker?* (Wintertime)

▶ Why can't the women stay in their present campsite? (It does not offer them protection from harsh winter weather.)

▶ In what direction are the women migrating? (Northward)

▶ What other migrations does the passage refer to? (The northward migration of animals and the southward migration of ducks and geese)

## Skills Development

**Infer**  Develop the idea that winter climates vary according to the particular climatic zone. (Students will learn more about climate zones in Chapter 20.) Have students identify phrases in the passage that describe the wintertime weather of Amana's location. Then ask:

▶ Based on this description of wintertime, what U.S. locations are not possible settings for this passage? (Answers should include the Southeast states, southern California, Hawaii, and Alaska.)

▶ What U.S. location could very well be the setting of this passage? (Central plains)

# Science and Literature Connection

### Legend Days

*The following excerpt is from the novel* Legend Days *by Jamake Highwater.*

By autumn their travois was loaded with pemmican, and the time had come for them to follow the animals north and to pick a good camping place where they might find protection from the howling blizzards and snows of winter. The sun glowed orange and golden in the midafternoon as shadows crossed the silent grasses, bringing night earlier and earlier each day. It was a sad time for the women, for now they faced a long and lonely winter of solitude. It was also a sad time for Amana. For as many seasons as she could recall, her tribe had always assembled into a vast winter encampment. All the small bands that spent the summer alone in their far-flung hunting grounds joined together in a glistening community of tipis, sending up smoke and the sounds of laughter and winter games. How nice it used to be when all the people gathered together in the time of the Cold-Maker.

"Aih," Grandmother Weasel Woman exclaimed as she embraced Amana with an expression of sorrow in her face, "but we are alone now. All the people were taken by the sickness and we are alone. So we must fend for ourselves through the hard wintertime."

They broke camp before sunrise, and in a cool breeze that pressed hard upon them from the mountains, they started on their way. Amana and blind Weasel Woman pulled the heavy travois while Crow Woman, with the aid of a cottonwood cane, stumbled along after them, singing into the wind.

They left the shelter of their handsome valley in the mountains and followed a shady forest trail that wound through the rusty-brown foothills. Already the first frosts had turned the grasses umber and dry. Then they descended over high ridges and turned northward along the prairies that spread out beneath the giant peaks. The crickets sang and on every side were the broad meadows and rolling swells of brown grasslands. The small lakes were filled with noisy flocks of ducks and geese pausing on their southward migrations.

On their journey the women followed the Old North Trail, the most traveled of all the ancient routes of the Northwest. It ran along the great chain of mountains called the Backbone of the World, winding over the smooth, rounded ridges and then down long slopes, through wide meadows, and across blue streams and gray rivers, clear and icy cold.

At the head of a broad and windy valley they saw the peak of Chief Mountain, a lone spur of rock, a huge wall rising into the clouds above the surrounding plain.

The women were exhausted from their long, hard journey. Each day they pressed forward, and at night they made camp in groves of shaking aspen, among big cottonwoods in river valleys, and on the banks of swift-flowing streams. But during all these difficult days they saw no one. They found no tracks of other travelers. And they could hear no trace of

# Skills in Science

## Reading Skills in Science

1. The women embarked on this journey in order to find a safe place to camp for the winter. Other members of the tribe succumbed to an epidemic. Grandmother Weasel Woman reminded Amana about the sickness.

2. The women's campsite was located in a valley in the mountains that offered them little protection from harsh winter weather. They are traveling northward into a mountain chain where natural landforms will protect them from the weather.

## Writing Skills in Science

1. Possible causes of the smoke include a forest fire, an erupting volcano, and the discovery of a group of people from a different tribe. Student entries might include topographic descriptions that highlight how they have found a safe haven from the elements.

2. The Backbone of the World is a mountain range most likely formed by folding and faulting, whose "smooth, rounded ridges" are probably well-weathered by erosion. Chief Mountain, a "huge wall" rising above the plain, is either an exposed footwall, or a hanging wall exposed by a reverse fault.

## Activities

**Communicate** Students should describe a location with natural barriers, such as hills or mountains, that would protect them against harsh winter weather.

**Make a Model** Students' maps should show the main physical features described in the passage.

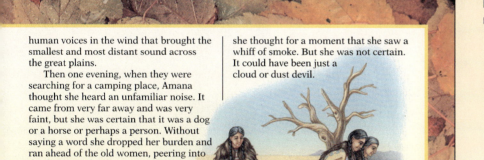

human voices in the wind that brought the smallest and most distant sound across the great plains.

Then one evening, when they were searching for a camping place, Amana thought she heard an unfamiliar noise. It came from very far away and was very faint, but she was certain that it was a dog or a horse or perhaps a person. Without saying a word she dropped her burden and ran ahead of the old women, peering into the darkening landscape. In the distance, where the endless plains reached the sky, she thought for a moment that she saw a whiff of smoke. But she was not certain. It could have been just a cloud or dust devil.

## Skills in Science

### Reading Skills in Science

1. **Find Details** Why did Amana and the other women go on this journey? What had happened to the other members of Amana's tribe? How do you know?

2. **Find the Main Idea** Describe the relationship that exists between the type of landforms that make up the setting of the passage and the reason for the women's journey.

### Writing Skills in Science

1. **Predict** Imagine that you are Amana. Write an entry in your diary describing what caused the whiff of smoke referred to at the end of the passage. Then add an entry that describes a day in your life one month from now.

2. **Find Causes** Choose two topographical features described in this passage and explain how they may have formed. Give evidence for your response.

### Activities

**Communicate** If you lived in a tipi at the location you live now, would you be protected from howling blizzards and winter snows? Is there a nearby location where the natural land features would help protect you from harsh winters? Imagine that you had to set up a winter encampment using a tipi. Describe the best place to set up camp. Explain why you chose the location.

**Make a Model** Make a topographical map of the region where the women traveled. You will need to use your imagination to fill in some parts of the map.

### Where to Read More

*The Shape of the World.* Chicago: Rand McNally, 1991. This beautifully illustrated text is a companion volume to a six-part PBS series telling the story of the exploration, mapping and measurement of earth. Complete with pictures of the earth as viewed from space.

**U** nit 3 explores the chemistry of the earth and its minerals. Chapter 8 discusses the properties of matter, and explains chemical and physical changes. The periodic table of the elements is shown and explained. Chapter 9 illustrates what minerals are, how they are formed, and how earth scientists classify them. The chapter closes with a discussion of how people use minerals. Chapter 10 describes rocks and the rock cycle. The chapter outlines the constant rock cycle within the earth, and illustrates how the three main types of rocks—igneous, sedimentary, and metamorphic—form and change as a result of this cycle.

## Introducing the Unit

### Directed Inquiry

Have students study the photograph. Ask:

▶ How would you describe the different kinds of rocks in this picture? (Students will notice the various patterns, colors, and textures of the rocks.)

▶ Why do the rocks look so different from each other? (Students may suggest that different processes created the rocks, or that the rocks are from different parts of the earth.)

▶ How did these rocks get here? (Students may suggest that a glacier, such as the one in the background, might have left the rocks when it receded, or that they were formed and exposed by volcanic forces.)

▶ If you were a geologist, what kinds of information might these rocks reveal to you? (Answers will vary. Rocks tell what mineral resources are available in an area, give evidence of plate tectonic force, show continents have moved, what sort of wind and water erosion has occurred, and what the land was like in the distant past, for example.)

### Writing About the Photograph

Suggest that students imagine they are on a cross-country hiking expedition. Their party has just reached the site shown in the photograph. They will be setting up camp for the night. Have students write a journal entry in which they describe the surrounding land.

Unit **3**
## Composition of the Earth

*Chapters*

**8** Earth Chemistry

**9** Minerals

**10** Rocks and the Rock Cycle

# Data Bank

Use the information on pages 612 to 625 to answer the following questions about topics explored in this unit.

## Classifying

What kinds of minerals are classified as sulfides? What kinds of minerals are classified as silicates?

## Comparing

Which rock is more common in the United States, metamorphic rock or igneous rock?

## Reading a Table

What are the chemical symbols for the minerals gold, calcite, and gypsum?

## Interpreting a Map

List the classes of rocks that are found in Alaska.

The photograph to the left is of metamorphic and other types of rocks in Alaska. What else do you see in the photograph?

## Overview

Earth chemistry is studied in this chapter. The first section discusses the structure and properties of matter. The second section describes the chemical and physical changes of matter that occur in chemical reactions. The final section includes a discussion of the periodic table and elements most commonly found in the earth.

## Advance Planner

▶ Bring Epsom salts for TE page 163.

▶ Obtain a jigsaw puzzle for TE page 163.

▶ Prepare baking soda, beakers, and vinegar for TE page 171.

▶ Provide plastic or foam cups, spoons, thermometers, calcium chloride, baking soda (sodium bicarbonate), graduated cylinders, clock with second hand or timers, colored pencils, graph paper, paper towels, regular pencils for SE Activity 8, page 174.

▶ Reproduce and cut apart a periodic table for TE page 176.

## Skills Development Chart

| Sections | Classify | Communicate | Design and Experiment | Infer | Interpret Data | Observe |
|---|---|---|---|---|---|---|
| **8.1** Skills WarmUp | ● | | | | | |
| Skills WorkOut | | | ● | | | |
| **8.2** Skills WarmUp | | | | | | ● |
| Skills WorkOut | | | | ● | | |
| Consider This | | ● | | ● | | |
| Activity 8 | ● | ● | | ● | ● | ● |
| **8.3** Skills WarmUp | | | | | | ● |
| SkillBuilder | | | | | ● | |
| Skills WorkOut | | | | | | ● |

## Individual Needs

▶ **Limited English Proficiency Students** Ask students to list the boldface vocabulary and any other terms they don't know in their science portfolios, leaving several lines between each term. Ask them to give a definition of each term using their own words. Then have them write a sentence or two specifically relating each term to the study of the earth.

▶ **At-Risk Students** Invite students to make an earth chemistry scrapbook. Have them copy each item from the concept summary on page 181 at the top of a separate page of their science portfolios. Then ask them to illustrate each item with appropriate and illustrative labeled diagrams, drawings, and pictures cut from magazines. They can use their scrapbooks to review the concepts in the chapter.

▶ **Gifted Students** Encourage students to find out more about isotopes, particularly the unstable ones called radioisotopes. Ask them to use these questions to guide their research: How many isotopes occur in nature? What are radioisotopes? How do science and industry make use of isotopes? Have them present an illustrated report using their findings.

## Resource Bank

▶ **Bulletin Board** Attach the title *Elements of the Earth* to the bulletin board. Divide the board into three sections titled *Where They Are Found, Phases,* and *Forms.* Have the class discuss appropriate subcategories for each section based on the chapter. Then add labels for these subcategories. Finally, ask students to make cards for various elements and place them under the labels that reflect their natural state or states. For example, the labels under *Forms* might be "Elemental Matter," "Compounds," and "Mixtures." Under a label students would place a card naming an element that fits the category. An element like oxygen would appear in several categories. Cards can give additional information appropriate to the element in that category. The oxygen card under "Compounds" might list the names or formulas of some of its natural compounds. Students may have to do some research to find out more about the elements.

| Section | Core | Standard | Enriched | Section | Core | Standard | Enriched |
|---|---|---|---|---|---|---|---|
| **8.1 Structure of Matter** pp. 159–167 | | | | **8.3 The Earth's Elements** pp. 175–180 | | | |
| **Section Features** Skills WarmUp, p. 159 Skills WorkOut, p. 167 | ● | ● ● | ● ● | **Section Features** Skills WarmUp, p. 175 SkillBuilder, p. 179 Skills WorkOut, p. 180 | ● ● | ● ● ● | ● ● ● |
| **Blackline Masters** Review Worksheet 8.1 Skills Worksheet 8.1 Integrating Worksheet 8.1 | ● ● | ● ● ● | ● ● ● | **Blackline Masters** Review Worksheet 8.3 Enrich Worksheet 8.3 Skills Worksheet 8.3 Integrating Worksheet 8.3 Vocabulary Worksheet 8.3 | ● ● ● ● | ● ● ● ● ● | ● ● ● ● ● |
| **Color Transparencies** Transparencies 16, 17 | ● | ● | ● | **Overhead Blackline Transparencies** Overhead Blackline Master 8.3 and Student Worksheet | ● | ● | ● |
| **8.2 Energy and Changes in Matter** pp. 168–174 | | | | **Laboratory Program** Investigation 13 | | | ● |
| **Section Features** Skills WarmUp, p. 168 Skills WorkOut, p. 172 Consider This, p. 172 Activity, p. 174 | ● ● ● | ● ● ● ● | ● ● ● ● | **Color Transparencies** Transparencies 19a, 19b | ● | ● | ● |
| **Blackline Masters** Review Worksheet 8.2 | | | | | | | |
| **Color Transparencies** Transparency 18 | ● | ● | ● | | | | |

# Bibliography

The following resources can be used for teaching the chapter. See page T–46 for supplier codes.

**Library Resources**

Ardley, Neil. The World of the Atom. New York: Gloucester Press, 1990.

Hann, Judith. How Science Works. Pleasantville, NY: The Reader's Digest Association, Inc., 1991.

Matsubara, T. The Structure and Properties of Matter. New York: Springer-Verlag New York Inc., 1982.

Tocci, Salvatore. Chemistry Around You. New York: Arco Publishing, Inc., 1985.

**Technology Resources**

*Internet*

**PLANETDIARY** at *http://www.planetdiary.com*
• Review geological news by clicking on *Current Phenomena.*

*Software*

All About Science I. Mac, Dos. ESI.
Learning All About Matter. Mac, Dos. LS.
Science Elements. Win. ER.
SuperStar Science. Mac, Win. ER.

*CD-ROMs*

Interactive Earth. SFAW.

*Laserdiscs*

Living Textbook. (See barcodes on pages in this chapter.) Optical Data.
Atoms and Molecules. AM.

*Videos*

All About Matter. FM.

**Audio-Visual Resources**

Element Probe: An A/V Game for Teaching the Chemical Elements. Slides. UL.
An Introduction to the Atom. Filmstrip. NGSES.
Periodic Table. Film. EME.

### Writing Connection

Ask students to imagine they've shrunk to the size of a grain of sand and are wandering among the objects in the photograph. Have them write a few paragraphs describing what they see. Some students may want to share their paragraphs with the class.

## Introducing the Chapter

Have students read the description of the photograph. Ask if they agree or disagree with the description.

### Directed Inquiry

Have students study the photograph. Ask:

▶ How would you describe what you see in this photograph? What do you think is actually shown? (Students may relate the image to feathers, plants, or crystals. They will probably agree that the photograph shows ice crystals.)

▶ How did these ice crystals form? (Water vapor in the air condensed to liquid water, which then froze. At some temperatures, ice crystals may also form directly from water vapor.)

▶ How does this photograph relate to the subject of the chapter? (Answers may vary. Students might say it illustrates the three phases of matter: solid, liquid, and gas. They might also say that water is one of the most abundant chemical compounds on earth, or that it is made of two extremely common earth elements, oxygen and hydrogen.)

## Chapter Vocabulary

| | |
|---|---|
| atom | isotope |
| chemical bond | matter |
| compound | molecule |
| element | organic matter |
| ion | phase change |

# Chapter 8  Earth Chemistry

### Chapter Sections

**8.1** Structure of Matter

**8.2** Energy and Changes in Matter

**8.3** The Earth's Elements

### What do you see?

❝The picture resembles frost on a window. You can see many crystal shapes, and there are convoluted spiderlike branches pressed against the glass. The frost probably formed when the dew on a window froze. The sunlight is shining through the ice giving the appearance of the yellow color.❞

*Mark Adato
Hanby Junior High School
Wilmington, Delaware*

To find out more about the photograph, look on page 182. As you read this chapter, you will learn about the chemistry of the earth.

## *Themes in Science*

**Scale and Structure** Matter can be broken down into increasingly smaller parts. Atoms, the smallest units of matter, are made of subatomic particles.

## *Integrating the Sciences*

**Physical Science** Explain that matter can convert into energy. Have students identify at least five kinds of energy, such as sound, light, heat, and electricity. Ask students to infer how matter can change into energy.

**Section Objectives**
For a list of section objectives, see the Student Edition page.

**Skills Objectives**
Students should be able to:

**Classify** kinds of matter.

**Design an Experiment** to separate parts of a mixture.

**Communicate** the names and numbers of atoms in given compounds.

**Vocabulary**
matter, atoms, ion, element, isotopes, chemical bonds, molecule, compound

# 8.1 Structure of Matter

## Objectives

▶ **Describe** the structure of atoms.

▶ **Explain** what an element is.

▶ **Compare** and **contrast** three kinds of chemical bonds.

▶ **Communicate** the information contained in chemical formulas.

### ▼ ACTIVITY

**Classifying**

*Down in It*

Make a list of ten different substances, or kinds of matter, that you can see from where you sit. Imagine that you can make yourself so small that you can go inside each piece of matter. Based on what you think you would see while inside, classify the items in your list into several groups.

**SKILLS WARMUP**

**W**hat is everything on the earth made of? You probably think that there isn't just one answer to that question. After all, there are plants, animals, rocks, mountains, oceans, and many other different things on the earth. But, in spite of the differences, everything on the earth is made of **matter**. Matter is anything that takes up space and has mass. Mass, measured in kilograms, is the amount of matter making up an object.

If you look around, you see examples of matter everywhere. In fact, you are made of matter. Your chair, desk, textbook, pencil, and lunch are made of matter. The classroom windows, and the trees and buildings you see outside, are also made of matter. Even the air you breathe is made of matter.

Look at Figure 8.1. What examples of matter do you see? You may think that matter is only found on the earth, but look at the sky one night. Did you know that the stars are made of matter, too?

## Properties of Matter

Because the properties of matter are different, it's easy to tell them apart. For example, rocks are usually solid, hard, and heavy. Water is a clear liquid that sometimes turns into ice or steam. Wood and coal are solids that burn easily. Apples, cheese, and peanuts are forms of matter that are good to eat.

You can probably think of many other properties of matter. All of the properties of matter fall into one of two categories. They are either physical properties or chemical properties.

## MOTIVATE

### *Skills WarmUp*
To help students practice describing the structure of matter, have them do the Skills WarmUp.
**Answer** Lists should include ten items. Classifications should be based on how they imagine their objects to look at an atomic level.

## Prior Knowledge
Gauge how much students know about the structure of matter by asking the following questions:

▶ How does wood change when it burns?

▶ Why does ice float?

▶ Where can you find oxygen?

**Answer to In-Text Question**

① **The rocks and trees are solid, the clouds are vapor, or a gas. The kinds of matter also differ in color, size, texture, mass, etc.**

**Figure 8.1** ▲
This landscape is made of many different kinds of matter. How do they differ from each other? ①

## TEACH ▪ *Continued*

### Skills Development

**Interpret Data** Have students study Table 8.2. Ask: What elements in the table besides iron and gold have symbols that come from very old names? How do you know? (Sodium, silver, lead; their symbols do not resemble their current names.)

### Discuss

Give students additional chemical formulas, such as $H_2O$, NaCl, $CaCl_2$, $C_6H_{12}O_6$, and $SO_2$, and have them describe the chemical make-up of the compounds.

### Answers to In-Text Questions

① **One atom**

② **Nitrogen**

③ **Hydrogen**

④ **There are three hydrogen atoms in the molecule.**

⑤ **One atom**

 ### *Social Studies Connection*

Have students discuss the use of alphabetic symbols and abbreviations in everyday life. Point out examples of symbol systems, such as the two-letter post office abbreviations for states, or the three-letter symbols for airports. Have students create their own symbol system for a set of objects they choose.

### *History Connection*

Many elements have been known to people for centuries. Give students a list of some of these elements (gold, silver, iron, sodium, copper, lead, mercury, potassium) and have them infer why these elements were known long before the others.

**Table 8.2   Chemical Symbols of Common Elements**

| Element | Chemical Symbol |
|---------|-----------------|
| Hydrogen | H |
| Carbon | C |
| Nitrogen | N |
| Oxygen | O |
| Sodium | Na |
| Silicon | Si |
| Sulfur | S |
| Chlorine | Cl |
| Calcium | Ca |
| Iron | Fe |
| Silver | Ag |
| Gold | Au |
| Lead | Pb |
| Uranium | U |

## Chemical Symbols and Formulas

Scientists all over the world use the same set of symbols to name elements and describe chemical compounds. Every element is represented by a *chemical symbol*. A chemical symbol may be a capital letter or a capital letter followed by a small letter.

Look at Table 8.2 to see the symbols of some common elements. You'll notice that some chemical symbols seem to have nothing to do with the names of their elements. These symbols actually come from very old names for the elements. The symbol for iron, Fe, comes from *ferrum*, the Latin word for iron. The symbol for gold, Au, comes from the Latin word *aurum*.

Combinations of chemical symbols, called *chemical formulas*, are used to represent compounds. A chemical formula tells how many atoms of each element are present in a compound. Look at the chemical formula $CO_2$ in Figure 8.10. Notice that the number 2 is a *subscript* that tells how many atoms of an element are present. How many atoms of carbon are there in the compound $CO_2$, or carbon dioxide? ①

The symbol for carbon is C.

The symbol for oxygen is O.

No subscript after carbon means that only one atom of carbon is in each molecule.

The subscript 2 means that two atoms of oxygen are in each molecule.

What element is represented by the symbol N? ②

What element is represented by the symbol H? ③

How many atoms of N are there in a molecule of ammonia? ⑤

What does the subscript after ④ the H mean?

**Figure 8.10   Examples of Chemical Formulas** ▲

## Integrating the Sciences

**Life Science** Explain that most foods are mixtures of proteins, carbohydrates, fats, vitamins, and minerals. Write the formula $C_6H_{12}O_6$ on the board. Tell students it stands for glucose, the simplest carbohydrate compound. Then ask students to name the elements and the number of atoms of each one that combine to form glucose. Have students use references to find a chemical formula for one type of protein, a fat, a vitamin, and a mineral.

## Answer to Link

Explanations should reflect the definition of an atom, isotope, and compound.

## Skills WorkOut

To give students practice in separating a mixture, have them do the Skills WorkOut.

**Answers** Answers will vary. Students may suggest filtering out the sand, allowing the water to evaporate, and using a magnet to extract the iron. Be sure they list a procedure.

## EVALUATE

### WrapUp

**Reteach** Have students define and then explain the relationship between each group of terms you place on the chalkboard: physical and chemical properties; ionic bonds, covalent bonds, and metallic bonds; and elements, compounds, and mixtures. (Kinds of matter have physical and chemical properties; all chemical bonds involve electrons; elements can occur alone, in compounds, or in mixtures.)

Use Review Worksheet 8.1.

### Check and Explain

1. Answers should correspond to Figure 8.4 on p. 161.

2. An element is one kind of atom. Elements differ in the number of subatomic particles their atoms contain.

3. All bonds join atoms together and involve electrons. However, ionic bonds transfer electrons, covalent bonds share electrons between two or more atoms, and metallic bonds share electrons among many atoms.

4. 1 carbon atom and 3 hydrogen atoms; 1 calcium atom, 1 carbon atom, and 3 oxygen atoms; 2 iron atoms and 3 oxygen atoms

**Answer to In-Text Question**

⑥ Answers will vary and may include broth, soda, or fruit juice.

---

### Science and You *Mixtures You Eat*

Do you like spaghetti, burritos, sandwiches, and pizza? These popular foods are forms of matter that you can eat. Which form of matter are they? Are they elemental matter, compounds, or mixtures? If you look closely at these foods, you can see that they are made of different substances mixed together. For example, pasta and tomato sauce make spaghetti. A burrito may contain rice, beans, meat, vegetables, and spices.

Many foods are obviously mixtures. You can see the different kinds of matter that make them up. However, some mixtures can look like pure substances. For example, think about the mayonnaise on a sandwich. White, creamy mayonnaise looks like a pure substance. Actually, mayonnaise is a mixture of three very different substances: oil, vinegar, and eggs. Mixed together, the substances form tiny droplets. Milk also looks like a pure substance. Milk is really a mixture of water, droplets of fat, proteins, and dissolved milk sugar.

Some food items are examples of the type of mixture called a solution. Vinegar, for example, is a solution. It contains molecules of a weak acid, acetic acid, mixed with molecules of water. The two kinds of molecules mix together so thoroughly that the solution looks the same throughout. In a solution, the particles are very small and can't be separated by filtering. Also, light can easily pass through, so a solution is often transparent. What other food solutions can you think of? ⑥

### Check and Explain

1. Describe the three subatomic particles that make up atoms.

2. What is an element? How do atoms of one element differ from atoms of another element?

3. **Compare and Contrast** How are ionic, covalent, and metallic bonds similar? How are they different?

4. **Communicate** For each of the following compounds, list the names of the elements that make up the compound and the number of atoms of each element present. The chemical formulas of the compounds are: $CH_3$, $CaCO_3$, $Fe_2O_3$.

---

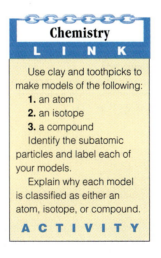

### ▼ ACTIVITY

**Designing an Experiment**

*The Perfect Mix*

You have a mixture of sand, salt, tiny pieces of iron, and water. Design a procedure, or series of steps, that will let you separate all the parts of the mixture.

**SKILLS WORKOUT**

---

### Chemistry
### L I N K

Use clay and toothpicks to make models of the following:
1. an atom
2. an isotope
3. a compound

Identify the subatomic particles and label each of your models.

Explain why each model is classified as either an atom, isotope, or compound.

**A C T I V I T Y**

---

### Themes in Science

**Energy** Phase changes and changes in chemical composition both result from energy changes.

### Writing Connection

Ask students to write short stories that hinge on some physical or chemical change. For example, students could write a detective story in which someone heats a piece of paper and discovers a message written on it in invisible ink.

## Section Objectives

For a list of section objectives, see the Student Edition page.

## Skills Objectives

Students should be able to:

**Observe** and define changes in matter.

**Infer** common properties of combustible substances.

**Infer** what happens to molecules if mixed liquids become warm.

**Interpret Data** about changes in energy during chemical reactions.

## Vocabulary

phase change

## MOTIVATE

### Skills WarmUp

To help students identify changes in matter, have them do the Skills WarmUp.

**Answer** Lists will vary; when classified, examples labeled as chemical changes should result in formation of a new substance.

### Prior Knowledge

To gauge how much students know about energy and changes in matter, ask the following questions:

▶ Are rust and iron the same or different substances? Water and ice? Paper and ash?

▶ What besides ice can melt?

▶ How do smells travel?

▶ What happens to food when you cook it?

### Answers to In-Text Questions

① **Physical**

② **Answers will vary. A familiar example is rusting iron.**

---

### ▼ ACTIVITY

#### Observing

*Changing Matter*

Describe ten different changes in matter that you've observed. When you have finished reading this section, decide which of the changes you described were chemical and which were physical.

#### SKILLS WARMUP

**Figure 8.11**
Is cutting paper an example of a physical change or a chemical change? ▼ ①

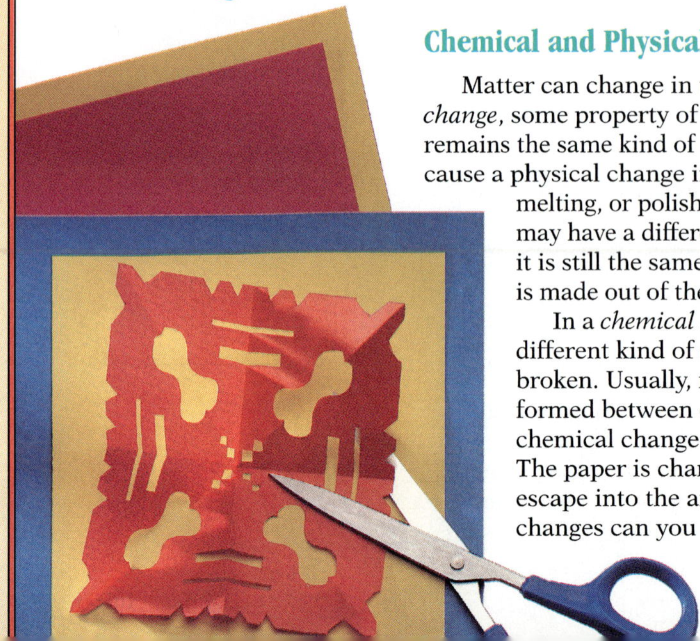

---

## 8.2 Energy and Changes in Matter

### Objectives

▶ **Give examples** of physical changes.

▶ **Explain** how a chemical change differs from a physical change.

▶ **Compare** and **contrast** phase changes.

▶ **Infer** what happens to the molecules of a substance from observations of changes in the substance.

Outside, icicles are melting in the sun. The plant on the windowsill is beginning to bloom. The carrot you left on your desk is drying out. The sandwich you ate is being digested in your stomach. The icicles, plant, carrot, and sandwich are all examples of matter that is changing in some way.

All the time, changes in matter are taking place in, on, and around the earth. Rocks are eroding, clouds are forming, dead organisms are decaying. How do all these changes in matter occur?

### Chemical and Physical Changes

Matter can change in two basic ways. In a *physical change*, some property of the matter changes, but it remains the same kind of matter. For example, you can cause a physical change in metal by bending, cutting, melting, or polishing it. Afterwards, the metal may have a different size, shape, or surface, but it is still the same substance you started with. It is made out of the same atoms.

In a *chemical change*, matter changes into a different kind of matter. Chemical bonds are broken. Usually, new chemical bonds are formed between different atoms. A common chemical change takes place when paper burns. The paper is changed into ash and gases that escape into the air. What other chemical changes can you think of? ②

## Integrating the Sciences

**Physical Science** On the chalkboard, write the following ideas that help explain the particle model of matter. Have students copy the ideas into a notebook.

▶ The particles that make up all forms of matter are too small to be seen.

▶ Even the tiniest speck contains a huge number of particles.

▶ The tiny particles in matter are constantly moving.

▶ Particles vary in size, shape, arrangement, motion, and individual properties.

## Phase Changes

If you put water in the freezer, it will turn to ice. If you boil water, some of the water will disappear into the air as a gas, or vapor. Ice, liquid water, and water vapor are all forms of the same substance: $H_2O$. Therefore, changes from one form to another are physical changes.

The solid, liquid, and gas forms of a substance are called phases. A change from one phase to another is called a **phase change**. Phase changes are one of the most important types of physical changes in matter.

Particles of a substance are constantly moving. The phase is determined by how the particles move. Study Figure 8.12 to see how particles move in different phases of matter.

**Solid**
The particles in a solid vibrate but are held in fixed positions. A solid has a definite shape and volume.

**Figure 8.12
Phases of Matter** ▼

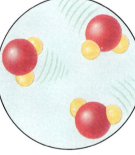

**Liquid**
The particles in a liquid touch each other but are free to move around. Liquids have a definite volume but no definite shape. They take the shape of their container.

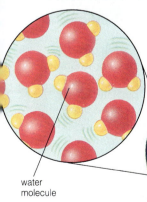

 water molecule

**Gas**
The particles in a gas move rapidly, mostly staying far apart. A gas, therefore, has neither a definite shape nor a definite volume. It will fill whatever space is available.

### Enrich

Remind students that ice can change to water and then to water vapor. Now tell them that dry ice is solid carbon dioxide that changes directly to the gas carbon dioxide instead of going through the liquid phase. Iodine is another substance that changes phases this way. A phase change in which matter changes from a solid directly into a gas is called sublimation.

### *Explore Visually*

Have students study Figure 8.12 and the descriptions of phases. Then ask:

▶ How would you describe a solid? (It has a definite shape and volume.)

▶ How would you describe a liquid? (It has a definite volume but no definite shape; it takes the shape of its container.)

▶ How would you describe a gas? (It has neither a definite shape nor a definite volume; it fills the available space.)

▶ How do the particles of a solid move? (They can vibrate, but they are held in fixed positions.)

▶ How do the particles of a liquid move? Why? (They are free to move around and change positions because they are not held in fixed positions.)

▶ How do the particles of a gas move? (They move rapidly and stay far apart.)

## Discuss

Have students study Table 8.3. Ask: In what two phase changes is heat removed? (Condensation and freezing)

## Critical Thinking

**Find Causes** Have students think about fire extinguishers and carbonated drinks. Ask: What happens when the valve of the extinguisher is opened or when you first open the drink? Why? (Gas escapes because it is under higher pressure inside the container.)

### Answer to In-Text Question

① **Heat energy is added; it cools, or loses heat energy.**

## *Integrating the Sciences*

**Astronomy** Point out that matter in the plasma phase makes up much of the universe. In fact, the sun and other active stars are made mostly of plasma. Ask students to infer what gases form plasmas. (Helium and hydrogen)

**Physical Science** You may wish to explain Boyle's Law, which describes the relationship between pressure and volume. The law states that if a sample of gas is kept at a constant temperature, compressing its volume will increase the pressure the gas exerts.

---

**Table 8.3   Phase Changes**

| Change | Name |
|---|---|
| Solid to liquid | Melting |
| Liquid to gas | Evaporation |
| Gas to liquid | Condensation |
| Liquid to solid | Freezing |

**Figure 8.13 ▶**
How is solid rock changed into the liquid phase? What occurs ① when liquid rock becomes solid?

**Figure 8.14**
Lightning changes matter from the gas phase to the plasma phase. ▼

## Energy in Phase Changes

For a substance to change from one phase to another, the movement of its particles must change. One way to make such a change is to add or remove energy. Energy can be added or removed from a substance by changing its temperature.

The temperature of a substance is really a measure of its particles' energy of movement, or kinetic energy. If heat energy is added, the particles move faster. Adding heat energy makes a solid change into a liquid, and a liquid change into a gas. Removing heat energy makes a gas change into a liquid, and a liquid change into a solid.

Pressure changes can also cause a phase change because pressure exerts a force on particles. For example, by increasing its pressure a gas can change to a liquid. The increasing pressure forces the gas particles closer to each other, forming a liquid. The liquid can be changed back into a gas by decreasing the pressure. The decreasing pressure allows the particles in a liquid to move farther apart and form a gas.

At temperatures and pressures on the earth, nearly all matter exists in either the solid, liquid, or gas phase. However, at extremely high temperatures, such as those that exist in the sun, another phase change can occur. Gases can change into another form of matter called a *plasma*. A plasma is made of free electrons and charged ions that form from the nuclei of atoms. Matter exists as plasma in lightning bolts and in stars.

## Integrating the Sciences

**Physical Science** On the chalkboard, write the following ideas that help explain the particle model of matter. Have students copy the ideas into a notebook.

▶ The particles that make up all forms of matter are too small to be seen.

▶ Even the tiniest speck contains a huge number of particles.

▶ The tiny particles in matter are constantly moving.

▶ Particles vary in size, shape, arrangement, motion, and individual properties.

## Phase Changes

If you put water in the freezer, it will turn to ice. If you boil water, some of the water will disappear into the air as a gas, or vapor. Ice, liquid water, and water vapor are all forms of the same substance: $H_2O$. Therefore, changes from one form to another are physical changes.

The solid, liquid, and gas forms of a substance are called phases. A change from one phase to another is called a **phase change**. Phase changes are one of the most important types of physical changes in matter.

Particles of a substance are constantly moving. The phase is determined by how the particles move. Study Figure 8.12 to see how particles move in different phases of matter.

**Solid**
The particles in a solid vibrate but are held in fixed positions. A solid has a definite shape and volume.

**Liquid**
The particles in a liquid touch each other but are free to move around. Liquids have a definite volume but no definite shape. They take the shape of their container.

**Gas**
The particles in a gas move rapidly, mostly staying far apart. A gas, therefore, has neither a definite shape nor a definite volume. It will fill whatever space is available.

**Figure 8.12
Phases of Matter ▼**

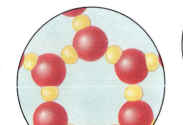

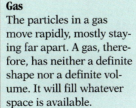

water molecule

### Enrich
Remind students that ice can change to water and then to water vapor. Now tell them that dry ice is solid carbon dioxide that changes directly to the gas carbon dioxide instead of going through the liquid phase. Iodine is another substance that changes phases this way. A phase change in which matter changes from a solid directly into a gas is called sublimation.

### Explore Visually
Have students study Figure 8.12 and the descriptions of phases. Then ask:

▶ How would you describe a solid? (It has a definite shape and volume.)

▶ How would you describe a liquid? (It has a definite volume but no definite shape; it takes the shape of its container.)

▶ How would you describe a gas? (It has neither a definite shape nor a definite volume; it fills the available space.)

▶ How do the particles of a solid move? (They can vibrate, but they are held in fixed positions.)

▶ How do the particles of a liquid move? Why? (They are free to move around and change positions because they are not held in fixed positions.)

▶ How do the particles of a gas move? (They move rapidly and stay far apart.)

TEACH ▪ *Continued*

## Discuss

Have students study Table 8.3. Ask: In what two phase changes is heat removed? (Condensation and freezing)

## Critical Thinking

**Find Causes** Have students think about fire extinguishers and carbonated drinks. Ask: What happens when the valve of the extinguisher is opened or when you first open the drink? Why? (Gas escapes because it is under higher pressure inside the container.)

## Answer to In-Text Question

① **Heat energy is added; it cools, or loses heat energy.**

## Integrating the Sciences

**Astronomy** Point out that matter in the plasma phase makes up much of the universe. In fact, the sun and other active stars are made mostly of plasma. Ask students to infer what gases form plasmas. (Helium and hydrogen)

**Physical Science** You may wish to explain Boyle's Law, which describes the relationship between pressure and volume. The law states that if a sample of gas is kept at a constant temperature, compressing its volume will increase the pressure the gas exerts.

**Table 8.3  Phase Changes**

| Change | Name |
|---|---|
| Solid to liquid | Melting |
| Liquid to gas | Evaporation |
| Gas to liquid | Condensation |
| Liquid to solid | Freezing |

**Figure 8.13 ▶**
How is solid rock changed into the liquid phase? What occurs
① when liquid rock becomes solid?

**Figure 8.14**
Lightning changes matter from the gas phase to the plasma phase. ▼

### Energy in Phase Changes

For a substance to change from one phase to another, the movement of its particles must change. One way to make such a change is to add or remove energy. Energy can be added or removed from a substance by changing its temperature.

The temperature of a substance is really a measure of its particles' energy of movement, or kinetic energy. If heat energy is added, the particles move faster. Adding heat energy makes a solid change into a liquid, and a liquid change into a gas. Removing heat energy makes a gas change into a liquid, and a liquid change into a solid.

Pressure changes can also cause a phase change because pressure exerts a force on particles. For example, by increasing its pressure a gas can change to a liquid. The increasing pressure forces the gas particles closer to each other, forming a liquid. The liquid can be changed back into a gas by decreasing the pressure. The decreasing pressure allows the particles in a liquid to move farther apart and form a gas.

At temperatures and pressures on the earth, nearly all matter exists in either the solid, liquid, or gas phase. However, at extremely high temperatures, such as those that exist in the sun, another phase change can occur. Gases can change into another form of matter called a *plasma*. A plasma is made of free electrons and charged ions that form from the nuclei of atoms. Matter exists as plasma in lightning bolts and in stars.

## Themes in Science

**Patterns of Change/Cycles** All chemical reactions cause substances to change in predictable ways. Explain that elements combine and separate in chemical reactions according to certain patterns.

**Energy** Many chemical reactions give off some form of energy. In all chemical reactions, energy is conserved. Point out that a chemical equation accounts for total mass and energy in a chemical reaction.

## Chemical Reactions

A chemical reaction is another name for a chemical change. Chemical reactions occur constantly in the earth's atmosphere, in the oceans, in rocks, and in soil. In your body, chemical reactions change the food you eat into substances your body's cells can use.

In any chemical reaction, starting materials, called reactants, are changed into products. The same atoms are present in the reactants and products, but they are combined differently. Chemical bonds in the reactants are broken. New chemical bonds are formed to create the products. For example, when elemental iron combines with oxygen gas, the product is iron oxide, or rust.

The product of a chemical reaction has different chemical and physical properties than the reactants do. For example, chlorine is a poisonous gas. Sodium is a soft, shiny metal. But sodium and chlorine combine in a chemical reaction to form ordinary table salt.

**Chemical Equations** A chemical reaction can be expressed in a kind of sentence called a chemical equation. Chemical equations use chemical formulas to represent the reactants and the products. Study the chemical equation shown in Figure 8.16. Notice that reactants and products have the same number and kinds of atoms, but in a different arrangement.

**Figure 8.15** ▲
What substances combine in this chemical reaction? ②

**Figure 8.16    Example of a Chemical Equation** ▼

| Reactants | Yield Sign | Products |
|---|---|---|
| On the left side of a chemical equation are the starting materials, or reactants. When there is more than one reactant, a plus sign separates them. | The arrow means "yields" or "produces." It shows the direction of the change. | New substances formed in a chemical reaction are its products. The products are shown at the right of the yield sign. What are the products of this chemical reaction? ③ |

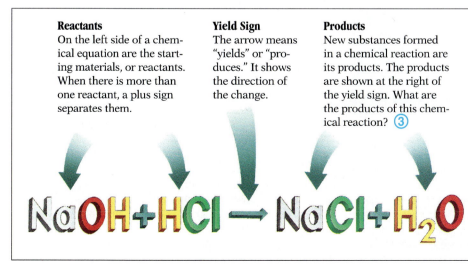

$$NaOH + HCl \rightarrow NaCl + H_2O$$

## Class Activity

Have students work in cooperative groups. Each group should place a spoonful of baking soda in a beaker and then add a spoonful of vinegar to it. Have students observe what happens and then state what happened in a sentence. (Students should describe the reactants and products in the chemical reaction.)

## *Explore Visually*

Have students study Figure 8.16. Then ask:

▶ What are the reactants in this chemical equation? (NaOH and HCl)

▶ What does the arrow in the chemical equation show? (The direction of change)

▶ What are the products in this equation? (NaCl and $H_2O$)

▶ How have the compounds changed? (Atoms have switched places so that the products differ from the reactants.)

▶ What can you state about the numbers and kinds of atoms on each side of the equation? (They are the same. There are one Na, one Cl, one O, and two H atoms on each side.)

## Answers to In-Text Questions

② Wood and oxygen
③ NaCl and $H_2O$

### TEACH ▪ *Continued*

## Skills WorkOut

To help students infer what makes a substance combustible, have them do the Skills WorkOut.
**Answer** Answers will vary; students may say that all the substances contain carbon.

## Skills Development

**Infer** Have students consider the role of adding heat energy in starting a chemical reaction. Ask: What does lighting the wick do for a candle? (It adds heat energy required for a reaction to occur.)

## Consider This

**Think About It** Answers will vary. Students should evaluate the costs and benefits of having such laws. Many students will say they would pay higher prices to be safer.
**Write About It** Answers will vary, but be sure students give the reasons for their positions.

### STS Connection

**Research** Have each student choose three toxic chemicals to research. Tell students to answer these questions for each chemical:

▶ How is it produced?

▶ What is it used for? In what product is it found?

▶ What is dangerous about it? What potential health effects does it have?

---

### ▼ ACTIVITY

#### Inferring

*Up in Flames*

Make a list of ten substances that have the chemical property of being combustible. What do you think the molecules of all these substances have in common?

#### SKILLS WORKOUT

**Energy in Chemical Reactions** Energy is absorbed or released in a chemical reaction. Chemical bonds in the reactants break and new chemical bonds form to make the products. Energy changes occur in this process because each kind of chemical bond contains a certain amount of energy. Sometimes, the chemical bonds of the products contain less energy than those of the reactants. Then the reaction releases energy, usually in the form of heat or light. For example, combustion is a chemical reaction that releases both kinds of energy. Sometimes, the chemical bonds of the products contain more energy than the chemical bonds of the reactants. Then the reaction absorbs energy.

Energy also affects the speed of chemical reactions. Generally, chemical reactions occur faster at higher temperatures. The heat energy makes the particles of the reactants move about faster. They are more likely to collide with each other and start a reaction.

## Consider This

### Should People Be Warned About Harmful Chemicals?

Every day, many people are exposed to harmful chemicals. The health effects of these chemicals may not show up for many years. So, scientists cannot easily link chemicals to health problems. However, cases of illness and death probably caused by chemicals in food, water, and air have increased as the general use of chemicals has grown.

Because of health concerns, some workers have demanded that they be told if harmful chemicals are in their workplace. Consumers have demanded that products include warning labels telling of any risks. In response, state governments passed a number of "right to know" laws. Such laws are necessary, say their supporters, for people to be able to protect their health.

Others argue, however, that such laws may go too far. It is very difficult to determine whether many chemicals actually are harmful, or at what levels people should be concerned. Also, the laws are very expensive for companies to obey. The more warnings and labels that are required, the higher the cost of products.

**Think About It** Do you support "right to know" laws? Would you pay higher prices for products in order to be better informed of dangers?

**Write About It** Write a paper discussing your position on the issue of "right to know" laws.

### Science and Technology *Buckyballs*

Imagine designing and building a custom-made molecule. You could design matter with unique and useful physical or chemical properties. Scientists have discovered many ways to make custom-made molecules from carbon atoms. A carbon atom can form up to four covalent bonds with other atoms. Carbon atoms can combine to make straight chains, branched chains, and rings.

In 1985, scientists discovered how to link 60 carbon atoms together to form a structure shaped like a hollow soccer ball. They named the new substance buckminsterfullerene. The name honors the scientist R. Buckminster Fuller, who designed a building with a similar shape called a geodesic dome. Molecules of the substance are sometimes called buckyballs.

The unusual structure of buckyballs gives them many important uses. Buckyballs link together in different ways to create new materials. Atoms of other elements can be placed inside or on the surface of the hollow buckyballs.

One use of buckyballs is to create substances called superconductors. Superconductors let an electric current flow with little resistance. Buckyballs coated with atoms of fluorine produce a heat-resistant lubricant. A larger buckyball containing 70 carbon atoms has been used to grow thin films of diamond. These diamond films could be produced cheaply as tough coatings for tools, ball bearings, and surgical blades. Buckyballs may have many other possible uses.

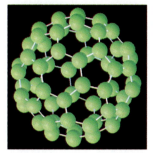

**Figure 8.17** ▲
A computer helped create this image of a buckyball molecule.

### Check and Explain

1. Describe two examples of a physical change.

2. How is a chemical change different from a physical change?

3. **Compare and Contrast** Describe two kinds of phase changes. How are they alike? How are they different?

4. **Infer** You observe that when two liquids are mixed together, they become warm. What can you infer is happening to the molecules in each liquid?

**Time** 40 minutes    **Group** 3

**Materials**

30 plastic or foam cups

20 spoons

10 thermometers

calcium chloride

baking soda (sodium bicarbonate)

10 graduated cylinders

clock with second hand, or 10
timers

colored pencils, 10 each of 3
colors

graph paper

paper towels

## Analysis

1. Calcium chloride and water; the combination produces the highest temperature.

2. Baking soda and water; the mixture cools.

3. Answers will vary. Make sure the answers reflect the information in the graph.

4. Independent variables: substances mixed together; dependent variable: temperature change

## Conclusion

Energy changes, as shown by observed changes in temperature, are evidence that chemical reactions have occurred. Some reactions release energy; others absorb energy.

## Extension

Students should observe gas production from the water, calcium chloride, and baking soda mixture. The gas released is carbon dioxide.

### *Prelab Discussion*

Have students read the entire activity. Discuss these points before beginning:

▶ Discuss how a thermometer can be used to measure energy changes.

▶ Ask students why the temperature is measured five separate times for each mixture.

▶ Ask students to suggest the reason for using foam cups instead of glass beakers or other types of containers.

## *Activity 8*  *How can you measure energy changes?*

*Skills*  Measure; Make a Graph; Interpret Data

### Task 1  Prelab Prep

1. Collect the following items: labels, calcium chloride, baking soda, 3 plastic or foam cups, 2 spoons, water, a graduated cylinder, a thermometer, a timer or clock, paper towels, graph paper, a pencil, 3 different colored pencils.

2. Label one cup *baking soda*, one cup *calcium chloride,* and one cup *baking soda + calcium chloride + water.*

### Task 2  Data Record

1. On a separate sheet of paper, copy Table 8.4.

2. Record your temperature measurements for the three chemical reactions in the data table.

3. You will use the data you collect in the table to graph the energy changes in the three chemical reactions.

**Table 8.4    Temperature Changes During Chemical Reactions**

| Reactants | Temp (°C) | | | | | |
|---|---|---|---|---|---|---|
| | 0 min. | 1 min. | 2 min. | 3 min. | 4 min. | 5 min. |
| Baking Soda + Water | | | | | | |
| Calcium Chloride + Water | | | | | | |
| Baking Soda + Calcium Chloride Water | | | | | | |

### Task 3  Procedure

1. Measure 15 mL of water in the graduated cylinder and add it to the baking soda cup.

2. Place the thermometer in the cup.

3. Measure one spoonful of baking soda and place it in the cup with the water.

4. Immediately measure the temperature of the combined reactants and record it in the data table.

5. Continue to measure the temperature at one minute intervals for five minutes. Record your temperature measurements in the data table.

6. After five minutes, remove the thermometer and wipe it clean with a paper towel.

7. Repeat steps 1 to 6 for calcium chloride + water, and for baking soda + calcium chloride + water.

8. On the graph paper, prepare a line graph with temperature on the vertical axis and time on the horizontal axis. Graph the temperature measurements for all three chemical reactions on the same graph, using a different color pencil for each.

### Task 4  Analysis

1. Which chemical reaction gave off the most energy? How could you tell?

2. Which chemical reaction absorbed the most energy? How could you tell?

3. Describe the graph for the chemical reaction that included both baking soda and calcium chloride. What does this tell you about the chemical reaction?

4. Identify the independent and dependent variables in this activity.

### Task 5  Conclusion

Write a short paragraph explaining how energy changes relate to chemical reactions.

### *Extension*

Test each of the three chemical reactions to find out how much gas each produces. Conduct each of the chemical reactions in self-lock plastic bags. Try to write simple chemical equations for each of the reactions. Use the equations to reveal the gas produced.

## Themes in Science

**Diversity and Unity** All elements have different properties, but they share a basic atomic structure in which a nucleus is surrounded by one or more electrons.

## History Connection

Tell students that Russian scientist Dimitri Mendeléev created the first periodic table in 1869. Many elements had not yet been discovered, so Mendeléev's table had empty spaces for the "missing" elements.

**Section Objectives**
For a list of section objectives, see the Student Edition page.

**Skills Objectives**
Students should be able to:

**Observe** the organization of a calendar.

**Observe** the elements in a period of the periodic table.

**Interpret Data** in the periodic table.

**Vocabulary**
organic matter

# 8.3 The Earth's Elements

## Objectives

▶ **Describe** the organization of the periodic table.

▶ **List** elements that are most common in the crust, atmosphere, and ocean.

▶ **Generalize** about the location of metals and nonmetals in the periodic table.

▶ **Interpret data** contained in the periodic table.

▼ **ACTIVITY**

**Observing**

*Your Days Are Numbered*
Look at the calendar below. What do the days identified as the 4th, 11th, 18th, and 25th have in common?

**SKILLS WARMUP**

**MOTIVATE**

**Skills WarmUp**
To introduce students to the structure of the periodic table, have them do the Skills WarmUp.
**Answer** All four are Wednesdays.

## Misconceptions

Students may think that all elements are metals. Others may think that elements are either metals or gases. Explain that the elements are classified as metals, nonmetals, and metalloids. Point out that some metals do not look or feel like familiar metals, that nonmetals are not all gases, and that metalloids have properties of both metals and nonmetals.

**Answer to In-Text Question**

① The days are placed in order and put in columns according to the day of the week.

If you had a collection of 90 different tapes or CDs, how would you organize them? One possible way would be to put them in rows on shelves, in alphabetical order. Then you could find any CD quickly. Or you could organize them by type of music. Whichever way you choose, some kind of organization is useful. It would take a long time to go through a stack of 90 CDs that were in no order at all.

Organization is also useful in understanding the chemical elements. However, in the case of the elements, the goal of organization is different. The goal is to make sense of patterns that the elements show in their chemical and physical properties.

## Patterns in the Elements

Many years ago, scientists noticed that certain elements had very similar properties. The elements with atomic numbers 2, 10, 18, and 36 all existed as gases and didn't react chemically with other elements. The metals lithium, sodium, and potassium were all so reactive they never existed as pure metals. Scientists thought that each set of similar elements should be grouped together. They also thought that elements should be organized in order of increasing atomic number.

Look at the calendar in Figure 8.18. The dates increase by one each day. Also notice that all the dates in a single column have a similar "property." They are the same day of the week. The elements can be arranged in a calendarlike way to form what is called the periodic table of the elements.

**Figure 8.18** ▲
How does a calendar organize the days of a month? ①

## TEACH

### Explore Visually

Have students study Figure 8.19. Ask:

▶ What does the number in each square represent? (The element's atomic number)

▶ What other information can you find in each square? (The element's symbol, name, and atomic mass.)

▶ What are the vertical columns in the table called? (Groups)

▶ What are the horizontal rows called? (Periods)

▶ How many groups does the table have? (18)

▶ How many periods does the table have? (7)

▶ How are the elements within a group similar? Why? (They have similar properties because their atoms have similar arrangements of electrons.)

▶ Why don't the elements 104–109 have symbols or names? (Their names are not officially assigned.)

### Enrich

Use Enrich Worksheet 8.3.

### Cooperative Learning

Reproduce a periodic table and cut it apart by elements. Challenge cooperative groups to put the table back together like a puzzle. When they finish, ask them to explain the process they used to reassemble the table.

### Portfolio

Tell students to make a list of elements, then go on an element hunt. Each time they can name a substance or product containing an element, they can put a check mark next to the element. Have students search the labels on daily vitamins, food products, plant fertilizers, and cleaning products to find elements. Tell students to keep their checklists in their portfolios.

## The Periodic Table

On these pages, you will tour the periodic table. During the tour, you will learn more about how the table is put together and the patterns that make it useful. The periodic table is an important tool in the study of earth science.

**Figure 8.19**
**Periodic Table of the Elements** ▶

**Groups** Vertical columns are called groups. Elements within a group can have many similar properties. Their properties are similar because their atoms have a similar arrangement of electrons.

**Group Number** Groups of elements are identified by numbers from 1 to 18, beginning at the left side of the table.

**Periods** The seven horizontal rows are called periods. Period 1 contains only hydrogen and helium. Elements 57 to 70 and 89 to 102 fit into periods 6 and 7.

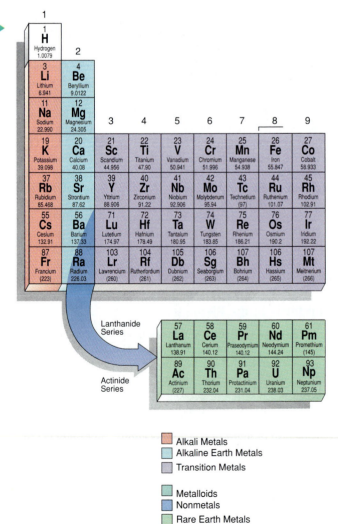

## Integrating the Sciences

**Everyday Science** Have students choose ten metals from the periodic table and research everyday uses of these metals. For example, copper, or Cu, is commonly used in wiring. Silver (Au) is used in photographic film. Have students list the elements and their uses and present them to the class. Collectively, the class can make a large chart that shows a variety of metals and their uses.

▶ Which elements are in Period 1? (Hydrogen and helium)

▶ Which elements are in Group 1? (Hydrogen, lithium, sodium, potassium, rubidium, cesium, and francium)

▶ Which elements are in Period 2? (Lithium, beryllium, boron, carbon, nitrogen, oxygen, fluorine, and neon)

▶ Which elements are in Group 18? (Helium, neon, argon, krypton, xenon, and radon)

▶ Where are the nonmetals in the periodic table? (In the upper right corner of the table to the right of the zigzag line, except hydrogen)

▶ Where are the metals? (To the left of the zigzag line)

▶ What are metalloids? (Elements that have properties of both metals and nonmetals)

▶ Where are the metalloids in the periodic table? (They border the zigzag line.)

▶ Why are two rows of elements from periods 6 and 7 separated from the rest of the table? (To make the table a more convenient size)

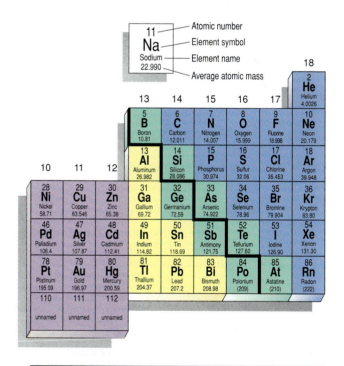

**Nonmetals** Nonmetals occupy the upper-right corner of the periodic table. All nonmetals, except hydrogen, are to the right of the zigzag line.

**Metals** Most of the elements are metals. They occupy the space in the periodic table to the left of the zigzag line.

**Metalloids** Elements that have properties of both metals and nonmetals are metalloids (MEHT uh LOYDZ). Metalloids border both sides of the zigzag line that separates the metals from the nonmetals.

**Rare Earth Metals** The two rows of elements from periods 6 and 7 are separated from the rest of the table to make it a more convenient size. These are the rare earth metals.

## Skills Development

**Interpret Data** Have students study both graphs. Then ask:

▶ How much of the earth's crust is made up of carbon, the element present in all organic matter? (Carbon must be one of the elements that make up 9% of the earth's crust. Carbon, therefore, makes up less than 9% of the earth's crust.)

▶ How much carbon dioxide is present in the atmosphere? (The atmosphere contains less than 1% carbon dioxide.)

## Integrated Learning

Use Integrating Worksheet 8.3.

**Answers to In-Text Questions**

① 74.3%

② They are metallic elements.

③ Nitrogen and oxygen

### Integrating the Sciences

**Life Science** The human body is made of over 20 elements. Have students find out the main elements in humans. They can present their findings to the class as a circle graph showing the percentage of the human body that each element makes up. Have them compare the graphs to those on pages 178 and 179. Have students discuss which elements are common to the earth's crust, the atmosphere, the ocean, and humans.

### Elements of the Earth's Crust

Most of the elements in the periodic table are found in the earth's crust. Some elements are very common, and others are very rare. Look at Figure 8.20. It shows the chemical makeup of the earth's crust. How much of the crust is made of just oxygen and silicon? ①

Most of the atoms of silicon and oxygen in the crust are chemically bonded together. Combined with one or more metal elements, oxygen and silicon form compounds called silicates. Silicates are the most common kind of rocky material in the crust.

The thin layer of soil on the surface of the crust is different in makeup from the crust itself. In addition to tiny bits of rock, soil contains **organic matter**. Organic matter comes from, or is produced by, living or dead organisms. All organic matter contains the element carbon, a nonmetal. Other elements in organic matter include the nonmetals oxygen, hydrogen, and nitrogen.

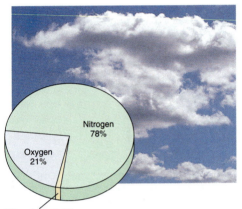

Figure 8.21 ▲
What two elements are most abundant in the atmosphere? ③

### Elements of the Atmosphere

Elements found in the atmosphere are usually in the gas phase. Look at Figure 8.21. What elements are most common? Nitrogen gas exists as molecules of two nitrogen atoms each, shown by the chemical formula $N_2$.

Oxygen is also common in the atmosphere. Unlike oxygen in the crust, most oxygen in the atmosphere exists as elemental matter. Molecules of oxygen gas, $O_2$, contain two oxygen atoms. Oxygen gas in the atmosphere is important to many living organisms. Some oxygen is chemically combined with hydrogen in the form of water molecules. Water in the gas phase is invisible, but tiny droplets of water in the atmosphere form clouds.

Carbon in the atmosphere is contained in molecules of carbon dioxide, or $CO_2$. Plants use $CO_2$ and energy from sunlight to make glucose. Glucose made by plants is the source of much of the carbon in the organic matter of the soil and in living organisms.

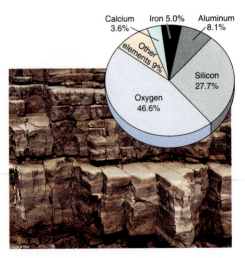

Figure 8.20 ▲
② What do calcium, iron, and aluminum have in common?

## Integrating the Sciences

**Marine Biology** The solubility of oxygen is less than 1% in the coldest part of the ocean. By comparison, the atmosphere contains about 21% oxygen. The amount of dissolved oxygen in the ocean varies from zero to approximately 9 ml/L of seawater, and most of it is produced by plants living on the ocean's surface layer. Diffusion of oxygen from the ocean accounts for over 50% of atmospheric oxygen. Oxygen diffuses into the atmosphere from the oceans because seawater can hold just a small fraction of the oxygen produced by marine plants.

## Elements of the Ocean

If you've tasted ocean water, you know it's not pure water. Ocean water is a mixture of gases and solids dissolved in water. Most of the solids are salts. Salts are ionic compounds containing a metal and one or more nonmetals.

The most abundant salt in ocean water is sodium chloride, or table salt. It is made up of ions of the metal sodium and ions of the nonmetal chlorine. Look at Figure 8.22. What are the most common elements in ocean water? ④

The gases dissolved in ocean water are the same ones that make up the atmosphere. They are nitrogen ($N_2$), oxygen ($O_2$), and carbon dioxide ($CO_2$). The amount of dissolved gases varies greatly by depth and water temperature. Ocean organisms remove dissolved $O_2$ from the water for use in their life processes just as you remove $O_2$ from the air you breathe.

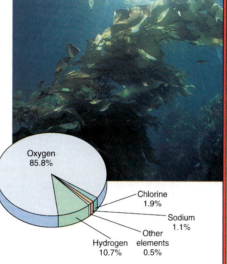

Oxygen 85.8%

Chlorine 1.9%

Sodium 1.1%

Other elements 0.5%

Hydrogen 10.7%

**Figure 8.22 ▲**
In what chemical form does most of the ocean's oxygen and hydrogen exist? ⑤

## SkillBuilder *Interpreting Data*

### Using the Periodic Table

The periodic table contains a great deal of information packed into a small space. For example, if you know the name of an element, the periodic table will tell that element's symbol and atomic number. Practice using the periodic table on pages 176–177 by answering the questions below.

1. List all the elements in Group 17.

2. Find sodium (Na) in the periodic table. How many protons does an atom of sodium have in its nucleus? How do you know?

3. Find nickel (Ni). How many electrons does an atom of nickel have?

4. Which is likely to have the greater mass, a cubic centimeter of titanium, or the same volume of zirconium?

5. Use the periodic table to complete the table below.

Make a list of the different kinds of information you can get from the periodic table. Give an example of each.

| Symbol | Name | Atomic Number | Group Number |
|--------|------|---------------|--------------|
| H | | | |
| | | 6 | |
| | | 8 | |
| Mg | | | |
| | | 13 | |
| | Silicon | | |

## Skills WorkOut

To help students use the periodic table, have them do the Skills WorkOut.

**Answers**  The group number is 9. Familiar elements in the same period are gold, mercury, and lead.

## EVALUATE

## WrapUp

**Portfolio**  Duplicate periodic tables that have blank squares. Have students fill in the blank squares and indicate the metals, nonmetals, and metalloids. Suggest that they add the completed tables to their portfolios.

Use Review Worksheet 8.3.

## Check and Explain

1. By properties and in order of increasing atomic number

2. Oxygen and silicon; most exist in silicates.

3. Metals are located to the left of the zigzag line in the periodic table, and nonmetals are located to its right.

4. Argon, chlorine, phosphorus, silicon, aluminum, magnesium, and sodium; polonium, tellurium, selenium, and oxygen; elements in the same group

### Integrating the Sciences

**Environmental Science**  Compounds called *chlorofluorocarbons* destroy ozone in the upper atmosphere. Chlorofluorocarbons are used to manufacture many products, including plastic foams, and as refrigerants in refrigerators and air conditioners. Write *chlorofluorocarbon* on the board and have students use the periodic table to infer which elements make up these compounds.

▼ **ACTIVITY**

**Observing**

*Where's My Iridium?*
Find iridium in the periodic table. What is its group number? What familiar elements are in the same period as iridium?

**SKILLS WORKOUT**

### Science and Society  *Chemical Clues*

Did you know that many of the earth's secrets have been unlocked by studying an element or compound? For example, the element iridium (Ir) occurs around the world in a thin layer of clay about 65 million years old. Iridium is also found in asteroids. The earth's iridium layer provides evidence that an asteroid collided with the earth 65 million years ago. U.S. scientists Luis and Walter Alvarez proposed that the collision may have caused the extinction of the dinosaurs.

Other elements also provide clues to the earth's past. For example, silicon, iron, oxygen, and many other elements occur in rocks and soil. Carbon has been found in wood, bones, and carbon dioxide bubbles in ancient ice. These elements provide evidence that the earth's atmosphere has changed. The amount of oxygen gas ($O_2$) has increased greatly over the last 2.8 billion years. This change had a major effect on living organisms, climate, and the earth's crust.

Studying chemical compounds is also important in understanding changes taking place on the earth today. Since the 1970s, the amount of ozone ($O_3$) in the upper parts of the atmosphere has decreased. Ozone is a form of oxygen that blocks out harmful ultraviolet radiation from the sun. Ozone is destroyed by chemical compounds released into the atmosphere by people. Finding out which compounds destroy ozone is an important step in solving the problem.

### Check and Explain

1. How are the elements organized in the periodic table?

2. Which two elements are most abundant in the earth's crust? In what form do atoms of these elements exist in the crust?

3. **Generalize**  Where are metals located in the periodic table? Where are nonmetals located?

4. **Interpret Data**  What other elements are in the same period as sulfur? What other elements are in the same group? Which elements are likely to have properties similar to those of sulfur?

## Check Your Vocabulary

1. molecule
2. matter
3. organic matter
4. atom
5. compound
6. isotope
7. chemical bond
8. elements
9. phase change
10. ion

## Write Your Vocabulary

Students' sentences should show that they know the meaning of each word as well as how to use it in a sentence.

Use Vocabulary Worksheet for Chapter 8.

## Chapter 8 Review

### Concept Summary

**8.1 Structure of Matter**

▶ All things are made of matter. Matter is anything that takes up space and has mass. Each type of matter has unique chemical and physical properties.

▶ Atoms are the building blocks of matter. Atoms are made up of electrons, neutrons, and protons.

▶ The number of protons in an atom's nucleus determines what element it is.

▶ Atoms of the same element with different numbers of neutrons are isotopes.

▶ Atoms are joined together by ionic, covalent, and metallic bonds.

▶ Matter exists as elemental matter, compounds, and mixtures.

**8.2 Energy and Changes in Matter**

▶ A physical change in matter is a change in its physical properties.

▶ A chemical change alters the chemical bonds joining the atoms of matter.

▶ Matter on the earth exists in the solid, liquid, or gas phase. A change in phase is a physical change caused by the addition or removal of heat energy.

**8.3 The Earth's Elements**

▶ The elements are organized in a systematic way in the periodic table.

▶ The earth's crust, atmosphere, and oceans vary in the elements that make up their matter.

### Chapter Vocabulary

| | | |
|---|---|---|
| matter (8.1) | isotope (8.1) | compound (8.1) |
| atom (8.1) | chemical bond (8.1) | phase change (8.2) |
| ion (8.1) | molecule (8.1) | organic matter (8.3) |
| element (8.1) | | |

### Check Your Vocabulary

Use the vocabulary words above to complete the following sentences correctly.

1. Two or more atoms joined by covalent bonds form a(n) ____ .

2. Everything you can touch is made of ____ .

3. Matter created or derived from living things is ____ .

4. A nucleus surrounded by electrons makes up a(n) ____ .

5. A substance made of two or more elements chemically bonded is a(n) ____ .

6. Two atoms with 6 protons each but different numbers of neutrons are examples of a(n) ____ .

7. Interactions between two atoms or ions create a(n) ____ .

8. Hydrogen, oxygen, and iron are examples of ____ .

9. Water undergoes a(n) ____ when it becomes ice.

10. When an atom loses or gains an electron, it becomes a(n) ____ .

### Write Your Vocabulary

Write sentences using the vocabulary words above. Show that you know what each word means.

## Check Your Knowledge

1. Answers will vary, but may include color, shape, texture, hardness, density, ductility, buoyancy, and solubility.

2. Oxygen

3. Solid, liquid, gas, and plasma

4. An ion is an atom that has gained or lost electrons.

5. A metallic bond

6. Elements are arranged by increasing atomic number and in columns, called groups. Elements in a group share similar properties and electron arrangements.

7. The proton

8. Gas

9. The reactants, the "yield" sign, and the products

10. 8

11. evaporates

12. protons

13. a compound

14. subscripts

## Check Your Understanding

1. No; for an ionic bond to form, there must be an electrostatic attraction between oppositely charged ions. Covalent bonds do not form between ions.

2. Gas; because the space between the molecules of a gas can be compressed, it is possible to squeeze a given quantity (mass) of a gas into a smaller volume. Reducing the volume of a constant mass of gas will result in a higher density. Accept "solid" as an answer if the student has in mind a compressible solid, such as foam.

3. In water vapor, the molecules are free to move rapidly in any direction (until they collide with each other or with the walls of a container). In water, the molecules can slide freely around each other, but do not have large spaces between molecules. In ice, the molecules are held tightly in place but are able to vibrate.

4. Determining the densities of the two blocks will establish whether they are the same or different metals.

5. proton, nucleus, atom, molecule

6. chemical: b; physical: a, c, d

7. a. sodium (Na) ion (positive)

   b. chlorine (Cl) ion (negative)

   c. neon atom

8. From water vapor in the atmosphere

---

## Chapter 8 Review

### Check Your Knowledge

Answer the following in complete sentences.

1. Name four properties of solids.

2. What element is most abundant in the crust, atmosphere, and oceans?

3. Name the four phases of matter.

4. What is the difference between an atom and an ion?

5. What kind of bond holds together the atoms of a metal?

6. How are groups of elements arranged in the periodic table? How are the groups identified?

7. What subatomic particle carries a positive charge?

8. What phase of matter has neither a definite volume nor a definite shape?

9. What are the three basic parts of a chemical equation?

Choose the answer that best completes each sentence.

10. An oxygen atom with a mass number of 16 has 8 protons and (0, 8, 9, 16) neutrons.

11. A liquid (evaporates, melts, condenses, freezes) to form a gas.

12. Atomic number describes the number of (electrons, neutrons, protons, nuclei) in the atoms of an element.

13. An ionic solid is (elemental matter, a compound, a mixture, an isotope).

14. In the chemical formula of a compound, the number of atoms of each element is shown by (chemical symbols, subscripts, charges, yield signs).

### Check Your Understanding

Apply the concepts you have learned to answer each question.

1. Can two negative ions be joined by a chemical bond? Explain.

2. When the pressure of a certain substance is increased, it becomes more dense. Is it a solid, liquid, or gas? Explain how you know.

3. Compare and contrast the movement and arrangement of $H_2O$ molecules in water, ice, and water vapor.

4. **Application** You have two blocks of metal that look the same and have the exact same size and shape. How can you determine if the two blocks are the same metal or different metals?

5. Arrange the following by size, from smallest to largest: molecule, proton, atom, nucleus.

6. **Classify** The following are properties of iron. Which are chemical properties? Which are physical properties?

   a. Density is 7.87 $g/cm^3$.

   b. Combines with oxygen to form rust.

   c. Shiny.

   d. Melts at 1,535°C.

7. For each particle described below, give the name of the element and tell whether it is an atom, a negative ion, or a positive ion.

   a. 11 protons, 10 electrons.

   b. 17 protons, 18 electrons.

   c. 10 protons, 10 electrons.

8. **Mystery Photo** The photograph on page 158 shows ice crystals on a window. Where do you think the molecules making up the crystals came from?

## Develop Your Skills

1. a. 9; 5

   b. Mass number rises with atomic number, but not at a constant rate. Students may note that with each increase of 1 in atomic number, mass number increases by either 1, 2, or 3. Students may note also that the mass number is approximately twice that of the atomic number.

   c. Answers will vary. The relative proportions of protons and neutrons in the elements vary.

2. a. Carbon-14

   b. 6 protons and 8 neutrons

## Make Connections

1.

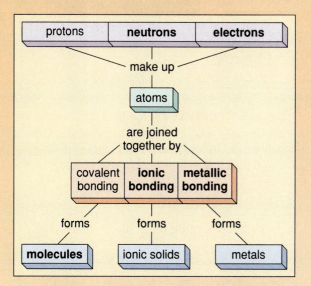

2. Silicon and gallium arsenide, along with compounds of yttrium, barium, copper, and oxygen are being investigated for superconductivity. Possible uses include electric power transmission wires with no resistance to current flow, generators and motors that can be made smaller than current ones, and more efficient electromagnets.

3. Dalton was the first to realize that each element was made of a different type of atom, and that these atoms combined to form all matter. Rutherford introduced the idea that the atom was made up of a small, positively charged nucleus surrounded by negatively charged electrons. Thompson discovered the ratio of the electron's charge to its mass. Bohr theorized that electrons orbit the nucleus in discrete energy levels.

4. Student reports will vary. Communities test their water for the presence of bacteria, minerals, and potentially harmful chemicals.

---

### Develop Your Skills

Use the skills you have developed in this chapter to complete each activity.

**1. Interpret Data** The graph below shows the atomic number and mass number of the most common isotopes of the first eight elements.

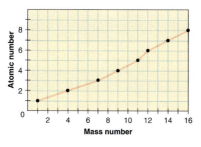

a. What is the mass number of the element with an atomic number of 4? How many neutrons are in the nucleus of this isotope of the element?

b. Describe the relationship between atomic number and mass number.

c. Why do you think the isotopes on the graph don't line up to form a straight line?

**2. Data Bank** Use the information on page 622 to answer the following questions.

a. By measuring the amounts of certain unstable isotopes contained in rocks and fossils, scientists can determine their age. Which element and isotope is used to date fossils containing organic matter?

b. How many protons and how many neutrons do atoms of this isotope contain?

### Make Connections

**1. Link the Concepts** Below is an incomplete concept map showing how some of the main concepts in this chapter link together. Copy the map, then complete it, using words and ideas from the chapter.

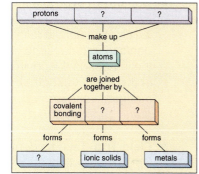

**2. Science and Technology** Buckyballs are one kind of substance being used to make superconductors. Research other types of superconducting materials and find out their possible uses.

**3. Science and Social Studies** Find out how the model of the atom has changed over time. Focus your research on the scientists John Dalton, J. J. Thomson, Ernest Rutherford, and Niels Bohr.

**4. Science and Society** Contact your local water department or water company and ask for the latest chemical analysis of the drinking water supplied to your home. Use this information to make a wall chart for your classroom showing the substances contained in your water and their amounts. Identify any substances that might be harmful.

## Overview

Chapter 9 illustrates what minerals are, and how they are formed and classified. The first section defines minerals, then explores what minerals are made of and how they are grouped according to crystal systems. The second section outlines the properties by which minerals are identified. Chapter 9 closes with a discussion of how people use minerals.

## Advance Planner

▶ Provide rocks for SE page 185.

▶ Provide granulated sugar and string for TE page 187.

▶ Collect beakers, pipe cleaners, spoons, hot plates, alum, salt, tape, and goggles for SE page 191.

▶ Provide chalk, glass, and steel wool for SE page 195.

▶ Provide streak plates, copper pennies, kitchen knives, glass pieces, and mineral samples for SE page 196.

▶ Obtain calcite crystals for TE page 196.

## Skills Development Chart

| Sections | Classify | Communicate | Measure | Observe | Predict | Research |
|---|---|---|---|---|---|---|
| **9.1** Skills WarmUp | | | | ● | | |
| Skills WorkOut | | | | | | ● |
| Activity 9 | | | ● | ● | | |
| **9.2** Skills WarmUp | | | | | ● | |
| SkillBuilder | ● | | | | | |
| **9.3** Skills WarmUp | ● | | | | | |
| Historical Notebook | | ● | | | | |

## Individual Needs

▶ **Limited English Proficiency Students** Have students write down the names of all the minerals they see mentioned as they read through the chapter. Remind them to include minerals from the tables and figures, too. Have them make a chart with the following column heads: mineral, major group (as in Table 9.1), crystal system, properties, uses. Then ask them to list each mineral and fill in their charts according to the information given in the chapter. Explain that the charts will not be complete; if they want to, allow them to finish them using other sources. Encourage them to illustrate their charts with diagrams and pictures from magazines.

▶ **At-Risk Students** Encourage students to work in groups to create posters about gold. Have them investigate the properties of gold, its uses, where it is found, why it is valued, and how it has been regarded by various cultures throughout history. Invite groups to display their posters in an exhibit.

▶ **Gifted Students** Invite students to find out about silicon chips and their relationship to minerals. Students should investigate why these chips are important in modern technology, how they operate, and how they are made. If possible, provide them with actual chips to use in their investigation and in a classroom exhibit of their findings.

## Resource Bank

▶ **Bulletin Board** Title the bulletin board *All About Aluminum*. Make a diagram that outlines the process by which aluminum is refined from the ore bauxite. Ask students to add captions about the amount of energy and the impact on the environment involved in the production of this metal from ore. Invite students to add to the board a diagram showing how aluminum is recycled and appropriate captions about energy and the environment.

▶ **Field Trip** Take students on a geological field trip on which they collect rock samples. Encourage them to field test the rocks and identify as many minerals as they can. Have them conduct more tests in the classroom. Contribute the samples to a classroom collection of minerals.

| Section | Core | Standard | Enriched | Section | Core | Standard | Enriched |
|---|:---:|:---:|:---:|---|:---:|:---:|:---:|
| **9.1 Mineral Formation and Structure** pp. 185–191 | | | | **Blackline Masters** Review Worksheet 9.2 Skills Worksheet 9.2 | • • | • • | • • |
| **Section Features** Skills WarmUp, p. 185 Skills WorkOut, p. 187 Activity, p. 191 | • • | • • | • • • | **Overhead Blackline Transparencies** Overhead Blackline Master 9.2 and Student Worksheet | • | • | • |
| **Blackline Masters** Review Worksheet 9.1 Integrating Worksheet 9.1a Integrating Worksheet 9.1b Integrating Worksheet 9.1c | • • • | • • • • | • • • • | **Laboratory Program** Investigation 14 Investigation 15 | | • | • • |
| **Color Transparencies** Transparencies 20, 21 | • | • | • | **9.3 Use of Minerals** pp. 200–204 | | | |
| **9.2 Mineral Identification** pp. 192–199 | | | | **Section Features** Skills WarmUp, p. 200 Historical Notebook, p. 203 | • • | • • | • • |
| **Section Features** Skills WarmUp, p. 192 SkillBuilder, p. 196 | • • | • • | • • | **Blackline Masters** Review Worksheet 9.3 Skills Worksheet 9.3 Vocabulary Worksheet 9.3 Enrich Worksheet 9.3 | • • • | • • • • | • • • |

# Bibliography

The following resources can be used for teaching the chapter. See page T–46 for supplier codes.

**Library Resources**

Bates, R. L. *The Challenge of Mineral Resources.* Hillside, NJ: Enslow Publishers, Inc., 1991.

Bates, R. L. *Industrial Minerals: How They Are Found and Used.* Hillside, NJ: Enslow Publishers, Inc., 1988.

Farndon, John. *How the Earth Works.* Pleasantville, NY: The Reader's Digest Association, Inc., 1992.

Parker, S. *Rocks & Minerals.* Eyewitness Series. New York: Alfred A. Knopf, 1991.

Symes, R. F., and R. R. Harding. *Crystal and Gem.* Eyewitness Series. New York: Alfred A. Knopf, 1991.

**Technology Resources**

*Software*

*Earth.* Mac, Dos, Win. ER.

*Earth Science.* Mac, Win. ER.

**CD-ROMs**

*Interactive Earth.* SFAW.

**Laserdiscs**

*Living Textbook.* (See barcodes on pages in this chapter.) Optical Data.

*Gems and Minerals: The Ultimate Rock Video.* Videodiscovery.

**Videos**

*Identifying Minerals: Searching for Clues.* FM.

**Audio-Visual Resources**

*Introduction to the Minerals.* Still frame. 15 min. CABISCO.

*Recognizing Rock-Making Minerals.* Film. EB.

*Rocks and Minerals: How We Identify Them.* Film. C/MTI.

### Writing Connection

Ask students to imagine that the object in the photograph is a doorway into a special world of crystals. Have them write stories about what they see as they enter the doorway and explore. Students may wish to share their stories with the class.

## Introducing the Chapter

Have students read the description of the photograph. Ask if they agree or disagree with the description.

### Directed Inquiry

Have students study the photograph. Ask:

▶ How would you describe the image in the picture? (Students may say that it looks like layers of crystals and rock around a cavity. They may also come up with more fanciful descriptions, such as a nest of precious gems.)

▶ What properties help you identify this object? (Students should mention such properties as color, shine, hardness, and heaviness.)

▶ How do you think this rock was formed? (Answers will vary. You might explain that the layers formed as water evaporated, in a way similar to the formation of stalactites.)

▶ What are some features that this formation has in common with all minerals? (Students may mention the crystals and the fact that it is naturally formed and not alive.)

## Chapter Vocabulary

| | |
|---|---|
| cleavage | Mohs scale |
| fracture | ore |
| gem | specific gravity |
| luster | streak |
| mineral | |

---

# Chapter 9  Minerals

### Chapter Sections

**9.1** Mineral Formation and Structure

**9.2** Mineral Identification

**9.3** Uses of Minerals

### What do you see?

❝I see an amethyst cut crosswise. It was formed like all crystals, through many years. The colors are caused by different elements when it was being formed.❞

*Eliza Bivins*
*Westwood Center for Health and Science*
*Grand Rapids, Michigan*

To find out more about the photograph, look on page 206. As you read this chapter, you will learn about the composition and uses of minerals.

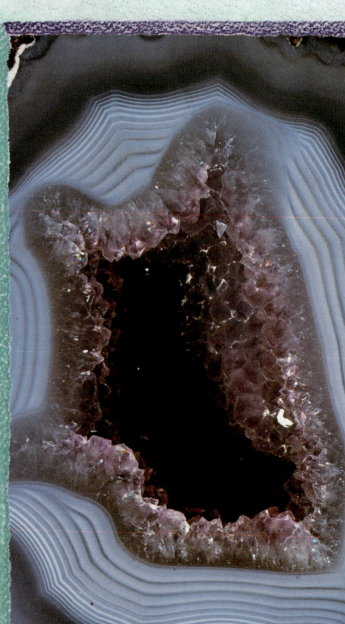

## Themes in Science

**Scale and Structure** The crystal structure of a particular mineral is always the same. Crystal structure is one of many stable patterns in the natural world.

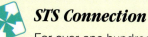

## STS Connection

For over one hundred years, scientists have tried to create crystals like those found in nature. Today, synthetic crystals are very important for technological uses. In fact, such crystals are built into nearly every optical or electronic device produced today. Synthetic crystals, unlike natural crystals, can be made without any flaws. In addition, they can be created to grow a certain shape and size and then used for specific purposes.

# 9.1 Mineral Formation and Structure

## Objectives

▶ **Define** mineral.

▶ **Describe** the chemical composition of mineral groups.

▶ **Distinguish** between minerals and nonminerals.

▶ **Make models** of mineral crystal systems.

---

**▼ ACTIVITY**

**Observing**

*Rock Features*

Closely inspect several rocks. Do you notice different colors, patterns, or textures within the same rock? How do you explain these differences?

**SKILLS WARMUP**

---

If you go outside and pick up the nearest rock, what are you holding in your hand? You might answer that you are holding part of the earth's crust. You might add that the rock is made up of certain elements that are common in the crust. What you probably don't know is that the elements in the rock are arranged in certain patterns.

## Characteristics of Minerals

Most rocks contain more than one mineral. Each mineral may be scattered throughout the rock as tiny particles too small to see. In other rocks, the mineral particles are visible as large specks. Some rocks are chunks of just one mineral.

There are over 2,000 different kinds of minerals in the earth's crust, but all of them share five characteristics. These characteristics can be stated in one definition. A **mineral** is a natural, inorganic solid with a definite chemical composition and a particular crystalline structure. The following explanations will help you understand these characteristics.

1. *A mineral is formed in nature.* Minerals come from the earth's crust, not from the laboratory or factory. When people chemically change materials from the earth's crust, they are no longer minerals. For example, glass and concrete are not minerals, even though they are made from substances that originally came from minerals.

**Figure 9.1**
The orange-colored chalcedony is a mineral. Is the chunk of coal a mineral, too? ▼ ①

**Section Objectives**
For a list of section objectives, see the Student Edition page.

**Skills Objectives**
Students should be able to:

**Observe** a rock's physical composition.

**Research** how quartz crystal forms.

**Infer** where quartz crystal examples may be found.

**Make a Model** of two basic crystal systems.

**Measure** the growth of crystals.

**Vocabulary**
mineral

---

**MOTIVATE**

### Skills WarmUp

To help students become more familiar with the characteristics of minerals, have them do the Skills WarmUp.
**Answer** Observations will vary. The differences have to do with the processes by which the minerals were formed.

### Misconceptions

Students may think that all minerals are either metals or a source of metals. Remind students that they are familiar with many minerals that are not metallic—for example, salt, quartz, talc, sulfur, and diamond.

**Answer to In-Text Question**
① **No; coal is organic.**

---

**The Living Textbook:
Earth Science Sides 1-2**

Chapter 34          Frame 07714
Mineral Definition (2 Frames)
Search:                    Step:

## Critical Thinking

**Classify** After students read about the characteristics of minerals, ask: Crude oil is formed in nature, so why isn't it classified as a mineral? (It is organic and not a solid.)

**Compare and Contrast** Have students think about the chemical formula for quartz. Ask: How is $SiO_2$ like $CO_2$, and how is it different? (Both have two oxygen atoms, but one chemical formula has silicon in it and the other has carbon in it. One formula represents a solid and the other represents a gas. Also, $SiO_2$ describes the *ratio* of atoms in a structure with a variable number of total atoms, whereas $CO_2$ represents a single molecule.)

## Skills Development

**Observe** Have students look at samples of quartz and wulfenite. Ask: How many sides do quartz crystals have compared to wulfenite crystals? (Wulfenite crystals have four sides; quartz crystals have six sides.)

### Integrating the Sciences

**Chemistry** Remind students of what a chemical formula is. Ask:

▶ What information is given in a chemical formula? (How many atoms of each element are present in a compound)

▶ As an example, ask: What does the chemical formula $CaCO_3$ stand for? (Calcium carbonate)

### STS Connection

Crystals are used in electronics, industrial tools, medicine, communications, and control circuits. All the functions necessary to a computer can be coordinated on a single tiny computer chip called an integrated circuit. Have student volunteers find out how silicon computer chips are made and present their findings to the class.

**Figure 9.2** ▲
Quartz (left) and wulfenite (right) each have a particular crystalline structure.

2. *A mineral is inorganic.* The word inorganic is used to describe things not made of living matter or matter produced by living things. Wood is not a mineral because it comes from trees. Coal is not a mineral because it is formed from the remains of plants.

3. *A mineral is a solid.* Minerals must be solid for their atoms to form characteristic patterns. Magma is a natural substance found in the earth, but it is not a mineral because it is not a solid.

4. *A mineral has a definite chemical composition.* A mineral always contains the same elements in the same proportions. A chemical formula can be written for each mineral, and the formula never changes. The mineral quartz, for example, is always made up of two oxygen atoms for every silicon atom. The chemical formula for quartz is $SiO_2$. Some minerals are exceptions to this rule because the amounts or kinds of elements in their makeup can vary. But chemical formulas for these minerals can still be written because the variations are within certain limits.

5. *A mineral has a particular crystalline structure.* The atoms of a mineral are arranged in a way that forms a particular geometric shape, or crystal. Each mineral always has the same crystalline structure. Mineral crystals are usually too small to be seen without a microscope.

## Mineral Formation

Minerals are formed slowly by two natural processes. In the first process, melted rock, or magma, cools to form solid mineral crystals. In the second process, water containing dissolved minerals evaporates, leaving behind mineral crystals.

**Cooling of Magma** Recall that in the asthenosphere, much of the earth's rocky material is hot and partially liquid. Some of this magma works its way upward through cracks in the crust, where it collects and cools. During the cooling process, atoms in the magma rearrange. They begin to "lock" into place, forming crystals.

The chemical makeup of the magma determines which kinds of minerals it can form. The rate at which the magma cools determines the size of the mineral crystals. Slow cooling produces large crystals, and rapid cooling produces small crystals.

Many minerals come from cooling magma. Some examples are olivine, plagioclase (PLAY jee uh KLAYS) feldspar, and quartz. Minerals with magma origins are often recovered through mining. These minerals can also reach the earth's surface through folding, faulting, uplift, and erosion.

**Precipitation** Minerals dissolved in liquids form mixtures called solutions. When the liquid part of a mineral-containing solution evaporates, the minerals are left behind. This process is called *precipitation* (pree SIHP uh TAY shuhn). If you ever made rock candy from a sugar solution, you precipitated a solid from a solution.

The largest mineral solution on the earth is the ocean. The ocean contains the compound sodium chloride. When ocean water evaporates, sodium chloride forms the mineral halite. Other compounds dissolved in ocean water form other minerals through precipitation. Minerals also precipitate from hot springs, geysers, springs, and streams.

Look at the mineral crystals in Figure 9.3. It shows a rock called a geode (JEE ohd). Hot, mineral-containing water once filled the geode. When the water evaporated, the mineral crystals lining the inside of the geode were left behind.

**Figure 9.3**
The mineral crystals inside a geode form by precipitation. ▼

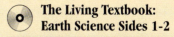

## TEACH ▪ Continued

### Skills Development

**Infer** Ask students to explain why carbonates are not organic, even though they contain carbon. (They are not formed by or from living things.)

### Directed Inquiry

Have students study Table 9.1. Then ask the following questions:

► What are the six important mineral groups? (Silicates, carbonates, oxides, sulfates, sulfides, and halides)

► What elements do all silicates contain? (Silicon and oxygen)

► What elements do all halides contain? (Chlorine or fluorine)

► What element is in all oxides? (Oxygen)

---

**The Living Textbook:**
**Earth Science Sides 1-2**

Chapter 26       Frame 03433
Hematite (3 Frames)
Search:             Step:

---

**The Living Textbook:**
**Earth Science Sides 1-2**

Chapter 26       Frame 03456
Dolomite (3 Frames)
Search:             Step:

---

**The Living Textbook:**
**Earth Science Sides 1-2**

Chapter 26       Frame 03468
Flourite (3 Frames)
Search:             Step:

### *Integrating the Sciences*

**Chemistry** Have students look at the periodic table on pages 176 and 177 in Chapter 8. Tell them that one of the groups in the periodic table is called the *halogens*. Then ask them to infer which mineral group in Table 9.1 takes its elements from the halogens. (Halides; chlorine and fluorine are halogens, and the group name has the same prefix.)

### *Language Arts Connection*

Have students study the mineral groups in Table 9.1. Then have them list mineral groups with names ending in *-ide* and mineral groups with names ending in *-ate*. Have students explain the meanings of these suffixes and how they apply to the names of the two groups. (Oxides, sulfides, and halides are all chemical compounds, which is the definition of *-ide*. The *-ate* in silicates, carbonates, and sulfates indicates a chemical derivative.)

---

## Mineral Composition

You learned that each kind of mineral has its own unique chemical makeup, or composition. However, there are chemical similarities among many of the most common minerals. For example, many minerals contain the elements silicon (Si) and oxygen (O). Earth scientists group these minerals together and call them the silicate minerals.

In a similar way, some minerals contain the elements carbon and oxygen to form a carbonate group ($CO_3$). Minerals containing the carbonate group are called carbonate minerals.

In addition, there are four other important mineral groups: oxides, sulfates, sulfides, and halides. Each is named for the nonmetal elements shared by the minerals in the group. Oxides contain oxygen. Sulfates contain sulfur and oxygen, and sulfides contain only sulfur. Halides contain chlorine or fluorine. The six major mineral groups are described in Table 9.1.

**Table 9.1  Major Mineral Groups**

| Silicates | Carbonates | Oxides |
|---|---|---|
| Si + O + one or more metals | $CO_3$ + one or more metals | O + one or more metals |
| Examples: quartz, feldspar, dioptase, mica, topaz, olivine | Examples: calcite, dolomite, siderite, rhodochrosite | Examples: magnetite, hematite, corundum |
| Dioptase | Rhodochrosite | Corundum |

| Sulfates | Sulfides | Halides |
|---|---|---|
| $SO_4$ + one or more metals | S + one or more metals | Cl or F + a metal |
| Examples: gypsum, barite | Examples: galena, sphalerite, bornite | Examples: halite, fluorite |
| Barite | Sphalerite | Fluorite |

## Math Connection

Have students study the definitions of the crystal systems in Table 9.2. Have students work in cooperative groups, and assign the groups the task of rewriting each crystal system definition using mathematical symbols. Tell students to assign each axis a capital letter and each angle between axes a lowercase letter, and to use the following symbols: = and ≠. Provide this example: Tetragonal crystal system: $A = B \neq C$, $a = b = c = 90°$. Have the groups compare their results. (Cubic: $A = B = C$, $a = b = c = 90°$; Orthorhombic: $A \neq B \neq C$, $a = b = c = 90°$; Monoclinic: $A \neq B \neq C$, $a \neq b = c = 90°$; Triclinic: $A \neq B \neq C$, $a \neq 90°$, $b \neq 90°$, $c \neq 90°$; Hexagonal: $A = B = C \neq D$, $a = b = c = 60°$, $d = 90°$.)

**Use Integrating Worksheet 9.1b.**

## Crystal Structure

The crystal shapes of most of the earth's minerals are classified into six different groups. Each group of crystal shapes is called a crystal system. The six crystal systems are shown in Table 9.2. Each crystal system is defined by a certain arrangement of three or four lines called axes. Each axis represents one dimension of the crystal's three-dimensional shape. The relationship of the axes to one another determines the three-dimensional shape.

Crystal shape is determined by the arrangement of the atoms that make up a mineral. A mineral's characteristic crystal shape is the most stable way its atoms can arrange. The shape of a mineral's crystals is the same no matter how large they are. Sometimes crystals become very large, so the crystalline arrangement is easy to see. These beautiful minerals are valuable because they are rare. However, most crystals are very small. Some are so small that microscopes or X-rays are needed to reveal the crystal's pattern.

**Table 9.2  Basic Crystal Systems**

| Cubic | Tetragonal | Orthorhombic |
|---|---|---|
| Three axes of equal length intersect at 90° angles. | Same as cubic, except the vertical axis is longer or shorter than the others. | Three axes of different lengths intersect at 90° angles. |
| Examples: halite, galena, pyrite | Examples: cassiterite, chalcopyrite | Examples: olivine, topaz |

| Monoclinic | Triclinic | Hexagonal |
|---|---|---|
| Same as orthorhombic, except one axis is oblique, or not at a 90° angle, to the others. | Three unequal axes intersect at oblique angles to one another. | Three equal horizontal axes intersect at 60° angles. The vertical axis is longer or shorter than the others. |
| Examples: mica, gypsum | Examples: plagioclase feldspar, turquoise | Examples: calcite, quartz |

## Skills Development

**Interpret Data**  Have students study Table 9.2, then ask:

▶ How is each crystal system defined? (Each has a certain arrangement of three or four axes.)

▶ How do the tetragonal and cubic arrangements differ? (In the tetragonal arrangement, the vertical axis is longer or shorter than the horizontal axes.)

▶ How do the orthorhombic and triclinic arrangements differ? (Orthorhombic axes intersect at 90° angles; triclinic axes intersect at oblique angles.)

▶ If you find a crystal with six sides plus a top and bottom, how would you classify it? (Hexagonal)

**The Living Textbook:
Earth Science Sides 1-2**

Chapter 25          Frame 03284
Cubic (14 Frames)
Search:                    Step:

**The Living Textbook:
Earth Science Sides 1-2**

Chapter 25          Frame 03226
Orthorhombic (13 Frames)
Search:                    Step:

**The Living Textbook:
Earth Science Sides 1-2**

Chapter 25          Frame 03255
Hexagonal (24 Frames)
Search:                    Step:

## Apply

Have students discuss the mineral elements contained in a typical school lunch or an imaginary meal. Encourage them to use resources and read labels to find out which minerals they can ingest from common foods.

## EVALUATE

### WrapUp

**Review** Place six columns on the chalkboard. Ask students to name the major mineral groups and place one name over each column. Have the class give examples of minerals for each group.

Use Review Worksheet 9.1.

### Check and Explain

1. A mineral is a natural, inorganic solid with a definite chemical composition and a particular crystal structure.

2. Check student answers against Table 9.1 for accuracy.

3. **a.** A clam shell is formed by a living organism. **b.** An iron nail is not formed in nature. **c.** A brick is not formed in nature. **d.** Concrete is not formed in nature and does not have a definite chemical composition.

4. Models will vary, but should correspond to Table 9.2.

## *Integrating the Sciences*

**Health** Have students look at the labels on bottles of multiple vitamin tablets to determine which minerals, other than those listed on this page, people need for good nutrition. Point out that calcium is the most abundant mineral in the human body. A constant, daily supply of calcium is important, because our bodies continuously break down and rebuild bone tissue. Every cell in the body requires calcium. Have students make a list of foods that provide calcium. (Dairy products low in fat, canned fish, tofu, turnip, mustard greens, salad dressings made with vinegar or citrus juices, and foods rich in vitamin C and magnesium—these help absorb the calcium.)

**Use Integrating Worksheet 9.1c.**

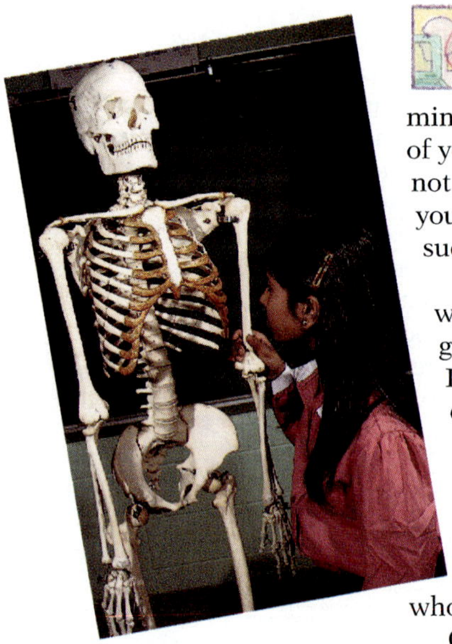

**Figure 9.4** ▲
Bones contain large amounts of calcium and phosphorus, elements which come originally from minerals in the earth.

### Science and You   *Minerals for Life*

If you read the labels on food products and vitamins, you may know that minerals are a necessary part of your diet. However, the minerals your body needs are not the same as the minerals you just read about. What you need are certain elements that come from minerals, such as iron, calcium, phosphorus, and iodine.

In the earth, these elements are usually combined with other elements to form minerals in rocks. But to get them into your body, you can't simply eat rocks! Instead, you eat parts of plants that extracted these elements from mineral particles in the soil. You can also get these elements by eating parts of animals that have eaten plants.

Iron is necessary for the formation of red blood cells. Red blood cells carry oxygen throughout your body. When you eat meat, liver, nuts, and whole-grain cereal, you get the iron you need.

Calcium and phosphorus help your body produce healthy bones and teeth. They also aid in blood and tissue formation. These elements are present in whole-grain cereal, meat, milk, and vegetables.

A chemical released by your thyroid gland regulates many of the processes that occur in your body. This gland depends on iodine for proper functioning. Foods containing iodine include seafood and iodized salt. You and rocks do have something in common: You are both formed from some of the same elements.

### Check and Explain

1. Write a definition of *mineral* that includes all five characteristics.

2. Describe the chemical composition of each major mineral group.

3. **Reason and Conclude** Explain why each of the following is not a mineral.

   a. Clam shell     c. Brick
   b. Iron nail      d. Concrete

4. **Make a Model** Using cardboard and tape, make three-dimensional models of two of the basic crystal systems.

### Prelab Discussion

Have students read the entire activity. Discuss a few points before beginning:

▶ Discuss the purpose of rolling the pipe cleaner in the powdered chemical. Point out the pipe cleaner's concentrated surface area.

▶ Explain that heating the water increases the quantity of salt or alum that can be dissolved in it. You may wish to state that the solubility of most solids increases with the temperature of the liquid solution.

**Time** 30 minutes    **Group** pairs

**Materials**

30 100-mL beakers

30 pipe cleaners

15 spoons

8 hot plates

30 pencils

alum, 0.75 kg

sodium chloride, 0.5 kg

masking tape

oven mitt or tongs

safety goggles

## Activity 9  How do you grow crystals?

*Skills*  Measure; Observe

### Task 1  Prelab Prep

1. Collect the following items: 2 beakers, water, 2 pipe cleaners, spoon, hot plate, oven mitt or tongs, 2 pencils, 2 pieces of masking tape, alum (potassium aluminum sulfate), table salt (sodium chloride), safety goggles.
2. With the masking tape and pencil, label one beaker *Alum* and the other *Sodium chloride*.
3. Put on your safety goggles.

### Task 2  Data Record

1. On a separate sheet of paper, copy Table 9.3.
2. Throughout the next several weeks, record your observations in the data table.

### Table 9.3  Observations of Crystal Growth

| Date | Alum Crystals | Sodium Chloride Crystals |
|------|---------------|--------------------------|
|      |               |                          |
|      |               |                          |
|      |               |                          |

### Task 3  Procedure

1. Fill the beaker labeled *Alum* half full of water.
2. On the hot plate, heat the water to boiling. With the oven mitt or tongs, remove the beaker from the hot plate. **CAUTION! Be careful when handling a beaker of hot water.** Set the beaker on a heat-resistant surface.
3. Slowly add alum to the beaker of hot water, stirring constantly. Keep adding alum until no more of the chemical will dissolve.
4. Allow the solution to cool for several minutes.
5. Dampen a pipe cleaner. Roll the pipe cleaner in the remaining powdered alum.

6. Wrap one end of the pipe cleaner around the middle of a pencil. Place the pencil on the rim of the beaker so that the pipe cleaner hangs in the center of the solution.
7. Repeat steps 1 to 6 for sodium chloride.
8. Set the beakers where they will not be disturbed.
9. Observe the beakers every school day for the next two weeks. Each time you make an observation, examine the crystals, and record what you see in your data table.

Note: If no crystals form after several days, remove the pipe cleaner, roll it again in the powdered chemical, and put it back in the solution.

### Task 4  Analysis

1. Did crystals form in each beaker?
2. If crystals grew, where did they form in each beaker? Why?
3. How do the crystals of alum differ from the crystals of sodium chloride?
4. Did the alum and the sodium chloride crystals grow at the same rate?

### Task 5  Conclusion

Write a short report describing the growth of crystals. Include drawings in your report.

### Everyday Application

Try making rock candy using the same procedure for growing crystals. Use sugar for your chemical and use heat-resistant kitchenware instead of labware. Compare the shape of the sugar crystals to the shape of the alum and sodium chloride crystals.

### Extension

Do crystals formed in nature grow like the crystals you made in this activity? Discuss possible ways that a solution of a mineral and water could form and then dry out to form crystals.

## Analysis

1. Crystals should have formed in each beaker.
2. The crystals should have formed on the pipe cleaner and possibly at the bottom of the beaker. The solid chemical on the pipe cleaner provides a surface on which the crystals can form.
3. Salt: cubic; alum: tetragonal
4. Answers can vary. Check to see whether answer agrees with the table of observations.

## Conclusion

Accept any reasonable summary of the results.

## Everyday Application

Point out to students that it is important to use clean kitchenware when making rock candy, especially if they want to sample it.

## Extension

In the activity, a heated solution cools, allowing the crystals to form. In nature, some crystals form in this way, while others form when water evaporates from a solution. Solutions can form as rainwater dissolves minerals from rock. The runoff can end up in puddles. After the water in the puddles evaporates, crystals can be left behind.

**Section Objectives**

For a list of section objectives, see the Student Edition page.

**Skills Objectives**

Students should be able to:

**Predict** the relative hardness of minerals.

**Classify** some common minerals.

**Measure** the hardness of minerals.

**Vocabulary**

streak, luster, cleavage, fracture, specific gravity, Mohs scale

## MOTIVATE

### Skills WarmUp

To help students understand the concept of mineral hardness, have them do the Skills WarmUp.

**Answer** Results depend on the samples tested. See Table 4 on page 195 for the relative hardness of several common minerals.

### Prior Knowledge

To gauge how much students know about mineral classification, ask the following questions:

▶ How can you tell if two minerals are pieces of the same sample?

▶ Can one mineral be shinier than another mineral? Harder or softer? More red or less red?

**Answer to In-Text Question**

① **The large sample on the left is pyrite.**

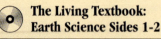
**The Living Textbook:
Earth Science Sides 1-2**

Chapter 25          Frame 03292
Pyrite (1 Frame)
Search:

### Portfolio

To illustrate the idea that distinguishing physical properties can be useful in identifying minerals specifically but also things in general, have students do this exercise. Work with them to make a list of about 12 groups of objects in which specific objects differ but can be identified by their common characteristics. Start with this list and add more: Bicycles, Video Games, Clouds, and Coins. For each group, have students make a list of characteristics that are relevant in identifying or naming a specific object within the group. (For bicycles, relevant characteristics include size and style of tires, number of gears, style of brakes, and construction of frame.) Students can keep their lists in their portfolios.

### ▼ ACTIVITY

#### Predicting

*Scratch Tests*

What do you think will happen when you scratch a mineral with a penny? Will you get different results with different minerals? How might the results of such a test be useful?

**SKILLS WARMUP**

**Figure 9.5**
Which is pyrite and which is gold? ▼ ①

## 9.2 Mineral Identification

### Objectives

▶ **List** the six properties of all minerals.

▶ **Identify** special properties of minerals.

▶ **Compare** and **contrast** mineral cleavage and fracture.

▶ **Measure** the hardness of minerals.

**P**icture a snake in your mind. You probably imagined an animal with scales and no legs. If you were to describe your snake, it would be different from the ones your classmates might describe. In nature, too, each kind of snake has unique characteristics that distinguish it from other snakes. What characteristics distinguish the snake you imagined? Physical properties, such as color, shape, and size, are useful for identifying snakes. Certain physical properties are also useful for identifying minerals.

### Properties of Minerals

A prospector panning for gold in a stream collects some shiny gold-colored nuggets. Can the prospector be sure the nuggets are gold? Many gold miners have been fooled by pyrite, a mineral that's also called "fool's gold." Look at Figure 9.5 and notice the similarities between these two minerals.

Pyrite and gold are both shiny and have similar colors. But by testing other properties, the prospector can tell whether the mineral is pyrite or gold. Other physical properties that the prospector may test include streak, luster, cleavage or fracture, specific gravity, and hardness.

How do you identify a mineral you find in the field or laboratory? First, you can ask a series of questions about the mineral. The questions can be answered by performing simple tests or making observations. Each test determines one of the mineral's important properties that will help identify the mineral. Since each mineral has a unique set of properties, you can identify the mineral that you find.

### Themes in Science

**Diversity and Unity** Minerals are diverse in color, streak, luster, cleavage, density, and hardness, but all have a crystalline structure and a definite chemical composition.

### STS Connection

Sometimes complex tools are required to positively identify a mineral specimen. A spectroscope, often used in the study of stars, is used to help distinguish between gemstones of similar color. A technique called *electron probe microanalysis* helps identify minerals through a scanning electron microscope (SEM). The SEM focuses a beam of light on the mineral and an X-ray spectrum is produced that shows the characteristics of the minerals.

**Luster** How does the mineral reflect light? Some minerals are shiny and others are dull. The way light reflects from the mineral's surface is called **luster**. If a mineral is shiny like a metal, it has a *metallic* luster. The galena in Figure 9.6 has a *metallic* luster.

All other types of luster are grouped together. They are called *nonmetallic* lusters. Nonmetallic lusters include pearly, silky, glassy, dull, and greasy. Describe the luster of the olivine in Figure 9.6.

**Streak** What color mark does the mineral leave on a tile? Many minerals make a mark when rubbed on a piece of unglazed porcelain tile called a streak plate. The mark is some of the mineral in powdered form. The color of the powder left on the streak plate is called the mineral's **streak**. What is the color of the streak of the mineral hematite in Figure 9.7? ②

Unlike color, the streak of a mineral does not vary, so streak is often a good identification test. Hematite varies in color from red to brown, but its streak is always red. A streak test is one way to distinguish between pyrite and gold. Gold has a gold streak, and pyrite has a black streak.

Galena                          Olivine

**Figure 9.6** ▲
Minerals vary in their luster.

**Color** What color is the mineral? Color may be the first property you notice about a mineral. However, very few minerals can be identified by their color. Most minerals vary greatly in color because of small amounts of impurities. For example, the mineral quartz comes in a variety of colors, including pink, brown, purple, white, and clear.

Color can often tell you if a certain element is contained in a mineral. Copper, for example, produces a green or blue color in a mineral. You can infer that most green or blue minerals, such as the azurite and malachite in Figure 9.8, contain copper. Knowing that a mineral contains a certain element greatly narrows down what it might be.

**Figure 9.7** ▲
Why is streak a more reliable property than color for mineral identification? ③

**Figure 9.8** ▲
You can see both azurite (blue) and malachite (green) in this sample.

### Enrich

Help students understand that some minerals have quite distinctive colors. The blue of azurite and the green of malachite are quite distinctive. So is the yellow of sulfur. However, color must be used with caution in identifying minerals. For example, fluorite can be violet, green, blue, yellow, pink, white, or colorless. Such a wide variation in color is rare, but minerals often occur in more than one color because of small amounts of impurities.

### Apply

Have students describe the color and luster of the minerals pictured on pages 185, 186, and 188.

**Answers to In-Text Questions**

② **Blood-red**

③ **Colors can vary, but the streak of the mineral is always the same.**

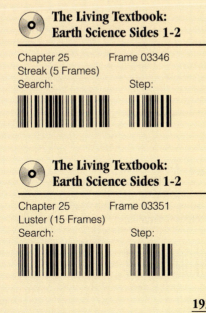

The Living Textbook:
**Earth Science Sides 1-2**

Chapter 25          Frame 03346
Streak (5 Frames)
Search:                    Step:

The Living Textbook:
**Earth Science Sides 1-2**

Chapter 25          Frame 03351
Luster (15 Frames)
Search:                    Step:

## TEACH ▪ Continued

### Discuss

Have students read about cleavage and fracture and study Figure 9.9. Ask:

▶ What is the cleavage of a mineral? (Cleavage is the way a mineral breaks along a flat surface or plane.)

▶ How does mica cleave? (Mica cleaves in one direction, forming flat thin sheets.)

▶ How does halite cleave? (Halite cleaves in three directions so that it breaks into small cubes.)

▶ How is the fracture of a mineral different from cleavage? (Fractures leave an uneven surface.)

### Skills Development

**Infer** Ask students: What did early people use quartz for? Why? (They used quartz to make cutting tools and arrowheads because it is hard and has conchoidal fracture, which produces sharp edges.)

**Measure** Have students suppose a mineral has a density of 6.7 g/cm³. Ask: What is its specific gravity? (6.7)

### Explore Visually

Have students examine the picture of halite. Ask them to identify the three cleavage planes. Suggest that they compare the picture to the cubic crystal system in Table 9.2.

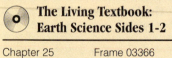

**The Living Textbook: Earth Science Sides 1-2**

Chapter 25        Frame 03366
Fracture (7 Frames)
Search:                Step:

### Math Connection

Ask students to explain why measures of density have units, whereas measures of specific gravity are numbers without units. (Density is a ratio of quantities with different units. Specific gravity is a ratio of two quantities with the same units. The units cancel out, and the ratio is reduced to a decimal value, leaving only a number.)

**Cleavage and Fracture** How does the mineral break? The broken surfaces on a mineral can be an important clue to identification. There are two types of mineral breakage: fracture and cleavage. A mineral that breaks along a flat surface, or plane, has **cleavage**. Minerals can have cleavage in one, two, three, four, or six directions. The mineral mica cleaves in one direction, forming flat, thin sheets. Halite cleaves in three directions. It breaks into smaller cubes.

Some minerals do not form smooth surfaces when they break. A mineral that leaves an uneven surface when it breaks has **fracture**. Fracture surfaces may be curved, splintery, or fibrous.

Minerals that break to form curving surfaces have *conchoidal* (kahn KOYD uhl) fracture. Quartz, shown in Figure 9.9, is one common mineral with conchoidal fracture. Minerals with conchoidal fracture have been used by people for thousands of years for making cutting tools and arrowheads.

**Specific Gravity** How dense is the mineral? Recall that density is how much matter is contained in a certain volume. Density is expressed as g/cm³.

The densities of minerals can also be compared by using the measure of **specific gravity**. Specific gravity is the ratio of a mineral's density to the density of water. Water is used as a basis of comparison because its density is 1 g/cm³. A mineral with a density of 5.3 g/cm³, for example, has a specific gravity of 5.3. It is 5.3 times more dense than water.

The specific gravity of most minerals varies from 2 to 5. Minerals made mostly of metal elements, however, may have a much higher density. The specific gravity of pure gold, for example, is 19.3.

In the field, specific gravity is hard to measure, so heft is used instead. *Heft* is measured by picking up the mineral, feeling its mass, and comparing it to an equal volume of another mineral. A prospector would find that gold has more heft than pyrite.

**Figure 9.9**
The type of cleavage or fracture a mineral shows can help in its identification. ▼

**Halite**
Cleavage along three planes

**Mica**
Cleavage along one plane

**Quartz**
Conchoidal fracture

## STS Connection

Discuss how the hardness of minerals can determine how people use them. Have students explain how soft minerals, such as talc, can be used. (Talc is used in talcum powder and crayons, gypsum is used in plaster of Paris, and calcite is used as chalk.) Then discuss how hard minerals, such as corundum and diamond, can be used. (Both can be used as abrasives, and diamonds are used in rock drills.)

## Integrating the Sciences

**Chemistry** The hardness of a mineral is determined by the strength of the chemical bonds connecting its atoms. Ask students to imagine what happens, on an atomic level, to a mineral when it is scratched by a harder mineral.

## Critical Thinking

**Generalize** Have students suppose they have two different minerals that look alike. One can be scratched by a fingernail and the other cannot. The hardness of a fingernail is about 2.5. The second mineral may be scratched by a penny and not by a fingernail. The hardness of a penny is about 3.5. The two minerals could be gypsum and calcite or talc and calcite. What other possibilities exist? (One could be calcite and the other a mineral with the hardness of gypsum. Both minerals could also be minerals not mentioned.)

## Class Activity

Have students try to scratch a piece of chalk and a piece of glass with a fingernail to determine which is softer. (Chalk) Then ask students to try to scratch glass with steel wool to determine which is softer. (Steel wool) If possible, use mineral samples on the Mohs scale and have students rank them by hardness.

## Answer to In-Text Question

① **10**

## Answer to Link

A possible explanation is that this plane represents a weaker bond than bonds that exist elsewhere in the model.

**Hardness** How hard is the mineral? Hardness is an important property for identifying minerals. Hardness is the ability of a mineral to resist being scratched. Harder minerals scratch softer minerals.

To make it easier to compare the hardness of different minerals, a German earth scientist named Friedrich Mohs (MOHZ) set up a hardness scale in the early 1800s. He arranged ten minerals in order of increasing hardness and assigned each a number from 1 to 10. These reference minerals are used to test and describe the hardness of minerals. This scale is called the **Mohs scale** of hardness.

Look at the Mohs scale in Table 9.4. Which mineral has a hardness of 10? Which mineral has a hardness of 1? The softest mineral, talc, can be scratched by all other minerals. Talc is in crayons and talcum powder. Diamond, the hardest known mineral, can scratch all other minerals.

When you test hardness, don't confuse a scratch with a streak. A soft mineral such as talc cannot scratch a harder mineral. But it may leave a streak that looks like a scratch!

In the field, you can test hardness with the field tests shown in the right-hand column of the table. Field tests do not require the test minerals from the Mohs scale. Instead, common items, such as a steel knife, are used.

**Figure 9.10** ▲
Diamond is the hardest known mineral. What number is it given on the Mohs scale? ①

**Table 9.4 Mohs Scale of Mineral Hardness**

| Mineral | Hardness | Field Test |
|---------|----------|------------|
| Talc | 1 | Easily scratched by a fingernail |
| Gypsum | 2 | Can be scratched by a fingernail |
| Calcite | 3 | Barely scratched by a copper penny |
| Fluorite | 4 | Easily scratched by a steel knife blade |
| Apatite | 5 | Can be scratched by a steel knife blade |
| Feldspar | 6 | Easily scratches glass |
| Quartz | 7 | Easily scratches glass and steel |
| Topaz | 8 | Scratches quartz |
| Corundum | 9 | No simple test |
| Diamond | 10 | No simple test |

## Chemistry
### L I N K

The cleavage of a mineral provides clues to how the mineral is structured. Collect some toothpicks, glue, and a butter knife.

**1.** Using the toothpicks and glue, build a "mineral" that you think will cleave in only one direction.

**2.** Allow the glue to dry, then test the cleavage of your mineral by trying to pry it apart with a butter knife or other flat instrument.

**3.** Draw a picture of your mineral and label the cleavage plane.

Why does your mineral break along this plane?

**A C T I V I T Y**

**The Living Textbook: Earth Science Sides 1-2**

Chapter 25      Frame 03325
Hardness (14 Frames)
Search:              Step:

## TEACH ▪ Continued

### Enrich

Tell students that the mineral calcite has special properties. Light bends when it passes through clear calcite crystals. If possible, have students view objects through clear calcite crystals.

### *SkillBuilder*

**Research** Provide each student or group with a set of standard mineral samples that vary in color, streak, and hardness. Each mineral used should appear in the Data Bank on pages 624–625. Point out that students should use this resource to help identify their minerals.

**Answers**

5. Answers will vary, but they may be able to identify some minerals. They may also need to test for fracture or cleavage, special properties, and heft to identify some samples.

6. Answers will vary; most will say hardness.

Reports will vary, but students should follow the procedure outlined in this SkillBuilder.

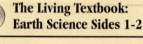
**The Living Textbook: Earth Science Sides 1-2**

Chapter 25      Frame 03380
Fluorescence (23 Frames)
Search:            Step:

---

 ## *Multicultural Perspectives*

The mineral magnetite was used by the Chinese to make the first compasses about 3,000 years ago. Compasses became important in early voyages of exploration and trade. Ask students how they would go about making a simple compass using a piece of magnetite.

---

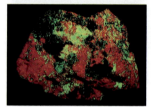

**Figure 9.11** ▲
Willemite shows the special property of fluorescence.

### Special Properties

All minerals have the physical properties of color, streak, luster, cleavage or fracture, specific gravity, and hardness. Some minerals have additional properties that can be used for identification. One special property is smell. Other special properties include magnetism and fluorescence (flor EHS uhns).

**Magnetism** Minerals containing iron or nickel are attracted to magnets. Some of these minerals can even act as magnets themselves. Magnetite is a magnetic mineral. Magnetite is also an important source of iron.

**Fluorescence** Some minerals display interesting characteristics when they interact with light. Exposure to ultraviolet light will make some minerals fluoresce, or glow. In Figure 9.11, the mineral willemite is shown fluorescing bright green after exposure to ultraviolet light.

## *SkillBuilder* *Classifying*

### *Identifying Common Minerals*

Unknown minerals can be identified by testing the minerals' properties. Copy the table to the right. Obtain a streak plate, a copper penny, a kitchen knife, a piece of glass, and unknown mineral samples for identification. Give a number to each sample, and label it with that number.

1. In your table, observe and record the color of each mineral.

2. Test each mineral's streak using a streak plate. Record the color of the streak for each mineral in your table.

3. Test each mineral's hardness using the field tests in Table 9.4. Record the hardness results in your table.

4. Try to identify each mineral by comparing your results to the chart of mineral properties on pages 624–625 of the Data Bank.

5. Based on the three properties you tested, could you identify any of your samples? If not, what additional properties do you need to test in order to identify the samples?

6. Which property was most helpful in identifying the minerals?

Write a short report describing how you would identify an unknown mineral you found while walking home from school.

| Sample Number | Color | Streak | Hardness |
|---|---|---|---|
| 1 | | | |
| 2 | | | |
| 3 | | | |

## Mineral Properties and Chemical Structure

Minerals are made of different chemical elements. But chemical makeup alone doesn't explain all the variations in minerals' properties. What matters most is a mineral's structure—the arrangement of its atoms or ions.

The effect of chemical structure on physical properties is easily seen in the silicates. All silicates contain silicon and oxygen. So they are similar in chemical makeup. However, silicates vary greatly in their properties.

All silicates share a structural unit called the silicon–oxygen tetrahedron (TEH truh HEE druhn). You can see in Figure 9.12 that this unit is made up of four oxygen atoms covalently bonded to one atom of silicon.

Silicon–oxygen tetrahedra bond to each other and to atoms or ions of other elements in many different ways. The tetrahedra can form single chains, double chains, sheets, and three-dimensional networks. Each type of structure results in a different set of physical properties. Study Figure 9.13. It compares two different types of structures.

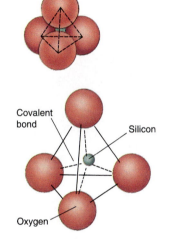

Covalent bond
Silicon
Oxygen

**Figure 9.12** ▲
The silicon–oxygen tetrahedron is the building block of all silicate minerals.

**Figure 9.13
Silicate Structures** ▼

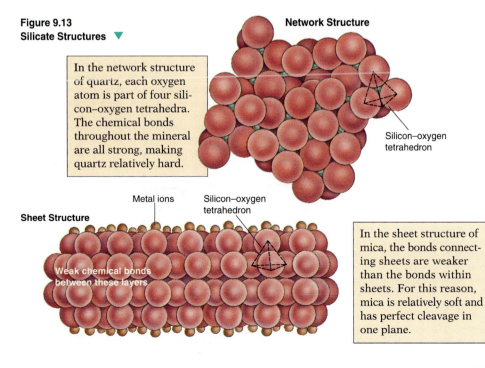

**Network Structure**

In the network structure of quartz, each oxygen atom is part of four silicon–oxygen tetrahedra. The chemical bonds throughout the mineral are all strong, making quartz relatively hard.

Silicon–oxygen tetrahedron

**Sheet Structure**

Metal ions
Silicon–oxygen tetrahedron

Weak chemical bonds between these layers

In the sheet structure of mica, the bonds connecting sheets are weaker than the bonds within sheets. For this reason, mica is relatively soft and has perfect cleavage in one plane.

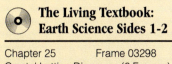

## Skills Development

**Interpret Data**  Have students study Table 9.5. Then ask:

▶ What element is the most common among rock-forming minerals? (Oxygen)

▶ To which mineral group do most of the rock-forming minerals belong? (Silicates)

▶ What mineral group is the second most common among rock-forming minerals? (Carbonate)

▶ Which minerals vary the most in color? (Quartz, plagioclase feldspar, dolomite)

▶ Which rock-forming minerals have variable chemical compositions? (Plagioclase feldspar, olivine, mica, pyroxene, and amphibole)

## Discuss

Point out that potassium feldspar and plagioclase feldspar make up about half of the earth's crust. These minerals are often combined with mica and quartz. Quartz is the hardest rock-forming mineral. Ferromagnesian minerals include olivine, pyroxene, and amphibole. They make up most of the earth's mantle.

## Integrating the Sciences

**Chemistry**  Have students study Table 9.5 and make a list of all the elements listed in the *composition* column by chemical symbol. Then ask students to use the periodic table on pages 176 and 177 in Chapter 8 to find the name of each element and to write down whether it is a metal or nonmetal.

## Common Rock-Forming Minerals

Of the thousands of minerals in the earth's crust, only about 20 are common. They are called the rock-forming minerals because they make up most of the earth's rocks. Some important rock-forming minerals are described in Table 9.5. The 11 rock-forming minerals listed in the table make up about 90 percent of the mass of the earth's crust. Why do you think that most of the rock-forming minerals are in the silicate group? Recall that almost three-fourths of the earth's crust is made of oxygen and silicon.

**Figure 9.14** ▲
Common rock-forming minerals include feldspar (front), olivine (center), and mica (rear).

**Table 9.5    Major Rock-Forming Minerals**

| Mineral | Composition | Mineral Group | Hardness | Color |
|---------|-------------|---------------|----------|-------|
| Quartz | $SiO_2$ | Silicate | 7 | Varies |
| Potassium feldspar | $KAISi_3O_8$ | Silicate | 6 | Pink |
| Plagioclase feldspar | Varies from $NaAISi_3O_8$ to $CaAl_2Si_2O_8$ | Silicate | 6 | Varies |
| Mica | Contains Si, O, Al, K, and other elements | Silicate | 2.5 | White to dark |
| Olivine | $(Mg, Fe)_2SiO_4$ | Silicate | 6.5 | Olive, yellowish, greenish |
| Pyroxene | Contains Si, O, Fe, and Mg | Silicate | 5–6 | Dark green to black |
| Amphibole | Contains Si, O, H, Fe, and Mg | Silicate | 5–6 | Dark green to black |
| Calcite | $CaCO_3$ | Carbonate | 3 | White, grey, yellow, colorless |
| Dolomite | $CaMg(CO_3)_2$ | Carbonate | 3.5–4.0 | Varies |
| Halite | $NaCl$ | Halide | 2.5 | White, colorless |
| Gypsum | $CaSO_4 \cdot 2H_2O$ | Sulfate | 2 | Reddish, white, grayish, yellowish, |

### Science and Technology
#### *Drilling with Diamonds*

When you think of diamonds, you probably imagine the glistening gems embedded in jewelry. But diamonds are also used for industrial purposes. Because of their hardness, diamonds can cut and drill through substances, such as rock, that are relatively hard.

The diamonds used in industry are not the same as those chosen for fine jewelry. Industrial diamonds have impurities or flaws, so they cannot be used as gems. Most industrial diamonds are also very small, like grains of sand.

Diamonds are most commonly used to coat the cutting surfaces of drill bits. Diamond drill bits for cutting through rock are ring-shaped hollow cylinders set with diamonds. The drill bit is attached to a drill that rotates at high speed. The bit penetrates the rock, leaving a sample of the rock inside it. The rock is then removed.

Diamond drill bits cut through rock much faster than bits made of other materials. They also last much longer. A high-grade steel bit cuts a path 8 km long before wearing down. A diamond bit, in contrast, cuts a path 2,000 km long before wearing down. You can see why diamonds are important for reasons other than just their brilliant luster.

**Figure 9.15** ▲
This diamond-tipped drill can cut through the hardest of rocks.

### Check and Explain

1. List the six properties that can be tested for identification of a mineral.

2. What is the property of fluorescence? How may it be used to identify a mineral?

3. **Compare and Contrast** Discuss the similarities and differences between cleavage and fracture.

4. **Measure** Using the Mohs scale of hardness on page 195, determine the hardness number for each of the following minerals.

   a. Scratches feldspar, but not topaz

   b. Scratched by your fingernail

   c. Scratches all the other minerals

   d. Scratched by a penny

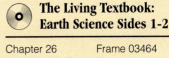

**Section Objectives**
For a list of section objectives, see the Student Edition page.

**Skills Objectives**
Students should be able to:

**Classify** gems based on observable characteristics.

**Infer** why most minerals are not found in their pure form.

**Vocabulary**
ore, gem

---

### Social Studies Connection

Assign each student in the class a state in the United States (beginning with the largest in area). Have each student look up his or her state in an encyclopedia or other reference to find out what metal ores are mined there. Then, as a class, make a table that lists the states by the metal ores that they mine.

### Multicultural Perspectives

In the 1970s, two Brown University scientists discovered that African people living on the western shores of Lake Victoria had produced carbon steel up to 2,000 years ago. The African steelmakers used preheated forced-draft furnaces, a method that is considered technologically advanced. The scientists discovered this steelmaking method was passed on orally from generation to generation by people of the Haya tribe in Tanzania.

---

## MOTIVATE

### Skills WarmUp

To help students recognize the characteristics used to classify gems, have them do the Skills WarmUp.
**Answer** Lists and classifications will vary. Groups may be based on color, shape, value, or other characteristics.

### Misconceptions

Students may think that minerals are only useful if they are precious or if hard metals can be extracted from them. Discuss some of the more unusual properties that make minerals useful. Examples are the electrical properties of the minerals in dry cells and digital displays, the pigments important to paints, the color and texture of marble important to sculpting and architecture.

**The Living Textbook:
Earth Science Sides 1-2**

Chapter 26     Frame 03504
Bauxite (4 Frames)
Search:       Step:

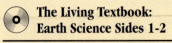

---

### ▼ ACTIVITY

**Classifying**

*Jewels*

**1.** Make a list of all the valuable stones and gems you can think of that are used in jewelry.
**2.** Classify the items on your list into two or more groups. Why did you choose the groups you did?

**SKILLS WARMUP**

**Figure 9.16**
The iron in steel comes from iron-containing minerals. ▼

---

# 9.3 Uses of Minerals

## Objectives

▶ **Describe** the use of ores.

▶ **List** some common uses of minerals.

▶ **Distinguish** between precious and semiprecious gems.

▶ **Infer** why metals are usually not found in their pure form in the earth's crust.

---

**D**id you know that every time you drink from a glass or bottle, you are using a product made from sand? Sand is a very plentiful material. Sand is mostly made of the mineral quartz, or $SiO_2$. Sand is melted down and molded or blown to make glass.

The quartz in sand is just one of the minerals of the earth that people use. Substances and products that come from minerals are all around you. You couldn't live your life without them.

### Metals from Minerals

People use minerals as a source of metals. Only a few metals, such as gold, silver, and copper, exist as pure metals in the earth's crust, and even these are rare. Most of the metals people use, therefore, must come from minerals or rocks that contain metal elements.

A mineral or rock that contains usable amounts of a metal is called an **ore**. Bauxite, for example, is an ore of aluminum. Feldspar also contains aluminum. But feldspar is not an ore because it contains too little aluminum to make extracting it worthwhile.

The process of removing a metal from its ore is called smelting. The ore is broken down into small particles and then heated to a high temperature. The atoms of metal separate from the rest of the mineral or rock and join in a molten mass. The molten metal is then collected.

Iron is produced by smelting the mineral hematite and other iron-containing minerals. Once extracted from its ores, iron can be processed to make steel. Many different industries use steel. For example, steel is used to build bridges, machine parts, and the frames of large buildings.

### Art Connection

Have students draw pictures of products listed in Table 9.6 and label each picture with the mineral used to make it. Post the drawings as a classroom display grouped by mineral. Have students write one-page reports on the mining and production of each mineral, and post the reports with the appropriate groups of drawings.

### Answer to Link

The life sciences consider minerals as the elements that are available in true minerals. An example is sodium, a metal element, available in the mineral halite (sodium chloride). Possible responses may include: calcium–bones, teeth, and muscle contraction; iron–hemoglobin production; potassium–water balance in cells, nerve and muscle action; phosphorous–bones and teeth.

## Skills Development

**Interpret Data** After students study Table 9.6, ask the following questions:

▶ What two materials may be used to make soap? (Borax and talc)

▶ What two minerals may be used to make medicines? (Calcite and sulfur)

▶ What is the mineral inside the wood of a pencil? (Graphite)

▶ What materials may be made from mica? (Glossy makeup, electronic parts, and insulation)

▶ What two minerals are used to make porcelain? (Borax and feldspar)

**Communicate** Have students research the uses and dangers of asbestos. Then hold a debate on the question of whether asbestos is useful or not. Be sure students clearly express their arguments.

**Answer to In-Text Question**

① **Glass is made from quartz, but it may also include some feldspar or halite.**

## Useful Minerals

Look at Table 9.6. It lists just a few of the many uses of minerals. As you can see, many products you use every day contain minerals.

The mineral gypsum is present in the walls of most modern houses and other buildings. Gypsum is mined in large, open pits. It is crushed and then used to make wallboard, or drywall. If you can easily push a tack into a wall, the wall is probably made of gypsum-filled wallboard.

Sulfur is a very useful mineral. In addition to the uses listed in Table 9.6, sulfur is important in the making of dyes, paints, fertilizers, insecticides, and plastics. Some of the world's richest sulfur deposits are on the Gulf Coast in Louisiana and Texas. Many deposits of sulfur are not easily mined because they are deeply buried. Gulf Coast sulfur is removed from the earth, however, without digging. Hot water, pumped into the sulfur deposit, melts the sulfur. It is then pumped to the surface and dried.

Some minerals are not in a usable form when they are mined from the earth. Like metal ores, however, they contain useful substances that must be separated from the mineral. Asbestos, for example, is separated from the mineral serpentinite.

**Figure 9.17** ▲
What mineral is used to make glass? ①

**Life Science**

**L I N K**

Research what types of minerals are important for human health.

In a data table, list at least five different minerals, where or how the minerals can be obtained, and which bodily functions the minerals help to perform.

**A C T I V I T Y**

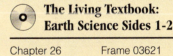
**The Living Textbook: Earth Science Sides 1-2**

Chapter 26    Frame 03621
Gypsum (1 Frame)
Search:

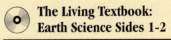

**The Living Textbook: Earth Science Sides 1-2**

Chapter 26    Frame 03634
Sulfur (1 Frame)
Search:

**Table 9.6    Mineral Uses**

| Mineral | Used to Make |
|---------|--------------|
| Borax | Soaps, cleansers, porcelain, dyes, inks |
| Calcite | Medicines, toothpaste |
| Feldspar | Pottery, glass, scouring powder, porcelain |
| Graphite | Pencils, dry lubricant, battery electrodes |
| Gypsum | Wallboard, plaster of Paris, fertilizer |
| Halite | Table salt, food preservatives, glass, paper |
| Mica | Glossy makeup, electronic parts, insulation |
| Quartz | Glass, watches, radios, televisions |
| Sulfur | Matches, medicines, rubber, gunpowder |
| Talc | Talcum powder, crayons, paints, soap |

## TEACH ▪ Continued

### Directed Inquiry

Have students study the pictures and paragraphs on this page. Then ask:

▶ What happens in a gas stove igniter when a quartz crystal is squeezed? (A spark lights the gas from the burner.)

▶ What is a transducer? (A device that changes one form of energy into another)

▶ Why is quartz a transducer in a gas stove igniter? (It changes pressure, or mechanical energy, into electrical energy.)

▶ How does a quartz oscillator vibrate? (An alternating electrical field causes the crystal to change shape slightly in one direction and then change shape slightly in the opposite direction many times per second.)

▶ How is the constant number of vibrations with a constant current useful in a watch? (The watch keeps accurate time because the crystal vibrates at a constant frequency.)

### Enrich

Use Enrich Worksheet 9.3.

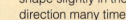
**The Living Textbook:**
**Earth Science Sides 1-2**

Chapter 25     Frame 03321
Quartz (2 Frames)
Search:      Step:

202

---

## STS Connection

**Research** The principle behind the gas igniter in the photograph is called *the piezoelectric effect*, or *piezoelectricity.* Have student volunteers research this phenomenon and report on its other uses.

### Quartz Vibrations

Quartz has many useful properties. It is very common, relatively hard, and can be melted down to make glass. Quartz also has an unusual property that has many important uses. Pressure produces electric charges across a quartz crystal. Because of this property, quartz is used as a *transducer* (tranz DOOS ur). A transducer is a device that changes one form of energy into another.

Scientists found that this special property of quartz also works in reverse. When an electrical charge is placed across a quartz crystal, the crystal changes shape slightly in one direction. If the electrical field is reversed, the crystal changes shape in the opposite direction. Therefore, if the electrical field alternates, the crystal will vibrate.

The number of vibrations per second stays constant if the frequency of the electrical current stays constant. This property is used to control the frequency of radio and television waves. It also makes a good timekeeper.

There is a quartz crystal inside this gas igniter. When the button is pushed, the crystal is squeezed, producing an electric charge. This charge causes a small spark. The spark lights the gas from the burner quickly and safely. ▼

▲ Electronic equipment may use oscillators made from slices of quartz. An oscillator vibrates. Oscillators in radios control the frequency of the radio waves received by the radio.

Have you seen a wristwatch with the word quartz on it? A thin slice of quartz in these watches helps keep accurate time. Electrical current from the watch battery makes the crystal vibrate at a constant frequency of over 30,000 times a second. ▼

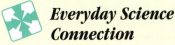

## Integrating the Sciences

**Life Science** Some gems are organic. They are derived from plants and animals. Examples include pearl, shell, coral, amber, and jet. Although they're not as hard as gemstones, they have been valued for thousands of years by many cultures. You may wish to have cooperative groups research the origins and common uses, past and present, of these five gems.

## Everyday Science Connection

Write the following list of birthstones on the board: January—garnet; February—amethyst; March—aquamarine; April—diamond; May—emerald; June—pearl; July—ruby; August—peridot; September—sapphire; October—opal; November—topaz; December—turquoise. Have students name their birthstones. Then discuss why people connect certain gems with people's birthdays.

## Critical Thinking

**Compare and Contrast** Have students think about how gems occur in the earth compared to how they appear as ornaments. Ask: What has to be done to gems such as diamonds to make them valuable? (They have to be removed from rock and carefully cut and polished.)

**Find Causes** Have students think about the durability of precious gems. Ask: Why do precious gems that were cut and polished years ago still look much the same today? (Gems are hard minerals that do not wear away quickly.)

## Gems

Rare and beautiful minerals that are cut and polished for use as ornaments are called **gems**. Gems are divided into two groups: precious and semiprecious. Precious gems are rare and valuable. Diamonds, rubies, sapphires, and emeralds are precious gems. Semiprecious gems include garnet, jade, opal, topaz, and certain kinds of quartz. Semiprecious gems are usually not as rare as precious gems, so they are not as valuable.

Gems are valued for their color, luster, and hardness. In jewelry, diamonds are treasured for their ability to break up light into dazzling colors. They are also used in drills and abrasives because of their hardness. Jade's silky luster makes it a valued mineral for ornaments, such as vases and sculptures. For centuries, gems have adorned many temples, homes, and people.

**Figure 9.18** ▲
Gems decorate fine jewelry.

## *Historical Notebook*

**Portfolio** Show students photographs of copper and bronze objects. Ask each student to write a paragraph comparing the color, luster, and other observable qualities of the two metals. Have students add their paragraphs to their portfolios.

**Answers**

1. Bronze is harder than copper, so bronze items are more durable.

2. Copper was easier to extract from its ore.

## *Historical Notebook*

### *Mineral Use Through Time*

For thousands of years, people have known that minerals provide many useful materials. Minerals have been used in their original forms and as sources for metals.

Copper was the first metal extracted from a mineral. Over 7,000 years ago in the Middle East, people found they could put the mineral malachite into fire to remove its copper. The molten copper was collected, cooled, and hammered into tools, ornaments, and containers.

About 3800 B.C., people discovered that adding tin to copper made bronze, an alloy harder than either of the two metals. After its discovery in the Middle East, the secret of bronze-making traveled to other parts of the world. In China, bronze was used for weapons, everyday items, and sculptures like the one shown here.

Iron was discovered much later than copper because it is more difficult to extract from its

ores. Iron was first refined in Egypt about 3,500 years ago. Because iron is a hard, durable metal, it became an important metal for making tools and weapons.

1. Why was bronze more useful than copper?
2. Why was copper discovered before iron?

## TEACH ▪ Continued

### Skills Development

**Infer** Have students imagine a rusty car door and a steel cooking pot. Ask which is more likely to be made of stainless steel. (The pot)

## EVALUATE

### WrapUp

**Reteach** List the following minerals on the chalkboard, then have students classify them as ores, gems, or other: jade (gem), mica (other), bauxite (ore), hematite (ore), sulfur (other), quartz (other or gem), sapphire (gem)

Use Review Worksheet 9.3.

### Check and Explain

1. A mineral or rock that contains usable amounts of a metal

2. Answers will vary, but most students will have used pencils that contain graphite, utensils that contain iron, and a television set or radio that contains quartz.

3. Precious gems are rare and valuable; semiprecious gems are not as rare as precious gems.

4. Most metals combine easily with other elements to form minerals.

### Cooperative Learning

Have students work in cooperative groups. Have one group of student volunteers do research to find out what kinds of alloys are used to make coins in the United States and why. (Pennies—copper-coated zinc; nickels—copper and nickel; dimes, quarters, half dollars, and dollars—pure copper core with outer layers of a copper and nickel alloy. Alloys are more economical than the silver and gold used in the past.) Assign another group the task of finding out what alloys were used to make coins in the past. Have this second group answer these questions: When did silver stop being used in coins? Why? (1965; silver became too expensive.) When was the last gold-containing coin made? (1933) When were pennies made of steel? (1943)

### Science and Technology
#### Improved Minerals

Did you know that pure metals are often recombined with other metals and nonmetals? The result of this combination is called an alloy. In many ways, an alloy is like an artificial mineral.

**Figure 9.19** ▲
Because they have to be light yet strong, aircraft are made of many different alloys.

Alloys have different properties from the elements that make them up. An alloy may be stronger, lighter, or more resistant to corrosion or rusting than a pure metal. For these reasons, alloys are more widely used in commercial products than pure metals.

Steel is an alloy made by combining iron and carbon. Different kinds of steel with special properties are produced by adding elements to the iron and carbon. For example, extremely sharp blades are made from a kind of steel that contains titanium. These blades are so sharp that they are used to cut regular steel.

A kind of steel that contains manganese hardens with impact. Earth-moving equipment contains this alloy because it can withstand continuous pounding. Stainless steel is a familiar kind of steel that resists corrosion. Stainless steel contains chromium and nickel.

Duraluminum® is an alloy of aluminum, copper, magnesium, and manganese. This alloy is hard, light, and able to withstand much tension without tearing apart. Because of this quality, duraluminum is used for many aircraft parts.

Another important alloy is brass. Brass is used in musical instruments, jewelry, and electrical appliances. Brass is a combination of copper and zinc.

### Check and Explain

1. What is an ore?

2. Make a list of products or substances you've used in the past week that contain minerals.

3. **Compare and Contrast** Explain the difference between precious and semiprecious gems.

4. **Infer** Why do most metals in the crust not exist in their pure form?

# Chapter 9 Review

## Concept Summary

### 9.1 Mineral Formation and Structure

▶ A mineral is a natural, inorganic solid with a definite chemical composition and a particular crystalline structure.

▶ Minerals are formed when magma solidifies and when minerals precipitate from solutions.

▶ Most minerals are classified as silicates, carbonates, oxides, sulfates, sulfides, or halides.

▶ Most minerals are classified into one of six basic crystal systems.

### 9.2 Mineral Identification

▶ Minerals have six basic properties that help in their identification: color, streak, luster, cleavage or fracture, specific gravity, and hardness.

▶ Hardness is measured on the Mohs scale.

▶ The most common minerals in the earth's crust are the rock-forming minerals.

### 9.3 Uses of Minerals

▶ Most metals come from minerals in the earth that have high metal content called ores.

▶ Some minerals are used in their original form to make a variety of products.

▶ Gems are cut or polished minerals valued for their rarity or beauty.

| Chapter Vocabulary | | |
|---|---|---|
| mineral (9.1) | cleavage (9.2) | Mohs scale (9.2) |
| streak (9.2) | fracture (9.2) | ore (9.3) |
| luster (9.2) | specific gravity (9.2) | gem (9.3) |

## Check Your Vocabulary

Use the vocabulary words above to complete the following sentences correctly.

1. The color of a mineral may vary, but the color of its ____ does not.

2. Minerals have either metallic or nonmetallic ____ .

3. Hardness is measured on the ____ .

4. Feldspar is a ____ , but coal and concrete are not.

5. When a mineral breaks along flat planes, it has ____ .

6. Minerals that break to form curved surfaces and jagged edges have conchoidal ____ .

7. A cut diamond is an example of a precious ____ .

8. Metals are separated from minerals called ____ .

9. The density of different minerals may be compared by measuring their ____ .

Explain the difference between the words in each pair.

10. cleavage, fracture

11. gem, crystal

12. specific gravity, density

## Write Your Vocabulary

Write sentences using the vocabulary words above. Show that you know what each word means.

## Check Your Vocabulary

1. streak

2. luster

3. Mohs scale

4. mineral

5. cleavage

6. fracture

7. gem

8. ores

9. specific gravity

10. Cleavage is uneven breakage; fracture is breakage on a flat surface.

11. Gems are rare and valuable and are cut or polished by humans; crystals are not necessarily rare or valuable and are formed naturally.

12. Specific gravity is a particular way of measuring and describing density.

## Write Your Vocabulary

Students' sentences should show that they know the meaning of each word as well as how to use it in a sentence.

Use Vocabulary Worksheet for Chapter 9.

## Check Your Knowledge

1. You need a copper penny, a knife with a steel blade, a piece of glass, and a piece of quartz.
2. See Table 9.5 for possible answers.
3. A metal is separated from its ore by smelting. The ore is broken down into small pieces and heated to a high temperature. The metal becomes molten and is separated from the rock.
4. Color is an unreliable way to identify minerals because impurities can give the same mineral different colors.
5. Minerals form either as magma solidifies as it cools or when minerals dissolved in water are left behind as the water evaporates.
6. A crystal system is the basic structure that gives shape to a crystal. See Table 9.2 for descriptions of six crystal systems.
7. The characteristic patterns of atoms in minerals are not found in gases, liquids, or plasmas.
8. Possible answers include: pearly, silky, glassy, dull, and greasy.
9. The highest measure of hardness is 10, the hardness of diamond.
10. Halides contain chlorine or fluorine combined with a metal.
11. False; silicate
12. False; many
13. True
14. False; oblique
15. False; may not
16. False; magnetism (or fluorescence)

## Check Your Understanding

1. If the mineral does not contain a useful amount of aluminum, it is not considered an ore.
2. They are all silicates and are important rock-forming minerals.
3. Carbonates contain carbon and oxygen in a carbonate group $(CO_3)$, while silicates contain silicon and oxygen.
4. The atoms of a mineral arrange themselves in a specific pattern. The pattern does not change in larger sizes.
5. Student answers may vary. The two may be samples of the same mineral, but the samples may have different impurities.

6. a. silicate
   b. sulfate
   c. halide
   d. oxide
   e. sulfide
7. Student answers may vary. The purple bands were formed in the same way as the amethyst: crystals formed as water disappeared, leaving minerals behind.
8. The density is 64 g/16 cm³ = 4 g/cm³; specific gravity is 4.
9. The curved surfaces formed make good cutting edges.

---

# Chapter 9 Review

## Check Your Knowledge

Answer the following in complete sentences.

1. What are the materials you need to perform field tests for hardness?
2. Name six rock-forming minerals.
3. How is a metal separated from its ore?
4. Why is color an unreliable property to use for mineral identification?
5. Describe two ways that minerals form.
6. What is a crystal system? Describe one.
7. Why must a mineral be solid to be called a mineral?
8. Name two kinds of nonmetallic luster.
9. What is the highest measure of hardness on the Mohs scale? What mineral has this hardness?
10. What elements do minerals in the halide mineral group contain?

Determine whether each statement is true or false. Write *true* if it is true. If it is false, change the underlined word to make the statement true.

11. Most of the earth's crust is made up of minerals in the <u>sulfate</u> group.
12. The mineral sulfur has <u>few</u> uses.
13. The streak left behind by a mineral on a streak plate is the mineral in its <u>powdered</u> form.
14. The axes of a triclinic crystal all meet at <u>90°</u> angles.
15. Hard organic matter <u>may</u> be classified as a mineral.
16. Not all minerals have the special property of <u>luster.</u>

## Check Your Understanding

Apply the concepts you have learned to answer each question.

1. Why is a mineral containing the element aluminum not necessarily an ore of aluminum?
2. What do the minerals amphibole, pyroxene, and olivine have in common?
3. How do carbonates and silicates differ in their chemical composition?
4. Why are the crystals of a mineral always the same shape, no matter what their size?
5. **Application** You have two mineral samples that vary in color but are identical in all other properties. What can you infer about the two samples?
6. **Classify** Each chemical formula below represents a particular mineral. Identify the mineral group to which each belongs.
   a. $NaAlSi_3O_8$
   b. $MgSO_4$
   c. $CaF_2$
   d. $AlO_3$
   e. $ZnS$
7. **Mystery Photo** The photograph on page 184 shows the polished cross section of a geode. The crystals on the inside of the geode are amethyst, a type of quartz. How do you think the purple bands surrounding the amethyst crystals were formed?
8. A sample of a mineral has a mass of 64 g and a volume of 16 cm³. What is its density? What is its specific gravity?
9. **Application** Why is a mineral with conchoidal fracture useful for making stone tools?

## Develop Your Skills

1. a. 19.3 times
   b. Oak wood will float in water. All except gold will float in liquid mercury.
2. a. Apatite
   b. Silver, gold, galena, magnetite, and iron; they are metals or metal ores.
3. Check maps for accuracy. Have students cite their sources.

## Make Connections

1.

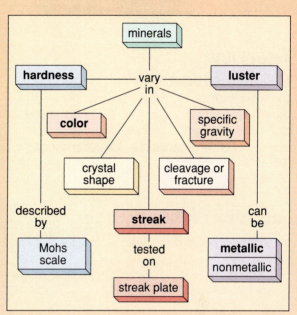

2. Student charts will vary.
3. Student reports will vary. Synthetic diamonds can be made by heating and compressing graphite, another form of pure carbon. The resulting diamonds are used to make extremely durable cutting and grinding tools like drill bits and saw blades.
4. Student reports will depend on location. Free information may be obtained by writing to the U.S. Bureau of the Mines, care of the Department of the Interior.

---

## Develop Your Skills

Use the skills you have developed in this chapter to complete each activity.

1. **Interpret Data** The table below shows the specific gravity of different substances.

| Substance | Specific Gravity |
|-----------|------------------|
| Aluminum  | 2.7              |
| Diamond   | 3.5              |
| Gold      | 19.3             |
| Mercury   | 13.5             |
| Oak wood  | 0.85             |
| Talc      | 2.7              |
| Water     | 1.0              |

   a. How much denser is gold than water?
   b. Which of the substances listed will float in water? Which will float in the liquid metal mercury?

2. **Data Bank** Use the information on pages 624-625 to answer the following questions.

   a. What mineral has a hardness of 5, a white streak, and a specific gravity of 3.2?
   b. Name two minerals with a specific gravity higher than 5.0. What do they have in common?

3. **Make a Map** In an atlas, find a map showing the location of important mineral deposits in the world. Make your own map, using this information.

## Make Connections

1. **Link the Concepts** Below is a concept map showing how some of the major concepts in this chapter link together. Only parts of the map are filled in. Complete the map, using words and ideas from the chapter.

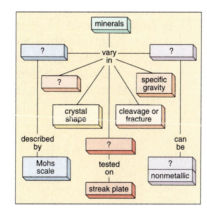

2. **Science and You** Compare the labels on three or more daily multiple-vitamin products. Make a chart that shows the minerals each product contains and their amounts.

3. **Science and Technology** Research how synthetic diamonds are made. In a few paragraphs, explain how these diamonds are created and their uses.

4. **Science and Economics** Find out what minerals, ores, or gems are mined in your state. Write a short report on the economic importance of these mining operations.

## Overview

Chapter 10 discusses the rock cycle. The first section defines the three main types of rocks and introduces the concept of the rock cycle. The second section explains rock classification and describes some ways igneous rocks are used. The third section discusses sedimentary rocks and sedimentation processes. Metamorphic rocks and types of metamorphism are the topics of the last section.

## Advance Planner

▶ Gather ingredients for peanut brittle for TE page 209.

▶ Obtain pumice for TE page 210; pumice, scoria, and granite are also needed for SE page 215.

▶ Obtain goggles, mothballs, candle, matches, a metal spoon, and a note card for TE page 217.

▶ Provide plaster of Paris for TE page 221.

▶ Collect sediments, toothpicks, glue, spoons, cups, and graduated cylinders for Activity 10, SE page 225.

▶ Obtain granulated sugar for TE page 226.

▶ Provide a topographic map for TE page 227.

## Skills Development Chart

| Sections | Classify | Compare | Hypothesize | Infer | Make a Model | Observe | Research |
|---|---|---|---|---|---|---|---|
| **10.1** Skills WarmUp | | | | ● | | | |
| Skills WorkOut | ● | | | | | | |
| SkillBuilder | ● | | | | | | |
| **10.2** Skills WarmUp | | ● | | | | | |
| **10.3** Skills WarmUp | | | ● | | | | |
| Activity 10 | | | ● | ● | ● | ● | |
| **10.4** Skills WarmUp | | | | | | | ● |
| Historical Notebook | | | | | | | ● |

## Individual Needs

▶ **Limited English Proficiency Students** Have students trace Figure 10.2, 10.5, 10.10, or 10.17. Ask students to write descriptive labels and other information for each figure using their own words.

▶ **At-Risk Students** Invite students to work in groups to make a rock-cycle game. Have them make a Rock deck and a Processes deck. The first deck should contain 12 to 15 cards each labeled *igneous, sedimentary,* or *metamorphic.* The second should have the same number of cards each labeled *melting/cooling, weathering/compacting,* or *heat and pressure.* Have students shuffle the decks and take turns drawing a card from each. Each player should tell how the kind of rock on the card was formed and one other fact about it. Then he or she should explain in detail how the process on the second card will change the rock. Allow other students in the group to challenge answers they think are incorrect.

▶ **Gifted Students** Encourage students to work together to make a class rock collection with samples of all three basic rock types and the various subgroups within each type. Allow students to use rock and mineral field guides to identify their specimens. Have them create an exhibit of their collection that uses labels and is arranged to show the different classifications of rocks presented in the chapter.

## Resource Bank

▶ **Bulletin Board** Attach some pictures of stone sculptures and sculptors from a variety of cultures to the bulletin board. Encourage students to add examples of their own. When the bulletin board is complete, hold a class discussion about the kinds of stone used, the techniques for working it, and the purpose of each example.

| Section | Core | Standard | Enriched | Section | Core | Standard | Enriched |
|---|---|---|---|---|---|---|---|
| **10.1 Rocks** pp. 209–214 | | | | **10.3 Sedimentary Rocks** pp. 220–225 | | | |
| **Section Features** Skills WarmUp, p. 209 Skills WorkOut, p. 212 SkillBuilder, p. 213 | ● ● ● | ● ● ● | ● ● ● | **Section Features** Skills WarmUp, p. 220 Activity, p. 225 | ● ● | ● ● | ● ● |
| **Blackline Masters** Review Worksheet 10.1 Reteach Worksheet 10.1 Integrating Worksheet 10.1 | ● ● ● | ● ● ● | ● | **Blackline Masters** Review Worksheet 10.3 Skills Worksheet 10.3 | ● ● | ● ● | ● |
| **Overhead Blackline Transparencies** Overhead Blackline Master 10.1 and Student Worksheet | ● | ● | ● | **10.4 Metamorphic Rocks** pp. 226–230 | | | |
| **Color Transparencies** Transparencies 22a, 22b, 23 | ● | ● | ● | **Section Features** Skills WarmUp, p. 226 Historical Notebook, p. 229 | ● ● | ● ● | ● ● |
| **10.2 Igneous Rocks** pp. 215–219 | | | | **Blackline Masters** Review Worksheet 10.4 Skills Worksheet 10.4 Vocabulary Worksheet 10.4 Integrating Worksheet 10.4 | ● ● ● ● | ● ● ● ● | ● ● |
| **Section Features** Skills WarmUp, p. 215 | ● | ● | ● | **Laboratory Program** Investigation 16 | ● | ● | ● |
| **Blackline Masters** Review Worksheet 10.2 | ● | ● | ● | | | | |

# Bibliography

The following resources can be used for teaching the chapter. See page T–46 for supplier codes.

**Library Resources**

Farndon, John. How the Earth Works. Pleasantville, NY: The Reader's Digest Association, Inc., 1992.

Parker, S. Rocks & Minerals. Eyewitness Series. New York: Alfred A. Knopf, 1991.

**Technology Resources**

*Internet*

PLANETDIARY at http://www.planetdiary.com
• Learn more about volcanoes in *Volcano* by clicking on *Phenomena Backgrounders.*
• Review geological news in *Current Phenomena.*

*Software*

Earth. Mac, Dos, Win. ER.

Rocks and Volcanoes. Mac, Win. ER.

*CD-ROMs*

Interactive Earth. SFAW.

*Laserdiscs*

Living Textbook. (See barcodes on pages in this chapter.) Optical Data.

*Videos*

The Rock Cycle: Understanding the Processes and Products of an Ever-Changing Earth. 30 min. 1992. MMI.

**Audio-Visual Resources**

Comparing Rocks. Film. EB.

The Earth: Discovering Its History. Film. C/MTI.

Introduction to the Rocks. Still frame. 15 min. CABISCO.

Recognizing Rock-Making Minerals. Film. EB.

Rocks and Minerals: How We Identify Them. Film. C/MTI.

# 10

## Introducing the Chapter

Have students read the description of the photograph. Ask if they agree or disagree with the description.

### Directed Inquiry

Have students study the photograph. Ask:

► What substance is shown in the photograph? (Students will probably say that the substance is rock.)

► What do you think has happened to the darker rock between the light stripes? Explain. (Students may say that the darker rock has been worn down by wind, water, or both. The shadow along the light stripes and the curved marks across the dark rock suggest this.)

► What might have happened to the rock that was worn away? (Students may say water dissolved it, or that it was carried away as particles by the wind and water and deposited elsewhere.)

► How do you think this picture is related to the rock cycle? (Students should recognize that the word *cycle* suggests change and the picture shows rock that has changed by a natural process.)

## Chapter Vocabulary

chemical rock
clastic rock
extrusive rock
foliated
igneous rock
intrusive rock

metamorphic rock
metamorphism
organic rock
rock cycle
sedimentary rock

### Portfolio

Share with students that during the late 1970s, pet rocks were very popular. Give each student a rock. Tell them to write a description of their pet rocks and that they are responsible for them until the chapter is completed. As students study rocks in this chapter, they can determine the texture, type, composition, and formation of their pet rocks. When the chapter is completed, have students classify their pet rocks. They can keep all of the information about their pet rocks in their portfolios.

## Chapter 10 Rocks and the Rock Cycle

### Chapter Sections

**10.1** Rocks

**10.2** Igneous Rocks

**10.3** Sedimentary Rocks

**10.4** Metamorphic Rocks

### What do you see?

"I see a rock's surface. I think it shows some type of erosion by rain. I think there was also wind erosion. I think that it will become soil for a plant."

*Latrina Young*
*Edison Learning Center*
*Dallas, Texas*

To find out more about the photograph, look on page 232. As you read this chapter, you will learn about different types of rocks and the rock cycle.

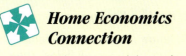

### *Home Economics Connection*

Have students record the recipe for making peanut brittle that is written on this page. If possible, make peanut brittle with the class. Then have students describe how making peanut brittle is like rock formation.

### *Geography Connection*

Have students use a map of the United States to list the names of cities, towns, and other locations that have the word *rock,* such as Rockport, Illinois, and Little Rock, Arkansas. Use the list of cities to determine whether locations in rocky areas, such as mountainous regions, use more rock names than areas with less rocks, such as sandy or swampy regions. Have students infer why *rock* is used in the names of many locations.

**Section Objectives**
For a list of section objectives, see the Student Edition page.

**Skills Objectives**
Students should be able to:

**Infer** how rocks form.

**Classify** rocks as igneous, metamorphic, or sedimentary.

**Classify** rocks by physical characteristics.

**Make a Model** of the rock cycle.

**Vocabulary**
igneous rock, sedimentary rock, metamorphic rock, rock cycle

## 10.1  Rocks

### Objectives

▶ **Identify** and **classify** the three types of rocks.

▶ **Explain** the role of heat in the rock cycle.

▶ **Describe** the main characteristics of rocks.

▶ **Make a model** of the rock cycle.

▼ **ACTIVITY**

**Inferring**

*Making Rocks*

Collect several rock samples. Examine the rocks. Based on the texture and appearance of each rock, what can you infer about how the rock formed? Explain your reasoning.

**SKILLS WARMUP**

**H**ave you ever made peanut brittle? What ingredients are needed to make this treat? Peanut brittle is made of nuts, butter, sugar, boiling water, and corn syrup. The mixture is heated, then spread to cool and harden. Once hard, it can be broken into pieces. Like peanut brittle, rocks contain different ingredients. In rocks, the "ingredients" are minerals. Unlike peanut brittle, rock formation takes millions of years.

### Types of Rocks

A rock is a made of one or more minerals. In Figure 10.1, you can see three rocks that contain the minerals feldspar and quartz. Although these rocks contain similar minerals, they formed in different ways. Rocks are classified according to how they formed. Rhyolite is classified as an **igneous** (IHG nee uhs) **rock**. Sandstone is a **sedimentary rock**. Quartzite is a **metamorphic rock**. Igneous, sedimentary, and metamorphic are the three main types of rocks.

Deep within the earth, high temperatures melt minerals to form magma. When magma cools and solidifies, igneous rock forms. Some magma solidifies beneath the surface. Some reaches the surface before hardening.

On the earth's surface, wind and water carry away pieces of minerals, rocks, and the remains of organisms. These particles settle to form layers of sediment. Over time, the sediment compacts, cements together, and hardens into sedimentary rock.

Through a series of changes involving heat and pressure, buried rock may form metamorphic rock. The original rock changes in appearance, structure, and composition.

Quartzite

Rhyolite

Sandstone

**Figure 10.1 ▲**
Each of these rocks belongs to a different group. Sandstone is sedimentary; rhyolite is igneous; quartzite is metamorphic.

**MOTIVATE**

### *Skills WarmUp*

To help students understand how rocks may be classified, have them do the Skills WarmUp.
**Answer**  Answers depend on samples collected. Students will probably relate rocks' appearances to how they have been worn down, or to what is inside them. Students might suggest wearing by water, wind, ice, or other rocks.

### Misconceptions

Students may think that rocks are as old as the earth. Explain that new rocks are constantly forming from old rock material as a part of the rock cycle. The oldest rocks discovered so far are still close to one billion years "younger" than the earth.

### Explore Visually

Have students reexamine Figure 10.2. Then ask:

► Name the forces in Figure 10.2 that change rocks from one kind to another in the rock cycle. How are these forces shown visually? (Erosion, cooling, heat and pressure, melting; with arrows)

► What type of rock would you find near the top of the volcano? (Igneous)

► What type of rock might be just beneath soil layers? (Sedimentary or igneous)

► What might the stonelike layer of the drawing represent? (Compressed slabs of sedimentary rock)

### Integrated Learning

Use Integrating Worksheet 10.1.

**Answers to In-Text Questions**

① Metamorphic rock can be weathered and eroded, producing sediments that can be compacted into sedimentary rock.

② Deep sedimentary rock can melt, forming magma. As magma cools, igneous rock is formed.

**The Living Textbook: Earth Science Side 2**

Chapter 46          Frame 23939
The Rock Cycle (Movie)
Search:                   Play:

### Themes in Science

**Patterns of Change/Cycles** The rock cycle represents a continuous flow of substances on the earth. During the rock cycle, one type of rock changes into another type of rock. Using Figure 10.2, have students describe the processes that can change rocks in the rock cycle. (Heat and pressure; melting and cooling; and sedimentation)

### Integrating the Sciences

**Physical Science** Point out to students that pumice contains many air holes. The air in pumice makes it less dense than water, allowing it to float. Obtain a piece of pumice and demonstrate the density difference between pumice and another type of rock. Be sure not to leave the pumice in water for very long. If the air holes fill with water, the pumice will eventually sink.

### The Rock Cycle

Cycles occur in many places on the earth. For example, during a frog's life cycle, the frog changes from a tadpole into an adult frog through a process called metamorphosis. Many insects go through a similar process as eggs develop into adults.

Rocks also go through cycles. The **rock cycle** is a series of processes in which rocks continuously change from one type to another. The rock cycle is shown in Figure 10.2. Follow the cycle as you read how rocks change form.

**Heat and Pressure** When rock is buried under the surface, heat and pressure may change the structure and appearance of the rock's minerals. Metamorphic rocks, such as marble or slate, may form.

If deeply buried sedimentary, igneous, or metamorphic rocks are exposed to even greater heat and pressure, the rocks melt to form magma. The rock cycle continues.

Figure 10.2
The Rock Cycle ▼

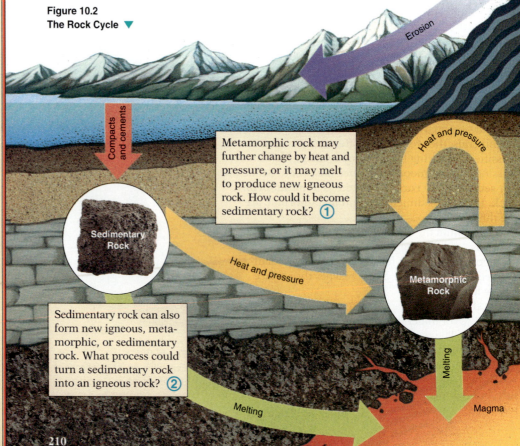

Erosion

Compacts and cements

Metamorphic rock may further change by heat and pressure, or it may melt to produce new igneous rock. How could it become sedimentary rock? ①

Sedimentary Rock

Heat and pressure

Heat and pressure

Metamorphic Rock

Sedimentary rock can also form new igneous, metamorphic, or sedimentary rock. What process could turn a sedimentary rock into an igneous rock? ②

Melting

Melting

Magma

## *Literature Connection*

Have students work in small groups to write a play about the rock cycle. Students may want to choose magma, the formation processes, or different types of rocks to be the characters in the play. Have each group present their rock-cycle play to the class.

## *History Connection*

Tell students that during the 1700s, geologists debated how rocks were formed. The Neptunists proposed that all types of rock originally settled out of water. They reasoned that this settling helped explain why rock beds appeared on the surface of the earth. The Plutonists proposed that rocks were formed by processes driven by heat in the earth's interior. Have students discuss reasons why both groups were correct.

## Directed Inquiry

After students read the text and study Figure 10.2, ask the following questions:

▶ How can heat and pressure affect the minerals in a rock? (They can change the structure or appearance of the minerals or even melt them.)

▶ What type(s) of rock can form magma? What type(s) of rock can magma form? (All three; igneous)

▶ In the rock cycle, what do erosion and magma have in common? (Answers will vary, but students should recognize that all rock can be eroded and all types of rock can melt into magma. Both represent recycling.)

## Reteach

Use Reteach Worksheet 10.1.

**Melting and Cooling**  Inside the earth, great pressures and high temperatures melt rocks and minerals. Here, igneous, sedimentary, and metamorphic rocks become magma. Some magma reaches the surface as lava. The lava cools and hardens, forming new igneous rock from the melted rock material.

Some magma pushes its way up through the surrounding rock. As it rises, the magma cools slowly. Eventually it hardens and forms new underground igneous rocks. Forces within the earth may push up great mountains of underground igneous rock.

**Sedimentation**  Sedimentary, igneous, and metamorphic rocks located near the surface are exposed when topsoil washes or blows away. Rain, wind, and running water break down surface rocks into tiny particles. The particles of many different rocks form layers of sediment. As new layers of sediment form, they push down on the older layers. Over time, the weight of the overlying layers presses the particles below tightly together. The buried sediments harden into new sedimentary rock. The type of sedimentary rock formed depends on the kinds of particles that collect in the sediments.

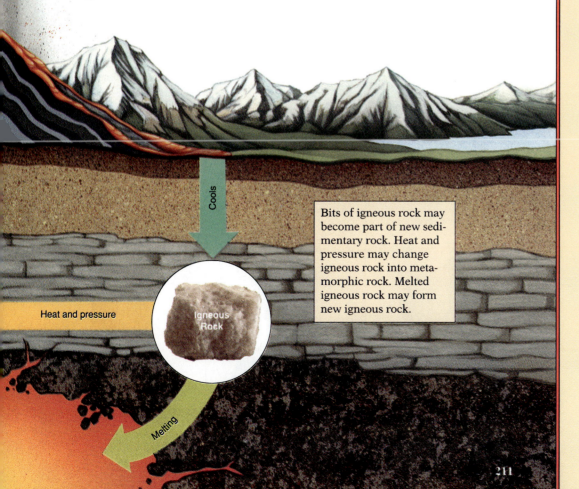

Cools

Heat and pressure

Igneous Rock

Melting

Bits of igneous rock may become part of new sedimentary rock. Heat and pressure may change igneous rock into metamorphic rock. Melted igneous rock may form new igneous rock.

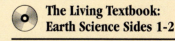

**The Living Textbook: Earth Science Sides 1-2**

Chapter 26          Frame 03682
Rock Cycle Diagram (1 Frame)
Search:

211

# TEACH · *Continued*

## *Skills WorkOut*

To help students classify, have them do the Skills WorkOut.

**Answer**  Answers will vary. Have students exchange their collections with other students as a check.

## Discuss

Ask students to name things that have many different textures, such as leaves or the coats of different species of dog. Ask students to list adjectives describing the varying textures. Then ask students what produces different textures in rocks and how textures help identify rocks.

## Research

Ask students to find out how many different minerals are found on the earth's crust. Ask students to list the 10 minerals that make up nearly all rocks. Write the list on the chalkboard and leave it there while you work through the chapter.

## Skills Development

**Infer**  Ask students to study Table 10.1. Have them infer which of these rocks most likely formed from melted material that cooled quickly. (Obsidian)

**Answer to In-Text Question**

① **All but shale and obsidian**

**The Living Textbook:
Earth Science Sides 1-2**

Chapter 26      Frame 03714
Sandstone (1 Frame)
Search:

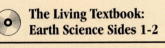

**The Living Textbook:
Earth Science Sides 1-2**

Chapter 26      Frame 03704
Obsidian (1 Frame)
Search:

## STS Connection

People who collect rocks as a hobby are called *rockhounds*. Rock-hounds may travel the world to collect rock samples. Some tools used by a rockhound include a hammer, hand lens, goggles, pen and notebook for recording locations, maps, and a rock identification guide. Find out if any students are rockhounds. Also, you can find a rockhound in the community and have him or her discuss the hobby of rock collecting with the class.

▼ **ACTIVITY**

**Classifying**

*Deep into Rocks*

1. Start a rock collection by gathering rock samples from places near where you live.
2. Use a hand lens to examine each rock.
3. Use a rock field guide to identify your rocks.
4. Classify the rocks as igneous, sedimentary, or metamorphic.

**SKILLS WORKOUT**

## Characteristics of Rocks

If you try to find your friend in a crowd, you probably look for certain physical characteristics. You might look for hair style or body build. Physical characteristics are important in identifying your friend. To identify a rock, you'd also examine its physical characteristics.

The texture of a rock is an important physical characteristic. The size, shape, and arrangement of the mineral grains that make up a rock determine its texture. Notice the different textures of the rocks in Table 10.1.

The size of the mineral grains in a rock helps determine the texture. Mineral grains that are large enough to see without a microscope give rocks a coarse-grained texture. These rocks look and feel rough. Some particles of coarse-grained rocks may come off when you rub or scrape them. Which rocks in Table 10.1 have coarse-grained textures? ①

**Table 10.1  Common Rock Textures**

| Grain Size | Example | Grain Shape | Example | Grain Pattern | Example |
|---|---|---|---|---|---|
| Coarse | Sandstone, granite | Smooth and round | Conglomerate | Banded | Gneiss |
| Fine | Shale, basalt | Sharp and angular | Breccia | Nonbanded | Granite |
| Glassy | Obsidian | Elongated | Slate | | |

## Social Studies Connection

The first tools, such as axes, scrapers, and knives, were made from stones. The period of time in which these were created is called the *Stone Age*. The Stone Age is divided into two parts. The Paleolithic Age is the period from 1.5 million years ago to about 8000 B.C. This is the time when people first developed stone tools. The Neolithic Age lasted until 3000 B.C. Have students research the culture of Stone Age people.

## Integrating the Sciences

**Life Science** Share with students that humans are not the only organisms to use stones. Sea otters use stones to crack open the shells of marine organisms. Chimpanzees and other primates use stones for cracking open nuts. Scientists have also observed chimpanzees throwing stones at one another to protect their territories.

## Discuss

After students study the text, ask the following questions.

► Why does shale have a fine-grained texture? (It is formed from clay, a fine-grained mixture.)

► Can obsidian be formed by compaction and cementation? Why or why not? (Probably not; texture is too smooth and glassy to be a sedimentary rock.)

► How are granite and gneiss similar? How are they different? (They seem to have the same composition, but their textures are different and gneiss has a banded grain pattern.)

## SkillBuilder

**Classifying** You may wish to provide some sample classifications before students begin their own.
**Answers**
1. Glassy and coarse textures are likely to be the easiest to identify.

2. Answers will vary depending on samples, but the coarse-grained group is likely to be largest.

3. Students may use grain shape and grain arrangement.

4. Answers will vary.

---

In Table 10.1, you can see shale. Shale is a sedimentary rock that forms from clay sediments. It has a fine–grained texture. The tiny grains can be seen only with a magnifying glass or a microscope.

Some igneous rocks, such as obsidian, don't contain any mineral grains. These rocks have a glassy texture. Obsidian is smooth and looks like dark glass.

Look at the conglomerate rock in Table 10.1. It is a sedimentary rock made of different kinds and sizes of rock. The grain shape in conglomerate affects the rock's texture. The large particles in conglomerate have smooth, rounded edges. In contrast, the particles in breccia (BREHCH ee uh) have sharp, angular edges.

Describe the grain pattern for each rock in Table 10.1. In most rocks, the grain pattern is random. In some rocks, such as slate and sandstone, the grains are spread evenly through the rock. These grains appear to line up in one direction. Other rocks, such as gneiss (NYS), have a banded pattern.

## SkillBuilder  *Classifying*

### Rock Groups

Copy the flowchart onto a sheet of paper. Use a hand lens to examine ten different rock samples that are identified with a number. Divide the ten rocks into three groups based on their texture. Record each sample number in the appropriate circle on the flowchart. Further divide the rocks in each texture group. Record the sample numbers and the characteristic you used for each new group. Compare your system of classification with the systems used by your classmates.

1. Which texture was the easiest to identify?

2. Which texture group had the most rocks?

3. What characteristics did you use for the additional groups? Why?

4. If you knew the minerals present in each rock, would you group them differently? Why?

Write a paragraph describing how a rock's physical characteristics help to identify it.

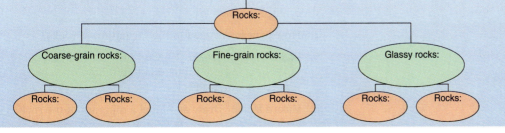

**The Living Textbook: Earth Science Sides 1-2**

Chapter 26          Frame 03712
Conglomerate (1 Frame)
Search:

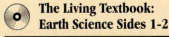

**The Living Textbook: Earth Science Sides 1-2**

Chapter 26          Frame 03717
Shale (1 Frame)
Search:

## Class Activity

Have students bring in pictures or even small samples of building materials. Have them determine which ones come from rocks and identify the rock source.

## EVALUATE

## WrapUp

**Reteach** Have students make a concept map showing how metamorphic rocks can become sedimentary, igneous, and other metamorphic rocks.

Use Review Worksheet 10.1.

## Check and Explain

1. Igneous, rhyolite; sedimentary, sandstone; metamorphic, quartzite

2. Heat and pressure can change buried rock into metamorphic rock. Enough heat can melt rock into magma; when magma cools, igneous rock is formed.

3. Igneous rock may have been weathered and eroded, mixed with other rock particles and remains of organisms, compacted, and then cemented to form sedimentary rock.

4. Check students' drawings for accuracy.

### Answer to In-Text Question

① **Brown sandstone, brick, cement**

---

## *Integrating the Sciences*

**Environmental Science** Tell students that quarrying is the type of open-pit mining employed to obtain rocks such as sandstone, granite, and marble. Quarrying separates rocks from the surface by blasting, drilling, and scooping. Quarrying destroys the natural vegetation and disrupts the habitat of many organisms. It also leaves scars on the landscape. Discuss with students how quarrying affects the land.

---

**Science and You**
*Is Your Home Made of Stone?*

**Figure 10.3** ▲
What types of rock materials were used to construct these row houses in Philadelphia, Pennsylvania? ①

Think about the outside and inside of your home, school, and other buildings in your neighborhood. What kinds of rock materials were used to construct these buildings? Some buildings have an exterior of brown sandstone, often called brownstone. Others are made of bricks, which are manufactured from clay or shale. Perhaps the outside walls of some buildings in your neighborhood are covered with stucco. Stucco is a mixture of sand, water, and cement.

Is there a fireplace in your home? What is it made of? Most likely, it is made of bricks or stones held together by cement. The cement used to bind together bricks, tiles, and stones begins as a mixture of limestone and shale or clay. The mixture is ground, heated, and then crushed into a fine, gray powder. Powdered cement was probably also used to build the foundation of your house. When water, sand, and gravel are added to powdered cement, the mixture forms concrete. The concrete is poured into wooden foundation forms, where it hardens. Houses and buildings are then built on top of this sturdy material.

Gypsum is a sedimentary rock that is heated to produce plaster of Paris. You may have used plaster of Paris in art class or to create scientific models. But did you know that plaster is also used in building construction? Plaster is mixed with water and sand or other materials, and then covered with cardboard to make wallboard. Wallboard is commonly used for the inside walls of houses, apartments, and offices.

---

## Check and Explain

1. Name the three main types of rocks, and give an example of each type.

2. How is heat involved in the formation of rocks?

3. **Reason and Conclude** Explain how the mineral particles in a piece of sandstone might have once been part of an igneous rock.

4. **Make a Model** Draw and label a diagram of the rock cycle. Use arrows to show how rocks are related.

### *Language Arts Connection*

Tell students that the term *extrusive* comes from the word *extrude*. The term *intrusive* comes from the word *intrude*. Have students use a dictionary to look up the meanings of the words *extrude* and *intrude*. Ask the students how the definitions relate to the two names for igneous rocks.

SECTION

# 10.2

**Section Objectives**

For a list of section objectives, see the Student Edition page.

**Skills Objectives**

Students should be able to:

**Compare** rock crystals.

**Infer** different densities of rocks.

**Vocabulary**

extrusive rock, intrusive rock

# 10.2 Igneous Rocks

## Objectives

- **Name** the two kinds of igneous rocks.
- **Explain** how igneous rocks form.
- **Classify** igneous rocks by characteristics.
- **Infer** what minerals are present in an igneous rock.

What image comes to mind when you think about the word "ignite"? Perhaps you imagine something being set on fire or bursting into flames. "Ignite" and "igneous" both come from the Latin word *ignis*, meaning "fire." In the formation of igneous rocks, heat plays an important role.

## Formation of Igneous Rocks

Recall that the rock-forming process determines the rock type. Rocks produced by the cooling and solidifying of magma are classified as igneous. Igneous rocks form either underground or on the earth's surface. Thus igneous rocks are further classified by where they form.

Lava on the surface solidifies to form **extrusive rock**. At or near the surface, lava cools rapidly, leaving little time for large grains to form. As a result, extrusive rock tends to have a fine-grained or a glassy texture. Rhyolite, basalt, and pumice (PUHM ihs) are examples of extrusive rocks.

Magma that solidifies beneath the surface forms **intrusive rock**. Deep magma cools very slowly, producing rocks with large grains of uniform size. Coarse-grained texture is characteristic of intrusive igneous rocks, such as granite and gabbro.

Notice the grains in the porphyritic (POR fuh RIHT ihk) rock shown in Figure 10.4. The grains are different sizes. The large crystals formed from magma cooling beneath the earth's surface. However, before the magma completely hardened, it was forced out. On the surface, the rest of the magma cooled rapidly, producing the fine grains.

**Figure 10.4**
How is a porphyritic rock different from other igneous rocks? ②

**ACTIVITY**

**Comparing**

*Rocks Float?*

Collect samples of pumice, scoria, and granite.

**1.** Use a hand lens to compare the crystals in each rock.

**2.** Try to float each rock in water. Which rock is the least dense? The most dense? Infer why there is a difference in the density of the rocks.

**SKILLS WARMUP**

## MOTIVATE

### *Skills WarmUp*

To help students understand the characteristics of igneous rocks, have them do the Skills WarmUp.
**Answer** Students will notice that the granite is the densest of the samples, and the pumice is least dense. Inferences will vary. Both the scoria and the pumice contain gas pockets as a result of hardened bubbles in molten materials.

### Misconceptions

Students may think that all rocks must sink in water. When they see a demonstration showing that pumice floats, students may think that the pumice is a synthetic material. If possible, show moving footage of lava flowing and bursting. Stop the tape at various points to indicate where rapidly cooling lava would contain bubbles.

## TEACH

### Enrich

Ask students to bring pictures or samples of pumice and granite to class. If they have rock samples available, have them use a hand lens to observe the textures.

**Answer to In-Text Question**

**② It cools at different rates.**

### TEACH ▪ *Continued*

#### *Explore Visually*

After students study Figure 10.5, ask the following questions:

▶ What can pumice do that most rocks cannot? (Float) Why? (Because it is filled with holes caused by gas bubbles)

▶ How is obsidian like scoria, and how is it different? (Both are extrusive rocks. Obsidian loses most of its gases before reaching the surface, so it looks glassy. Scoria has holes that are hardened gas bubbles.)

▶ What is the difference between magma and lava? (Magma lies beneath the earth's surface; lava is magma that reaches the earth's surface.)

▶ How does magma become lava? (By erupting, often through volcanoes)

▶ What are volcanoes made of? (Extrusive rock)

#### *Multicultural Perspectives*

Share with students that Native-American societies of the past chipped obsidian into blades and projectile points. Although other types of stone were also used, obsidian's glasslike texture was preferred because especially sharp points and edges could be sculpted from it.

Obsidian blades and points have been found in places far removed from volcanic areas. Have students infer how these artifacts reached distant locations. (They were carried long distances and often traded.)

**Figure 10.5**
**Formation of Extrusive and Intrusive Rocks** ▼

### Extrusive Rocks

Recall that extrusive rock forms from lava. When you hear the word "lava," you probably immediately think of volcanoes. Volcanoes are important in extrusive igneous rock formation. For this reason, extrusive rocks are also known as volcanic rocks.

Pumice is solidified foam. It forms when gases escape quickly from lava. Pumice is so light that it floats on water.

Hot lava erupts onto the surface and cools, forming fine-grained and glassy igneous rocks.

Obsidian is rapidly cooled lava that loses most of its gases before reaching the surface. This glassy rock is very brittle.

Scoria (SKOR ee uh) is similar to pumice. The holes are hardened gas bubbles.

Magma beneath the surface may rise rapidly. The sudden decrease in pressure releases trapped gases. The magma and gases shoot out through openings in the crust.

Magma

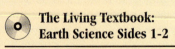

**The Living Textbook:**
**Earth Science Sides 1-2**

Chapter 26         Frame 03705
Volcanic Rocks (7 Frames)
Search:              Step:

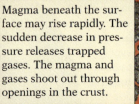

## Integrating the Sciences

**Chemistry** The size that crystals reach during crystal formation is dependent upon the rate of the cooling time. Demonstrate for students the relationship of crystal size and cooling. Obtain goggles, several mothballs, a candle, matches, a metal spoon, and a notecard. Place a mothball on the spoon and melt it over a candle flame. Pour the melted mothball material onto the notecard to cool. Place another mothball on the spoon and melt it over a candle flame. This time, allow the melted material to cool on the spoon. After the material has cooled, have students compare the crystals that formed on the notecard with those on the spoon. (The crystals on the spoon should be larger.) Ask: Which crystals are like intrusive rocks? Extrusive rocks? (Intrusive—spoon crystals; extrusive—notecard crystals) Caution: mothballs can be hazardous to humans.

### Intrusive Rocks

According to Greek myths, Pluto was the ruler of the Underworld. This Kingdom of the Dead was located "beneath the secret places of the earth." Because intrusive rocks form deep inside the earth, they are also called plutonic (ploo TAHN ihk) rocks.

Recall that a body of intrusive rock is called a pluton. Plutons are usually composed of granite. Plutons have an irregular shape and form the core of great mountain ranges. Huge bodies of intrusive rock are called batholiths.

Sometimes magma intrudes layers of existing sedimentary rock. The force of the magma pushes up part of the rock, causing it to bulge. As the magma cools, it forms an irregular or mushroom-shaped body called a *laccolith*. Locate the laccolith in Figure 10.5.

Eventually the magma stops moving. Over time, it solidifies and produces coarse-grained plutonic rocks.

Some magma pushes between existing rocks. As the magma rises, the pressure decreases. Dissolved gases slowly escape, and the magma thickens.

Pools of magma form at great depths within the earth. Here, pressure and overlying rocks hold in heat and dissolved gases. The magma stays hot and liquid for a long time.

▶ Where do intrusive rocks form? (Beneath the earth's surface)

▶ Explain how magma forms intrusive rock. (Magma rises between underground rocks, releasing dissolved gases as the pressure decreases. Gradually the magma thickens and hardens.)

▶ What does intrusive igneous rock look like? (Coarse-grained)

### Discuss

Have students describe the differences between a laccolith, an anticline, and a volcano. (A laccolith is a dome shape formed when magma pushes rock upward. Magma breaks the surface through a volcano. An anticline is caused by folding.)

### Skills Development

**Infer** Ask students to infer which takes longer to form, extrusive or intrusive rock. (Intrusive; the magma is insulated by overlying rocks and cools more slowly.)

## TEACH ▪ Continued

### Directed Inquiry

After students study the text and Figures 10.6 and 10.7, ask the following questions:

▶ What is basalt's characteristic color? What gives it that color? (Medium gray to gray-black; pyroxene)

▶ Why is mineral composition not enough to classify an igneous rock? (Fine-grained and coarse-grained rocks may have the same mineral composition but have been formed at different rates of cooling.)

▶ How are temperature and texture related? (Coarse-grained rocks are formed as magma cools very slowly; fine-grained rocks form as magma is cooled quickly.)

### Research

Have students find out the characteristic colors of pyroxene, olivine, biotite, and hornblende. Have them describe a rock containing quartz and each of these minerals.

### Answer to In-Text Question

① **Coarse-grained, nonbanded**

---

### Integrating the Sciences

**Astronomy** Analysis of moon rocks collected by Apollo astronauts showed that the rocks were igneous in origin. Types of breccia, basalt, and gabbro were found. The rocks' mineral compositions differed from similar igneous rocks found on the earth. Glasses were also brought back from the surface of the moon. It was discovered that the glasses do not belong to the igneous rock group; they are more similar to metamorphic rock. Scientists hypothesize that glasses formed when meteorites hit the moon's surface and vaporized the surface rocks. Ask students what information can be inferred from the moon rocks. (The rocks reveal that the moon had volcanic activity, meteorites cause large changes on the moon's surface, and the absence of sedimentary rocks reveals a lack of weathering.)

---

Feldspar · Biotite · Quartz

**Figure 10.6** ▲
The crystals in granite reveal its mineral composition. Different kinds of granite contain different minerals.

## Igneous Rock Identification

Igneous rocks are identified by texture and mineral composition. The minerals present in the magma that forms a rock determine its composition. Texture depends on how fast the magma cools.

**Texture** In coarse-grained rocks, the grains can be as wide as a pencil. You can easily see the grains. In fine-grained rocks, the grains are no wider than the thickness of paper. The grains are visible with a hand lens or a microscope. Rocks with glassy texture contain no grains. Many igneous rocks are porphyritic. Recall that porphyritic rocks have large crystals embedded in fine-grained rock. What texture is shown in Figure 10.6? ①

**Composition** The major minerals found in igneous rocks are quartz, feldspar, muscovite, biotite, pyroxene, olivine, and hornblende. Notice the mineral colors for granite in Figure 10.6. The colors in igneous rock are a clue to its mineral composition. Quartz, feldspar, and muscovite are light-colored minerals. The dark-colored minerals are pyroxene, olivine, biotite, and hornblende.

## Examples of Igneous Rocks

Compare the different igneous rocks shown in Figure 10.7. All three rocks are formed from magma, but no two look alike. The texture and the mineral composition vary for each rock.

**Figure 10.7**
Different igneous rocks vary in texture, color, and mineral composition. ▼

| **Diorite** | **Gabbro** | **Basalt** |
|---|---|---|
| Diorite is coarse-grained. It is gray or gray-green with white speckles. Its color comes from biotite, hornblende, and pyroxene. | Gabbro is coarse-grained. It is dark gray to black. It mainly contains pyroxene. Other minerals, such as olivine, may be present. | Basalt is a fine-grained rock with the same mineral composition as gabbro. It is medium gray to gray-black in color. |

## Architecture Connection

### Science and Society   Rock Architecture

Granite, gabbro, and basalt are hard, dense igneous rocks. The minerals in these rocks make them resistant to erosion and give them a pleasing appearance. Because rain and wind have little effect on these rocks, they have been used as building materials for thousands of years. For example, many European castles and churches were constructed from gabbro. Some roads in ancient Rome were paved with basalt. Although they were built centuries ago, many of the structures still stand. These roads and buildings remain as evidence of the durability of igneous rock.

In the 1800s and early 1900s, many buildings in the United States were built mainly of granite. The state capitol buildings in Arizona, Arkansas, California, Maine, and Vermont were built of granite native to those areas. Today few buildings are constructed of igneous rock. Although igneous rock is available in many regions, high removal and processing costs restrict its use for entire buildings. Granite, for example, must first be blasted or drilled out of the ground. The stone must then be cut and polished.

Some igneous rock is still used as decoration. Public buildings, such as libraries and courthouses, are partially constructed from or decorated with granite and gabbro. Is any part of the capitol building in your state built of igneous rock? How are these rocks used in other public buildings in your city or town?

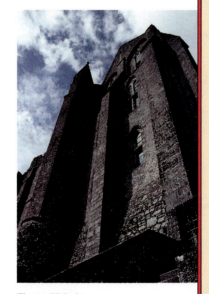

**Figure 10.8** ▲
Many old buildings, such as this castle in France, are constructed from igneous rock.

### Check and Explain

1. What are the two kinds of igneous rocks? How do igneous rocks form?

2. How does the texture of an igneous rock help identify its origin?

3. **Classify**   What two main characteristics are used to identify igneous rocks? Give examples of rocks in each category.

4. **Infer**   Suppose you see an old building made from very dark, almost black, coarse-grained rock. What minerals would the rock most likely contain? Explain your reasoning.

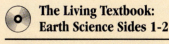

**Section Objectives**
For a list of section objectives, see the Student Edition page.

**Skills Objectives**
Students should be able to:

**Hypothesize** how chalk dust is formed from chalk.

**Observe** the process by which sedimentary rock layers form.

**Make a Model** of how sedimentary rock layers form.

**Vocabulary**
clastic rock, organic rock, chemical rock

---

## MOTIVATE

### Skills WarmUp

To help students understand the process of sedimentary rock formation, have them do the Skills WarmUp.
**Answer** Hypotheses might include applying pressure or running water.

### Prior Knowledge

To gauge how much students know about sedimentary rocks, ask the following questions:

▶ What is sediment?

▶ What kinds of material build up on the floor of a lake or ocean?

---

## TEACH

### Apply

Have students imagine a sediment deposit containing gravel, sand, and silt. Ask: Which particles will be on top? (Silt) Which particles will be on the bottom? (Gravel) Ask why levels form in this order. (Heaviest particles are deposited first.)

### Answer to In-Text Question

① **Wind, wave action, abrasion**

---

### Cooperative Learning

Have cooperative groups of three classify different types of sediment that can form sedimentary rock. Give each group a mixture of sediment sizes, shapes, and types. You may want to create mixtures by combining pebbles, sand, and gravel. Have each group spread its sediment sample onto a sheet of paper. Then students can divide the sediment components by size into at least three separate piles. Next have the groups combine the sediments and separate them into separate piles based on shape. Tell students to recombine the sediments and devise another way to separate the sediments. The groups can share their classification systems with the class.

---

▼ **ACTIVITY**

**Hypothesizing**

*Chalk It Up*

Obtain a piece of chalk. Hypothesize several ways that you could form chalk dust from the chalk.

Test your hypotheses. What natural processes could produce the same results?

**SKILLS WARMUP**

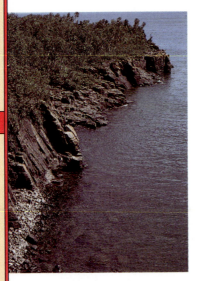

**Figure 10.9** ▲
Many different forces slowly break down this rocky cliff into sediment.

---

## 10.3 Sedimentary Rocks

### Objectives

▶ **Describe** the stages of sedimentary rock formation.

▶ **Identify** and **describe** the three types of sedimentary rocks.

▶ **Compare** and **contrast** the physical characteristics of sedimentary and igneous rock.

▶ **Make a model** of the sedimentation process.

---

Imagine you're on a beach along a rocky cliff. Near the cliff base are large boulders, stones, and pebbles. Some are as big as your fist and have sharp edges. These recently broke off the cliff. Others are no larger than dimes and have rounded edges worn by waves. Your feet move through tiny sand grains. Where the water meets the beach, you notice shells and seaweed. If you could see the ocean bottom, you'd find silt and mud forming a thick ooze. These are some of the various materials that make up sedimentary rock.

### Formation of Sedimentary Rocks

Sedimentary, igneous, and metamorphic rocks are all present on the earth's surface. An existing body of rock on the earth's surface is subjected to various forces of weathering and erosion. Rain, sun, wind, ice, pollution, and organisms break down exposed rock. What forces are acting on the rock shown in Figure 10.9? ①

Moving water transports rock particles of all sizes and deposits them as sediment. Rivers and streams carry loose sediment to lakes or oceans. As a water current slows, it drops sediment.

The size and density of the rock particles determine the order of the sediment deposited. Pebbles and gravel-sized particles are the first ones moving water deposits. Sand-sized particles are deposited next. Clay-sized particles and silt are the last particles that moving water deposits.

Layers of sediment slowly build up. The first sediment deposited is buried as more and more layers of sediment cover it. Over time, pressure from the stack of sediment hardens lower, older layers into sedimentary rock.

### Art Connection

Have students use plaster of Paris to make models of the different sedimentary rock structures. They may want to color the plaster of Paris for the different horizontal layers. Have students experiment to find out if a fan blowing over wet plaster will form ripple marks. For fossils, students can embed shells or bones in the plaster.

**Sedimentary Rock Processes** If you step on paper in a wastebasket to make more room, you use weight to decrease the paper volume. The same thing happens to sediment in water. Newly deposited particles don't fit together tightly, so the spaces fill with water. As more sediment deposits, the weight of new layers presses on underlying sediment. As the water squeezes out, the spaces get smaller, and the particles pack tightly together. The process of particles pressing together is called *compaction*.

During compaction, minerals dissolved in water may be left behind. The minerals form a thin film around the particles and bind them together. The process of sediment spaces filling and binding together with minerals is called *cementation*. Calcite and silica are common mineral cements.

You can see the processes of compaction and cementation represented in Figure 10.10. They are part of the lithification of sedimentary rock. *Lithification* is the hardening of sediment into rock.

**Figure 10.11** ▲
Mud cracks may form as fine-grained sediment dries out (above); water currents can produce ripple marks (below).

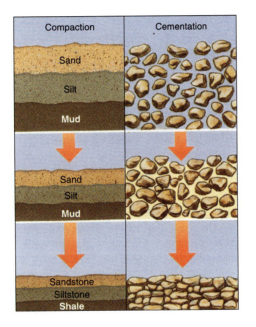

**Figure 10.10** ▲
Compaction presses sediments tightly together. Cementation glues the sediment into one mass.

**Sedimentary Rock Structures** Different structures, such as layering, ripple marks, and mud cracks form in sedimentary rock.

- Horizontal layering occurs in sediment laid down in calm water. Particle size, composition, and thickness may vary in each layer.

- Permanent ripple marks, such as those in Figure 10.11, form when wind or water constantly move over sediment.

- Cracks form on the rock's surface as muddy sediment dries and shrinks. You can see cracks in Figure 10.11.

- Fossils that form from the remains of organisms buried in sand, silt, clay, or mud may also become part of sedimentary rock.

## Class Activity

Provide small samples of sand, fine gravel, and clay. Have students wear aprons and make "mud pies" using each of the materials in turn. Ask students which materials made the best mud pies. Have them explain why in their own words. (Clay should work best because it can pack most tightly.)

## Reteach

Ask students to arrange the following sentences in the correct sequence:
Water deposits sediment such as pebbles and gravel. (1)
Minerals such as calcite and silica are left behind. (6)
Water deposits sediment such as sand and clay. (2)
Water is squeezed from lower layers of sediment. (5)
Sediment hardens into rock during lithification. (8)
Particles press together during compaction (4)
Layers of sediment form. (3)
Minerals bind particles together during cementation. (7)

## Critical Thinking

**Reason by Analogy** Ask students why sedimentary rock can be used as a "snapshot of history." (The rocks are laid down in layers, with the oldest usually at the bottom. The rock resembles a slice cut through time. The arrangement of layers can also tell what happened to the landscape geologically.)

## Directed Inquiry

After students study the text and Figure 10.12, ask the following questions.

▶ Name three kinds of clastic rock. (Breccia, conglomerate, sandstone and shale)

▶ How are conglomerate and breccia alike? How are they different? (Both are clastic rock and contain large rock fragments. The fragments in conglomerate are smooth and round; the fragments in breccia are angular and sharp.)

▶ What characteristics make conglomerate rock different from sandstone? (Conglomerate rock contains large rock fragments; sandstone texture may be fine or coarse.)

▶ What holds grains and fragments together in breccia and sandstone? (Mineral cement)

▶ Why can fossils be found in shale? (Shale is the hardened form of mud mixed with clay; fossils are often buried in mud.)

## Critical Thinking

**Reason and Conclude**  Ask students: If you wished to mine quartz, would you look for shale, conglomerate, or sandstone? Explain. (Sandstone; many sandstones are nearly all quartz.)

### *Themes in Science*

**Scale and Structure**  Sediments are small particles of rock, minerals, or organism remains. However, when sediments compact and cement together, large sedimentary rock structures form.

## Classification of Sedimentary Rocks

Sedimentary rocks are grouped according to composition and texture. Compacted and cemented particles form clastic sedimentary rock. Some deposits from living things form organic sedimentary rock. Minerals that were once dissolved in water make up chemical sedimentary rock.

**Clastic Rock**  Particles of eroded and weathered rock and mineral grains that compact and cement together form **clastic rock**. Particles in clastic rock range from coarse boulders to a fine sediment of silt and clay. The particle size determines the type of clastic rock.

▶ Conglomerate rock and breccia are made of various large rock fragments. In conglomerates, the fragments are smooth with round edges. In breccia, the fragments are sharp and angular. The spaces between fragments fill with material that cements them into a single rock.

▶ Grains of sand can become sandstone, as shown in Figure 10.12. Sandstone textures vary from coarse to fine. Many sandstones are almost all quartz grains. However, sandstone may also contain feldspar, biotite, pyroxene, or olivine. The color of sandstone depends on its mineral grains and the impurities in the cement that binds the grains together.

▶ Silt and clay are composed of tiny mineral particles. Silt and clay mixed together with water make mud. When mud with a lot of clay compacts, it hardens into shale. Because plant or animal remains buried in mud preserve well, you can often find fossils in shale.

**Figure 10.12** ▲
When sand cements together, it forms the clastic rock, sandstone. Sandstone formations, like these in Bryce Canyon, can extend for many kilometers.

**Organic Rock** Sedimentary rock that is formed from living things or their remains is called **organic rock.** Limestone is the most common organic rock. Coal is also an organic rock.

Limestone is mainly made of calcium carbonate. Ocean organisms, such as coral, clams, and mussels, extract calcium carbonate from water to form their shells and other hard parts. When these organisms die, layers of shells deposit on the ocean bottom. Over time, the fragments compact and cement together, forming limestone.

Chalk is a fine-grained, white limestone that formed on the bottom of ancient seas. Unlike most limestones, chalk is soft and rubs off easily. Figure 10.13 shows chalk deposits located near Dover, England.

Coal forms in swamps from the decayed remains of land plants. As plants die, they gradually form thick layers that harden into peat. The peat deposits become buried under sediment of sand and clay. Over time, pressure changes peat into lignite, a dark-brown type of coal. With increased time and pressure, black coal forms.

**Figure 10.13** ▲
What do these chalk formations tell you about the history of this area in England? ①

**Figure 10.14** ▲
The Bonneville Salt Flats exist in land-locked Utah. How can you explain their formation? ②

**Chemical Rock** When minerals come out of solution and crystallize, they form **chemical rock**. Most chemical rocks are formed by the evaporation of water. When water evaporates, the dissolved minerals are left behind.

Rocks formed by water evaporation from oceans or desert lakes are called *evaporites*. Like igneous rocks, evaporites and other chemical rocks are held together by tightly interlocking mineral crystals.

You are probably familiar with the chemical rock halite, which you know as table salt. Large halite deposits may form when water in a sea inlet evaporates faster than water can enter. When saltwater lakes evaporate, they may leave behind large, flat deposits of halite, such as the Bonneville Salt Flats in Utah, shown in Figure 10.14. Ancient salt deposits exist in Kansas, Michigan, New Mexico, and Oklahoma.

Ocean water evaporation also causes the crystallization of the mineral gypsum. Gypsum is therefore usually found with deposits of halite. Gypsum is used in making cement, plaster of Paris, and wallboard. Gypsum deposits are found in Iowa, California, Michigan, Texas, New York, and New Mexico.

### Research

Have students use resources to find out how core-sampling technology has been used to learn about the history of the earth's atmosphere.

## EVALUATE

### WrapUp

**Reinforce** Write the words *clastic*, *organic*, and *chemical* on the chalkboard. Ask the class to describe the texture and composition of each type of rock. Write their answers on the board. (Clastic—coarse or fine, compacted and cemented particles; organic—coarse or fine, living things or their remains; chemical—coarse or fine, crystallized minerals)

Use Review Worksheet 10.3.

### Check and Explain

1. At a lake shore, beach, river bank, or river delta

2. Clastic—particles of rock, sandstone; organic—remains of living organisms, limestone; chemical—crystallized minerals, rock salt and gypsum

3. The grains in the igneous rock are likely to be of uniform size; in a sedimentary rock the grains are likely to be of mixed sizes.

4. Check student models for accuracy. Possible materials include mud, sand, pebbles, gravel, water, and glue.

### *Cooperative Learning*

Have students work in cooperative groups of four to classify sedimentary rocks as organic, clastic, or chemical. Give each group samples of limestone, sandstone, conglomerate, and halite (rock salt). Have each group test the samples with 5% hydrochloric acid. The rocks that fizz are organic. Then have each group use a hand lens to examine the rocks for particles and mineral grains. These rocks are clastic. You may want to have students taste a fresh sample of the last rock. It will taste salty; it is chemical. (Organic—limestone, clastic—sandstone and conglomerate, chemical—halite)

### Science and Technology
*History in Sediment*

One of the biggest challenges for scientists studying the earth is finding out about its early history. How do scientists learn about the earth's history? Sedimentary rock holds the key to many unanswered questions about the earth.

One important way sedimentary rock is used to study the earth is through core sampling. Since the late 1960s, several ocean-drilling projects have collected cores from layers of sediment and oceanic crust more than 1,000 m below the ocean floor. The cores are valuable because ocean sediments are not affected by erosion or chemical and biological activities that change surface sedimentary layers. In recent years, scientists have studied core samples from the Indian Ocean. From the core samples, they learned that the gradual formation of the Himalaya Mountains from plate collisions actually occurred 10 million years earlier than they had originally hypothesized.

Sediments from core samples also helped scientists discover that the climate in Antarctica has not always been cold. In fact, they discovered that Antarctica was warm and populated with ferns and beech trees until about 40 million years ago. The evidence for an iceless Antarctica came mainly from sediment deposits beneath the polar seas.

**Figure 10.15** ▲
The long tubes will drill deep into the Mediterranean Sea to remove core samples.

### Check and Explain

1. Where can you observe the beginning stages of sedimentary rock formation? Give several examples.

2. Identify and describe the three kinds of sedimentary rocks. Give an example of each kind.

3. **Compare and Contrast** Suppose you find a coarse-grained rock while walking in the mountains. How could you tell that the rock is sedimentary rather than igneous?

4. **Make a Model** Construct a model that shows how sedimentary layers form in a lake. What materials did you use to make the model?

## Prelab Discussion

Have students read the entire activity. Discuss a few points before beginning:

▶ Review the concept of geologic time. Discuss other processes that take place over millions of years.

▶ Review the role of pressure in sedimentary rock formation.

▶ Ask students to describe concrete and how it functions.

**Time** 3 days, 40 minutes preparation

**Group** pairs

**Materials**

1 kg gravel

1 kg sand

1 kg powdered clay

15 medium-size jars

15 timers or clock with a second hand

15 spoons

15 cups

graduated cylinders

1 L diluted white glue solution

1 box of toothpicks

## Activity 10   How do sedimentary layers form?

**Skills**   Model; Hypothesize; Observe; Infer

### Task 1   Prelab Prep

1. Collect the following materials: gravel, sand, clay, graduated cylinder, jar, water, timer with a second hand, spoon, cup, diluted white glue solution, several toothpicks.
2. Crumble the clay into particles.

### Task 2   Data Record

On a separate sheet of paper, copy Tables 10.2 and 10.3. In Table 10.2, keep a record of any changes in the layers you observe.

### Task 3   Procedure

1. Fill the jar 3/4 full of water.
2. Drop in a pinch of one type of sediment. Watch it fall. Time the length of the fall. Record the settling rate in your data table.
3. Repeat step 2 for the other two types.
4. Hypothesize what would happen if you poured a mixture of the three types of sediment into the jar. Record your hypothesis on a separate piece of paper.
5. Measure three spoonfuls of each sediment. Mix them together and pour the mixture into the water. Record the settling order in your data table.
6. Pour out the excess water from the jar. Measure 50 mL of the diluted white glue solution. Evenly distribute the solution over the sediment layers in the jar.
7. Set the jar in a warm, dry place.

**Table 10.2   Sediment Characteristics**

| Sediment Type | Sediment Size | Settling Rate | Settling Order |
|---------------|---------------|---------------|----------------|
| Gravel | | | |
| Sand | | | |
| Clay | | | |

8. The next day, use toothpicks to test the hardness of the layers. Continue to keep the jar in a warm, dry place. Observe the layers each day for several days. Record your observations in Table 10.3.

**Table 10.3   Observations**

| Day 1 | Day 2 | Day 3 |
|-------|-------|-------|
| | | |
| | | |
| | | |

### Task 4   Analysis

1. **Observe**   What happened to the glue solution after several days?
2. What did the glue solution represent?
3. What happened to the sediment layers after several days? Which layer was the first to harden?
4. Did the water in the jar represent fast- or slow-moving water? Why?
5. What kinds of sedimentary rock did you form for each layer?

### Task 5   Conclusion

Write a paragraph describing how this model is similar to the natural processes involved in the formation of sedimentary rock layers. How is it different?

### Everyday Application

The compaction and cementation of sediments in the activity are similar to the formation of concrete. How are they alike? How do they differ?

### Extension

Develop a model using simple materials to show how igneous rock forms. Compare this model to your model for sedimentary rock formation.

## Analysis

1. Over several days, the glue solution seeped through the layers of sediment in the jar and hardened.
2. The glue solution represents the mineral cements that hold sedimentary rock together.
3. The sediment layers dried out and hardened after several days. The top layer should have hardened first.
4. Slow-moving, because it was not flowing over the sediment.
5. Conglomerate rock formed.

## Conclusion

Student answers will vary. The model is similar in that different sized particles settle out at different rates, time is needed for the sediment to dry out, and a cement is needed to hold the particles together. Differences include the short time in which "rock" is formed and the cement.

## Everyday Application

Student answers will vary.

## Extension

Student models may vary. Make sure models are accurate.

## Section Objectives
For a list of section objectives, see the Student Edition page.

## Skills Objectives
Students should be able to:

**Research** the term "metamorphism."

**Predict** where samples of metamorphic rock will be found.

## Vocabulary
metamorphism, foliated

## MOTIVATE

### Skills WarmUp
To help students research metamorphic rock, have them do the Skills WarmUp.

**Answer** *Meta-* and *-morph* mean "change," and "form," so *metamorphic* means "changed form."

### Prior Knowledge
To gauge how much students know about metamorphic rocks, ask the following questions:

▶ What is metamorphosis? Name some examples.

▶ What do all different kinds of marble have in common?

## TEACH

### Skills Development
**Observe** Heat a small amount of granulated sugar and a few drops of water in a pan. Have students describe what they observe. (The heat melts the crystals and the mass turns first to syrup then to a black, charred substance.) Ask students how this process resembles metamorphism. (Heat changed the structure, appearance, and composition of the sugar and water.)

226

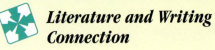

## Literature and Writing Connection
Read excerpts from Robert Louis Stevenson's story *The Strange Case of Dr. Jekyll and Mr. Hyde.* Discuss the metamorphosis of the character in the story. Then have students write a story about metamorphosis from the perspective of a piece of shale or slate. Student volunteers may want to share their stories with the class.

## Integrating the Sciences
**Physical Science** Heat and pressure are related. If the pressure were reduced in a vacuum pump holding a container of water, the water would start to boil. This illustrates how increased pressure increases the temperature within the earth.

---

### ▼ ACTIVITY
#### Researching

*Find It Under "M"*

Use a dictionary to look up the meaning of the prefix *meta*. Also find the meaning of the suffix *morph*. Using these two definitions, define the word "metamorphic."

**SKILLS WARMUP**

---

# 10.4 Metamorphic Rocks

## Objectives

▶ **Identify** common metamorphic rocks and their parent rocks.

▶ **Describe** the conditions necessary for metamorphism to take place.

▶ **Compare** and **contrast** contact and regional metamorphism.

▶ **Predict** the conditions necessary to form foliated or nonfoliated metamorphic rock.

---

When you see a butterfly, it's hard to imagine it was once a caterpillar. What happened to its many legs and its jaws? A butterfly is the result of a process called metamorphosis. During metamorphosis, the caterpillar's structure and appearance change to form a butterfly.

Rocks also go through a type of metamorphosis. In fact, both igneous and sedimentary rock can change into metamorphic rock. The texture, color, and composition of the original rock differ greatly from the new metamorphic rock formed.

### Formation of Metamorphic Rocks

Changes in structure, appearance, and composition of rock beneath the surface is called **metamorphism.** Metamorphism is caused by intense heat and high pressure acting on rock.

Magma may partially melt a rock mass. Under heat and pressure, the minerals recrystallize and small mineral grains enlarge. New minerals replace the original minerals. Mineral grains may pack more tightly and align, creating bands.

Shale is a fine-grained, clastic rock that contains clay. During metamorphism, the mineral mica replaces some of the clay to form slate. With continued heat and pressure, the mica grains enlarge, and new minerals are added. The minerals form bands. The rock changes to schist (SHIHST). Schist is shown in Figure 10.16. Schists are coarse-grained metamorphic rocks derived from slate or shale.

**Figure 10.16**
Shale may first change to slate, before changing into schist, the rock shown below. ▼

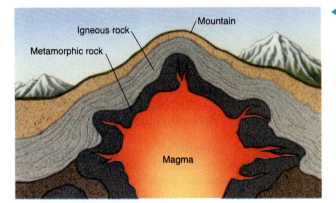

**Contact Metamorphism** What happens to an egg when it's fried? As it fries, an increase in temperature causes chemical changes in the egg. The part closest to the heat cooks first. The egg changes color and texture. Even if the outside of the egg looks done, the inside may have just begun to cook. During contact metamorphism, rocks go through a similar process.

Contact metamorphism takes place when magma intrudes country rock. The heat from the magma alters the rock. The rock in contact with the magma "cooks" first. Which rock in Figure 10.17 would the magma ① affect first? Minerals in the magma and the rock mix. New mineral combinations form in the country rock.

Different changes take place farther from the heat source. Rocks composed mainly of one kind of mineral recrystallize with little mixing.

**Regional Metamorphism** Small areas of rock are affected by contact metamorphism. In contrast, regional metamorphism affects thousands of kilometers of rock. Regional metamorphism occurs at the margins of continents, where large areas of rock become deeply buried. Intense forces act on the buried rock. Pressure may cause rocks to buckle and fold. Heat and pressure cause minerals to recrystallize and change structure.

Deeply buried rocks may come into contact with a magma chamber. Some rocks may melt completely, forming intrusive igneous rocks. Other rocks altered by contact with the magma form metamorphic rocks.

**Figure 10.18**
Regional metamorphism occurs at continental plate boundaries. ▼

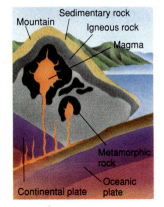

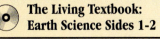

## Critical Thinking

**Compare and Contrast** Ask how sedimentary and foliated rocks are similar and different. (Both have layers; sedimentary layers are formed by particles of different sizes while foliated rock layers consist of different minerals.)

**Classify** Give the following description of a rock to students and have them decide if the rock is foliated or nonfoliated: All black from a distance but close-up has faint stripes and forms a smooth plate. (Foliated)

### Language Arts Connection

Have students look up the meaning for the word *foliate.* Ask them how the definition describes foliated or nonfoliated rocks. (*Foliated* means "to divide or beat into leaves or a thin foil," as in the parallel bands of foliated rocks. *Nonfoliate* is the absence of division, as seen in nonfoliated rocks.)

## Metamorphic Rock Classification

Metamorphic rock grains have uniform size. They are arranged either randomly or in parallel bands. Metamorphic rocks are classified according to the arrangement of their mineral grains.

**Foliated Rocks** The pressures that accompany metamorphism affect grain structure. The grains in sedimentary and igneous rocks tend to be random. Look at Figure 10.19. What happens to the grain arrangement when pressure is applied from one direction? The grains line up and lock together in bands.

Metamorphic rock with grains arranged in parallel bands are **foliated.** Banding gives foliated rocks a striped appearance. In rocks that contain several minerals, the grains may separate into bands of different minerals. The presence of sheet minerals, such as mica, causes foliated rocks to break into smooth plates. This property makes slate a useful rock for chalkboards and roofing material.

Foliated rocks differ from layered sedimentary rocks. The separate layers in sedimentary rock consist of different sized particles, not different minerals. Clastic rock particles are cemented and compacted, not interlocked like the minerals in foliated rock. Chemical rocks have mineral crystals, but the size varies, and the crystals are random.

**Nonfoliated Rocks** In contact metamorphism, equal pressure surrounds the rock mass. Little or no grain rearrangement occurs. These metamorphic rocks are nonfoliated. Nonfoliated rocks don't have bands. Most nonfoliated rocks originate from single-mineral rocks.

Because the grains in nonfoliated rocks form at the same time, the grains are similar in size. This property can distinguish metamorphic rock from igneous rock. Compare the grains in the igneous rock granite shown below on the left, with those in the nonfoliated rock marble in Table 10.4. Igneous rock grains form at different times, producing various grain sizes. The metamorphic rock grains are more uniform in size.

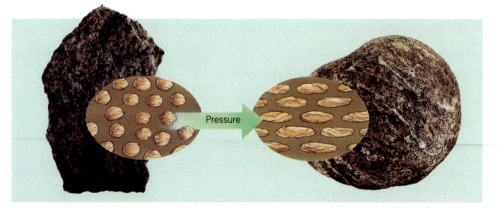

Pressure

**Figure 10.19** ▲
The random arrangement of minerals in rocks rearranges under pressure to form bands.

## Examples of Metamorphic Rocks

You can identify some metamorphic rocks by observing the parent rocks from which they formed. Compare the metamorphic rocks to the parent rocks in Table 10.4. How do they differ? ①

Marble is coarser-grained than its parent rock, limestone. Layers or fossils that were in limestone are not seen in marble, but impurities can form patterns.

The sedimentary rock sandstone changes into quartzite. It is a hard rock with tightly linked quartz sand grains.

Regional metamorphism changes shale into slate. Clay and mudstone also change into slate. Unlike its parent rock, slate contains mica and splits into thick slabs.

**Table 10.4   Metamorphic Rocks and Their Parent Rocks**

| Parent Rock | Metamorphic Rock |
| --- | --- |
| Limestone | Marble |
| Sandstone | Quartzite |
| Shale, clay, mudstone | Slate |

## Historical Notebook

### Marbles from the Past

Marble is a metamorphic rock that has been valued by people for centuries for its beautiful textures and colors. The Taj Mahal in India, shown at the right, is a famous monument made of a variety of marbles. It was completed in 1643 by Emperor Shah Jahan in memory of his wife.

The main building, or mausoleum, of the Taj Mahal complex is made of pure white marble. This type of marble is the most valuable marble. The mausoleum stands on a marble block 7 m high. The main arch rises to 33 m. Inside the mausoleum, the marble tombs of the emperor and his wife are carved and decorated with precious stones.

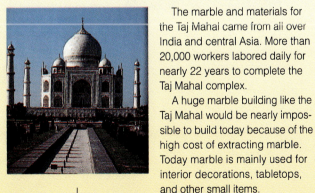

The marble and materials for the Taj Mahal came from all over India and central Asia. More than 20,000 workers labored daily for nearly 22 years to complete the Taj Mahal complex.

A huge marble building like the Taj Mahal would be nearly impossible to build today because of the high cost of extracting marble. Today marble is mainly used for interior decorations, tabletops, and other small items.

1. Why do you think Emperor Jahan chose marble to build the Taj Mahal?

2. **Research** Find out the history of another famous building that was made from marble, such as the Parthenon in Greece.

## TEACH ▪ Continued

### Research

Have students find out why the Leaning Tower of Pisa leans and what proposals have been made to keep it from completely collapsing. Ask students to explain how a knowledge of bedrock could have kept the Leaning Tower straight.

## EVALUATE

### WrapUp

**Portfolio**  Have students make a concept map using the terms *contact metamorphism, regional metamorphism, foliated, nonfoliated, mix, recrystallize, magma,* and *country rock.* Tell them they may use some terms more than once. Have them add their maps to their portfolios.
Use Review Worksheet 10.4.

### Check and Explain

1. (Metamorphic first, parent second) marble, limestone; quartzite, sandstone; slate and schist, shale; gneiss, granite.

2. Increased heat and pressure

3. Both apply heat and pressure; contact changes the rocks in contact with magma; regional changes large amounts of rock where continental plates collide.

4. Foliated rocks would be more likely near rocks containing a variety of minerals; nonfoliated rocks would be more likely near single-mineral formations. Both kinds of rock could be found above underground magma chambers.

---

## INTEGRATED LEARNING

 ### Social Studies Connection

Explain to students that many old country fences and houses are made from stone. In order to clear the fields for plowing, many stones had to be removed. Piling the stones into fences and incorporating them into buildings was a way to put the stones to good use.
Use Integrating Worksheet 10.4.

 ### Science and Technology
### Building on Bedrock

How can a tall building like the Empire State Building stand without toppling over? The reason is because the building is built on a layer of solid rock called bedrock. Because few materials are strong enough to support the great weight of a tall building, bedrock is very important in construction.

Bedrock can be igneous, metamorphic, or sedimentary in origin. It can be located below or at the earth's surface. When choosing a building site, builders must locate and identify the bedrock.

To locate bedrock, detailed geological maps are studied. Sonar, a device that uses reflected sound, may help detect bedrock. In some cases, bedrock is located by measuring the speed of seismic waves as they move through the earth. If the bedrock is difficult to identify, engineers must sometimes drill into the earth. A camera is then used to take photographs that will help identify the bedrock.

Before laying a foundation, workers may drive steel pipes, called piles, into the bedrock. The piles are then filled with concrete. For skyscrapers and other tall buildings, the concrete may be reinforced with steel rods called footings. The piles and footings are important because they support the weight of the entire building. Once they are in place, construction can begin.

**Figure 10.20** ▲
Before a large structure can be built, piles are driven into the bedrock for support.

### Check and Explain

1. Name four examples of metamorphic rocks, and identify their possible parent rocks.

2. What conditions are necessary before metamorphic rock will form?

3. **Compare and Contrast**  How are contact and regional metamorphism similar? How are they different?

4. **Predict**  Suppose you are searching for metamorphic rocks for your rock collection. Where would you most likely find samples of foliated and nonfoliated rock on the earth's surface?

## Check Your Vocabulary

1. rock cycle

2. sedimentary rock

3. metamorphism

4. igneous rock

5. chemical rock

6. metamorphic rock

7. clastic rock

8. extrusive rock

9. foliated

10. intrusive rock

11. organic rock

Use Vocabulary Worksheet for Chapter 10.

## Chapter 10 *Review*

### Concept Summary

**10.1 Rocks**
- ▶ The main types of rocks are igneous, sedimentary, and metamorphic.
- ▶ The rock cycle is a series of processes that recycles rocks.
- ▶ Depending on the conditions, a rock may change into another type of rock.
- ▶ Rocks are identified by their texture and grain size. Rock textures include coarse-grained, fine-grained, and glassy.

**10.2 Igneous Rocks**
- ▶ Igneous rock forms from magma.
- ▶ Extrusive igneous rock comes from magma cooling on the surface. Intrusive igneous rock forms by magma solidifying beneath the surface.
- ▶ Igneous rocks are identified by texture and mineral composition.

**10.3 Sedimentary Rocks**
- ▶ When loose sediments settle, compact, and cement together, sedimentary rock forms.
- ▶ Layers, ripples, and mud cracks are found in sedimentary rocks. Fossils occur in sedimentary rocks.
- ▶ Sedimentary rock can be clastic rock, organic rock, or chemical rock, depending on the origin of the rock particles.

**10.4 Metamorphic Rocks**
- ▶ Heat and pressure can change any rock into metamorphic rock.
- ▶ Metamorphic rock can form by contact or regional metamorphism.
- ▶ Metamorphic rocks are classified as foliated or nonfoliated.

### Chapter Vocabulary

| | | |
|---|---|---|
| igneous rock (10.1) | extrusive rock (10.2) | chemical rock (10.3) |
| sedimentary rock (10.1) | intrusive rock (10.2) | metamorphism (10.4) |
| metamorphic rock (10.1) | clastic rock (10.3) | foliated (10.4) |
| rock cycle (10.1) | organic rock (10.3) | |

### Check Your Vocabulary

Use the vocabulary words above to complete the following sentences correctly.

1. Rocks can change from one type into another type during the _____ .

2. Rocks formed by the compaction and cementation of sediments are _____ .

3. Changes in the appearance, structure, and composition of rocks is _____ .

4. Rocks formed from the cooling and hardening of magma are _____ .

5. Minerals coming out of solution and crystallizing form _____ .

6. Country rock exposed to heat and pressure may change to _____ .

7. A sedimentary rock made of compacted and cemented particles is _____ .

8. Magma that reaches the surface, then cools and hardens, makes _____ .

9. Metamorphic rocks that have mineral grains arranged in bands are _____ .

10. Magma that cools and hardens under the surface forms _____ .

11. Rock made from living organisms or their remains is called _____ .

## Check Your Knowledge

1. Sun, wind, ice, pollution, and organisms can break down rock to form sediment.
2. The textures of rocks are coarse, fine, and glassy.
3. Compaction, cementation, and lithification are the processes involved in forming sedimentary rock.
4. A fossil is the preserved remains of an organism.
5. Contact and regional metamorphism are the two ways metamorphic rock can form.
6. Volcanic rock is another name for extrusive igneous rock because solidified lava from a volcano can form igneous rock.
7. Marble is a nonfoliated metamorphic rock.
8. Sedimentary rock structures include: layering, ripples, and mud cracks.
9. Coal is an organic sedimentary rock.
10. Intrusive rock is also called plutonic rock, after the mythical ruler of the underworld, Pluto.
11. Chemical rock is typically formed by the evaporation of water.
12. organic
13. glassy
14. bands
15. extrusive
16. cementation

7. The formation of both igneous and metamorphic rock can involve heat. Igneous rock, however, is formed after molten rock cools, while metamorphic rock is formed when existing solid rock is changed by heat and pressure.
8. Igneous rocks look different depending on the conditions under which they formed. The rate at which they cooled and their mineral content are their most important differences.
9. Student answers may vary, but may include: flowing into a pocket between existing rocks forming an intrusive rock or being expelled in a volcanic eruption, becoming pumice, obsidian, or scoria.
10. Student answers may vary. Possible answers include: breaking the rock open to determine its texture and the size, shape, and pattern or grain.
11. Horizontal layering, ripple marks, a predominant color

## Check Your Understanding

1. Pumice is solidified foam that forms when lava cools quickly. Obsidian is formed from rapidly cooled lava that lost most of its gases. Scoria is similar to pumice.
2. Dead organisms can easily be buried by the layers of sediment that form sedimentary rocks.
3. The clay in shale is gradually replaced by mica to form slate. Over time, heat and pressure causes the mica grains to enlarge, and new minerals are added. The result of these changes is schist.
4. Extruded rocks are usually fine-grained while intrusive rocks are coarse-grained.
5. The word *metamorphic* means changing form. Metamorphic rock changes form during its creation.
6. Since buried sediments harden into sedimentary rock, the type of rock formed depends on the kinds of particles that collect in the sediments.

---

## Chapter 10 Review

### Check Your Knowledge

Answer the following in complete sentences.

1. List three ways that rock breaks down to form sediment.
2. What are the different rock textures?
3. List the processes involved in forming sedimentary rock.
4. What is a fossil?
5. Name the two ways that metamorphic rock can form.
6. What is another name for extrusive igneous rock? Why?
7. Give an example of a nonfoliated metamorphic rock.
8. List three sedimentary rock structures.
9. What kind of sedimentary rock is coal?
10. What is another name for intrusive igneous rock? Why?
11. How is chemical rock typically formed?

Choose the answer that best completes each sentence.

12. Chalk is an example of (clastic, organic, chemical, igneous) rock.
13. Rocks that don't contain any mineral grains have a (coarse-grained, fine-grained, mixed-grain, glassy) texture.
14. Foliated rocks have (layers, cracks, bands, ripples).
15. Volcanic lava that cools and solidifies forms (metamorphic, intrusive, extrusive, organic) rock.
16. The process of minerals filling the spaces between sediments to bind them together is called (cementation, sedimentation, compaction, lithification).

### Check Your Understanding

Apply the concepts you have learned to answer each question.

1. Describe the different kinds of extrusive rocks that can form from a volcanic explosion.
2. Explain why fossils are commonly found in sedimentary layers.
3. Discuss how the texture and mineral composition of shale changes to form schist.
4. How can you tell if an igneous rock is extrusive or intrusive by looking at it?
5. Explain why the name "metamorphic" is appropriate for this type of rock.
6. Explain how the composition of sedimentary rocks reveals their origin.
7. **Compare** Discuss how the formation of igneous rock is similar to the formation of metamorphic rock. How is it different?
8. If all igneous rocks are formed from magma, why don't they look the same?
9. **Extension** Imagine you are a little blob of magma floating beneath the earth. Discuss all the possible changes you could go through during your very long life.
10. **Application** You find an interesting rock while walking home from school. Discuss how you could determine whether it is an igneous, sedimentary, or metamorphic rock.
11. **Mystery Photo** The photograph on page 208 shows the surface of a sedimentary rock. The stripes are areas where the rock is harder than the rest of the cemented particles. List features common to sedimentary rocks that you can see in this photograph.

## Develop Your Skills

1. a. 0–6 km and 0–150°C
   b. Deeper than about 48 km, hotter than about 600°C
   c. Slate and schist; 8–24 km, 150–350°C. Gneiss; 40–48 km, 600–750°C
   d. With increasing depth and heat, the rocks change from sedimentary, to low temperature metamorphic, to high temperature metamorphic, to igneous.

2. a. Sedimentary
   b. Mainly sedimentary; students may also name metamorphic and intrusive igneous
   c. Extrusive igneous, metamorphic, sedimentary, and intrusive igneous

## Make Connections

1. Concept maps will vary. The map below shows a possible organization of the concepts listed.

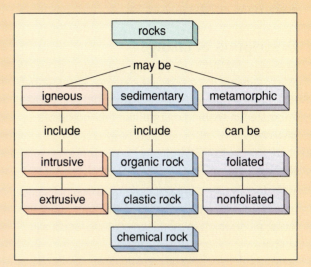

2. Student answers will vary. Make sure students correctly identify each material as either igneous, sedimentary, or metamorphic. Examples include: brick/clay, limestone—sedimentary; granite—igneous; marble, slate—metamorphic.

3. Review student art.

4. Student answers may vary. Conglomerate rock is made up of particles of varying sizes and textures within a matrix, just as the cookies contain chips, the bread contains nuts and the peanut brittle contains peanuts.

5. Student reports will vary. Students should be able to state why characteristics of the rock suited its function as a tool. Drawings and diagrams might illustrate flint knapping and how the stones were hafted to wood or bone. Reports may also address misconceptions, such as the expression "arrowhead," which is broadly applied to knives, choppers, scrapers, drills, awls, and lance points.

## Develop Your Skills

Use the skills you have developed in this chapter to complete each activity.

1. **Interpret Data** The graph below shows the effect of burial depth and temperature on various rocks.

   a. At what ranges of depth and temperature are sedimentary rocks found?
   b. At what ranges of depth and temperature are igneous rocks found?
   c. Name the metamorphic rocks listed in the graph. What are the depth and temperature ranges for these rocks?
   d. What is the relationship between the types of rocks formed and depth? Temperature?

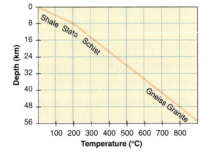

2. **Data Bank** Use the information on page 617 to answer the following questions.

   a. What is the most common class of rock found in the United States?
   b. What is the most common class of rock found in Canada?
   c. List the classes of rocks that are found in Mexico.

## Make Connections

1. **Link the Concepts** Draw a concept map showing how the following concepts from the chapter link together. Add terms to connect, or link, the concepts.

   rocks           igneous
   chemical rock   sedimentary
   extrusive       nonfoliated
   intrusive       organic rock
   clastic rock    foliated
   metamorphic

2. **Science and You** Make a list of all the building materials in your home and your school that contain rock. Then identify each of the building materials as igneous, sedimentary, or metamorphic rock.

3. **Science and Art** Make a rock sculpture using the sedimentary rock material, plaster of Paris. Decorate your sculpture with pebbles. Use the sedimentary rock, chalk, to color your sculpture.

4. **Science and Home Economics** Make peanut brittle, chocolate chip cookies, or banana nut bread. Describe how the steps in cooking one of the above recipes is similar to the formation of a conglomerate rock.

5. **Science and Social Studies** The Stone Age was a period in human history that lasted over 2 million years. Research how ancient people living during the Stone Age used rocks as tools. Make a replica or drawing of one of the stone tools. Present your replica or drawing to the class, and explain how the tool was used.

## About the Literary Work

"A Journey to the Centre of the Earth" was adapted from *A Voyage to the Center of the Earth*, written by Jules Verne in 1864.

## Description of Change

The passage was taken from a two-page section of text. It reflects the vocabulary, syntax, and general flavor of the original selection. It should get students interested in reading more about this incredible journey.

## Rationale

The excerpt was selected because it discusses the earth's interior, as well as rock types and characteristics, all of which relate to the science lessons in Unit 3.

## Vocabulary

commence, Ruhmkorf coil apparatus, sombre, engulf, bowels, abrasures, stalactites, limpid, variegated, insensible, luminous

## Teaching Strategies

### Directed Inquiry

After students finish reading, discuss the story. Be sure to relate the story to the science lessons in this unit. Ask the following questions:

▶ What is the focus of this story? (The observations of explorers as they travel below the earth's surface)

▶ The passage describes the explorers carrying a *Ruhmkorf coil apparatus*. What do you suppose is the purpose of this device? (To protect the explorers from the inflammable and combustible gases that surround them once they are inside the earth)

▶ The professor announces that the interior of the earth "has never [been] visited by humans since the first creation of the world." Do you agree with him? Why or why not? (It depends what is meant by the "interior of the earth." People have not yet been below the earth's crust. However, students might say that underground caverns have been visited or were once inhabited by people during the ice ages.)

## Skills Development

**Compare and Contrast**  Ask students what makes the rocks observed by the explorers different from more familiar kinds of rocks. (Scientists classify igneous rocks formed by the hardening of magma as either extrusive or intrusive. Extrusive igneous rocks form from magma that cooled and hardened on the surface of the earth while intrusive igneous rock forms from magma that never reached the earth's surface. The rocks observed by the explorers are intrusive igneous rock because they are observed deep under the earth's surface.)

**Infer**  Remind students that the time it takes magma to cool and solidify determines the size of the crystals contained in volcanic rock. The faster the magma solidifies, the smaller the crystals will be. Ask students to go back and find the section of the passage that describes the size of the crystals observed in the volcanic rock that lined the tunnel. Ask: What does this indicate about the time frame of the cooling process? (The passage indicates that the volcanic rocks were quite porous and contained crystals that were easily visible to the naked eye. This would indicate that the cooling process was slow.)

# Science and Literature Connection

## A Journey to the Centre of the Earth

*The following excerpts are from the novel* A Journey to the Centre of the Earth *by Jules Verne.*

"Now, Harry," cried the Professor, in an enthusiastic tone of voice, "we are truly about to take our first step into the Interior of the Earth; never before visited by humans since the first creation of the world. You may consider, therefore, that at this precise moment our travels really commence."

As my uncle made this remark, he took in one hand the Ruhmkorf coil apparatus, which hung around his neck, and with the other he put the electric current into communication with the worm of the lantern. And a bright light at once illuminated that dark and gloomy tunnel!

The effect was magical!

"Forward!" cried my uncle. Each took up his burden. Hans went first, my uncle followed, and I going third, we entered the sombre gallery!

Just as we were about to engulf ourselves in this dismal passage, I lifted up my head, and through the tube-like shaft saw that Iceland sky I was never to see again!

Was it the last I should ever see of any sky?

The stream of lava flowing from the bowels of the earth in 1229 had forced itself a passage through the tunnel. It lined the whole of the inside with its thick and brilliant coating. The electric light added very greatly to the brilliancy of the effect.

The great difficulty of our journey now began. How were we to prevent ourselves from slipping down the steeply-inclined plane? Happily, some cracks, abrasures of the soil, and other irregularities, served the place of steps; and we descended slowly, allowing our heavy luggage to slip on before, at the end of a long cord.

But that which served as steps under our feet became in other places stalactites. The lava, very porous in certain places, took the form of little round blisters. Crystals of opaque quartz, adorned with limpid drops of natural glass suspended to the roof like lustres, seemed to take fire as we passed beneath them.

"Magnificent, glorious!" I cried, in a moment of involuntary enthusiasm. "What a spectacle, uncle! Do you not admire these variegated shades of lava, which run through a whole series of colors, from reddish-brown to pale yellow—by the most insensible degrees? And these crystals—they appear like luminous globes."

"You are beginning to see the charms of travel, Master Harry," cried my uncle. "Wait a bit, until we advance farther. What we have as yet discovered is nothing—onward, my boy, onward!"

We had journeyed the entire day through this gallery when we noticed a difference in the walls of the gallery. It was a glorious sight to see how the electric light brought out the sparkles in the walls of the calcareous rocks and the old red sandstone. Some magnificent specimens of marble projected from the sides

# Skills in Science

## Reading Skills in Science

1. The passage is fictional. It describes an exploration that humans could not possibly undertake because of high temperatures and pressure and the inability to get through dense, solid layers of the earth.

2. The explorers enter the earth in Iceland. This is indicated by the sentence ". . . saw the Iceland sky I was never to see again!"

## Writing Skills in Science

1. Passages will vary but may include descriptions of other rock formations observed deep underground.

2. The explorers observe varieties of sedimentary and intrusive igneous rock.

## Activities

**Find Causes** Variations in the chemical composition of the magma produce color differences in the volcanic rock. High-silica rocks are light-colored while low-silica rocks are dark-colored.

**Communicate** In Iceland, hot water from geothermal areas is piped into homes for heating and cooking use. Check students' diagrams for accuracy.

---

of the gallery; some of an agate gray with white veins of variegated character, others of a yellow spotted color, with red veins; farther off might be seen samples of color in which cherry-tinted seams were to be found in all their brightest shades.

## Skills in Science

### Reading Skills in Science

1. **Classify** Classify this passage as either fiction or nonfiction. Provide evidence for your classification.

2. **Find Context Clues** In which country did the explorers enter the center of the earth? Identify the sentence from the passage that contains this information

### Writing Skills in Science

1. **Infer** Imagine you are accompanying the narrator in his journey to the center of the earth. What do you see? Write an entry in your diary describing your experiences.

2. **Classify** Write a paragraph identifying the rock types viewed by the explorers on their journey. Provide evidence for your classification.

### Activities

**Find Causes** The passage describes lava having a great variety of color. Use reference tools to determine the cause of this color variation.

**Communicate** The country in which the explorers began their journey is unique in that it uses the heat of volcanic material as an energy source. Use reference materials to find out how this is accomplished. Make a diagram to illustrate your findings with the class.

### Where to Read More

*Digging Deeper* by Sandra Markle. New York: Lothrop, Lee and Shepard Books, 1987. Learn more about various topics such as plate tectonics, erosion, and mineral resources by reading this text, complete with experiments and activities!

nit 4 is an investigation of the forces of change in the earth's surface and how the changes relate to geological history. Chapter 11 presents weathering and soils. The chapter discusses weathering as the source of soil, then explains world soil characteristics and classification. Chapter 12 explores the forces of erosion, including discussion of river and stream deposition, wave erosion, ice erosion, and glaciation. Chapter 13 addresses the history of life on the earth, opening with a discussion of the theory of evolution and the classification of organisms. The chapter describes how fossils form and how to interpret fossils. The chapter closes with an examination of life through geologic time.

## Introducing the Unit

### Directed Inquiry

Have students study the photograph and read the caption. Ask:

▶ How would you describe the rock formation in this picture? (Students might describe the archlike shape, the sun-baked coloration, and the smooth texture.)

▶ What is the surrounding landscape like? (Students might say that the landscape looks barren and filled with rock formations showing the same effects of wear.)

▶ What do you think the weather is like in this place? Why? (The rock formations suggest that the place is windy and has a lot of sun. The lichens and the sparse growth of leafy plants suggest lack of rain and cold temperatures.)

▶ Which of the following factors most likely caused the formations in the picture: water, rain, ice, wind, people or animals, or chemical reactions? Explain why. (Water, rain, ice, and chemical reactions have all been important in producing these features. The formations are in an arid region where temperature extremes and occasional flash floods occur.)

### Writing About the Photograph

Suggest that students write what they think this area will look like in two thousand years. Remind them that the forces of weathering and erosion are constantly at work. Tell them to be very detailed in their descriptions.

Unit 4

# Changes on the Earth's Surface

*Chapters*

**11** Weathering and Soils

**12** Forces of Erosion

**13** History of Life on Earth

# Data Bank

Use the information on pages 612 to 625 to answer the following questions about topics explored in this unit.

### Interpreting a Diagram

In which climate does the regolith reach a depth of about 15 meters?

### Inferring

Why do you think the Ganges River has the highest silt load shown?

### Interpreting a Table

How many years ago did the Miocene epoch begin? What is the most recent epoch?

### Reading a Map

What is the approximate silt load of the Amazon River?

The photograph to the left is of Arches National Park in Utah. How did this unusual rock structure form?

## Data Bank Answers

Have students search the Data Bank on pages 612 to 625 for the answers to the questions on this page.

**Interpreting a Diagram**  The regolith reaches a depth of about 15 meters in the temperate climate. The answer is found on the diagram Climate and Weathering on page 613.

**Inferring**  Answers will vary. The Ganges River is part of the drainage system of the steep Himalayan Mountains. Tremendous volumes of sediment are being shed from these mountains. Slope, rainfall, and soil type all affect the silt load. Refer to the map *Silt Loads of Major Rivers* on page 612.

**Extension**  Have students research why the Ganges has such a high silt load.

**Interpreting a Table**  The Miocene epoch began about 24 million years ago. The most recent epoch is the Pleistocene. The answers are found in the table The Cenozoic Era on page 612.

**Reading a Map**  The approximate silt load of the Amazon River is 1,000,000,000 tons per year (1000 $\times 10^6$). The answer is found on the map Silt Loads of Major Rivers on page 612.

**Extension**  Have students calculate the silt loads of all other rivers shown on the map.

**Answer to In-Text Question**

Many years of weathering and erosion along parallel fractures in the soft sandstone; some rainfall may have caused chemical erosion from weak acids formed on the rock surface.

**CHAPTER 11**

## Overview

Chapter 11 presents a discussion of weathering and soils. The first section introduces mechanical and chemical weathering. The second section discusses the source, properties, and characteristics of soil, including organisms that dwell in soil. Types of world soils are classified in the third section, which includes a discussion of overgrazed grasslands.

## Advance Planner

▶ Obtain a mass weight, copper wire, a clamp, and a stand for TE page 241.

▶ Supply chalk, straws, water, cups, lemon juice, and vinegar for SE page 243.

▶ Gather clear plastic bottles, breakfast cereal, or bits of discarded paper for TE page 248.

▶ Collect two samples of freshly dug soil for TE page 249, and hand lenses, paper, and pens for SE page 251.

▶ Supply paper cups, small wood blocks or rocks, shallow dishes or saucers, coffee or paper filters, sand, soil, gravel, measuring cups, metric rulers, scissors, and a clock or watch with second hand for SE Activity 11, page 252.

▶ Obtain two jars with lids, two different soil samples, water, a measuring cup, and a spoon for TE page 256.

## Skills Development Chart

| Sections | Classify | Communicate | Infer | Interpret Data | Observe | Predict |
|---|---|---|---|---|---|---|
| **11.1** Skills WarmUp |  |  |  |  |  | ● |
| Skills WorkOut |  |  |  |  | ● |  |
| **11.2** Skills WarmUp |  |  | ● |  |  |  |
| Historical Notebook |  |  |  |  |  |  |
| Skills WorkOut |  |  |  |  | ● |  |
| Activity 11 |  | ● |  | ● | ● |  |
| **11.3** Skills WarmUp | ● |  |  |  |  |  |
| Consider This |  | ● |  |  |  |  |

## Individual Needs

▶ **Limited English Proficiency Students** Ask students to make a summary of each section of the chapter in their own words using the headings in the sections as a guide. They should include the boldface chapter vocabulary in their summaries. Encourage them to illustrate each section with original drawings and pictures cut from magazines.

▶ **At-Risk Students** Invite an expert on soil from a state or county agricultural organization to talk with students about the kinds of soil found in the area and what crops grow best there. Have students prepare a list of questions for the speaker beforehand. The questions should relate topics in the chapter to area conditions. Students may also want to know what kinds of professions need data about the soil.

▶ **Gifted Students** Have students work in groups of three or four. Ask each group to examine a different agricultural practice and its effects—good and bad—on the soil around the world and through history. Practices could include irrigation, fertilization, crop rotation (and lack of it), slash-and-burn agriculture, and grazing. Have each group present its findings in a report to the rest of the class.

## Resource Bank

▶ **Field Trip** With the help of the students, plan a field trip to different places in your area that show clear examples of the different kinds of weathering. Go on the field trip, and ask students to take notes on each site. Have them make sketches and take photographs of each kind of weathering.

▶ **Bulletin Board** Hang up photographs from the field trip and any others students find or take that show weathering. Have students label each with its location and the kind of weathering. Have students discuss the examples and determine whether people should try to slow down or stop the process in each case, why or why not, and how they might go about preventing it. Students may have to do some research about the prevention of weathering.

| Section | Core | Standard | Enriched | Section | Core | Standard | Enriched |
|---|---|---|---|---|---|---|---|
| **11.1 Weathering** pp. 239–244 | | | | **Ancillary Options** *CEPUP*, The Waste Hierarchy: Where Is 'Away'? *Multiculturalism in Mathematics, Science, and Technology*, pp. 39–40 | ● | ● ● | ● ● |
| **Section Features** Skills WarmUp, p. 239 Skills WorkOut, p. 243 | ● | ● ● | ● ● | | | | |
| **Blackline Masters** Review Worksheet 11.1 Reteach Worksheet 11.1 Skills Worksheet 11.1 | ● ● | ● ● ● | ● ● ● | **Laboratory Program** Investigation 17 | | ● | ● |
| **Overhead Blackline Transparencies** Overhead Blackline Master 11.1 and Student Worksheet | ● | ● | ● | **Color Transparencies** Transparencies 24, 25 | ● | ● | ● |
| **11.2 Soils** pp. 245–252 | | | | **11.3 World Soil Types** pp. 253–258 | | | |
| **Section Features** Skills WarmUp, p. 245 Historical Notebook, p. 251 Skills WorkOut, p. 251 Activity, p. 252 | ● ● | ● ● ● | ● ● ● ● | **Section Features** Skills WarmUp, p. 253 Consider This, p. 254 | ● ● | ● ● | ● ● |
| **Blackline Masters** Review Worksheet 11.2 Integrating Worksheet 11.2a Integrating Worksheet 11.2b | ● ● | ● ● ● | ● ● ● | **Blackline Masters** Review Worksheet 11.3 Skills Worksheet 11.3 Integrating Worksheet 11.3 Vocabulary Worksheet 11.3 | ● ● ● | ● ● ● ● | ● ● ● ● |
| | | | | **Color Transparencies** Transparency 26 | ● | ● | ● |

# Bibliography

The following resources can be used for teaching the chapter. See page T–46 for supplier codes.

**Library Resources**

Bourgeois, Paulette. *The Amazing Dirt Book*. New York: Addison-Wesley, 1990.

Farndon, John. *How the Earth Works*. Pleasantville, NY: The Reader's Digest Association, Inc., 1992.

Herda, D. J. and Margaret L. Madden. *Land Use and Abuse*. New York: Franklin Watts, 1990.

**Technology Resources**

*Internet*

**PLANETDIARY** at *http://www.planetdiary.com*
- Learn more about animals and plants in *Fauna* and *Flora* by clicking on *Phenomena Backgrounders*.
- Find meteorological and geological news in *Current Phenomena*.

*Software*

*Earth Science*. Mac, Win. ER.
*Geology: Science 2*. Dos. ESI.

*CD-ROMs*

*Interactive Earth*. SFAW.
*Small Blue Planet: The Real Picture World Atlas*. Mac, Dos. ESI.

*Laserdiscs*

*Living Textbook*. (See barcodes on pages in this chapter.) Optical Data.

*Videos*

*Discovering the Changing Surface of Our Earth*. 30 min. MMI.
*Folding, Flooding, and Faulting: How the Earth is Shaped*. 60 min. Blue Sky Associates.

**Audio-Visual Resources**

*The Earth: Discovering Its History*. Film. C/MTI.
*Erosion: Carving the Landscape*. Still frame. 15 min. CABISCO.
*The Shape of the Land*. Still frame. 15 min. CABISCO.
*Soils: An Introduction*. Film. EB.

# 11

## Introducing the Chapter

Have students read the description of the photograph. Ask if they agree or disagree with the description.

### Directed Inquiry

Have students study the photograph. Ask:

▶ Where was this photograph taken? (Students should recognize that the picture was taken in a cave.)

▶ How would you describe the vertical structures within the cave? What material are they made of? (Students may say they look like columns, tree roots, icicles, or drips made out of rock.)

▶ How do you think these structures might have been formed? (Students may suggest that water with dissolved minerals formed drops on the cave ceiling. The hard mineral was left behind after the water evaporated. The bits of mineral built up over time into these stalactites.)

▶ How do the structures in the photograph relate to weathering? (Students might say that the cave was hollowed out by weathering when water seeped into the rock and wore it away or dissolved it. They may also infer that stalactites are formed by a kind of weathering.)

## Chapter Vocabulary

| | |
|---|---|
| carbonation | oxidation |
| exfoliation | parent rock |
| horizon | podsol |
| humus | regolith |
| laterite | soil profile |
| leaching | |

238

### Writing Connection

Ask students to write a mystery or scary story that takes place inside the cave in the photograph. Tell students to study the photograph and jot down details about the color, size, and shape of cave structures. Ask them to use these details in their descriptions and plots. You may wish to have volunteers read their stories to the class.

Chapter **11**

# Weathering and Soils

### Chapter Sections

**11.1** Weathering

**11.2** Soils

**11.3** World Soil Types

### What do you see?

❝I see caves, a rock structure. It looks like one of the caverns in Carlsbad Caverns. They were made some billions of years ago when the water table lowered. Water penetrated through the hairline cracks in an immense block of limestone, gradually forming chambers and corridors. Calcium carbonate deposits formed from evaporating lime-laden ground water.❞

*April Stachura*
*Carman Ainsworth Junior*
*High School*
*Flint, Michigan*

To find out more about the photograph, look on page 260. As you read this chapter, you will learn about weathering and soils.

238

## *Portfolio*

Have students list the results of mechanical weathering that they see on their way to and from school. Students may want to keep their lists in their portfolios. When students visit a store, a relative's house, or take a class outing, they can add to their lists.

**Section Objectives**

For a list of section objectives, see the Student Edition page.

**Skills Objectives**

Students should be able to:

**Predict** the makeup of earth's surface in a million years.

**Observe** the effects of weak acids on chalk.

**Predict** weathering in different rocks.

**Vocabulary**

exfoliation, oxidation, leaching, carbonation

## 11.1 Weathering

### Objectives

▶ **Describe** the causes of mechanical weathering.

▶ **Describe** the causes of chemical weathering.

▶ **Compare** and **contrast** mechanical and chemical weathering.

▶ **Predict** rates of weathering.

---

▼ **ACTIVITY**

**Predicting**

*Not in a Million Years*

Imagine that you can travel through time. What do you think the earth's surface will look like after one million years? What do you think causes these changes?

**SKILLS WARMUP**

---

**MOTIVATE**

### *Skills WarmUp*

To help students understand the effects of weathering, have them do the Skills WarmUp.

**Answer** Students' predictions will vary a great deal, but all should mention the breaking down of materials. For example, they might predict that mountain ranges would be lower.

### Misconceptions

Students may think that the only reason pavement becomes worn is because it is used by people. Explain that this is one kind of weathering (animal weathering). You might point out another example of mechanical weathering (ice pockets or plant growth), as well as an example of chemical weathering (acid rain, acid from fungus).

T hink about an area of pavement near your home or school. Over time, cracks develop. Sometimes tiny plants grow in the cracks. Ants and other insects often build their homes under the cracks. If left alone and not repaired, the pavement eventually crumbles apart as a result of the constant action of the rain, sun, plants, and animals.

The changes in the pavement over time are caused by a process called weathering. Weathering is the process by which exposed rocks and other materials break down. The surface of the earth is constantly wearing away due to the process of weathering.

### Mechanical Weathering

Breaking rock into smaller pieces by mechanical or physical means is called mechanical weathering. You can see the effects of mechanical weathering if you break a rock into small pieces with a hammer. Mechanical weathering results in smaller pieces of rock, but the rock type doesn't change.

Most rocks break into small, irregularly shaped pieces. But some rocks break off in large sheets, leaving a rounded surface underneath. For example, look at the granite dome in Figure 11.1. The granite originally formed underground, under great pressure from overlying rock. Over time, the ground above the granite wore away, and the pressure on the granite decreased. As a result, the outer layers of granite expanded, cracked, and flaked off in a process called **exfoliation** (EHKS foh lee AY shuhn). Extreme changes in temperature can also cause exfoliation.

**Figure 11.1** ▲

Half Dome, in Yosemite National Park, is an example of an exfoliation dome.

⊙ **The Living Textbook: Earth Science Sides 1-2**

Chapter 9        Frame 01962
Exfoliation (1 Frame)
Search:

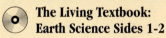

239

*Explore Visually*

Have students study the illustrations and text on these two pages. Then discuss mechanical weathering by asking the following questions:

▶ What happens to a rock as water seeps into cracks and freezes? (The expanding ice pushes the cracks farther apart. In time, the rock itself can split apart.)

▶ How is a root growing in a rock like ice wedging? (The root expands as it grows, pushing the crack farther apart in much the same way that ice widens cracks.)

▶ What animals may split rocks apart as they dig and burrow in cracks? (Insects, such as ants and termites)

**Answer to In-Text Question**

① **Answers will vary. Examples include rubbing and bumping against rocks, as well as pounding on rocks with hooves as they travel.**

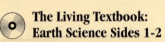
**The Living Textbook:
Earth Science Sides 1-2**

Chapter 9          Frame 01955
Tree Splitting Rock (2 Frames)
Search:          Step:

---

*Integrating the Sciences*

**Environmental Science**  People are a major cause of mechanical weathering. For example, people remove rock to plant fields and build roads. Ask students to make a list of other ways that people cause mechanical weathering.

## Causes of Mechanical Weathering

Mechanical weathering occurs in many different ways. Study the causes of mechanical weathering on these pages. An important cause of mechanical weathering is the freezing and thawing of water. Recall that water expands when it freezes. If you fill a jar with water, cap it with a lid, and put it in the freezer, the expanding ice will break the glass or push the lid off. Water breaks rocks apart in the same way.

**Ice Wedging**
Water from rain or melting snow enters the cracks in a rock. If the air temperature drops below freezing, the water in these cracks changes into ice. The expanding ice slowly pushes the cracks farther apart. Over a long period of time, the cracks widen so much that the rock can split apart. ▼

**Plant Weathering** ▲
The wind carries seeds from plants into cracks in the rocks. The seeds sprout, and the plants begin growing. As each plant grows, the roots exert pressure on the sides of a crack. Over time, the root pressure causes the crack to widen.

Small weedy plants often grow in the rock cracks. But even large trees can grow right out of rocks!

**Animal Weathering**
Animals dig into rocky areas to search for food or to build homes. For example, insects such as ants and termites split rocks apart as they constantly dig and burrow in cracks. The insects carry rock and dirt particles to the surface, sometimes forming a hill or mound. Animal burrows allow air and water inside the rock, so it weathers faster. What other ways might animals cause weathering? ▼ ①

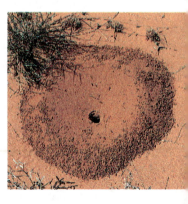

## STS Connection

When engineers design freeway overpasses or bridges, they often leave a gap, called an expansion joint, between sections. Since overpasses and bridges are built with concrete made from rocks, they expand and contract as temperatures change. The gap between sections allows the concrete to expand and contract without building up stress.

## Integrating the Sciences

**Physical Science** When a material is heated, its molecules move faster and collide with one another, and the material expands. Demonstrate expansion in a solid. Attach a mass weight to one end of a copper wire. Fasten the other end of the wire to a clamp on a stand. Heat the wire and observe what happens to the mass weight.

▶ How do daily temperature changes affect rocks? (Heat from the sun causes the surface layer of rocks to expand during the day. At night the surface layer contracts. These changes in temperature cause rocks to crack and flake off.)

▶ What is water abrasion? (Particles in moving water scrape and tumble against rocks and wear down the rocks over time.)

▶ How is water abrasion like the use of sandpaper? (Water in rivers and streams carries particles that scrape against rocks and wear them down in a way that is similar to sandpaper's effect on objects.)

▶ What is wind abrasion? (It is the blowing of sand and dust against rocks so that, in time, the rocks are polished and flattened on their windward sides.)

▶ How is wind abrasion like water abrasion? (Both involve particles acting abrasively to break down materials over time.)

## Misconceptions

Not all geologists agree that abrasion is a form of weathering. Some geologists think that the processes of water and wind abrasion should be considered only as kinds of erosion. Tell students that they may encounter this disagreement if they continue to study geology.

---

Temperature changes make rocks expand and contract. Where there are extreme daily temperature changes, such as in a desert, expansion and contraction can help make rocks break apart. Another important mechanical weathering process is called abrasion. Think about what happens when you use sandpaper to smooth a piece of wood or an emery board to file your fingernails. When gravity, wind, or moving water causes rocks to rub against each other, the rocks wear down or break into smaller pieces.

### Water Abrasion

Rivers and streams carry particles of sand or rock. The particles scrape and tumble against other rocks as the water moves by. The abrasion wears down the rocks over a period of time.

On the coast, ocean waves also carry particles of sand and rock. As the waves strike the shoreline, the particles scrape and smooth the rocks on shore. ▼

### Temperature Change ▲

The sun warms up the surface of rocks. The heat causes the surface layer of each rock to expand. The inside of the rock remains cool. At night, this process is reversed. The surface layer of the rock gets cold and contracts. The inside of the rock is warmer than the outside. This daily expansion and contraction can help cause the weakened surfaces of exposed rocks to slowly crack and flake off.

### Wind Abrasion ▲

Wind can carry sand, dust, and small rock particles over long distances. In dry regions, the wind easily picks up loose sand and dust. As the particle-laden wind blows against exposed rocks, the particles scrape against the rock surfaces. Over a long period of time, wind abrasion can polish and flatten the windward sides of rocks.

## TEACH ▪ Continued

### Skills Development

**Observe** Have students look at the brick or cement surfaces of old buildings or old tombstones in a cemetery. Ask: What causes the surfaces to wear down the way they do? (The weak acids in rainwater eat away the stone in time.)

### Directed Inquiry

Have students study the illustrations and text on this page. Ask the following questions:

▶ What are the most common causes of chemical weathering? (Water, oxygen, and carbon dioxide from the air)

▶ What is rust? (It is iron that has combined with oxygen from the air.)

▶ What happens to rocks that contain iron when they are exposed to air? (The iron combines with oxygen to form iron oxide, or rust, which crumbles easily and causes the rocks to break apart eventually.)

▶ What happens to rocks as water combines with gases in the air to form acids? (The acids dissolve rocks or change the composition of rocks.)

▶ How are clay minerals formed? (When feldspar minerals and water combine)

**The Living Textbook: Earth Science Sides 1-2**

Chapter 9      Frame 01952
Oxidation (1 Frame)
Search:

242

### *Integrating the Sciences*

**Chemistry** Review chemical change and physical change. Ask: What happens during mechanical weathering? (Rock is broken into pieces by physical means.) What happens during chemical weathering? (Rock breaks down because its chemical makeup is changed.) How are the products of these two processes different? (Mechanical weathering produces smaller pieces of rock; chemical weathering changes the rock into something new.)

### Answer to Link

Most likely, the rusty wool gave off more debris. The process of chemical weathering produces iron oxide (rust). The iron oxide is weakly bonded to the steel wool and is more susceptible to mechanical weathering than the unrusted wool.

### Chemistry
#### LINK

Obtain two pieces of uncoated steel wool, water, and a sheet of white paper.

1. Wet one piece of wool.

2. Set both pieces of steel wool out for two days.

3. The following day, place the pieces on the sheet of paper and grind them firmly for two minutes.

Which piece of wool gave off more debris? Why?

#### ACTIVITY

## Chemical Weathering

Weathering that changes the chemical composition of rock is called chemical weathering. You can see chemical weathering at work if you look at old building stones or tombstones made of marble or granite. The surface of the stones is dissolved by a weak acid in rainwater. The acid eats away the stone, rounding the edges, smoothing away areas of lettering, and forming surface pits and holes.

## Causes of Chemical Weathering

The most common causes of chemical weathering are water, oxygen, and carbon dioxide from the air. Study the causes of chemical weathering shown below.

**Oxidation** ▲
What happens if you leave a steel hammer outside for a few days? It develops rust. Rust is the result of a type of chemical weathering called **oxidation**. Iron combines with oxygen in the air to form a substance called iron oxide, or rust. Rust isn't as strong as iron. Rust crumbles easily. When exposed to air, rocks containing iron become "rusty" and eventually fall apart.

**Water** ▶
Water can dissolve many minerals. Water also combines with gases in the air to form acids that can dissolve or change the composition of rocks.

As water dissolves the minerals, rocks either change in composition or fall apart. As shown in the photograph to the right, feldspar minerals combine with water to become clay minerals. The clay mineral kaolinite is an important ingredient of fine porcelain. ▶

## Social Studies Connection

Sulfuric acid in acid rain is destroying many of the world's ancient ruins, including the Parthenon in Athens, Greece; the Colosseum in Rome, Italy; and the Taj Mahal near Agra, India. The acid wears away the surfaces of these structures, as shown in the photograph of the lion's head. Discuss with students why acid disintegration of ancient ruins is a great loss to all people.

Chemical weathering breaks down minerals. Recall that minerals are the chemical compounds that make up rocks. Even though minerals are solids, many dissolve in water. A rock that contains a water-soluble mineral will slowly dissolve when the rock is exposed to water.

Acids also dissolve many minerals. Acids form when gases in the air dissolve in rainwater. For example, carbon dioxide dissolves in rainwater to form carbonic acid. Acids produced by plants and fungi break down rocks and help to form soil.

Rainwater carries dissolved minerals deeper into the ground in a process called **leaching**. Leaching changes the chemical composition of a soil. Leaching makes the surface soil mineral-poor. The leached minerals are deposited deeper down, forming a mineral-rich layer.

### ▼ ACTIVITY

#### Observing

**The Acid Test**

Observe the effect of weak acids on chalk. You can make a solution of carbonic acid by blowing through a soda straw into a glass of water. Lemon juice and vinegar are other weak acids you can try. What do your observations tell you about weak acids and chemical weathering?

**SKILLS WORKOUT**

### Sulfuric Acid

Burning coal and natural gas release sulfur dioxide gas into the air. Water vapor in the air combines with sulfur dioxide to form sulfuric acid. Sulfuric acid is a strong acid that easily dissolves rock and metals. When sulfuric acid falls to the earth as acid rain, it can harm plants and fishes. ▼

### Carbonation ▲

Weathering produced by carbonic acid is called **carbonation**. You can see the effects of carbonation on limestone and marble. The rock develops small pits or holes. Underground, carbonic acid dissolves limestone deposits. As the rock is eaten away, caverns and sinkholes form.

### Plant and Fungal Acids ▲

Some plants and fungi make acids that dissolve rocks and minerals. For example, the root tips of some plants produce a weak acid. The acid helps the roots burrow into cracks in the rock.

Lichens sometimes hug the surface of rocks. They often look like green, orange, or brown patches. Lichens contain fungi that produce a weak acid. The acid dissolves the surface of the rock beneath them.

## Skills WorkOut

To help students understand chemical weathering, have them do the Skills WorkOut.
**Answer** Weak acids react with chemicals in rock. But, the acids work slowly, so major changes take place over a long period of time.

## Directed Inquiry

Have students study the illustrations and text on this page. Ask the following questions:

▶ What is weathering caused by carbonic acid called? (Carbonation)

▶ What may form as a result of carbonic acid dissolving limestone deposits underground? (Caverns and sinkholes)

▶ How does sulfuric acid form in the air? (Water vapor combines with sulfur dioxide from burning coal and natural gas.)

▶ How does sulfuric acid affect rocks and metals? (It dissolves them easily.)

## Reteach

Use Reteach Worksheet 11.1.

 **The Living Textbook: Earth Science Sides 1-2**

Chapter 20          Frame 02712
Lichens (3 Frames)
Search:                    Step:

 **The Living Textbook: Earth Science Sides 1-2**

Chapter 9          Frame 01947
Acid Rain Damage (1 Frame)
Search:

## WrapUp

**Portfolio** Have students draw examples of each kind of mechanical and chemical weathering. Tell them to leave their drawings unlabeled. Have students exchange their work with other students and try to determine the kinds of weathering represented in their classmates' drawings. Afterward, students can label their drawings and keep them in their portfolios.

Use Review Worksheet 11.1.

## Check and Explain

1. Ice wedging (widens cracks), plant and animal weathering (roots of plants and digging and movement of animals widen cracks), temperature change (heat of day and cold nights crack rocks), and water and wind abrasion (particles wear away rocks)

2. Oxidation (iron and oxygen form rust, which weakens rocks), water (dissolves or changes minerals), carbonic acid, sulfuric acid, and acid in plants and fungi (dissolve rocks)

3. Rocks are broken apart by mechanical weathering, but are changed by chemical weathering. Over time, rocks are broken down by both kinds of weathering.

4. The rock with cracks would weather faster due to ice wedging and plant and animal weathering. Weathering is most rapid in warm, moist climates.

### Art Connection

Have students take rubbings from inscriptions on stone tombstones, keystones, manhole covers, or metal jewelry. Discuss why art historians might take rubbings from ancient monuments. (The rubbings serve as an easily stored record if the monument is destroyed.)

**Figure 11.2** ▲
Over time, the inscriptions on this granite obelisk have nearly disappeared.

### Science and Society    *Lost Inscriptions*

Ancient peoples around the world built monuments and buildings of stone. Many monuments are covered with detailed inscriptions carved thousands of years ago. The inscriptions record information about events and people in the distant past.

Ancient Egyptians inscribed stone temples and pointed stone towers called obelisks. Ancient people in Central America inscribed stone pyramids, temples, and pillars called stelae. In Asia, people inscribed stone pillars and temples, such as the one at Angkor Wat in Cambodia.

Exposed stone monuments are subject to weathering. Over time, weathering can wear away inscriptions, and the information they contain may be lost. The speed of weathering depends on the climate. Look at Figure 11.2. The granite obelisk now called Cleopatra's Needle was carved in Egypt more than 3,500 years ago. Very little weathering took place in Egypt's hot, dry climate.

In 1881, the obelisk was given by the Egyptian government as a gift to the people of New York City. When the obelisk arrived in New York, its inscriptions were clear and readable. But New York's temperate, humid climate weathered the stone quickly. Extremes of heat and cold caused mechanical weathering. City air caused chemical weathering by carbonation and sulfuric acid. After 100 years in New York City, the obelisk's inscriptions have almost disappeared.

### Check and Explain

1. What are the causes of mechanical weathering? Explain the effects of each cause.

2. What are the causes of chemical weathering? Explain the effects of each cause.

3. **Compare and Contrast** How are mechanical and chemical weathering different? How are they alike?

4. **Predict** Which rock would weather faster, a smooth rock or one with many cracks? Explain your choice. How would climate affect the rate of weathering? Explain.

## Themes in Science

**Diversity and Unity** All soils are formed from weathering and contain rock fragments, decayed organic matter, air, and water. However, the concentration and composition of each part of soil varies with the region where the soil forms. For this reason many different types of soil are found throughout the world.

# 11.2 Soils

## Objectives

▶ **List** the properties of soil.

▶ **Explain** how new soil forms.

▶ **Generalize** about how different soils can be produced in different areas.

▶ **Make a model** of a soil profile of a mature soil.

▼ **ACTIVITY**

### Inferring

*More Than Dirt*

Even if you live in a city, soil is important to you. List some ways that soil is part of your life. What would life be like without soil?

**SKILLS WARMUP**

I f you dig down under any grassy area, forest, or garden, you find layers of soil. A look into a deep hole often reveals many different-colored soil layers. Notice the soil layers in Figure 11.3. Over the course of a long car trip, you may observe that the soil doesn't look the same everywhere. Soil in fields and along the roadside varies in color and texture from place to place.

Soil covers most of the earth's land surfaces. Soil is essential for land plants, trees, and animal life. Plants grow by drawing up water and nutrients from the soil. Plants growing in soil provide food for people and animals. Many animals build their homes in the soil.

## Sources of Soil

Soil results from many years of weathering of the rocks on the earth's surface. All of the loose, weathered material that covers the surface of the earth is called the **regolith**. Soil is the top layer of the regolith that supports plant growth. The soil layer is usually 1-m to 3-m deep. The rock, the weathering processes, and the rate of weathering influence the type of soil that develops.

Soil contains rock fragments, decayed plant and animal matter, air, and water. All soils are not alike. The rock fragments come from different kinds of rocks. The plant and animal material varies. For example, soil samples from the East Coast, Midwest, Southwest, and West Coast regions of the United States look very different. Soil samples taken from different parts of the world show even more variety.

**Figure 11.3** ▲
Look at the cross-section of soil at this construction site. What soil materials do you see under the layer of paving? ①

### Section Objectives
For a list of section objectives, see the Student Edition page.

### Skills Objectives
Students should be able to:

**Infer** how soil affects life.

**Observe** particles and organisms in soil.

**Model** mature soil.

**Interpret Data** about the permeability of sand, soil, and gravel.

### Vocabulary
regolith, parent rock, soil profile, horizon, humus

**MOTIVATE**

### Skills WarmUp
To help students understand the importance of soil, have them do the Skills WarmUp.
**Answer** Students' lists will vary. Examples might include: parks, food for trees and farm crops. Students should convey the idea that life would be impossible without soil.

### Misconceptions
Students may think that soil is inorganic. Point out that one ingredient of any soil is bacteria, whose respiration gives soil its odor. The bodies of dead bacteria also make up much of the organic bulk of soil.

**Answer to In-Text Question**

① **Answers may include rock fragments, plants, and water.**

🔘 **The Living Textbook: Earth Science Sides 1-2**

Chapter 34          Frame 07875
Soil Definition (2 Frames)
Search:                    Step:

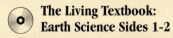

## TEACH

### Skills Development

**Infer** Have students consider how the parent rock influences the kind of soil formed. Ask: If sandstone is the parent rock, what would you expect to find in the soil that is formed? (You would expect to find sand.)

### Directed Inquiry

Have students study the illustrations and text on this page. Ask the following questions:

▶ What forces split parent rock into blocks or boulders? (Mechanical and chemical weathering processes)

▶ What happens to parent rock as more surface is exposed? Why? (Weathering increases because more surfaces are exposed to weathering.)

▶ What happens when plants begin to grow on the weathered rocks? (They attract insects and other animals, and fungi grow around their roots.)

▶ What happens to the dead plant and animal materials? (They are decayed by bacteria and fungi to form a top layer of organic matter.)

▶ What does topsoil contain? (Decayed matter, plant roots, living organisms, sediment)

▶ How does the burrowing of earthworms affect mature soil? (The action mixes organic matter with tiny rock particles under the topsoil.)

**The Living Textbook: Earth Science Sides 1-2**

Chapter 34          Frame 07877
Soil Diagram (1 Frame)
Search:

246

### Language Arts Connection

Have students discuss the general meaning of the words *parent*, *immature*, and *mature*. Record a class definition of each word on the board. Then ask students to explain how each term describes a phase in soil development.

## Soil Development

One of the main ingredients of soil is rock fragments from bedrock or other rock. The rock that breaks apart to produce the fragments found in a soil is called its **parent rock**. The mineral composition of the parent rock affects the composition of the resulting soil.

The types of weathering processes that break down the parent rock also affect the type of soil that forms. Climate and living organisms also play an important role. Decaying plant and animal matter mix with rock fragments and clays as a soil develops. Study the illustrations on this page to see how soil forms from parent rock.

**Weathered Parent Rock** The parent rock develops cracks. Mechanical and chemical weathering processes split the parent rock into blocks or boulders. As more surface is exposed, weathering increases. Large fragments break into smaller ones. Water and carbonic acid dissolve minerals in the rock. The rock fragments begin to disintegrate.

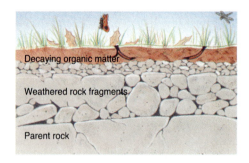

**Immature Soil** Small hardy plants start to grow. The plants attract insects and other small animals. Fungi grow around the plant roots. Dead plant and animal materials build up and are decayed by bacteria and fungi. The decaying organic material forms a layer on top of and within the weathered rock.

**Mature Soil** Plants and dead plant debris cover the soil surface. Under the surface, the topsoil contains a mix of decayed organic matter, plant roots, living organisms, and sediment. Earthworms and other burrowing organisms mix some organic matter with tiny rock particles. Water leaches out minerals and fine clay particles. A layer of mineral-rich clay forms above the weathered parent rock.

## Integrating the Sciences

**Life Science** Have students list ideal soil conditions for a vegetable garden. Make sure that students consider the size and shape of the soil particles, plant nutrients, and the acid level of the soil.

**Use Integrating Worksheet 11.2a.**

**Chemistry** Plant nutrients dissolved in water form ions. Ions have a positive or a negative charge. The surface of soil particles are also charged. Have students look at Figure 11.5 and determine the charge of soil particles in the drawing. (Negative) Ask which ions are attracted to these particles and why. (Positive, because opposite charges attract)

### Skills Development

**Infer** Ask: What shape do clay particles have? Why? (Since water doesn't tend to move easily through it, its particles must fit together more tightly. Therefore, they must be angular or flat.)

### Critical Thinking

**Compare and Contrast** Have students compare particle shape and size with respect to water retention. Ask: Which shape and size is easiest for allowing water to pass through? The most difficult? (Large, rounded particles are easiest for allowing water through. Small, flat particles are the most difficult for allowing water through.)

**Find Causes** Ask: Why is watering important to plant growth? Why is it harmful to overwater a garden with fertile soil? (Plant nutrients dissolve in water and are taken into plants with water intake. Water can also wash nutrients out of the soil if too much runs off the parent rock.)

### Ancillary Options

If you are using CEPUP modules in your classroom for additional hands-on activities, experiments, and exercises, begin *The Waste Hierarchy: Where Is "Away"?* Activities 1–6.

If you are using the blackline masters from *Muticulturalism in Mathematics, Science, and Technology*, have students read about George Washington Carver and complete pages 39 to 41.

### Soil Properties

In addition to mineral composition, soils have many other properties.

**Particle Shape** Some soil particles are rounded, some are flat, and some are angular. The particle shape affects the amount of pore space in the soil. Rounded particles don't pack together very tightly. So a soil with rounded particles has more pore space and can hold more water. Water moves easily through interconnected pore spaces. If the particles are angular or flat, they fit together more tightly. As a result, there isn't as much pore space. Water can't move through as easily.

**Particle Size** Clays contain the smallest particles. Slightly larger particles are called silt. Sand particles are slightly larger than silt particles. Particle size affects the amount of pore space in a soil. Soils with a mixture of particle sizes have less pore space. Smaller particles fill in the spaces around the larger ones. Compare the effects of particle size and shape in Figure 11.4.

**Fertility** A fertile soil contains many plant nutrients. Look at Figure 11.5. Available nutrients, dissolved in water, are part of the soil solution. Some of the nutrients cling to the surface of soil particles. The six most important plant nutrients are nitrogen (N), phosphorus (P), potassium (K), calcium (Ca), magnesium (Mg), and sulfur (S). Nitrogen, phosphorus, and sulfur come from the action of bacteria and the decay of plants and animals. Other nutrients come from the weathering of mineral-rich bedrock.

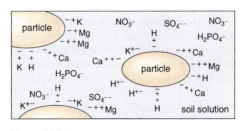

**Figure 11.5** ▲
Plant nutrients are dissolved in water.

**Acid Level** Two factors affect a soil's acid level. One factor is the type of organic matter in the soil. The other factor is the kind of minerals that weather out of the parent rock. For example, pine needles produce acids as they decay. So the soil in a pine forest is very acidic. Chemical weathering of igneous parent rocks also produces acidic soils.

The acid level of a soil affects plant growth. Farmers and gardeners need to know how acidic or basic, and how fertile their soil is before deciding what to plant. They can send soil samples to be tested in a laboratory. Then they can either choose appropriate plants or adjust the soil. They can add fertilizers to infertile soils and lime to acidic soils.

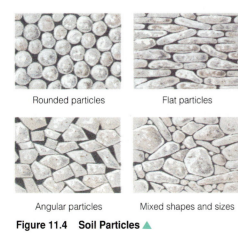

Rounded particles      Flat particles

Angular particles      Mixed shapes and sizes

**Figure 11.4   Soil Particles** ▲

◄ **TEACH ▪ Continued**

## Enrich

Tell students that soil scientists are called *pedologists* after the term *ped*, the Greek word for soil or ground, and *ology*, which means the study of. Pedologists describe soils by the characteristics of the soil horizons, including color, texture, structure, and chemical conditions.

## Class Activity

Use a clear plastic bottle and common materials, such as rice, breakfast cereal, or bits of discarded paper, to make a soil profile model. Have students use tape and markers to label the various horizons. Ask students to choose one soil horizon and describe its history and makeup.

## Integrated Learning

Use Integrating Worksheet 11.2b.

### Themes in Science

**Stability and Equilibrium** Mature soils have reached equilibrium. A mature soil typically consists of a top layer of living vegetation, three soil horizons, and parent rock material. Each layer has a stable structure and a specific location in the soil profile.

## Soil Profiles

What do you see if you dig a hole down through the regolith to the bedrock? The side of the hole shows a **soil profile**. A soil profile is a cross section of the layers of soil.

All mature soils have three distinct layers, called **horizons**. However, in some soils, the boundary between each horizon is gradual and hard to see. Also, the boundaries between horizons can be wavy or irregular instead of flat. Study the soil horizons in Figure 11.6. Each horizon looks different from the others and is different in composition.

The uppermost layer is the *A* horizon, also called the topsoil. The *A* horizon contains rock particles mixed with **humus** (HYOO muhs). Humus is decayed plant and animal matter. It gives the soil a rich,

dark color. Humus is a major source of plant nutrients. It has a spongy texture and helps the soil hold water. Humus also keeps the soil from becoming packed down.

Beneath the *A* horizon lies the *B* horizon, also called the subsoil. As water moves down through the *A* horizon, it leaches out minerals such as iron. The water also moves small clay and silt particles. The particles and dissolved minerals build up in the *B* horizon. Therefore, the *B* horizon has a higher clay and iron content and is sometimes a reddish color.

Below the *B* horizon and just above the bedrock is the *C* horizon. The *C* horizon is the layer of rock that is actively weathering. Small rock particles build up at the top of the *C* horizon. Large particles stay near the bottom. The *C* horizon rarely contains organic matter.

**Figure 11.6  Sample Soil Profile** ▼

On top is usually a layer of undecayed plant and animal material.

The *A* horizon is a mixture of tiny rock particles and humus. Pore spaces allow air and water in.

The *B* horizon is made up of minerals, silt, and clay particles leached down by water.

The *C* horizon contains rock fragments weathered from the parent rock.

Below the *C* horizon is unaltered parent rock.

## Math Connection

Have students use the information in Table 11.1 to make a bar graph comparing the number of organisms in soil. Tell students to convert the number of organisms per m² to scientific notation with the same base 10 exponent. For example, all of the numbers can be converted to scientific notation based on $10^5$. After students complete their bar graphs, ask: Which organism is the most plentiful? (Bacteria) Which organism is the least plentiful? (Mites)

## Soil Organisms

Think about the smell of freshly turned soil. The earthy odor you think of as the smell of soil is produced by a soil organism called *Streptomyces*. In addition to supporting plant growth, soil itself contains a large number of organisms. Some soil organisms are large enough to see, but most are microscopic. The most common soil organisms are bacteria and fungi. Just 1 g of soil may contain several million bacteria, an equal amount of fungi, and more than 100,000 protozoa.

Larger, but still tiny soil organisms include mites, springtails, nematodes, and insect larvae. Some examples are shown in Figure 11.7. Study Table 11.1 to compare the numbers of organisms in an area of soil 1 m² at the surface and extending down to the bedrock. Most soil organisms feed on organic matter in the soil, or on other soil organisms. The number of organisms living in the soil varies with local conditions. For example, fungi are the most common organisms in the acid soil of a forest, but bacteria are more common in neutral grassland soil.

Many larger animals also live in the topsoil. Worms, insects, grubs, slugs, gophers, moles, groundhogs, and rabbits are just a few of them. These animals perform several important functions. By digging through the soil, animals help to maintain the flow of water and air into the soil. Through their bodily functions—such as eating, digesting, and excreting—the animals help change the soil chemically. Finally, when they die, they become part of the soil itself as their bodies decay into humus.

**Table 11.1   Soil Organisms**

| Organism | Number per m² |
|---|---|
| Bacteria | $2.6 \times 10^{14}$ |
| Fungi | $8 \times 10^{12}$ |
| Algae | $3 \times 10^{10}$ |
| Protozoa | $7 \times 10^{12}$ |
| Nematodes | 250,000 |
| Springtails | 100,000 |
| Mites | 50,000 |
| Crustaceans | $4 \times 10^{13}$ |

Springtails

Nematodes and fungi (200x)

Pseudoscorpion (32x)

▲ **Figure 11.7**
Millions of tiny organisms like these live in the soil.

## Class Activity

Have students work in small groups. Provide each group with two samples of freshly dug soil. One sample should be moist and the other dry. Have students smell the two kinds of soil. Explain that *Streptomyces* produces chemical by-products when it is active. The chemicals give soil much of its odor. Ask:

▶ Which soil type, the moist or dry sample, has the stronger odor? (Moist)

▶ What does this tell you about *Streptomyces*? (Water makes the soil organism active.)

## Critical Thinking

**If . . . Then Arguments** Have students discuss the flaw in the following argument: If there are several million bacteria, an equal number of fungi, and more than 100,000 protozoa in 1 gram of soil, then there is no space for sand and other inorganic particles in that sample. To aid the discussion, give students the following average sizes of these organisms: bacteria—1.5 microns, or 0.0015 millimeter; fungi—5 microns, or 0.005 millimeter; protozoa—20 microns, or 0.02 millimeter. (Bacteria, fungi, and protozoa are so minute in size that there is plenty of room in 1 gram of soil to accommodate large numbers of soil organisms and still have room for inorganic particles.)

**Themes in Science**

**Systems and Interactions** Soil has an important role in land ecosystems. Its many functions maintain the flow of energy between plants, animals, and the atmosphere.

### Explore Visually

Have students study this page. Discuss soil ecology by asking the following questions:

▶ What are decomposers? What do they do for soil? (Decomposers are the bacteria and fungi in the soil that decompose dead plants and animals; release nutrients into soil.)

▶ What do soil bacteria have to do with the nitrogen and phosphorus cycles? (One group of bacteria releases phosphorus from organic matter. Another group takes in nitrogen gas from the air and puts it in the soil.)

▶ Which organisms are producers, and which are consumers? (Plants are producers, and animals are consumers.)

▶ What happens to the water plants take in from the soil? (It moves up through their stems and out through their leaves.)

▶ What do plants use to produce plant materials? (Energy from the sun, minerals from the soil, and carbon dioxide from the air)

▶ What gases do plants take in and release? (They take in carbon dioxide and release oxygen.)

▶ What gases do animals take in and release? (They take in oxygen and release carbon dioxide.)

▶ How do animals get energy? (They eat plants or other animals.)

## Soil Ecology

Soil plays an important role in energy flow and nutrient cycling. Study Figure 11.8. Plants, which depend on mineral nutrients from soil, capture the sun's energy and store it. Animals use the captured energy, in the form of plant material, as food. For this reason, plants are called producers, and animals are called consumers.

Soil organisms, such as bacteria and fungi, are called decomposers. They break down dead leaves, wood, and animal remains, releasing mineral nutrients back into the soil.

Soil bacteria are part of the global nitrogen and phosphorus cycles. One group of soil bacteria releases phosphorus from organic matter. Another group of soil bacteria takes in nitrogen gas from the air and puts it in the soil.

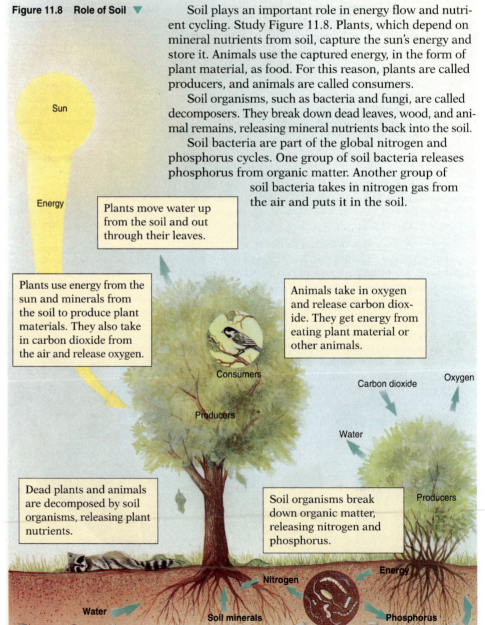

**Figure 11.8 Role of Soil ▼**

Sun

Energy

Plants move water up from the soil and out through their leaves.

Plants use energy from the sun and minerals from the soil to produce plant materials. They also take in carbon dioxide from the air and release oxygen.

Animals take in oxygen and release carbon dioxide. They get energy from eating plant material or other animals.

Consumers

Producers

Carbon dioxide

Oxygen

Water

Dead plants and animals are decomposed by soil organisms, releasing plant nutrients.

Soil organisms break down organic matter, releasing nitrogen and phosphorus.

Producers

Energy

Nitrogen

Water

Soil minerals

Decomposers

Phosphorus

## Multicultural Perspectives

Agriculture first developed in Egypt's Nile Valley and in Mesopotamia, a region between the Tigris and Euphrates rivers. Ancient Mesopotamia includes areas in today's Iraq and portions of Iran, Syria, and Turkey. Locate these areas on a climate map. Ask students what type of soil might be common in these areas today.

## Art Connection

Have students make drawings, collages, or sculptures from clay products, such as modeling clay, pencil lead, bricks, or glossy photos clipped from magazines.

# Historical Notebook

## Ancient Agriculture

In prehistoric times, people hunted animals and gathered wild plants for food. But at least 18,000 years ago, people began farming. Ancient farmers poked holes in the ground with sticks and planted seeds they collected from wild grass. They farmed areas such as river deltas, where the ground was soft and easy to work. Wheat, barley, lentils, and chickpeas were grown in Africa 18,000 years ago. Corn was grown in North America 7,000 years ago. Rice began to be cultivated in Asia about 6,000 years ago.

As farming became a way of life, people developed farming technology. By 6,000 years ago, farmers were plowing their fields using animals dragging logs. About 4,800 years ago, the sickle was developed. The sickle, used for harvesting, had a curved handle made of wood or bone and a flint stone for a blade. About 3,500 years ago, metal plows began to be used.

1. Why did ancient people farm river deltas? What other areas might they have used as farm technology improved? Explain.

2. **Research** Many farmers still use sickles, plows, and other tools developed thousands of years ago. Do library research on farming techniques in other parts of the world. Write a one-page report.

### Science and You  *Everyday Uses of Soil*

You may eat from dinner plates made from a soil component, clay. Clay is easy to shape and hardens when dry. When fired at high temperatures, clay becomes very hard and shiny. You may attend classes in a brick building. Bricks are also made from fired clay. Even your pencil contains clay. The clay is mixed with graphite, a soft black mineral, and then fired to make pencil lead. Clay also coats the shiny paper you see in magazines.

## Check and Explain

1. List three important properties of soil.

2. Describe how a soil forms.

3. **Generalize** Why do different locations have different kinds of soil?

4. **Model** Draw or make a soil profile of a mature soil.

## ▼ ACTIVITY

### Observing

**Down in the Dirt**

Obtain a sample of fresh soil.

1. Using a hand lens, examine the soil closely.

2. Describe the types of soil particles you observe and any soil organisms you find.

3. Make a drawing to record your observations.

**SKILLS WORKOUT**

## Historical Notebook

**Answers**

1. Ancient people farmed deltas because the soil was soft and easy to work. Low and flat areas were used later because sickles and plows could be used there.

2. Students should mention subsistence farming, which is common in Africa, Asia, and Latin America.

## Skills WorkOut

To help students observe substances contained in soil, have them do the Skills WorkOut.
**Answer** Encourage students to be specific in their descriptions of the particles they observe.

## EVALUATE

## WrapUp

**Review** Diagram a typical soil ecosystem on the chalkboard. Use Figure 11.8 on page 250 as a guide. Include blank boxes in the diagram. Have volunteers fill in the blanks with the appropriate labels. Then have student volunteers describe the flow of energy in soil ecology.

Use Review Worksheet 11.2.

## Check and Explain

1. Mineral composition, particle shape and size, and fertility

2. Parent rock weathers, plants grow, insects and other animals move in, fungi and bacteria decompose dead materials, earthworms turn the soil over, and clay and minerals leach out of the topsoil.

3. Different locations have different parent rock, climates, and organisms living in or on the soil.

4. Students should show the three soil horizons, the parent rock, and the layer of undecayed materials on top.

**Time** 30 minutes   **Group** 3

**Materials**

30 paper cups

30 small wood blocks or rocks

10 shallow dishes or saucers

30 coffee filters, or paper filters

sand

soil

gravel

10 measuring cups

10 metric rulers

10 pairs of scissors

clock or watch with second hand

## Analysis

1. Students' rates will vary. Make sure the calculated rate agrees with the time and volume data.

2. The gravel should have the highest drainage rate, while the soil should have the lowest. Make sure students' answers agree with data.

3. Gravel, sand, soil

4. Gravel, sand, soil

## Conclusion

The larger the particles are, the more permeable the soil sample.

## Extension

Mixing the samples together would yield a permeability lower than any of the three soil types alone. The smaller particles of the sand and the soil would fill up the spaces between bits of gravel. A possible hypothesis: A mixture of sand, soil, and gravel is less permeable than soil, sand, or gravel alone.

---

## TEACHING OPTIONS

### Prelab Discussion

Have students read the entire activity. Discuss these points before beginning:

▶ Remind students of the definition of *permeable*.

▶ Discuss the importance of the size and number of holes poked in the bottom of the cups.

▶ Discuss the effect of the filter paper on the data.

## *Activity 11*  *How permeable is it?*

**Skills**  Model; Observe; Interpret Data

### Task 1  Prelab Prep

1. Collect the following items: 3 paper cups; pencil; scissors; 3 pieces of filter paper or coffee filters; one sample each of sand, soil, and gravel; metric ruler; measuring cup; water; clock or watch; 3 small blocks of wood or 3 small rocks; a shallow dish or saucer.

2. Using your pencil point, make eight small holes in the bottom of each cup. Label the cups *Sand, Soil,* and *Gravel.*

3. Cut circles from the filter paper to fit into the bottom of each cup.

### Task 2  Data Record

1. Copy Table 11.2. Record the amount of water poured into each cup and the time the water takes to drain.

2. After the experiment, calculate the drainage rate for each type of soil. Record the drainage rate in your table.

### Task 3  Procedure

1. Mark a line 5 cm up from the bottom of each cup. Fill to this line with the sand, soil, or gravel, according to the label on the cup.

2. Look at Figure 11.9. Set the sand-filled cup in the dish on top of the blocks or rocks. Be sure the blocks don't cover the holes.

3. Measure out 100 mL of water. Start timing as you pour the water into the cup. Finish timing when no more water drains from the cup. Record the time on your chart.

**Figure 11.9 ▲**

4. Pour the water in the shallow dish into your measuring cup. Record this amount.

5. Repeat steps 2, 3, and 4 with the other two cups.

### Task 4  Analysis

1. In Table 11.2, calculate the drainage rate for each sample. Divide the amount of water that drained into the saucer by the time it took to drain. Record the drainage rates.

2. Which sample had the highest drainage rate? Which sample had the lowest rate?

3. List the samples in order of particle size from largest to smallest.

4. If a sample with the highest drainage rate is the most permeable, order the samples from most permeable to least permeable.

### Task 5  Conclusion

Write a short paragraph explaining how particle size can affect the permeability of a soil sample.

### *Extension*

How might permeability be affected if the samples were mixed together? Propose a hypothesis, and test it.

**Table 11.2  Permeability Data**

| Soil Type | Time | Amount of Water | Drainage Rate |
|-----------|------|-----------------|---------------|
| Sand | | | |
| Soil | | | |
| Gravel | | | |

### Cooperative Learning

Have students work in pairs to make a table showing the countries that contain each soil type. Use a world map and the map in Figure 11.10 to classify the locations of the six types of soil.

**Section Objectives**
For a list of section objectives, see the Student Edition page.

**Skills Objectives**
Students should be able to:

**Classify** soils by location.

**Classify** soils based on characteristics.

**Vocabulary**
podsol, laterite

## 11.3 World Soil Types

### Objectives

▶ **Describe** seven types of soil.

▶ **Identify** soil types by geographic location and climate.

▶ **Compare** and **contrast** the major soil types

▶ **Classify** soils by their characteristics.

**▼ ACTIVITY**

**Classifying**

*I Just Mopped the Floor*

What type of soil is usually found near a beach? What type of soil would you find in a swamp? If your shoes were covered with dark, slimy mud, which area did you walk through, a beach or a swamp? Explain.

**SKILLS WARMUP**

D id you know that detectives can use soil samples from suspects' shoes to prove they were at the scene of a crime? How does identifying soil help solve a crime? The reason is that soil varies from place to place.

Although there are thousands of different soils, people have developed ways to classify soils into groups. One way to classify soils is by the environment in which the soil was formed. For example, soil formed in a tropical environment differs from soil formed in a desert environment. Look at Figure 11.10. Notice the distribution of soil types formed in different environments around the world.

**MOTIVATE**

### Skills WarmUp

To help students understand how soil types are related to location, have them do the Skills WarmUp. **Answer** Sand; dark, nutrient-rich soil; through a swamp. Swamps have wet dirt that is much more likely to be muddy than sandy.

### Misconceptions

Students may think that all soil is the same, even though it has different names. Remind students of the distinct soil components they may have handled, such as ceramic clay, sand, peat, or concrete. Explain that each of these components, in varying amounts, would form soil with different properties.

**Figure 11.10  Map of Soil Types ▼**

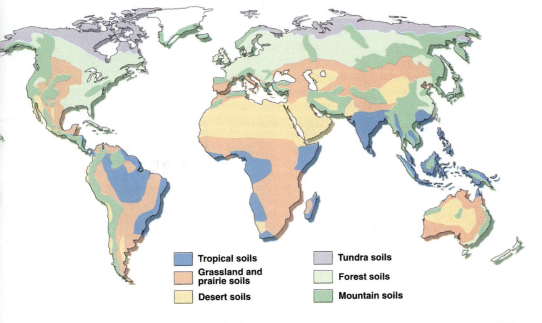

| | | |
|---|---|---|
| ■ Tropical soils | ■ Tundra soils | |
| ■ Grassland and prairie soils | ■ Forest soils | |
| ■ Desert soils | ■ Mountain soils | |

### Skills Development

**Infer** Have students compare the *A* horizon in forest soils to the *B* horizon. Ask: Why is the *B* horizon usually red or brown in color? (This indicates the presence of red or brown minerals, such as iron. It is these minerals that leach from the *A* horizon and build up in the *B* horizon.)

### Consider This

**Think About It** Answers will vary. Evaluations should take into account what will happen to people if the cutting of forests is restricted, or if people are allowed to cut as many trees as they want.

**Debate It** Students should choose a position after reading about the issue and then be ready to defend their position with reasons.

**Answer to In-Text Question**

**① Rainwater, leaves and needles, organic acids**

## Integrating the Sciences

**Environmental Science** Tropical forests, home to the greatest diversity of species on earth, are being cleared for lumber, farms, villages, and roads. Researchers estimate that an area of tropical forest the size of Great Britain is destroyed every year. If this trend continues, researchers predict that 15 percent to 20 percent of all species will be extinct by the year 2000.

## Forest Soils

Forest soils occur in areas of heavy rainfall and changing temperatures. Look at the soil profile of a forest soil in Figure 11.11. Above the topsoil is a layer of dead leaves, needles, and twigs. Rainwater leaches organic acids from the dead plant material into the topsoil. The acidic water leaches minerals and clay particles out of the topsoil. As a result, the lower part of the *A* horizon of a forest soil is usually thin, sandy, and light-colored.

Insoluble iron, aluminum, and clays build up in the *B* horizon. Therefore, the *B* horizon is usually red or brown in color. Although the composition of forest soils varies, the acidic leaching causes a similar

**Figure 11.11 ▲**
What materials help produce forest soils? ①

soil profile to form. A soil formed in this way is called a **podsol**. Podsols are generally not very fertile because of the thin topsoil. Trees can grow because they have deep roots.

## Consider This

### Should the Cutting of Forests Be Restricted?

All over the world, people have been cutting down forests. Sometimes, the forests have grown back. But worldwide, about 30 to 50 percent of the forests that were cut down have not grown back.

People cut down forests mainly to clear land for farming and to obtain firewood and lumber. As the world's population grows, people need more farmland to grow food. In many areas, firewood is essential for cooking and heating. People need lumber to build homes. In rural areas, the lumber industry provides needed jobs.

Forests play an important role in the environment. The trees give off oxygen and take in carbon dioxide. They also move water up from the soil into the atmosphere. Through these processes, a forest helps maintain the balance of gases and moisture in the air. When a forest is cut down, the balance of gases in the air is affected. After a forest is cut down, newly exposed soils can blow or wash away. Also, cutting forests destroys the homes of other plants and animals.

**Think About It**
What might happen to people and the environment if the cutting of forests is restricted? If people cut as much as they want?

**Debate It** Find out more about all sides of the forest-cutting issue. Choose a position.

## Social Studies Connection

In 1803 the United States bought the Louisiana Territory from France. The territory included more than 2 million square kilometers of prairie and grasslands stretching from the Mississippi River to the Rocky Mountains. Have students find out what states were later formed from the Louisiana Territory.

## Multicultural Perspectives

For centuries the Great Plains of the United States were home for many Native American tribes. Plains tribes included the Commanche, Cheyenne, Sioux, and many others. Have each student write a report or create an informative poster on one Plains tribe. Student volunteers may want to present their report to the class or to display their posters on a bulletin board.

## Prairie Soils

Prairie soil regions don't get quite as much rain as forest soil regions. So there is less leaching of minerals, and the topsoil is very deep and rich in humus and nutrients. Look at Figure 11.12. Prairie soils are fertile and productive soils. A major crop grown in prairie soil regions is corn.

Prairie soil regions in the central United States contain deposits of fine-grained angular particles called *loess* (LOH ehs). The particles were produced as moving glaciers scoured rocks during the last ice age. As the glaciers retreated, meltwater formed many streams and deposited glacial sediments in front of the melting ice. Strong winds picked up and carried away silt-sized particles and piled them up into thick layers.

Winds can carry the fine prairie soil particles away if they are not held together by plant roots. For example, during a drought in the 1930s, the dry, bare soils were blown away by the wind. The area in which this disaster occurred was named the Dust Bowl. The land lost all of its topsoil, so no crops could grow.

## Grassland Soils

Grassland soils get even less rain than prairie soils. Because of the smaller amount of rainfall, the grassland topsoil isn't leached very much. The soil mineral calcium isn't dissolved away. The calcium remains in the *A* horizon, giving the topsoil a whitish color. Look at the soil profile of a grassland soil in Figure 11.13. Soils in drier grassland regions often contain whitish calcium deposits.

The thick grassland topsoil is rich in humus from decaying grass stems and leaves. Food crops that are grasses, such as wheat and rye, grow well in grassland areas around the world. Grassland areas also support large herds of grazing animals, such as buffalo, cattle, and sheep. Important grassland areas around the world include the Great Plains region of North America, the pampas region in South America, and the steppes regions of central Asia.

**Figure 11.12** ▲
This tallgrass prairie has soil with a very thick layer of organic matter.

**Figure 11.13** ▲
A grassland soil has less organic matter than a prairie soil.

## Critical Thinking

**Compare and Contrast**  Have students compare and contrast forest soils and prairie soils. Ask the following questions:

▶ What is the difference between the amounts of humus and nutrients contained in the two soils? Why? (Prairie soils have more humus and nutrients than forest soils. Because prairie soils get less rainfall than forest soils, less leaching occurs.)

▶ If a forest were cut down to use the land for food crops, would soil of the cleared forest be as productive as prairie soil? Why or why not? (Cleared forest soil would not be as productive as prairie soil. Forest soil has fewer nutrients in it due to the leaching of its minerals.)

▶ Have students compare the profile of a grassland soil in Figure 11.13 with the profile of a prairie soil in Figure 11.12. Ask: Which soil is richer and more productive? Why? (The prairie soil is more productive. It has a thick layer of organic matter and gets more rainfall than the grassland soil.)

## Integrated Learning

Use Integrating Worksheet 11.3.

## Enrich

Tell students that the Soil Survey of the United States Department of Agriculture uses a system that consists of ten orders of soils: alfisols, aridisols, entisols, histosols, inceptisols, mollisols, oxisols, spodosols, ultisols, and vertisols. Ask students which of these ten orders they think probably describes desert soils. (Aridisols, judging from the root "arid")

## Discuss

Have students think about the development of mountain soils. Ask:

▶ Why can't mature soils build up on mountains? (Gravity pulls them downhill.)

▶ Where does organic matter build up on mountains? (In depressions)

▶ Why does the side of the mountain facing the wind have better soils and more trees and shrubs than the opposite side? (The side facing the wind has more rainfall.)

▶ In what part of the world can you find thicker mountain soils? Why? (They are found in tropical mountain areas because soil can develop rapidly.)

### Cooperative Learning

Have students work in cooperative groups of three to determine the organic content of soil. Obtain two lidded jars, two different soil samples, water, a measuring cup, and a spoon. Fill each jar one-third full with a different soil sample. Add the same amount of water to each jar. Secure the lids and shake each jar for one minute. Leave the jars undisturbed for one day. Then compare the amount of floating organic material in each jar. The jar with the most floating material has the greater concentration of organic matter.

## Desert Soils

In areas of little or almost no rainfall, desert soils form. Desert soils are only slightly weathered and leached. As a result, desert soils are rich in minerals. Look at the profile of a desert soil in Figure 11.14. Only plants adapted to dry conditions, such as cacti, grow in deserts. Because of the scarcity of plants, there is little organic matter available to form humus.

Despite the lack of humus, desert soils can be very fertile because of the high mineral content. Farmers in the western United States use irrigation to add water to the desert soil. With water, sunshine, and minerals, crops grow easily. But years of irrigation can make the soil become salty. Fresh water contains salts. As the water evaporates, it leaves the salt behind. Crops don't grow well in salty soil. The flow of irrigation water also leaches out the needed soil minerals.

**Figure 11.15** ▲
A thin layer of rocky soil can form on the slopes of mountains.

## Mountain Soils

In the mountains, the soils are usually rocky and thin. Mountain slopes are too steep for mature soils to develop. As soon as soil builds up, gravity starts to pull it downhill. Look at the mountain in Figure 11.15. On the high slopes, there are only weathered chunks of rock, with little organic matter. Where trees and shrubs grow, organic matter can build up in depressions, producing a thin rocky layer of acidic soil.

Rainfall and wind cause soil conditions to vary from one side of a mountain to the other. On the side facing the wind, there is usually more rainfall. The rainy side can usually support the growth of trees and shrubs. But on the opposite side, there will be almost no trees or shrubs.

Mountain soils aren't usually good places to grow crops because of the steep slopes and thin soil. But in tropical mountain areas, thicker soils can develop. In South America and Africa, farmers grow coffee in the mountain soil.

**Figure 11.14** ▲
A desert soil has very little organic matter and is rich in minerals.

## *Integrating the Sciences*

**Life Science** A surprisingly large number of animal species are adapted to the harsh conditions of the tundra. Some of these animals include the Arctic wolf, Arctic fox, ermine, caribou, collared lemming, snowshoe hare, rodents, and migratory birds. The tundra has a short growing season and supports only small plants. Ask students to infer how so many animals survive this harsh environment.

## Tundra Soils

In polar regions with very cold temperatures and little rainfall, tundra soils form. The deep layer of subsoil in polar regions is permanently frozen and is called *permafrost*. Above the permafrost is a soil layer that freezes in the winter and thaws out in the summer. When it thaws, the soil stays waterlogged because the water can't drain off through the permafrost. Evaporation occurs very slowly because of low air temperatures. Humus forms very slowly in these conditions. Therefore, tundra topsoil is usually black or brown and contains undecayed plant material. Look at the soil profile of a tundra soil in Figure 11.16.

Plants that grow in tundra soil are usually small with shallow roots. Tundra plants must grow quickly to take advantage of the short summer. Because only a small amount of organic matter is produced each year, tundra soils take a long time to build up. If disturbed, tundra soils recover very slowly.

## Tropical Soils

Tropical soils form in areas of heavy rainfall and year-round warm temperatures. Chemical weathering occurs rapidly, and very thick layers of mineral soil build up. But the frequent rains cause heavy leaching. Almost everything, including the quartz, is leached out. Only aluminum clays and iron oxide, or rust, remain. These two minerals don't dissolve easily in water. The resulting soil, called **laterite** (LAYT er IGHT), is rusty red in color, due to the iron oxide.

The topsoil of laterites contains little humus. Humus can't build up because organic matter decays quickly in a tropical environment. The nutrients are immediately used for new plant growth. Look at the soil profile of a tropical soil in Figure 11.17. The topsoil lacks minerals because of the leaching.

If the tropical rain forest is cut down, the soil changes dramatically. Without the trees, the clay-rich soil bakes in the sun to a bricklike hardness.

**Figure 11.16** ▲
Tundra soils have a layer of undecayed plant material on top of permafrost.

A
B
C

**Figure 11.17** ▲
Tropical soils have thick layers of leached clays.

## Skills Development

**Infer** Ask students why tundra soils contain undecayed plant material. (During the summer, the soils are waterlogged because water cannot drain off through the permafrost. As a result, the plant material in the soil cannot decay.)

## Research

Have students use references to find out what happens when tropical rain forests are logged or burned to provide land for grazing animals and farming. Have them find out what happens to the soil over time and how people and animal life are affected by changes in the soil.

## Critical Thinking

**Compare and Contrast** Have students compare tropical soils to forest soils. Ask: How are the soils alike and how are they different? (They are alike in that both have heavy rainfall and, as a result, heavy leaching. They differ in that tropical soils have year-round warm temperatures and thick layers of mineral soil. Tropical soils have less humus because humus is rapidly broken down and used for new plant growth in tropical environments.)

## TEACH ▪ *Continued*

### Research

Have students use references to find out about the deserts of the Middle East. Pose the question: Is overgrazing responsible for the formation of these desert areas?

## EVALUATE

### WrapUp

**Review** Have students list each type of soil on one side of a flashcard and their characteristics on the other. Have them quiz one another on the soils.

Use Review Worksheet 11.3.

### Check and Explain

1. Forest soils—changing temperatures, heavy rains; prairie soils—less rain than forests, has loess; grassland soils—plains region with less rain than prairies; desert soils—little or no rain; mountain soils—cold temperatures, little rain; tropical soils—heavy rain, year-round warm temperatures; tundra soils—very cold temperatures and very little rainfall

2. Laterite is a rusty red soil made of iron oxide and clays.

3. Forest soils and tropical soils undergo extensive leaching. Prairie and grassland soils have less leaching because they have less rainfall.

4. The type of soil is prairie soil because it has loess, some leaching, rich humus, and rich nutrients.

### *Themes in Science*
#### Patterns of Change/Cycles

Large herds of grazing animals have affected the natural cycle of soil production in some grasslands. These herds have destroyed the plant cover through overgrazing. The lack of plant cover exposes the soil to erosion by wind and water, and changes grasslands into deserts. This interruption of the natural cycle has changed the land's productivity.

**Figure 11.18** ▲
Cattle have overgrazed the grasses on one side of the fence. No plants remain to hold the soil in place.

### Science and Society
#### *Overgrazed Grasslands*

Do you think a Dust Bowl disaster could happen today? What might happen to cause one to occur? Drought is an important factor. But people learned from the Dust Bowl disaster of the 1930s that the way they manage the land has an important impact. For example, they learned that fields need some sort of plant cover, such as grass or clover, when no crops are growing. Plant roots help hold the soil in place. Today many farmers follow this plan to protect their soil.

People use grasslands to graze herds of cattle and sheep. When a small number of animals graze over a large area, the grass can grow back, and the grasslands aren't damaged. But if there are too many animals in an area, they can damage the grasslands. They eat too much of the grass, destroy its roots, and trample it under their hooves. Look at Figure 11.18. Too many grazing animals can strip large areas of grass. Without the grass, the bare topsoil blows away in the wind. A once productive grassland can turn into a desert.

In Africa, overgrazing and droughts have caused serious problems in the last few years. Parts of Australia and the United States also suffer from overgrazing. A recent study by the United States government found that more than half of the grazing land now in use is in poor or fair condition due to overgrazing.

### Check and Explain

1. List seven types of soil. Where in the world is each type found?

2. What is a laterite?

3. **Compare and Contrast** Describe two soils that undergo extensive leaching of minerals. Compare them to two soils in which less leaching occurs. What conditions seem to cause leaching?

4. **Classify** You have been given a soil sample from an unknown location. It is composed of fine-grained angular fragments, and the soil is somewhat leached. The topsoil is rich in humus and nutrients. What type of soil is your sample?

# Chapter 11 *Review*

## Concept Summary

### 11.1 Weathering
▶ Mechanical weathering breaks rock into pieces by physical means.
▶ The causes of mechanical weathering include ice wedging, plant weathering, animal weathering, temperature change, water abrasion, and wind abrasion.
▶ Chemical weathering alters the chemical composition of rock.
▶ The causes of chemical weathering include oxidation, water dissolving and leaching minerals, carbonation, sulfuric acid, and plant and fungal acids.

### 11.2 Soils
▶ Soil, the upper part of the regolith, is a mixture of parent rock, decayed plant

and animal matter called humus, and rock fragments.
▶ Soils have measurable properties that include particle shape, particle size, fertility, and acid level.
▶ A soil profile shows the distinct layers, or horizons, present in soil. Mature soils have three horizons.
▶ Soil supports the survival of plants and many other living organisms.

### 11.3 World Soil Types
▶ Soil is classified by mineral and humus composition, and the environment where the soil was formed.
▶ The seven different world soil types are forest soils, prairie soils, grassland soils, desert soils, mountain soils, tundra soils, and tropical soils or laterites.

## Chapter Vocabulary

| | | | |
|---|---|---|---|
| exfoliation (11.1) | carbonation (11.1) | soil profile (11.2) | podsol (11.3) |
| oxidation (11.1) | regolith (11.2) | horizon (11.2) | laterite (11.3) |
| leaching (11.1) | parent rock (11.2) | humus (11.2) | |

## Check Your Vocabulary

Use the vocabulary words above to complete the following sentences correctly.

1. Iron combining with oxygen to form rust is a type of chemical weathering called ＿＿＿ .

2. All of the loose, weathered material on the earth's surface is the ＿＿＿ .

3. The decayed plant and animal matter in soil is called ＿＿＿ .

4. The process of mechanical weathering when rock cracks and flakes off is called ＿＿＿ .

5. Forest soils are usually ＿＿＿ .

6. The process of dissolving and moving minerals from the upper soil is ＿＿＿ .

7. The cross section of soil that shows distinct layers is a ＿＿＿ .

8. A type of chemical weathering caused by carbonic acid is ＿＿＿ .

9. The rock that breaks down to produce soil particles is called ＿＿＿ .

10. Red soils often found in tropical regions are ＿＿＿ .

11. The distinct layers seen in a soil profile are called ＿＿＿ .

## Write Your Vocabulary

Write sentences using the vocabulary words above. Show that you know what each word means.

## Check Your Vocabulary

1. oxidation
2. regolith
3. humus
4. exfoliation
5. podsols
6. leaching
7. soil profile
8. carbonation
9. parent rock
10. laterites
11. horizons

## Write Your Vocabulary

Students' sentences should show that they know the meaning of each word as well as how to use it in a sentence.

Use Vocabulary Worksheet for Chapter 11.

## Check Your Knowledge

1. Answers may include ice wedging, plant weathering, animal weathering, temperature change, water abrasion, and wind abrasion.
2. Soil properties include particle shape, particle size, fertility, and acid level.
3. Tropical, grassland, prairie, desert, tundra, forest, and mountain
4. Answers may include oxidation, water, carbonic acid, sulfuric acid, and plant and fungal acids.
5. Permafrost is a permanently frozen layer of subsoil found in polar regions.
6. Mature soils have three horizons: A (topsoil), B (subsoil), and C (weathered parent rock).
7. Answers may include bacteria, fungi, algae, protozoa, nematodes, springtails, mites, and crustaceans.
8. *Podsol* is another name for forest soil.
9. Acid rain can contain sulfuric acid.
10. The two types of weathering are chemical and mechanical.
11. Nitrogen, phosphorus, potassium, calcium, magnesium, and sulfur
12. mechanical
13. A
14. bacteria and fungi
15. exfoliation
16. soil
17. water

## Check Your Understanding

1. Pollutants from factories and vehicles dissolve in rainwater, creating acid rain that chemically weathers rocks.
2. Answers will vary.
3. Both types of abrasion involve the wearing away of rock by the scraping of small, moving particles. The difference is in the way the small particles are carried.
4. Animals contribute to chemical weathering because they produce carbon dioxide. They cause mechanical weathering by digging and burrowing in rock.
5. Water or wind abrasion and acid rain can smooth the edges of stone.
6. The parent rock develops cracks. The cracks gradually split the rock into blocks or boulders. The boulders weather into smaller and smaller particles. Plants begin to grow in the immature soil and form a decaying layer on top of the weathered rock. Over time, decaying organic matter and other living organisms form topsoil.

7. The acid level in soil determines the types of plants or crops that can be grown.
8. Living plants, animals, and microorganisms contribute to the creation of soil by breaking down rock. Some organisms dig into the soil, allowing water and air to flow through. By eating, digesting, and excreting, soil organisms change the soil chemically. When they die, their bodies decay into humus.
9. Students' answers will vary, but may include: eating vegetables grown in the soil; breathing oxygen produced by plants grown in soil. Starvation and suffocation would change lives.
10. Student answers will vary. The effects of weathering would moderately change the landscape in 100 years, but would show a significant change in 1,000 years.
11. The soil may be forest or tropical, because both types of soil are subject to leaching of minerals.

---

## Chapter 11 Review

### Check Your Knowledge

Answer the following in complete sentences.

1. List three causes of mechanical weathering.
2. What are the properties of soil?
3. What are the seven different types of soil found around the world?
4. List four causes of chemical weathering.
5. What is permafrost?
6. How many horizons exist in mature soils? Name the horizons.
7. List five different types of organisms found in soil.
8. What is another name for acidic forest soils?
9. What chemical is found in acid rain?
10. What are the two types of weathering?
11. List the six important plant nutrients.

Choose the answer that best completes each sentence.

12. Ice wedging is a type of (mechanical, chemical, plant, animal) weathering.
13. Humus is found in horizon (A, B, C, D).
14. The most common soil organisms are (bacteria and fungi, protozoa, bacteria and nematodes, mites).
15. Temperature changes cause (exfoliation, chemical weathering, oxidation, carbonation).
16. The top layer of regolith is (bedrock, humus, soil, parent rock) that extends down to 3 m below the surface.
17. The particle shape of soils determines the amount of (clay, water, sulfur, living things) the soil can hold.

### Check Your Understanding

Apply the concepts you have learned to answer each question.

1. Explain how industrial society increased the weathering of rocks.
2. What type of soil is common in the area where you live?
3. Compare water and wind abrasion. How are they the same? How are they different?
4. Explain how animals cause both chemical and mechanical weathering.
5. If you wanted to smooth the edges of a sharp stone, what types of chemical and mechanical weathering could you use?
6. Describe the events that take place to change parent rock into soil.
7. Why is the acid level in soil important to farmers?
8. Explain the role of plants and organisms in soil ecology.
9. **Extension** Make a list of the ways in which soil affects your life every day. How would your life be different if the soil were removed and replaced with concrete?
10. **Application** Describe the different types of weathering you see occurring as you travel from your home to school. How will the effects of weathering change the landscape in 100 years? In 1,000 years?
11. **Mystery Photo** The photograph on page 238 shows stalactites formed by water dissolving, leaching, and redepositing minerals. What might the soil be like above these underground caverns? Why?

## Develop Your Skills

**1.** **a.** Profile *a* shows grassland; the calcium salts are typical of grassland soil.

   **b.** Profile *b* has the most humus; profile *c* has the largest B horizon. (Note that the drawings are not done to the same scale.)

**2.** **a.** Tropical; about 80 m

   **b.** The more precipitation and the higher the temperatures, the greater the depth of the weathering.

**3.** Students' tables may vary. They should show the most common and least common soils as follows. North America: tundra or forest/desert; South America: tropical/desert; Europe: forest/grassland; Asia: forest or mountain/desert; Africa: grassland/mountain; Australia: desert or grassland/tropical; Antarctica (not on map): tundra only (by inference).

**4.** Desert soils are thin and have little organic matter due to the lack of plants. They also contain salt deposits near the surface due to evaporation of water from the soil. Forest soils develop with heavy rainfall and abundant vegetation. This creates thick soils with well-developed horizons.

## Develop Your Skills

Use the skills you have developed in this chapter to complete each activity.

**1. Interpret Data** The drawings below show different soil profiles.

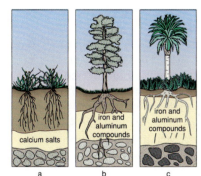

calcium salts | iron and aluminum compounds | iron and aluminum compounds
a | b | c

   a. Which soil profile shows a grassland soil. Why?

   b. Which soil profile has the most humus? The largest *B* horizon?

**2. Data Bank** Use the data on page 613 to answer the following questions.

   a. In which climate is the regolith deepest? How deep is the regolith?

   b. **Infer** How are precipitation and temperature related to depth of weathering?

**3. Classify** Make a table listing the seven major continents. Use Figure 11.10 to find the most common and the least common soil types for each continent.

**4. Compare and Contrast** What processes are probably most responsible for creating desert soils? Compare these to the processes most likely to create forest soil.

## Make Connections

**1. Link the Concepts** Below is a concept map showing how some of the main concepts in this chapter link together. Only part of the map is filled in. Finish the map, using words and ideas from the chapter.

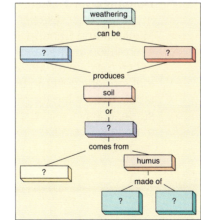

**2. Science and Society** Use recent magazines and newspapers to find out the impact of desertification on many African communities.

**3. Science and Literature** In John Steinbeck's novel, *The Grapes of Wrath*, a family is displaced from their home because of the Dust Bowl disaster. Read this book to find out how soil changed the lives of many people and the history of the United States.

**4. Science and Art** Jewelry often contains polished rocks. Obtain an unpolished rock. Use different types of abrasion processes to make a polished stone.

## Make Connections

**1.**

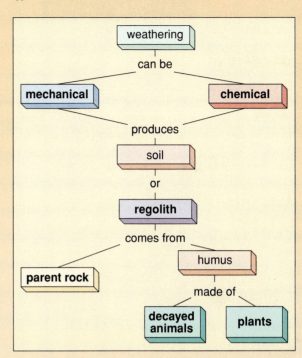

**2.** Students' answers will vary. In general, desertification affects communities by ruining crop and grazing land as dunes encroach. This often results in food shortages.

**3.** Students' reports will vary. The availability of fertile soil determines the type of agriculture that is practiced in specific regions. The Joads were forced to migrate to California when farmland in Oklahoma turned to desert.

**4.** Students can polish the rock by rubbing it against another rock under water, rubbing it with sandpaper, or shaking it in a container with gravel.

## Overview

This chapter explores the forces of erosion. The first section opens with the mass movement of earth caused by erosion and deposition. Section two covers water erosion. This section includes river and stream deposition, flood control, and wave erosion. The third section investigates ice erosion and glaciation. The final section discusses wind erosion.

## Advance Planner

▶ Collect small pans, soil, straws, water, and graduated cylinders for SE page 266.

▶ Collect June or July 1993 newspaper or magazine articles for TE page 269.

▶ Supply a plastic container with a lid and water for TE page 274.

▶ Obtain Jean M. Auel's *The Clan of Cave Bear* for TE page 275.

▶ Provide large pieces of ice, paper towels, pieces of wire, hard plastic, and sand for SE Activity 12, page 279.

▶ Gather paper towels, sand, and straws for SE page 281.

▶ Obtain pictures of Martian sand dunes for TE page 283.

## Skills Development Chart

| Sections | Classify | Communicate | Infer | Interpret Data | Make a Model | Observe | Predict |
|---|---|---|---|---|---|---|---|
| **12.1** Skills WarmUp | | | | | | | ● |
| **12.2** Skills WarmUp | | | | | | ● | |
| Skills WorkOut | | | ● | | | | |
| SkillBuilder | | | | ● | | | |
| **12.3** Skills WarmUp | | ● | | | | | |
| Historical Notebook | | ● | | | | | |
| Activity 12 | ● | | | | ● | ● | |
| **12.4** Skills WarmUp | | | | | | | ● |
| Skills WorkOut | | | | | ● | | |

## Individual Needs

▶ **Limited English Proficiency Students** Ask students to choose an area that they are familiar with, either where they now live or where they originally came from. Have them make an erosion scrapbook of the area by collecting photographs or drawing pictures that show different kinds of erosion found there. Ask them to write simple captions for the pictures describing what has happened to the land using the vocabulary in the chapter.

▶ **At-Risk Students** Have students work in small groups and have each one choose an agent of erosion: water, wind, or gravity. Encourage each group to create a model or models to demonstrate the erosion caused by the agent they chose. After they have planned and made their models, have them present a demonstration to the rest of the class. Groups should explain what they are demonstrating and be prepared to answer questions from their classmates.

▶ **Gifted Students** Ask students to choose a river that interests them because of its history, length, or other characteristics. Have them do research to find out about it, including its location, how it has shaped the land through which it flows, and what effect it has had on the people living near it. Have students make an exhibit about their river that shows the results of their research.

## Resource Bank

▶ **Bulletin Board** Use the bulletin board for an exhibit about Waterton-Glacier International Peace Park in Montana and Canada. From the U.S. Park Service obtain information, maps, and pictures of the park, which has active glaciers as well as landforms created by the ice that formerly covered the area. Invite students to make labels describing the pictures in geological terms. If any students have visited the area, ask them to contribute materials. The class may want to plan an imaginary trip to the park.

| Section | Core | Standard | Enriched | Section | Core | Standard | Enriched |
|---|:---:|:---:|:---:|---|:---:|:---:|:---:|
| **12.1 Gravity and Erosion** pp. 263–265 | | | | **Color Transparencies** Transparency 27 | ● | ● | ● |
| **Section Features** Skills WarmUp, p. 263 | ● | ● | ● | **12.3 Ice Erosion** pp. 274–279 | | | |
| **Blackline Masters** Review Worksheet 12.1 Reteach Worksheet 12.1 Skills Worksheet 12.1 | ● ● ● | ● ● ● | ● ● ● | **Section Features** Skills WarmUp, p. 274 Historical Notebook, p. 275 Activity, p. 279 | ● ● ● | ● ● ● | ● ● ● |
| **12.2 Water Erosion** pp. 266–273 | | | | **Blackline Masters** Review Worksheet 12.3 Integrating Worksheet 12.3 | ● ● | ● ● | ● ● |
| **Section Features** Skills WarmUp, p. 266 Skills WorkOut, p. 270 SkillBuilder, p. 270 | ● ● | ● ● ● | ● ● ● | **Color Transparencies** Transparencies 28, 29 | ● | ● | ● |
| **Blackline Masters** Review Worksheet 12.2 Skills Worksheet 12.2 Integrating Worksheet 12.2 | ● ● | ● ● ● | ● ● ● | **12.4 Wind Erosion** pp. 280–284 | | | |
| **Ancillary Options** *Multiculturalism in Mathematics, Science, and Technology,* pp. 164–166 | ● | ● | ● | **Section Features** Skills WarmUp, p. 280 Skills WorkOut, p. 281 | ● ● | ● ● | ● ● |
| **Laboratory Program** Investigation 18 | | ● | ● | **Blackline Masters** Review Worksheet 12.4 Vocabulary Worksheet 12.4 | ● ● | ● ● | ● ● |
| | | | | **Overhead Blackline Transparencies** Overhead Blackline Master 12.4 and Student Worksheet | ● | ● | ● |

# Bibliography

The following resources can be used for teaching the chapter. See page T–46 for supplier codes.

**Library Resources**

Farndon, John. *How the Earth Works.* Pleasantville, NY: The Reader's Digest Association, Inc., 1992.

Walker, Sally M. *Glaciers: Ice on the Move.* Minneapolis: Carolrhoda Books, Inc., 1990.

**Technology Resources**

*Internet*

**PLANETDIARY** at *http://www.planetdiary.com*
- Find out more about drought, floods, and the atmosphere in *Drought, Flood, and Atmosphere* by clicking on *Phenomena Backgrounders.*
- Review meteorological and geological news in *Current Phenomena.*

**Software**

*Microsoft Oceans.* Win. ER.
*Soil and Erosion.* Mac, Win. ESI.

*CD-ROMs*

*Interactive Earth.* SFAW.
*An Odyssey of Discovery for Science Insights:* Have students explore the activity *Aquarium* on the Living Science Disk. SFAW.
*Small Blue Planet: The Real Picture World Atlas.* Mac, Dos. ESI.

*Laserdiscs*

*Living Textbook.* (See barcodes on pages in this chapter.) Optical Data.

*Videos*

*Discovering the Changing Surface of Our Earth.* 30 min. MMI.
*Folding, Flooding, and Faulting: How the Earth is Shaped.* 60 min. Blue Sky Associates.

**Audio-Visual Resources**

*Erosion: Carving the Landscape.* Still frame. 15 min. CABISCO.
*Evidence for the Ice Ages.* Film. EB.
*The Water Cycle and Erosion.* 15 min. EME.

## Introducing the Chapter

Have students read the description of the photograph. Ask if they agree or disagree with the description.

### Directed Inquiry

Have students study the photograph. Ask:

► What does this photograph show? (Students may recognize a narrow, winding canyon from its closely spaced, eroded and weathered walls of rock and the area lit by the sun.)

► What natural process formed this canyon? (Students should say weathering and erosion.)

► What kinds of weathering and erosion do you think were at work here? (Students may mention water and wind abrasion, and water dissolving the rock.)

► What kind of an area do you think this canyon is located in? Why? (Although a river runs through the canyon, the wind erosion suggests a dry region. This canyon was likely cut by water from occasional heavy rains. Wind erosion made the rock surfaces jagged.)

## Chapter Vocabulary

| | |
|---|---|
| alluvial fan | mass movement |
| deflation | meander |
| deposition | moraine |
| erosion | outwash |
| glacier | rill |
| levee | till |

### Writing Connection

Ask students to study the photograph and write a list of nouns and adjectives that describe the place shown. Tell students to think of words describing sounds, textures, temperatures, and smells, as well as colors and shapes. Then have students use their lists to write a vivid description of a walk through the canyon.

Chapter **12**   Forces of Erosion

### Chapter Sections

**12.1** Gravity and Erosion

**12.2** Water Erosion

**12.3** Ice Erosion

**12.4** Wind Erosion

### What do you see?

❝I see weathered rocks. It also looks like a cave. So it's a weathered cave. The rock looks like sandstone. The weather made it this way by breaking down the earth's surface.❞

*Phillip Jackson*
*Bingham Middle School*
*Kansas City, Missouri*

To find out more about the photograph, look on page 286. As you read this chapter, you will learn how erosion and deposition change the surface of the earth.

### Multicultural Perspectives

The sphinx is a mythical beast common to several ancient cultures. Most often Egyptian sphinxes had the body of a lion and the head of a human. You may wish to have student volunteers report on the form and meaning of the sphinx in ancient Egypt and Greece.

### Themes in Science

**Evolution** The surface of the earth changes over time. These changes are due to the erosion and deposition of weathered rock on the earth's surface.

SECTION
# 12.1

**Section Objectives**
For a list of section objectives, see the Student Edition page.

**Skills Objectives**
Students should be able to:

**Predict** how water erodes land.

**Predict** how mass movement could affect a house.

**Vocabulary**
erosion, deposition, mass movement

# 12.1 Gravity and Erosion

## Objectives

- **Explain** the difference between erosion and deposition.
- **Name** the agents of erosion.
- **Predict** what conditions cause mass movement.
- **Compare** and **contrast** the different types of mass movement.

Imagine what the area where you live looked like 1,000 years ago. How do you think it differed from the way it looks today? For one thing, buildings and streets wouldn't have existed. The land may have had more hills. Since that time, human activity or natural causes may have worn away the hills. Maybe the land was more flat than it is today. Machines or wind and water may have deposited sediments to build up the land. You may not know it, but the land in your area is still changing. How do you think it will look 1,000 years from now?

### ACTIVITY
**Predicting**

*How to Make Mud*

What happens to a pile of dirt if you water it with a hose? Where will the dirt go when the water is turned off? What will happen to the dirt if the water comes out powerfully? Does the speed of the water affect the amount of dirt moved? Explain.

SKILLS WARMUP

## Erosion and Deposition

The materials on the surface of the earth are always changing. How has the structure in Figure 12.1 changed over time? Recall that rock is broken down by mechanical and chemical weathering. Weathered materials are picked up and transported to other places. The action of picking up and moving materials is called **erosion**. The agents of erosion are water, wind, ice, and gravity. Erosion results in the wearing away of the land.

The degree of erosion that occurs in an area depends on the amount of rain, the looseness of the soil, and the slope of the land. Therefore, a bare hillside erodes faster than a grass-covered hill or a flat field.

The dropping of weathered materials somewhere else is called **deposition** (DEHP uh ZISH uhn). Deposition aids in the creation of new landforms. Sometimes deposition occurs over a long period of time. Sometimes deposition moves materials rapidly over a short time.

**Figure 12.1**
What agent of erosion weathered this Egyptian sphinx? ▼ ①

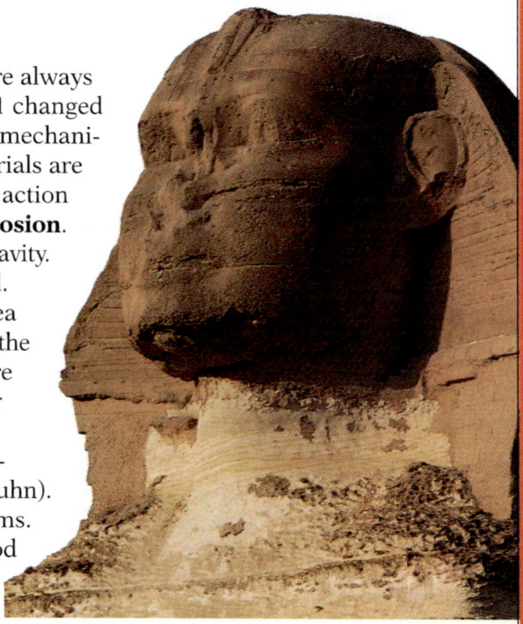

## MOTIVATE

### Skills WarmUp

To help students observe erosion, have them do the Skills WarmUp.
**Answer** A stream of water will wear away the pile. Loosened dirt particles will flow away from the pile. A powerful stream moves more particles because the water's force and volume increase. Yes, the faster the water, the greater the erosion because faster water has more energy.

### Misconceptions

Students may think of erosion as a force that involves only water. Explain that erosion occurs whenever material is picked up and moved. Ask for examples of wind erosion, such as dust moving across a baseball diamond.

## TEACH

### Discuss

Ask students what word is contained in *deposition*. Have them make a memory device to remind them of the meanings of *deposition* and *erosion*.

**Answer to In-Text Question**
① Wind

264

### TEACH ▪ *Continued*

#### Explore Visually

Have students study the illustrations on the page. Then ask the following questions:

▶ How is a landslide similar to a mudflow? How is it different? (Both are rapid, downward movements and both leave piles of material at the bottom of a slope. Landslides consist of rocks and soil, mudflows consist of wet fine-grained sediment.)

▶ How can you tell that a mass movement has occurred? (Objects once near the top of a slope have moved down.)

▶ Which two agents work together to produce slump? What does a slump look like? (Water and gravity; layers of soil or bedrock move downslope as a single unit, often leaving a curved scar.)

**Answers to In-Text Questions**

① **The tree is bowed downslope.**
② **It pushed everything in its path to the bottom of the slope.**

---

#### 💿 The Living Textbook: Earth Science Side 2

Chapter 37      Frame 12570
Erosion (Movie)
Search:                    Play:

#### 💿 The Living Textbook: Earth Science Sides 1-2

Chapter 18      Frame 02671
Land-, Mud-, and Rockslides (25 Frames)
Search:                    Step:

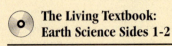

---

#### 📁 Portfolio

For the next several weeks have students identify, describe, and record the location of mass movements near school or home or in the news. Have them keep the data in their portfolios. If mass movement is visible in your area, have the students return to the selected sites after several weeks and observe how mass movement has changed the land.

---

**Landslides ▲**

The rapid movement of large amounts of rock and soil is a landslide. Landslides often occur after heavy rains or after earthquakes loosen materials on a steep slope. Landslides that occur on the sides of mountains can destroy entire towns. Piles of material at the bottom of a slope indicate a landslide location, as shown in the photograph above. Warning signs are often placed in landslide areas.

### Mass Movement

Gravity pulls downward on all objects. Gravity moves loose material on a slope. When gravity moves rocks or soil down a slope, it is called **mass movement**. Types of mass movements are classified by the size of material moved down the slope or by the speed of the movement.

**Creep ▲**

The gradual downslope movement of soil is called creep. Creep happens too slowly to notice while it's occurring. But over time, the results of creep can be seen. How can you tell from the photograph that creep is taking place? ①

**Slump**

◀ When weak layers of underlying materials move downslope as a single unit, slump occurs. Water and gravity acting together cause slump. Slump can occur in soil or bedrock cliffs. Slumps often leave curved scars.

**Mudflows**

In dry areas, fine sediment can collect in thick layers. When it rains, water loosens the sediment and increases its weight. As a result, after a heavy rainfall, the sediment mixed with water washes down the slope. This movement is called a mudflow. Mudflows are rapid movements that sometimes destroy everything in their path. How did the mudflow in the photograph affect the area? ▼ ②

### STS Connection

Off-road vehicles, or ORVs, include motorcycles, dune buggies, four-wheel-drive and all-terrain vehicles. ORVs greatly increase soil erosion. Until the mid-1970s, ORV owners could ride on most public lands. Now ORVs are restricted to areas set aside for this use. Because ORVs damage the environment, some people think they should be banned from public lands. Have students discuss how ORVs should be restricted.

### Answer to Link

The process of mass movement, or mass wasting, is modeled. Mass wasting involves erosion by gravity. Gravity pulls mass from high geologic areas and deposits it in low-lying areas, essentially smoothing out the topographical relief of the earth's surface.

### Class Activity

Ask students to look for patterns of erosion around the school. They might look for worn carpeting, work patterns in floor tile, or signs of wear on stairs. Have the class draw and label a diagram that shows their observations. Have students infer what may have caused the erosion and what could be done to slow or stop it.

### WrapUp

**Reteach**  List the following features on the chalkboard: rocks at the base of a slope, mud at the base of a slope, a curved scar, bowed trees. Ask students to identify which mass movements could cause each feature. (Landslide, mudslide, slump, creep)
Use Review Worksheet 12.1.

### Check and Explain

1. Erosion occurs as materials are picked up and moved away; deposition is dropping weathered materials.

2. Water, wind, ice, gravity

3. Check to see that the hill does not have a lot of loose rock and soil or thick layers of fine sediment. Curved scars and tilted trees could indicate slump or creep.

4. *Landslide*—fast; rocks and soil; *mudflow*—fast; fine sediment; *creep*—slow; soil; *slump*—slow or sudden; layers of soil or bedrock

### Reteach

Use Reteach Worksheet 12.1.

**Answer to In-Text Question**

③ **The two paths on the right look as if they were made by car wheels. The third path may have been made by people walking.**

### Science and You
### *You: An Agent of Erosion*

Have you ever thought of yourself as an "agent of erosion"? Probably not, but you are one. Here are a few examples. As you're walking home from school, you decide to take your usual shortcut through a field or yard. You notice that the grass where you walk is beginning to wear away. Soon there will be no grass at all, and you will have worn away a path. Your feet acted as agents of erosion by slowly wearing away the grass and topsoil.

When you get home, you turn on the hose to wash your bicycle. As you rinse your bicycle, you notice that water from the hose collects in small streams that run down the gutter on the side of the street. When the water stops moving or slows down, you notice that piles of dirt and leaves build up in the gutter. The water from the hose you are using acts as an agent of erosion when it removes soil and dirt from the ground. It also causes deposition, when the water slows down and creates piles of material.

When you finish, you climb on your erosion machine —or your bicycle—and ride to the park for a softball game. Over a long time, even the hard concrete of the sidewalk will slowly erode under the movement of your bicycle tires.

During the softball game, you get a chance to steal second base. You are called "safe" as you "erode" into second base!

### Check and Explain

1. How is erosion different from deposition? Give examples.

2. What are the four agents of erosion?

3. **Predict**  Suppose you want to build a house on the side of a hill. What preparations would ensure that mass movement wouldn't affect your house?

4. **Compare and Contrast**  Describe how the speed of the movement compares for each type of mass movement. Describe how the size of material moved varies for each type of mass movement.

**Figure 12.2** ▲
How do you think the paths in this forest setting were created? ③

### Physical Science
### L I N K

Collect the following: sand, water, a medium-sized bucket, a large plastic bag, and a sheet of graph paper.

**1.** Fill the plastic bucket with sand. Add just enough water to make the sand clump together.

**2.** Freeze the container of sand for a few hours.

**3.** Place the frozen sand onto the plastic bag.

**4.** Draw a profile of the frozen sand mass.

**5.** Repeat step 4 at one-hour intervals for four hours.

What geologic processes are modeled? How does gravity affect geologic features on the earth's surface?

**A C T I V I T Y**

### *Themes in Science*

**Scale and Structure** Most rivers begin with many short, steep streams that gradually merge into one long, sloping river.

### *Themes in Science*

**Systems and Interactions** River systems form when runoff follows a channel. The interaction of the flowing water with dirt causes erosion. A drainage system forms as the flowing water interacts with more flowing water. A drainage system includes rills that join to form gullies; gullies joining together to form streams; streams coming together to form the main river.

## Section Objectives
For a list of section objectives, see the Student Edition page.

## Skills Objectives
Students should be able to:

**Observe** how ground cover affects water erosion.

**Infer** how to control wave erosion.

**Interpret Data** about sediment deposits along a shore.

**Classify** landforms on different types of shorelines.

## Vocabulary
rill, meander, alluvial fan, levee

## MOTIVATE

### Skills WarmUp
To help students observe water erosion, have them do the Skills WarmUp.
**Answer** More soil will flow out with the water from the soil-only pan. The straw reduces erosion.

## Misconceptions
Students may think that erosion always takes a long time. Discuss how a strong rainfall affects dirt. Point out that small channels and muddy deposits can form very rapidly.

## Answer to In-Text Question
① **Rills are small channels in soil that join to form gullies. Water flows through rills and gullies, moving topsoil farther downhill.**

**The Living Textbook:
Earth Science Sides 1-2**

Chapter 9          Frame 01957
Gully Forming (5 Frames)
Search:                Step:

▼ **ACTIVITY**

### Observing

*Mud Pies*

   Collect some grass straw, two small pans filled with soil, a bucket, and about 300 mL of water.
   **1.** Cover the soil in one pan with straw.
   **2.** Hold the soil-only pan at a slight angle over the bucket.
   **3.** Pour 150 mL of water over the soil. Observe the water in the bucket.
   **4.** Repeat the process with the other pan.
   How does the straw affect the amount of erosion?

**SKILLS WARMUP**

**Figure 12.3**
How are rills different from gullies? ▼ ①

## 12.2 Water Erosion

### Objectives

▶ **Describe** how a river forms.

▶ **Relate** the stages of a river to water erosion.

▶ **Classify** wave formations according to the type of shoreline.

▶ **Compare** and **contrast** stream and wave deposits.

After a hard rain, you've probably seen muddy water running down your street or road. Dirt moves from place to place in moving water. When the water stops or slows down, the sediment forms piles. You may have seen piles of sand and dirt building up in gutters or ditches next to the street.

### Stream Erosion

As rainwater flows downhill, it forms **rills**, or small channels in the dirt. Look at Figure 12.3. Rills join to form larger channels called *gullies*. Water flows through rills and gullies carrying sediment downslope.

Once gullies reach a stream, more erosion occurs. A stream moves sediment. This constant motion erodes the stream bottom and sides, forming a valley. When streams enter rivers, the water slows and drops sediment.

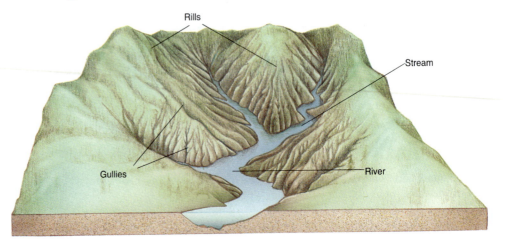

Rills

Stream

Gullies

River

## *Geography Connection*

A continental divide separates the flow of rivers to different sides of a continent. In North America, this divide is also called the Great Divide. Rivers east of the Great Divide flow into the Atlantic Ocean, and rivers to the west flow into the Pacific. The Great Divide follows the crest of the Rocky Mountains. Have students locate the Great divide on a map of North America. Have students determine which ocean the rivers in their area flow into.

## Stages of River Erosion

Rivers are classified by how much they erode the areas around them. The three stages of river erosion are referred to as young, mature, and old. These stages are shown in the photographs at right.

**Young River** Young rivers are often found in mountains. Downcutting and erosion of the landscape are very visible around a young river. Young rivers flow swiftly and they are very powerful agents of erosion. A young river has a lot of energy that creates rapids and waterfalls. The energy is often used to generate electricity. Features of young rivers include steep slopes and V-shaped valleys.

**Mature River** A mature river moves more slowly and its slope is gentler than a young river. Energy in a mature river is just great enough to carry its load. A mature river continues to erode the bottom of the riverbed. It also begins to erode its sides. As the riverbed shifts toward the outside of a bend in the river, the river forms a series of curves called **meanders**. Meanders erode the valley sides and widen the valley floor of a mature river. During heavy rains, the river sometimes overflows its banks to create a *floodplain* on the valley floor.

**Old River** In an old river, the water moves very slowly. An old river carves its way over the land, widening the broad, flat floodplain. Sometimes during a flood, the river cuts across a meander loop and forms a new path. Sediments build up at both ends of the meander loop, cutting it off from the rest of the river. In time, a separate lake, called an *oxbow lake*, forms.

**Figure 12.4a** ▲
This young river flows quickly to erode through Yellowstone Canyon in Wyoming.

**Figure 12.4b** ▲
The Koyukuk River in Alaska is a mature river. How is a mature river different from a young river? ②

**Figure 12.4c** ▲
The Chena River is an old river located near Fairbanks, Alaska. Notice the many meanders.

### Directed Inquiry

After students read the text and study Figures 12.4a, b, and c, ask the following questions:

▶ Which erodes more sediment, a young river or an old river? (Young river)

▶ Which is wider, an old river or a mature river? (Old)

▶ Which has steeper slopes, a young river or an old river? (Young)

▶ At what stage of erosion is a river most likely to flood? (Answers will vary; help students understand that flooding results from increased water volume in any river. Flooding is most common in mature and old rivers.)

▶ How might an oxbow lake form along the river in Figure 12.4c? (If the river takes a "shortcut" route across the meander, the rest of the loop could be closed off, forming an oxbow lake.)

### Integrated Learning

Use Integrating Worksheet 12.2.

**Answer to In-Text Question**

② **A mature river moves more slowly and across land that is less sloped than a young river.**

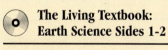

**The Living Textbook: Earth Science Sides 1-2**

Chapter 23          Frame 02974
Colorado River (4 Frames)
Search:                Step:

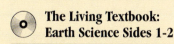

**The Living Textbook: Earth Science Sides 1-2**

Chapter 9           Frame 02029
Meanders/Oxbows (20 Frames)
Search:                Step:

## Discuss

Have students explain how the energy of a stream or river is related to the amount of sediment it deposits. (As a river or stream loses energy, it drops sediments.)

## Critical Thinking

**Find Causes** Ask students why large, coarse materials are the first to be deposited along a river. (They are heavy; they take the most energy to move and so would be the first to deposit when the river loses energy.)

## Classify

List the following phrases on the chalkboard. Have students tell whether each phrase describes a delta or an alluvial fan. thick wedge (AF), stream flows onto desert floor (AF), stream flows into still body of water (D), river comes to a standstill (D), forms at the base of a mountain (AF).

## Skills Development

**Communicate** Have students describe how the Mississippi Delta grew. (As the river flowed it gathered sediments. As it entered the Gulf of Mexico, it slowed and deposited sediments. As this process continued, the delta grew.)

### Integrating the Sciences

**Life Science** Conditions on a river delta create a unique ecosystem. The deltaic plain is rich in nutrients that settled to the bottom. The water is brackish, or a mixture of salt and fresh water. Some organisms common to this ecosystem are mud flat grasses, oysters, snails, crabs, and sea trout. Other animals, such as salmon and eels, migrate through these waters. These organisms can adapt to changing water conditions because their kidneys can increase or decrease the amount of water pumped into or out of the body. Have students gather information about one animal that lives in or migrates through this unique ecosystem.

## Stream and River Deposition

When a stream or river slows down, it loses energy. The energy loss causes a stream or river to drop the sediment it is carrying. The sediment may deposit on the sides of the river, within the channel, or at the mouth. As the river slows, large coarse materials are the first sediment to deposit. Fine sediment, like silt and clay, deposit last. The size of the sediment and the location of the deposit determine the types of landforms that are created. You can see examples of these landforms in the photographs below.

**Delta**
◀ At the mouth of a river, a triangular-shaped deposit called a *delta* may form. A delta forms when the river flows into a quiet, still body of water, such as a gulf, lake, or inland sea. Because the river almost comes to a complete standstill, most of its sediment deposits at the mouth. The delta shown here is located in Alaska. Large deltas also exist at the mouth of the Mississippi River and Nile River.

**Alluvial Fan** ▶
Sometimes water leaves a steep mountain slope and flows onto a flat area. The water slows down and drops its load, forming a thick wedge at the mountain base. This type of sediment deposit is called an **alluvial** (uh LOO vee uhl) **fan**. Alluvial fans commonly form in arid regions where streams flow onto the desert floor.

## *STS Connection*

During the summer of 1993, the Mississippi River and many of its tributaries flooded parts of South Dakota, Minnesota, Wisconsin, Iowa, Nebraska, Missouri, and Illinois. The high, fast-moving water broke through many levees that were built to control floods. Collect newspaper or magazine articles from June and July of 1993 for students to read. Discuss how the flooding affected towns and farmlands and ideas about the value of levees.

## Flood Control

Flooding occurs naturally as streams develop and river systems mature. However, flooding can cause problems for cities and farmlands located on floodplains. Some flooding is controlled naturally. During floods, sediment deposits in a long ridge, called a **levee**, next to mature or old rivers. Levees help prevent a river from spilling over its banks.

People also help control flooding by creating artificial lakes and levees. Artificial levees are built from dirt or concrete. People can also help by keeping fields covered with plants and by conserving forests. Soil conservation prevents excess runoff during heavy rainfall.

**Floodplain** ▶

Sediment builds up on floodplains after repeated flooding. Floodplains can be narrow or many kilometers wide. Floodplains are often excellent agricultural areas because flood deposits add nutrients and minerals to the soil on both sides of the river. The floodplain in this photograph is located in Kenya, Africa.

**Levee**

◀ Levees are composed of large grain sediment that deposits first when the river overflows its banks. The deposits build up and eventually raise the river banks. In this way, levees help control future floods. If repeated flooding occurs along a river, the natural levees may be quite high. The natural levee shown here is located near the Green River in Utah.

## Skills Development

**Predict** Ask students to predict where they would find the best farmland: along a young river, a mature river, or an old river. Why? (In the floodplain of a mature or old river where nutrients and minerals are added to the soil by repeated flooding)

**Infer** Have students explain why rivers form levees at or near river banks even though the floodplain may be several kilometers wide. (Natural levees are formed of large-grain sediment too heavy to carry a great distance inland.)

## Enrich

Ask students why people live in floodplains even though they risk losing land, personal property, and homes to flooding. (Answers will vary. These locations provide farming, processing, and transportation jobs. The areas are often attractive.)

## Ancillary Options

If you are using the blackline masters from *Multiculturalism in Mathematics, Science, and Technology*, have students read about the Zuni and complete pages 164 to 166.

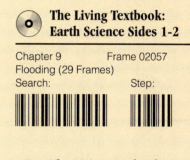

**The Living Textbook: Earth Science Sides 1-2**

Chapter 9          Frame 02057
Flooding (29 Frames)
Search:                    Step:

**The Living Textbook: Earth Science Sides 1-2**

Chapter 9          Frame 02004
Ganges Flood Plain (1 Frame)
Search:

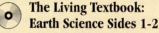

## Skills WorkOut

To help students learn about controlling wave erosion, have them do the Skills WorkOut.

**Answer** Answers will vary; actual methods include building sea walls, harbors, and jetties.

## Reteach

Ask students which kinds of wave erosion are suggested by the words *pressure, breaking,* and *dissolving.* (Hydraulic action, abrasion, chemical weathering)

## SkillBuilder

**Answers**

1. d, b, e, a, c

2. Sample d contained the most gravel and coarse sand. These sediments are the heaviest and are carried less distance as the river loses energy.

3. Sample c has the most light sediments, silt and clay. Because they are easiest to move, these deposits are farthest away from the river's mouth.

4. Answers will vary. For example, still in the water

5. Answers will vary. For example, along the river bed

Student reports should relate the size and distance a particle moves to the energy of the wave. Waves deposit larger sediments first and smallest sediments last, thereby sorting sediments by size.

### Integrating the Sciences

**Life Science** Explain that many saltwater animals are adapted to life on wave-pounded shores. For instance, strong shells protect mussels and snails. Ask students to research other adaptations and share them with the class.

---

▼ **ACTIVITY**

**Inferring**

*Erosion Control*

Waves pounding on a shoreline can cause damage to roads and buildings nearby. Infer how wave erosion could be controlled. Compare your ideas to various methods that people actually use to control wave erosion.

**SKILLS WORKOUT**

### Wave Erosion

A physical process called hydraulic action occurs when waves pound on cracks in rocks. First, a wave fills a crack with water. Before the water drains from the crack, another wave forces more water into the crack. This pressure causes the crack to get bigger. Eventually the rock breaks apart into smaller pieces that are further eroded by waves.

Another physical process that breaks up rocks is abrasion. The waves roll and tumble rocks against each other and break them into smaller pieces. These pieces are then eroded. The sediment carried by the waves can act like sandpaper, rubbing away at the rocks.

Finally, ocean water can chemically weather the rocks. The ocean water dissolves minerals in the rock, causing the rock to fall apart. These smaller pieces are picked up by the waves and further eroded.

### SkillBuilder  *Interpreting Data*

**ACTIVITY ACTIVITY**

#### Sedimentation and Sorting

When a river enters an ocean, the water slows down and drops its sediments. These sediments are then moved along the shore by the waves. The sediments drop out of the waves according to the density and size of the different sediment particles.

The graph shows the average sediment sizes of samples taken along a 1.6 km stretch of beach next to the mouth of a river. Study the graph, then answer the questions.

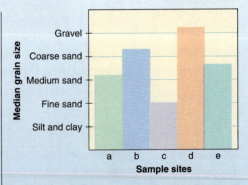

1. List the sites in order, from the largest to the smallest sediment size.

2. Which sample came from the site closest to the river's mouth? Why?

3. Which sample came from the site farthest away from the river's mouth? Why?

4. Where would you expect to find sediment sizes even smaller than these samples?

5. Where would you expect to find sediment sizes larger than these samples?

Write a short report explaining how waves sort sediments by size.

## Formations from Wave Erosion

Have you ever seen any of the shoreline formations below? Waves constantly change the shape of the shoreline. Both sand on a beach and rocky shorelines are eroded continuously by the waves. Along a rocky coast, wave erosion results in beautiful landforms.

**Sea Arch**

If the rock in a sea cave becomes eroded through, a natural arch may form. This natural arch is called a sea arch. Compare the sea arch in this photograph to the sea cave shown above. If erosion continues, the sea arch may collapse and leave behind a column of rock, or a sea stack.

**Sea Cave**

◀ When a coastal area consists of several types of rock that erode at different rates, landforms develop. Waves pounding against a cliff that contains weak rock may hollow out a hole. This rock cavity is called a sea cave. Find the sea cave in the photograph.

**Sea Stack** ▲

A sea stack is a tall tower of resistant rock standing offshore. It is the rock left standing from a steep wall of rock, or a sea cliff, after the waves eroded all of the weaker surrounding rock. Locate a sea stack in the photograph.

**Sea Cliff**

◀ When a rocky shore erodes at approximately the same rate all along an area, a steep wall of rock forms. This wall is called a sea cliff. Sea cliffs may extend along a rocky coast for many kilometers. At the base of a sea cliff, a platform called a sea terrace may form.

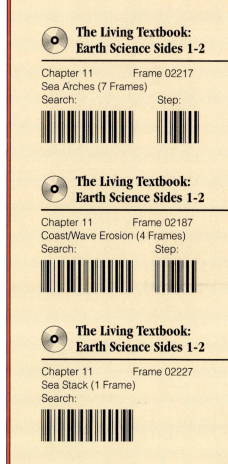

## Apply

After students read the page and study Figure 12.5, ask:

▶ How is a sea cliff or a sea arch related to a sandy beach? (Some of the particles the waves erode from a rocky coast can end up along a beach.)

▶ Why do most beaches have sand-sized particles? (Friction from waves breaks rocks into small particles.)

## Skills Development

**Infer** Ask students to imagine they are planning to sail along the U.S. Atlantic coastline. Have them explain why they would want a recent map of the coastline. (The coastline is constantly changing because of erosion and deposition.)

**Answer to In-Text Question**

① **A spit is connected to the shore, but a sand bar is not.**

**The Living Textbook:
Earth Science Sides 1-2**

Chapter 11          Frame 02271
Beaches (4 Frames)
Search:               Step:

**The Living Textbook:
Earth Science Sides 1-2**

Chapter 11          Frame 02325
Spits (8 Frames)
Search:               Step:

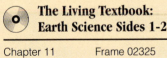

### Art Connection

Ask students to bring in photographs of beaches from magazines or family vacations. Have students use the photographs to draw or paint a beach scene. Discuss with the students why beaches are often chosen as the subject of paintings or photographs.

## Wave Deposits

Sediment is constantly deposited by waves. This material was eroded from the coastline or brought to the ocean by rivers. These sediments deposit as the water slows down. Over a long period of time, the deposited sediments collect along the shore. A shoreline that is covered with sand, gravel, or other sediment forms a *beach*.

Looking at Figure 12.5, you might think that beach sediment stands still. However, if you could color some of the sand and watch it over a period of several hours or days, you would see that the sand actually moves along the beach. The sand is continuously eroded and deposited along the shoreline by waves and currents.

Currents are like rivers that flow offshore in the water along a beach. Currents move large amounts of sediment parallel to the shore. When these currents meet a change in the direction of the shoreline or deeper water, they suddenly slow down and deposit the sediment. This deposit is called a *spit*. Look at an example of a spit in Figure 12.6. A spit extends out from a beach across a bay or inlet.

Sand bars are features similar to spits but not connected to the beach. Sand bars may form offshore when breaking waves pull the sand from the beach into the water. This creates sand bars that are parallel to the beach.

Sand carried by waves and currents to the head of a bay or inlet may form small pocket beaches. Over a long period of time, the deposition of spits and beaches fills in the bays and inlets with sand, making the coastline more regular. This deposition of sediment straightens out the coastline.

Waves are most commonly found in the ocean. However, large lakes, such as the Great Lakes, also have waves. Large lakes create some of the same landforms that oceans do.

**Figure 12.5** ▲
Although this beach in Kauai, Hawaii looks quiet, the sand is actually being moved along the shoreline by the pounding waves.

**Figure 12.6** ▲
The Dungeness Spit in the state of Washington is a large natural spit. How does a spit differ from a sand bar? ①

## Integrating the Sciences

**Environmental Science** Wetlands are swamps, marshes, bays, and lagoons that provide homes for many species of plants and animals. Wetlands are often filled in or dredged for housing, recreation, industry, agriculture, and shipping. Dredging often drains swamps that adjoin wetland areas. Protection laws and regulations help safeguard some wetlands. The federal government also buys wetlands and adds them to the National Wildlife Refuge System. Have students research wetland destruction and reclamation and share what they learn with the class.

### Science and Society  *Harbor Dredging*

Wave erosion and deposition move sand from one place to another. Sand often deposits in bays where the water has less energy to move the sediment. Over time, bays fill with sand deposits.

Bays are important sites for shipping. Bays provide ships with harbors for loading and unloading cargo. Therefore, the natural filling-in of the bay with wave deposits interferes with shipping. Sand bars can block the entrance to the harbor, and the bottom of the bay can become too shallow for large ships. New shipping channels are created by removing sediment that settled on the bottom of the harbor.

Many communities that surround harbors rely on dredging to keep the harbors operating. A dredging operation consists of a barge or platform that sits out in the bay. A large pump connects to several pipes. The pump sucks up the sediments on the bottom of the bay through one pipe. It then pumps out the collected sediment, either offshore or downshore through another pipe. The redepositing of sediments can cause changes in the natural erosion and deposition patterns in other areas of the shoreline.

How often dredging is done depends on how much sediment is deposited. In some harbors along sandy coastlines, such as Florida's, dredges operate nonstop.

**Figure 12.7** ▲
Dredges can be stationary or mobile. This floating dredge deepens submarine channels.

### Check and Explain

1. Using drawings and words, describe how a river forms from runoff.

2. How does a river's pattern of erosion change as it develops through the young, mature, and old river stages?

3. **Classify** Would you find each landform on a rocky or sandy shoreline: spit, sea stack, sea cliff, beach, or sea arch?

4. **Compare and Contrast** How are wave and river deposits similar? How are they different?

---

Ask students to explain how harbor dredging can form new beaches downshore or change the composition of the ocean floor offshore. (Answers will vary; students should recognize that material removed from a harbor by dredging is deposited elsewhere and may greatly change the sea-floor topography and ecology of the deposit site.)

## EVALUATE

### WrapUp

**Reteach** List the following features on the chalkboard: moving water, sediment, erosion, deposition, meanders, floodplain, delta, alluvial fan. Make a second list including moving water, sediment, erosion, deposition, sea arch, sea cave, sea cliff, beach. Ask students to make two concept maps, using the terms from each of the lists. (Check concept maps for distinctions between erosion results and deposition results.)

Use Review Worksheet 12.2.

### Check and Explain

1. Although answers will vary, students should indicate that runoff forms rills and gullies; gullies join to make streams and streams join to make rivers.

2. A young river is very active at eroding. A mature river is balanced between the amount of erosion it does and the sediment it transports. An old river does less eroding and more transporting of sediment.

3. Sandy, rocky, rocky, sandy, rocky

4. In both deposits, largest materials deposit first and smaller materials travel farther. Wave deposits occur along shorelines; river deposits occur at shorelines, deltas, or alluvial fans and during flooding across the floodplain.

### Section Objectives
For a list of section objectives, see the Student Edition page.

### Skills Objectives
Students should be able to:

**Communicate** adjectives that describe glaciers.

**Make a Model** of a valley eroded by glaciers.

**Classify** glacial formations.

**Observe** and **Model** glacial erosion.

### Vocabulary
glacier, outwash, moraine, till

---

## MOTIVATE

### Skills WarmUp
To give students practice in describing glaciers, have them do the Skills WarmUp.
**Answer** Adjectives might include *massive, frozen, slow-moving,* and *ancient.*

### Misconceptions
Even though students may understand how slowly glaciers move, they may think glaciers develop quickly. Explain that many seasons of snowfall must first produce an ice mass great enough to melt the bottommost layers.

**The Living Textbook:**
**Earth Science Sides 1-2**

Chapter 8      Frame 01629
Valley/Continental Glacial Systems
(2 Frames)
Search:         Step:

---

### Integrating the Sciences

**Physical Science** Demonstrate the force of ice expansion. Completely fill a lidded plastic container with water. Place the lid on the container, making sure there is no air inside the container, and tape the lid on tightly. Put the container in a freezer. After the water has turned to ice, remove the container and observe what happened. (Ice expands as it forms. The container lid will break loose from the tape to make room for expansion.)

---

### ▼ ACTIVITY

#### Communicating

*What a Glacier Is . . .*
  In one minute, write as many adjectives as you can think of to describe glaciers. As a class, compile your list of adjectives on the chalkboard. Then narrow the list down to the ten best adjectives.

**SKILLS WARMUP**

---

## 12.3  Ice Erosion

### Objectives

▶ **Explain** how glaciers form.

▶ **Describe** the process of ice erosion.

▶ **Classify** landforms as the result of glacial erosion or glacial deposition.

▶ **Make a model** of a valley glacier and label its parts.

---

Like giant bulldozers, glaciers move very slowly. But they are capable of eroding and depositing large amounts of materials. Glacial movement produces many distinctive landforms.

### Glaciers

When the amount of snow is so great that it can't completely melt, **glaciers** form. As the layers of snow pile up, the weight on the underlying snow increases. Eventually this weight tightly packs the snow underneath, forming glacial ice. The pressure on the ice at the bottom becomes so great that it partially melts. The entire ice mass starts moving. A glacier is formed.

The two types of glaciers are shown below. Glaciers that form in high mountain valleys are called *valley glaciers*. Glaciers that cover large areas in polar regions, like Antarctica, are called *continental glaciers*.

**Figure 12.8**
The photograph on the left is a valley glacier. The one on the right is Greenland, which is a continental glacier. ▼

## Literature Connection

Read passages from the book *The Clan of the Cave Bear,* by Jean M. Auel. Explain that the book is a fictional account of the lives of ice-age people living in Europe during the Pleistocene epoch, and that the author did extensive research on tool making and other aspects of prehistoric life.

A glacier moves by sliding over the thin layer of water due to melting on the bottom of the ice mass. Once the glacier starts to slide, gravity pulls the ice mass downhill. Gravity moves glaciers a few meters to 100 m per year.

### Ice Ages

Glaciers have been a feature on the earth's surface for a long time. In the past, the climate of the earth has been cooler, and large glaciers covered much of the earth. These periods of cooling are referred to as ice ages. Look at Figure 12.9. Where did glaciers cover the earth in the recent past? ①

During the last ice age, continental glaciers covered the northern part of North America. The western United States had many valley glaciers at the same time. The glaciers of the last ice age caused many of the landforms in these areas.

**Figure 12.9** ▲
During the last ice age, did glaciers cover the area where you live? ②

## Historical Notebook

### Ice Age Societies

If you imagine Ice Age culture, you may think of people dressed in animal hides standing around a cave fire. However, scientific findings show that Ice Age people had a complex society. Evidence from Ice Age base camps reveals that these people lived in dwellings, made clothing, and created art.

Ice Age people probably didn't live in caves at all. In fact, an excavation site in the Ukraine uncovered a village built from the bones of wooly mammoths. At other sites, archeologists discovered wood and stone that may have been used for housing.

Caves were an important part of Ice Age culture, however. Many caves have been found decorated with art. Caves may have served as sacred places or places to record history.

Engravings and cave drawings give clues to Ice Age clothing. Ice Age art shows people wearing parkas, collared shirts with sleeves, and boots.

Site findings of beads and shark teeth suggest that they also adorned themselves with jewelry.

1. What findings suggest that Ice Age people had a complex culture?

2. **Write** Describe a typical day if you lived during the Ice Age.

### Discuss

Ask students how glaciers and mass movements, such as mudslides, are related. (Both respond to the force of gravity and move downhill.)

### *Historical Notebook*

**Enrich** Suggest that students research the discovery of Lascaux Cave, shown in the photograph. Have them write a report about what the discoverers found in the cave. (Four teenagers found paintings of horses, bulls, and deer.)

**Answers**

1. Bones, wood, and stone used for housing; paintings with parkas, boots, collars, and sleeves; beads and shark teeth from possible jewelry

2. Answers will vary; students should refer to the cooler climate.

### Integrated Learning

Use Integrating Worksheet 12.3.

**Answers to In-Text Questions**

① Figure 12.9 suggests large portions of the northern hemisphere.

② Students living in most states north of Tennessee should answer yes.

 **The Living Textbook: Earth Science Sides 1-2**

Chapter 8          Frame 01645
Valley Glacier (1 Frame)
Search:

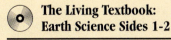

## *Language Arts Connection*

The French word *cirque* is derived from a Latin term meaning *circus*. Ask students to infer the connection between the ancient word for *circus* and the word used to describe bowl-shaped holes carved out of a mountainside.

---

◀ **TEACH** ▪ *Continued*

## Critical Thinking

**Reason by Analogy** As students begin to study pages 276 and 277, ask them to think of water erosion and deposition as an analogy to glacial erosion and deposition. How are they similar and different? (Answers will vary. An outwash plain is like a delta; both erode land underneath and to the side; a glacier moves slower than water.)

### *Explore Visually*

After students study Figures 12.10 and 12.11, ask the following questions:

▶ What is a cirque? How is it formed and where is it found? (A bowl-shaped hole carved from a mountainside by a glacier)

▶ Which is a glacier likely to leave behind, a U-shaped valley or a V-shaped valley. Why? (As a glacier moves through a V-shaped valley it erodes the sides, widening the valley to form a U-shape.)

▶ How might glaciers form a ridge or sharp mountain peak? (Several cirques close together can result in the formation of a sharp peak.)

**The Living Textbook:**
**Earth Science Sides 1-2**

Chapter 8          Frame 01655
Glacial Erosion (35 Frames)
Search:          Step:

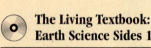

**The Living Textbook:**
**Earth Science Sides 1-2**

Chapter 8          Frame 01657
Cirques/U-Shaped Valleys (7 Frames)
Search:          Step:

**276**

---

### Glacial Erosion

As a glacier moves, it causes erosion. The melted water from the glacier's surface or bottom seeps into cracks in rock and freezes. Ice wedging causes the rock to break apart. The rock fragments stick to the glacial ice and are plucked out as the glacier moves. These pieces of rock stuck to the bottom and sides of a glacier act like sandpaper. As the glacier moves, it scrapes and scratches the bedrock and soil underneath and along its sides. As shown in Figure 12.10, many landforms result from glacial erosion.

Unlike valley glaciers, continental glaciers tend to level large surface areas through the scraping and grinding of thick ice. Large areas carved out by continental glaciers can fill with water when the glaciers retreat. The Great Lakes along the Canadian border and the Finger Lakes in New York are examples of this process.

**Figure 12.10**
**Landforms from Glacial Erosion** ▼

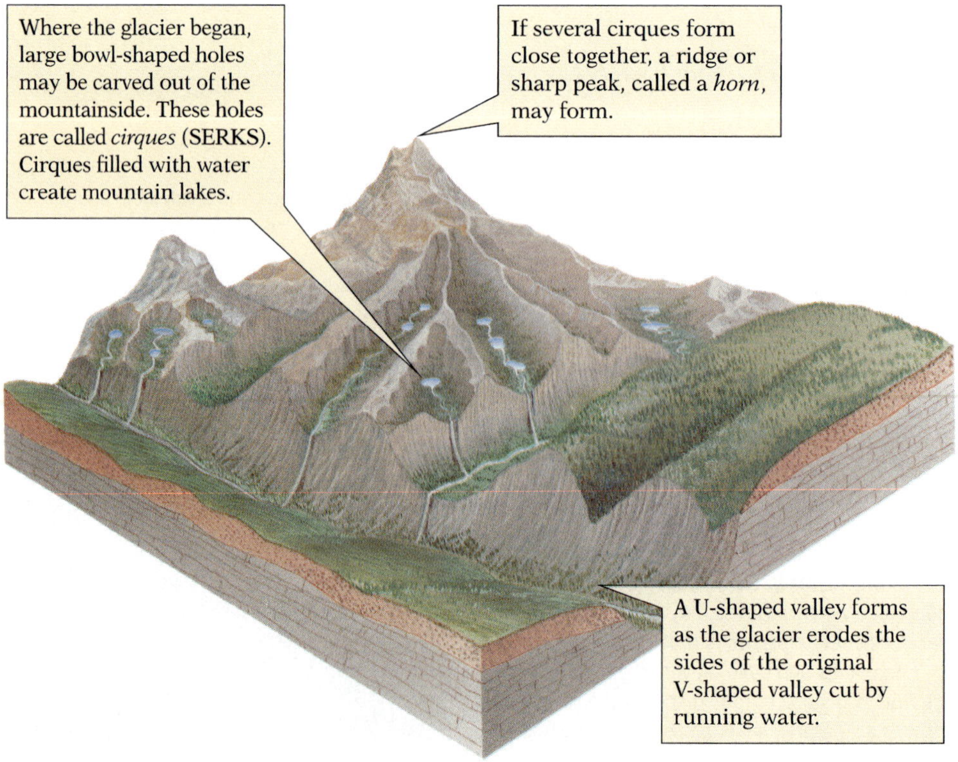

Where the glacier began, large bowl-shaped holes may be carved out of the mountainside. These holes are called *cirques* (SERKS). Cirques filled with water create mountain lakes.

If several cirques form close together, a ridge or sharp peak, called a *horn*, may form.

A U-shaped valley forms as the glacier erodes the sides of the original V-shaped valley cut by running water.

## Themes in Science

**Diversity and Unity** Glacial deposition and erosion produce a wide variety of formations on the surface of the earth. Although each individual formation is unique, similar formations can be found anywhere in the world where glaciers have molded the land.

▶ How are a delta and an outwash plain alike? How are they different? (Both result from deposition. A delta consists of fine sediment carried downstream by a river; an outwash plain is a sorted and layered deposit from a meltwater stream.)

▶ How do a moraine and an outwash plain differ? (Moraine till is a jumble of different-sized sediments deposited by glacial ice. In an outwash plain layered, sorted sediment is deposited by glacial meltwater.)

▶ What happens when a large block of ice breaks away from a glacier? (The ice may become covered with sediment. When the ice melts, the sediment collapses and forms a hole. If the hole fills with water, it forms a kettle lake.)

### Glacial Deposits

Landforms also result from glacial deposits, as shown in Figure 12.11. As the ice moves to the front of the glacier, it carries along rocks and other sediments. The glacier drops some rocks as it moves. However, much sediment is carried to the front of the glacier. The meltwater streams that flow from the glacier carry some of the sediment. Deposits from meltwater streams are similar to an alluvial fan. The heaviest sediments drop out before the lighter ones, resulting in a sorted and layered deposit. This sorted and layered sediment is called **outwash**.

If the weather warms up, the glacier begins to melt faster than the ice accumulates. The glacier retreats and drops its sediment load in a big pile or ridge called a **moraine**. Moraines left behind during the last ice age helped to form Long Island, Cape Cod, and Nantucket. A moraine contains an assortment of sediment sizes. This mixture of sediments in a moraine is called **till**. When cemented together, till forms conglomerate sedimentary rock.

**Critical Thinking**

**Reason and Conclude** Ask students why they think Wisconsin's Kettle Moraine State Forest has this name. (It is in an area where continental glaciers left deposits and many kettle lakes were formed.)

**Figure 12.11**
**Landforms from Glacial Deposition** ▼

At the front of a glacier, melting water deposits sediments. The sediments form deltalike areas called *outwash plains*.

At the head of an outwash plain, there is often a large ridge of till. This ridge, called a moraine, is left behind by a retreating glacier.

Kettle lake

Outwash

A large block of ice may break off from a retreating glacier. The ice becomes covered with sediment. The ice melts, creates a hole under the sediment, and collapses. If water fills the hole, it forms a *kettle lake*.

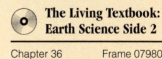

**The Living Textbook:
Earth Science Side 2**

Chapter 36          Frame 07980
Glacier Melting (Movie)
Search:                  Play:

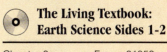

**The Living Textbook:
Earth Science Sides 1–2**

Chapter 8          Frame 01859
Outwash (27 Frames)
Search:                  Step:

## Enrich

Divide the class into two groups. One group should research the benefits of Antarctic exploration; the second should research the environmental costs of Antarctic exploration. Have the groups present their findings and hold a class discussion about the pros and cons of Antarctic research.

## EVALUATE

### WrapUp

**Review** Have students work in groups to describe or define each of the following terms: *glacier, continental glacier, valley glacier, cirque, ice age, outwash, moraine, till.*

Use Review Worksheet 12.3.

### Check and Explain

1. Unmelted layers of snow build up and turn to ice. Eventually, pressure on bottom layers melts some of the lowest ice, and the glacier starts moving.

2. Ice wedging causes rocks to break apart. The rock fragments stick to the glacial ice making it like sandpaper. The glacier scrapes and scratches the rock.

3. *Glacial Deposition:* till, outwash plain, kettle lake, moraine. *Glacial Erosion:* cirque, U-shaped valley, horn.

4. Check students' drawings for accuracy. The eroded landscape should include a cirque, horn, and U-shaped valley.

**The Living Textbook: Earth Science Sides 1-2**

| | |
|---|---|
| Chapter 13 | Frame 02380 |

Aerial Photos of Antarctica (22 Frames)
Search:          Step:

## Integrating the Sciences

**Health** Overexposure to severe cold can result in frostbite and hypothermia. Frostbite occurs when body tissues are frozen. In severe cases, frostbitten fingers and toes have to be amputated. Hypothermia occurs when a person's body temperature drops below 95°F (35°C). Deep hypothermia can result in death. Ask students to suggest ways that scientists in the Antarctic could avoid overexposure to the cold temperatures. (Limit time spent outside; wear proper clothing that covers exposed skin; know how to treat overexposure.) Students may also want to research first aid techniques for frostbite and hypothermia.

### Science and Technology
### *Working in Antarctica*

Imagine your classroom is as cold as your freezer on warm, sunny days. That is actually the normal summertime climate for the nearly 4,000 scientists who live and work in Antarctica. Imagine what it's like in the winter! The scientists must bundle up to avoid frostbite. They pull their instruments on sleds and often ski or travel by snowmobile to their testing sites. For studies in more remote areas, scientists travel in airplanes equipped with skis for landing.

In Antarctica, scientists study glaciers, earth history, the atmosphere, wildlife, and volcanoes. Much of the research involves direct observation and sample collecting. Many Antarctic studies use remote-controlled equipment. Instruments are set up at the testing site. Probes collect information and beam it to satellites, which relay the information back to the scientists. This type of technology is very important for conducting year-round research, since the winter temperatures in Antarctica can drop to as low as –57°C.

In one Antarctic study, scientists are using a roving robot. The robot has eight walking legs and high-resolution cameras for eyes. The robot is attached by a cable to a transporter. It will send information to the transporter for storage in case the robot is destroyed during its mission. If all goes well, however, the robot will collect samples and return to the transporter for a safe trip back to camp.

**Figure 12.12** ▲
Scientists need special tools to study the extreme conditions in the Antarctic.

### Check and Explain

1. How do glaciers form?

2. Explain how glaciers erode a mountain.

3. **Classify** Make a table with one column labeled *Glacial Deposition* and the other column labeled *Glacial Erosion*. Classify each of the following in the proper column in the table: cirque, U-shaped valley, till, outwash plain, horn, kettle lake, moraine.

4. **Make a Model** Draw a view of a mountainous landscape. Then draw the same area after erosion by a valley glacier. Label the various glacial formations.

**Time** 40 minutes    **Group** pairs

**Materials**

15 pieces of ice (water frozen in paper cups will work)

15 pieces of stiff wire

15 squares of hard plastic

15 handfuls of sand

paper towels

### Prelab Discussion

Have students read the entire activity. Discuss a few points before beginning:

▶ Review how glaciers move and erode surfaces.

▶ Discuss what the ice and sand represent.

▶ Discuss the limitations of the model used in this activity.

▶ Discuss how force and pressure are related. Remind students that the same force can produce different pressures, depending on the area over which it is applied.

## Analysis

1. Slow, firm push; this models the high, constant pressure exerted by accumulating layers of snow and ice in a glacier.

2. Picking up the sand slowly

3. By pulling slowly and steadily, or by slowly pushing the wire completely through the ice

4. The high pressure was melting the ice at the point of contact.

5. The melted ice refreezes, picking up the sand.

6. The ice with sand embedded scratches the plastic in the same way that rocks carried in glacial ice scrape the ground.

---

## Activity 12  *How can you model a glacier?*

*Skills*  Observe; Model; Infer

### Task 1  Prelab Prep

Collect the following materials: a large piece of ice, paper towel, a piece of wire, a square of hard plastic, a handful of sand.

### Task 2  Data Record

On a sheet of paper, copy Table 12.1. Record all your observations in the table.

**Table 12.1  Glacial Erosion Model**

| Event | Observations |
|---|---|
| Inserting wire quickly | |
| Inserting wire slowly | |
| Smooth ice on plastic | |
| Picking up sand quickly | |
| Picking up sand slowly | |
| Sandy ice on plastic | |

### Task 3  Procedure

1. Place the paper towel on your desk. Put the piece of ice on the paper towel. Try to quickly force the wire into the ice. Record your observations.

2. Slowly but firmly push the end of the wire against the ice. Hold it there for several minutes. Record your observations.

3. Place the plastic square on your desk. Rub the piece of ice back and forth on the plastic square. Observe the surface of the plastic. Record your observations.

4. Place the sand in a layer on the plastic square. Try to quickly pick up the sand with the ice. Record your observations.

5. Slowly but firmly push the ice down onto the sand. Leave the ice on the sand for several

minutes. Remove the ice from the sand, and record your observations.

6. Clean the plastic square of sand. Rub the sandy side of the ice back and forth on the plastic square. Observe the surface of the plastic. Record your observations.

### Task 4  Analysis

1. Which method worked the best for pushing the wire into the ice? How did inserting the wire demonstrate how glaciers melt?

2. Which method worked best for picking up the sand?

3. How could you remove a wire stuck in ice without destroying the ice block?

4. What was happening at the site where the wire or sand was slowly pushed into the ice?

5. What happened when you released the slow steady pressure?

6. Which caused the greatest change on the surface of the plastic, the smooth ice or the ice embedded with sand? How did this model demonstrate the effect of glaciers upon bedrock?

### Task 5  Conclusion

Write a short paragraph explaining how your glacier model is similar to actual glaciers.

### *Everyday Application*

Explain how inserting the wire into the ice is similar to the process that enables a figure skater to move across the ice.

### *Extension*

Design a model that shows glacial deposition. Test the model that you design. Decide how it is similar to actual glacial deposition and how it is different.

## Conclusion

Glaciers move as the weight of ice and snow causes ice at the bottom to melt. Loose rocks picked up by the glacier abrade the ground as the glacier moves over it. Both of these processes are modeled in this activity.

## Everyday Application

The pressure between the blades and the ice causes a thin layer of ice to melt. The skater glides on this layer of water.

## Extension

Student models will vary. Make sure the models are accurate and that students describe the similarities and differences between their models and actual glaciers.

**Section Objectives**
For a list of section objectives, see the Student Edition page.

**Skills Objectives**
Students should be able to:

**Predict** how wind erosion affects surfaces.

**Make a Model** of particle movement.

**Make a Model** of sand dunes.

**Vocabulary**
deflation

## *Themes in Science*
**Energy** The energy of wind erosion begins with the sun. Wind is a form of solar energy. The sun's radiation sets up convection currents that transfer kinetic energy to the particles in the moving air.

## *Social Studies Connection*
Windmills were first used in Europe around the 12th century. Windmills used wind energy to pump water, grind grain, and power sawmills. Windmills are now also widely used to generate electricity. Have students discuss the use of windmills they have seen or have read about.

---

## MOTIVATE

### *Skills WarmUp*
To help students predict the effects of wind erosion, have them do the Skills WarmUp.
**Answer** The sandpaper rubs off some of the paint. Students may suggest that wind could do this by blowing sand against the pencil.

### Prior Knowledge
Gauge how much students know about wind erosion by asking the following questions:

▶ How does a windy place look compared to a place where there is no wind?

▶ Where does the dust from a dust cloud go?

▶ Where do sand dunes come from?

---

## TEACH

### Discuss
Ask students why wind erosion is more common in dry areas than in wet areas. (Water makes soil particles too heavy for wind to carry and promotes vegetation cover) Have them describe conditions that enable wind erosion to occur. (Drought; soil left unplanted)

**280**

---

### ▼ ACTIVITY
#### Predicting

*Sandblasting*

Rub the painted ridges of your pencil across a small piece of sandpaper. What happened to the paint? What does the surface of the pencil feel like? Explain what happened. How could wind do the same thing?

#### SKILLS WARMUP

---

## 12.4 Wind Erosion

### Objectives

▶ **Describe** the conditions necessary for wind erosion to occur.

▶ **Explain** how sand particles move.

▶ **Compare** and **contrast** abrasion and deflation.

▶ **Make models** of the different types of sand dunes.

---

If you have ever gotten dirt or sand in your eyes on a windy day, you know that the wind can move dirt. Wind causes erosion, just like running water, waves, and glaciers do. Wind not only erodes areas, it also deposits materials to make unique landforms. If you have ever been to a beach, you probably have seen the most common landform deposited by winds: the dunes.

### Energy in Wind

As with running water and waves, the energy of the wind determines the size of the materials it carries. As wind blows across the ground, it lifts and moves dry, loose surface materials. Weak winds have little energy, so they carry only small particles like dust. Strong winds have more energy. The energy creates more of an uplifting force. Strong winds are often more turbulent. The more turbulent the wind, the more sediments it carries. Just as the turbulence of running water prevents sediments from dropping out, the turbulence of strong wind prevents heavier particles from dropping. A constant, strong wind can develop a large dust cloud, like the one shown in Figure 12.13.

Most wind erosion occurs in the dry areas of the world, such as deserts. In wetter areas, water causes the soil particles to clump together, forming pieces that are too heavy for the wind to pick up. However, if a drought causes the ground to dry out and the soil is bare, wind erosion can occur anywhere. Wind erosion can also occur if the soil is left unplanted for a long period of time. Plants keep the soil from being blown away.

**Figure 12.13** ▲
Beside strong winds, several other factors contribute to dust storms, such as arid climates, droughts, and poor planting practices.

### *Themes in Science*

**Scale and Structure** The movements and collisions of many individual, tiny grains of sand are responsible for shaping sand dunes that are giant by comparison.

## Skills WorkOut

To help the students understand how wind moves particles, have them do the Skills WorkOut.
**Answer** If students blow carefully, the sand grains will move and soon form long, fine ridges that can serve as models for sand dunes. If students blow hard the sand will scatter and not form ridges.

## Critical Thinking

**Compare and Contrast** Ask students how the movement of particles by wind is like the movement of sediment by water. (In each case large particles move only a short distance, medium particles move farther, and the smallest particles are carried the farthest.)

## Skills Development

**Communicate** Have one student draw the leap-frog path of a sand grain on the chalkboard. Ask a volunteer to draw arrows representing the force of the wind moving the sand grain. Have another student draw arrows representing the force of gravity acting on the sand grain.

**Answers to In-Text Questions**

① **It stops at the top of the dune; it is probably a large particle.**

② **It hops over other grains of sand and goes farther than the grain followed by the green arrow; it is a small particle.**

## Particle Movement

Follow the movement of the sand grains shown in Figure 12.14. How would you describe the movement of the particles? Sand particles are too heavy to be held up in the air for a long time. The sand grains are lifted into the air by the wind. Then they roll forward and collide with other sand grains. The collision sends the first grains up and over the other grains. The wind provides a horizontal force that sends the grains forward. Gravity pulls the grains back down to the ground. The result is that the sand grains follow a rounded path as they leap-frog along.

When a sand grain lands on the ground, it is picked up again by the wind or buried in the loose sand, which throws other grains in the air. This occurs simultaneously with many other sand grains, producing a cloud-like layer of moving sand just above the ground, as shown in Figure 12.14.

This type of movement also separates the sediment into different sizes. Large particles are left behind, close to their source. Medium-sized particles only move a short distance away. The smallest particles are carried the farthest. In both strong and weak winds, however, particles are carried only a few centimeters to a meter above the ground. The movement of particles over a distance is due to the energy transfer from one particle to another.

▼ **ACTIVITY**

### Making a Model

*Sand Dunes*

**1.** Cover a hard surface, such as your desk or a section of the floor, with paper towels.
**2.** Place a small pile of sand in the center of the towels.
**3.** Using a drinking straw, slowly and carefully blow the sand across the towels. What happens to the sand? Do shapes form? What would happen if you blew hard? How is this a model of sand dune formation by wind?

**SKILLS WORKOUT**

**Figure 12.14**
Wind causes sand particles to move in little leaps. What happens to the sand particle followed by the green arrow? What ① happens to the sand particle followed by the red arrow? ▼ ②

## Apply

Ask students to turn back to page 263. Have them explain how the face of the Sphinx has been changed by wind erosion. (Abrasion has worn away its features.)

## Enrich

Ask students if they have ever heard of sandblasting. Tell them that sandblasting is a technique used to clean stone, engrave metal, and smooth glass. Compressed air forces sand through a hose; the sand acts as an abrasive.

### Answers to In-Text Questions

① **The worn rock has ripples suggesting that original rock had layers of differing hardness. Abrasion has worn more of the softer rock away, leaving the harder layers.**

② **The wind carried away the fine-grained loose sediment and left behind the larger rocks.**

 **The Living Textbook: Earth Science Sides 1-2**

Chapter 23          Frame 02842
Arches (30 Frames)
Search:                    Step:

**The Living Textbook: Earth Science Sides 1-2**

Chapter 10          Frame 02167
Desert Pavement (2 Frames)
Search:                    Step:

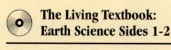

 *Cooperative Learning*

Have students work in cooperative groups of three or four to make erosion collages. Tell students to use magazine photographs that illustrate formations made by wind, running water, glaciers, gravity, and waves. Some students may want to donate vacation photographs that illustrate erosion formations. Tell students to decide how to divide the work: collecting photographs of each type of erosion formation, designing the collage, and assembling the collage. When students finish their collages, display them on a bulletin board titled "Nature's Sculptors."

**Abrasion**   If you've ever felt the sand whip across your legs on a windy day at the beach, you have experienced abrasion. Sand grains wear away the surface of buildings, telephone poles, and rocks by abrasion. The sand-filled air is like a moving piece of sandpaper.

The effect of windblown sand depends on the hardness of a rock's surface. If a rock is the same hardness along the entire surface, the windblown sand smoothes and polishes the rock's surface. If a rock surface is made of various types of rock with different hardnesses, the windblown sand causes abrasion at different rates. The surface of the rock becomes rippled rather than smooth, as shown in Figure 12.15.

The abrasion of rock by wind erosion can sometimes result in unusual landforms. For example, the forces of abrasion may eventually cut through rock layers, forming arches. Tall towers may be left standing after the wind carries away the soft material that surrounded hard inner layers. However, it takes many years for windblown sand to

**Figure 12.16** ▲
Desert pavement is a hard, stony surface. How did this desert pavement in Arizona form? ②

erode large rock surfaces. Most erosion of large rocks is due to running water.

**Deflation**   The process of wind carrying away loose sediment is called **deflation**. Deflation comes from the Latin word meaning "to blow away." Deflation occurs primarily in desert regions. As the wind blows along the ground, it scoops up and carries away the loose sediment, such as dust and sand. The larger pebbles left behind form a hard, stony surface called *desert pavement*. Look for the rocks in the desert pavement in Figure 12.16.

In areas where the sediment is mostly fine–grained dust, deflation can cause serious problems. Turbulent winds can create dust storms. Unlike heavier sand grains, winds lift dust particles high into the air and move them long distances. Recall the area in the United States that became known as the Dust Bowl in the 1930s. The Dust Bowl disaster was caused by deflation. Deflation removed most of the fertile soil in the Great Plains after several years of severe drought.

**Figure 12.15** ▲
Abrasion causes the wearing away of rock. How can you tell that this rock is composed of several different types of rock? ①

## Integrating the Sciences

**Astronomy** Pictures of Mars' surface reveal extensive regions of sand dunes. Obtain pictures of Martian sand dunes. Ask students to infer what sand dunes reveal about Mars. (Mars has strong winds. Analysis shows that wind up to 150 km/hr may exist on the planet.)

### Wind Deposits

When wind slows down, it drops the sediments it is carrying. The type of landform produced by the deposited sediments depends on the size and amount of particles, the wind direction, and the amount of wind from a single direction. Deposits formed by windblown sand are called *dunes*. Deposits formed by windblown dust are called *loess*.

Dunes form when an obstacle, such as a rock or a plant, causes wind to slow. The sand piles up and blocks the wind, causing more sand to deposit. Dunes have a gentle slope facing the wind and a steep slope away from the wind. As the wind blows, it pushes the sand up and over the top of a dune. This constant motion causes the dune to move forward.

One type of sand dune is a crescent, or horn-shaped, dune. These dunes have horns that point in the direction of the wind. They occur where land is very flat and hard, and there is little sediment and few plants.

Transverse dunes are long, continuous sand ridges. They form at right angles to the wind direction in areas with a large supply of sediment. Transverse dunes are commonly found at the beach or in large deserts.

Longitudinal dunes form in areas with strong winds and little sediment. These dunes run parallel to the wind direction. Longitudinal dunes form in desert areas with moderate amounts of sand.

## Explore Visually

After students study the illustrations, ask these questions:

▶ What kind of dunes form in areas with strong winds and little sediment? What direction do the dunes face? (Longitudinal; parallel to the wind direction)

▶ Which kind of dune forms at right angles to the wind? Where does it form? (Transverse; in areas with a lot of sediment.)

▶ Where will you find a crescent dune? What does it look like? (Where land is flat and hard with little sediment and few plants; a crescent or an animal horn)

## Critical Thinking

**Generalize** Ask students: If you visit a crescent dune on a calm day, how can you tell which way the wind usually blows? (The dune's gentler slope faces the wind and its steeper slope faces away from the wind.)

**The Living Textbook: Earth Science Sides 1-2**

Chapter 10          Frame 02142
Dunes (11 Frames)
Search:                    Step:

**The Living Textbook: Earth Science Sides 1-2**

Chapter 10          Frame 02137
Longitudinal/Transverse/Crescent Dunes (3 Frames)
Search:                    Step:

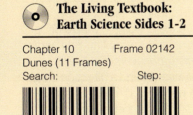

## TEACH ▪ *Continued*

### Research

Have students research what U.S. farmers are doing to protect the soil from erosion. (Conservation methods include minimum tillage, contour planting, terracing, and strip cropping.)

## EVALUATE

### WrapUp

**Reinforce** Ask students to explain how the wind of a tornado can lift large objects. (It contains a great deal of energy and is very turbulent.)

Use Review Worksheet 12.4.

### Check and Explain

1. Dry desert sand dune, sand dune covered with some beach grass, bare field of damp earth, grass-covered field

2. In a leap-frog fashion—they move upward, roll forward, collide with other grains, and fall to earth.

3. In both, the wind moves fine sediment particles. In abrasion, sand particles wear away rock surfaces; in deflation, loose sediment is carried away, leaving larger sediments behind.

4. Check students' drawings and descriptions for accuracy. *Crescent:* point in wind's direction, land is very flat, little sediment; *transverse:* at right angles to wind's direction, large supply of sediments; *longitudinal:* run parallel to wind's direction, little sediment, strong winds

 **Multicultural Perspectives**

People live in many desert regions including the Middle East, Northern Africa, and Central Australia. Have students research the foods desert people eat and their methods of farming and finding water.

**Figure 12.17** ▲
The increasing deserts in Africa have caused food shortages and climatic changes.

### Science and Society   *The Moving Desert*

About one-third of the earth's land surface is covered by deserts. Although some of these deserts occur because of warm temperatures and a lack of rain, many deserts have been formed or expanded by human activity. As shown in Figure 12.17, Africa has been severely affected by desert expansion. The spreading Sahara Desert removes about 100 000 hectares of useful land every year. Many human activities contribute to the spreading of deserts, a process known as desertification. These include overgrazing, poor farming practices, and overpopulation.

The primary activity responsible for increasing the size of deserts is farming. In many areas of the world, such as parts of Africa, China, and the United States, farmers cut down trees and remove the grasses to create more fields for farming. The trees and grasses help hold the soil in place. Without plants, the soil is left open to the attack of the wind. If a drought occurs or if the water in an area is used up, the soil dries out. Much of the soil blows away.

In many areas of the world, the balance between the vegetation and the climate is quite delicate. If the balance is upset, the area cannot recover, and a desert forms. Fortunately, scientists are recognizing this situation and are studying ways to avoid the problem. Proper water use and crop planting could help make these areas productive again.

### Check and Explain

1. Place the following in order as examples of areas with the most to the least erosion: a grass-covered field, a bare field of damp earth, a dry desert sand dune, a sand dune covered with some beach grass.

2. Describe how sand particles move.

3. **Compare and Contrast** How are deflation and abrasion alike? How are they different?

4. **Make Models** Create a separate drawing for each type of sand dune. Include in each drawing the type of surrounding area in which the sand dune would form.

# Chapter 12 Review

## Concept Summary

### 12.1 Gravity and Erosion
▶ Weathered materials are eroded by the action of water, wind, ice, and gravity. Deposition piles these materials elsewhere.
▶ Gravity causes mass movement. Types of mass movement are landslides, mudflows, slump, and creep.

### 12.2 Water Erosion
▶ Rivers are classified as young, mature, or old depending on how much they erode an area.
▶ When a river slows down, it deposits sediments to form deltas, levees, floodplains, and alluvial fans.
▶ Wave erosion forms sea cliffs, sea caves, sea stacks, and sea arches. Wave deposits form beaches, spits, and bars.

### 12.3 Ice Erosion
▶ Great amounts of snow form valley glaciers and continental glaciers.
▶ Ice wedging, scraping, and scratching are glacial processes. Glacial erosion forms a variety of land features.
▶ Melting glaciers leave behind till and outwash deposits. Formations from these deposits include outwash plains, moraines, and kettle lakes.

### 12.4 Wind Erosion
▶ The wind picks up and carries particles in the air, or causes deflation. These particles may abrade rock surfaces.
▶ Particle movement by wind follows a leap-frog path.
▶ The most common wind deposits are dunes and loess.

### Chapter Vocabulary

| | | | |
|---|---|---|---|
| erosion (12.1) | rill (12.2) | levee (12.2) | outwash (12.3) |
| deposition (12.1) | meander (12.2) | glacier (12.3) | moraine (12.3) |
| mass movement (12.1) | alluvial fan (12.2) | till (12.3) | deflation (12.4) |

## Check Your Vocabulary

Use the vocabulary words above to complete the following sentences correctly.

1. An old river has many curves, or ____.

2. Sediments deposited along the sides of rivers are called ____.

3. Glacial deposits that contain an assortment of sediment sizes are called ____.

4. A thick wedge of sediment that sometimes forms at a mountain base is called ____.

5. Glacial deposits that result in sorted and layered sediment are called ____.

6. The moving of materials by wind, water, ice, or gravity is ____.

7. The process by which wind carries away loose sediment is called ____.

8. The movement of rocks or soil by gravity down a slope is ____.

9. Small channels in the dirt that are formed by rainwater flowing down a slope are called ____.

10. A glacial deposit of till formed at the head of an outwash plain is a ____.

11. The dropping of weathered materials in a new place is called ____.

12. A large mass of moving ice and snow is a ____.

## Check Your Vocabulary

1. meanders
2. levees
3. tills
4. alluvial fan
5. outwash
6. erosion
7. deflation
8. mass movement
9. rills
10. moraine
11. deposition
12. glacier

## Write Your Vocabulary

Students' sentences should show that they know the meaning of each word as well as how to use it in a sentence.

Use Vocabulary Worksheet for Chapter 12.

## Check Your Knowledge

1. The three types of dunes are crescent, transverse, and longitudinal.

2. A gully is a large channel formed by water running downhill.

3. Mass movement is caused by gravity. On a flat field, gravity has no place to pull material.

4. The three stages of river erosion are young river, mature river, and old river.

5. A glacier is a large, heavy mass of slowly moving ice.

6. The two types of glaciers are continental and valley.

7. Wave action can break rocks by hydraulic action, abrasion, and chemical weathering.

8. Student answers will vary but may include: type of rock; type of soil; terrain; amount of rainfall; amount of wind; presence of rivers, lakes, or oceans; amount of vegetation.

9. The types of mass movement are landslide, creep, slump, and mudflow.

10. The agents of erosion are water, wind, ice, and gravity.

11. Desert pavement is the hard, stony surface left behind after wind carries away small, loose sediment.

12. The type of wind deposit formed depends on the size and amount of particles, the wind direction, and the amount of wind from a single direction.

13. water

14. continental

15. abrasion

16. coarse material

17. wave deposition

## Check Your Understanding

1. Farmers can protect their land by keeping soils planted and using water properly.

2. As snow piles up, deeper layers are compacted into ice. The pressure on the layer in contact with the ground causes the ice to melt. Gravity then causes the glacier to slide down the slope.

3. When a surface made of one type of rock is abraded, the result is a smooth, polished surface. When a surface made of many rock types is abraded, the result is a rippled, uneven surface.

4. Sand bars and dunes are similar because both are formed by deposition of sediments.

5. A mountain lake forms by glacial erosion when a bowl-shaped hole is carved out by a glacier at its source. A kettle lake forms by glacial deposition when a large block of ice breaks off from a retreating glacier.

6. Wind to scoop up and carry the dust, gravity to pull the particles to the ground

7. River deposition is controlled with levees, dams, and dredging.

8. Dunes, loess, alluvial fans

9. These valleys were most likely created by the action of valley glaciers that eroded an area formed by a young river.

10. When the rows are perpendicular to the slope of the hill, soil erosion is slowed because water is prevented from running off quickly.

11. Student answers may vary, but will likely include wind and/or water.

## Chapter 12  Review

### Check Your Knowledge

Answer the following in complete sentences.

1. List the three types of dunes.

2. What is a gully?

3. Why is mass movement more common on a steep slope than on a flat field?

4. List the three stages of river erosion.

5. What is a glacier?

6. Name the two different types of glaciers.

7. Describe three ways that rocks are broken up by wave action.

8. List the factors that affect the amount of erosion in an area.

9. What are the different types of mass movement?

10. List the agents of erosion.

11. What is desert pavement?

12. What factors determine the type of wind deposit that will form?

Choose the answer that best completes each sentence.

13. An alluvial fan is an example of (water, wind, wave, glacial) deposition.

14. Greenland is a (valley, continental, retreating, advancing) glacier.

15. Smooth and polished rocks are a result of wind (deflation, differential erosion, abrasion, deposits).

16. When water slows down, the first sediments to drop out are (silt, clay, fine material, coarse material).

17. Spits, beaches, and bars are examples of (stream erosion, stream deposition, wave erosion, wave deposition).

### Check Your Understanding

Apply the concepts you have learned to answer each question.

1. Describe how farmers can protect their farms from the effects of wind erosion.

2. Explain how glaciers move.

3. Describe the effects of differential wind erosion on rocks.

4. Which wind and water formations are similar in appearance? Discuss why these formations look similar although they were formed by different types of erosion.

5. Compare how a mountain lake and a kettle lake form.

6. What two agents of erosion are necessary to form loess deposits?

7. Describe two ways that river deposition is controlled by humans.

8. **Classify** Using all the agents of erosion, make a list of the different types of depositions that form only in arid regions.

9. **Find Causes** Many valleys in the mountains of Scotland are very wide and have steep sides. Explain how they were formed.

10. **Application** Farmers plow in circles around a hill instead of up and down. Explain this in terms of soil erosion.

11. **Mystery Photo** The photograph on page 262 is a closeup of the rocks in Antelope Canyon in Arizona. What agents of erosion shaped this canyon? How can you tell?

## Develop Your Skills

1. a. 300 cm/s

   b. 5 cm/s

   c. Boulders drop out first because they are too heavy to be carried by any but the strongest current.

   d. Silt and clay drop out last because they are the lightest and most easily carried in water.

   e. Between 100 and 50 cm/s; between 50 and 25 cm/s

2. a. Ganges River

   b. Mississippi River

   c. Delta

3. Student designs will vary. A likely setup will include a tub with sand piled in one end and water in the other, and a mechanical means of creating waves, such as a ruler that is moved back and forth.

## Make Connections

1.

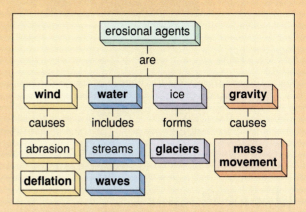

2. Student reports will vary.

3. Student artwork will vary. Make sure that all pictures are accurate examples of erosion.

4. Student reports will vary. The Dust Bowl formed after the combined effects of over-farming, over-grazing, and a severe drought destroyed the grasslands of the southern Great Plains. Wind erosion of the topsoil accelerated until there was little or no fertile topsoil left. This could have been prevented by protective farming and live-stock practices, and planting trees to stop winds.

5. Make sure students provide accurate descriptions of all the examples of erosion in your area. School building examples might include depressions worn into steps, worn railings, and worn spots in paint. Park examples might include worn paths, gullies caused by rain water, worn monuments and benches, and crumbling sidewalks.

---

## Develop Your Skills

Use the skills you have developed in this chapter to complete each activity.

**1. Interpret Data** The graph below shows the effect of stream speed on the type of sediments carried.

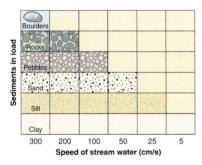

a. At which speed does a stream carry the largest load?

b. At which speed does a stream carry the smallest load?

c. Name the sediments that drop from the load first. Why?

d. Name the sediments that drop from the load last. Why?

e. At what speed do pebbles drop from the load? Sand?

**2. Data Bank** Use the information on page 612 to answer the following questions.

a. Where is the largest silt deposit located?

b. Where is the largest silt load deposit in North America?

c. **Infer** What formation would you expect to find at the mouth of each river?

**3. Design an Experiment** The sand on a beach is constantly in motion. Map the path of sand moving along a beach.

## Make Connections

**1. Link the Concepts** Below is a concept map showing how some of the main concepts in this chapter link together. Only parts of the map are filled in. Complete the map, using words and ideas from the chapter.

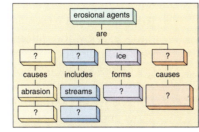

**2. Science and Society** During the late 1960s, desertification in Africa resulted in the deaths of 250,000 people. Conduct research to find out how famine relief is administered throughout the world. List organizations that are involved in famine relief.

**3. Science and Art** Use magazines or travel brochures to find pictures of the results of all types of erosion. Cut out the pictures and glue them on a sheet of paper, making an erosion collage.

**4. Science and Social Studies** The Dust Bowl of the 1930s affected the lives of many people in the United States. Find out how the Dust Bowl began. How could the Dust Bowl have been prevented?

**5. Science and You** Take an erosion walk around your school or a local park. Record and describe each agent of erosion that you find.

## Overview

This chapter addresses the history of life on the earth. The chapter opens with a discussion of the theory of evolution and a classification of organisms. The second section describes how fossils form and are categorized. The third section explains how to interpret fossils. The fourth section closes the chapter with an examination of life through geologic time.

## Advance Planner

▶ Gather old magazines for TE page 291.

▶ Provide assorted nuts and washers (about 300 pieces) and 5 m of butcher paper for Activity 13, SE page 293.

▶ Collect paper, objects with rough surfaces, pencils, crayons for SE page 294.

▶ Obtain Darwin's *Zoology of the Voyage of the Beagle* for TE page 294.

▶ Supply modeling clay for TE page 295.

## Skills Development Chart

| Sections | Classify | Gather Data | Infer | Make a Model | Measure | Observe | Organize Data |
|---|---|---|---|---|---|---|---|
| **13.1** Skills WarmUp | ● | | | | | | |
| Skills WorkOut | ● | | | | | | |
| Activity 13 | | | | ● | ● | | ● |
| **13.2** Skills WarmUp | | | | | | ● | |
| SkillBuilder | | | ● | | | | |
| **13.3** Skills WarmUp | | | ● | | | | |
| **13.4** Skills WarmUp | | ● | | | | | |
| Skills WorkOut | | | | | | ● | |

## Individual Needs

▶ **Limited English Proficiency Students** Have students sketch or trace Figure 13.15, 13.16, or 13.18, leaving out the captions. Have students write descriptive labels for the figures using their own words. In the space below each figure, have them name the era represented and list other information about the era.

▶ **At-Risk Students** Have students work together in pairs or groups to create graphic organizers such as charts or tree diagrams for the information presented in the chapter. Each group should choose one section and decide how best to present the material graphically. A group may want to use more than one graphic organizer to cover its section. Have groups present their organizers to each other and exchange copies to use in reviewing the chapter.

▶ **Gifted Students** Invite students to investigate the life of Charles Darwin, particularly his voyage to South America and the Galápagos Islands. Students may want to read part or all of his diary, *The Voyage of the Beagle,* to help with their research. They should find out not only what he saw and did on the voyage but also how the things he learned led him to formulate his theory of evolution. Encourage students to present what they learn as a series of newspaper articles or dramatized television broadcasts by a "reporter" traveling with Darwin aboard the *Beagle*.

## Resource Bank

▶ **Bulletin Board** Have students work together to make a clock to show the different geological periods from the earth's beginning to the present. They should use different colors for sections of the clock face representing different geological eras. They may want to differentiate periods by using different shades of the era colors and to show important geological events by marking the edges. In determining the time analogies of their clock, students should think of the earth's beginning as noon and the present as midnight. A movable hand can point to different events. Students may want to add small pictures of rocks and fossils around the clock face to illustrate the different periods.

| Section | Core | Standard | Enriched | Section | Core | Standard | Enriched |
|---|---|---|---|---|---|---|---|
| **13.1 Evolution of Life** pp. 289–293 | | | | **13.3 Interpreting Fossils** pp. 298–301 | | | |
| **Section Features** Skills WarmUp, p. 289 Skills WorkOut, p. 292 Activity, p. 293 | ● ● | ● ● ● | ● ● ● | **Section Features** Skills WarmUp, p. 298 | ● | ● | ● |
| **Blackline Masters** Review Worksheet 13.1 Skills Worksheet 13.1 | ● ● | ● ● | ● | **Blackline Masters** Review Worksheet 13.3 Integrating Worksheet 13.3 | ● ● | ● ● | ● ● |
| **Overhead Blackline Transparencies** Overhead Blackline Master 13.1 and Student Worksheet | ● | ● | ● | **Laboratory Program** Investigation 19 | ● | ● | |
| **Color Transparencies** Transparency 30 | ● | ● | ● | **Color Transparencies** Transparencies 31, 32 | ● | ● | ● |
| **13.2 The Fossil Record** pp. 294–297 | | | | **13.4 Life Through Geologic Time** pp. 302–308 | | | |
| **Section Features** Skills WarmUp, p. 294 SkillBuilder, p. 296 | ● ● | ● ● | ● ● | **Section Features** Skills WarmUp, p. 302 Career Corner, p. 307 Skills WorkOut, p. 308 | ● ● | ● ● ● | ● ● ● |
| **Blackline Masters** Review Worksheet 13.2 | ● | ● | ● | **Blackline Masters** Review Worksheet 13.4 Reteach Worksheet 13.4 Skills Worksheet 13.4 Integrating Worksheet 13.4 Vocabulary Worksheet 13.4 | ● ● ● ● ● | ● ● ● ● ● | ● ● ● |
| | | | | **Color Transparencies** Transparencies 33, 34, 35, 36 | ● | ● | ● |

# Bibliography

The following resources can be used for teaching the chapter. See page T–46 for supplier codes.

### Library Resources

*Kricher, J. C. Peterson First Guide to Dinosaurs. Boston: Houghton Mifflin, 1990.*

*Parker, Steve, with Raymond L. Bernor, editor. The Practical Paleontologist. New York: Simon and Schuster, 1990.*

*Rydell, Wendy. Discovering Fossils. Mahwah, NJ: Troll, 1984.*

*Taylor, Paul D. Fossil. New York: Alfred A. Knopf, Inc., 1990.*

*U.S. Geological Survey. Geologic Time. Washington, DC: U.S. Department of the Interior.*

### Technology Resources

#### Internet

**PLANETDIARY** at *http://www.planetdiary.com*
• Find out more about animals and plants on Earth in *Fauna* and *Flora* by clicking on *Phenomena Backgrounders.*
• Find geological news in *Current Phenomena.*

#### Software
*Earth. Mac, Dos, Win. ER.*
*Eyewitness Virtual Reality: Dinosaur Hunter. Mac, Win. ER.*
*Origins of Mankind. Mac, Win. ER.*
*Sim Earth Classic. Mac, Dos, Win. ER.*

#### CD-ROMs
*Interactive Earth. SFAW.*
*An Odyssey of Discovery for Science Insights:* Have students explore the activity *Dig It* on the Earth and Space Disk. *SFAW.*

#### Laserdiscs
*Living Textbook.* (See barcodes on pages in this chapter.) *Optical Data.*

#### Videos
*Dinosaurs of the Gobi (NOVA). PBS.*
*Fossils: Clues to the Past. 23 min. 1983. NGSES.*

### Audio-Visual Resources
*Age of Mammals. Filmstrip. T–L.*
*Evolution: Four Billion Year Legacy. Film. Fl.*
*Message from a Dinosaur. Film. EB.*
*Prehistoric Life. Filmstrip. 1983. SVE.*

# 13

## Introducing the Chapter

Have students read the description of the photograph. Ask if they agree or disagree with the description.

### Directed Inquiry

Have students study the photograph. Ask:

▶ What is this a photograph of? (It is a fossil of a sea animal's shell. Tell students it is an ammonite fossil from the Cretaceous period, which occurred over 70 million years ago. When alive, the ammonite was a marine mollusk.)

▶ When this organism was alive, was the shell made of rock? What do you think happened? (No; rock gradually replaced the original shell material.)

▶ How does this photograph illustrate the topic of this chapter? (The fossil is of an organism that lived millions of years ago.)

▶ What do you think scientists learn about the history of life on the earth from fossils like this? (By comparing fossils from earlier and later times than this one, they can learn about the various life forms that existed at a given period and they can trace the development and extinction of a type of life.)

## Chapter Vocabulary

cast
evolution
extinction
half-life
invertebrate
kingdom
mold

petrified
principle of
    superposition
species
trace fossil
vertebrate

### Art Connection

Ask students to name the type of shape represented by the fossil in the photograph. (Spiral) Make a class list of spiral objects. Show or pass around examples, such as snail shells, young fern fronds, springs, and photographs of spiral staircases. Have students create their own spiral objects using scissors, construction paper, and glue or tape. When they are finished, ask:

▶ How would you describe a spiral?

▶ Where else in nature and in society have you seen spiral shapes? (In plant life, shells, architecture, and models of DNA, for example)

▶ How might some organisms benefit from having a spiral shape? (A spiral shape helps conserve space; it is stronger and more compact than a long shell.)

Chapter **13**    ## History of Life on Earth

### Chapter Sections

**13.1** Evolution of Life
**13.2** The Fossil Record
**13.3** Interpreting Fossils
**13.4** Life Through Geologic Time

### What do you see?

❝I believe this is a prehistoric fossil of a seashell. It died and sank into mud and the mud dried, turning the seashell into a fossil.❞

*Hector Rivera*
*Fleming Junior High*
*Lomita, California*

To find out more about the photograph, look on page 310. As you read this chapter, you will learn about the information found in rocks that tells the history of the earth.

*Themes in Science*

**Evolution** Both the earth's surface and the organisms living on it have undergone continuous change for billions of years. Evidence of these changes led to the development of the theory of evolution.

 *Art Connection*

Have students draw pictures of a prehistoric scene showing some animals and plants that lived at some time in the remote past. Ask them to resist looking through the rest of the chapter for ideas. When the drawings are complete, have students explain why they chose the organisms that they included in their drawings. When they finish reading the chapter, have them evaluate the accuracy of their drawings.

**Section Objectives**
For a list of section objectives, see the Student Edition page.

**Skills Objectives**
Students should be able to:

**Classify** organisms by similar characteristics.

**Classify** a library's organizational system.

**Observe** evolutionary relationships among organisms.

**Make a Model** of a classification system.

**Vocabulary**
species, evolution, extinction, kingdom

## 13.1 Evolution of Life

### Objectives

▶ **Explain** how fossils provide evidence for evolution.

▶ **State** the theory of evolution.

▶ **Describe** how organisms are classified.

▶ **Classify** groups of organisms according to the five-kingdom classification system.

 **ACTIVITY**

**Classifying**

*Pets of All Sorts*

Make a list of all the kinds of animals people keep as pets. Then classify the animals into three or more groups. What characteristics define each group?

**SKILLS WARMUP**

You set the dial of your time machine to 320 million years before the present and press the transport button. A moment later, you're standing in a swampy forest of strange-looking trees. You trudge through the muck to the edge of a lake and look around. Fish are swimming in the water. An animal that looks like a salamander sits by the water's edge. A flying insect buzzes overhead. There's no sign of any birds, furry animals, or flowers.

You can't actually visit the past in this way, but earth scientists can tell you what the past was like. Their information about the past comes from the study of fossils. Fossils help scientists learn about the history of the earth and the organisms living on its surface.

### Earth's Changing Organisms

(1) What types of organisms left the fossils shown in Figure 13.1? Fossils tell scientists what kinds of organisms lived during each period in geologic time. For example, in rocks 280 million years old, there are fossils of reptiles. Rocks more than 40 million years older than these, however, contain no reptile fossils. Based on this evidence, scientists hypothesize that if you traveled back more than 320 million years you would not find any reptiles. But you would find many kinds of plants and animals that do not exist today.

Similarly, if you traveled back in time 500 million years, the organisms you'd see would be different from those of any other period. Fossil evidence shows that the kinds of organisms inhabiting the earth's surface have changed over time.

**Figure 13.1** ▲
The organisms that left these fossils have been extinct for millions of years.

**Skills WarmUp**
To give students practice classifying organisms, have them do the Skills WarmUp.
**Answer** Lists may include reptiles, fishes, insects, amphibians, birds, and mammals. Make sure students identify the common characteristics they use to group the organisms.

**Prior Knowledge**
Gauge how much students know about the evolution of organisms by asking the following questions:

▶ How long have bacteria lived on the earth?

▶ When did dinosaurs live?

▶ Did human beings live alongside dinosaurs?

▶ Can the appearance of a kind of organism change from generation to generation?

**Answer to In-Text Question**
(1) **Dinosaurs, or ancient reptiles**

290

## TEACH

### Directed Inquiry

After students have read the page and studied Figure 13.2, ask the following questions:

▶ What theory applies to the way species change over time? (Evolution)

▶ What did Darwin call the hypothesis he used to describe how species change over time? (Natural selection)

▶ How does natural selection relate to adaptation? (Traits of individuals that are well adapted to their environments are likely to survive from one generation to the next.)

### Discuss

Have students describe the environments in which horses live today. Ask how the horses have adapted to these environments. (Answers might include the horse's size, ability to run, diet, long tail, grass-eating teeth, and hooves.)

### Integrating the Sciences

**Environmental Science** Discuss with students how the extinction of organisms today compares to the extinction of organisms through geologic time. Ask: If extinction is a natural process in the evolution of life, why is it considered a problem that organisms are becoming extinct today? (Some organisms are rapidly becoming extinct due to the activities of humans.)

### Themes in Science

**Diversity and Unity** Through the process of evolution, living things have become diverse in body structure, diet, and behavior. Yet all organisms are unified on a basic level because they evolved from a common ancestor long ago.

## Theory of Evolution

Each kind of organism is called a **species** (SPEE sheez). All the members of a species have nearly the same traits, and they reproduce to make more organisms like themselves. Scientists identify species that lived in the past by studying their fossil remains.

If different species lived on the earth at different periods of time, then species must change. Charles Darwin reached this conclusion over 100 years ago. He worked out a theory of **evolution**. In biology, evolution is the process by which species change over time.

Darwin hypothesized that slight differences in traits make some individuals in a species better able to survive than others. These individuals are better *adapted* to their environment. More of their offspring tend to survive compared to other individuals. Their special traits are passed on to the next generation. Darwin called his hypothesis *natural selection*.

Natural selection is the process by which the traits of the species as a whole change over time, as shown in Figure 13.2.

Changes in the earth's environment affect evolution. Environmental changes may cause the **extinction**, or dying out, of species that can't adapt to the changes. Changes in climate and sea level have resulted in the origin of new species and the extinction of others.

The movement of the earth's tectonic plates also had an important role in evolution. The breakup of Pangaea created separate continents. The environments of the continents eventually became different. Organisms on each continent, therefore, evolved differently.

The theory of evolution states that all living things are related. Scientists hypothesize that all species now alive came from one or a few simple life forms. Look at Figure 13.3. It is a simplified evolutionary tree showing how the many kinds of organisms alive today may have evolved from the first cells.

**Figure 13.2** ▼
The modern horse evolved from a small mammal that lived during the early Tertiary period.

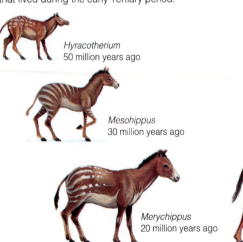
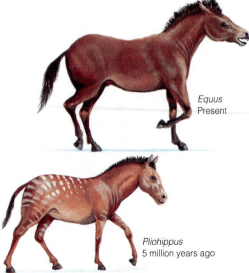

*Hyracotherium*
50 million years ago

*Mesohippus*
30 million years ago

*Merychippus*
20 million years ago

*Equus*
Present

*Pliohippus*
5 million years ago

### Cooperative Learning

Make an illustrated version of the evolutionary tree in Figure 13.3 for display on a bulletin board. Have students collect magazine photographs of a variety of organisms. Then have them work as a group to place the photographs in the correct groups shown in the tree. Answer students' questions about the classification of any difficult organisms.

### Portfolio

Organisms from each of the five kingdoms are sources of food for people. Have students list examples of foods from each kingdom. Challenge them to make up a menu for a single meal that includes a food from each kingdom.

### Directed Inquiry

Have students study Figure 13.3 and Table 13.1. Then ask:

▶ Which organisms in the figure would you classify as animals? (Sponges, jellyfish, worms, arthropods, mollusks, starfish, animals with backbones)

▶ How would you classify seaweeds? (Protists)

▶ What distinguishes seaweeds from plants? (Answers will vary. Plants have a more complex organization and are always many-celled.)

▶ What distinguishes seaweeds from fungi? (Seaweeds do not absorb nutrients from other organisms.)

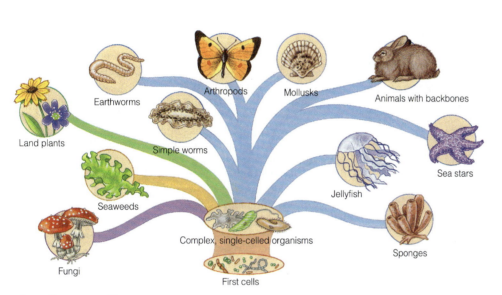

Earthworms
Arthropods
Mollusks
Animals with backbones
Land plants
Simple worms
Seaweeds
Sea stars
Jellyfish
Complex, single-celled organisms
Sponges
Fungi
First cells

**Figure 13.3** ▲
This tree diagram shows the ancestry of some major groups of modern organisms.

## Classification of Organisms

Many very different groups of organisms have evolved on the earth. Look at Figure 13.3. Notice that each branch of the evolutionary tree contains organisms more closely related to each other than to organisms on other branches. The major branches of the evolutionary tree in Figure 13.3 are the basis for a system of classification.

The system most widely used today to classify organisms divides them into five large groups called **kingdoms**. Each kingdom is made up of species with a similar body organization and method of nutrition, or way of getting food. The five kingdoms are described in Table 13.1. What kingdom do you belong in?

The monerans (MOHN ehr uhnz) are distinguished by the simple structure of their cells. This structure is similar to that of the first cells. Members of the other four kingdoms have cells with specialized parts surrounded by membranes.

### Table 13.1 The Five Kingdoms

| Kingdom | Major Characteristics | Groups |
|---|---|---|
| Monerans | Simple cells | Bacteria, blue-green algae |
| Protists | Complex cells; one-celled or many-celled organisms | Protozoa, seaweeds |
| Fungi | Absorb nutrients from other organisms | Mushrooms, yeasts, molds |
| Plants | Many-celled; use photosynthesis for energy and growth | Ferns, mosses, cone-bearing and flowering plants |
| Animals | Many-celled; eat food | Sponges, worms, insects, fishes, reptiles, birds, mammals, and many others |

## Skills WorkOut

To give students an opportunity to apply their classification skills, have them do the Skills WorkOut.
**Answer** Students should note that the library classifies by subject, title, and author.

## WrapUp

**Reteach** Ask students to describe the weather in your area over the past week. Have them discuss how plants and animals are adapted to these conditions. Ask them to list some traits that provide evidence for the adaptations.

Use Review Worksheet 13.1.

## Check and Explain

1. The theory that describes how species change over time.

2. They show that species have changed over time.

3. To starfish; as shown on the diagram, starfish and animals with backbones split off from the same branch.

4. Check diagrams for accuracy based on Table 13.1.

**Answer to In-Text Question**

① Answers may include alphabetical, numerical, social, and political or economic systems of classification.

## Multicultural Perspectives

All human cultures have certain classification systems for the things in their environments. The classification systems are based on how the people in the culture use and view the things around them. For example, the Inuits have developed a classification system for snow that includes 17 words to describe *white*. Find a description of the classification system of a nonindustrial society from the tundra, rain forest, or desert, and present it to students for discussion.

## ▼ ACTIVITY

### Classifying

**Books in Order**

1. Go to your library and find out how books are classified.

2. Make a chart or diagram that shows the library's classification system.

Where can you find books about dinosaurs? About jewelry? Sports?

**SKILLS WORKOUT**

### Science and You  *Everyday Classification*

Classification systems help scientists explain the relationships among organisms. But classification is not only used by scientists. In fact, you use some type of classification system nearly every day. You use them in stores, at school, at home, and many other places.

How do you use classification systems in stores? Think, for example, what it would be like finding apples in the store if there were not a produce section. You'd have to travel throughout the store before you could locate the apples. They could be anywhere! The grocery store would be more like a flea market, where items can be found in almost any location.

How do you use classification systems in school? The library is one obvious place. Your school may have its own classification system for grouping books. They may be grouped by author, title, or subject. Many school libraries use the Dewey Decimal Classification System. This system divides books into ten main groups. Each main group is broken into more specific fields.

How do you use classification systems at home? You may have your music or video collection classified. Maybe you arrange your collection by type, such as jazz or comedy, just like most music and video stores do. Maybe your collection is arranged alphabetically. You can probably find a number of classification systems in your bedroom. Your shoes may be placed in a certain part of your closet. Your summer clothes are probably separated from your winter clothes. What other examples of everyday classification systems can you name? ①

## Check and Explain

1. What is the theory of evolution?

2. How do fossils provide evidence for evolution?

3. **Observe** Study Figure 13.3. Are animals with backbones more closely related to arthropods or to starfish? Why?

4. **Classify** Copy the evolutionary tree in Figure 13.3. Then use the five-kingdom classification system to divide the tree into five sections, each corresponding to a kingdom.

292

### Prelab Discussion

Have students read the entire activity. Discuss these points before beginning:

▶ Review the five-kingdom classification system.

▶ Discuss how physical characteristics can be used to classify things. Give examples from students' experience.

▶ Ask students if they think there is a single best classification scheme.

**Time** 40 min    **Group** pairs

**Materials**

Assorted nuts and washers (about 300 pieces)

Butcher paper, about 5 m

### Analysis

1. Student answers will vary, but should mention and describe charts made by other students in the class.

2. Students should give their first major grouping, such as washers versus nuts, or big versus little.

3. A useful name will include characteristics that distinguish the object from all other kinds of nuts or washers.

4. Directions should clearly describe each "trait" that corresponds to a division in the chart. The most complete sets of directions will function like dichotomous keys.

5. The chart in this activity models an evolutionary tree because it groups items based on similar characteristics and it moves from less similar to more similar as you read outward.

### Conclusion

Student conclusions will vary, but should agree with the scheme used in the chart.

### Extension

Classification schemes and charts will vary.

---

## Activity 13   How do you classify a group of items?

*Skills*  Observe; Classify; Model; Communicate

### Task 1  Prelab Prep

Collect the following items: container of assorted washers and nuts, piece of butcher paper, pencil.

### Task 2  Data Record

1. At the top of the piece of butcher paper, copy the chart shown in Figure 13.4. Leave room to make the chart larger.

2. Show all your groupings of objects in the chart.

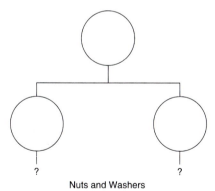

Nuts and Washers

**Figure 13.4** ▲

### Task 3  Procedure

1. Pour the contents of the container onto a table. Divide the contents into two groups based on similar characteristics.

2. Record the name and characteristics of each group on your chart.

3. Divide each of the two groups into two or three smaller groups. The items in each group must share at least one common characteristic. Give a name to each group based on the group's characteristics.

4. Record the characteristics of each group on your chart.

5. Continue to separate the items into smaller groups until each group contains only one type of item. Remember that items in a group must have characteristics that make them different from the items in the other groups.

6. Record the characteristics for each of the groups that you make on your chart.

7. Share your chart with your classmates. Communicate what characteristics you chose to distinguish each group.

### Task 4  Analysis

1. How is your chart different from those of your classmates?

2. Which groups were the easiest to distinguish between? The most difficult?

3. **Observe**  Choose one item. Using the chart, record all the characteristics for that item based on all the different groups it belongs to. How does the name you chose for that item reflect its characteristics?

4. If someone picked an item from the group at random, how would you describe to that person how to classify it the same way you did? Write a set of step-by-step directions that someone could use to classify any item from the group.

5. How does your chart model the classification of organisms in an evolutionary tree?

### Task 5  Conclusion

Imagine that your washers and nuts are organisms and that they have evolved to reach their present forms. Describe all the steps in the evolutionary process you recorded on your chart.

### Extension

Make a classification chart for other items, such as nails and screws, beads, or items in a desk.

### Section Objectives

For a list of section objectives, see the Student Edition page.

### Skills Objectives

Students should be able to:

**Observe** imprints and how they relate to fossils.

**Infer** how a fossil site develops.

**Infer** how North America has changed geologically.

### Vocabulary

petrified, mold, cast, trace fossil

## MOTIVATE

### Skills WarmUp

To help students sharpen their observation skills, have them do the Skills WarmUp.

**Answer** Responses will depend on the objects students choose. Some benefits to finding fossil remains may be a better understanding of the types of organisms that lived in Earth's past and how these organisms have changed through geologic time.

### Misconceptions

Students may think that the fossil record documents all life on earth. Explain that the fossil record contains many gaps. Some organisms did not leave fossils. Discovery of new fossils also changes the fossil record regularly.

### Answers to In-Text Questions

① **Answers will vary, but should include the idea of being buried by sediments.**

② **Metamorphic and igneous rocks are subjected to high temperatures and/or pressures that would destroy fossils.**

### Social Studies Connection

Read passages from Darwin's *Zoology of the Voyage of the Beagle* that describe his discovery of fossils in South America (beginning with Chapter V, "Bahia Blanca"). Have students make inferences about people's knowledge of geologic time 100 years ago. Discuss what the discovery of fossils meant to the scientists of the time.

### Themes in Science

**Evolution** Fossils provide information about organisms that lived millions of years ago. The fossil record provides evidence for how living things have changed over time.

▼ **ACTIVITY**

**Observing**

*Hints of Life*

**1.** Place a sheet of paper over a flat object that has a rough surface.

**2.** Rub a pencil or crayon over the paper.

**3.** Repeat with two or three other objects.

**4.** Trade your rubbings with someone else's and try to identify the rubbings you receive.

What are some benefits to finding the slightest remains of a once-living organism?

**SKILLS WARMUP**

## 13.2 The Fossil Record

### Objectives

▶ **Describe** the conditions under which fossils may form.

▶ **Distinguish** among the different types of fossils.

▶ **Explain** how molds and casts differ.

▶ **Infer** geologic history from the fossil record.

Millions of years ago, organisms related to today's sea stars, crabs, and clams lived on a muddy ocean floor beside a giant reef wall. One day, a huge landslide buried these animals in thick layers of mud. Millions of years later in Siberia, a woolly mammoth wandered the icy plains in search of food. Suddenly the ground gave way, and the animal fell into a deep crack in the frozen ground.

Both the ocean-floor organisms and the mammoth became fossils. The fossils of the ocean-floor organisms were found in shale 2,400 m above sea level in the Canadian Rocky Mountains. When scientists found the mammoth, it was still frozen and perfectly preserved. Fossils such as these make up the *fossil record*—the record of the history of life on the earth.

### Formation of Fossils

The ocean-floor organisms and the woolly mammoth were both unusual. Most organisms that lived on the earth did not leave any fossil remains. Usually an organism is destroyed when it dies. Another organism may eat it, or it decays. If it has hard parts, such as bones or shells, they are often broken, crushed, or scattered about.

For an organism to become a fossil, it must be protected from destructive forces and decay. This usually happens when sediments bury an organism that is alive or recently dead. When the sediments become rock, the organism may be preserved as a fossil. For this reason, most fossils are found in sedimentary rock. Why do you think metamorphic and igneous rocks contain few fossils? ②

**Figure 13.5**
How do you think these fish ① became fossilized? ▼

## Types of Fossils

Fossils are classified according to how they formed and what is preserved. A fossil may be all or part of an organism. Some fossils are not parts of organisms at all, but traces, such as footprints or burrows.

**Petrified Fossils**   Most of the dinosaur bones that scientists have found are not the organisms' actual bones. They are mineralized copies of the original bones, called **petrified** (PEHT ruh fyd) fossils.

The process of petrification begins when bones, wood, shells, or other parts of living things are covered by sediment. The matter making up these parts is dissolved by seeping water. Minerals in the water slowly replace the original matter. As a result, the parts turned to stone. Even though their matter changed, the parts still have the shape and details of the original part. Can you see the growth rings in the petrified wood shown in Figure 13.6?

**Figure 13.6** ▲
The wood in these petrified trees was completely replaced by stone.

**Molds, Casts, and Imprints**   Have you ever made a handprint in plaster of Paris? The same type of process formed many fossils. In this process, the remains of an organism buried by sediment slowly become rock. Water seeps through the rock and dissolves the hard parts of the organism, leaving a hole, or cavity, in the rock. This cavity in the shape of an organism is a fossil. This type of fossil is called a **mold**. Later, minerals may seep into and fill the cavity to form a **cast**. Look at the cast and mold in Figure 13.7.

Molds of thin objects are called imprints. A leaf pressed into sediment makes a pattern. This pattern is preserved when the sediment turns to rock.

**Figure 13.7** ▲
Which is the cast of this ancient trilobite? ③

**Trace Fossils**   Footprints, tracks, trails, and burrows left by animals can be preserved as **trace fossils**. These fossils provide evidence about the size, shape, and habits of an animal. For example, the trace fossil footprints of early humans are evidence that they walked upright.

**Coprolites**   Waste materials from animals may be petrified, forming a fossil called a coprolite (KAHP ruh lyt). Particles of food, such as plant parts, are often preserved in the coprolite. They give information about what the animal ate and the organisms living at that time.

## Discuss

Tell students that the La Brea tar pits contain fossils of llamas, which now live only in South America, and fossils of camels, which now live only in Africa and Asia. Ask students how they might explain the presence of these fossils. (Answers will vary. Students may suggest that plate tectonics played a role. Actually, scientists think camels and ancestors of llamas migrated from North America to the other locations during the Pleistocene Ice Age.)

## SkillBuilder

**Research**  Have students use resources to learn more about the La Brea tar pits. Suggest that they write a story about how one of the fossils ended up there.

**Answers**  Student answers will vary. Possible answers include the following:

1. Since leopards eat their prey in trees, the remains of a leopard's meals are likely to be near trees.

2. He or she could have been eaten by a leopard.

3. They may have been scattered elsewhere, dissolved, or eroded away. Or, leopards may have eaten the small bones, not discarding them as they did the large bones.

4. It is not possible to know for certain because the fossils accumulated a long time ago. However, scientists may generate a hypothesis supported by all the evidence. The hypothesis for this site is that leopards dropped the bones into the cave as they ate their prey in the trees.

## Answer to In-Text Question

① **No matter has been removed from it or changed into a different kind of matter.**

## *Integrating the Sciences*

**Chemistry**  Organisms trapped in ice, tar, and tree resin may become unchanged fossils. In contrast, organisms buried in mud or other sediments may become petrified fossils or molds and casts. Ask students:

▶ What properties do ice, tar, and tree resin share that enable them to preserve the matter of an organism? (They are fluid so they can flow around and trap things. Also, they become solid and hard through evaporation.)

▶ What properties of sediments and the rocks they become result in the matter of an organism being gradually removed or replaced by other matter? (Minerals in the sediments are removed by water. These minerals replace the original material.)

**Figure 13.8** ▲
Why is this insect classified as an unchanged fossil? ①

**Unchanged Fossils**  In petrified fossils, molds, and casts, little or none of the matter from the original organism remains. In some fossils, however, matter from the organism was not changed or removed. Such a fossil is called an unchanged or unaltered fossil.

The woolly mammoth preserved in frozen ground is an unchanged fossil. Another type of unchanged fossil is shown in Figure 13.8. It was formed when an insect got trapped in sticky plant sap. The sap hardened over time, becoming a substance called amber. Inside the amber is the insect's perfectly preserved body.

In the most common type of unchanged fossil, the soft parts of the body decayed, but the bones or other hard parts remained unchanged. This commonly occurred when an animal was trapped and buried in a tar pit. The unchanged fossil bones of wolves, sabertooth cats, bison, horses, sloths, and camels were found in the La Brea tar pits in Los Angeles, California.

## SkillBuilder  *Inferring*

ACTIVITY

### Case Study of a Fossil Site

Interpreting information obtained from fossils is like detective work. Numerous fossil bones have been found in limestone caves at Swartkrans in South Africa. Use clues from the fossil evidence below to determine how the fossils might have accumulated in the cave.

▶ The fossils are embedded in breccia, a sedimentary rock made of rock particles cemented together with limestone.

▶ The fossils include the skull of an early human child with two puncture wounds, a leopard jaw with a few teeth, and large bones from many types of mammals.

▶ Fossils from small bones such as ribs and vertebrae are not present.

▶ Trees grow near the opening of the cave. The trees protect the cave opening.

▶ The cave entrance is a hole in the ground that continues as a vertical shaft.

▶ Leopards are known to eat their prey in trees.

1. Why might the location of trees near the cave entrance be important?

2. How might the early human child have received its wounds?

3. Why might small animal bones be absent from the cave?

4. Is it possible to know for certain how the fossils accumulated in the cave? Why?

Write a story about how the fossil bones got into the cave over a million years ago. Make sure your explanation fits all the pieces of evidence given above. You may want to include a drawing or diagram.

## Geography Connection

Have students use an encyclopedia or other reference to find the state fossils. The students should notice that some states will not have official state fossils. On a wall map of the United States, place the name of each fossil on the appropriate state.

▶ Ask students if they recognize a pattern in the distribution of states that have official fossils and those that do not. (Students should note a similar geologic pattern across fossil and non-fossil states.)

▶ Challenge students to locate and identify each state (without looking at the wall map) when given the fossil name.

## The Incomplete Fossil Record

The record of past life and events is not complete. Many organisms, especially those with soft bodies, did not leave fossils. Many fossils remain covered in undisturbed layers of rock. Many fossils and rocks were destroyed by metamorphism and other forces. Other fossils and evidence of environmental change have been found, but remain unexplained.

### Science and Society
*What's Your State Fossil?*

Does your state have a state fossil? The state fossil of Nebraska is the mammoth. All four species of extinct mammoths once lived in Nebraska. Mammoth skeletons are displayed in a museum in Lincoln, Nebraska.

Nevada's state fossil is the ichthyosaur, a reptile that lived in the ocean during the Mesozoic Era. A 15 m-long ichthyosaur was found in Nevada. *Stegosaurus*, a short-legged, plant-eating dinosaur weighing over 4 metric tons, is Colorado's state fossil. *Stegosaurus* is famous for the plates on its back. Arizona selected petrified wood as its state fossil. The largest collection of petrified wood in the world is found in Arizona in the Petrified Forest National Park.

Other state fossils include Alaska's woolly mammoth, Ohio's trilobite, and California's saber-toothed cat. If your state does not have a state fossil, what do you think would be a good choice? ②

**Figure 13.9** ▲
Crinoids, or sea lilies, are common fossils from the Paleozoic and Mesozoic Eras. The crinoid is the state fossil of Missouri.

## Check and Explain

1. Why did most organisms that lived on earth leave no fossil remains?

2. How is a mold different from a cast?

3. **Find Causes** Fossils of ocean organisms are much more common than fossils of organisms that lived on land. How do you explain this fact?

4. **Infer** In the center of North America, there are sedimentary rocks containing the fossils of ocean organisms. Based on this evidence, what can you infer about the geologic history of North America?

## Skills Development

**Hypothesize** Ask students to think about where in their state they would most likely find fossils. Have them write a hypothesis that states why they chose this place. Ask them how they would test their hypotheses.

### EVALUATE

## WrapUp

**Reinforce** Ask students to explain the difference between a trace fossil and a mold or cast. (Trace fossils provide evidence about an animal's habits; molds and casts show the animal's shape. A trace fossil may be a cast.)
   Use Review Worksheet 13.2.

## Check and Explain

1. Their bodies decayed or were eaten, bones and shells were scattered, or their remains eroded away.

2. The mold is a cavity left by an organism, and the cast fills the cavity.

3. Answers will vary. Ocean organisms have a better chance of being quickly buried and preserved in sand or silt, while land dwellers are more exposed to decay and erosion.

4. The center of North America was once under an ocean.

**Answer to In-Text Question**
② Answers will vary. Be sure students can explain their choices.

**Section Objectives**
For a list of section objectives, see the Student Edition page.

**Skills Objectives**
Students should be able to:

**Infer** the relative ages of objects.

**Measure** fossil age using radiometric data.

**Vocabulary**
principle of superposition, half-life

## MOTIVATE

### Skills WarmUp

To help students infer the relative age of different objects, have them do the Skills WarmUp.
**Answer** Items will vary. Check student rankings for accuracy and reasonable selection of evidence.

### Prior Knowledge

Gauge how much students know about dating fossils by asking the following questions:

▶ How can scientists learn the age of a fossil?

▶ Which is likely to be older, a fossil or the rock around it?

▶ Which would be closer to the earth's surface, a 10,000-year-old fossil or a 2 million-year-old fossil?

### Skills Development

**Define Operationally** Ask students for examples of the principle of superposition from everyday life. To get them started, point out that gravel on roads is usually "younger" than the dirt or concrete below it.

**Social Studies Connection**

Discuss with students how the paleontologist's job of interpreting fossils compares with the historian's job of writing about human history. Ask:

▶ How does each type of evidence used by historians compare to a fossil? (Pieces of evidence are preserved over time and provide information much like fossils.)

▶ How do historians date and order events? How does this differ from the ways in which paleontologists date and order events in geologic time? (Historians date and order events with respect to the appearance of human beings on the earth, whereas paleontologists date and order events with respect to geology and earth events.)

▼ **ACTIVITY**

**Inferring**

*Age Before Beauty*

Select five items in the classroom and rank them from oldest to youngest. What evidence did you use to make your ranking?

**SKILLS WARMUP**

## 13.3 Interpreting Fossils

### Objectives

▶ **Explain** the principle of superposition.

▶ **Determine** the relative age of fossils.

▶ **Describe** the process of radiometric dating.

▶ **Measure** the absolute age of a rock using the concept of half-life.

If dinosaurs lived tens of millions of years ago, how do scientists know so much about them? All knowledge about dinosaur size, appearance, diet, and behavior comes from fossils. For example, the distance between dinosaur footprints was used to estimate how fast the animals walked or ran.

One very important kind of information provided by fossils is when different species lived on the earth. By knowing the order in which species appeared, scientists can infer evolutionary relationships. To determine the age of different fossils, earth scientists use methods of relative and absolute age dating.

### Relative Age Dating

**Figure 13.10**
The deeper a rock layer, the older the fossils it contains. ▼

On a trip to the Grand Canyon, you find a fossil in sedimentary rock near the rim of the canyon. Will this fossil be older or younger than a fossil you find near the canyon bottom? Since you know that layers of sedimentary rock get older as you move down, you can infer that the fossil near the rim is younger. By making this inference, you have described the *relative age* of the fossil.

You may not realize it, but your inference was based on the **principle of superposition**. The principle of superposition states that younger rock layers are formed on top of older rock layers. This principle is the basis for most relative age dating of fossils.

## *Themes in Science*

**Energy** Disruptions of the rock layers at the earth's surface are caused primarily by the movement of tectonic plates. These movements are the result of heat energy in the earth's interior causing convection in the mantle.

## Disruptions of Rock Layers

Layers of sedimentary rock do not always stay where they form. Recall that rocks in the earth's crust may deform by folding or faulting. Folding can turn rock layers upside down or sideways. Faulting can make rock layers of different ages line up next to each other.

Erosion by water, wind, and ice removes layers of rock and creates gaps within layers. Sedimentary rock layers may also be disrupted by molten igneous rock moving into cracks and hardening to form an igneous dike.

The disruptions of sedimentary rock layers make relative age dating more difficult. But even the most deformed or eroded rock layers can be interpreted if you remember a few simple rules:

▶ Rock layers are horizontal before they deform.

▶ A fault or igneous dike did not exist when the layers formed, and is younger than the layers it cuts across.

Look at Figure 13.11. Study the rock layers and then answer the questions.

### Life Science
### L I N K

Construct a clay model of disrupted rock layers. In the model, include faults, folds, and fossils. See Figure 13.11 for ideas. Collect the following items: modeling clay, tissue paper, a trash bag, small objects (to represent fossils), thin wire, and graph paper. Separate rock layers with the tissue paper. Use the wire for making fault blocks and unconformities. On a sheet of graph paper, draw the rock layers as they would appear if undisrupted. Describe how your development of the model is similar to the processes that take place in the earth's crust.

**A C T I V I T Y**

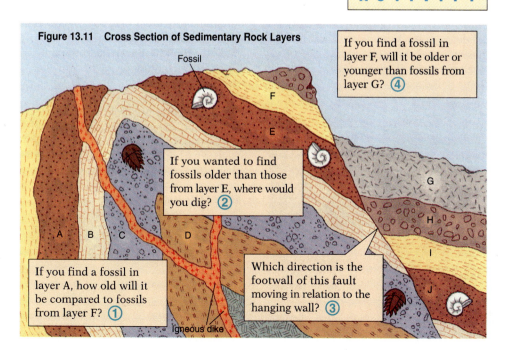

**Figure 13.11   Cross Section of Sedimentary Rock Layers**

Fossil

If you find a fossil in layer **F**, will it be older or younger than fossils from layer **G**? ④

F

E

If you wanted to find fossils older than those from layer **E**, where would you dig? ②

A   B   C   D

G

H

I

Which direction is the footwall of this fault moving in relation to the hanging wall? ③

J

If you find a fossil in layer **A**, how old will it be compared to fossils from layer **F**? ①

Igneous dike

## Reteach

Have students turn to the photograph of a fault on page 117. Ask them to identify the oldest and youngest layers of rock. (The youngest layers are on the surface.)

## Skills Development

**Observe**  Have students study Figure 13.11 and match the layers that have been disrupted. (A, E, and J; F and I; students may also match unlabeled layers.)

### Answers to In-Text Questions
① **Older**
② **Into layers B and C, starting where layer B reaches the surface**
③ **Upward**
④ **Older**

### Answer to Link

Models and descriptions should reflect some of the concepts discussed in Chapters 6 and 12, as well as in Chapter 13.

## Skills Development

**Calculate** Give students the following problems to solve:

▶ If a sample contains 25% carbon-14 and 75% carbon-14 decay product, how many half-lives have passed? (2) How old is the sample? (11,460 years)

▶ If a sample contains 1/8 undecayed isotopes and 7/8 decay product, how many half-lives have passed? (3)

**Infer** Ask students which isotope from Table 13.2 they would use to date the mold of a fish from the Tertiary Period (1.6 to 66 million years ago). (Most students will choose potassium-40 because the mold is not likely to contain organic material.)

## Integrated Learning

Use Integrating Worksheet 13.3.

**Answer to In-Text Question**

① **Half the sample of undecayed atoms**

### Integrating the Sciences

**Physical Science** Have students locate in the periodic table on pages 176–177 each of the radioactive isotopes listed in Table 13.2. Based on the atomic numbers given in the periodic table, have students determine the number of protons and neutrons contained in the nuclei of each isotope. (Th-232: 90 protons, 142 neutrons; K-40: 19 protons, 21 neutrons; C-14: 6 protons, 8 neutrons)

 ### Math Connection

Have students convert the bar graph in Figure 13.12 into a line graph. Challenge them to extend their graphs to four or five half-lives.

## Absolute Age Dating

The relative age of a fossil from the bottom of the Grand Canyon is older than one from the rim. But how can you determine the age in years of these fossils? You use absolute age dating. Absolute dating is based on a "clock" that accurately measures the passage of time.

**Radioactive Isotopes** The most accurate clock for absolute age dating is the decay of the radioactive isotopes of certain elements. An atom of a radioactive isotope contains an unstable ratio of neutrons to protons in its nucleus. It will *decay*, or release some matter and energy from the nucleus. Radioactive decay forms a new, more stable element called a decay product.

**Half-Life** Look at Figure 13.12. When many atoms of a radioactive isotope are present in a piece of matter, they do not all decay at the same time. Each atom has an equal chance of decaying. But over a certain amount of time, only some will decay.

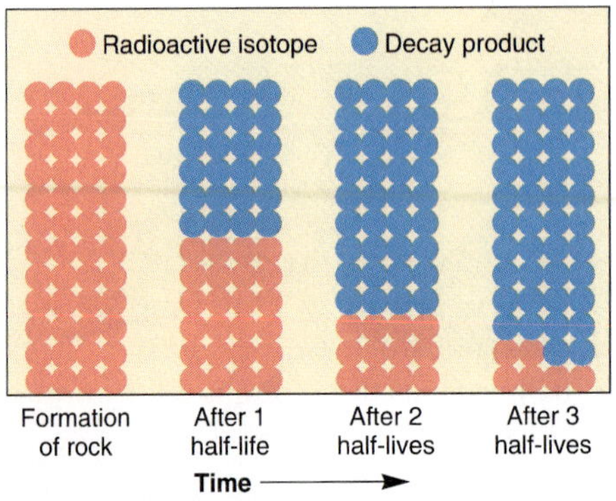

Scientists describe the rate of an isotope's decay by how long it takes for *half* of the atoms in a sample to decay. This measure of decay is called the isotope's **half-life**. The half-lives of isotopes vary from fractions of a second to billions of years. Radioactive decay makes a good clock for absolute age dating because half-lives are unchanging.

**Radiometric Dating** How do scientists use radioactive decay to date rocks and fossils? Many rocks contain small amounts of radioactive isotopes when they first form. And all organisms collect radioactive isotopes during their lives. After a rock forms or an organism dies, these isotopes start to decay at a regular rate. Each radioactive atom turns into an atom of another element.

Scientists measure the amount of the radioactive isotope present in the rock or fossil. They compare this amount to the amount of the decay product present. The ratio of the two amounts is used to calculate the amount of time that has passed since the formation of the rock or the death of the organism.

Look at Table 13.2. Different radioactive isotopes are used for dating different kinds of objects. Isotopes with long half-lives are best for dating old rocks. The isotope carbon-14 is used to date fossils that still contain organic material.

● Radioactive isotope ● Decay product

Formation of rock | After 1 half-life | After 2 half-lives | After 3 half-lives

**Time** ⟶

**Figure 13.12** ▲

How many atoms decay during a half-life? ①

**Table 13.2  Isotopes Used for Radiometric Dating**

| Isotope | Half-Life (Years) | Used to Date |
|---------|-------------------|--------------|
| Thorium-232 | 14 billion | Very old rocks |
| Potassium-40 | 1,300 million | Old rocks and fossils in them |
| Carbon-14 | 5,730 | Fossils less than 50,000 years old |

## Integrating the Sciences

**Health**  Computed axial tomography was first developed as a tool in medicine. Have students research its uses in that field. Ask:

▶ How have CAT scans helped doctors discover the sources of health problems? (They can see internal structures without having to operate.)

▶ Why is CAT technology an improvement over X-rays? (They are three dimensional.)

### Science and Technology
#### Probing Fossils with New Tools

Could dinosaurs see color? How well could they smell? How smart were they? Modern technology is helping scientists find answers to these and other questions.

Fossil bones can hold a lot of information. Unfortunately much of that information must remain hidden. To learn everything a fossil has to tell, scientists must break it apart to look inside. But scientists usually do not want to destroy a fossil.

A new technology, called computed axial tomography, or CAT, helps scientists "see" inside a fossil without destroying it. CAT scans give scientists three-dimensional images of a fossil and its interior. A CAT scan is made by placing the fossil inside a doughnut-shaped ring. The ring rotates and takes top-to-bottom X-ray scans. A computer puts all the scans into one three-dimensional image, such as the one in Figure 13.13. This picture can be rotated on the computer screen.

CAT scans of fossils from the meat-eating dinosaur *Nanotyrannus* show that it had a brain twice as large as first predicted. The spaces filled by the parts of the brain used for smell and sight suggest that this dinosaur could see colors and had an excellent sense of smell. Using these techniques to learn more about fossils helps scientists get a much better picture of what dinosaurs were really like.

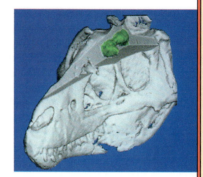

**Figure 13.13** ▲
Using CAT technology, a scientist can "slice" open a fossil without actually touching it.

### Check and Explain

1. How is the principle of superposition used to find the relative age of fossils?

2. What does it mean if the half-life of a radioactive isotope is 13,000 years?

3. **Infer**  Fossil A is the youngest of three fossils, and fossil C is oldest. When you find that the absolute age of fossil B is 140 million years, what can you infer about fossils A and C?

4. **Measure**  A rock sample contains 0.05 g of potassium-40 and 0.05 g of its decay product. Using Table 13.2, determine the age of a fossil contained in the sample.

## Section Objectives
For a list of section objectives, see the Student Edition page.

## Skills Objectives
Students should be able to:

**Gather Data** on historical events.

**Observe** characteristics that help determine absolute age.

**Organize Data** about the appearance and extinction of organisms.

**Vocabulary**
invertebrate, vertebrate

## MOTIVATE

### Skills WarmUp
To give students practice gathering time-ordered data, have them do the Skills WarmUp.
**Answer** Student timelines will vary. Be sure they circle at least two events.

### Misconceptions
Students may think that all ancient species are extinct. Tell them that some marine animals have changed only slightly since the Paleozoic Era, and many insects have changed only slightly since the Mesozoic Era.

### Class Activity
Have several volunteers copy the geologic time chart onto the chalkboard. As you discuss the eras in class, have volunteers add significant evolutionary events to the appropriate parts of the chart.

### Physical Education Connection

Have students see how far they can jump back into time. Convert the scale of geologic time into centimeters (one centimeter equals one million years). On the school grounds, measure the length of each period in the earth's history, using centimeters for millions of years. Label the intervals with the name for each period as shown in Figure 13.14. Have students stand at zero, or the present, and broad jump back into history. Keep a record of each jump. Have students analyze and graph the data to find out which periods were landed in most and which periods were landed in least.

### ▼ ACTIVITY

#### Gathering Data

*In Your Lifetime*

Refer to the timeline you made in the Skills WarmUp in Chapter 4, page 82. Add to your timeline some important historical events. Then circle the events that you think have been most important during your life and in history.

**SKILLS WARMUP**

## 13.4 Life Through Geologic Time

### Objectives

▶ **Name** some common types of organisms from each era of geologic time.

▶ **Explain** why the Precambrian Era has a poor fossil record.

▶ **Describe** human evolution.

▶ **Organize data** that shows the major events in the history of life on the earth.

If you could travel back in time, what point in the earth's history would you go to? Would you choose to go back about 10 million years, when mastodons and other large mammals lived in North America? Or would you want to travel back 150 million years to see *Seismosaurus*, a dinosaur that was over 40 m long and weighed 60 to 80 metric tons? What about going back 250 million years to explore the supercontinent Pangaea?

You will now take a short tour through the earth's history. You will learn what kinds of organisms lived in each of the four eras of geologic time, and when new types of organisms appeared on the earth. Study the "road map" of geologic time in Figure 13.14 before you begin your tour. You may also want to review the charts of geologic time on page 85, which show the relative lengths of the eras and periods.

**Figure 13.14
The Eras and Periods
of Geologic Time ▼**

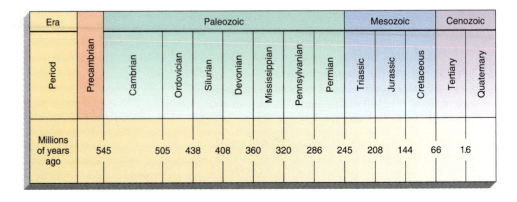

| Era | | Paleozoic | | | | | | | Mesozoic | | | Cenozoic | |
|---|---|---|---|---|---|---|---|---|---|---|---|---|---|
| **Period** | Precambrian | Cambrian | Ordovician | Silurian | Devonian | Mississippian | Pennsylvanian | Permian | Triassic | Jurassic | Cretaceous | Tertiary | Quaternary |
| **Millions of years ago** | 545 | 505 | 438 | 408 | 360 | 320 | 286 | 245 | 208 | 144 | 66 | 1.6 | |

302

## Integrating the Sciences

**Chemistry** Oxygen accumulated in the atmosphere as a result of organisms using photosynthesis to meet their energy needs. Write the simplified equation for photosynthesis on the board: $6CO_2 + 6H_2O \xrightarrow{\text{sunlight}} C_6H_{12}O_6 + 6O_2$. Then ask:

▶ For every molecule of $CO_2$ used in photosynthesis, how many molecules of $O_2$ were formed? (6)

▶ Where did organisms get the $CO_2$ they used in photosynthesis? (From volcanoes)

▶ Why is *sunlight* written above the arrow in the equation? (It is necessary for the reaction to occur.)

## Discuss

Ask students where most Precambrian organisms lived and have them explain their answer. (In the sea; most examples given are of marine organisms. Organisms colonized land 400 million years ago, in the Paleozoic Era.)

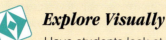

### Explore Visually

Have students look at Figure 13.15. Then ask:

▶ What animals are in this picture? (Sponge-like organisms on the sea floor, sea pens, jellyfish, and various types of worms)

▶ Where are the algae in this picture? (The leaf-like structures)

▶ What do all of these life forms have in common? (They all live in water. Students may also say that the organisms all need sunlight, or are made of cells.)

## Reteach

Use Reteach Worksheet 13.4.

## Integrated Learning

Use Integrating Worksheet 13.4.

Soft-bodied animals, much like today's jellyfish, probably swam in late Precambrian seas.

Many-celled algae grew up toward the light coming from the surface.

Animals resembling modern sponges lived attached to the bottom.

**Figure 13.15**
**Life Near the End of the Precambrian Era** ▲

## Precambrian Era

For about the first 1,000 million years of the earth's history, no life existed. During this time, the atmosphere formed. Heavy rains fell, and an ocean eventually covered all the land. The first living things appeared in this ancient ocean. They were simple cells without any specialized parts. But they were able to reproduce.

Scientists do not know when these first cells appeared. The oldest known fossils are about 3,500 million years old. These fossils, called *stromatolites* (stroh MAT uh lyts), were formed by colonies of ancient monerans trapped by layers of sediment. Over hundreds of millions of years, monerans and others like them released oxygen as part of their life processes. The oxygen accumulated in the atmosphere. By about 2,500 million years ago, the atmosphere had a significant amount of this vital gas.

Monerans were the only life forms on the earth until about 1,900 million years ago. At this time, the first complex cells evolved. They contained specialized parts, or organelles. They are classified in the protist kingdom.

The first many-celled organisms probably appeared a little over 1,000 million years ago. Scientists found a fossil of a red alga that is at least 2 billion years old. By the end of the Precambrian Era, 545 million years ago, numerous many-celled organisms lived in the ocean. These included animals that resembled modern sponges and jellyfish.

There were also organisms in the fungi and plant kingdoms. However, scientists do not know very much about these organisms because few left any fossils. They all had soft bodies that decayed rapidly when they died. Look at Figure 13.15 to see how a shallow sea may have appeared near the end of the Precambrian Era.

### Explore Visually

Have students examine Figure 13.16, then ask the following questions:

▶ Which of the animals in the picture are vertebrates? (Fish, shark, amphibian)

▶ Which organisms in the picture are invertebrates? (Dragonfly, crab-like organisms, starfish, crustacean, mollusks, squid-like organism)

▶ Which plants look like modern horsetails? (Those slightly right of center)

### Research

Have students use resources to find out about some organisms that survived the Paleozoic Era, such as gastropods, crustaceans, and echinoderms. Ask them to describe how these organisms were adapted to their environments.

### Enrich

Tell students that plant life from the swamp forests that flourished during the Paleozoic Era formed much of the oil and coal we now use as fuel.

### Art Connection

Have students use what they know about fishes and amphibians to show the evolution from fishes to amphibians in several stages. The stages should show how fins evolved into legs. At the same time, each stage should represent an organism that could have lived and was adapted to its environment.

## Paleozoic Era

The appearance of animals with hard parts, such as shells, marks the beginning of the Paleozoic Era. These animals left the first abundant fossils. Unlike the Precambrian Era, the Paleozoic has a rich fossil record.

Fossil evidence shows that the oceans in the early Paleozoic Era contained diverse organisms. All the animals of the early Paleozoic Era were **invertebrates**, or animals without backbones. The first **vertebrates**, animals with backbones, were fishlike organisms. They appeared in the Ordovician period. During the Silurian period, the first organisms left the ocean to live on land. These were simple plants, which had evolved from many-celled algae.

**Figure 13.16**
**Life at the Beginning of the Mississippian Period** ▼

The first animals to live on land, about 400 million years ago, were arthropods similar to today's millipedes. The first air-breathing vertebrates were amphibians, which evolved from fish during the Devonian period. They lived partly on land and partly in water.

The Mississippian period began about 360 million years ago. Huge swamp forests covered much of the land. These forests were made up of seedless, fernlike plants and the first primitive seed plants. The first reptiles appeared during the Pennsylvanian period.

Near the end of the Paleozoic Era, the earth's landmasses came together to form Pangaea. Many places where life flourished, such as the shallow seas, disappeared. Most of Pangaea became very dry. As a result of these changes, many organisms became extinct around 245 million years ago. These mass extinctions mark the end of the Paleozoic Era.

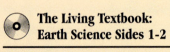

**The Living Textbook:**
**Earth Science Sides 1-2**

Chapter 27      Frame 03820
Paleozoic Fossils (8 Frames)
Search:           Step:

Seedless plants similar to modern ferns and horsetails grew as high as trees.

Winged insects buzzed through the humid air of the swamp forests.

The seas were filled with invertebrates, representing every major group alive today.

Amphibians were the first vertebrates to live on land.

### *Portfolio*

Have students make lists of all the facts they know about dinosaurs. Have students use the lists to compare dinosaurs to mammals. They can keep the lists in their portfolios.

### *Cooperative Learning*

Working in cooperative groups of four, have students list and describe famous dinosaurs portrayed in stories, movies, or television. Then have the students compare their lists of dinosaur facts from their portfolios to the famous dinosaurs. Have them discuss the scientific accuracy of the famous dinosaurs.

### *Explore Visually*

Have students look at Figure 13.17. Ask the following questions:

▶ What were the dominant vertebrates in the Mesozoic Era? (Dinosaurs)

▶ What were the dominant plants in the Mesozoic Era? (Students should infer that seed plants dominated.)

▶ How did the Mesozoic Era differ from the Paleozoic Era? (More land animals; flowering plants evolved; Pangaea split into continents.)

▶ What do the Mesozoic and Paleozoic eras have in common? (Both eras ended with mass extinctions. Species common to both would include fishes, insects, amphibians, reptiles, and ferns.)

▶ Which kinds of organisms shown still exist today? (Birds, flowering plants, small mammals)

## Skills Development

**Communicate**  Have each student write a paragraph describing the break-up of Pangaea and its effect on the environments in which organisms lived. Have several volunteers read their paragraphs to the class.

## Mesozoic Era

About 250 million years ago, certain reptiles evolved into the first dinosaurs. Over the next 160 million years, dinosaurs continued to evolve a variety of shapes, sizes, habits, and diets. During this time, the Mesozoic Era, dinosaurs dominated the earth.

From the study of fossil evidence, scientists learned that many dinosaurs were probably warm-blooded. They were active animals, and some could run much faster than you. Some dinosaurs probably lived in groups and took care of their young.

Many of the groups of organisms common today first appeared during the Mesozoic Era. The first mammals evolved about the same time as the dinosaurs. They were small and active at night. The first birds appeared a little later, probably during the Jurassic period.

Toward the end of the Mesozoic Era, the first flowering plants evolved from seed plants. Flowering plants adapted to a variety of environments, from dry to wet and from cold to hot. Flowering plants now greatly outnumber all other kinds of plants.

The earth's landmasses changed greatly during the Mesozoic Era. At the beginning of the era, there was only the supercontinent Pangaea. By the end of the era, Pangaea had broken into the major continents present today.

The Mesozoic Era ended about 66 million years ago, when many species, including most of the dinosaurs, died out. These mass extinctions were the result of major changes in the earth's environment and climate. Some of the changes may have been triggered by the impact of a large meteorite.

**Figure 13.17  Life in the Jurassic Period** ▼

Many dinosaurs depended on the palmlike cycads for food.

The first birds probably evolved from a type of dinosaur.

The first mammals were small and shy.

Flowering plants appeared during the Mesozoic Era.

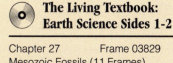

### Class Activity

Have students use references to find out how the evolution of marsupials was affected by geography during the Cenozoic Era. Have them prepare a bulletin-board display to illustrate where marsupials have flourished.

### Explore Visually

Have students look at Figure 13.18, then ask:

▶ Where are the flowering plants in the picture? (On the ground; the trees)

▶ Which animals in the picture are plant-eaters? (The zebra-like, rhinoceros-like, and elephant-like animals)

▶ Where did meat-eating animals hunt? (On grassy plains)

▶ What is the biggest difference between this scene and the illustration in Figure 13.15? (Students should mention that the illustration of the Precambrian Era is made up entirely of sea life, while the organisms shown in Figure 13.18 all live on dry land.)

### Integrating the Sciences

**Life Science**  Have students do research to find out the common characteristics of mammals. Discuss how mammals were better adapted to living in an era with repeated glaciation.

### Themes in Science

**Scale and Structure**  The size and the structure of organisms changed as they adapted to their environment. Some organisms became smaller, while others became larger. The structure of the organisms also changed as the animals evolved. For example, certain plant eaters evolved hooves.

### Cenozoic Era

The era in which you now live, the Cenozoic Era, began 66 million years ago. If the Mesozoic Era can be called the Age of Dinosaurs, then the Cenozoic Era is the Age of Mammals. The small mammals present in the Mesozoic Era evolved rapidly during the early Cenozoic Era. Some became plant-eaters, evolving hooves and a larger body size. They grazed on the increasing numbers of flowering plants. Others became meat-eaters, specializing in the hunting of plant-eaters.

By about 30 million years ago in the Tertiary period, the ancestors of most modern mammals had evolved. On land, there were horses, rhinoceroses, monkeys, mastodons, camels, antelopes, tigers, and lions. In the ocean, there were whales and dolphins.

The climate during most of the Cenozoic Era has been relatively cool and dry. Advances of glaciers shaped the land. An ice age with several periods of glaciation occurred during the last 2 million years. The human species, *Homo sapiens*, evolved during this time of repeated glaciation and warming.

**Figure 13.18
Life in the
Tertiary Period** ▼

Many plant-eating mammals grazed on the grassy plains that covered much of the land.

Meat-eating mammals, such as the ancestors of today's tigers, lions, and dogs, fed on the herds of grazing animals.

Flowering plants evolved many different forms.

**The Living Textbook:
Earth Science Sides 1-2**

Chapter 27          Frame 03840
Cenozoic Fossils (11 Frames)
Search:               Step:

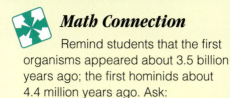

## Math Connection

Remind students that the first organisms appeared about 3.5 billion years ago; the first hominids about 4.4 million years ago. Ask:

▶ How old are hominids compared to the age of life on the earth? (Hominids are about one-eight hundredth as old as the earth's first organisms.)

## Human Evolution

The first humanlike organisms, or hominids (HAHM uh nihdz), appeared about 4.4 million years ago. They lived on the ground and walked upright on two legs. Hominids evolved into several different species. Most early hominid species eventually became extinct. But one species survived to evolve further.

Scientists have found the fossils of many hominid species, but they are not sure which ones are direct human ancestors. About 1.6 million years ago, a hominid called *Homo erectus* existed. Scientists hypothesize that it is an ancestor of modern humans.

*Homo erectus* evolved into *Homo sapiens* sometime between 500,000 and 300,000 years ago. The first modern-looking humans appeared about 100,000 years ago, probably in Africa. They are called the Cro-Magnons (KROH MAG nuhnz). Cro-Magnons had spread to most continents by about 30,000 years ago.

**Figure 13.19** ▲
These are fossils of hominids that lived about 1.5 million years ago.

## Career Corner  *Paleontologist*

### Who Finds and Studies Fossils?

How would you like to discover a new kind of dinosaur? If you become a paleontologist (PAY lee uhn TAHL uh jihst), such a discovery is possible. A paleontologist studies the organisms of the past. Much of the study focuses on fossils, as they provide evidence about ancient life.

Paleontologists use fossils to trace the evolution of life. Pollen in ice, ripple marks in sandstone, the oxygen content in minerals, and other findings are used by paleontologists to describe ancient environments. Paleontologists date fossils using methods you learned about, as well as others.

Most paleontologists spend some of their time in the field. They hunt for fossils and take great care in removing and preserving them. They also work in laboratories, where fossils are studied and dated.

Paleontologists use knowledge of anatomy, geology, biology, physics, chemistry, and mathematics in their work. To prepare for a career as a paleontologist, you should take a variety of science courses in high school. You can also start fossil collecting as a hobby.

Most paleontology jobs require an advanced degree. However, with some experience or college training, you can work in the field or a laboratory assisting paleontologists.

## Directed Inquiry

After students have read the text on human evolution, ask the following questions:

▶ What characteristics distinguished hominids from most other mammals? (They lived on the ground and walked upright on two legs.)

▶ Do any other animals today share these characteristics? (Examples include flightless birds, such as ostriches.)

▶ What characteristics distinguish today's humans from all other animals? (Answers will vary and may include opposable thumbs, language, and so on.)

## Career Corner

**Portfolio**  Have students choose one of the following scientists and write a brief report on where they worked and their major contributions to science. Encourage students to include as much biographical detail in the report as they wish. Have them keep their reports in their portfolios.
Mary Leakey
Louis Leakey
Charles Lyell
Mary Anning
Henry F. Osborn
Baron Cuvier
Pierre Teilhard de Chardin

## Skills WorkOut

To help students apply their observation skills to the dating of objects, have them do the Skills WorkOut.

**Answer** Student selections will vary. Absolute age can often be determined by stamped or written dates. Check answers for accuracy.

## Apply

Have students imagine they are planning a dig in the area. Ask where they would look for fossils and what kind they would be likely to find.

## WrapUp

**Reinforce** Have students review pages 303–306 and list the organisms that evolved from other organisms. (Plants from many-celled algae, amphibians from fishes, dinosaurs from reptiles, flowering plants from seed plants) Have them draw tree diagrams that illustrate these developments.

Use Review Worksheet 13.4.

## Check and Explain

1. Dinosaurs and cycads; mammals and flowering plants; marine organisms, seedless plants

2. Most organisms were soft-bodied and decayed rapidly; animals with hard body parts appeared.

3. Answers will vary; students may suggest that mammals were no longer prey for dinosaurs, or that mammals were able to fill the roles (plant eaters, meat eaters) once occupied by dinosaurs.

4. Check timelines for accuracy.

### STS Connection

Many people want dinosaur fossils of their own. Because some people are willing to pay large amounts of money for fossils, fossil hunters often break laws to collect fossils for sale. Discuss the following:

▶ Should fossils be used only for scientific purposes?

▶ Is it wrong to collect fossils for sale, even if it is legal?

▶ What can be done about the increase in theft of fossils from public lands?

### ▼ ACTIVITY

**Observing**

*Absolute Age*

Select five items in the classroom that can be given an absolute age. How can you tell the absolute age of each item?

**SKILLS WORKOUT**

### Science and You  *Going on a Dig*

In many places, fossils are more common than you may think. Many fossil beds are open to amateur fossil collectors. Do you have fossil beds near where you live? If you do, you may be able to start a collection of traces of plants and animals that lived millions of years ago.

The best place to find fossils in your area is where sedimentary rocks are at the surface. A deep road cut or a canyon wall may expose layers of sedimentary rock representing millions of years of geologic time. Coastlines where the ocean erodes tall cliffs often have visible fossil layers. Gravel and sand pits and limestone quarries are also good sites for finding fossils. The sedimentary rocks that are often used to make buildings, fences, and sidewalks may contain fossils! Look closely at structures made from rocks.

If you find fossils that you want to collect, you may need a rock hammer to break free the chunks of rock containing the fossils. Be careful not to break the fossils. A field guide to fossils will help you identify what you've found. A field guide may also help you find fossils by showing you what unfamiliar ones may look like.

Most fossils in national and state parks are protected and shouldn't be removed. These fossils may be valuable for scientific study. Before removing fossils from private land, be sure to get permission from the owner.

### Check and Explain

1. What group of organisms was dominant on the earth during the Mesozoic Era? The Cenozoic Era? The Paleozoic Era?

2. Why are fossils from the Precambrian Era rare? What happened at the beginning of the Paleozoic Era to make fossils more common?

3. **Find Causes** Why did mammals begin to evolve rapidly right after the dinosaurs died out? Explain your reasoning.

4. **Organize Data** Make a timeline that dates the appearance and extinction of important groups of organisms.

## Chapter 13 *Review*

### Concept Summary

**13.1 Evolution of Life**
▶ Fossils help scientists reconstruct the history of life on earth.
▶ Darwin's theory of evolution explains how species change over time.
▶ Organisms are classified into five kingdoms according to similarities in body organization and method of nutrition.
▶ The organisms in each kingdom share an evolutionary history. They are more related to each other than to organisms in other kingdoms.

**13.2 The Fossil Record**
▶ If an organism is protected from decay and destruction when it dies, it may become a fossil.
▶ Fossils are classified into groups depending on how they form.

**13.3 Interpreting Fossils**
▶ The relative ages of rocks and fossils are determined by using the principle of superposition.
▶ Radiometric dating is a way of finding the absolute age of a rock or fossil. It is based on the constant rate of decay of radioactive isotopes.

**13.4 Life Through Geologic Time**
▶ Life first appeared during the Precambrian Era.
▶ Organisms with hard parts evolved during the Paleozoic Era.
▶ Mammals, birds, and flowering plants appeared during the Mesozoic Era, while dinosaurs dominated the earth.
▶ Modern types of mammals evolved during the Cenozoic Era.

### Chapter Vocabulary

| | | |
|---|---|---|
| species (13.1) | petrified (13.2) | principle of superposition (13.3) |
| evolution (13.1) | mold (13.2) | half-life (13.3) |
| extinction (13.1) | cast (13.2) | invertebrate (13.4) |
| kingdom (13.1) | trace fossil (13.2) | vertebrate (13.4) |

### Check Your Vocabulary

Use the vocabulary words above to complete the following sentences correctly.

1. All organisms belong to one of five ____ .
2. When mineral-containing water seeps into a fossil mold, a ____ may form.
3. The theory of ____ explains how species change over time.
4. An animal with a backbone is a ____ .
5. A dinosaur footprint is an example of a ____ .
6. An impression in rock left by a shell is an example of a ____ .
7. All members of a ____ have nearly the same basic traits.
8. Scientists use the ____ to find the relative age of fossils.
9. Each radioactive isotope has a ____ .
10. All the organisms living in the early Paleozoic Era were ____ .
11. Environmental changes may cause the ____ of a species.
12. A bone whose matter is slowly replaced by minerals becomes ____ .

### Write Your Vocabulary

Write sentences using the vocabulary words above. Show that you know what each word means.

### Check Your Vocabulary

1. kingdoms
2. cast
3. evolution
4. vertebrate
5. trace fossil
6. mold
7. species
8. principle of superposition
9. half-life
10. invertebrates
11. extinction
12. petrified

### Write Your Vocabulary

Students' sentences should show that they know the meaning of each word as well as how to use it in a sentence.

Use Vocabulary Worksheet for Chapter 13.

## Check Your Knowledge

1. The first organisms were monerans.
2. A layer of rock is older than the layer right above it.
3. An atom of a radioactive isotope must eventually decay.
4. Examples include organisms preserved in frozen ground, in amber, or in a bog or tar pit.
5. Dinosaurs evolved from reptiles.
6. Plants photosynthesize, and animals eat food. Plants and animals also have different evolutionary histories.
7. The bone becomes petrified as minerals replace the original organic matter.
8. Folding, faulting, erosion, and igneous intrusions can disrupt sedimentary rock layers.
9. False; tree diagram
10. False; Paleozoic
11. True
12. True
13. False; Precambrian
14. True

## Check Your Understanding

1. When the environment changes, different traits may be favored over others because they help the organisms that have them be adapted to the changes. Organisms possessing beneficial traits will survive and have offspring; those without the trait(s) will not.
2. Accept any reasonable answer. The mass extinctions are easily visible as breaks in the fossil record, and the mass extinctions separate one characteristic set of organisms from another.
3. Only the imprint of the leaf is definitely a fossil; the others are similar to fossils, but do not preserve remains from an older time in geologic history.
4. It is possible that the insect and the plant species made it possible for each other to survive: the plant could have provided food for the insect while the insect provided a means of pollination for the plant.

5. Either folding turned the rock layers in the area upside down, or erosion removed the upper layers of rock.
6. The classification of organisms is based on similarities that are a result of evolution. Organisms that are members of the same kingdom have evolved from a common ancestor.
7. Over 150 million years longer
8. The ammonite looks like a snail shell. The crystals formed when minerals dissolved in water crystallized as the water left.

## Chapter 13  Review

### Check Your Knowledge

Answer the following in complete sentences.

1. The first organisms to live on the earth belonged to which kingdom?
2. How old is a sedimentary rock layer compared to the layer directly above it?
3. What must happen, sooner or later, to an atom of a radioactive isotope?
4. Give an example of how an unchanged fossil may form.
5. From what kind of organism did the dinosaurs evolve?
6. How do plants differ from animals?
7. How does the bone of a dead organism become petrified?
8. List three ways that layers of sedimentary rock may be disrupted.

Determine whether each statement is true or false. Write *true* if it is true. If it is false, change the underlined word(s) to make the statement true.

9. The relationships between different groups of organisms can be shown with an evolutionary bar graph.
10. The first vertebrates appeared during the Cenozoic Era.
11. A mold must form before a cast.
12. The radioactive isotopes in a rock begin to decay when the rock is formed.
13. Organisms that lived in the Paleozoic Era left few fossils.
14. A species evolves through the process of natural selection.

### Check Your Understanding

Apply the concepts you have learned to answer each question.

1. Why do changes in the environment affect the evolution of a species?
2. **Critical Thinking**  Both the Paleozoic and Mesozoic Eras ended at times of mass extinction. Why do you think scientists chose these times in geologic history to mark the ends of eras and the beginnings of new eras?
3. **Classify**  Which of the following is a fossil? If it is not a fossil, explain why not.
   a. Bird tracks in hardened mud.
   b. A chicken in your freezer.
   c. The imprint of a leaf in a rock.
   d. A bone you dig up in your backyard.
4. New species of insects began to evolve rapidly about the same time that flowering plants appeared. Why might this be so?
5. **Critical Thinking**  You find a 200-million-year-old fossil in the uppermost layer of some sedimentary rock. How is this possible?
6. Explain the relationship between the evolution of life and the classification of life into kingdoms.
7. **Compare and Contrast**  How much longer did dinosaurs live on the earth than humans have lived?
8. **Mystery Photo**  The photograph on page 288 shows the fossil of an ammonite, which lived during the Cretaceous period. What modern animals do you think are most closely related to ammonites? How do you think the crystals formed inside the fossil?

## Develop Your Skills

**1.** a. 50 grams

b. 50 years; one-half of a 100-gram sample will decay in 50 years.

c. The shapes of the curves would be very similar.

**2.** a. Uranium-238

b. Nitrogen-14

c. Uranium-235, Potassium-40, Uranium-238, Thorium-232, Rubidium-87

## Make Connections

**1.** Concept maps will vary. The map below shows a possible organization of the concepts listed.

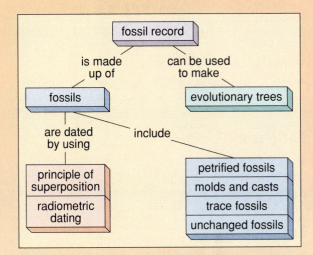

**2.** Student answers may vary. Some important discoveries have been made at the La Brea tar pits in Los Angeles; in the great dinosaur fields of Alberta, Canada, and Jensen, Utah; and the Olduvai Gorge in Africa.

**3.** Student stories will vary. Encourage students to use details in describing the time period they choose.

**4.** Answer depends on location.

**5.** Drawings will vary.

**6.** Analysis proved that the skull was of a human and the jawbone was from an ape.

## Develop Your Skills

Use the skills you have developed in this chapter to complete each activity.

**1. Interpret Data** The graph below shows the decay of a radioactive isotope over time.

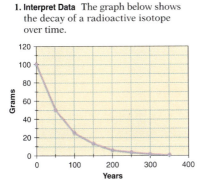

a. How much of the isotope is present after 50 years?

b. What is the half-life of this isotope? How do you know?

c. If you graphed the decay of another radioactive isotope in a similar way, how would the shape of the curve compare to the shape of this curve?

**2. Data Bank** Use the information on page 622 to answer the following questions.

a. What radioactive isotope has a half-life nearly equal to the age of the earth?

b. What is the decay product of carbon-14?

c. What radioactive isotopes could be used to date a fossil from the Paleozoic Era?

## Make Connections

**1. Link the Concepts** Construct a concept map showing how the concepts from this chapter link together. Add terms to connect, or link, the concepts: unchanged fossil, evolutionary tree, trace fossil, principle of superposition, fossil, radiometric dating, fossil record, petrified fossil, mold, cast.

**2. Science and Geography** Research to find out where important fossils have been found. Make a map that shows where the fossils were discovered.

**3. Science and Writing** Choose a time in the earth's history you would like to visit in a time machine. Write a story about what you see when you get there.

**4. Science and Society** Find out if your state has a state fossil. If not, do research to find out what types of organisms have been found as fossils in your state. Write a letter to one of your state legislators explaining why a certain fossil should be adopted as the state fossil.

**5. Science and Art** Find pictures of different kinds of fossils, such as trilobites and ammonites. Use the shapes and patterns of one or more of these fossils to make a design or drawing.

**6. Science and Society** Do research on Piltdown Man, a skull and jawbone found in England in 1911. The Piltdown Man was believed to be the fossil remains of an ancient human ancestor. Find out how the bones were discovered to be a hoax.

## About the Literary Work

"Tales of a Dead King" was adapted from *Tales of a Dead King* by Walter Dean Myers, copyright 1983 by Walter Dean Myers. Reprinted by permission of William Morrow and Co., Inc.

## Description of Change

This is a short passage from the novel that gives the reader a good sense of the desert terrain.

## Rationale

The passage was chosen because it makes use of concepts from the science lessons in this unit, such as the processes of deposition and erosion.

## Vocabulary

Nubian, Egyptian, equidistant

## Teaching Strategies

### Directed Inquiry

After students finish reading, discuss the story. Be sure to relate the story to the science lessons in this unit. Ask the following questions:

▶ The dunes that are mentioned in the passage are likely to be of what type? (Transverse; because transverse dunes are common in large deserts with lots of sand)

▶ What do you suppose an Egyptologist does? (Studies Egyptian antiquities)

▶ How is it that the narrator had not noticed that they had been traveling in a circle? (The desert topography is relatively featureless, and the topography quickly changes.)

## Critical Thinking

**Reason and Conclude**  Have students reread Ahmed's puzzled responses to Karen and the narrator. Ask:

▶ Why do you think there were no signs of digging at the sites to which Ahmed led Karen and the narrator? Do you think Ahmed had forgotten where the sites were? Give evidence to support your answer. (Ahmed probably knows the desert very well and has found the original digging sites. It is likely that the windblown, shifting sands of the desert erased any evidence of Dr. Leonhardt's visit.)

▶ Karen contradicts Ahmed and insists that Dr. Leonhardt must have dug many feet in his search for artifacts rather than just probing the surface. Who is right, Karen or Ahmed? Why? (Ahmed is probably right. It is likely that many feet of sand have piled up on the site since Dr. Leonhardt's visit so that now it is necessary to dig much more deeply.)

# Science and Literature Connection

A hmed grunted and began to drive. He drove for about an hour through some of the most desolate land I had ever seen. Finally he stopped and pointed toward a small dune.

"There," he said.

He pulled the jeep to a stop. The wind had picked up and the sand cut into our faces. Ahmed lowered his hood and produced a scarf from somewhere which he handed to Karen. We walked slowly over to the dune, up to our shoe tops in the loose sand.

We looked around the site. There were no signs of digging at all. I went to the crest of the dune, or as near to it as I could, to see if there was anything under it. Nothing. I looked off in the distance. The Nile was a half mile away. It was the part of the river that had overflowed when the Aswan dam was built, and that had engulfed what little greenery there was. I could see a few patches of grass growing out of the silt deposits along the water's edge, and the remains of a Nubian village.

I got back to the jeep at the same time Ahmed and Karen returned from the other side of the dune.

"You see anything?" she said.

"Nothing," I said.

The next site was a good half hour's drive away. This time Ahmed stopped at a rock formation very close to the Nile. He showed us what he said was the exact spot in

### *Tales of a Dead King*

*The following excerpt is from the book* Tales of a Dead King *by Walter Dean Myers.*

which Dr. Leonhardt had been digging. We drew a large circle around the spot, about twelve feet in diameter, and began to probe with sticks. There was one area that might have been dug up before, but we couldn't tell for sure. We pushed the sticks into the soft earth carefully, so as not to break anything we might find under the earth's surface.

"I don't think this is the place," Karen called back. "If Dr. Leonhardt had really dug here the ground should have been looser."

"Ahmed, why isn't the ground looser here if Dr. Leonhardt dug here as you say?" I asked.

# Skills in Science

## Reading Skills in Science

1. The story takes place in the Egyptian desert. Karen and the narrator are attempting to find an archaeological dig site.

2. The wind, which is an agent of both erosion and deposition, could move great amounts of sand in such a way that the landscape could change significantly. This would make it almost impossible to find the dig site.

## Writing Skills in Science

1. The Nile flooded annually, leaving silt behind. Silt provides fertile soil for crops.

2. Ancient artifacts would normally be covered by centuries of sediment deposition buildup. They might be buried far below the earth's surface. Due to the forces of erosion and deposition, the depth of the artifacts could vary considerably from place to place. In this particular environment, wind erosion might actually remove enough sediment to expose the artifacts.

## Activities

**Collect Data** The Aswan High Dam, completed in 1970, ended the annual flooding of the Nile, trapping the river's silt in Lake Nassar. Without the silt, Egyptian farmers have been forced to use more artificial fertilizers. But the dam generates electricity and provides a steady flow of water for farming.

**Communicate** Nubia was an ancient region of Africa. It covered what is now Sudan. The most important Nubian peoples, the Kush, lived from 1000 B.C. to about A.D. 350, creating a center of ironworking, learning, and trade.

---

"He don't dig," Ahmed said. "He never dig. He just push a stick into the ground, like you."

"In that case," Karen said, rubbing her nose. "He wasn't serious about digging here. Anything that he would have been interested in wouldn't be anywhere near enough to the surface to find with a probe. You would have to dig at least six to fourteen feet, depending on the amount of erosion in the area, before you could even think about using a probe."

"I don't think that Ahmed understands that," I said. "Better explain it to him carefully."

"Dr. Leonhardt's an Egyptologist," Karen said. "Anything he would be looking for would be either above the ground, like a pyramid, or many feet below the ground, covered by years of dirt blowing over it. You understand?"

"I understand," Ahmed said. "But that's what he did. Like I say."

We went around to two more sites where Ahmed said that Dr. Leonhardt had been digging. We didn't see any signs of digging at all.

"I think," Karen said as we got back into the jeep, "that we are being had by Mr. Ahmed. You, of course, noticed that we are traveling in a direction for which there is a constant equidistant point?"

"Huh?"

"We're traveling in a circle!" she said.

I asked Ahmed to stop the jeep and I got out. I couldn't see very much where I was, so I walked up to the base of a small hill and began climbing. When I had gone up about thirty feet, I looked around. Sure enough, there was the same deserted Nubian village I had seen before, but now I was looking at it from the other side. Either Ahmed was taking us for a ride or Dr. Leonhardt was taking everybody for a ride.

## Skills in Science

### Reading Skills in Science

1. **Accurate Observations** Where does this story take place? What are Karen and the narrator trying to do?

2. **Infer** In what ways would the forces of erosion and deposition slow the efforts to find the location where Dr. Leonhardt was digging? Explain.

### Writing Skills in Science

1. **Find Causes** Explain how silt was deposited along the edge of the Nile. Why are the silt deposits one of the only places where grass grows?

2. **Generalize** Explain why Dr. Leonhardt would have to dig at least six to fourteen feet if he were trying to find ancient Egyptian artifacts. Is this true for every place he might dig? What factors influence how deep he must dig?

### Activities

**Collect Data** Gather information on the Aswan High Dam. How has the dam's construction affected the areas downriver from the dam? Explain how the building of the dam has affected farming in nearby areas.

**Communicate** Make a diagram or draw a picture of what the Egyptian Nubian village in this story might look like. Use reference materials at a library to collect information about the Nubians.

### Where to Read More

*Going on a Dig* by Velma Ford Morrison. New York: Dodd, Mead & Co. An excellent introduction to the hands-on science of archaeology; explains why artifacts are buried and describes the procedure of a dig, giving many examples along the way.

# UNIT

## Introducing the Unit

### Directed Inquiry

Have students study the photograph and read the caption. Ask:

▶ What is causing this water to flow so rapidly? (Gravity)

▶ Where is the water coming from? (Possible sources are rainwater, melting snow from mountain tops, or a spring.)

▶ Where will the water flow to? (Students may suggest that the stream becomes a river that finally runs into the ocean or into a larger body of fresh water.)

▶ Where else is the water in this picture going? (Plants are using water, and the water is both soaking into the ground and evaporating.)

▶ What are some of the differences between this water and ocean water? (Students will mention the saltiness. They should also note that fresh water is located inland, underground, and in ice caps; and that it moves in rivers and seeps through the ground.)

▶ How are oceans and bodies of fresh water alike? (Both change the land around them; lakes and oceans both contain currents.)

### Writing About the Photograph

Have students imagine that they can step into this photograph and go beyond it, into the environment shown. Have them describe what they see in a poem.

Unit 5 explores the waters of the earth. Bodies of water and water movements are studied both in terms of physical properties and their importance to living things. Chapter 14 discusses fresh water, tracing its movements over, under, and across the earth's surface. The chapter emphasizes how life depends on available fresh water, and also explains how water can be contaminated. Chapter 15 examines ocean water and how it moves. Currents, waves, and tides are discussed. The chapter also considers efforts to harness the tremendous mechanical energy of the tides. Chapter 16 is an exploration of the ocean basins, from the life zones of the open ocean to the topography of the ocean floor. The chapter describes the tools and technology used by scientists to study the ocean, and concludes with a discussion of some of the valuable food and mineral resources in the ocean.

Unit 5

# Earth's Waters

### Chapters

14  Fresh Water

15  Ocean Water

16  Ocean Basins

# Data Bank

Use the information on pages 612 to 625 to answer the following questions about topics explored in this unit.

## Calculating

Approximately how much deeper is the Atlantic Ocean than the Arctic Ocean?

## Making a Graph

Construct a line graph that shows the heights of the day tides. The *x*-axis should show the times; the *y*-axis should show the tide heights in meters. Be sure to label your graph.

## Reading a Map

Locate and name at least three rivers in the United States that run through the Great Plains.

The photograph to the left was taken in Olympic National Park in Washington state. Is the water shown running through a creek or a river? How can you tell?

Have students search the Data Bank on pages 612 to 625 for the answers to the questions on this page.

**Calculating** The Atlantic Ocean is approximately 2,500 meters deeper than the Arctic Ocean. The answer is found in the graph World's Largest Oceans and Seas on page 622.

**Extension** Have students locate all the seas listed in the graph on a world map.

**Making a Graph** Students' graphs should accurately reflect the information given in the Tide Table, Week of January 24–30 on page 616.

**Reading a Map** The Missouri, North Platte, South Platte, Platte, Arkansas, Yellowstone, Red, and Brazos rivers are the major rivers shown that run through the Great Plains. The answer is found on the Physical Map of the United States on pages 620 and 621.

**Extension** Have students find and list all major rivers than run through the eastern United States.

**Answer to In-Text Question**

The water is moving swiftly and is near the river's source. A creek is a slower-moving tributary.

**CHAPTER 14**

## Overview

Fresh water is discussed in this chapter. Section one explains the physical and chemical properties of water and describes the importance of water to living things. The next section describes surface water and its location. The third section discusses water beneath the surface, exploring ground water, its zones, movement, and potential contaminants.

## Advance Planner

▶ Gather a glass, marker, tape, and coffee filter for TE page 318 (top). Collect wax paper, toothpicks, glue, tennis balls, and table-tennis balls for TE page 318 (side).

▶ Obtain sugar, cooking oil, candle wax, salt, and flour for TE page 319.

▶ Supply dry sponges for SE page 321. Prepare beakers, plastic wrap, rubber band, and a small rock or marble for TE page 321.

▶ Gather funnels, aquarium gravel, sand, and plastic containers for TE page 329.

▶ Collect Epsom salt, jars, cotton string, washers, and note cards for TE page 331.

▶ Prepare jars or beakers, clear plastic tubing, markers, and masking tape for SE Activity 14, page 334.

## Skills Development Chart

| Sections | Classify | Define Operationally | Make a Model | Measure | Observe | Communicate | Predict |
|---|---|---|---|---|---|---|---|
| **14.1** Skills WarmUp | | | | ● | | | |
| SkillBuilder | | | | | | | ● |
| Skills WorkOut | | | ● | | | | |
| **14.2** Skills WarmUp | | ● | | | | | |
| Skills WorkOut | ● | | | | | | |
| **14.3** Skills WarmUp | | | | | ● | | |
| Consider This | ● | | | | ● | ● | |
| Activity 14 | ● | ● | ● | | ● | ● | |

## Individual Needs

▶ **Limited English Proficiency Students** Tape record the definitions and pronunciations of the chapter's boldface terms. Tell students which figures and definitions in the text illustrate the terms. Have them use the tape recorder to listen to the information about each term. Next have students define the terms using their own words. Have them make their own tape recordings of the words and their definitions. They can use this tape to review important chapter concepts.

▶ **At-Risk Students** Have students work in groups to make models of stalactites and stalagmites. Have each group dissolve as much washing soda as possible in two jars of very warm water. Next have them attach a paper clip to each end of a length of yarn and place each end in a jar. Put a saucer between the jars and leave a few days. In less than a week, students should see a stalactite forming in the middle of the yarn and a stalagmite growing up on the saucer. Have groups present their experiments, explaining their procedure, how their stalactites are similar and different from actual ones, and how the activity relates to the subject of the chapter.

▶ **Gifted Students** Encourage groups of students to find out more about the fresh water in their area through research and interviews. Have one group map a circular area 5–25 km in diameter with the school as the center. Their map should show the surface water. Ask another group to make a map or diagram that shows the water beneath the surface. A third group should learn about threats and damage to the fresh water of the area. Have all groups present their findings in an exhibit.

## Resource Bank

▶ **Bulletin Board** Have students contribute pictures and maps of the floods of 1993 to the bulletin board. Have them add captions to their pictures. Where possible, have them show before and after views of flooded areas. Their contributions can show causes of the flood, relief efforts, and types of damage, as well as the flood plain, levees, and other physical features.

▶ **Field Trip** If possible, take students on a field trip to a local water plant to learn the process by which water is collected and purified for drinking and other household uses. Encourage students to ask questions based on what they have learned from the chapter.

| Section | Core | Standard | Enriched | Section | Core | Standard | Enriched |
|---|:---:|:---:|:---:|---|:---:|:---:|:---:|
| **14.1 Water and Its Properties** pp. 317–323 | | | | **Laboratory Program** Investigation 20 | | ● | ● |
| **Section Features** Skills WarmUp, p. 317 | ● | ● | ● | **Color Transparencies** Transparency 38 | ● | ● | ● |
| SkillBuilder, p. 319 | ● | ● | ● | **14.3 Water Beneath the Surface** pp. 329–334 | | | |
| Skills WorkOut, p. 321 | ● | ● | | **Section Features** Skills WarmUp, p. 329 | ● | ● | ● |
| **Blackline Masters** Review Worksheet 14.1 | ● | ● | ● | Consider This, p. 332 | ● | ● | ● |
| Skills Worksheet 14.1a | ● | ● | ● | Activity, p. 334 | ● | ● | ● |
| Skills Worksheet 14.1b | ● | ● | ● | **Blackline Masters** Review Worksheet 14.3 | ● | ● | ● |
| Integrating Worksheet 14.1 | ● | ● | | Integrating Worksheet 14.3 | ● | ● | ● |
| **Overhead Blackline Transparencies** Overhead Blackline Master 14.1 and Student Worksheet | ● | ● | ● | Vocabulary Worksheet 14.3 | ● | ● | ● |
| **Color Transparencies** Transparencies 37a, 37b | ● | ● | ● | **Ancillary Options** *CEPUP,* Investigating Groundwater: The Fruitvale Story | | ● | ● |
| **14.2 Surface Water** pp. 324–328 | | | | *One-Minute Readings,* p. 58 | | ● | ● |
| **Section Features** Skills WarmUp, p. 324 | ● | ● | ● | **Laboratory Program** Investigation 21 | ● | ● | |
| Skills WorkOut, p. 327 | ● | ● | ● | Investigation 22 | | | ● |
| **Blackline Masters** Review Worksheet 14.2 | ● | ● | ● | **Color Transparencies** Transparencies 39a, 39b | ● | ● | ● |
| Reteach Worksheet 14.2 | ● | ● | ● | | | | |
| Skills Worksheet 14.2 | ● | ● | ● | | | | |
| Integrating Worksheet 14.2 | | ● | ● | | | | |

# Bibliography

The following resources can be used for teaching the chapter. See page T–46 for supplier codes.

## Library Resources

Farndon, John. *How the Earth Works.* Pleasantville, NY: The Reader's Digest Association, Inc., 1992.

Gay, Kathlyn. *Water Pollution.* New York: Franklin Watts, Inc., 1990.

Hoff, Mary, and M. M. Rodgers. *Our Endangered Planet: Groundwater.* Minneapolis, MN: Lerner, 1991.

Hoff, Mary, and M. M. Rodgers. *Our Endangered Planet: Rivers and Lakes.* Minneapolis, MN: Lerner, 1991.

MacEachern, D. *Save Our Planet: 750 Everyday Ways You Can Help Clean Up the Earth.* New York: Dell Publishing Co., 1990.

## Technology Resources

### Internet

**PLANETDIARY** at *http://www.planetdiary.com*

- Discover more about floods in *Flood* by clicking on *Phenomena Backgrounders.*
- Explore meteorological news in *Current Phenomena.*

### Software

*Earth Science.* Mac, Win. ER.
*Oceans.* Mac, Dos, Win. ER.

### CD-ROMs

*Interactive Earth.* SFAW.

*An Odyssey of Discovery for Science Insights:* Have students try the activity *Recycler* on the Earth and Space Disk, and the activity *Aquarium* on the Living Science Disk. *SFAW.*

### Laserdiscs

*Living Textbook.* (See barcodes on pages in this chapter.) Optical Data.

### Videos

*Discovering Our Rivers, Lakes, and Oceans.* 30 min. MMI.
*The Water Cycle and Erosion.* 15 min. EME.

### Audio-Visual Resources

*Water Below.* Film. U.S. Geological Survey.

# 14

### *Writing Connection*

A haiku is a form of unrhymed Japanese poetry that consists of three lines with a total of 17 syllables. The three lines have a five-seven-five syllable pattern. Read a haiku to the class. Then have students write a haiku about the stream shown in the photograph. Ask volunteers to read their haiku to the class.

## ◀ Introducing the Chapter

Have students read the description of the photograph. Ask if they agree or disagree with the description.

### Directed Inquiry

Have students study the photograph. Ask:

▶ What does this photograph show? (Students will say a creek or stream flowing over and past rocks.)

▶ Is the water in this stream likely to be fresh water or salt water? Why do you think so? (This is fresh water because rivers and streams are fresh.)

▶ Why is this water moving the way it does? (Streams and rivers move because of the pull of gravity. This stream seems to be moving rapidly, which suggests that it is moving down steep mountains or that the source has an abundant water supply.)

▶ Where do you think the water in this stream came from? Where will the water end up? (Students may say the water comes from rain or snow that has fallen at a higher altitude, and that the stream will probably join another stream or river and end up in the ocean.)

## ◀ Chapter Vocabulary

aquifer
divide
permeability
photosynthesis
polar molecule
porosity

transpiration
tributary
universal solvent
water table
watershed

## Chapter 14 Fresh Water

### *Chapter Sections*

**14.1** Water and Its Properties

**14.2** Surface Water

**14.3** Water Beneath the Surface

### *What do you see?*

❝I see a stream running along rocks. The stream is running out of a lake or river, carrying particles of the soil and rocks. It is the fall, because there are leaves on the ground. The stream is very clear, because it has not rained there in a long time. I wonder if there are any fish in the water.❞

*Brent Leopard
Riverside Middle School
Saluda, South Carolina*

To find out more about the photograph, look on page 336. As you read this chapter, you will learn about the earth's fresh water.

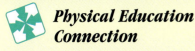

**Section Objectives**
For a list of section objectives, see the Student Edition page.

**Skills Objectives**
Students should be able to:

**Measure** a day's worth of water usage.

**Predict** the effects of surface tension.

**Make a Model** of runoff.

**Make a Model** of a molecule traveling through the water cycle.

**Vocabulary**
polar molecule, universal solvent, photosynthesis, transpiration

# 14.1 Water and Its Properties

## Objectives

▶ **Describe** the amount of fresh water on the earth.

▶ **Relate** the structure of water molecules to the physical and chemical properties of water.

▶ **Explain** why living things need water.

▶ **Generalize** about the role of energy in the water cycle.

▶ **Make a model** tracing the path of a water molecule through the water cycle.

▼ **ACTIVITY**

**Measuring**

*Down the Drain*

How much water do you use in a day? Use the following estimates in your calculations:

| | |
|---|---|
| toilet | 20 L/flush |
| glass of water | 0.25L |
| faucet | 15L/min |
| 5-minute shower | 75 L |

Compare your answers with those of your classmates.

**SKILLS WARMUP**

Think about the many ways you use water every day. You drink it, bathe in it, and water plants with it. When you turn on the tap, fresh water comes out. Where does the fresh water come from? Your home's supply of fresh water may come from a river, a lake, or an underground well.

When the weather is warm, you may use water for sports or recreation. You may go swimming, fishing, or boating. If you swam in the ocean, you would notice that ocean water is different from fresh water. Ocean water is salty because it has a large amount of minerals and salts dissolved in it. Fresh water isn't salty.

### The Earth's Fresh Water

Earth is sometimes known as the water planet. Almost 75 percent of the earth's surface is covered by water. Notice in Figure 14.1 that most of the earth's water is salty ocean water. About 2 percent of the earth's fresh water is frozen in glaciers and ice caps. Another 0.6 percent lies deep underground. The atmosphere contains 0.001 percent of Earth's water. The rest of the earth's fresh water exists on the surface or in soil moisture.

To think about the amount of fresh water on the earth, you can use a mental model. For example, imagine fifty 2-L bottles filled with water. These bottles represent all the earth's waters. The amount of usable fresh water would only be enough to fill one 354-mL can!

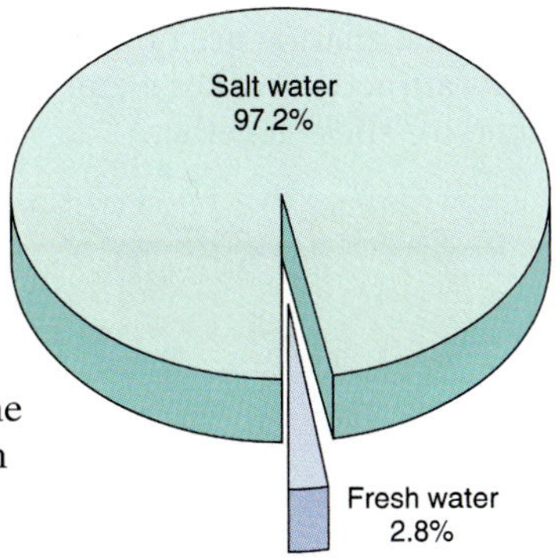

Salt water
97.2%

Fresh water
2.8%

**Figure 14.1** ▲
How much of the total water on earth is fresh water? How much of it is salt water? ①

---

**MOTIVATE**

### Skills WarmUp
To help students measure water consumption, have them do the Skills WarmUp.
**Answer** Totals will vary. You may wish to remind students of how they use water indirectly—by using products that require water to manufacture. Extend the activity by calculating yearly use.

### Misconceptions
Students may think that the only difference between salt water and fresh water is taste. Explain that the two are different in many ways. One example is density. Students who are swimmers may have noticed that they float higher in ocean water. Point out also that ocean water not only tastes salty but is toxic to use directly for drinking water.

**Answer to In-Text Question**
① 2.8%; 97.2%

## Class Activity

Divide the class into four or five groups. Have students in each group place one or two drops of water on a sheet of waxed paper. Have them use a toothpick to push a small drop close to a larger drop. Ask them to describe what happens. (The pushed water drop "jumps" to the larger drop.) Then ask students to describe what happens as they pull one of the larger drops apart by dragging a toothpick through it. (The water drop seems to stretch.) Ask them which properties of water can help explain their observations. (Answers will vary, but the drop "jumps" because the molecules are polar. The drop "stretches" because of surface tension.)

## Skills Development

**Make a Model**  Have students use glue, a tennis ball, and two table tennis balls to make a model of a water molecule.

## Critical Thinking

**Reason and Conclude**  Ask students to describe what they think the earth would be like if water became denser as it froze. (Answers will vary. Students might suggest that lakes and ponds would freeze solid during cold winters, and that much of the frozen water at the Poles would sink, affecting ocean levels.)

## Integrated Learning

Use Integrating Worksheet 14.1.

### Integrating the Sciences

**Physical Science**  The attraction between water molecules allows the force of capillary action to pull water up into fibers, plants, and soil. Demonstrate capillary action using a glass, water, a nonpermanent marker, tape, a pencil, and a coffee filter cut into a strip. Use a marker to draw a line about 3 cm from the bottom of the filter strip. Tape the other end of the strip to the pencil. Put a small amount of water in the glass. Rest the pencil on the rim of the glass so that the end of the strip just touches the water. You may need to adjust the water level. Observe what happens to the mark on the filter paper. (The mark travels up the filter paper with the water. Several colors may form due to different water solubilities of the colored inks in the marker.)

## Properties of Water

Water is the only compound that occurs in all three phases at normal earth temperatures. Think about an ice-covered lake. Ice is water's solid phase. Beneath the ice is liquid water. Water vapor forms in the air above the ice.

Water has other unique properties. It gains and loses heat energy slowly compared to other compounds. Also, water's solid phase is less dense than its liquid phase. Ice floats on top of liquid water. In addition, liquid water dissolves many different substances.

Water's physical and chemical properties are due to the structure of its molecules. Look at Figure 14.2. Each water molecule has two hydrogen atoms and one oxygen atom.

Water is a **polar molecule.** The parts of a polar molecule have slight electric charges. A water molecule's hydrogen atoms have a slight positive charge. The oxygen atom has a slight negative charge.

Recall that opposite charges attract and like charges repel. In liquid water and ice, water molecules align so that opposite charges are next to each other. This attraction makes water molecules tend to "stick" together.

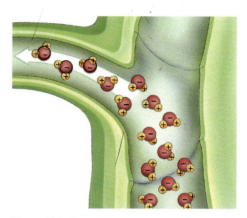

**Figure 14.3** ▲
Water molecules follow one another.

**Physical Properties**  When you heat a pan of water on a stove, which heats faster, the metal pan or the water? Water gains heat energy slowly. Recall that heat is the energy of moving molecules. It takes a large amount of heat energy to separate polar water molecules and get them moving. Water also retains heat.

Water forms a skinlike layer on its surface due to surface tension. Surface tension gives water droplets a rounded shape. Surface tension occurs because water molecules attract each other. The attraction between water molecules also makes them act like beads on a string. When a force pulls one molecule, others follow, as shown in Figure 14.3.

Ice is less dense than liquid water. Water is densest at 4°C. Usually, the molecules in a solid are closer together than those in a liquid. But, like charges repel, so polar water molecules can't get very close together. In ice, water molecules form large, open structures called crystals.

Water isn't easily compressed. If you try to push an object down into it, the water pushes back. The upward pressure on the object can cause it to float.

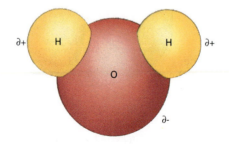

**Figure 14.2** ▲
A polar molecule has electric charges. Locate the charges in this water molecule.

**Chemical Properties** Water has another unique property. It can dissolve many other substances. Think of all the liquids you drink: milk, lemonade, juice, and so on. These liquids are actually mixtures of water with other substances such as sugar, fruit pulp, butterfat, and milk protein.

Water is called the **universal solvent** because it can dissolve more substances than any other liquid. Due to their polar nature, water molecules attract ions or polar molecules that make up other substances. Water molecules hold the ions or polar molecules in solution, as shown in Figure 14.4.

Water can't dissolve substances such as oils. Oils are made of nonpolar molecules. Nonpolar molecules are insoluble in water.

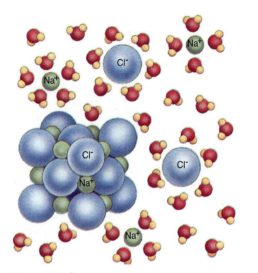

**Figure 14.4** ▲
Ions form when salt dissolves in water.

## *SkillBuilder* Predicting

ACTIVITY

### Surface Tension

Surface tension is one of the properties of water. Use these questions to make predictions about the effects of surface tension:

▶ Are water droplets always round?

▶ Can you float a needle on the surface of a glass of water?

Write down your predictions. Then try the following activities to test your predictions. Drop some beads of water onto a tray or your desktop. Make the following observations.

1. What shape are the beads of water?

2. Does their shape change as you make them larger by adding more water?

Next, fill a glass to the top with water. Carefully lay a needle on the surface and observe what happens. Answer the following questions.

3. If metal is heavier than water, why does the metallic needle float?

4. Try to make the needle sink. Can you do it?

Write a brief report explaining how these activities demonstrate surface tension.

## Discuss

Ask students to explain which two processes of the water cycle are phase changes that are the reverse of each other. (Condensation, vapor to water, is the reverse of evaporation, water to vapor.)

### Explore Visually

After students study Figure 14.5, ask the following questions:

▶ How do plants and the sun contribute to the water cycle? (Plants move water up from the soil. The sun's heat energy evaporates water.)

▶ What part do dust particles from the upper atmosphere play in the water cycle? (Water vapor condenses on dust, forming clouds.)

▶ Where does precipitation go when it reaches the earth's surface? (It may soak into the ground, collect in low-lying areas, run off the ground, or freeze.)

▶ What is runoff? Where does it go? (Rainwater that runs off the land; streams and rivers)

### *Themes in Science*

**Patterns of Change/Cycles** The water cycle is a closed system that moves water continuously from one place to another on the earth. The fact that water can change phases between liquid and gas within a small temperature range makes the water cycle possible.

## The Water Cycle

Water moves continuously from one place to another on the earth because of the water cycle. Water that falls on you as rain may have come from a distant ocean. Water that flows out of your tap may have once been part of the Amazon River! Study the water cycle in Figure 14.5.

Radiant energy from the sun drives the water cycle. Heat energy makes liquid water change phase to water vapor. This phase change is called *evaporation*. Water doesn't have to reach its boiling temperature (100°C) to evaporate. Even at lower temperatures, some water molecules escape a liquid to form vapor. When water evaporates, dissolved minerals or salts are left behind.

As the water vapor rises into the air, it cools. At cooler temperatures, a phase change called *condensation* occurs. Water vapor condenses into liquid droplets that form clouds. Clouds can move water over long distances. Eventually, the water falls to the earth as rain, sleet, hail, or snow. All forms of water that fall from the atmosphere are called *precipitation*.

**Figure 14.5**
**The Earth's Water Cycle** ▼

**Condensation**
In the atmosphere, water vapor condenses on dust particles forming clouds. Under some conditions, water droplets form rain or snow and then fall as precipitation.

**Evaporation**
The heat energy of the sun evaporates water from oceans, lakes, rivers, streams, puddles and dew. Plants move water to their leaves where it evaporates.

## Writing Connection

Have students imagine that they are water molecules. Ask students to write stories about the places they visited and the people and objects they encountered as they moved through the water cycle.

After precipitation reaches the earth's surface, several things can happen. In cold areas, snow and ice remain on the ground. Rainwater soaks into the ground or runs along the surface in rivers and streams. Lakes and ponds of standing water form. As water moves across the land surface, it dissolves minerals and wears away rock. Most of the water eventually flows into the oceans. At any point, the water may evaporate into the atmosphere.

### Water Resources

Fresh water is constantly being made in the water cycle. Precipitation is the source of the earth's fresh water. But each year, 75 percent of the precipitation falls into the oceans. Only 25 percent of the precipitation falls on the earth's land surfaces. Humans, animals, and land plants rely on this limited amount for their water needs. Therefore, it's important not to waste fresh water or pollute freshwater lakes, rivers, and streams.

### ▼ ACTIVITY

**Making a Model**

*Soak It In*

How much water does a sponge hold? Start with a dry sponge and water.

Carefully pour the water onto the sponge until the sponge is saturated. Then add more water. What happens? How does this relate to runoff?

**SKILLS WORKOUT**

**Precipitation**
Water falls as rain, snow, hail, or sleet. It soaks into the ground, runs off into streams and rivers, or remains frozen.

**Runoff**
Rainwater cannot soak into hard-packed, frozen, or saturated ground. It runs off the surface. Gravity pulls the water downhill.

**Collection**
Water collects in low-lying areas forming ponds, streams, rivers, and lakes.

**Underground Water**
Some water seeps through rocks and soil to form underground streams and reservoirs.

To help students make a model of runoff, have them do the Skills WorkOut.
**Answer** Exact quantities will vary. Excess water runs off. This resembles runoff that occurs when the ground is saturated.

### Skills Development

**Make a Model** Have students place about 2 cm of water in a large beaker or measuring cup. Place a smaller beaker inside the container. Loosely seal the large beaker using plastic wrap and a rubber band. Place a marble or small rock in the center of the plastic wrap. Let the assembly stand in direct sunlight for several hours. Ask students to explain how this is a model of the water cycle. (Water evaporates, condenses on the plastic wrap, and "rains" into both the large and small beaker.)

### Research

Have students research a natural or artificial reservoir in the state where they live. Ask what effect it has, if any, on the water supply in the surrounding region.

### Critical Thinking

**Uncover Assumptions** Ask students if they agree or disagree with this statement: *Fresh water is made during the water cycle, so there is a limitless supply for humans.* Have them give reasons for their choice. (Answers will vary. Students should avoid assuming that fresh water will always be both available and usable because of the water cycle.)

321

## TEACH ▪ *Continued*

### Portfolio

Ask students to draw a basic plant body that includes roots, shoot, and leaves. Then have them add to their drawings to show how water moves through the plant. Suggest that they keep their drawings in their portfolios.

## Enrich

Have students research the amount of water, as percent of weight, in several kinds of animals and plants. Have them present the information in bar graphs or on posters. Ask them to develop a conclusion about life's dependence on water. (Examples: elephant, ear of corn, 70%; earthworm, potato, 80%; tomato 95%. Water is essential to life.)

### Answers to In-Text Questions

① **It stands upright and spreads its leaves.**

② **The water vapor condenses and forms a cloud.**

### Answer to Link

The inside of the plastic bag should contain some moisture as a sign that transpiration is taking place through the plant leaf.

## *Integrating the Sciences*

**Health**  Have students list the purposes water serves in the human body. (Sweat controls body temperature, tears clean eyes, saliva moistens food, and blood carries oxygen and chemicals to cells.) Have students list the ways they replenish their body's water supply. (Drink water and other liquids that contain water, eat foods containing water)

---

### Life Science LINK

Collect the following items: a potted plant with large leaves, a non-seal sandwich bag, and string or tape.

**1.** Cover one leaf of the plant with the sandwich bag. Tie or tape the bag closed around the stem of the leaf.

**2.** Place the plant in a sunny area for a couple of hours.

**3.** Remove the bag and examine it. Describe your observations and explain what happened.

**ACTIVITY**

### Water and Living Things

Water is essential for all living things on the earth. Some living things spend their entire lives in water. Humans and other land animals carry water in their bodies. In fact, about 68 percent of your total body weight is from water. Most living things can survive longer without food than without water.

Animals and humans cycle water through their bodies. They take in water by drinking or eating. They release liquid water in body wastes and perspiration. They release water vapor as they exhale. For example, in Figure 14.6 you can see the "cloud" that forms when you exhale on a cold day. Water keeps your body cool in hot weather. Heat energy from your hot skin evaporates watery sweat, cooling off your skin.

Plants also need water to survive. They use light from the sun, water, and carbon dioxide to make sugars. This process is called **photosynthesis**. Plants need these sugars for their own growth. Plants bring up large amounts of water from the soil through their roots. Water carries nutrients from the soil and helps the plant stay upright and rigid, as shown in Figure 14.6.

Water moves upward through a plant, eventually exiting into the air through tiny holes in the leaves. This process is called **transpiration** (TRAN spuh RAY shun). Large amounts of water return to the atmosphere by transpiration. Most of the water that evaporates from the earth's land surfaces does so through transpiration.

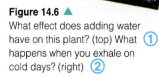

**Figure 14.6 ▲**
What effect does adding water have on this plant? (top) What ① happens when you exhale on cold days? (right) ②

322

## STS Connection

As the demand for water increases all over the world, scientists are researching ways to increase the supply of fresh water. Some scientists have proposed seeding clouds to increase rainfall in drought areas, towing icebergs to areas with water shortages, and building desalinization plants in dry areas near oceans. Have students write pros and cons for each proposal or choose one to defend in a debate.

### Science and You  *Your Water Use*

On average, each person in the United States uses about 240 L of water each day. Study Table 14.1. How does your water use compare? The average daily water use of 240 L doesn't include indirect water uses.

The manufacturing of products uses large amounts of water. For example, it takes about 200 000 L of water to produce a car and 800 L to produce a Sunday newspaper. Agriculture also uses huge amounts of water. It takes about 500 L of water to produce one egg and 4,000 L to produce one quart of milk. Including indirect uses, the average person uses over 6,000 L per day.

The fresh water used in homes, schools, and businesses comes from one of several sources. These water sources are underground wells, lakes, reservoirs, or rivers and streams. All these sources receive their fresh water from precipitation. People also make some fresh water directly from ocean water by desalting it.

All the water people use is part of the larger water cycle. Water used for crops and other plants moves directly into the air through transpiration. Waste water from homes and businesses goes through a cleaning process before it flows back into a river or the ocean. If you live in a rural area, the waste water may go into a septic tank or a large underground hole. Wastes stay in the tank or hole, and the cleaned water seeps into the ground. If you live in a city, a system of underground pipes carries your waste water to a sewage-treatment plant. At the treatment plant, the water is filtered and cleaned. Treated water enters a nearby river or ocean.

**Table 14.1**
**Household Water Uses**

| Activity | Amount of Water Used (L) |
|---|---|
| Shower | 50–77 |
| Tub bath | 96–116 |
| Washing hands | 4–8 |
| Flushing toilet | 19–27 |
| Brushing teeth | 19–39 |
| Washing dishes | 20–77 |
| Using automatic dishwasher | 27–58 |

### Check and Explain

1. Describe in your own words what fresh water is. How much of the earth's water is fresh water?

2. Explain how the structure of a water molecule relates to three properties of water.

3. **Generalize**  Write a general statement describing the role of the sun's energy in the water cycle.

4. **Make a Model**  Draw and label a diagram that traces the path of a water molecule through the water cycle. Be sure to label the diagram.

## Skills Development

**Observe**  Have students start a "water diary" by recording how they use water every day for a week. Encourage them to make note of even brief uses such as rinsing a glass or wetting a cloth. Ask them to think about ways they can change their habits and conserve water.

## EVALUATE

### WrapUp

**Reteach**  Draw a large circle on the chalkboard. Ask volunteers to turn the circle into a diagram of the water cycle. Ask other volunteers to describe what happens at each stage of the cycle. (The main steps are evaporation, condensation, and precipitation.)

Use Review Worksheet 14.1.

### Check and Explain

1. Students should suggest that fresh water, 2.8% of the earth's water, does not have large amounts of minerals and salts dissolved in it.

2. The water molecule is polar, with slight negative and positive charges. This accounts for properties such as surface tension, water's slowness to heat or cool, and water's ability to dissolve more substances than any other liquid.

3. Answers will vary. Sample answer: Heat energy from the sun changes water to water vapor, which eventually condenses and falls to earth as precipitation.

4. Check student diagrams for accuracy.

For a list of section objectives, see the Student Edition page.

**Skills Objectives**
Students should be able to:

**Define Operationally** the flow of rainwater.

**Classify** glacial areas as continental or valley glaciers.

**Predict** how fresh water affects life.

**Organize Data** comparing rivers and glaciers.

**Vocabulary**
tributary, watershed, divide

### Skills WarmUp

To give students practice in observing the flow of surface water, have them do the Skills WarmUp.
**Answer** Observations will vary. Rainwater may evaporate, run into streets through downspouting, or run directly into an underground drainage system. The rainwater's course might be changed by varying sunshine, blocked downspouting, or backed-up sewers.

### Prior Knowledge

Gauge how much students know about the flow of surface water by asking the following questions:

▶ How does a dam work?

▶ How does water change the land?

▶ What happens to water from melting snow?

**TEACH**

### Skills Development

**Communication** Ask students to use the terms *runoff, gullies, streams, rivers,* and *ocean* in a concept map.

---

**INTEGRATED LEARNING**

### Multicultural Perspectives

Many cultures have legends about a great flood that covered the world. The Inuits in the Arctic describe a terrible flood that killed all but those who escaped on a raft. The Incas of South America tell of a great flood caused by the god who created the Inca people. The Book of Genesis recalls a flood that lasted for 40 days and nights. The only survivors were Noah, his family, and pairs of animals that they carried on an ark. Some geologists think that much of the earth was flooded when a huge ice cap covering North America melted during the last ice age. The melting ice caused the oceans to rise around the world.

▼ **ACTIVITY**

**Defining Operationally**

*Rain Tracks*

Based on your experience and observations, what happens to rainwater that falls on buildings where you live? Write down your observations. What could happen that might change the path of the rainwater?

**SKILLS WARMUP**

**Figure 14.7** ▲
Heavy rain can cause flooding.

## 14.2 Surface Water

### Objectives

▶ **Describe** three ways in which fresh water exists on the surface of the earth.

▶ **Describe** a watershed and its drainage systems.

▶ **Predict** what life on earth might be like if fresh water didn't accumulate on the surface.

▶ **Organize data** about rivers and glaciers.

Think about a natural landscape that exists in your part of the country. You might think of a leafy forest with many lakes, rivers, or streams. Or you may think of a grassland or a desert with very little surface water. Why are these landscapes so different?

Landscapes are different because fresh water isn't distributed equally over the earth's surface. You can find fresh water on the surface as running water, standing water, or frozen water. The amount of surface water in an area depends on the amount of precipitation it receives. Some areas suffer severe droughts. Areas like the one in Figure 14.7 have frequent rainstorms and floods. Other areas are covered in snow and ice for most of the year.

### Running Water

Recall that water from rain or melted snow may soak into the ground, evaporate, or flow over the surface as runoff. Recall that runoff forms rills and gullies, and flows into rivers and streams. Running water is water in rivers and streams that flows downhill because of gravity. As running water flows, it carves the landscape, forming streambeds and deep river valleys.

Running water plays an important role in the water cycle by carrying water back to the oceans. Besides returning to the ocean, the water in rivers and streams can also evaporate into the air or soak into the ground. Depending on the amount of rain or snow, a river or stream may flow just for a few months, or all year.

**Art Connection**

Have students create a relief map showing the drainage system of a major river. Students can find information in world atlases and books of aerial or Landsat photographs. Students may want to sculpt a three-dimensional map out of clay, then paint it to show the rivers and other features.

**Figure 14.8** ▲
How many tributaries can you see flowing into this river? ①

**Streams and Rivers** Streams flow into larger streams that flow into rivers. Rivers flow into the ocean. Together, the streams and rivers form a pattern called a *drainage system*.

On a map or satellite photograph, a drainage system often forms a treelike pattern. A drainage system can also look like a pattern of rectangles, a trellis, or the spokes of a wheel. The pattern depends on the type of landforms and rocks in an area.

A small stream that flows into a larger one is called a **tributary** (TRIB yoo TAIR ee). A complex drainage system has many tributaries. Notice the tributaries in the satellite photograph in Figure 14.8.

Rivers serve as a source of fresh water for drinking by humans and animals. They can also transport goods and people over long distances. Most of the world's major cities developed along rivers. Land along river banks is important for agriculture. Plenty of water is available for crops, and the soils are usually rich in plant nutrients.

**Watersheds** The surrounding land area that supplies runoff to the streams of a drainage system is called a **watershed**. Watersheds vary in size from less than one square kilometer to thousands of square kilometers.

Watersheds that supply runoff to different drainage systems are usually separated by a ridge of land. The ridge separating the drainage systems is called a **divide**. Gravity makes water flow downhill. Therefore, a divide prevents water from getting from one drainage system to another.

Like watersheds, divides can be small or large. Look at Figure 14.9. In North America, the Rocky Mountains and the Sierra Madre Occidental make up the ridge that forms the Continental Divide. Streams to the east of the Continental Divide drain into the Atlantic Ocean or the Gulf of Mexico. Streams to the west of the Continental Divide drain into the Pacific Ocean.

**Figure 14.9** ▲
Into which ocean does the water drain from the area where you live? ②

## Class Activity

Have a volunteer draw a drainage system on the chalkboard. Have other students label streams, rivers, and three or four tributaries. Have the class decide where to add a divide to the diagram. (Completely to the right or left; it would not divide the drainage system.) Then ask them which direction the water in the system flows. (Away from the divide)

## Critical Thinking

**Find Causes** Ask students to locate the ten largest U.S. cities on a map. Have them determine the distance from each city to a river. Ask students why they think population centers are located close to water.

## Integrated Learning

Use Integrating Worksheet 14.2.

### Answers to In-Text Questions

① **Dozens**

② **East of the continental divide, Atlantic Ocean; west of the divide, Pacific Ocean**

### TEACH ▪ *Continued*

## Directed Inquiry

After students read the text and study the illustrations, ask these questions:

▶ How do ponds and lakes form? (Running water stops flowing when it reaches low areas in a drainage system; the standing water eventually forms a lake or pond.)

▶ How is a reservoir similar to a lake? How is it different? (Both are large areas of standing water. A reservoir is an artificial lake that stops or interrupts the flow of a river.)

▶ How does sunlight affect ponds? (Ponds are usually shallow enough for sunlight to reach the bottom, allowing plant and animal life to thrive.)

▶ How do people artificially create areas of standing water? Why? (By building dams, which form reservoirs; reservoirs store fresh water and can be used to control flooding.)

## Research

Divide the class into five groups and assign each group a Great Lake. Have each group find the area and average depth of its lake and report to the class. Ask the class what is unique about the Great Lakes. (They are the largest freshwater system of lakes on the earth.)

## Reteach

Use Reteach Worksheet 14.2.

### *Themes in Science*

**Scale and Structure** Rivers, streams, and runoff are narrow structures that flow into broad, low areas to create lakes or ponds. Lakes and ponds are small water structures when compared to the entire water system of the earth.

### *Geography Connection*

Have students use a state map to locate three nearby lakes, ponds, or reservoirs. Then ask students to identify the rivers that flow into these standing bodies of fresh water.

### Standing Water

When running water reaches a low area in a drainage system, the water stops flowing. Over time, the low area fills with standing water. A body of standing water, called a lake or pond, forms. Some water evaporates, but water added from precipitation, streams, and runoff keeps the lake or pond full.

**Lakes ▶**

Lakes form in large, deep depressions in the earth's crust. Lakes are usually so deep that sunlight doesn't penetrate to the bottom. The Great Lakes on the United States–Canadian border are so large that they have waves and tides like an ocean.

**◀ Ponds**

Ponds form in small depressions. Usually, ponds are shallow enough for sunlight to reach the bottom. Therefore, ponds tend to support lush plant growth and animal life. Ponds may be seasonal, occasionally drying up.

**Reservoirs ▶**

Artificial lakes, called reservoirs, form when a dam stops the flow of a river. People build reservoirs to store fresh water and control flooding. People aren't the only ones who dam rivers. Beavers build dams to form deep ponds that won't freeze solid in winter.

## Integrating the Sciences

**Physical Science** Two forces act on an iceberg to make it float. The downward force is gravity. The upward force, which opposes gravity, is called the *buoyant force*. Float an ice cube in water to model an iceberg. Point out the two forces acting on the ice cube.

## Social Studies Connection

On April 14, 1912 a British luxury passenger ship named the *Titanic* hit an iceberg in the North Atlantic and sank. Over 1,000 people drowned during this disaster. Interested students may wish to further research the *Titanic* tragedy and the recent discovery of the wreckage.

## Skills WorkOut

To help students classify glacial areas, have them do the Skills WorkOut.

**Answer** Greenland, Iceland, some Arctic Islands, and Antarctica have continental glaciers. All other areas have valley glaciers.

## Discuss

Ask students if they think glaciers and icebergs contribute fresh water to the earth. Have them explain their reasoning. (Yes. Glacial meltwater contributes fresh water directly in the form of meltwater streams. Icebergs melt in salt water, and water vapor from the ocean is part of the cycle that provides fresh water.)

## Skills Development

**Infer** Occasionally the glaciers of Greenland and Antarctica are called *polar ice caps*. Ask students why this is a descriptive name. (The ice covers the continents like a cap and is located near the earth's north and south poles.)

### Frozen Water

Most of the world's fresh water is frozen. Near the poles or in very high mountains, all the snow doesn't melt each summer. Permanent snowfields form. Snow accumulates year after year. Eventually, the weight of the new snow presses the old snow together, forming ice.

A snowfield turns into a sheet of ice called a glacier. You can model this process by packing a snowball together with gloved hands. Pressure from your hands turns the snow into ice. Recall that valley glaciers form in high mountain valleys. Continental glaciers cover areas such as Greenland or Antarctica and move by the pull of gravity.

When a continental glacier reaches the ocean, large pieces break off and float away. These pieces are called icebergs. Icebergs are dangerous to ships. Only a small part of an iceberg is visible above the water's surface.

Glaciers and snowfields play an important role in the water cycle through melting and evaporation. During the short summers, some of the ice melts. Meltwater streams form, supplying fresh water to many areas.

### ▼ ACTIVITY

**Classifying**

*Glaciers on the Move*

1. Study the map of glacial areas on this page.
2. Compare it to a relief map of the world found in an atlas.
3. Using the information from the relief map, classify each of the glacial areas as a valley glacier or a continental glacer.

**SKILLS WORKOUT**

**Figure 14.10**
Locate the places on the earth where glaciers currently exist. ▼

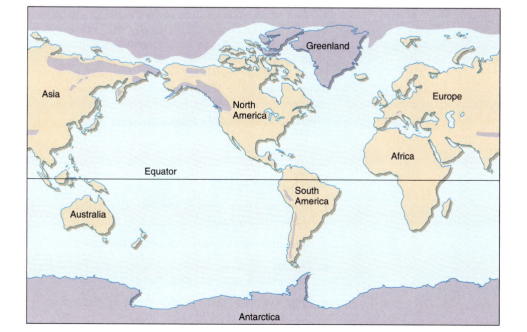

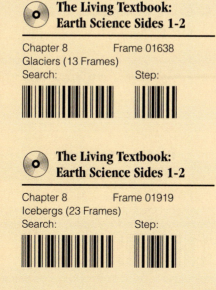

**The Living Textbook: Earth Science Sides 1-2**

Chapter 8      Frame 01638
Glaciers (13 Frames)
Search:      Step:

**The Living Textbook: Earth Science Sides 1-2**

Chapter 8      Frame 01919
Icebergs (23 Frames)
Search:      Step:

327

## TEACH ▪ Continued

### Class Activity

Have students research the 1993 Mississippi River flood. Have one group present information about how levees saved some towns and cities, but threatened to damage others. Have a second group report on how the flooding affected settlements along the Mississippi tributaries.

## EVALUATE

### WrapUp

**Review** Have students locate the school on a map. Then have them find the distance to the nearest river or river system. Ask them to identify several tributaries, the drainage system, the direction of water flow, and the divide that influences that direction.

Use Review Worksheet 14.2.

### Check and Explain

1. As frozen, running, and standing water

2. A watershed is a land area supplying runoff to a drainage system that carries water to an ocean.

3. Answers will vary. However, all students should recognize that fresh water is necessary for plants and animals to survive.

4. Check student tables for accuracy.

**The Living Textbook: Earth Science Sides 1-2**

Chapter 30          Frame 04567
Mississippi Delta (1 Frame)
Search:

328

---

## Integrating the Sciences

**Environmental Science** Certain areas along rivers in the United States are prone to flooding—for example, farms located on fertile flood plains and low-lying towns and cities built on the river banks. In some areas engineers have built dams, levees, and channels to control floods. However, these flood-control projects change the rivers' natural flooding cycle and their ecosystems. Have students discuss the benefits and risks to river environments caused by building flood-control projects.

### Science and Technology
#### The Wandering River

The Mississippi River is the third longest river in the world. It has more than 200 tributaries, and has the fourth-largest watershed in the world. The river affects more than 100 million people in 31 states and parts of Canada. Many cities and towns use the river for drinking water and for farming. The river is also a very important water highway. Barges move constantly along the river carrying cargo. At the river's end is the port of New Orleans, an international shipping center on the Gulf of Mexico. The Mississippi River hasn't always been in the same place. About every 1,000 years, it changes its course, cutting a new riverbed and abandoning its old one. The worst flood in the recorded history of the Upper Mississippi River basin occurred in the summer of 1993. Towns and farmland in many midwestern states were covered in river water. Crops and homes were destroyed.

**Figure 14.11 ▲**
By monitoring the water that flows from the Mississippi River, flooding is controlled.

In Louisiana, the Mississippi river has been trying to change its course westward to the Atchafalaya River. If the Mississippi changed course, the port of New Orleans would dry up. Morgan City, at the mouth of the Atchafalaya, would be destroyed by floods. After a major flood in 1927, the Army Corps of Engineers began a massive flood-control project. They built the structure shown in Figure 14.11 to control the amount of Mississippi river water entering the Atchafalaya. They also built levees and deepened the Atchafalaya channel. This flood-control project helped to spare this part of the Mississippi from the disastrous flood of 1993.

### Check and Explain

1. What are three ways in which fresh water exists on the earth's surface?

2. Describe a watershed and a drainage system.

3. **Predict** What do you think life on earth would be like if there were no fresh water on the surface?

4. **Organize Data** Make a table showing how a river and a glacier are alike and different.

### Cooperative Learning

Have students work in cooperative groups to observe differences in soil porosity. Each group will need a funnel, screen, aquarium gravel, sand, 100 mL of water, and a plastic container. Each group should place the screen in the funnel. Put a layer of gravel on the funnel. Then create another layer of sand above the gravel. Pour the water through the screen and collect it in the container. Measure the amount of water in the container. Record the amount of water absorbed by the soil. Repeat, using different proportions of earth materials. Compare results.

## 14.3 Water Beneath the Surface

### Objectives

▶ **Explain** what forms groundwater and **describe** groundwater zones.

▶ **Describe** the movements and activities of groundwater.

▶ **Predict** changes in the groundwater.

▶ **Classify** earth materials by permeability.

▼ **ACTIVITY**

**Observing**

*Taking in Water*

Think of some items that you could use to clean up some spilled water. List them in order of their usefulness. How are the most useful items alike? What characteristic do they share?

**SKILLS WARMUP**

T hink about what happens when you water a garden or a potted plant. Where does the water go? The water soaks into the ground or soil. On a global scale, a huge amount of water from precipitation soaks into the ground. The amount of water in the ground is more than all the water in the world's rivers and lakes combined. Some underground water comes to the surface in springs and as part of rivers, streams, and lakes.

### Groundwater

The water that soaks into the ground from rain or melted snow is called *groundwater*. Recall that soils and some rocks have pore spaces between the dirt or rock particles. Groundwater fills in these pore spaces. The amount of groundwater a rock or soil holds depends on how much pore space exists between the grains of the material.

The percentage of a material's volume that is pore space is called **porosity**. High-porosity rocks and soil can hold more water than those with low porosity. Look at Figure 14.12. Notice that the porosity of sandstone is high.

If the pore spaces are well connected, water flows easily through the rock. Such a rock has high **permeability**. For example, sand, gravel, and sedimentary rocks, such as sandstone, have high permeability. Shale and clay have low permeability. Rocks with low permeability are called *impermeable*. Water does not flow through them.

**Figure 14.12** ▲
Sandstone has high porosity and high permeability.

**Section Objectives**
For a list of section objectives, see the Student Edition page.

**Skills Objectives**
Students should be able to:

**Observe** characteristics of items that soak up water.

**Predict** what could lower the water table.

**Classify** sediment permeability.

**Observe** the similarities between a siphon and an artesian well.

**Vocabulary**
porosity, permeability, water table, aquifer

◀ **MOTIVATE**

### Skills WarmUp

To help students understand the porosity of materials, have them do the Skills WarmUp.
**Answer** Lists will vary. They may include such items as sponges, rags, or cat litter. In general, more porous materials hold more water.

### Prior Knowledge

To gauge how much students know about groundwater, ask the following questions:

▶ Where does the water in a well come from?

▶ What makes water rush into a deep hole dug on a beach?

▶ Where can cities get water if they are not near a river, stream, lake, or reservoir?

**The Living Textbook:**
**Earth Science Side 2**

Chapter 44       Frame 22681
Permeability (Movie)
Search:              Play:

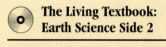

## TEACH

### Explore Visually

After students study Figure 14.13, ask the following questions:

▶ How are a well and a spring alike? How are they different? (Both get water from an aquifer. Water is pumped to the surface in a well; in a spring, the water table meets the surface.)

▶ What two zones does groundwater create? (Zone of aeration and zone of saturation)

▶ What do these zones look like in the diagram? (Answers will vary. Pores in the aeration zone are filled with air; pores in the saturation zone are filled with water.)

▶ How are underground caves and caverns formed? (Carbonic acid in rainwater moves through the rock and dissolves rocks, such as limestone, forming caves or caverns.)

▶ What kinds of rock or rock layers play a part in forming an aquifer? (Permeable rock above impermeable rock)

### Decision Making

If you have classroom sets of *One-Minute Readings*, have students read Issue 34, "Underground Toxic Wastes" on page 58. Discuss the questions.

### Ancillary Options

If you are using CEPUP modules in your classroom for additional hands-on activities, experiments, and exercises, begin *Investigating Groundwater: The Fruitvale Story.*

### Integrated Learning

Use Integrating Worksheet 14.3.

### STS Connection

The water table in an aquifer can drop if more water is removed than is replaced. Overpumping aquifers for human use has caused the land to sink under cities such as Mexico City, Venice, Italy, and Houston, Texas. Some of these cities have sunk several meters. The problem was solved in Venice when the Italian government limited people's use of underground water. In Mexico City, scientists have proposed pumping water back into the acquifer to prevent further sinking.

## Groundwater Zones

As water from rain or melted snow soaks into the ground, gravity pulls the water downward. When the water reaches an impermeable layer, such as shale, the water spreads out. When the water can't spread out further, the water level rises. To make a mental model of this, think of filling a glass of crushed ice with water. The bottom of the glass is impermeable. As you add water, it fills in the spaces between the ice particles. The water level in the glass rises.

Groundwater creates two distinct underground zones. These zones are shown on the left in Figure 14.13. In the lower zone, called the zone of saturation, all the pore spaces contain water. In the upper zone, called the zone of aeration (AIR AY shun), the pore spaces are filled with air. The boundary line between the two zones is called the **water table.** Below the water table, the rocks and soil are saturated with water. Above the water table, the pore spaces are filled with air.

The water table isn't always at the same depth. The water table can change depths at different times of the year, depending on the amount of rainfall. When it rains more, the water table is higher. After a long dry spell, the water table is lower.

The type of rock or soil beneath the surface also affects the water table. In areas where an impermeable layer is close to the surface, the water table is higher. If the impermeable layer is deeper, the water table is lower.

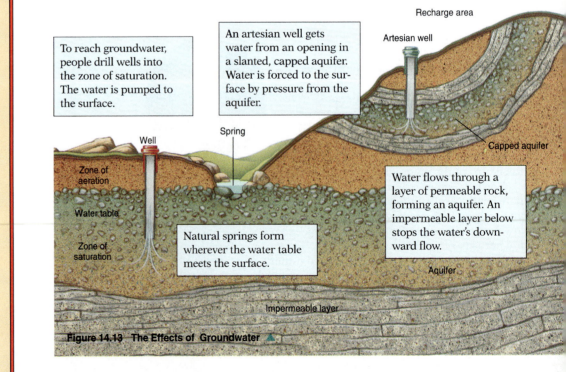

To reach groundwater, people drill wells into the zone of saturation. The water is pumped to the surface.

An artesian well gets water from an opening in a slanted, capped aquifer. Water is forced to the surface by pressure from the aquifer.

Water flows through a layer of permeable rock, forming an aquifer. An impermeable layer below stops the water's downward flow.

Natural springs form wherever the water table meets the surface.

Recharge area

Artesian well

Capped aquifer

Well

Spring

Zone of aeration

Water table

Zone of saturation

Aquifer

Impermeable layer

**Figure 14.13 The Effects of Groundwater** ▲

330

### Cooperative Learning

Have students work in pairs to model the formation of stalagmites and stalactites. Give each pair Epsom salts, two baby food jars, cotton string, metric ruler, scissors, two washers, water, and a notecard. Then tell them to follow these steps: Fill each jar half full with Epsom salts. Add water to cover the Epsom salts. Place the jars 10 to 12 cm apart. Place the notecard on the table between the two jars. Cut a piece of string long enough to stretch from the bottom of one jar to the other jar. Tie a washer at each end of the string. Place one washer in each jar. Position the string so that it hangs above the notecard between the two jars. Let the jars stand undisturbed for a week. Observe what happens. (Stalagmites will form on the notecard. Stalactites will form on the string above the stalagmites.)

### Moving Groundwater

Groundwater can travel through layers of rock or sediments that act like pipelines. Groundwater can dissolve rocks, forming underground caverns. Hot springs and geysers are groundwater returning to the surface.

**Aquifers** A layer of permeable rock or sediment containing groundwater is called an **aquifer** (AH kwih fur). Aquifers usually form in sandstone, sand, or gravel, above or between layers of impermeable rock.

Aquifers are important sources of fresh water. People drill wells into an aquifer and pump water out. The largest aquifer in the United States is the sand and gravel Ogallala Aquifer. It stretches from South Dakota to Texas.

**Caverns and Sinkholes** Recall that carbon dioxide in the air combines with rainwater to form carbonic acid. As the acidic rainwater moves down through the ground, it chemically reacts with some rocks. Limestone easily dissolves away, forming caves and caverns.

Water drips into the cavern from the rock layers above, carrying dissolved minerals. When the water evaporates, the minerals are left behind. Look at Figure 14.13. If the water evaporates on the cavern ceiling, an icicle-like *stalactite* forms. If the water evaporates on the floor, it forms a pillar of minerals called a *stalagmite*.

If a layer of limestone weakens from being dissolved, it can suddenly collapse. The resulting hole is called a *sinkhole*. Areas of the southern and central United States have many sinkholes.

- ▶ Would you expect to find caverns beneath an aquifer? Why or why not? (No; the layer below an aquifer is impermeable rock, so water could not pass through.)

- ▶ What would happen if the soil in an aquifer's recharge area were polluted? (The water in the aquifer would be in danger of becoming polluted as well.)

- ▶ Why is the water in both caverns shown in the diagram at the same level? (Both caverns are in an area where the water table is the same.)

### Portfolio

Ask students to draw an underground cavern. Have them write descriptions of how the cavern formed and label stalagmites and stalactites. Suggest that they keep their drawings and descriptions in their portfolios.

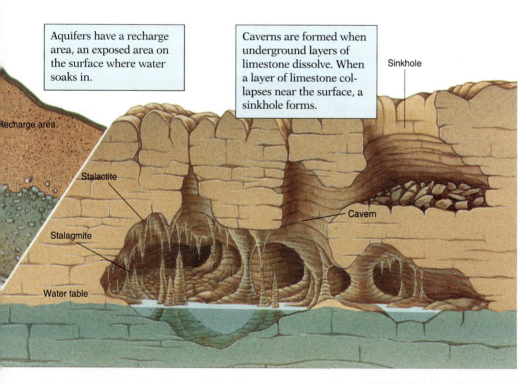

Aquifers have a recharge area, an exposed area on the surface where water soaks in.

Caverns are formed when underground layers of limestone dissolve. When a layer of limestone collapses near the surface, a sinkhole forms.

Sinkhole

Recharge area

Stalactite

Stalagmite

Cavern

Water table

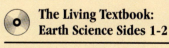

**The Living Textbook: Earth Science Sides 1-2**

Chapter 17      Frame 02636
Cave Formations (1 Frame)
Search:

**The Living Textbook: Earth Science Sides 1-2**

Chapter 17      Frame 02644
Sinkholes (2 Frames)
Search:      Step:

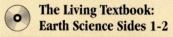

## Skills Development

**Infer** Ask students if the water table near a geyser is close to the earth's surface. (Probably not; water would have to be deep enough to be heated by magma.)

## Consider This

**Think About It** Answers will vary; students may indicate that no matter who cleans up, the cost will ultimately be passed on to the consumers.
**Debate It** Students should be able to give reasons supporting their positions.

## Enrich

Some students may wish to investigate the government's role in protecting consumers. Allow them to join the debate, taking the position that the government should share the cost of cleaning up aquifers. You may wish to remind students where governments get the money necessary for such projects.

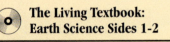

**The Living Textbook: Earth Science Sides 1-2**

Chapter 6          Frame 01565
Yellowstone (21 Frames)
Search:          Step:

### Themes in Science

**Energy** In a geyser the earth's heat increases the temperature of groundwater in an underground chamber. The energy of the molecules increases and builds up pressure in the chamber. The building pressure eventually forces the heated water out of an opening.

**Hot Springs and Geysers** Some groundwater rises to the surface as hot water, in hot springs or geysers. A hot spring is any body of water with a temperature higher than the human body's. A geyser is a fountain of hot water ejected from the ground. Geysers can rise 30–60 m. They are caused by the periodic release of superheated steam that forms in underground chambers.

Groundwater can be heated either by contact with igneous rock from volcanism or by contact with warm rock deep in the earth. In the western United States, most hot springs and geysers result from water heated by igneous rock from volcanism. In the eastern United States, the water in hot springs, such as at Warm Springs, Georgia, is heated in deep regions.

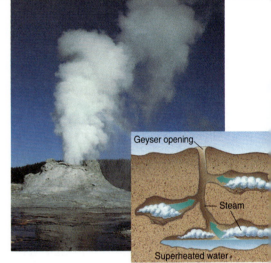

**Figure 14.14** ▲
After pressure builds, this geyser erupts in Yellowstone National Park, Wyoming.

## Consider This

### Who Pays for the Cleanup?

Cleaning up groundwater pollution can be a difficult and costly job. Polluted groundwater moves slowly through aquifers, spreading the pollution over many kilometers. Natural processes can remove some pollutants. The aquifer itself can filter out dirt. Certain bacteria help clean up water by digesting some kinds of pollutants. However, some industrial pollutants cannot be easily removed from water.

Industries, such as agriculture and electronics, use toxic chemicals. Toxic chemicals can enter an aquifer

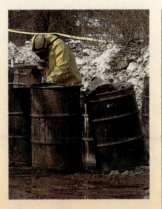

when farmers apply pesticides to the soil. Aquifers are polluted when industrial solvents are dumped or accidentally spilled. In the past,

many toxic chemicals entered aquifers before anyone realized the danger.

**Think About It** Who is responsible for cleaning up the aquifers? Who should pay for it? Should the companies pay for this, possibly putting small companies out of business? Or should the costs be passed on to the consumers?

**Debate It** Have a class debate on the issue of who should pay for the cleanup of aquifers. Half the class can take the side of the company owners and the other half the side of consumers.

### Portfolio

Have students collect magazine and newspaper articles about freshwater pollution. Have students identify the pollutant in each article and determine where in the water cycle the pollution occurs. Tell students to keep the articles in their portfolios.

### Science and Society
#### Protecting Groundwater

Did you know that pollutants in one place can end up in someone's drinking water hundreds of kilometers away? Recall that water is the universal solvent. As rainwater travels through materials above the ground, it dissolves many substances. The rainwater soaks into the ground, carrying the dissolved substances into the groundwater. If the dissolved substances are harmful, the groundwater becomes polluted. Polluted groundwater can enter aquifers that supply drinking water to people many kilometers away.

Old landfills and dumps pose a major hazard to groundwater because of the chemicals in paints, cleansers, and household or industrial wastes. When rainwater moves down through a landfill or dump, the water dissolves some of the chemicals. The rainwater can soak into the ground and reach the water table, polluting the groundwater.

One way that groundwater can be protected is by using the principle of impermeability. Just as impermeable layers keep water in an aquifer, they can also help keep polluted water out. New landfills, such as the one in Figure 14.15, have a lining of impermeable clay, asphalt, or plastic. Water containing dissolved materials from the landfill can't soak into the ground. After a landfill is full, it can be capped with another impermeable layer. The impermeable cap prevents rainwater from entering the landfill and dissolving any chemicals. The groundwater is then further protected from pollution.

**Figure 14.15** ▲
The landfill shown here is considered a sanitary legal landfill because it has a clay lining.

### Check and Explain

1. What is groundwater? Describe two distinct groundwater zones.

2. Describe three movements and activities of groundwater.

3. **Predict** What will happen to the water table in an area during a prolonged drought? What else could affect the water table the same way?

4. **Classify** Order the following from least to most permeable: gravel, sand, clay, sandstone.

### Class Activity

Have students research the location of landfills in their area. Help them learn if the local landfills are lined with an impermeable material and what other measures are being taken to protect the ground water in their area. Have students create a bulletin board display of their research.

### WrapUp

**Reinforce** Draw a simplified version of Figure 14.13 on the chalkboard. Have students label the groundwater zones. Have them add to the diagram to indicate ways in which people draw water from the aquifer.

Use Review Worksheet 14.3.

### Check and Explain

1. Water that soaks into the ground from rain or melted snow. The zone of aeration has pore spaces filled with air; the zone of saturation has pore spaces containing water.

2. Water can travel under the surface through layers of rock or sediments in an aquifer. Acidic groundwater can dissolve layers of limestone to form caverns and sinkholes. Super-heated groundwater emerges as a geyser.

3. Answers will vary. For example, the water table will sink, drawing out more water than the aquifer's recharge area soaks in.

4. Clay, sandstone, sand, gravel

Time 40 minutes   Group 3

**Materials**

20 jars or beakers

10 pieces of clear plastic tubing, 50–75 cm each

10 markers

masking tape

## Analysis

1. The water was pulled through
the tube by gravity pulling
down on the water in the tube
and the cohesion between the
molecules.

2. The water stopped moving
when the upper jar emptied
and air entered the tube.

3. Before, all the water was in jar
A; after, almost all the water
was in jar B.

4. The water rising in the cup at
the bottom of the siphon is a
model of pressure from a slanted aquifer forcing water up in
an artesian well.

## Conclusion

Accept any logical conclusion.
Water is always under the influence
of gravity, so water flows in natural
springs due to the effects of gravity
and the pressures caused by water
being pulled down by gravity.

## Everyday Application

As long as one end of the hose or
tube can be located below the
level of the end in the water, an
aquarium or pool can be emptied
using a siphon.

## Extension

For the system to work, one end of
the tube must be lower than the
other. As soon as jar B is lifted
higher than jar A, the water will
begin to flow back into jar A.

### Prelab Discussion

Have students read the entire activity.
Discuss a few points before beginning:

▶ Ask if anyone has used a siphon
before. Ask how students think a
siphon works.

▶ Discuss the properties of water, especially cohesion among water molecules
and surface tension.

▶ Review artesian wells and aquifers.
Discuss possible ways to model them.

## Activity 14  *How are a siphon and an artesian well similar?*

*Skills*  Observe; Hypothesize; Model

### Task 1  Prelab Prep

1. Collect the following items: 2 jars of approximately the same size, a marker and masking
tape, a 50- to 75-cm long piece of clear
plastic tubing.

2. Using the marker and masking tape, label
one jar A and the other one B.

### Task 2  Procedure

1. Fill jar A half full of water. Mark the level of
the water on the outside of the jar with the
marker. Set the jar on the desk.

2. Look at Figure 14.16. Place the empty jar B
on a chair or the floor so that it is lower than
jar A. Be sure that the plastic tube can reach
both jars.

3. Your teacher will have prepared a bucket
or sink half-filled with water. Hold the plastic
tube in both hands. Dunk the entire tube into
the bucket or sink. After the tube fills completely with water, tightly cover both ends
with your thumbs. Now lift the tube out of
the water.

4. Look at Figure 14.16. Covering both ends of
the tube tightly, carry the water-filled tube
back to your jar setup. Place one end of the
tube, still covered, into each jar. Be sure that
the end in jar A is underwater.

5. Without letting go of the tube, release both of
your thumbs at the same time and observe
what happens. This system is called a
siphon.

6. When the water stops moving through the
tube, mark the water levels on both jars.
Compare the changes in the water level
in each jar.

### Task 3  Analysis

1. What caused water to move through the tube?

**Figure 14.16 ▲**

2. What caused the water to stop moving?

3. How did the water levels compare before the
activity? How did the levels compare after
the activity?

4. How is your siphon like an artesian well?
Compare your setup to the aquifer in
Figure 14.13. Is your siphon like an aquifer?
Explain.

### Task 4  Conclusion

Write a short paragraph explaining how the flow
of water in a natural spring compares to the flow
of water in a siphon.

### *Everyday Application*

Have you ever seen someone empty a swimming
pool or an aquarium? Explain how a siphon system might be used to empty a swimming pool
or an aquarium.

### *Extension*

Do you think this system would work if the jars
were at the same level? What if jar B were higher
than jar A? Try lifting jar B, when it is about 1/4
full of water, higher than jar A. Explain what
happens. Why?

## Check Your Vocabulary

1. watershed
2. polar molecule
3. water table
4. porosity
5. photosynthesis
6. permeability
7. universal solvent
8. divide
9. aquifer
10. transpiration
11. tributary

## Write Your Vocabulary

Students' sentences should show that they know the meaning of each word as well as how to use it in a sentence.

Use Vocabulary Worksheet for Chapter 14.

# Chapter 14 Review

## Concept Summary

### 14.1 Water and Its Properties
▶ Only about 3 percent of all the water on the earth is fresh water.
▶ Water is a polar molecule. The polar nature of the water molecule gives water many unique properties, such as gaining and losing heat slowly and the ability to dissolve many different substances.
▶ Water moves continuously from one place to another on the earth because of the water cycle. The driving force is energy from the sun.
▶ Precipitation is the source of fresh water on the earth.

### 14.2 Surface Water
▶ Fresh water exists on the earth's surface as running water in rivers and streams, standing water in lakes and ponds, and frozen water in glaciers.

▶ A watershed is a land area that supplies runoff to streams and rivers.
▶ Glaciers move slowly downhill because of gravity.

### 14.3 Water Beneath the Surface
▶ Water that soaks into the ground is called groundwater. The amount of water that soaks in depends on the ground's porosity and permeability.
▶ Groundwater forms distinct underground zones: the zone of saturation, the zone of aeration, the boundary between them, and the water table.
▶ Groundwater travels through aquifers, layers of permeable rock or sediment. Groundwater can return to the surface in springs, geysers, artesian wells, rivers, streams, and lakes.

## Chapter Vocabulary

| | | | |
|---|---|---|---|
| polar molecule (14.1) | transpiration (14.1) | divide (14.2) | water table (14.3) |
| universal solvent (14.1) | tributary (14.2) | porosity (14.3) | aquifer (14.3) |
| photosynthesis (14.1) | watershed (14.2) | permeability (14.3) | |

## Check Your Vocabulary

Use the vocabulary words above to complete the following sentences correctly.

1. Surface runoff from a ____ enters streams and rivers.
2. The atoms in a water molecule carry a slight electric charge because water is a ____ .
3. Underground, the boundary between the zone of saturation and the zone of aeration is the ____ .
4. The ____ of a rock or soil is a measure of the amount of water that can pass through.
5. Plants need water to make sugar in a process called ____ .

6. Water passes easily through a rock or soil that has high ____ .
7. So many different substances dissolve in water that it is called the ____ .
8. A high ridge that separates one watershed from another is a ____ .
9. A layer of permeable rock that contains moving groundwater is an ____ .
10. Water evaporates from leaf surfaces in the process of ____ .
11. A stream that flows into a larger river is a ____ of that river.

## Check Your Knowledge

1. The earth is called the water planet because almost 75 percent of its surface is covered by water.

2. A polar molecule has an uneven distribution of positive and negative charge, giving it a slightly positive end and a slightly negative end.

3. Earth's fresh water is produced in the water cycle by condensation and precipitation of water originally evaporated from surface water.

4. Water evaporates from the earth's surface. Water vapor condenses in the upper atmosphere forming clouds. The water in the atmosphere falls to the earth as rain, sleet, snow, or hail. Rainwater and melt water collect in bodies of water and aquifers.

5. Animals and plants take in water. Plants release water vapor through transpiration; animals release water vapor as a by-product of respiration and in body wastes.

6. Water in North America drains into either the Pacific Ocean or the Atlantic Ocean and Gulf of Mexico.

7. Fresh water exists as ice, as vapor in the atmosphere, as liquid in surface bodies of water, and as liquid in underground aquifers.

8. Water can soak into the ground because rock or soil is permeable.

9. Ground water travels long distances underground by flowing through layers of permeable rock and above or between layers of impermeable rock. An example is the Ogallala Aquifer.

10. water cycle
11. molecular structure
12. precipitation
13. evaporates
14. porosity

## Check Your Understanding

1. Ocean water has large amounts of salt and minerals dissolved in it; fresh water does not. Salt water makes up 97.2% of the water on the earth.

2. Glaciers form when snow accumulates and the pressure of the layers causes the snow to turn to ice. Most of the earth's fresh water is frozen in glaciers and snowfields.

3. The structure of its molecules gives water the ability to dissolve many different substances, allows it to retain heat, makes individual molecules stick to each other, and forms a solid that is less dense than the liquid form.

4. Water from the Amazon evaporates. The vapor rises and condenses into clouds, which are carried by the wind. The water falls as rain and flows into an aquifer or body of water from which it is drawn.

5. Boiling the salt water evaporates fresh water and leaves salt behind. The vapor can be collected and condensed into liquid fresh water.

6. Different parts of the earth have different amounts of surface water due to differences in terrain which allow water to collect or run off, and due to the amount of precipitation. The amount of surface water in an area determines the types and numbers of living things that can survive in the area.

7. A well can run dry if the water table lowers as a result of a dry spell, or if the underground water source is depleted faster than it is replenished. The owners could dig the well deeper.

8. a. The water comes from snow melting higher up in the mountains. b. The water is likely going toward a larger stream or river that will eventually empty into an inland basin. c. Water flows downhill. d. The creek carries water to places where it collects and evaporates.

---

## Chapter 14 Review

### Check Your Knowledge

Answer the following in complete sentences.

1. Why is the earth sometimes called the water planet?

2. What is a polar molecule?

3. Where does the earth's fresh water come from?

4. Describe the water cycle. What is its driving force?

5. How do plants and animals participate in the water cycle?

6. Why can the North American continent be described as having two large watersheds?

7. What are four ways in which fresh water exists on the earth?

8. Why can water soak into the ground?

9. How does groundwater travel long distances underground? Give an example.

Choose the answer that best completes each sentence.

10. Water moves continuously from one place to another on the earth because of the (water table, water cycle, aquifers, watersheds).

11. The physical and chemical properties of water are due to its (surface tension, solid phase, boiling temperature, molecular structure).

12. The earth's fresh water comes from (lakes, rivers, glaciers, precipitation).

13. When water (condenses, evaporates, collects, flows), dissolved salts and minerals are left behind.

14. The amount of water a rock or soil can hold depends on its (permeability, density, porosity, mass).

### Check Your Understanding

Apply the concepts you have learned to answer each question.

1. How does ocean water compare with fresh water? Discuss the abundance of each on the earth.

2. Explain how a glacier forms. What role do glaciers play in the global water cycle?

3. How does the structure of a water molecule affect water's physical and chemical properties? Discuss two examples.

4. **Critical Thinking** Explain how water molecules from the Amazon River could end up coming out of the water tap in your home.

5. **Extension** Devise a way to produce fresh water from salt water.

6. **Critical Thinking** Why do different places on the earth's surface have different amounts of surface water? What effect does the amount of surface water have on a land area?

7. **Application** Sometimes, a well that has been used for many years will suddenly run dry. Explain why this happens. What could the well owners do to get water to come out of the well again?

8. **Mystery Photo** The photograph on page 316 shows a creek in California on the eastern side of the Sierra Nevada Mountains.

   a. Where did the water in the creek come from?

   b. Where is the creek water going?

   c. Why does the creek water flow in one direction only?

   d. Explain the role of the creek in the water cycle.

## Develop Your Skills

**1.** a. highest porosity is *a*; lowest is *c*

b. highest permeability is *a*; lowest is *c*

c. Layer *a* will hold the most water.

**2.** Drainage systems can be shaped like the branches of a tree, the spokes of a wheel, a pattern of rectangles, or a trellis.

**3.** If its recharge area undergoes a long drought, an aquifer may dry up.

**4.** If large amounts of water are pumped from an aquifer, the land can collapse.

**5.** a. San Francisco Bay

b. 7 or 8; Answers may include Wisconsin, Illinois, Red, Arkansas, Wabash, Ohio, or Missouri rivers.

## Make Connections

**1.**

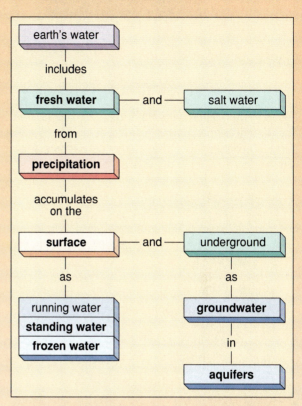

**2.** Student reports will vary. Look for concepts taught in this chapter.

**3.** Student reports will vary depending on whether water in your community comes from a lake, river, or aquifer.

**4.** Student posters will vary. Make sure students illustrate and compare at least 2 methods.

---

## Develop Your Skills

Use the skills you have developed in this chapter to complete each activity.

**1. Interpret Data** The drawings below show magnified cross sections through three different samples of rock or soil.

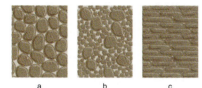

a. Which one has the highest porosity? The lowest porosity?

b. Which one has the highest permeability? The lowest permeability?

c. Which one will hold the most water?

**2. Make a Model** Draw three patterns that drainage systems can take. Label the tributaries on each of the model drainage systems.

**3. Predict** What will happen to an aquifer if the surface of its recharge area undergoes a long drought?

**4. Infer** What might happen to the land in areas where large amounts of water are pumped from aquifers?

**5. Data Bank** Use the information on pages 620–621 to answer the following questions.

a. Into which bay does the Sacramento River drain?

b. How many tributaries can you see flowing into the Mississippi River? Identify two of them by name.

## Make Connections

**1. Link the Concepts** Below is a concept map showing how some of the main concepts in this chapter link together. Only part of the map is filled in. Complete the map, using words and ideas from the chapter.

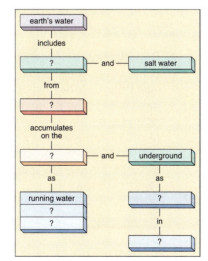

**2. Science and Social Studies** Do library research, and write a report on the history of a major city that developed along a river.

**3. Science and You** Find out where your community's supply of fresh water comes from. Write a report on the water's source and its quality.

**4. Science and Society** Do library research on modern sewage-treatment methods. Create a poster or bulletin board illustrating and comparing the different methods.

## Overview

This chapter explores ocean water. The first section begins with an observation of the properties of ocean water. The second section investigates currents and their influence on ocean life. The third section explains how waves are formed and measured. The last section discusses tide patterns and concludes with a discussion of tidal power.

## Advance Planner

▶ Obtain a clear container, a straw, clay, a permanent marker, and salt for TE page 340. Collect wood, containers, and salt for TE page 341.

▶ Provide glasses, water, salt, plastic wrap, and rubber bands for SE page 342. Supply toothpaste for TE page 342.

▶ Provide drinking glasses, labels, pen, blue food coloring, dropper, salt, plastic spoon, and stir stick for SE Activity 15, page 344.

▶ Gather chalk, globes, and beach balls for TE page 345.

▶ Collect shallow pans, straws, and construction paper for TE page 351.

▶ Obtain a copy of *The Great Wave at Kanagawa* for TE page 354.

## Skills Development Chart

| Sections | Communicate | Hypothesize | Infer | Interpret Data | Make a Model | Observe | Research |
|---|---|---|---|---|---|---|---|
| **15.1** Skills WarmUp | | | | | | ● | |
| Skills WorkOut | | | | | ● | | |
| Activity 15 | ● | ● | ● | | ● | ● | |
| **15.2** Skills WarmUp | | | | | ● | | |
| SkillBuilder | | | | ● | | | |
| Skills WorkOut | | | | | | | ● |
| **15.3** Skills WarmUp | | | | | | ● | |
| Skills WorkOut | | | ● | | | | |
| **15.4** Skills WarmUp | ● | | | | | | |
| Skills WorkOut | | | | ● | | | |

## Individual Needs

▶ **Limited English Proficiency Students** Have students use the boldface heads to make up "What are/is . . ." questions for each section in the chapter. For example, "What is the origin of ocean water?" Have them write each question on a separate page of their science portfolios. As they read each section, have them write two- or three-sentence answers to the questions. They should use their own words as well as the boldface terms in their answers. Have students use diagrams to illustrate their answers. Allow students to meet in groups of four or five to discuss what they have written. Encourage them to make changes or additions to their answers and use the questions and answers to review the chapter.

▶ **At-Risk Students** Have students work in groups and ask them to pick an area of one of the oceans that includes a section of coast. Encourage them to find out more about the properties of their area's water, its currents, waves, and tides. Have groups display their findings as a map with explanatory captions and, if possible, pictures from magazines.

▶ **Gifted Students** Ask students to consider the effect on the world's oceans if the earth had no winds. Have them find out some more about the action of the wind on the ocean. Then ask them to write an essay describing what the ocean would be like without it. They should take into account currents, waves, properties of water, and ocean life in their essay.

## Resource Bank

▶ **Bulletin Board** Invite students to bring in a photograph of the ocean that appeals to them and attach it to the bulletin board. Have them write two descriptions of their picture: one in straightforward scientific language and one as a poem. Display the descriptions on the bulletin board also, but separate from the pictures. Encourage students to try to match the descriptions with the corresponding pictures. Have a class discussion about the different styles of writing.

| Section | Core | Standard | Enriched | Section | Core | Standard | Enriched |
|---|:---:|:---:|:---:|---|:---:|:---:|:---:|
| **15.1 Properties of Ocean Water** pp. 339–344 | | | | **Section Features** Skills WarmUp, p. 351 Skills WorkOut, p. 351 | ● ● | ● ● | ● ● |
| **Section Features** Skills WarmUp, p. 339 Skills WorkOut, p. 342 Activity, p. 344 | ● ● | ● ● ● | ● ● ● | **Blackline Masters** Review Worksheet 15.3 Enrich Worksheet 15.3 Skills Worksheet 15.3 | ● ● | ● ● ● | ● ● ● |
| **Blackline Masters** Review Worksheet 15.1 Skills Worksheet 15.1 Integrating Worksheet 15.1 | ● ● | ● ● ● | ● ● ● | **Color Transparencies** Transparencies 44a, 44b | ● | ● | ● |
| **Color Transparencies** Transparencies 40, 41 | ● | ● | ● | **15.4 Tides** pp. 356–360 | | | |
| **15.2 Ocean Currents** pp. 345–350 | | | | **Section Features** Skills WarmUp, p. 356 Career Corner, p. 359 Skills WorkOut, p. 360 | ● ● | ● ● ● | ● ● ● |
| **Section Features** Skills WarmUp, p. 345 SkillBuilder, p. 346 Skills WorkOut, p. 350 | ● | ● ● ● | ● ● ● | **Blackline Masters** Review Worksheet 15.4 Vocabulary Worksheet 15.4 | ● ● | ● ● | ● ● |
| **Blackline Masters** Review Worksheet 15.2 Integrating Worksheet 15.2 | ● | ● ● | ● ● | **Overhead Blackline Transparencies** Overhead Blackline Master 15.4 and Student Worksheet | ● | ● | ● |
| **Laboratory Program** Investigation 23 | ● | ● | | **Laboratory Program** Investigation 24 | ● | ● | ● |
| **Color Transparencies** Transparencies 42, 43 | ● | ● | ● | **Color Transparencies** Transparency 45 | ● | ● | ● |
| **15.3 Ocean Waves** pp. 351–355 | | | | | | | |

# Bibliography

The following resources can be used for teaching the chapter. See page T–46 for supplier codes.

## Library Resources

Carson, Rachel. *The Sea Around Us.* Racine, WI: Golden Press, 1958.

Farndon, John. *How the Earth Works.* Pleasantville, NY: The Reader's Digest Association, Inc., 1992.

Gay, Kathlyn. *Water Pollution.* New York: Franklin Watts, Inc., 1990.

## Technology Resources

### Internet

**PLANETDIARY** at *http://www.planetdiary.com*
- Learn more about earthquakes in *Earthquake* by clicking on *Phenomena Backgrounders.*
- Review geological news in *Current Phenomena.*

### Software
*Hothouse Planet. Mac, Win. ESI.*
*Oceans. Mac, Dos, Win. ER.*

### CD-ROMs
*Interactive Earth. SFAW.*

### Laserdiscs
*Living Textbook. (See barcodes on pages in this chapter.) Optical Data.*

### Videos
*Discovering Our Rivers, Lakes, and Oceans. 30 min. MMI.*
*Ocean Currents and Winds. 15 min. EME.*

### Audio-Visual Resources
*Currents. Film. T–L.*
*Waves on Water. Film. EB.*

## Writing Connection

Ask students to imagine that they're spending a day on an ocean beach where many large waves break near shore. Have students write a story about their day at the beach that describes how the waves influenced the events of the day.

## Introducing the Chapter

Have students read the description of the photograph. Ask if they agree or disagree with the description.

### Directed Inquiry

Have students study the photograph. Ask:

▶ What does this photograph show? From what angle is it seen? (Students will probably say that it shows a wave breaking as it reaches the shore. The wave is seen from the side, rather than head-on.)

▶ What does this view of a wave show about how waves break? (Waves seem to be swept upward from the ocean bottom and then topple forward in a large curl.)

▶ What happens when large waves strike objects, such as a sand castle, on a beach? What does this suggest about them? (Students should say that the sand castle will probably be destroyed by the waves. This suggests that waves are powerful and can change shoreline features.)

▶ What do you think creates waves on oceans and lakes? (Students may mention the wind; some may think of earthquakes.)

## Chapter Vocabulary

| | |
|---|---|
| Coriolis force | semidiurnal |
| crest | thermocline |
| current | tide |
| estuary | trough |
| gyre | wave height |
| salinity | wavelength |

## Chapter **15** Ocean Water

### Chapter Sections

**15.1** Properties of Ocean Water

**15.2** Ocean Currents

**15.3** Ocean Waves

**15.4** Tides

### What do you see?

❝This picture looks like the inside of a wave. The wave was formed by either the wind or the water's current. The water is moving in a tunnel-like way. In the next few seconds it will probably come crashing down near the shore and another will form further out and do the same.❞

*Sylvia Lucero*
*Park Junior High School*
*Antioch, California*

To find out more about the photograph, look on page 362. As you read this chapter, you will learn about the earth's ocean water.

## Themes in Science

**Evolution** The world ocean has changed continuously through time. Ocean water has become more salty. The size of the large oceans and small seas has changed as the continents moved. The size and chemical composition of the ocean continues to evolve.

# 15.1 Properties of Ocean Water

## Objectives

▶ **List** substances that are dissolved in ocean water.

▶ **Explain** how a thermocline forms.

▶ **Compare** and **contrast** properties of ocean water.

▶ **Predict** the solubility of salt in water at different temperatures.

**ACTIVITY**

**Observing**

*Pondering the Ocean*

You have probably visited an ocean beach or seen one on television. What have you observed about the ocean water? Make a list of your observations.

**SKILLS WARMUP**

Suppose you have a glass of pure water, a glass of fresh water, and a glass of ocean water. You evaporate all the water. What will be left behind in each glass? Pure water contains only water molecules, so nothing will be left behind. Fresh water contains a very small amount of dissolved minerals and salts, so a whitish film may be left on the glass. Ocean water contains large amounts of dissolved salts and other minerals, so a crust of salts and minerals will form on the inside of the glass.

## Origin of Ocean Water

How did ocean water originally form? When the earth formed billions of years ago, its surface was very hot. There were many active volcanoes. The volcanoes sent molten rock and gases from inside the earth out to its surface. One of the gases released was water vapor. The released gases slowly gathered in a layer over the earth's surface to form the atmosphere.

Over time, the earth's surface and atmosphere cooled. As the water vapor cooled, it formed droplets of liquid water. The water droplets combined and fell to the earth's surface as rain. The rainwater flowed over the surface forming streams and rivers. The flowing water pooled in large, interconnected basins, forming a world ocean.

Recall that today's world ocean is divided into several large oceans and smaller seas. The oceans include the Atlantic, Pacific, Indian, and Arctic oceans. The largest of these is the Pacific Ocean, shown in Figure 15.1.

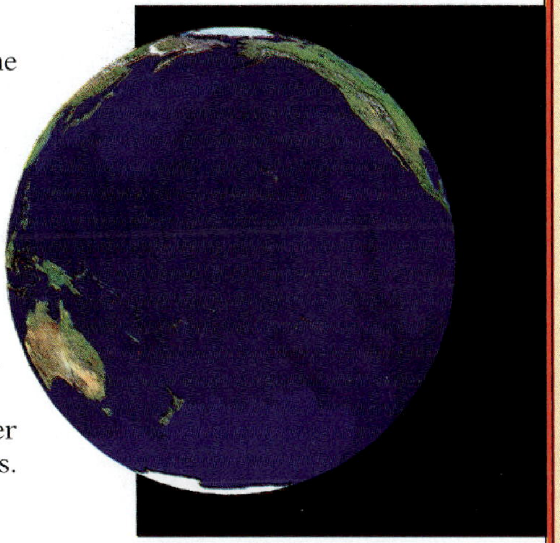

**Figure 15.1** ▲
The Pacific Ocean covers about 34% of the earth. It contains over 50% of the earth's salt water.

**SECTION**

**15.1**

**Section Objectives**
For a list of section objectives, see the Student Edition page.

**Skills Objectives**
Students should be able to:

**Observe** ocean water characteristics.

**Make a Model** of desalination.

**Predict** what will happen to refrigerated salt water.

**Hypothesize** how temperature and salinity affect density.

**Vocabulary**
salinity, estuary, thermocline

**MOTIVATE**

**Skills WarmUp**
To help students observe properties of ocean water, have them do the Skills WarmUp.
**Answer** Lists will vary; they may include observations from all the senses.

**Prior Knowledge**
Gauge how much students know about the properties of ocean water by asking the following questions:

▶ How does ocean water taste?

▶ Would you like to live on an ocean beach? Why or why not?

▶ What are some animals that live only in the ocean? What are some animals that live only in fresh water? Can any animals live in both places?

**Research**
Have students use a globe or world map to list the names of the world's seas. Then have them find out how each sea got its name.

Chapter 15 Ocean Water **339**

## Skills Development

**Calculate** Have students study Table 15.1. Then have them add all the grams of salt in 1 kg of ocean water. Ask: What percent of the salt in ocean water is sodium chloride? (27.2 g is 77.5 percent of total salts, 35.1 g.)

## Answers to In-Text Questions

① **Sodium chloride**

② **The areas of highest salinity are the Mediterranean Sea, the middle of the Atlantic Ocean, and a section off the east coast of South America. The areas of lowest salinity are the Hudson Bay region in Canada and estuaries, such as where the Mississippi River flows into the Gulf of Mexico. The salinity of most of the world's ocean is between 34 and 35 parts of salt per 1,000 parts ocean water.**

## Integrating the Sciences

**Physical Science** Density determines whether an object will sink or float in a fluid. Demonstrate how changing the density of water affects how an object floats. Construct a flotation device by inserting a straw into a ball of clay. Make cm markings on the straw with a permanent marker. Obtain a two-liter, clear container. Fill the container two-thirds full with water. Place the flotation device into the container. Add different amounts of table salt to the water. Have students observe the flotation device. (The device should float higher in the water as the density of the water is increased.)

**Table 15.1**
**Salts in Ocean Water**

| Salt | Grams in 1 kg Ocean Water |
|------|---------------------------|
| Sodium chloride | 27.2 |
| Magnesium chloride | 3.8 |
| Magnesium sulfate | 1.7 |
| Calcium sulfate | 1.3 |
| Potassium sulfate | 0.9 |
| Calcium carbonate | 0.1 |
| Magnesium bromide | 0.1 |

**Figure 15.2**
Study the map. Where are the areas of highest salinity? The areas of lowest salinity? What is the salinity of most of the world ocean? ▼ ②

## Chemical Properties of Ocean Water

Ocean water is a mixture of dissolved gases, salts, and tiny amounts of many elements. Small amounts of these substances dissolve in rivers as they flow across the land. After reaching the ocean, some of the water evaporates, but the dissolved substances remain behind. Eventually, the substances are either deposited in sedimentary rock or used by ocean organisms.

The major dissolved gases in ocean water are nitrogen, oxygen, and carbon dioxide. The major dissolved salts are shown in Table 15.1. What is the most common salt in ocean water? Dissolved salts give ocean ① water a property called **salinity** (suh LIN uh tee). Salinity is the number of grams of salts in 1 kg of water. The average salinity of ocean water is 34.5 g/kg.

Salinity varies from one part of the ocean to another. Look at Figure 15.2. High salinity occurs in regions of high evaporation, low rainfall, and warm water. Warm water can hold more dissolved salts than cold water. Low salinity occurs for several reasons. Where large rivers flow into the ocean, fresh river water mixes with ocean water. A bay or inlet of low-salinity water called an **estuary** (ES choo AIR ee) forms. Low salinity also occurs in areas of high rainfall or melting ice.

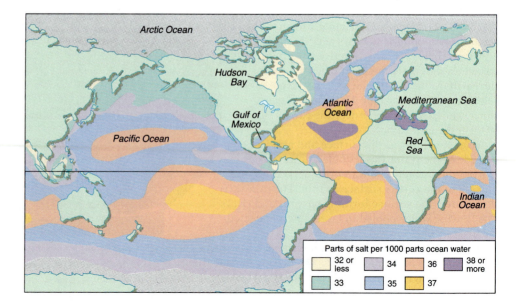

Arctic Ocean

Hudson Bay

Atlantic Ocean

Mediterranean Sea

Gulf of Mexico

Pacific Ocean

Red Sea

Indian Ocean

Parts of salt per 1000 parts ocean water
- 32 or less
- 33
- 34
- 35
- 36
- 37
- 38 or more

340

## Integrating the Sciences

**Physical and Life Science** When people dive to great ocean depths, the air they breathe must have the same pressure as the surrounding water. If the pressure is less, the diver's body can be crushed by the high, surrounding water pressure. As a result of breathing high-pressure air, nitrogen becomes concentrated in the diver's blood and tissue fluids. If the pressure around the diver is lowered too quickly, the nitrogen can form gas bubbles in the organs and bloodstream. This condition, known as the *bends,* can lead to death. To avoid the bends, deep-sea divers are raised to the surface in stages. By stopping at each stage, the body slowly adjusts to the lowering pressure.

## Physical Properties of Ocean Water

The physical properties of ocean water vary at different points in a water column. Look at Figure 15.3. A water column is a cross section reaching from the ocean floor to the surface at one location.

**Temperature**  Only the top of the water column is directly warmed by the sun. Surface movements mix the warmed water, transferring heat downward to a depth of 100 to 400 m. Mixing makes the water about the same temperature throughout this zone. The actual surface water temperature varies. Summer surface temperatures are higher than those in winter.

The surface water temperature also varies from place to place. Solar energy heats ocean water the most near the earth's equator and the least at the poles. For example, summer surface zone temperatures range from 28°C near the equator to 2°C near the poles.

Just beneath the surface zone, the water temperature decreases rapidly. A zone of rapid temperature change is called a **thermocline** (THUR moh KLYN). A thermocline forms because warm surface water floats on top of the colder water. The depth of the thermocline varies with location and season. Below a thermocline, the water temperature decreases only slightly.

**Density**  Pure water has a density of 1 g/cm³. The density of ocean water ranges from 1.026 to 1.028 g/cm³. Salinity and temperature both affect the density of ocean water. High-salinity water is denser than low-salinity water, if the waters are the same temperature. Cold water is denser than warm water. The

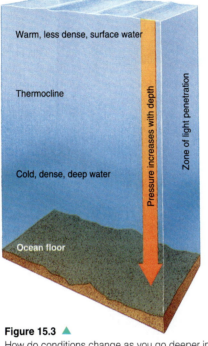

**Figure 15.3** ▲
How do conditions change as you go deeper in a water column? ③

colder water becomes, the more closely its molecules pack together.

**Pressure**  Imagine you have a bucket filled with berries. When you pour the berries out, you notice that the berries at the bottom of the bucket are squashed. Why did this happen? The combined weight of all the berries pressed down on the berries at the bottom.

A water column in the ocean behaves the same way. Deep in the water column, the combined weight of all the water above presses downward. Near the bottom, the pressure is much greater than near the surface. At a depth of 10 m, the pressure from the water above is about equal to the weight of a small car pressing on an area of 1 square meter.

## Skills Development

**Infer**  Ask students: Why is high-salinity water more dense than low-salinity water at the same temperature? (There are more particles, and more mass, in a given volume.)

## Class Activity

Have students work in small groups. Give each group two pieces of wood of the same kind, size, and weight; two clear containers with equal amounts of water; and some salt. Have students dissolve the salt into one container of water. Have students place one piece of wood in the container of salt water and one in the container of fresh water. Have them note which piece of wood floats higher in the water. (The wood in the salt water floats higher.)

## Integrated Learning

Use Integrating Worksheet 15.1.

**Answer to In-Text Question**

③ Temperature decreases; density and pressure increase.

### Skills WorkOut

To help students make a model of a desalination plant, have them do the Skills WorkOut.

**Answer** Evaporation is involved in removing salts from water. Condensation is necessary for collecting fresh water.

### Critical Thinking

**Reason and Conclude** Animals live in the deepest part of the ocean where there is very great outside pressure. Ask students what special features, or adaptations, might help these organisms live at great depths. (Some answers may include high internal pressure and strong shells or skeletons.)

### Enrich

Show the class pictures of coral formations. Explain that they are created by animals that take calcium from sea water to form deposits of calcium carbonate, or limestone.

### Answer to In-Text Question

① **Multicellular algae use dissolved nitrate for growth. Clams use calcium in their shells, and diatoms use silica to build their shells.**

### STS Connection

Diatoms are added to toothpaste as an abrasive. Have students rub a dab of toothpaste between their fingers to feel how the silica in diatom shells helps make toothpaste gritty.

### Literature Connection

According to a Danish legend, two female giants make the ocean salty. After the giants were captured by a Scandinavian king, they were ordered to grind salt from two magic stones. The giants ground so much salt that their boat sank to the ocean floor. They are still at the bottom of ocean, grinding salt. You may wish to have students find other legends or myths focusing on the ocean.

---

### ▼ ACTIVITY

#### Making a Model

*Water with the Sun's Help*

Fill a glass one-third with water. Dissolve 3 g of salt in the water. Cover the glass with plastic wrap. Place the glass in a sunny window. After one day, remove the plastic wrap and taste the drops of water that formed there. How is your model like a desalination plant?

#### SKILLS WORKOUT

**Figure 15.4** ▲
How does each of these organisms depend upon ocean water for its survival? ①

### Ocean Water and Living Things

Organisms that live in the ocean use substances dissolved in ocean water to survive. Look at Figure 15.4. Algae use dissolved nitrate ($NO_3^-$) for growth. Some animals extract calcium to build thick, hard shells. Microscopic plantlike organisms called diatoms use silica ($SiO_2$) to build tiny, intricate shells.

Many ocean organisms depend on sunlight. For example, diatoms and algae need sunlight for photosynthesis. Recall that sunlight can't penetrate very deeply into the ocean. Therefore, these organisms must live in shallow water near the shore or float on the surface of the ocean.

Some organisms move up and down in the water column by changing their density. For example, fishes have a swim bladder that fills with gases from their bloodstream. When its swim bladder is filled, a fish is less dense than the water around it. Therefore, the fish rises in the water column. When the swim bladder empties, the fish becomes more dense and sinks in the water column.

Water pressure also affects organisms that live in the ocean. Organisms that live in very deep water must withstand extremely high pressure. Organisms that live where the water level changes must withstand changes in pressure.

### Science and Technology
#### Drinkable Ocean Water

If you have ever accidentally swallowed a mouthful of ocean water, you know that it tastes awful. But, the bad taste isn't the only reason you shouldn't drink ocean water. Ocean water has too much salt for your body to process. Too much salt makes your body lose water. The salt concentrates in your cells, pushing out the water. Instead of quenching your thirst, drinking ocean water makes you more thirsty!

In some areas of the world, there isn't enough fresh water available, so people have to get their drinking water from the ocean. Salt is removed from ocean water through a process called desalination.

## Integrating the Sciences

**Life Science** Desalination plants also use reverse osmosis to remove salt from water. Fishes that live in salt water must also remove salt from their bodies. Have students infer how marine fishes get rid of the extra salt in their bodies. (Marine fishes use a process called osmoregula-

tion. In an adaptation that keeps fresh water in their systems, they drink sea water and then give off salt through their gills. They also produce only a small amount of urine, which conserves fresh water in their bodies.)

◀ **Figure 15.5**
The Yuma Desalting Plant in Arizona uses the reverse osmosis method to desalt water. The plant can desalt nearly 275 million liters of water per day.

In the most common method of desalination, ocean water is pumped into a chamber and then heated. The water turns to steam. The steam rises into another chamber, where it cools and condenses. Salt is too heavy to be carried in the steam and is left behind. Water from condensed steam is fresh and drinkable. Most desalination plants that use this process must burn fossil fuels to heat the water.

Another desalination method uses a membrane through which water, but not salt, can pass. Water is forced through the membrane in a process called reverse osmosis. Usually the process is powered by fossil fuels, but one design uses power from ocean waves.

## Check and Explain

1. What substances are dissolved in ocean water?

2. What is a thermocline? Explain how it forms.

3. **Compare and Contrast** Compare the following properties of ocean water: composition, temperature, salinity, and density. Explain the relationships among these properties.

4. **Predict** Imagine you have a glass of water at room temperature. You mix salt into the water until no more will dissolve. Then you put the glass in the refrigerator. Predict what will happen to the salt in the water.

### WrapUp

**Reteach** Ask students to describe how swimming in ocean water is different from swimming in fresh water. Have them discuss which kind of water is easier to swim in and why it is easier. (Ocean water is easier to swim in than fresh water because its greater salinity and density make it easier to float.)

Use Review Worksheet 15.1.

### Check and Explain

1. Minerals, gases, and salts

2. A zone of rapid temperature change that occurs when warm surface water floats on top of colder water

3. Answers will vary. Composition of the water can vary as its physical properties change. Temperature decreases with depth; salinity and density increase with depth.

4. The salt may begin to collect on the sides of the glass as the water evaporates; salt may also precipitate in the bottom of the glass without continued stirring.

**Time** 30 minutes    **Group** 3

**Materials**

20 small drinking glasses

20 large drinking glasses

20 stir sticks

10 droppers

blue food coloring

salt

10 plastic spoons

cold tap water

warm tap water

### *Prelab Discussion*

Have students read the entire activity. Discuss the following points before beginning:

▶ Emphasize the importance of pouring carefully. Point out that some liquid is likely to spill during this procedure.

▶ Alert students to carefully observe the initial movements of the different types of water as the food coloring will eventually spread throughout the water.

▶ Ask students to predict the results of the activity.

## Analysis

1. The water in glass *3* was more dense because it sunk below the water in glass *1*.

2. The water in glass *1* was warm, so it was less dense than the water in glass *3*.

3. The water in glass *4* was more dense because it sank below the water in glass *2*.

4. Glass *2* has less salt.

## Conclusion

Density decreases as the temperature increases. As salinity increases, density also increases. A change in salinity or temperature could cause water to sink and form deep ocean currents.

## Extension

Hypothesis: The water in glass *2* will float on the 8-spoonful solution because the solution has a higher salinity and is denser.

## *Activity 15*  *How do temperature and salinity affect density?*

***Skills***  Interpret Data; Observe; Model; Hypothesize

### Task 1 Prelab Prep

1. Collect the following items: 2 large drinking glasses, 2 small drinking glasses, labels, pen, warm and cold tap water, blue food coloring, dropper, salt, plastic spoon, stir stick.

2. Number the labels *1, 2, 3,* and *4*. Label the large drinking glasses *1* and *2*. Label the small drinking glasses *3* and *4*.

### Task 2 Data Record

1. On a separate sheet of paper, copy Table 15.2.

2. Use the data table to record all of your observations.

**Figure 15.6** ▲

**Table 15.2    Density Comparisons**

| Glass Number | Water Type | Observations |
|---|---|---|
|  |  |  |
|  |  |  |
|  |  |  |
|  |  |  |

### Task 3 Procedure

1. Add warm tap water to glass *1* until half full.

2. Add cold tap water to glass *3* until it is nearly full. Add three drops of food coloring and stir.

3. As shown in Figure 15.6, slowly pour the water in glass *3* down the inside of glass *1*. Record your observations in the data table.

4. Add warm tap water to glass *4* until it is nearly full. Add three drops of food coloring and 5 spoonfuls of salt. Stir well.

5. Add warm tap water to glass *2* until it is half full. Add 2 spoonfuls of salt. Stir well.

6. As shown in Figure 15.6, slowly pour the water in glass *4* down the inside of glass *2*. Record your observations in the data table.

### Task 4 Analysis

1. Which was more dense, the water in glass *1* or the water in glass *3*? Explain.

2. Why did the water in glass *1* have a different density than the water in glass *3*?

3. Which was denser, the water in glass *2* or the water in glass *4*? Explain how you know.

4. Why did the water in glass *2* have a different density than the water in glass *4*?

### Task 5 Conclusion

Write a short paragraph explaining the relationship between temperature and density. Then write another paragraph explaining the relationship between salinity and density. Relate your conclusions to the movement of deep currents in the ocean.

### *Extension*

Imagine you had another small glass with 8 spoonfuls of salt dissolved in it. Suppose you poured this solution into glass *2* after completing step 6 of the procedure. Make a hypothesis about what would happen. Test your hypothesis.

## Cooperative Learning

Have students work in cooperative groups to model the Coriolis effect on a three-dimensional object. Have each group obtain a piece of chalk and a globe, beach ball, or other large spherical object. As one student rotates the sphere, have another student try to draw a straight line from pole to pole with the chalk. Have students observe the shape of the line made by the chalk on the sphere. Ask: How did this process model the Coriolis effect? (The rotating motion of the sphere produced a curved line. The sphere represents the earth and the line represents the effect of the Coriolis effect on winds and water.)

### Section Objectives
For a list of section objectives, see the Student Edition page.

### Skills Objectives
Students should be able to:

**Make a Model** of movements affected by the Coriolis effect.

**Interpret Data** about ocean currents.

**Research** the effects of El Niño.

**Predict** the effects of Coriolis effect on air travel.

### Vocabulary
current, Coriolis force, gyre

# 15.2 Ocean Currents

## Objectives

▶ **Describe** the major ocean current patterns in the Pacific and Atlantic oceans.

▶ **Identify** two factors that drive ocean currents.

▶ **Compare** and **contrast** surface currents and deep currents.

▶ **Predict** the effects of the Coriolis force.

▼ **ACTIVITY**

**Modeling**

*At the Edge*

Imagine you are riding at the center of a merry-go-round. You want to throw a ball to a friend at the edge of the merry-go-round. Where would your friend have to sit to be able to catch the ball? Draw a picture showing what would happen.

**SKILLS WARMUP**

Imagine a boat adrift in the ocean near the continent of Antarctica. Which way do you think the boat would move? The boat would travel in a clockwise direction. The boat would be carried along in a flow of water called a current. A **current** is a flow of water moving through the ocean. A strong ocean current flows in a clockwise direction around Antarctica.

Currents flow through all parts of the ocean. Surface currents flow horizontally on or near the top of the ocean. Deep currents flow horizontally far beneath the surface. Ocean water also flows vertically. Water can flow down toward the ocean floor or up toward the surface.

### Surface Currents

Think about what happens when you blow on hot cocoa to cool it off. The surface of the hot cocoa moves in the direction that you blow. Wind moves ocean water in a similar way, creating surface currents.

Surface currents are driven by winds that blow for long distances over the ocean surface. The winds blow in a curved path because of the **Coriolis** (KOHR ee OH liss) **effect**. The Coriolis effect, caused by the earth's rotation, bends the earth's winds and ocean currents.

To understand how the Coriolis effect works, look at Figure 15.7. A person tries to draw a straight line on a rotating turntable. Although the line is being drawn straight, the surface on which it is drawn is moving. The motion of the surface produces a curved line.

**Figure 15.7**
What happens as this person tries to draw a straight line on the rotating turntable? ▼

### MOTIVATE

*Skills WarmUp*
To help students model the Coriolis effect, have them do the Skills WarmUp.
**Answer** Drawings will vary depending on the direction in which the merry-go-round is turning. The friend would have to sit behind the spot toward which the ball is thrown. A picture would show the ball following a curved path, as in Figure 15.7.

### Misconceptions
Students may think that all ocean currents exist on the surface of the water. Explain that currents flow in all levels of the ocean. Also point out that currents at different levels in the same section of the ocean can flow in different directions.

## TEACH

### *Explore Visually*

Have students study the text and Figure 15.8. Then ask:

▶ In what direction do the northeast tradewinds blow? (Southwest) The westerlies? (Northeast) The southeast tradewinds? (Northwest)

▶ What does the name tell you about each of the prevailing winds? (Tells the direction from where the wind originated)

▶ What causes the prevailing winds to curve? (The rotation of the earth in an easterly direction)

### *SkillBuilder*

#### Answers

1. In a few cases the surface and deep currents are in the same places; in many they are not. The deep currents tend to be along the eastern sides of the continents. The surface currents tend to be on both sides of the continents.

2. Surface currents and deep currents often flow in opposite directions. Off the east coast of South America, however, the surface and deep currents flow in the same direction.

3. They tend to follow the edges of the continents for long distances and they are curved.

Reports will vary; they should explain the general patterns of current flow.

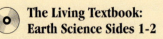

### The Living Textbook: Earth Science Sides 1-2

Chapter 24      Frame 03014
Global Wind Patterns (1 Frame)
Search:

346

### Social Studies Connection

Have students infer why some prevailing winds are called "tradewinds." Tell students that during the 1500s, many European countries searched for ocean passages that would open new lands to trade and settlement. Northeast winds carried sailors across the Atlantic to the Americas. The winds were called tradewinds because they carried sailing ships across the oceans to new trading territories.

**Figure 15.8 ▲**
The prevailing winds in the northern and southern hemispheres push the ocean's surface waters in circular currents.

**Surface Currents and Wind Patterns**   The earth rotates in an easterly direction. The earth's motion makes winds blowing toward the equator curve westward. In a similar way, winds blowing toward the poles curve eastward. Notice in Figure 15.8 that the winds form roughly circular patterns north of the equator. They also form circular patterns south of the equator. Surface currents in the ocean form similar patterns. Imagine a windblown surface current traveling south toward the equator. At the same time, the ocean basin moves eastward because the earth is rotating. Therefore, the current curves slightly to the west.

If winds change direction, so do the surface currents. In summer, winds blow from the northern Indian Ocean toward Asia. The winds cause a surface current that moves in a clockwise circle. In winter, winds blow from Asia toward the ocean. The surface current changes direction, moving in a counterclockwise circle.

## *SkillBuilder*   *Interpreting Data*

### *Ocean Currents*

The waters of the world ocean are constantly moving. In every ocean basin, there are surface currents and deep currents. All these currents exist at the same time. Therefore, in any part of the world ocean, surface water may move in a completely different direction than the deep water in the same area. For example, surface water in the North Atlantic Ocean moves in a clockwise circular motion. Meanwhile, a deep current in the same ocean carries dense water from Greenland toward the equator along the ocean bottom.

Study the map of surface currents on page 347. Place a sheet of tracing paper over the map. Using a pencil, trace the outlines of all the continents. Using a colored pencil, carefully trace all the surface currents. Be sure to include the arrows so you know in which direction the currents are moving.

Place your map of surface currents over the map of deep currents on page 348. Line up the continents so that the outlines on the two maps match exactly. Using a different colored pencil, trace the deep currents. You now have a map that shows how surface currents move in relation to deep currents. Use the combined information on your map to answer the following questions.

1. Compare the locations of the surface currents and deep currents in each ocean.

2. What differences do you see in the directions that surface currents flow and the directions that deep currents flow?

3. How are the currents similar?

Write a short report summarizing the movements of surface currents and deep currents in the world ocean.

## Geography Connection

Have students investigate how surface currents affect climate, using maps of average winter and summer temperatures for each continent. Tell students to compare temperatures along the coast to see if warm equatorial currents or cold polar currents affect the climate. If you prefer to focus on one continent, the climates along coastal South America show clear climate differences. Temperatures are higher along the Atlantic side, which receives warm currents. The cooler Pacific side is affected by cold polar currents.

**Surface Currents in the World Ocean**   Study the major surface currents in the world ocean shown in Figure 15.9. Notice that warm currents flow from the equator and cold currents flow from the poles. Surface currents form a circular pattern called a **gyre** (JY ur). Gyres in the Northern Hemisphere flow clockwise. In the Southern Hemisphere, gyres flow counterclockwise.

Along the equator in the Pacific, Atlantic, and Indian oceans, warm currents flow west. In the Pacific and Indian oceans, a weak countercurrent flows east between the northern and southern currents. Around the continent of Antarctica, a current flows east.

In the North Atlantic Ocean, the North Equatorial Current flows into the Gulf Stream. The Gulf Stream flows north, meets the Labrador Current, and turns east to form the North Atlantic Drift Current. As the North Atlantic Drift Current approaches Europe, it splits in two. The northern branch moves toward the North Pole. The southern branch becomes the Canary Current that rejoins the North Equatorial Current.

In the North Pacific Ocean, the North Equatorial Current flows into the Kuroshio Current. The Kuroshio Current moves north along the coast of Asia, then joins the eastward-flowing North Pacific Current. Eventually it turns south and becomes the California Current.

### Physical Science LINK

Collect the following materials: a small plastic ball (about 15 cm in diameter), string, a ruler, food coloring, water, and a clear container.

**1.** Add water to the container.

**2.** Using the ruler and string, suspend the ball in the water.

**3.** Spin the ball and slowly add drops of food coloring to the top of the ball.

Describe the flow of the food coloring around the ball. How is this flow related to ocean currents?

**ACTIVITY**

**Figure 15.9**
How do the currents differ north and south of the equator? ▼ ①

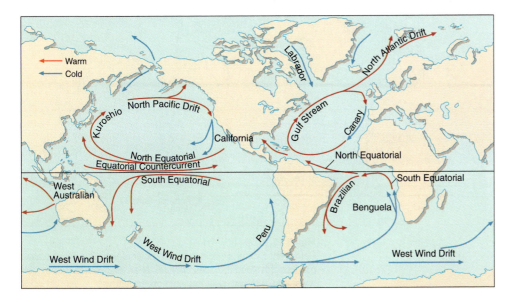

## Enrich

Inform students that because the Gulf Stream is a warm current, northern Europe has a warmer climate than it would otherwise have. As the Gulf Stream nears the coasts of northern Europe, it splits into two currents, and only part of it, the North Atlantic Drift, moves toward the North Pole. Have students study these currents on the map in Figure 15.9.

## Discuss

Have students note that the West Wind Drift flows along Antarctica. Ask: What happens to the West Wind Drift off the southern coast of South America? (It splits to form the cold-water current called Benguela. As this current warms, it becomes the warm-water current called the Brazilian.)

## Integrated Learning

Use Integrating Worksheet 15.2.

### Answer to In-Text Question

① **North of the equator, they move clockwise; south of the equator, they move counterclockwise.**

### Answer to Link

The flow of the food coloring should bend to the right if ball is spun in an Earth-wise rotation. Flow should bend left if ball is spun the opposite direction. This activity models the coriolis effect for the northern hemisphere of the earth. Ocean currents in the northern hemisphere are deflected to the right due to the coriolis effect.

**The Living Textbook:
Earth Science Sides 1-2**

Chapter 24        Frame 03015
Currents (2 Frames)
Search:              Step:

## Directed Inquiry

Have students study the text and Figure 15.10. Ask:

▶ Why do you think deep currents are also called density currents? (Colder water has a higher density than warm water, so it sinks. The cold, dense water forms deep currents.)

▶ In which direction do deep ocean currents tend to flow? (Northward or southward)

▶ Which current seems to contradict the flow pattern? (North Atlantic current along the east coast of South America)

## Critical Thinking

**Predict**  After students have read about upwelling, ask: Where would you go for the best fishing in the ocean? Why? (Where there are upwellings; the water is rich with nutrients and ocean life.)

## Themes in Science

**Stability and Equilibrium**  The difference in density between warm and cold water has produced equilibrium between the surface and the deep-ocean water. The two ocean layers do not mix, so each of their movements has formed a stable, independent system. The stability of each system depends on the separation of water layers and the Coriolis effect. The flow of surface currents and deep currents has a predictable pattern that can be mapped.

## Deep Currents

Recall that density differences between warm surface waters and cold deep waters keep them from mixing. Because the waters don't mix, the movement of surface currents usually has little effect on colder deep water. In fact, while surface currents move in gyres, deep ocean currents flow from the poles toward the equator.

Deep currents are kept in motion by density differences. The densest water in the ocean forms at the North and South poles. There, the surface water is very cold. As ice forms, salts concentrate in the remaining water. The result is very dense cold water with high salinity. The dense polar water sinks downward to the deep ocean. The water continues to flow as a deep current toward the equator.

Besides density, the Coriolis effect also affects deep currents. Look at the map in Figure 15.10. Notice that deep currents tend to flow either northward or southward. But as the currents flow, the Coriolis effect bends them toward the western side of the ocean basins.

Where winds blow in a constant direction parallel to the coast, surface currents and deep currents can mix. For example, along the Pacific coast of Chile, the wind blows northward. The wind pushes the warm surface waters away from the coast. Cold, deep water moves upward to take the place of the surface water. The upward movement of deep water is called *upwelling*. Where upwelling occurs, the water is rich with nutrients that it brings up from the ocean floor. Marine animals are plentiful in these nutrient-rich waters.

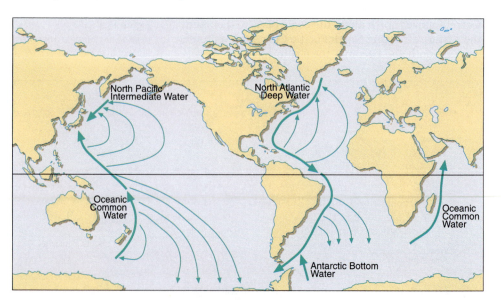

**Figure 15.10 ▲**
Cold, dense water sinks in the south polar region. The dense water moves north along the ocean bottom. At an intermediate depth, cold water from the north polar region moves south.

## Language Arts Connection

Have students look at Figure 15.11. Ask them if *longshore current* and *rip current* are appropriate names for these water movements and have them explain why. (Many students will think they are appropriate because longshore currents flow lengthwise along a shore. Rip currents look as though they have torn away from a series of longshore currents.) Ask students how the name *undertow* explains the behavior of this current. (*Tow* means "to pull," so an undertow is a current that pulls things under the water.)

## Directed Inquiry

Have students study this page and note the differences between rip currents, longshore currents, and undertows. Then ask:

► What is the difference between shoreline currents and surface and deep currents? (Shoreline currents travel short distances; surface and deep currents travel thousands of kilometers.)

► What shoreline currents form where waves approach the shore at an angle? (Longshore currents)

► What shoreline currents form when water carried to the shore pulls back toward the ocean? (Undertows)

► What shoreline currents are narrow, powerful streams of water that flow at a right angle to the shore? (Rip currents)

► How can a person escape a rip current? Why? (Swim parallel to the shore; the rip current is narrow and perpendicular to the shore.)

► What happens if a swimmer tries to swim toward the shore while caught in a rip current? (The person will make little progress and soon become tired because the current is very strong.)

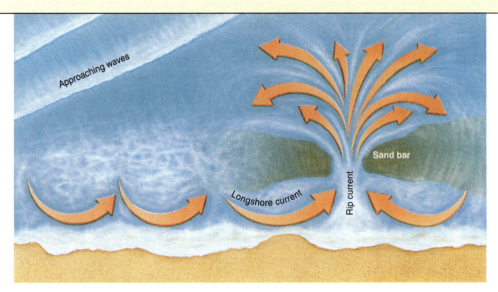

**Figure 15.11** ▲
Small, localized currents form as waves break on a shoreline.

## Shoreline Currents

Near the shoreline, local currents form that travel only short distances, such as a few kilometers or a few hundred meters. The distances these currents travel are like a trip across town or across the schoolyard. In contrast, surface currents and deep currents travel thousands of kilometers.

One type of shoreline current forms where waves approach a shore at an angle. After ocean waves hit the shore, the water flows back toward the ocean. The continuous back-and-forth motion of the waves forms a zigzag current parallel to the shore. Look at the zigzag current, called a *longshore current*, in Figure 15.11.

Along some shores are parallel ridges of rock or sand. Longshore currents can become trapped between the shore and the ridge. If there is an opening in the ridge, the longshore current can break through forcefully. The water in the longshore current is pulled out toward the open ocean. A narrow, powerful stream of water flows away at a right angle to the shore. This narrow stream is called a *rip current*.

Rip currents can be dangerous to swimmers. Swimmers are sometimes caught in a fast-moving rip current and pulled out to deeper water. Look at Figure 15.11. How do you think a swimmer can escape a rip current? Because a rip current is rather narrow, a swimmer can escape by swimming parallel to the shore.

A rip current is sometimes confused with an *undertow*. An undertow forms when water carried to shore in waves pulls back toward the ocean. If you stand on a beach and let small waves wash up around your ankles, the undertow drags the sand out from under your feet. An undertow isn't usually strong enough to be dangerous, unless the wave action is very strong or the ocean bottom drops away sharply. Public beaches with dangerous undertow conditions are often marked with warning signs.

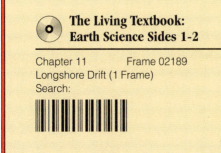

**The Living Textbook: Earth Science Sides 1-2**

Chapter 11          Frame 02189
Longshore Drift (1 Frame)
Search:

## Skills WorkOut

To help students understand El Niño, have them do the Skills WorkOut.

**Answer** Reports will vary, but should include climatic and economic effects.

## EVALUATE

## WrapUp

**Portfolio** Have students take the maps they made for the SkillBuilder and label the currents. Let them quiz one another on the directions of different currents. Then have them place the maps in their portfolios.

Use Review Worksheet 15.2.

## Check and Explain

1. They flow clockwise along the equator and the sides of the continents.

2. The Coriolis effect and surface winds

3. They differ in depth, water density, and often, direction. They're both influenced by the Coriolis effect, density, and both bend to the sides of the ocean basins.

4. South and west because the direction of the prevailing winds affects the plane's actual flight path.

 *STS Connection*

From 1964 to 1970, about 20 percent of the world fishery was represented by anchoveta, a small Pacific anchovy. But a severe El Niño in 1972 decreased the anchoveta catch so much that officials banned anchoveta fishing by 1982. Although other factors contributed to the decrease in anchoveta, the effects of El Niño triggered the eventual decline of this industry.

*Multicultural Perspectives*

Marine aquaculture, or mariculture, is a method of breeding and raising fishes and shellfish under controlled conditions. Mariculture has been used to cultivate ocean food crops in Asia for many years. More than 80 percent of today's mariculture takes place along Asia's coasts. Mariculture has contributed greatly to the world's food supply. You may wish to have students research specific mariculture methods used by people in Asia.

▼ **ACTIVITY**

**Researching**

*Current Disasters*

Use library references to research the El Niño that occurred in 1982 and 1983. Find out how it caused storms, floods, and droughts around the world. Also find out how it affected the fishing industry. Report your findings to the class.

**SKILLS WORKOUT**

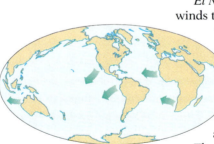

**Figure 15.12** ▲
In areas of upwelling, winds blow warm surface water away from the coast. Cold, deep water moves up to fill the space.

 **Science and Society**
*Upwelling and Fisheries*

Did you know that most of the world's supply of seafood comes from just a few places? Places where upwelling occurs, shown in Figure 15.12, are the world's most productive fishing grounds. Cold, deep water contains large amounts of plant nutrients, such as nitrogen and phosphates. Upwelling brings the cold, nutrient-rich water back to the ocean surface. The nutrients support the growth of diatoms and other plantlike organisms that serve as food for fishes.

The upwelling area off the western coast of South America is usually one of the world's most productive fisheries. Sometimes, however, the upwelling stops. A series of events called El Niño keeps the cold, nutrient-rich water from rising to the surface.

*El Niño* is a disturbance of ocean currents and winds that occurs every three to eight years. It begins when the westward trade winds weaken. These winds normally push warm surface water away from the coast of South America, allowing upwelling to occur. When the trade winds weaken, the warm equatorial current flows eastward toward the coast. The warm surface waters block upwelling along the coast.

The warming of the coastal waters and the lack of nutrients kill many microscopic organisms. Fishes and birds that feed on these organisms die of starvation or migrate elsewhere. The people who depend on fishing can't make a living during El Niño years.

## Check and Explain

1. Describe surface currents in the North Pacific Ocean and the North Atlantic Ocean.

2. What two factors cause ocean currents to form?

3. **Compare and Contrast** How do surface currents and deep currents differ? How are they similar?

4. **Predict** What direction would a plane have to travel to reach a city directly south of its starting point if the winds were blowing to the east? Explain why.

### Cooperative Learning

Have students work in cooperative groups of two or three to discover how waves form. Have each group obtain a shallow pan, water, several straws, and construction paper. Then tell them to follow this procedure: Fill the pan three-fourths full with water. Record what happens as one student blows gently across the top of the water through a straw. Wait for the water to settle. Then record what happens as a student blows vigorously across the top of the water. Wait for the water to settle. Add small pieces of torn construction paper to the water's surface. Record what happens to the construction paper as a student blows gently across the water's surface.

## 15.3 Ocean Waves

### Objectives

▶ **Explain** how waves form.

▶ **Identify** the parts of an ocean wave.

▶ **Explain** how to measure wave motion.

▶ **Define operationally** how a water particle moves as a wave passes.

▼ **ACTIVITY**

**Observing**

*Wave Motion*

Watch while part of the class performs the "wave" as done at sporting events. Describe how the people and the wave moved.

**SKILLS WARMUP**

H ow can you make waves in a tub of water? When you push down on the water with your hand, the water starts moving. An up-and-down movement travels the length of the tub. The periodic up-and-down movement of water is a *wave*.

Ocean waves form when wind pushes against the ocean's surface. Friction from the wind pushing against the water makes ripples form. The wind pushes against a ripple in much the same way that it would push against a sail. As the wind pushes against the surface of the ripple, energy is transferred from the wind to the water. The increasing energy makes the ripple grow into a wave. The larger a wave surface becomes, the more energy it can absorb from the wind.

### Mechanics of Wave Motion

When you watch a wave move, the water appears to move forward. Actually, the water itself barely moves. It is wave energy that moves forward through the water, not the water particles. As the wave energy pulses forward, the water particles move in a circular, up-and-down motion. A cork placed in the water would bob up and down with the same motion. Look at Figure 15.13. Notice that each water particle returns to the point from which it started.

When a wave moves through water, not all of the energy transfers forward. Some energy transfers downward. However, the motion of the water particles decreases as the depth increases, as shown in Figure 15.13. Below a certain depth, there is no wave motion at all and the water particles stop moving.

**Figure 15.13**
How does wave motion compare to the water particle motion? ▼ ①

Wave motion

Water particle motion

Section Objectives
For a list of section objectives, see the Student Edition page.

**Skills Objectives**
Students should be able to:

**Observe** how waves move.

**Infer** the relationships among crest, trough, height, and wavelength.

**Define Operationally** how water particles move in water waves.

**Vocabulary**
crest, trough, wave height, wavelength

### MOTIVATE

#### Skills WarmUp
To help students understand waves, have them do the Skills WarmUp.
**Answer** Descriptions will vary, but should note that individuals do not change locations.

#### Misconceptions
Students may think that particles in water waves move through water in the same direction as the waves. Use the analogy of a boat moving up and down as waves pass under it. Ask: Which way is the boat moving in comparison to the waves? (Perpendicular—the boat moves up and down as the waves pass under it.) Point out that the movement of water particles in waves resembles the boat's movement.

**Answer to In-Text Question**

① **The wave moves forward; the water particle returns to its original position.**

## Skills WorkOut

To help students understand wave characteristics, have them do the Skills WorkOut.

**Answer** The vertical distance between the wave's crest and trough is the wave height, and the horizontal distance from the crest of one wave to the crest of the next wave is the wavelength.

## Directed Inquiry

Have students study Figure 15.14 and the text on this page. Then ask:

▶ What is a crest? (The highest point of a wave)

▶ What is a trough? (The lowest point of a wave)

▶ What are swells? (Smooth, low hills of water)

▶ What causes waves in water? (Wind blowing across the water's surface gives energy to the water.)

▶ How long are ocean wavelengths? (From several meters to several kilometers)

▶ What is the period of a wave? (The time it takes one wavelength to pass a given point)

**Infer** What can you infer about the wind when waves occur? (Its strength and direction)

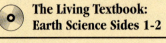

**The Living Textbook: Earth Science Sides 1-2**

Chapter 11          Frame 02188
Wave Diagram (1 Frame)
Search:

## Integrating the Sciences

**Physical Science** Point out that light and sound energy also move in waves that have the same parts as water waves. The wave height of a sound wave affects loudness; as the wave height increases, the sound becomes louder. Wavelength affects pitch; as the wavelength increases the pitch lowers. Have students look at Figure 15.14 and imagine that the wave represents a sound wave. Ask: Where is the sound loudest? (Right before the wave breaks) Where is the pitch the highest? (Right before the wave breaks)

### ▼ ACTIVITY

**Inferring**

*Wave Structure*

Look at the drawing of the wave on this page. What is the relationship of the wave's crest and trough to its wave height and wavelength?

**SKILLS WORKOUT**

**Figure 15.14**
**Ocean Waves** ▼

## Characteristics of Waves

If you watch the surface of the ocean over a period of time, you will see many waves of different sizes. The waves move in many directions. As the wind blows across the water's surface, it transfers energy to the water. When the wind is stronger, more energy is transferred. When the direction of the wind changes, it produces waves that move in a different direction.

Ocean waves begin to form far from land, in deep water. The wind blows over long distances of open ocean, causing unevenly spaced, ragged ridges of water to form. As the wave energy begins to travel through deeper water, the shape of the waves change. The waves form an even series of smooth, low hills of water called *swells*. No matter what its size or shape, an ocean wave always has certain characteristics. Study the characteristics of a wave in Figure 15.14.

Wavelengths of an ocean wave may vary from several meters up to several kilometers. The wavelength of an average swell is about 1,000 m. The time it takes one wavelength to pass a given point is called the *period* of the wave. The periods of most ocean waves range from 1 to 25 seconds.

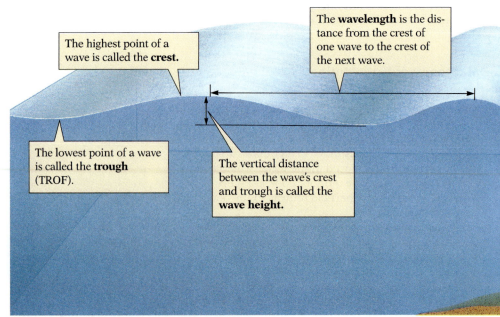

The highest point of a wave is called the **crest.**

The **wavelength** is the distance from the crest of one wave to the crest of the next wave.

The lowest point of a wave is called the **trough** (TROF).

The vertical distance between the wave's crest and trough is called the **wave height.**

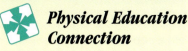

## Physical Education Connection

Surfing is popular in places with ocean shorelines where large waves break near the beach. Surfers ride a wave by standing on a surfboard at the bottom of a breaking wave. The energy of the wave pushes the surfer and the surfboard to the shore. Ask students to name other sports or water activities that use the power of breaking waves. (Students may mention boogie boarding and body surfing.)

## Wave Action and Energy

A wave that forms a series of low swells in the open ocean changes when it gets closer to shore. Study how the wave changes in Figure 15.14. Notice that the wave height increases and the wavelength decreases. These changes start when the wave reaches shallow water. When the water depth is less than one-half the wavelength, the wave energy reaches its lowest point. As the wave contacts the ocean floor, some of the wave energy transfers upward, increasing the wave height.

As the wave contacts the ocean floor, friction gradually slows down the deeper part of the wave. However, the crest of the wave keeps moving. Eventually the crest of the wave gets so far ahead that the water topples forward. The wave breaks and washes onto the shore as swirling, foaming water.

Waves carry a large amount of energy. When a wave breaks, all the energy is released against the shore. The wave energy can destroy property along a shore and disrupt boating and shipping activities. For this reason, some communities build breakwaters to slow the waves. A breakwater is a high, sloping wall built at an angle to the shore.

A breakwater forces the waves to break away from shore. Behind the breakwater, the water near the shore stays calm. The shore is protected from the destructive force of the waves. However, sand tends to build up on the side of the breakwater that faces the ocean, while the shore behind it gets narrower. Behind the breakwater, longshore currents carry sand away from the shore. The sand can't be replaced because the longshore currents can't carry sand from one side of the breakwater to the other.

After the wave breaks, the wave energy pushes water up onto the beach.

A wave's energy reaches to a depth of about one-half its wavelength. If the water is shallower than that depth, the wave will start to break.

Water from incoming waves flows back out again, causing longshore currents and undertows.

## Explore Visually

Have students study Figure 15.14. Then ask:

► What happens to the wave height and wavelength when the wave reaches shallow water? (Wave height increases and wavelength decreases.)

► What happens to a wave when the water is shallower than one-half its wavelength? (It starts to break.)

► What happens to the crest of the wave as it nears the shore? (It topples forward.)

► What happens when incoming waves flow back out? (Longshore currents and undertows form.)

► How do shells and other things from the sea end up on beaches? (Wave energy pushes the water that carries them onto the shore, and gravity pulls them down.)

## Skills Development

**Observe** Show students an aerial photograph of a major coastal U.S. port, such as New York, San Francisco, Boston, or Galveston. Have them identify breakwaters and other structures that may help protect the shore from waves.

## Enrich

Use Enrich Worksheet 15.3.

**The Living Textbook: Earth Science Side 2**

Chapter 38          Frame 14334
Waves (Movie)
Search:                    Play:

### TEACH ▪ *Continued*

#### *Explore Visually*

Have students study Figure 15.15. Then ask:

▶ How do tsunamis originate? (An earthquake moves the ocean floor.)

▶ What does a tsunami look like in deep water? (Low swells)

▶ What happens when a tsunami reaches the shore? Why? (The waves rise to great heights because the wavelength is so long.)

▶ Why are tsunamis so destructive? (Their energy is transferred to the shore.)

#### *History Connection*

One of the most devastating tsunamis in recent years occurred on May 22, 1960. The earthquake that produced the tsunamis occurred off the coast of Chile. But tsunamis struck coasts as far away as Los Angeles, California, and Honshu, Japan. The tsunamis caused millions of dollars in damage and killed hundreds of people. Have students research other major tsunamis.

#### *Art Connection*

Obtain a copy of the famous Japanese print *The Great Wave at Kanagawa.* Ask students to study the print of the tsunami, then make their own drawings or paintings of a tsunami.

### Earthquakes and Ocean Waves

The most dramatic and destructive ocean waves are not caused by the wind, but by earthquakes. An earthquake deep underground may cause part of the ocean floor to shift upward suddenly. Notice in Figure 15.15 that the motion pushes the overlying waters upward, forming a bulge of water. As the bulge of water settles back down, it sets off a series of giant waves. The giant earthquake-generated wave, called a *tsunami* (soo NAH mee), travels at speeds of over 700 km/hr.

In the open ocean, the swells of a tsunami are low, only about 0.5 m high on the surface. They can pass unnoticed under ships. Although the swells don't look very large, they carry an enormous amount of energy. A tsunami can have a wavelength of about 250 km. Recall that the energy of a wave reaches a depth of about one-half its wavelength. Therefore, the energy of a tsunami can reach 125 km beneath the ocean surface.

As tsunamis approach the shore, all the energy stored in the deep waves transfers upward. The wave heights increase dramatically, up to 30 m. Huge breakers come crashing onto shore, one after another. Tsunamis are very destructive, destroying beaches, homes, and anything else along the shore.

Predicting tsunamis is difficult. They often can't be detected until they reach shore. Monitoring earthquakes beneath the ocean floor is the only way to find out if tsunamis may be coming.

**Figure 15.15**
Earthquakes on the ocean floor set tsunamis in motion. In deep water, the waves travel easily, but when they near the shore, they rise to great heights. As they crash on shore, they can destroy property and kill people nearby. ▼

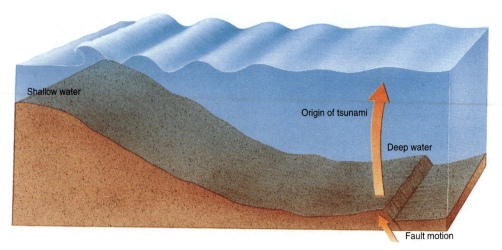

Shallow water

Origin of tsunami

Deep water

Fault motion

## *Themes in Science*

**Energy** Two waves can interact so that energy in the waves combines, resulting in one large wave with greater energy. Two waves can also interact so that the waves cancel each other, forming a smaller wave with much lower energy.

### Science and Society  *Rogue Waves*

Imagine sailing a boat through a storm. The water is choppy, the waves are high, but you are still in control of the boat. Suddenly a huge gust of wind tips the boat to one side. Then, even more suddenly, an immense wave towers above the boat and comes crashing down. The wave pushes the boat farther over. Before you can set the boat upright, a second huge wave sinks it!

This terrifying set of events actually happened to the crew of the sailing ship *Marques*. The 35-m sailing ship was sunk on June 3, 1984, with the loss of 19 of its 28 crew members. The cause of this maritime disaster wasn't just the storm winds, but a rogue wave. Rogue waves are immense waves, sometimes as large as 20 m high. They are called rogue waves because they seem to come out of nowhere, then disappear quickly.

Rogue waves can occur when two ordinary waves collide. Usually when waves collide, their crests and troughs don't "match up." What this means is that the trough of one wave meets with the crest of the other wave. The two waves partially cancel each other out, forming a smaller wave, as shown in Figure 15.16a. Occasionally, the waves do match up. The crest of one wave meets with the crest of the other. The two waves add their energy together as shown in Fig. 15.16b. A crest forms that is much higher than either of the two smaller crests. That high crest is the rogue wave. As the two waves continue to move off in different directions, the rogue wave disappears.

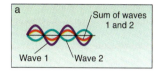

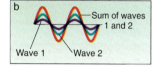

**Figure 15.16** ▲
When two waves arrive at the same point, they may combine in two different ways.

### Check and Explain

1. How do ocean waves form?

2. Name the parts of an ocean wave.

3. **Reason and Conclude** Imagine you are on the deck of a boat on a calm day. How can you determine the period of the waves passing under the boat?

4. **Define Operationally** Imagine a small piece of driftwood floating in the ocean. Describe its motion as a wave passes under it. What does this tell you about how a water particle moves as a wave passes?

## Section Objectives
For a list of section objectives, see the Student Edition page.

## Skills Objectives
Students should be able to:

**Communicate** about gravitational attraction between two objects.

**Interpret Data** to relate a new or full moon to tide fluctuations.

**Predict** how tides affect fishing.

## Vocabulary
tide, semidiurnal

## MOTIVATE

### Skills WarmUp
To help students understand tides, have them do the Skills WarmUp.
**Answer** Pictures will vary but all should show a force that each object exerts on the other.

### Misconceptions
Students may think that gravity only attracts objects toward the earth. Students who have seen daily tide patterns may find it easier to acknowledge the gravitational pull of other bodies. Point out that all masses attract each other, not just stars, moons, and planets.

### Enrich
Tell students that tidal areas support some animals that humans use as food. One example is the soft-shell crab harvested from tidal flats along the east coast of North America when the tide is out.

## Themes in Science

### Systems and Interactions
Gravity is the attracting force between two objects. The pull of the moon's gravity causes the ocean waters on the earth to rise and fall against the landmasses. Because the earth/moon system has a definite gravitational pull and pattern of movement, the action of gravity on the earth's waters is cyclic and predictable.

## ▼ ACTIVITY

### Communicating

*Gravity's Pull*
Draw a picture showing the gravitational attraction between two objects.

### SKILLS WARMUP

All areas of the world ocean pass under the moon every 24 hours and 50 minutes. The moon's gravity produces a high tide in the places directly under and opposite it.

**Figure 15.17** ▲

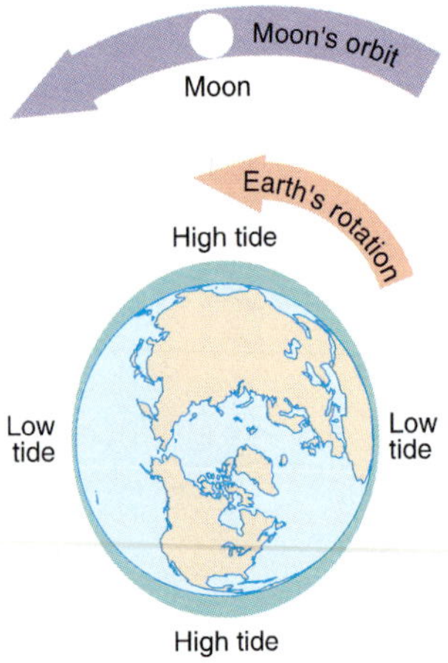

Moon's orbit

Moon

Earth's rotation

High tide

Low tide

Low tide

High tide

## 15.4  Tides

### Objectives

▶ **Describe** the effect of gravity on the earth's water.

▶ **Explain** why tides change.

▶ **Compare** and **contrast** the different types of daily tide patterns.

▶ **Predict** the effects of tides on fishing.

What happens when you jump up in the air? You come back down, of course. You come down because of the gravitational attraction between you and the earth. All matter exerts a gravitational pull on all other matter. The gravitational pull is stronger when the objects are large or close together.

### Gravity and Ocean Water

The sun and the moon are large objects that exert a gravitational pull on the earth. They exert the same amount of pull on the earth's land and water surfaces. However, liquid water shows the effects of the gravitational pull more than the solid earth. Every day, the level of the ocean surface rises and falls because of the gravitational pull of the moon and the sun. The daily changes in water level are called **tides.**

The gravitational pull of the moon on the ocean is strongest on the side of the earth nearest the moon. The ocean bulges on that side, as shown in Figure 15.17. On the opposite side from the moon, the solid earth is closer to the moon than it is to the ocean. The moon's gravity pulls the solid earth toward the moon and away from the ocean, causing a bulge. Therefore, on the opposite side of the earth, another bulge forms in the ocean. The sun's gravity also causes a bulge. But the bulge is smaller because the sun is farther away than the moon.

As the earth rotates, high tides occur in areas of the earth's surface beneath the bulges. *High tide* is the highest level that ocean water reaches on the shore. Low tides occur in areas between the bulges. *Low tide* is the lowest level that ocean water reaches on the shore.

## Themes in Science

**Energy** Two waves can interact so that energy in the waves combines, resulting in one large wave with greater energy. Two waves can also interact so that the waves cancel each other, forming a smaller wave with much lower energy.

### Science and Society *Rogue Waves*

Imagine sailing a boat through a storm. The water is choppy, the waves are high, but you are still in control of the boat. Suddenly a huge gust of wind tips the boat to one side. Then, even more suddenly, an immense wave towers above the boat and comes crashing down. The wave pushes the boat farther over. Before you can set the boat upright, a second huge wave sinks it!

This terrifying set of events actually happened to the crew of the sailing ship *Marques*. The 35-m sailing ship was sunk on June 3, 1984, with the loss of 19 of its 28 crew members. The cause of this maritime disaster wasn't just the storm winds, but a rogue wave. Rogue waves are immense waves, sometimes as large as 20 m high. They are called rogue waves because they seem to come out of nowhere, then disappear quickly.

Rogue waves can occur when two ordinary waves collide. Usually when waves collide, their crests and troughs don't "match up." What this means is that the trough of one wave meets with the crest of the other wave. The two waves partially cancel each other out, forming a smaller wave, as shown in Figure 15.16a. Occasionally, the waves do match up. The crest of one wave meets with the crest of the other. The two waves add their energy together as shown in Fig. 15.16b. A crest forms that is much higher than either of the two smaller crests. That high crest is the rogue wave. As the two waves continue to move off in different directions, the rogue wave disappears.

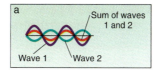

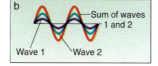

**Figure 15.16 ▲**
When two waves arrive at the same point, they may combine in two different ways.

### Check and Explain

1. How do ocean waves form?

2. Name the parts of an ocean wave.

3. **Reason and Conclude** Imagine you are on the deck of a boat on a calm day. How can you determine the period of the waves passing under the boat?

4. **Define Operationally** Imagine a small piece of driftwood floating in the ocean. Describe its motion as a wave passes under it. What does this tell you about how a water particle moves as a wave passes?

### Research

Have students use references to research other maritime disasters caused by rogue waves. What might be done to prevent such disasters?

### EVALUATE

## WrapUp

**Portfolio** Ask students to draw a series of waves and label the parts. Then have students draw and explain how waves change as they move toward the shore. Suggest that students keep the drawings in their portfolios.

Use Review Worksheet 15.3.

## Check and Explain

1. Wind blows across the water's surface and transfers energy to the water.

2. Crest, trough, wave height, and wavelength; students may include period.

3. Start timing when the boat is at the top of a swell and stop timing when the boat is on top of the next swell. Or, time how long it takes for ten waves to occur and then divide by ten.

4. The wave makes the wood rise and dip. The water particle moves in the same way and returns to the point from which it started.

**Section Objectives**

For a list of section objectives, see the Student Edition page.

**Skills Objectives**

Students should be able to:

**Communicate** about gravitational attraction between two objects.

**Interpret Data** to relate a new or full moon to tide fluctuations.

**Predict** how tides affect fishing.

**Vocabulary**

tide, semidiurnal

---

## MOTIVATE

### Skills WarmUp

To help students understand tides, have them do the Skills WarmUp.
**Answer** Pictures will vary but all should show a force that each object exerts on the other.

### Misconceptions

Students may think that gravity only attracts objects toward the earth. Students who have seen daily tide patterns may find it easier to acknowledge the gravitational pull of other bodies. Point out that all masses attract each other, not just stars, moons, and planets.

### Enrich

Tell students that tidal areas support some animals that humans use as food. One example is the soft-shell crab harvested from tidal flats along the east coast of North America when the tide is out.

**Themes in Science**

**Systems and Interactions**

Gravity is the attracting force between two objects. The pull of the moon's gravity causes the ocean waters on the earth to rise and fall against the landmasses. Because the earth/moon system has a definite gravitational pull and pattern of movement, the action of gravity on the earth's waters is cyclic and predictable.

▼ **ACTIVITY**

**Communicating**

*Gravity's Pull*

Draw a picture showing the gravitational attraction between two objects.

**SKILLS WARMUP**

## 15.4 Tides

### Objectives

▶ **Describe** the effect of gravity on the earth's water.

▶ **Explain** why tides change.

▶ **Compare** and **contrast** the different types of daily tide patterns.

▶ **Predict** the effects of tides on fishing.

**W**hat happens when you jump up in the air? You come back down, of course. You come down because of the gravitational attraction between you and the earth. All matter exerts a gravitational pull on all other matter. The gravitational pull is stronger when the objects are large or close together.

### Gravity and Ocean Water

The sun and the moon are large objects that exert a gravitational pull on the earth. They exert the same amount of pull on the earth's land and water surfaces. However, liquid water shows the effects of the gravitational pull more than the solid earth. Every day, the level of the ocean surface rises and falls because of the gravitational pull of the moon and the sun. The daily changes in water level are called **tides.**

The gravitational pull of the moon on the ocean is strongest on the side of the earth nearest the moon. The ocean bulges on that side, as shown in Figure 15.17. On the opposite side from the moon, the solid earth is closer to the moon than it is to the ocean. The moon's gravity pulls the solid earth toward the moon and away from the ocean, causing a bulge. Therefore, on the opposite side of the earth, another bulge forms in the ocean. The sun's gravity also causes a bulge. But the bulge is smaller because the sun is farther away than the moon.

As the earth rotates, high tides occur in areas of the earth's surface beneath the bulges. *High tide* is the highest level that ocean water reaches on the shore. Low tides occur in areas between the bulges. *Low tide* is the lowest level that ocean water reaches on the shore.

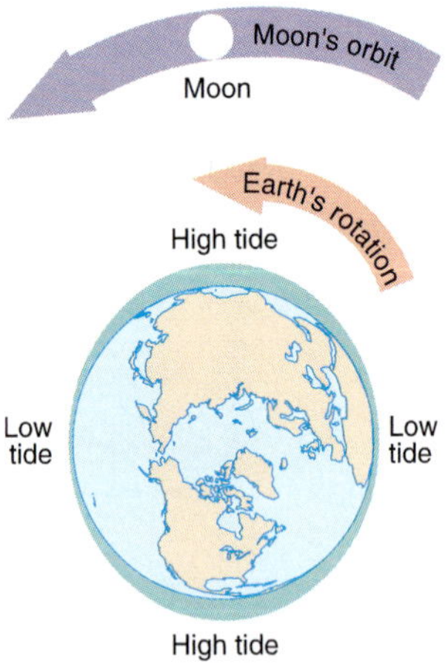

**Figure 15.17** ▲

All areas of the world ocean pass under the moon every 24 hours and 50 minutes. The moon's gravity produces a high tide in the places directly under and opposite it.

356

### Language Arts Connection

Have students look up the meaning of *diurnal* in the dictionary. (*Diurnal* means "daily.") How does the word describe diurnal tides? (Low and high tides occur once each day.) Have students define the prefix *semi-*. Then ask how this prefix modifies diurnal to describe semidiurnal tides. (*Semi-* means "half, or occurring halfway through a specified period of time." An area with semidiurnal tides has high and low tides twice every day.)

### Integrating the Sciences

**Life Science** In living things, biological clocks produce behaviors appropriate to cycles in nature. For instance, fiddler crabs become active according to the time of tides. Have students research other examples of biological clocks that adapt organisms to cycles in nature.

**Figure 15.18** ▲
In the Bay of Fundy in Canada the water level varies 15 meters between high and low tide.

### Daily Tide Patterns

Every coastal area has at least one high tide and one low tide every day. An example of extreme high and low tides occurs at the Bay of Fundy in Nova Scotia, Canada. The water level there changes drastically, as you can see in Figure 15.18.

Many factors influence daily tide patterns. The location on the earth's surface, the shape of the ocean floor and the coastline, and the Coriolis effect are some of the important factors. Tide patterns repeat every 24 hours and 50 minutes. Because a complete cycle actually takes slightly more than one day, tides occur at different times each day.

**Semidiurnal Tides** Some areas experience two high tides and two low tides each day. This pattern is known as a **semidiurnal** (SEH mee dye UR nuhl) tide pattern. The Atlantic coast of the eastern United States has a semidiurnal tide pattern.

**Diurnal Tides** Other areas have only one high tide and one low tide each day. This pattern is called a diurnal (daily) tide pattern. Diurnal tide patterns occur in the southeastern United States along the Gulf of Mexico.

**Mixed Tides** Areas such as the Pacific coast of the western United States have a mix of diurnal and semidiurnal tide patterns. Compare the daily tide patterns in the graphs in Figure 15.19. Which one is the daily tide pattern in the ocean nearest you? ①

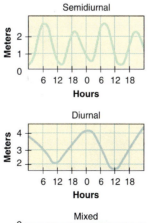

**Figure 15.19** ▲
Compare the line graphs of daily tide patterns. Which tide pattern involves the most water movement? ②

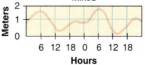

### TEACH ▪ *Continued*

### *Explore Visually*

Have students study Figure 15.20. Then ask:

▶ What daily tide cycles occur when the sun, moon, and earth line up? (Spring tides)

▶ What part of the monthly tide cycle produces neap tides? (When the moon, sun, and earth form a right angle)

▶ How much time passes between a period of spring tides and a period of neap tides? (6 to 8 days)

▶ How many times during the cycle do the sun, the moon, and the earth line up each month? (Twice)

▶ Which tides are due to combined gravity of the sun and the moon? (Spring tides)

▶ Which tides are due to gravity pulling in different directions? (Neap tides)

▶ How can you tell spring tides from neap tides on the graph? (The spring tides have longer lines between high and low tides.)

### *Themes in Science*

**Patterns of Change/Cycles** The orbit of the moon around the earth follows a regular cycle. This cycle of movement influences the patterns of the tides. Because the tides are caused by the orbiting moon, the tides also have a monthly cycle.

## Monthly Tide Cycles

The graph in Figure 15.20 shows how the tide heights vary during one month. The daily tides cycles with the greatest difference between high and low tides are called *spring tides*. The daily tides cycles with the least difference between high and low tides are called *neap tides*. Periods of spring tides and neap tides occur twice each month. The differences in tide heights are caused by the changing positions of the sun and moon.

**Figure 15.20**
**Monthly Tide Cycle** ▼

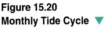

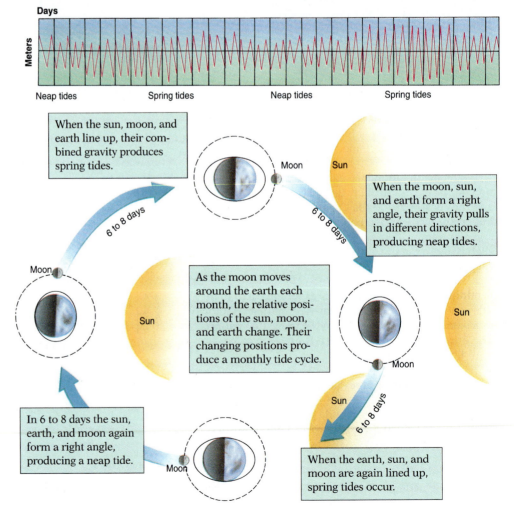

## Integrating the Sciences

**Environmental Science** Mussels and oysters live in the intertidal zone. Because these organisms accumulate pollutants, they have become important indicators for the presence of pollutants. Each year the Environmental Protection Agency collects oysters and mussels from more than 100 locations in the United States. By measuring the level of pollutants in these organisms, scientists can monitor pollution levels along the coasts of the United States.

## Tides and Living Things

Some organisms live on the shore between the level of the highest high tides and the lowest low tides. If you walk along a beach at low tide, you might see sand dollars, hermit crabs, seaweed, and other organisms. As the tides change, these organisms may be covered with ocean water or exposed to the air and sun. Some burrow in the wet sand or hide under rocks or seaweed to escape drying out.

Fishes living near shore are also affected by tides. At high tide, many fishes come closer to the shore. They feed on algae and other organisms that can't be reached at low tide. The life cycle of the grunion depends on tide cycles. Grunion swim onto the beach to spawn during the highest spring tides. They bury their eggs in the sand. The eggs develop until the next spring tide. The rising waters stimulate the eggs to hatch, and the young grunion swim out to the ocean.

**Figure 15.21** ▲
Grunions live and spawn in the warm waters off of Southern California and Baja Mexico.

## *Career Corner*  *Merchant Mariner*

### Who Moves Goods Across the Oceans?

Every time you visit a mall or supermarket, you see goods from faraway places. Clothes may come from Hong Kong, Korea, Europe, or Sri Lanka. Bananas from Costa Rica and coffee from Kenya are in many markets. How do these goods get to your hometown? Merchant ships carry all kinds of goods across the oceans. The people who operate these ships are called merchant mariners.

Some merchant mariners serve as captains and deck officers. The captain is in charge of all the ship's operations. Officers supervise navigation and ship maneuvers. Navigators estimate the ship's position and plan the route using electronic and celestial, or star, navigation. A meteorologist monitors weather conditions. Engineers, machinists, and pipe fitters maintain and repair the ship's engines and all shipboard systems. Skilled workers operate the engines and perform maintenance and repair work.

To become a merchant mariner, you need practical seagoing skills, such as boat handling and navigation. Officers and engineers need college courses in physics,

chemistry, oceanography, and electronics. Specialized maritime colleges offer further training. If you think you would like a career as a merchant mariner, you can write to the California Maritime Academy in Vallejo, California.

---

## Research

Have students use references to find out about tide pools. Have them find out what organisms live there, and how they survive the changing conditions in a tide pool.

## *Career Corner*

**Discuss** Have students answer the following questions:

▶ Which person on a ship is most concerned about currents and tides? Why? (The navigator; this person plans the route and keeps track of the ship's position on the ocean.)

▶ What types of jobs are needed to operate ships? (Captain, deck officers, navigators, meteorologists, engineers, machinists, pipe fitters, and skilled workers)

## TEACH ▪ *Continued*

### Skills WorkOut

To help students interpret data about tides, have them do the Skills WorkOut.

**Answer** Answers will vary, but students should find that either a new moon or a full moon produces higher tides.

### Skills Development

**Infer** Ask students whether a tidal power plant will generate more energy during spring tides or neap tides. Why? (Spring; more water moves over the turbines.)

## EVALUATE

### WrapUp

**Reteach** Draw a monthly tide cycle similar to the one in Figure 15.20 on the chalkboard. Have students explain the cycle of tides and why they occur.

Use Review Worksheet 15.4.

### Check and Explain

1. The gravitational pull of the sun and moon affect the ocean more than the solid earth. The moon's gravity produces high tides on the side of the earth nearest it and opposite it.

2. Because the moon takes nearly a month to orbit the earth

3. A semidiurnal pattern shows two high tides and two low tides each day; a diurnal pattern shows one high tide and one low tide each day.

4. Answers will vary. High tide carries water closer to habitation and brings fishes closer to shore. Low tide exposes tide pools.

---

### *Portfolio*

Have students list the pros and cons of using tides for an alternative energy resource. Students may want to research tidal energy further to make more informed decisions. Have students keep the lists and their research in their portfolios. When the class studies alternative energy resources in Chapter 21, have students add other energy resources to the pro and con lists in their portfolios.

**Figure 15.22** ▶
On the Rance River in France, vehicles drive on the roadway above while the tides generate electricity below.

▼ **ACTIVITY**

**Interpreting Data**

*The Moon and the Tides*

1. Every day for two weeks, look at a daily tide table in a newspaper.
2. Each day, record the time and height of the highest tide. When was the highest tide?
3. Using a calendar or almanac, find out if that day had a new moon or a full moon.

**SKILLS WORKOUT**

 **Science and Technology** *Tidal Power*

Did you know that the ocean can be an energy source? There are vast amounts of energy in ocean waves and currents. However, the most promising ocean-linked power plants use energy from tides. One such tidal power plant is located at the mouth of the Rance River in France.

At the tidal power plant, there is a huge dam across the river, as shown in Figure 15.22. Along the dam, below the water's surface, are tunnels for the water to flow through. Inside the tunnels are large spinning blades called turbines. As the tide flows in and out, the moving water turns the turbines. The spinning turbines operate generators that produce electricity. The electricity then travels to distribution stations.

The amount of electricity generated at a tidal plant varies with the amount of water that moves through the dam. The energy is available only when the turbines are turning. However, tidal power plants can help reduce the need to burn fossil fuels for generating electricity.

### Check and Explain

1. How does gravity cause tides?

2. Why do tides change over the course of a month?

3. **Compare and Contrast** What is the difference between a semidiurnal tide pattern and a diurnal tide pattern?

4. **Predict** When would a person going fishing on a beach have the best chance of catching a fish? Explain your answer.

## Check Your Vocabulary

1. tides
2. crest
3. trough
4. salinity
5. thermocline
6. current
7. estuary
8. gyre
9. Coriolis effect
10. wave height
11. wavelength
12. semidiurnal

## Write Your Vocabulary

Students' sentences should show that they know the meaning of each word as well as how to use it in a sentence.

Use Vocabulary Worksheet for Chapter 15.

# Chapter 15 Review

## Concept Summary

### 15.1 Properties of Ocean Water
▶ Ocean water contains dissolved gases, salts, and traces of different elements.
▶ The boundary between warm surface water and colder water below is a thermocline.
▶ The density of ocean water varies with temperature and salinity. Water pressure increases with depth.
▶ Organisms extract substances, like silica, from ocean water.

### 15.2 Ocean Currents
▶ The Coriolis effect bends winds and ocean currents.
▶ Wind-driven surface currents form clockwise gyres in the Northern Hemisphere and counterclockwise gyres in the Southern Hemisphere.

▶ Deep currents flow from the poles to the equator.
▶ The interaction between waves and the shoreline causes longshore currents, rip currents, and undertows.

### 15.3 Ocean Waves
▶ Wind friction produces surface waves.
▶ Ocean waves have a crest, trough, wave height, and wavelength.
▶ Earthquakes on the ocean floor cause giant waves called tsunamis.

### 15.4 Tides
▶ The gravitational pull of the sun and moon causes tides.
▶ The changing positions of the earth, sun, and moon result in a monthly cycle of spring tides and neap tides.

### Chapter Vocabulary

salinity (15.1)  current (15.2)  crest (15.3)  wavelength (15.3)
estuary (15.1)  Coriolis effect (15.2)  trough (15.3)  tide (15.4)
thermocline (15.1)  gyre (15.2)  wave height (15.3)  semidiurnal (15.4)

## Check Your Vocabulary

Use the vocabulary words above to complete the following sentences correctly.

1. Daily changes in water level caused by gravitational pull are called ____ .
2. The highest part of a wave is its ____ .
3. The lowest part of a wave is its ____ .
4. The number of grams of salts per kilogram of ocean water is ____ .
5. As you move deeper in the water column, a ____ , or zone of rapid temperature change, occurs.
6. A flow of water moving through the ocean is a(n) ____ .
7. A bay or inlet where a river enters the ocean is a(n) ____ .

8. The clockwise or counterclockwise flow of surface currents forms a ____ .
9. The bending of ocean currents by the earth's rotation is called the ____ .
10. The distance between the highest and lowest points of a wave is the ____ .
11. The horizontal distance from one wave crest to the next is the wave's ____ .
12. A ____ tide pattern has two low tides and two high tides each day.

## Write Your Vocabulary

Write sentences using the vocabulary words above. Show that you know what each word means.

## Check Your Knowledge

1. Water vapor from erupting volcanoes condensed and collected in basins

2. Dissolved salts enter the oceans from rivers. Some of the water evaporates, leaving the salts behind. Gradually, the amount of dissolved salt increases as more water enters and evaporates, leaving salt behind.

3. It forms because warm surface water floats on top of colder water below.

4. Three physical properties of ocean water are temperature, density, and pressure.

5. Cold water is denser because its molecules pack more tightly together than those of warmer water. High-salinity water is denser because of the larger quantity of dissolved salts in a given volume of water.

6. Water pressure increases.

7. The Coriolis force is the force between the rotating earth and the fluids (water and air) that flow on and above it. This force bends the surface currents in oceans and the wind currents in the atmosphere.

8. Surface currents are driven by winds blowing over the ocean. Deep currents are driven by density differences between cooler and warmer water.

9. A rip current is a powerful outward stream of water flowing at a right angle to the shore. An undertow forms when water carried in by a wave runs back off the beach into the ocean.

10. Tides are caused by the gravitational pull of the moon and sun.

11. False; greater
12. True
13. False; low
14. True
15. False; less
16. True

## Check Your Understanding

1. Salinity varies by region depending on the presence of estuaries, the evaporation rate, amount of rainfall, and water temperature.

2. Waves form as wind transfers energy to the water. Waves travel as water molecules transfer this energy from one to another.

3. Because a rip current is narrow, a swimmer can escape one by swimming parallel to the shore.

4. A breakwater prevents sand from being deposited on the beach as quickly as it is swept out to sea by longshore currents.

5. Answers will vary depending on location. Encourage students to look at the nearest coastal area, even if it is not nearby.

6. a. The wave in the picture has already broken, so the water is less than one-half the wavelength deep.

   b. Friction between the ocean floor and the bottom layer of water slows this layer down while the top layer continues at a faster speed, causing the wave to curl.

   c. Waves can create longshore and rip currents.

7. Answers will vary. People may believe that sea salt is healthier because it is more "natural" than refined salt with additives.

8. The water rising to the surface in an upwelling zone carries dissolved nutrients and small organisms from the depths of the ocean. This nutrient-rich water can support large populations of fish.

9. At a depth of 20 m, one would probably not be affected by surface waves.

---

## Chapter 15 Review

### Check Your Knowledge

Answer the following in complete sentences.

1. How did the oceans form?

2. Why is ocean water salty?

3. How does a thermocline form?

4. What are three physical properties of ocean water?

5. Which is denser, cold water or warm water? High-salinity water or low-salinity water? Explain.

6. What happens to water pressure as you go deeper into the water column?

7. What is the Coriolis force? How does it affect the ocean's surface currents?

8. How do deep ocean currents differ from surface currents?

9. What is a rip current? How is it different from an undertow?

10. What causes tides?

Determine whether each statement is true or false. Write *true* if it is true. If it is false, change the underlined word to make the statement true.

11. The water pressure at a depth of 600 m is <u>less</u> than at a depth of 60 m.

12. The water in an estuary has <u>lower</u> salinity than most ocean water.

13. A tsunami forms <u>high</u> wave crests as it travels across the open ocean.

14. In the Northern Hemisphere, surface currents form <u>clockwise</u> gyres.

15. Warm water is more dense than cold water.

16. In areas of upwelling, <u>cold</u> water rises to the surface.

### Check Your Understanding

Apply the concepts you have learned to answer each question.

1. Why do some parts of the world ocean have higher salinity than other parts?

2. Explain how an ocean wave forms and travels.

3. **Application** What should a swimmer who is caught in a rip current do to get back to the shore? Explain.

4. **Critical Thinking** In some beach communities with large breakwaters, the beach has virtually disappeared. Why?

5. **Extension** What type of daily tide pattern occurs in the coastal areas nearest your home? Describe what happens to the water level there during one day.

6. **Mystery Photo** The photograph on page 338 shows a breaking ocean wave. Study the photograph, and answer the following questions.

   a. What do you think the water depth is like where the picture was taken? Explain.

   b. Why does the water move the way it does?

   c. What kinds of currents can be caused by the wave?

7. **Application** Some people think sea salt from evaporating ocean water is more healthy than salt from chemical means. Why might they think this?

8. **Application** Why are the world's most productive fishing areas in upwelling zones?

9. **Extension** Imagine you are scuba diving 20 m beneath the ocean surface. How would the ocean's wave action affect you?

## Develop Your Skills

**1. a.** Spring tides occurred around the 14th and the 30th; neap tides occurred around the 7th and the 23rd.

**b.** This location has mixed diurnal tides, and may be located along the Pacific coast of the United States.

**2.** In the summer, the surface layer of the ocean is heated more, creating a greater temperature difference with deeper water.

**3.** A fish would be able to find more food near the surface because microorganisms depend, either directly or indirectly, on the sun for survival. A possible experiment could involve sampling water at various depths and counting the number of microorganisms in a given volume of water.

**4.** Accept any reasonable model. For example, one could hang a smooth spherical object from a string, put several drops of vegetable oil on the object, start the object spinning, and watch the path of the oil as it runs down the spinning object.

**5. a.** Sunday-noon, Monday-12:35 P.M., Tuesday-1:58 A.M., Wednesday-2:25 A.M., Thursday-2:56 A.M., Friday-3:31 A.M., Saturday-4:12 A.M.

**b.** Sunday-6:25 P.M., Monday-6:54 P.M., Tuesday-7:23 P.M., Wednesday-7:54 P.M., Thursday-8:27 P.M. and 8:58 A.M., Friday-10:01 A.M., Saturday-11:07 A.M.

**c.** Because the position of the moon changes each day

## Make Connections

**1.**

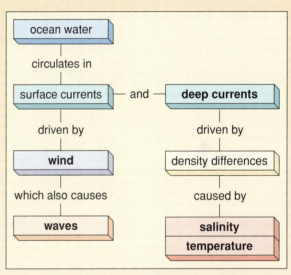

**2.** Student reports will vary. Students should find that trade routes paralleled ocean currents and prevailing winds.

**3.** If your school is located away from a coastal area, students will have to look at an out-of-town newspaper for this information.

**4.** Water can be desalinated by evaporation or by a process called reverse osmosis, in which pressure is exerted on contained salt water to force fresh water through a membrane, leaving behind the dissolved salts.

---

### Develop Your Skills

Use the skills you have developed in this chapter to complete each activity.

**1. Interpret Data** The graph below shows the tidal cycle in one U.S. location for the month of November.

   **a.** On which days of the month did spring tides occur? On which days did neap tides occur?

   **b.** What type of daily tide pattern does the place have? Where is it likely to be located?

```
Meters  2
        1
        0
           2  4  6  8  10 12 14 16 18 20 22 24 26 28 30
          1  3  5  7  9 11 13 15 17 19 21 23 25 27 29
                        November
```

**2. Infer** Thermoclines form more often in summer than in winter. Why?

**3. Hypothesize** Think about conditions near the ocean surface and deep underwater. Where do you think a fish living in the ocean would be able to find more food? Describe a possible experiment to test your hypothesis.

**4. Make a Model** Describe how to use a basketball, globe, or other spherical object to demonstrate the Coriolis effect.

**5. Data Bank** Use the information on page 616 to answer the following questions.

   **a.** At what times do high tides occur each day?

   **b.** At what times do low tides occur each day?

   **c.** Why are the times different each day?

### Make Connections

**1. Link the Concepts** Below is a concept map showing how some of the main concepts in this chapter link together. Only part of the map is filled in. Complete the map, using words and ideas from the chapter.

**2. Science and Social Studies** Ocean currents were very important in determining trade routes and ports of call for sailing ships. Do library research on sailing ships and the routes they traveled. Make a poster comparing the trade routes and ocean surface currents.

**3. Science and Math** Look up the tide times and heights from newspaper listings for the past month. Construct a bar graph showing the high-tide and low-tide heights for each day. Describe the patterns you find.

**4. Science and Technology** Do library research on methods of desalinating ocean water. Write a report comparing the different methods.

## Overview

Chapter 16 discusses ocean basins. The first section begins with the tools, methods, and purposes of ocean exploration. The next section describes ocean floor topography, including continental margins, trenches, and ridges. The final section explores life zones in the ocean and closes the chapter with a discussion of how materials from the ocean are used by people.

## Advance Planner

▶ Provide plastic bottles and droppers for TE page 367.

▶ Gather pebbles, pans, and an opaque liquid or dark-colored water for SE page 368.

▶ Collect modeling clay, straws, butter knives, scissors, and waxed paper for SE Activity 16, page 371.

▶ Obtain a map or globe of the world that displays ocean floor topography for TE page 373 and 375.

▶ Provide glasses and a thermometer for TE page 379.

▶ Gather diatomaceous earth for TE page 384.

## Skills Development Chart

| Sections | Compare/Contrast | Hypothesize | Infer | Make a Graph | Make a Model | Reason/Conclude |
|---|---|---|---|---|---|---|
| **16.1** Skills WarmUp | | | | | | ● |
| Skills WorkOut | | ● | | | | |
| Historical Notebook | | | | | | ● |
| Activity 16 | | | ● | | ● | |
| **16.2** Skills WarmUp | | | ● | | | |
| Skills WorkOut | | | | | ● | |
| SkillBuilder | | | | ● | | |
| **16.3** Skills WarmUp | ● | | | | | |
| Skills WorkOut | | | | ● | | |

## Individual Needs

▶ **Limited English Proficiency Students** Ask students to work in groups to write a simple travelogue describing what they would see in a journey in a submersible like Alvin. Their journey should cross continental margins and ocean floor features. A travelogue might describe some horizontal and vertical life zones. Encourage them to define the chapter vocabulary and write clear sentences in their travelogues. Group members can each record a different part of their travelogue and use the tape to review chapter concepts.

▶ **At-Risk Students** Encourage students to work in groups to plan an underwater photographic safari. Have groups start by making a list of the different environments that exist in the ocean. Then have them list what kinds of life they would expect to find and photograph in these conditions. Finally, ask them to list or draw the equipment they would like to take with them.

▶ **Gifted Students** Invite students to learn more about how humans have changed the ocean through their travels on it and their use of its resources. Ask them to prepare a state-of-the-oceans report describing present pollution, over-fishing, and other threats to the ocean and its life. Then have them explain why cleaning up the ocean and safeguarding its life forms is important. Finally, challenge them to create a plan that will do these things. Have them present their reports and plans orally to the class.

## Resource Bank

▶ **Bulletin Board** Title the bulletin board *Ocean Occupations.* Attach pictures of people engaged in various occupations that involve the ocean and its resources. Invite students to provide labels and captions identifying and describing these occupations and the training needed for them. Encourage students to add additional examples of such occupations.

▶ **Field Trip** Take the class on a field trip to an aquarium or a pet store that sells saltwater organisms. Encourage students to make inferences and ask questions about what areas and life zones these organisms come from and how they are adapted for life in their part of the ocean.

| Section | Core | Standard | Enriched | Section | Core | Standard | Enriched |
|---|---|---|---|---|---|---|---|
| **16.1 Ocean Exploration** pp. 365–371 | | | | **Overhead Blackline Transparencies** Overhead Blackline Master 16.2 and Student Worksheet | ● | ● | ● |
| **Section Features** Skills WarmUp, p. 365 Skills WorkOut, p. 368 Historical Notebook, p. 369 Activity, p. 371 | ● ● | ● ● ● ● | ● ● ● ● | **Laboratory Program** Investigation 25 | ● | ● | |
| **Blackline Masters** Review Worksheet 16.1 Skills Worksheet 16.1 Integrating Worksheet 16.1 | ● ● ● | ● ● ● | ● | **Color Transparencies** Transparencies 46a, 46b | ● | ● | ● |
| **16.2 Ocean Floor Topography** pp. 372–378 | | | | **16.3 Life Zones in the Oceans** pp. 379–384 | | | |
| **Section Features** Skills WarmUp, p. 372 Skills WorkOut, p. 377 SkillBuilder, p. 377 | ● ● | ● ● ● | ● ● | **Section Features** Skills WarmUp, p. 379 Skills WorkOut, p. 382 | ● ● | ● ● | ● |
| **Blackline Masters** Review Worksheet 16.2 Reteach Worksheet 16.2 Skills Worksheet 16.2 | ● ● ● | ● ● ● | ● ● | **Blackline Masters** Review Worksheet 16.3 Integrating Worksheet 16.3 Vocabulary Worksheet 16.3 | ● ● ● | ● ● ● | ● ● ● |
| | | | | **Ancillary Options** *One-Minute Readings,* pp. 64, 65, 66–67 | ● | ● | ● |
| | | | | **Color Transparencies** Transparencies 47, 48 | ● | ● | ● |

# Bibliography

The following resources can be used for teaching the chapter. See page T–46 for supplier codes.

**Library Resources**

Carson, Rachel. *The Sea Around Us.* Racine, WI: Golden Press, 1958.

Cox, Vic. *Ocean Life: Beneath the Crystal Seas.* New York: BDD Promotional Book Company, Inc., 1990.

Pope, Joyce. *Seashores.* Mahwah, NJ: Troll Associates, 1990.

**Technology Resources**

*Internet*

**PLANETDIARY** at *http://www.planetdiary.com*
- Find out more about volcanoes by exploring *Volcano*; first, click on *Phenomena Backgrounders.*
- Discover more about oceanic organisms in *Fauna* and *Flora* by clicking on *Phenomena Backgrounders.*

*Software*

Oceans. Mac, Dos, Win. ER.
Oceans Below. Mac, Win. ER.
Undersea Adventure. Mac, Win, Win 95. ER.

*CD-ROMs*

Interactive Earth. SFAW.

*Laserdiscs*

Living Textbook. (See barcodes on pages in this chapter.) Optical Data.

*Videos*

Discovering Our Rivers, Lakes, and Oceans. 30 min. MMI.
The Living Ocean. 25 min. 1985. NGSES.
Physical Oceanography. CABISCO.

**Audio-Visual Resources**

Challenge of the Oceans. Film. CRM.
Earth Beneath the Sea. Film. CRM.

 *Writing Connection*

In Roman mythology, Neptune ruled over the oceans of the earth. When Neptune was angry, he caused great storms that sank ships and flooded coastal towns. His favorite pet was the dolphin, whom he kept safe from harm. Have students invent and write about their own mythical ruler of the ocean. Students might consider using the animal shown in the photograph as their ruler's favorite pet.

## ◆ Introducing the Chapter

Have students read the description of the photograph. Ask if they agree or disagree with the description.

### Directed Inquiry

Have students study the photograph. Ask:

▶ How would you describe the image in this photograph? (Answers will vary. Students may say that it looks like a transparent flower with glowing lines. They may realize that the green areas are seaweed and the transparent object is a kind of jellyfish.)

▶ What are some unusual features of the jellyfish shown in the photograph? (Its transparency, luminous glow, and jelly-like body)

▶ How might these features help this organism survive? (Students may suggest that being transparent could help it elude predators; the glow might attract food; its jelly-like body could resist changes in water pressure.)

▶ How does the photograph relate to ocean basins? (It shows organisms that are adapted to living in the ocean.)

## ◆ Chapter Vocabulary

| | |
|---|---|
| abyssal plains | habitat |
| benthos | littoral zone |
| continental rise | nekton |
| continental shelf | neritic zone |
| continental slope | plankton |
| ecosystem | seamount |

Chapter **16**  Ocean Basins

### Chapter Sections

**16.1** Ocean Exploration

**16.2** Ocean-Floor Topography

**16.3** Life Zones in the Oceans

### What do you see?

❝I see an organism that is transparent and is outlined by a white zipper-like line. I think it might be some kind of squid or jellyfish. I think it lives in the ocean because it looks like it is surrounded by some seaweed. It is clear so it can hide from predators.❞

*Peter Wu*
*Parkhill Jr. High School*
*Dallas, Texas*

To find out more about the photograph, look on page 386. As you read this chapter, you will learn about the ocean basins and the kinds of organisms that live in oceans.

## Social Studies Connection

Learning about the earth's oceans has aided technology. A submarine transatlantic telegraph cable was successfully laid between Newfoundland and Ireland in 1866. It marked the start of rapid communication across the sea. After four failed attempts over 12 year's time, American Cyrus W. Field finally laid the cable, using the British steamship the *Great Eastern*. By 1900, 15 transatlantic cables crossed the ocean floor.

The third attempt, conducted in August of 1958, was briefly successful. The laying of this cable enabled the first transatlantic telegraph message to be sent. However, after one month, this cable also failed.

**Section Objectives**
For a list of section objectives, see the Student Edition page.

**Skills Objectives**
Students should be able to:

**Reason and Conclude** why ocean basins remain largely unexplored.

**Hypothesize** a method of underwater mapping.

**Evaluate Sources** of information gathered by different research vessels.

**Model** a core sample.

# 16.1 Ocean Exploration

## Objectives

▶ **Give examples** of two oceanic research vessels.

▶ **Describe** five tools and methods used to study the oceans and the ocean floor.

▶ **Infer** how to make a bathymetric map.

▼ **ACTIVITY**

**Reasoning**

*Ocean Basin Property*
The earth's ocean basins have been called the "last frontier on this planet." Make a list of possible reasons.

**SKILLS WARMUP**

I magine trying to figure out what's at the bottom of a sealed box. How can you find out what's there if you can't see inside the box? About 70 percent of the earth's surface is somewhat like the sealed box. That part of the earth's surface is covered by a deep layer of ocean water. For hundreds of years, scientists have searched for ways to learn more about the part of the earth's surface beneath the oceans.

## Oceanic Research Vessels

Until about 120 years ago, most information about the oceans came from people involved in fishing or trade. Their knowledge was mostly practical, having to do with navigation. Then, in 1872, the research vessel HMS *Challenger* began a 127 500-km voyage to study the world ocean. The voyage lasted three years. Scientists measured the depths of the ocean with long, weighted ropes. They observed currents, measured ocean temperatures, and collected samples of sediments and living organisms. The *Challenger's* data filled 50 large books!

Later, other research vessels were launched. In 1925, the *Meteor* began a two-year voyage to study currents in the Atlantic Ocean. Scientists measured water temperature and salinity. They also used sound waves to measure ocean depths. In 1968, the *Glomar Challenger* began a series of very successful voyages over a 15-year period. *Glomar Challenger* carried drilling equipment to collect samples of ocean-floor crust and sediments. The *JOIDES Resolution*, launched in 1985, continues the work today. Scientists use many other research vessels to learn about ocean life.

**Figure 16.1** ▲
What can scientists learn by studying the ocean? ①

**MOTIVATE**

## Skills WarmUp
To help students understand the importance of ocean exploration, have them do the Skills WarmUp.
**Answer** Answers will vary. Students may suggest that the oceans have remained relatively unexplored because they are so vast, so deep, or dangerous.

**TEACH**

## Discuss
Have students brainstorm about the benefits of ocean exploration.

**Answer to In-Text Question**
① **Scientists study many things including winds, wave heights, currents, weather patterns, and ocean depths.**

🔘 **The Living Textbook: Earth Science Sides 1-2**

Chapter 24          Frame 03165
Glomar Challenger (3 Frames)
Search:                    Step:

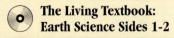

## TEACH ▪ Continued

### Directed Inquiry

After students study the text and pictures, ask the following questions:

▶ Describe a map of the ocean floor made with sonar. (It shows the topography of the ocean floor.)

▶ What equipment on a submersible enables scientists to observe the ocean floor? (Cameras, lights, robot arms, observation windows)

▶ What information could a submersible collect? (Information about organisms in deep oceans, ocean floor topography, and activity along tectonic plates)

▶ What information do satellites provide and how is it presented? (Data about water temperatures, currents, and surface heights; ocean life is translated into maps and photographs.)

### Integrated Learning

Use Integrating Worksheet 16.1.

**The Living Textbook:
Earth Science Sides 1-2**

Chapter 24          Frame 03169
Coring (6 Frames)
Search:          Step:

**The Living Textbook:
Earth Science Sides 1-2**

Chapter 24          Frame 03175
Sonar Plotters (1 Frame)
Search:

---

## Integrating the Sciences

**Physical Science**   Sound travels through different mediums at different speeds. Sound travels through ocean water at a speed of 1,500 m/s, through fresh water at a speed of 1,497 m/s, through air at 346 m/s, and through aluminum at 5,000 m/s. Ask students to consider why sound travels at such varying speeds. (Sound travels fastest through substances that have a tightly packed molecular structure. Sound travels much faster in aluminum than in air, because aluminum molecules are closer together than air molecules.)

---

## Tools and Methods of Ocean Research

As tools and methods have improved, people have learned more about the oceans. For example, you can measure ocean depth more accurately with sound waves than with a weighted rope. One older way of studying the ocean floor, called scraping, is still used today. Scraping involves dragging a heavy object, called a dredge, along the ocean floor. The dredge picks up loose rocks, sediments, and bottom-dwelling organisms. The samples are raised to the surface for study. Some modern tools and methods used to gather data about the deep ocean and the ocean floor are described here.

**Coring**

In coring, a ship uses a drilling rig to drive long metal tubes down into the ocean floor. The tubes fill up with layers of sediment and rock. Aboard ship, the layers are removed as a long cylindrical sample called a core. Cores as long as 1,500 m have been obtained. A core sample provides data about the age and composition of the ocean floor. Core samples have been collected from all parts of the ocean floor, even the deepest trenches. ▼

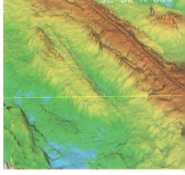

**Sonar ▲**

Sonar uses sound waves to map the ocean floor. A transmitter on a ship sends a sound wave toward the ocean floor. The sound wave reflects off the ocean bottom back to a receiver on the ship. Scientists know how fast sound travels through ocean water. By measuring the time it takes the sound wave to make one round trip, they can determine the depth of the ocean.

With modern tools and methods, the type and amount of data that can be collected have increased greatly. Satellites make it possible to survey conditions over the entire ocean surface several times each day. In a submersible (suhb MUR suh buhl), scientists can travel to the deep ocean bottom and make direct observations. Remote-controlled submersibles collect data even more efficiently and at less cost.

### Submersibles

◀ Submersibles are underwater research vessels. All submersibles are designed to withstand the tremendous pressure of ocean water deep below the surface. Submersibles carry cameras and scientific instruments. One type of submersible is shown in the photograph. It is operated by remote control from the surface. Others are piloted by people who make direct observations.

### Satellites

In 1978, a satellite ▶ named *Seasat* was launched to study the oceans from space. *Seasat* orbited the earth for about three months. *Seasat* used electronic instruments to collect data about water temperatures, currents, surface heights, and ocean life. The data were transmitted to receiving stations on the earth's surface. Computers translated the data into photographs and very accurate maps.

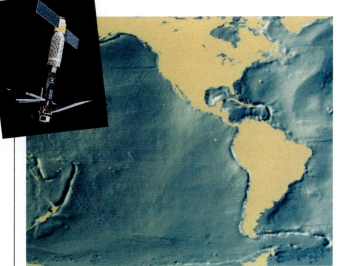

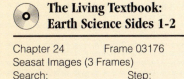

## TEACH ▪ *Continued*

### Skills WorkOut

In order to help students understand ocean floor mapping, have them do the Skills WorkOut.

**Answer** Answers will vary. For example, use a pipe cleaner or stick to probe the liquid. By observing how much of the pipe cleaner is submersed, students can infer the depth of the liquid.

### Skills Development

**Compare and Contrast** Give students topographic and bathymetric maps to study. Ask them to indicate the highest and lowest points on each one. Then have students list the similarities and differences between the maps. Ask them which map they think would be easier to make and why.

### Enrich

Have students research the origin of the measurement *fathom*. Then demonstrate a fathom for the class, and tell how it was used to determine ocean depths. (The fingertip to fingertip arm span of an average height man is a fathom, about 1.8 m. Ropes or cables bore knots a fathom apart. These ropes were cast into the ocean, the length noted, and the rope retrieved.) Have students compute the depth of the ocean at "Full fathoms five. . . ." (About 30 feet or 9 meters)

### Answer to In-Text Question

① **Bathymetric maps and topographic maps look similar. Contour lines on a bathymetric map indicate depth instead of height.**

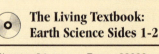

**The Living Textbook: Earth Science Sides 1-2**

Chapter 24     Frame 03090
Bathymetry Diagrams (4 Frames)
Search:        Step:

368

---

### *Language Arts Connection*

Have students use a dictionary to look up the Greek origin of the words *bathymetric* and *isobar*. To obtain a clear understanding of each word, students should find the origin for each of the following: *bathy-*, *metric*, *iso-*, and *isobath*.

(*Bathy-* comes from *bathys*, meaning "deep"; *metric* comes from *metry*, meaning "measure"; *iso-* comes from *isos*, meaning "equal"; and *-bath*, in the word *isobath*, comes from *bathos*, meaning "depth.")

---

### ▼ ACTIVITY

#### Hypothesizing

*Can't See a Thing*

**1.** Place pebbles in a pattern in the bottom of a pan.
**2.** Cover the pebbles with an opaque liquid, such as tempera paint or dark-colored water.
**3.** Hypothesize about how someone could determine the pattern of the pebbles without draining the pan.
**4.** Test your hypothesis.

### SKILLS WORKOUT

**Figure 16.2**
How does this bathymetric map compare to a topographic map?
▼ ①

### Mapping the Ocean Floor

Although the ocean floor is more than 70 percent of the earth's surface, it has been the last part to be mapped. For a long time, the overlying water made mapping extremely difficult. Some of the ocean floor is covered by a layer of water more than 10 000 m deep!

One of the first maps of the ocean floor was made by Matthew Fontaine Maury, a United States naval officer. He gathered data about winds, tides, currents, and ocean depths from mariners in different parts of the world. In 1855, he used this information to construct a simple topographic map of the floor of the North Atlantic Ocean. Recall that a topographic map uses contour lines to show surface shapes and elevations. A topographic map of the ocean floor is called a *bathymetric* (BATH uh MEHT trihk) map. Study the bathymetric map in Figure 16.2. Each contour line on a bathymetric map is called an *isobath* (EYE soh bath).

To determine the shape of the ocean floor, mapmakers needed depth measurements from many different locations. The weighted-rope method of measuring depth, called depth sounding, was not very good for mapmaking. Depth sounding was only effective in somewhat shallow waters. Also, depth sounding was slow. It took several months to measure just a small area of the ocean floor.

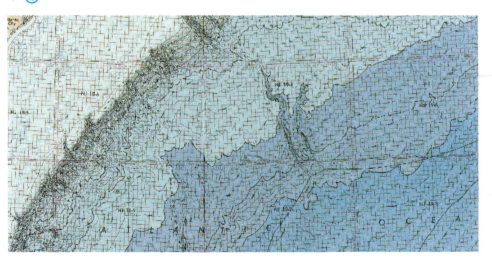

## Integrating the Sciences

**Life Science**  Most organisms get energy directly or indirectly from sunlight. However, organisms living at great ocean depths do not receive sunlight. Some of these organisms get energy from chemicals in hot water vents. The most prominent chemical is hydrogen sulfide. Many species of bacteria use hydrogen sulfide to build organic molecules. These bacteria are consumed by other organisms in the hydrothermal community.

## Answer to Link

A heightened sense of hearing would enable you to distinguish the changes in the sound of echoes as you move closer to or away from objects. This ability would help you to navigate a room without the use of your sight.

---

In 1925, scientists aboard the research vessel *Meteor* measured the depth of the ocean with sonar. Sonar enabled them to measure the ocean's depth continuously as the ship moved. They made a detailed record of how the depth changed as the ship moved over a wide area. They used the depth records to make a map of the shape of the ocean floor.

The launching of *Seasat* in 1978 introduced an even more efficient mapping technique. *Seasat* carried a device called a radar altimeter. The radar altimeter measured the distance between the satellite and the ocean surface within 10 cm. The data showed that the height of the ocean surface varied with the shape of the ocean floor beneath it. The surface height above an ocean trench was lower than the surface height above an underwater mountain. The differences in ocean surface height provided new information for more complete maps of the ocean floor.

### Life Science
### L I N K

Obtain a blindfold and a large sheet of cardboard.
**1.** Have a partner blindfold you.
**2.** Your partner then holds the cardboard at head level some distance in front of you.
**3.** Slowly, move forward making sounds in the direction of your partner.
Depending on your echo, determine when to stop before touching the cardboard.
How would a heightened sense of hearing help you in a darkened room?

### A C T I V I T Y

---

## Historical Notebook

### Life on the Ocean Floor

For many years, people thought the bottom of the deep ocean was a barren and lifeless desert. It was thought to be lifeless because of the lack of sunlight. However, this hypothesis turned out to be incorrect. In 1977, scientists discovered life on the Pacific Ocean floor at a depth of 2,500 m. In 1985, life was discovered at depths below 3,600 m on the Atlantic Ocean floor. These organisms were found along the mid-Atlantic Ridge by cameras lowered from vessels on the ocean surface.

Organisms on the deep ocean floor do not use energy from sunlight to survive. Instead, they use chemical energy from sulfur-rich water. The sulfur-rich water streams from vents in the ocean floor. Water temperatures near some Pacific Ocean vents ranged between 8° and 12°C. The normal bottom water temperature at these depths is about 2°C.

Living near the vents on the Atlantic Ocean floor were worms, anemones, fast-moving shrimps, crabs, and fishes up to 25 cm long. One vent was named the Snake Pit. This vent supported organisms like those listed above, as well as snakelike swimming animals that were about 30 to 60 cm long. Near the Pacific Ocean vents, scientists found tube worms over 1 m long, large mussels, white crabs, and some giant clams up to 25 cm long.

1. Why did scientists think that life couldn't exist on the ocean floor?

2. How do ocean-floor organisms stay alive without sunlight?

3. **Research**  Do library research to find out what organisms live on the Pacific Ocean floor. Compare them to the organisms on the Atlantic Ocean floor. How are they the same? How do they differ?

---

## Directed Inquiry

After students study pages 368 and 369, ask the following questions:

▶ What information did researchers need to relate the *Seasat* data to ocean depths? Explain. (Only the distance from the satellite to the water's surface; ocean floor depths correspond proportionally to the water's height.)

▶ How can varying ocean surface heights be used to map the ocean floor? (By comparing surface heights and known depths, researchers discovered a relationship between the two measurements. This allows surface height to be used as an indicator of depth for locations of unknown depth.)

## Historical Notebook

**Reason and Conclude**  Ask students to explain why retrieving live samples from the ocean floor is difficult. (Organisms adapted to live near vents are accustomed to warm water and great pressures. The change in temperature and pressure necessary to bring organisms to the surface may destroy them.)

**Answers**
1. Researchers thought that all living organisms required energy from the sun. No sunlight reaches the ocean floor.

2. Ocean-floor organisms derive energy from the chemical energy in sulfur-rich water.

3. Answers will vary with individual research.

**The Living Textbook: Earth Science Sides 1-2**

Chapter 24          Frame 03180
Altimeter Readings (4 Frames)
Search:                  Step:

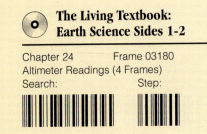

## Cooperative Learning

Have students work in cooperative groups of two or three to design their own deep ocean floor research vessel. Make sure the students consider the following factors in their designs: great water pressure, extreme temperatures, little or no light, sample collection, and data gathering. Students may want to draw or build models of their research vessels. Student volunteers can present their models to the class.

# EVALUATE

## WrapUp

**Reteach** Have students describe each of the four current technologies for exploring the ocean. Ask them to classify the method as direct or indirect observation. Have them draw an example of the data collected by each method. (Coring: direct; sonar, submersibles, and satellites: indirect; check student drawing for accuracy.)

Use Review Worksheet 16.1.

## Check and Explain

1. Answers will vary, but students should describe two of the following: the 1872–1875 *HMS Challenger* voyage; the 1925–1927 *Meteor* voyage; the *Glomar Challenger* voyage; the current *JOIDES Resolution* voyage.

2. Coring extracts an intact portion of the ocean floor; sonar measures the depth of the ocean; satellites collect data about water temperatures, currents, and surface heights; submersibles collect pictures, videos, and samples from ocean depths; scraping collects ocean floor rocks, sediments, and organisms.

3. The *Meteor*, because they rely on the reflection of sound waves and are probably more accurate; measurements from the *HMS Challenger* are more subject to human error.

4. A bathymetric map could be plotted by measuring the proportional differences in gravitational force over an ocean region.

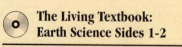

**The Living Textbook: Earth Science Sides 1-2**

Chapter 24          Frame 03039
ALVIN Images (31 Frames)
Search:                    Step:

370

## Science and Technology
### *Alvin, Jason, and ABE*

Imagine you had never seen any of the earth's land surfaces. Could you describe them using only topographic maps, satellite images, rocks, and soil samples? For many years, descriptions of the ocean floor were based on such indirect observations.

Submersibles make it possible for scientists to directly observe the deep ocean floor. Submersibles called *bathyscaphs* (BATH ih skafs) are like small submarines. The bathyscaph *Alvin* has made more than 1,600 dives. While exploring the East Pacific Rise, scientists aboard *Alvin* discovered geyserlike vents in the ocean floor. Streams of hot, mineral-rich water flowed from the vents. The earth's mantle heated the water to more than 350°C.

The most promising tools for exploring the deep sea are robotic submersibles. For example, *Jason* is an underwater robot equipped with video cameras, computers, and manipulator arms. Another robot, *ABE*, can be programmed to explore an area on its own. *ABE*, also called the *Autonomous Benthic Explorer*, can collect data more than 6 km under the water for up to one year.

**Figure 16.3** ▲
*Alvin* returns from one of its many dives.

## Check and Explain

1. Describe the voyages of two oceanic research vessels.

2. What are five tools and methods used to study the oceans and the ocean floor? Describe the kind of information each tool or method provides.

3. **Evaluate Sources** Which would you consider more accurate and reliable, a bathymetric map drawn from information gathered by HMS *Challenger,* or one drawn from information gathered by the ship *Meteor*? Give reasons for your answer.

4. **Infer** The earth's gravitational force is slightly stronger in the region of an ocean trench than it is near an oceanic mountain. How might such gravity differences be used to make a bathymetric map?

### Prelab Discussion

Have students read the entire activity. Discuss these points before beginning:

▶ Ask students what geological process is being modeled in step 4 of the Prelab Prep.

▶ Suggest that students model folding and faulting if they have time.

**Time** 40 minutes    **Group** 3

**Materials**

modeling clay (3 different colors)

30 plastic drinking straws

10 butter knives

10 small scissors

waxed paper

## Analysis

1. Answers will vary. Similarities and differences will be due to the varying thicknesses of the layers of the clay block.

2. Depending on the variation from the edges of the block to the center, students may or may not have been able to predict the appearance of the core samples.

3. The layer closest to the bottom of the straw represents the oldest layer.

4. The layer closest to the top of the straw represents the youngest layer.

5. Core samples will differ because of differences in the clay blocks, such as the order of colors of the layers, and the varied compactness of the layers. Samples will also vary if they are taken at different angles.

## Conclusion

Accept any reasonable conclusion. Actual ocean floor core samples will be larger, may have more layers, and the layers will not be of uniform composition.

## Extension

Make sure that the inferences made are reasonable.

## Activity 16  *What can you learn from a core sample?*

**Skills**  Model; Infer; Generalize

### Task 1  Prelab Prep

1. Collect the following items: 3 different-colored pieces of modeling clay (each piece about the size of a golf ball), square of waxed paper, butter knife, 3 plastic drinking straws, small scissors.

2. Soften each piece of clay by squeezing it in your hands.

3. Flatten each piece of clay into a slab. Vary the width and length of the slabs. Let the thickness vary between 0.5 and 1 cm. Each slab should be somewhat uneven.

4. Stack the clay slabs on top of each other to form a block. Place the clay block on the waxed paper. Compact the layers by pushing down on the clay block. Using the butter knife, trim the edges.

### Task 2  Data Record

On a separate sheet of paper draw a block and three cylinders, as shown in Figure 16.4. You will use this data sheet to record your observations.

**Figure 16.4** ▼

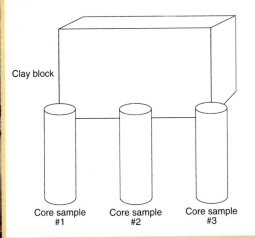

### Task 3  Procedure

1. Refer to the block you have drawn on your data sheet. Then draw a view of two sides of your clay block.

2. Push the straw through the layers of clay. Pull the straw out of the clay. On the block on your data sheet, record the location of your first core sample.

3. Use the scissors to cut open the straw lengthwise. Remove the clay plug, and place it on the waxed paper.

4. Draw the layers of core sample #1 on one of the cylinders on your data sheet.

5. Repeat steps 2 to 4 to create and examine core samples #2 and #3.

### Task 4  Analysis

1. **Observe**  Compare your three core samples. How were they alike? How were they different? What was the cause of the differences between the core samples?

2. Could you tell what each core sample would look like by first observing the sides of the clay block? Why?

3. Which layer of the core sample was the oldest? How could you tell?

4. Which layer of the core sample was the youngest? How could you tell?

5. **Infer**  How might your core samples differ from another group in the class?

### Task 5  Conclusion

How are the data from your model core sample similar to data from an actual core sample of the ocean bottom? How are they different?

### *Extension*

Attach the sides of all the clay blocks in the class together to form a model ocean floor. Take ten samples from the large clay block. Infer the geologic history of the model ocean floor from the core samples.

## Themes in Science

**Diversity and Unity** The land formations on the ocean floor are as diverse as those on the earth's surface. The conditions for each of these formations is very different; therefore, the processes that form the land vary. However, many of the structures present on the earth's surface can be seen in similar form on the ocean floor.

## Multicultural Perspectives

Students may be interested to know that a legend from the Inuit people of North America and Greenland says that a huge one-eyed spirit called *Sedna* controlled the marine animals. Sedna did not like humans because they hunted and killed seals and whales. Spirits friendly to humans, such as Agloolik, who lived under the ice, and Nootaikok, who ruled the icebergs, helped the Inuit hunters find food.

### Section Objectives
For a list of section objectives, see the Student Edition page.

### Skills Objectives
Students should be able to:

**Infer** which landforms may exist on the ocean floor, as well as on land.

**Make a Model** of plate boundaries.

**Make a Graph** comparing the depth of the Marianas Trench with measurements of land features.

**Predict** how two volcanoes will change after 10,000 years.

### Vocabulary
continental shelf, continental slope, continental rise, abyssal plains, seamount

---

## MOTIVATE

### Skills WarmUp

To help students understand the topography of the ocean floor, have them do the Skills WarmUp. **Answer** Lists will vary. Students might correctly indicate that features similar to most landforms exist on the ocean floor.

### Misconceptions

Students may think that the ocean floor is like the land they wade on at a beach. Explain that the ocean floor actually begins several miles offshore. Point out that the sand, rock, and soil present at shorelines is sediment from the dry land, and rests on the shelf-like edge of the landmass.

### ▼ ACTIVITY

**Inferring**

*The Ocean Floor*

Make a list of the different types of landforms that exist on the earth's continents. Review each land formation. Place an "O" next to each formation that you think may also exist on the bottom of the ocean.

**SKILLS WARMUP**

# 16.2 Ocean-Floor Topography

## Objectives

▶ **Describe** three features of the continental margin.

▶ **Identify** the major features of the ocean floor.

▶ **Compare** and **contrast** ocean trenches and ridges.

▶ **Predict** motion along underwater plate boundaries.

---

I magine what the earth's surface would look like if all the water drained from the ocean basins. What do you think the newly uncovered ocean floor would look like? For many years, people thought that most of the ocean floor was flat. They also thought a thick layer of sediments covered the entire ocean floor.

Modern oceanographic research shows that those early ideas about the ocean floor were incorrect. For example, the ocean floor has a variety of landforms similar to those on land. The ocean floor is dotted with volcanic peaks, many higher than any volcano on land. A system of underwater mountain ranges, called ridges, crosses each ocean basin. Other features of the ocean floor include canyons and vast, flat, featureless plains. The canyons are deeper than the Grand Canyon, and the plains are larger than any desert.

## Continental Margins

Have you ever gone to the shore at low tide and waded out into the water? Perhaps you thought you were walking on part of the ocean floor. However, the continent does not end right at the water's edge. The continent extends for some distance into the ocean. The part of a continent that extends out into the ocean is called the *continental margin*. The continental margin slopes downward toward the ocean floor. Three distinct regions make up the continental margin. Study the parts of the continental margin shown in Figure 16.6 on page 373. At some places, deep submarine canyons cut across the continental margin.

**Figure 16.5** ▲
These mountains in Iceland are part of the mid-Atlantic Ridge. The same mountains run thousands of kilometers along the floor of the Atlantic Ocean.

## Geography Connection

Obtain a map or globe of the world that displays ocean floor topography. Have students determine which of the continents have very wide continental shelves and which have very narrow ones. Ask the students if there is a pattern to the width of the continental shelves along continental edges. (Students should observe that most of the continents have a wide continental shelf on one side and a narrow continental shelf on the other side.)

**Continental Shelf**  A gently sloping surface, called the **continental shelf**, extends under the water from the shoreline. Sediments transported by rivers form most of the continental shelf.

The average width of a continental shelf is about 65 km. But the width may be much wider or narrower. Continental shelves are generally narrower in coastal areas, such as California, that are near tectonic plate boundaries.

**Continental Slope**  At the edge of the continental shelf, the **continental slope** drops off rather steeply toward the ocean floor. The continental slope is made up of the same materials as the continental shelf. The boundary between continental crust and oceanic crust occurs along the continental slope.

In some areas, almost no continental slope exists. One example is the Pacific coast of South America, where there are deep ocean trenches very close to the edge of the continental shelf.

**Continental Rise**  Look at Figure 16.6. The area from the continental slope to the deep ocean floor is called the **continental rise**. The continental rise is much less steep than the continental slope.

The continental rise is made of sediments. The sediments are carried from the continents and washed down the continental slopes. Continental rises vary in width from a few kilometers to hundreds of kilometers.

**Submarine Canyon**  In many places, continental margins are cut by deep submarine canyons. Rivers flowing to the ocean cut some of the canyons during the ice ages, when sea levels were lower. Moving masses of water and sediments, called turbidity currents, formed other submarine canyons. Turbidity currents are not related to other ocean currents. Because of the heavy load of sediments they carry, turbidity currents are very dense. They flow swiftly down the steep canyons in the continental slopes.

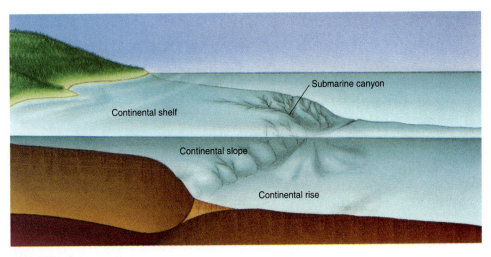

**Figure 16.6** ▲
Continental margins usually have three separate regions.

### Class Activity

Cut out the oceans and the continents from a large map of the world. Have students place the continents over the Pacific Ocean until the ocean is covered. (It will take all the continents to cover the Pacific.)

### Discuss

Have students discuss what part rivers play in the formation of continental margins. (Sediments carried by rivers make up the continental shelf, the continental slope, and the continental rise. Ice age rivers cut some submarine canyons.)

### Directed Inquiry

After students study the text and Figure 16.6, ask the following questions:

▶ If you were standing in ankle-deep water on the beach in the picture, what part of the continental margin would you be standing on? (Continental shelf)

▶ Which part of the continental margin is the steepest? (Continental slope)

▶ What parts of the ocean does the continental rise connect? (Continental slope and deep ocean floor)

▶ **Infer** the reason for the term "continental rise." (It's the area where the continental margin rises from the deep ocean floor.)

**373**

### Explore Visually

After students study the text and Figure 16.7, ask the following questions:

▶ Which ocean-floor features result from volcanic activity? Describe each one. (Seamounts—volcanic mountains rising more than 1000 m above the ocean floor; volcanic islands—seamounts that rise above the ocean surface; guyots—volcanic islands flattened by wave erosion)

▶ How are reefs and atolls similar? (Both are deposits of limestone skeletons of coral organisms.)

▶ What features form at converging and diverging plate boundaries? (Trenches form at converging plate boundaries; ridges, or underwater mountain ranges, form at diverging boundaries.)

### Reteach

Use Reteach Worksheet 16.2.

## Integrating the Sciences

**Chemistry** Scientists analyze the chemistry of ooze on the ocean floor to gain knowledge about the history of the earth. Much of the ooze is composed of the remains of foraminiferans, which are tiny protozoa with shells. Carbon dating and oxygen isotope analysis of the ooze relates to changes in foraminiferan populations. Changes in foraminiferan populations help scientists to determine the climate of the past.

## Ocean-Floor Features

The ocean floor has many features similar to those on land. Look at Figure 16.7. Volcanoes, sediments, and moving crustal plates shape the ocean floor.

**Abyssal Plains** Flat areas of the deep ocean floor are called **abyssal** (uh BIHS uhl) **plains**. Core samples from abyssal plains show layers of sediment deposited over thousands of years. The sediments fill in rough spots on the ocean floor, forming a smooth, flat surface.

Sediments vary in different parts of an abyssal plain. Near the continental margin are fine rock particles from land areas. Deep ocean sediments contain the remains of microscopic organisms. After the organisms die, they sink to the ocean floor, forming a sediment called ooze. The largest abyssal plains are in the Atlantic and Indian oceans, where large rivers deposit more sediments.

**Figure 16.7**
**Features of the Ocean Floor**
▼

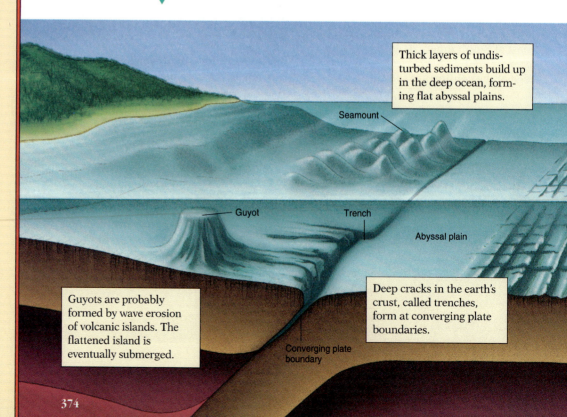

Thick layers of undisturbed sediments build up in the deep ocean, forming flat abyssal plains.

Seamount

Guyot

Trench

Abyssal plain

Guyots are probably formed by wave erosion of volcanic islands. The flattened island is eventually submerged.

Converging plate boundary

Deep cracks in the earth's crust, called trenches, form at converging plate boundaries.

## Math Connection

From the base on the ocean floor to the top, the island of Hawaii measures 10,000 meters tall. Have students measure their heights. Then have the students use their individual heights to calculate how many times taller Hawaii is than they are.

## Geography Connection

Use a map or globe of the world that displays the topography of the ocean floor to compare the length of the mid-Atlantic Ridge to different formations on the earth. Have students measure the length of the mid-Atlantic Ridge with a string, then cut the string to the length of the ridge. Have students use the string to compare the length of the ridge to various features on the earth's surface.

▶ What is ooze? Is it found near mid-ocean ridges? Explain. (Ocean sediment containing the remains of microscopic organisms; no, because ooze is a sediment that forms the flat surface of an abyssal plain away from the ridges)

## Skills Development

**Interpret Data** Ask students what they can infer from the presence of an atoll. (A volcanic island once stood there.)

**Organize Data** Ask students to make a concept web using the following items: rivers, sediment, abyssal plain, fine rock, ooze, deep ocean, continental margin.

## Critical Thinking

**Reason and Conclude** Ask students to explain how oceanic ridges can be used to locate a divergent plate boundary. (As plates diverge, a ridge forms on either side of the rift and one rift valley is formed. As the process continues, an even number of ridges forms—one on each side of the rift. Therefore, the central rift valley marks the location of the plate boundary.)

**Ridges** Each ocean basin has mountain ranges that form a ridge. For example, the mid-Atlantic Ridge runs through the Atlantic Ocean basin. Ridges form at diverging plate boundaries.

**Seamounts and Guyots** Volcanic mountains rising more than 1,000 m above the ocean floor are called **seamounts**. Seamounts form near mid-ocean ridges, or at volcanic "hot spots." Seamounts grow until plate movement carries them away from the plate boundary or hot spot. Some seamounts grow tall enough to form volcanic islands. When a volcanic island stops growing, wave action can flatten it, forming a *guyot* (GHEE oh).

**Reefs and Atolls** Coral reefs form in shallow water on continental shelves or along the shorelines of volcanic islands. If the volcanic island later sinks below the surface of the water, the ring of coral reefs is left behind. Such a formation is called an *atoll* (A tohl).

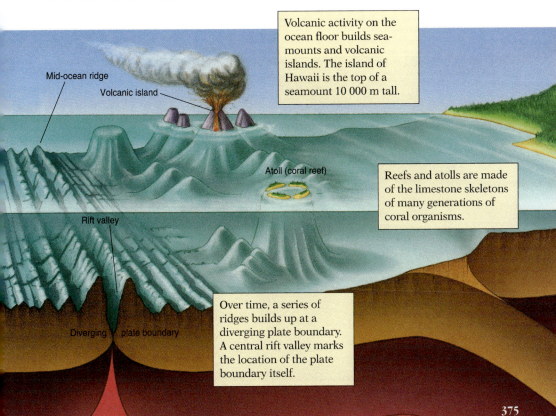

Volcanic activity on the ocean floor builds seamounts and volcanic islands. The island of Hawaii is the top of a seamount 10 000 m tall.

Mid-ocean ridge

Volcanic island

Atoll (coral reef)

Reefs and atolls are made of the limestone skeletons of many generations of coral organisms.

Rift valley

Diverging plate boundary

Over time, a series of ridges builds up at a diverging plate boundary. A central rift valley marks the location of the plate boundary itself.

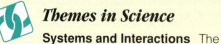

### Themes in Science

**Systems and Interactions** The interaction at plate boundaries form subduction zones. Subduction zones create deep cracks in the earth's crust that are called *trenches*.

---

## TEACH ▪ *Continued*

### Discuss

Have students discuss the forces that produce trenches. Ask them to study Figure 16.8 and locate two trenches—one on the east and one on the west side of the Pacific. Ask students how many plates are involved in creating a trench. (Two per trench)

### Class Activity

Divide the class into three cooperative groups and tell them they're going to make a map of tectonic plates showing subduction zones, major trenches, divergent boundaries, ridges, and rifts in the ocean floor. Have one group draw a large world map outlining the tectonic plates. Have the other two groups research the location of the features listed above in the Atlantic and the Pacific—one ocean per group. Then ask groups to share information to complete the map.

### Apply

Ask students to study Figure 16.8. Is Japan an island arc? (Yes. The islands have formed along a subduction zone.)

**Plate Boundaries and Trenches** Plate boundaries are geologically active areas. Volcanic eruptions, earthquakes, and mountain building occur at and near plate boundaries. Recall that at a plate boundary, the plates can interact in different ways. The plates may spread apart, slide alongside one another, or one plate may sink underneath the other.

Ocean trenches form where oceanic plates sink beneath continental plates or other oceanic plates. Recall that these areas are subduction zones. As the oceanic crust continues to sink, it eventually melts and becomes part of the mantle.

Look at the map in Figure 16.8. Notice the series of subduction zones along the western edge of the Pacific Ocean. The deepest trenches in the world ocean are in this part of the Pacific basin. There are five trenches more than 10 km deep. The deepest is the Marianas (MAIR ee AN uhs) Trench, located north of New Guinea. The Marianas Trench is more than 11 km deep and 70 km wide. The tallest mountain on land, Mt. Everest, would easily fit inside this deep trench.

**Figure 16.8**
Both land elevations and ocean depths are shown on this computer-generated map of the world. ▼

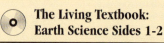

**The Living Textbook: Earth Science Sides 1-2**

Chapter 24     Frame 03089
Plate Boundaries (1 Frame)
Search:

## Social Studies Connection

Eight major islands and many small islets make up the Hawaiian islands. These islands are volcanic in origin. On the large island of Hawaii is Mauna Loa, a large, active volcano. Discuss with students how living on an island with an active volcano might affect the people that live on the island. Ask: How might the volcanic nature of the island affect where or how people construct buildings? Have students research the Hawaiian culture to find out how volcanic action has influenced its history and mythology.

Because of the large number of volcanoes around the Pacific Ocean basin, the area is called the Ring of Fire. Volcanoes in this area form in subduction zones. One plate sinks, and the material in it melts. Some of the molten material forms pockets of magma along the subduction zone. The magma can erupt to the surface, forming volcanoes. If the subduction zone is under the water, eruptions there may form a chain of volcanic islands. In Figure 16.8, notice the chains of volcanic islands alongside the trenches in the western Pacific. A chain of volcanic islands that forms along a subduction zone is known as an *island arc*.

On a global scale, the process of subduction balances the plate spreading that occurs at the mid-ocean ridges. In the subduction zones, material from the edge of one plate sinks down and melts. Some of the melted material is recycled into the mantle. At the ridges, material from the mantle wells up to form mountains.

### ▼ ACTIVITY

**Making a Model**

*Paper Boundaries*

Obtain two paper towels.

**1.** Moisten the paper towels with water.

**2.** Place the towels side by side on a table. Position each hand on the outer edge of each towel.

**3.** Slowly push the towel together until your hands meet.

How are the towels like plate boundaries?

**SKILLS WORKOUT**

## SkillBuilder *Making a Graph*

### Ocean Trenches

To understand how deep the Mariana Trench is, you need to compare it with other objects. Make a bar graph to compare each object listed in the table. Label the y–axis *Size (km)*. Label the horizontal x–axis *Object*. Record the name of each object under the correct bar on the graph. Use the graph to answer the questions.

| Object | Depth or Height (km) |
|---|---|
| Mariana Trench | 11.0 |
| Mt. Everest (China) | 9.0 |
| Mt. McKinley (Alaska) | 6.0 |
| Grand Canyon (Arizona) | 1.6 |
| Sears Tower (Illinois) | 0.5 |
| Tallest tree (California) | 0.1 |

**1.** How tall is the tallest mountain? The tallest building?

**2.** How tall is the tallest mountain in the United States?

**3.** Which object is the largest?

**4.** How many mountains the size of Mt. McKinley could fit into the Mariana Trench?

**5.** How many buildings the size of the Sears Tower could fit into the Mariana Trench?

**6.** How many times deeper is the Mariana Trench than the Grand Canyon?

Write a paragraph explaining how the depth of the Mariana Trench compares to the height or depth of other objects, such as the tallest tree, you, or the Grand Canyon.

## Skills WorkOut

To help students understand plate boundaries, have them do the Skills WorkOut.

**Answer** Check student models. One towel may slide one under another, or one may push the second upward making a fold in the towel. The towels model plates at subduction zones or converging plates.

## Portfolio

Ask students to imagine what it would be like to explore the Mariana Trench. They can write about the equipment they'd develop to explore the trench, the actual exploration, or data from the exploration. Students can keep their work in their portfolios.

## Skills Development

**Communicate** Have students draw a diagram to show that seafloor spreading and rift formation are balanced processes. (Matter melted at subduction zones is recycled into the mantle. At ridges, materials from the mantle form mountains.)

## SkillBuilder

Check student graphs for accuracy.

**Answers**

1. 9 km; 0.5 km

2. 6 km

3. Mariana Trench

4. Nearly two

5. About 22

6. 6.8 times deeper

Students' paragraphs will vary, but should illustrate their ability to compute relative measurements.

## EVALUATE

### WrapUp

**Reteach** Obtain a profile of the Atlantic and Pacific oceans. Have students make tags to identify features such as mid-oceanic ridges, trenches, continental margins, shelves, slopes, and rises. Have students identify the cause of each feature.

Use Review Worksheet 16.2.

### Check and Explain

1. Continental shelf, gently sloping surface from continent into ocean formed by river sediments; continental slope, a steep drop off from the shelf leading toward the ocean floor, also formed by river sediment; continental rise, a less steep region leading from the continental slope to the ocean floor

2. Abyssal plain; ocean trenches; mid-ocean ridges; guyots, seamounts, volcanic islands; coral reefs and atolls

3. Both are caused by plate movement. Rifts are caused by divergent (oceanic) plates and rise above the ocean floor; trenches are caused by converging continental and oceanic plates and are deep slashes in the ocean floor.

4. Predictions may vary, but students should suggest that the volcanoes will be farther apart due to sea floor spreading and probably shorter due to wave erosion.

**The Living Textbook:**
**Earth Science Sides 1-2**

Chapter 11          Frame 02333
Coral (4 Frames)
Search:                Step:

## Integrating the Sciences

**Environmental Science** Humans may have caused an imbalance in the Great Barrier Reef ecosystem that may lead to its destruction. The change in the ecosystem is due to a rising population of the Crown of Thorns starfish. The starfish feeds on the coral polyps that help form the coral reef. The rise in the starfish population may be due to the loss of the starfish's natural predators, one of which is the giant triton. The giant triton is a mollusk that is disappearing due to commercial fishing. Other starfish predators, such as the cod and grouper, have also been removed from the ecosystem for human consumption.

### Science and Society
#### *Great Barrier Reef Park*

The Great Barrier Reef of Australia is one of the most unique environments in the world. It extends for a distance of more than 2,000 km. Inside the main reef, islands have been set aside as national parks. The islands teem with tropical birds and other wildlife.

The Great Barrier Reef is almost 30 million years old. During its lifetime, the reef has grown and shrunk as the water level changed. After the last ice age, about 15,000 years ago, the water rose to its present level and the reef began to grow. The new growth took place on the eroded remains of older reefs.

The reef itself is made up of the limestone skeletons of coral organisms. In addition to the corals, the reef is home to many other organisms. There are more than 500 species of algae, or seaweed. Approximately 1,500 species of fish, 4,000 species of mollusks, and thousands of other animals live on or near the reef.

The Great Barrier Reef Marine Park Authority manages the reef. The Park Authority supervises commercial and sport fishing, research, reef preservation, and tourism. The reef is already a major tourist attraction. New hotels and an aquarium are being added to the area. The number of tourists may increase dramatically. The Park Authority's job will be to preserve the unique reef environment and manage the increased activity near the reef.

**Figure 16.9** ▲
Living corals coat the surface of the Great Barrier Reef.

### Check and Explain

1. Name and describe three features of the continental margin.

2. What are the major features of the ocean floor?

3. **Compare and Contrast** What do ocean trenches have in common with mid-ocean ridges? In what ways are the two regions different?

4. **Predict** Two volcanoes form on opposite sides of the mid-Atlantic Ridge. How will the size and location of these volcanoes change in 10,000 years?

## STS Connection

Manganese nodules exist on the ocean floor at depths of more than 2,000 meters. Several companies have tried testing recovery processes but the cost is too high. Have students infer how these nodules might have been recovered. They should take into consideration how oil is removed offshore, how crabs and lobsters are fished, and how salt water is collected. (Methods include robot divers and giant vacuum pumps.)

## Integrating the Sciences

**Environmental Science** Leakage from offshore oil wells may occur during normal operations. An average of 11,000 oil incidents occur in U.S. waters every year. This leakage of oil harms wildlife in general and marine life in particular. It soaks into the feathers of birds so that they are unable to fly. Oil kills plants and animals in the littoral zone. The oil then settles and affects organisms in the ocean's neritic zone.

## Skills Development

**Interpret Data** Ask students to list the minerals and other resources found in the ocean. Ask them which minerals come from organic sources and which come from inorganic sources. (Organic: calcium, petroleum, and natural gas; inorganic: salt, manganese, iodine, iron, copper, and nickel)

## Discuss

Ask students to consider the benefits and problems involved in mining the ocean floor. Have them discuss the issues of technology, pollution, and ownership of the open ocean.

**Minerals** Ocean water contains many dissolved minerals. Recall that many organisms remove minerals from ocean water as part of their life processes. Shellfish use calcium to make their shells. Some organisms remove iodine from ocean water. Seafood is an important source of iodine in the human diet.

Salt is an important mineral resource found in ocean water. The salt can be removed by the desalination process. People evaporate the water and collect the solid salt. Salt evaporation ponds are shown in Figure 16.14. The desalination process can also be used to collect fresh water from the ocean.

Small, rocklike deposits known as manganese nodules cover some parts of the ocean floor. Look at Figure 16.14. The nodules contain manganese, iron, copper, and nickel. At present, it costs more to collect these nodules than the minerals are worth. But in the future, the nodules may be a valuable resource.

**Oil** Large deposits of oil, or petroleum, and natural gas occur beneath the continental shelves. In North America, the largest offshore oil deposits are in the Gulf of Mexico. Oil-drilling platforms have been built offshore.

People depend greatly on oil to meet their energy needs. But oil is also a major source of ocean pollution. Oil spills and leaks from oil wells kill fishes, birds, and marine mammals, and damage beaches. Today governments in many parts of the world are taking steps to reduce the pollution of ocean water.

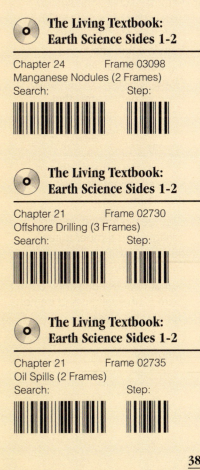

**The Living Textbook: Earth Science Sides 1-2**

Chapter 24          Frame 03098
Manganese Nodules (2 Frames)
Search:                    Step:

**The Living Textbook: Earth Science Sides 1-2**

Chapter 21          Frame 02730
Offshore Drilling (3 Frames)
Search:                    Step:

**The Living Textbook: Earth Science Sides 1-2**

Chapter 21          Frame 02735
Oil Spills (2 Frames)
Search:                    Step:

◀ **Figure 16.14** ▲
Salt is collected in evaporation ponds (left). Nodules from the ocean floor contain useful metals (above).

TEACH ▪ Continued

## Enrich

Bring in a sample of diatomaceous earth for students to observe. Have them soak some of the material in water and use a hand lens to see the skeletons. Diatomaceous earth is available as an organic gardening supply for controlling slugs, earwigs, and other leaf-sucking insects.

## EVALUATE

## WrapUp

**Reteach** Use the profile of the Atlantic and Pacific oceans from the previous section. Have students make tags to identify oceanic life zones and indicate what kinds of life live in each zone. Also ask them to write a short description of the conditions in each zone.
Use Review Worksheet 16.3.

## Check and Explain

1. Littoral—sunlit zone shallow water area between low and high tide; Neritic—sunlit zone from low tide line to the edge of the continental shelf; Oceanic—deep ocean beyond the continental shelf that includes all the zones: sunlit, twilight, bathyal, and abyssal zones)

2. Food in the form of fish and shellfish, minerals, and petroleum

3. Changes in habitat; in general, sunlight and temperatures decrease while water pressure increases. Water temperature is higher near ocean vents, but there is no sunlight and tremendous water pressure.

4. Check students' drawings for accuracy.

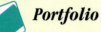
### Portfolio

Many everyday products come from seaweed. The chemicals extracted from seaweed, or algae, include carrageenan, agar, and algin. Students can find these chemicals listed on ingredient labels for dairy products, soups, dessert toppings, paints, polishes, and cosmetics.

Have students make a list of seaweed products from ingredient labels and title the list *Useful Products Made from Seaweed.* Students can keep the lists in their portfolios. You may want students to create lists of other useful products, such as those made from diatoms.

### Science and You
### *Clean Water from the Ocean*

How do some water filters clean the water? If you could take a small sample of the filter material and rub it between your thumb and forefinger, it would feel gritty. If you could examine it with a hand lens, you might see tiny particles of silica (SIL ih kuh). Silica is the compound that makes up most sand.

These filters contain a powdery material called diatomaceous (DY uh tuh MAY shuhs) earth. Diatomaceous earth is made up of the glasslike skeletons of diatoms. Diatoms are single-celled plantlike organisms with a silica skeleton. Diatoms live in great numbers in ocean water. After the diatoms die, their skeletons sink. They accumulate on the ocean bottom, forming a deposit of diatomaceous earth, also called diatomite.

Large diatomite beds built up near the continental margins and in places where shallow inland seas once existed. Large diatomite deposits are in California. One of these diatomite deposits covers an area of 10 km² and is more than 200 m deep.

In addition to its use as an abrasive, diatomite is used to make many other items. More than half of all the diatomite mined every year is used in filters for beverages and other liquids. The porous silica shells trap impurities while allowing liquid to pass through. Silica is also resistant to many chemicals. This property makes diatomite a useful filler in paints, paper, and other chemical products.

**Figure 16.15** ▲
Diatomite is made up of the skeletons of diatoms. The diatom shown above is greatly enlarged.

### Check and Explain

1. Name and describe the horizontal and vertical life zones of the ocean.

2. What resources do people get from the oceans?

3. **Find Causes** As you go deeper in the ocean, the types and numbers of organisms change. What causes these changes?

4. **Make a Model** Use references to make a drawing or diagram of a possible food web in the neritic zone. Present your model to the class.

## Check Your Vocabulary

1. continental slope
2. abyssal plains
3. nekton
4. continental shelf
5. littoral zone
6. ecosystem
7. continental rise
8. seamount
9. plankton
10. neritic zone
11. benthos
12. habitat

## Write Your Vocabulary

Students' sentences should show that they know the meaning of each word as well as how to use it in a sentence.

Use Vocabulary Worksheet for Chapter 16.

## Chapter 16 Review

### Concept Summary

**16.1 Ocean Exploration**
► Oceanic research vessels, such as *HMS Challenger* and *Glomar Challenger* made voyages to study the world ocean.
► Some tools and methods of ocean research include scraping, coring, sonar, submersibles, and satellites.
► Mapmakers determined the shape of the ocean floor from depth measurements taken at different locations.

**16.2 Ocean-Floor Topography**
► The continental margin extends into the ocean. It has three regions called the continental shelf, the continental slope, and the continental rise. Submarine canyons cross the continental margin.

► Some features of the ocean floor include abyssal plains, ridges, seamounts, guyots, reefs, and atolls.
► At subduction zones, ocean trenches and volcanos form.

**16.3 Life Zones in the Ocean**
► Many environmental factors, such as sunlight, temperature, and pressure, affect ocean habitats.
► Life zones in the ocean are divided horizontally and vertically.
► An ecosystem is an area in which organisms interact with each other and with their environment. Energy in an ecosystem is transferred in a food chain.
► People depend on the ocean for such resources as food, minerals, salt, oil, and fresh water.

### Chapter Vocabulary

| | | |
|---|---|---|
| continental shelf (16.2) | seamount (16.2) | benthos (16.3) |
| continental slope (16.2) | habitat (16.3) | plankton (16.3) |
| continental rise (16.2) | littoral zone (16.3) | nekton (16.3) |
| abyssal plains (16.2) | neritic zone (16.3) | ecosystem (16.3) |

### Check Your Vocabulary

Use the vocabulary words above to complete the following sentences correctly.

1. The boundary between the continental crust and the oceanic crust is the _____ .

2. Large, flat areas of the deep ocean floor are called _____ .

3. Swimming organisms, such as whales and squid, are known as _____ .

4. The sloping surface that extends from the shoreline of a continent is the _____ .

5. The area of shallow water between the high- and the low-tide line is the _____ .

6. In an _____ , organisms interact with each other and with the environment.

7. The area in the ocean between the continental slope and the ocean floor is the _____ .

8. A volcanic mountain that rises from the ocean floor is a _____ .

9. Microscopic organisms that float near the ocean surface are _____ .

10. The area from the low-tide line to the edge of the continental shelf is the _____ .

11. Organisms that live on the ocean floor are called _____ .

12. The place where an organism lives is called its _____ .

## Check Your Knowledge

1. Possible answers may include: coring, sonar, submersibles, and satellites.

2. A bathymetric map is a topographic map of the ocean floor.

3. A guyot results when a volcanic island is flattened by wave action.

4. Reefs form from the accumulation of coral skeletons. An atoll is a ring of coral reefs left behind after a volcanic island sinks into the ocean.

5. Factors include: sunlight, temperature, pressure, salinity, distance from shore, depth, and wave action.

6. Organisms living in the littoral zone include: crabs, clams, mussels, algae, seaweed, sea stars, sponges, and lobsters.

7. Many organisms are dependent on the estuary habitat for survival.

8. People get fish, plants, and minerals from the ocean.

9. Zooplankton are microscopic animals; phytoplankton are plantlike microscopic organisms.

10. Ridges form by lava flowing out at a diverging plate boundary.

11. Submarine canyons are underwater canyons found along the continental margins.

12. Sunlit zone, twilight zone, bathyal zone, and abyssal zone

13. abyssal
14. subduction zones
15. cores
16. ooze

## Check Your Understanding

1. Accept any reasonable answer. Possible answers include: habitat destruction; introduction of toxins; population growth when predators are killed or driven off; population decrease when prey are killed or driven off.

2. The littoral zone has strong sunlight, strong wave action, and changing water levels. The neritic zone has plenty of sunlight, a fairly constant temperature, and little wave action.

3. The continental shelf extends from the shoreline out into the ocean, where it drops off at the continental slope. From the continental slope, the crust drops off toward the ocean floor. The continental rise begins at the end of the continental slope and extends to the deep ocean floor.

4. The first mapping of the ocean floor was done using long, weighted ropes to take soundings.

Depth can be measured more accurately with sonar, which uses reflected sound waves, or radar altimetry, which uses reflected radio waves from a satellite.

5. Student answers will vary, but may include fish and seafood, salt and other minerals, and water.

6. Dolphins use echolocation to sense the environment around them, for hunting, navigating, and detecting predators.

7. Plankton: neritic; seaweed: littoral; lantern fish: oceanic; crab: littoral

8. Mapping the ocean floor can be performed using sonar or radar. Sampling the ocean floor is best done by drilling core samples. Traveling to the ocean floor in a submersible or sending a remote camera are ways to observe life on the ocean floor.

9. Early ocean floor exploration involved measuring the depth of shallow water using weighted ropes. Later, study was carried out by drilling core samples, using sonar and radar, and traveling below the surface in submersibles.

10. Student answers will vary.

## Chapter 16 Review

### Check Your Knowledge

Answer the following in complete sentences.

1. List three tools or methods that are used to study the ocean.

2. What is a bathymetric map?

3. What is a guyot?

4. Explain how reefs and atolls form.

5. List two environmental factors that affect ocean life.

6. Name an organism that lives in the littoral zone.

7. Why are estuaries important?

8. List two resources that people get from the ocean.

9. What are zooplankton? Phytoplankton?

10. What forms the ridges that are found in the major ocean basins?

11. What are submarine canyons? Where are they found?

12. Name four ocean vertical life zones.

Choose the answer that best completes each sentence.

13. The name of the deepest life zone in the ocean is the (sunlit, twilight, bathyal, abyssal) zone.

14. The areas where oceanic plates collide with and sink under continental or oceanic plates are called (atolls, subduction zones, mid-ocean ridges, guyots).

15. Vertical samples of ocean floor crust are called (scrapes, sonar, cores, submersibles).

16. Dead organisms that settle to the ocean floor form a sediment called (ooze, magma, limestone, coral).

### Check Your Understanding

Apply the concepts you have learned to answer each question.

1. **Critical Thinking** How could collecting manganese nodules or building more offshore oil platforms affect life in the ocean?

2. Compare conditions in the neritic zone to conditions in the littoral zone.

3. Describe how each of the following are related: continental rise, continental shelf, continental slope.

4. Describe how the ocean floor was first mapped. Compare this early technique to tools and methods used to map the ocean floor today.

5. **Application** Make a list of some different resources that come from the ocean. Which of these resources do you use? Which did you use today?

6. **Extension** Dolphins emit high-pitched sounds and listen for the echoes. Why do you think they do this?

7. Name the horizontal ocean life zone for each of the following: plankton, seaweed, lantern fish, crab.

8. Name the tools or methods that you would use to conduct the following studies: map the ocean floor, obtain a sample of the ocean floor, observe life on the ocean floor.

9. Discuss the history of ocean floor exploration.

10. **Mystery Photo** The photo on page 364 shows a closeup of a comb jelly. A comb jelly is part of the nekton in the sunlit zone. Infer how the comb jelly may adjust to changes in water pressure, salinity, and water temperature.

## Develop Your Skills

**1.** a. c

b. b; it looks like a fringe around the volcanic island.

c. a; the reef forms a wall around the island.

d. b, a, c

**2.** a. Pacific Ocean

b. Arctic Ocean

c. Pacific Ocean

d. About 1000 m

**3.** The mountains that form Hawaii are much taller than mountains on the continents. However, much of Hawaii is under the ocean. The Pacific abyssal plain is much larger than the Great Plains.

**4.** The food chain should be drawn: sunlight—phytoplankton—fish—squid—shark.

## Make Connections

**1.** Concept maps will vary. The map below shows a possible organization of the concepts listed.

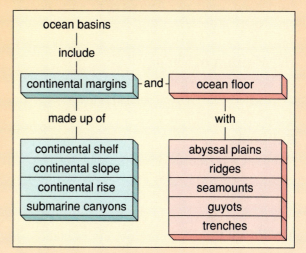

**2.** Student responses will vary. Surprisingly, much of the science-based technology—such as the submarine and the nuclear power source—turned out to be possible.

**3.** In general, requirements include above-average swimming ability and lung control, and knowledge of equipment use, safety rules, and diving regulations. The requirements exist to protect divers and the ecosystems in which they dive.

**4.** Accept any reasonable answer. Dumping in the ocean introduces substances that are not normally present. Marine organisms either die or survive, but they accumulate the toxins in their systems. Ocean dumping could be eliminated by reusing, recycling, and reducing the waste at the source.

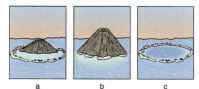

## Develop Your Skills

Use the skills you have developed in this chapter to complete each activity.

**1. Interpret Data** The drawing below shows three types of coral reefs.

a. Which drawing shows an atoll?

b. Which drawing do you think shows a fringing reef? Why?

c. Which drawing do think shows a barrier reef? Why?

d. Place the drawings in a sequence that would show the formation of an atoll.

**2. Data Bank** Use the information on page 622 to answer the following questions.

a. Which ocean is the largest?

b. Which ocean is the smallest?

c. Which ocean has the deepest average depth?

d. What is the average depth of the Arctic Ocean?

**3. Compare** Compare the height of the seamount that forms the island of Hawaii to the height of mountains on the surface of the earth. Use a map of North America and of the Pacific Ocean floor to compare the size of the Great Plains to the size of the abyssal plain.

**4. Make a Model** Draw a food chain using the following terms: sunlight, squid, phytoplankton, fish, shark.

## Make Connections

**1. Link the Concepts** Draw a concept map showing how the following concepts from the chapter link together. Add terms to connect, or link, the concepts.

| | |
|---|---|
| ocean basins | seamounts |
| trenches | submarine canyons |
| ridges | continental slope |
| ocean floor | continental shelf |
| abyssal plain | continental rise |
| guyots | |

**2. Science and Literature** The book *20,000 Leagues Under the Sea*, by Jules Verne, is a story about the adventures of a crew aboard an incredible underwater ship. Read this story. What parts of the story are scientifically possible? What parts are pure fantasy?

**3. Science and Physical Education** Scuba diving is a strenuous sport. In the United States, scuba divers must complete certain requirements before they can get a license to dive. Find out the requirements that must be completed before applying for a scuba license. Why do you think these requirements exist?

**4. Science and Society** For many years dumping wastes into the ocean was common. Currently, stricter controls are being placed on ocean dumping. How do you think ocean dumping affects life in the ocean? Infer how ocean dumping could be completely eliminated.

## About the Literary Work

"The Land I Lost" was adapted from *The Land I Lost* by Huynh Quang Nhuong, copyright 1982 by Harper and Row Junior Books. Reprinted by permission of Harper and Row.

## Description of Change

Passages describing the feeding patterns of eels were edited out of a short section of text.

## Rationale

Emphasis was placed on the importance of the watery environment to the life of the narrator, which is appropriate to the science lessons in this unit.

## Vocabulary

hamlet

## Teaching Strategies

### Directed Inquiry

After students finish reading, discuss the story. Be sure to relate the story to the science lessons in this unit. Ask the following questions:

▶ What type of animal is Tank? (Water buffalo)

▶ What is the narrator's relationship to Tank? (Tank is a type of work animal that the narrator also treats as a family pet.)

▶ What type of work is Tank described as doing in the selection? (Fishing for eels)

## Critical Thinking

**If . . . Then Arguments**  Ask students how the passage might have been different if Tank had not helped fish for the eels. (The narrator would probably not have been able to capture the same number of live eels. On his own, the narrator would need to organize friends' help or invent a tool in order to pull live eels from their nests.)

## Skills Development

**Infer**  Discuss with students the idea that organisms are suited to a particular type of environment. Ask:

▶ Is a river a freshwater or saltwater environment? (Freshwater)

▶ What does this indicate about the eels in this story? (They must be adapted to a freshwater environment.)

## Science and Literature Connection

### The Land I Lost

*The following excerpt is from the book* The Land I Lost *by Huynh Quang Nhuong.*

From the time [our buffalo, Tank, helped catch the giant white catfish], I had considered the idea of catching golden eels with Tank's help. There were two kinds of golden eels living in our area—one kind had bulging eyes, the other had beady eyes. Both were much sought after because their meat was excellent. These eels, when matured, reached two meters in length and weighed about five kilos.

The eels lived in muddy ditches that brought water to the fruit gardens, the banana groves, and the coconut groves when the level of the water in the river in front of our hamlet was high. They hid in deep holes that they dug in the hard clay soil beneath the mud of the ditch, usually near a tree planted on the border of the ditch. The roots of the tree were a natural barrier against intruders, and when an eel coiled its body around the root of a tree, it was almost impossible to pull it out.

One could lure an eel with almost any kind of bait, but we used earthworms because they were easy to find. We would dangle the worm at the nest's entrance, and sooner or later the eel would come out and bite the bait. We allowed the eel to swallow the bait far down into its stomach, instead of pulling the line right away, for if we pulled the line too soon we would only succeed in tearing off the eel's jaw during the struggle to pull it out of its nest. But with a hook in its stomach, it could not get away—no matter how hard it tried. Sooner or later, unless the fishing line broke, we would drag the eel out of its nest, dead or alive.

But a live eel got a better price than a dead one in the market, and since Tank had easily succeeded in pulling the white catfish out of the river for our old friend, I came up with the idea of letting him drag eels out of their nests for me. If he could pull an eel out quickly, I had a better chance to get the eel alive instead of dead.

First I had to find an eel's nest, but this was not difficult. One can know roughly the location of a nest by listening carefully to the sound an eel makes when it snaps at a victim. The sound made by its closing jaws is similar to that of a loud click and can be heard clearly from thirty or forty meters away, especially at night.

After finding the general area of a nest, I pinpointed the exact location by examining the mud. The mud around the main entrance of the nest is always more disturbed than the rest. Then I tied the end of a fishing line to Tank's horns and made the bait jump up and down on the mud covering the hole. The eel stuck its head out of the mud first, saw the bait clearly, snapped it up, and returned to its nest below. I loosened the line to let the eel swallow the bait into its stomach, then I signaled Tank to pull. Despite his tremendous strength, Tank needed quite a bit of effort to pull the eel out of its nest. But it

## Skills in Science

### Reading Skills in Science

1. Answers may vary. The meat from a live eel would be fresher and therefore it might be tastier than that from a dead eel.

2. Answers may vary. The hamlet may be in an area that receives sporadic rainfall, or the only other available water might be ocean water.

## Writing Skills in Science

1. Answers might include: water for irrigation; fishing for catfish and eels; river would be important to transportation; mud may be important for building.

2. The fruit gardens would be in danger and living things in the ditches might die.

## Activities

**Communicate** Food webs might include such organisms as aquatic plants, fish, mollusks, crustaceans, water birds, small mammals, and birds of prey. Check students' diagrams for accuracy.

**Collect Data** Answers depend on individual research. Eels are marine or freshwater fish. They are long and snakelike fishes with distinctive tails and a unique, migratory life cycle. All eels hatch in the sea, from which larvae are carried by ocean currents to various parts of the world. American and European mature eels migrate back to the Sargasso Sea, where they breed.

---

was the most exciting sight to see the wagging head of the eel stick out of the mud first, and then its big, trembling, golden body come slowly out of the hole. When the eel was on dry ground, it yanked, turned, and squirmed like an earthworm attacked by a swarm of fire ants.

Using this method, I caught several big eels; none of them could resist Tank more than fifty counts. When Tank started pulling, I counted, "One, two, three . . . "

Some strong eels reached forty-five, but the weaker ones were already on dry ground, wriggling, when I had not yet reached twenty. Often, when an eel had taken the bait, I yelled to my friends to come see Tank's work. When everybody arrived, I signaled Tank to pull. Some of my friends counted with me while the others yelled, clapped their hands, or cheered loudly for Tank.

### Skills in Science

#### Reading Skills in Science

1. **Infer** Why do you think a live eel was worth more at the market than a dead eel?

2. **Find Context Clues** The first sentence of the second paragraph infers that the people in the hamlet used water from the river to water their gardens and trees. Why do you think they must use river water? Explain.

#### Writing Skills in Science

1. **Reason and Conclude** What do you think life was like for the narrator in this remote village in Vietnam? Why was the river so important to the people? Identify four ways the people relied on the river. Explain your choices.

2. **Infer** Describe what might happen in the hamlet if a drought caused the water level in the river to become very low.

#### Activities

**Communicate** In a library, research the food chains commonly found in a river ecosystem. Make a diagram of a food web that illustrates the relationships among these food chains.

**Collect Data** Gather information about eels. Where do most types of eels live? What are some differences between freshwater eels and saltwater eels? Try to identify the species of eel in this story.

#### Where to Read More

*This is a River* by Lawrence Pringle. New York: MacMillan Company, 1972. This text explores the workings of a running-water ecosystem and describes how the actions of humans interferes with such a system.

his unit examines the earth's atmosphere and its importance to living things. Chapter 17 describes the composition, organization, and physics of the atmosphere. The last section explains how pollution is caused and why it must be reduced. Chapter 18 explains how clouds, humidity, and precipitation are related. Students learn to classify clouds and measure relative humidity. Chapter 19 illustrates how parts of the earth's atmosphere cause the changeable weather patterns around the world. Chapter 20 explains how weather patterns define climate zones. The chapter includes a discussion of life in the different climate zones and concludes with a discussion of climate changes, such as global warming.

## Introducing the Unit

### Directed Inquiry

Have students study the photograph and read the caption. Ask:

▶ How big is the storm in this picture? How can you tell? (It is bigger than the city and extremely high; the streaks are many times longer than the skyscrapers.)

▶ How far up can storms happen? (As high as the clouds)

▶ Why don't storms occur in outer space? (Storms are atmospheric phenomena; they require air masses to interact.)

▶ Infer what other forces are affecting the air over San Francisco. (The air is moving in gusts; warm and cold air masses have met; air pressure is changing; there is probably rain; hail may be forming.)

▶ How would you describe the weather you are having right now? (Answers depend on the weather. Students might describe the temperature, how windy it is, where the wind is coming from, or increasing or decreasing cloudiness. Some may mention air pressure.)

### Writing About the Photograph

Suggest that students write a dialogue between two airplane passengers who are flying through this storm.

Unit **6**

# Earth's Atmosphere

### Chapters

**17** The Atmosphere
**18** Water in the Atmosphere
**19** Weather
**20** Climate

# Data Bank

Use the information on pages 612 to 625 to answer the following questions about topics explored in this unit.

## Interpreting a Map

Where are the high pressure systems located on the weather map? Where are the low pressure systems located?

## Making a Graph

Make a bar graph that shows the maximum daily temperatures in January of all the cities listed in the table. Which cities have similar climates in January?

## Reading a Table

What are three major air pollutants? What are some causes of these pollutants?

The photograph to the left is of lightning over San Francisco, California. What kind of weather did San Francisco have that evening? During what season do you think the photograph was taken?

## Overview

This chapter explores the earth's atmosphere. The first section explains the composition of air and its characteristics. The next section outlines the layers of the atmosphere. The third section follows the changes in the atmosphere through time and the role of air pollution in such changes. The chapter concludes with a discussion of potential solutions to air pollution.

## Advance Planner

▶ Supply potatoes and drinking straws for SE page 393.

▶ Gather balloons, and measuring tape for SE page 396.

▶ Display cake pans and construction paper for SE page 398.

▶ Gather plastic bottles, straws, droppers, food coloring, markers, metric rulers, clay, and funnels for Activity 17, SE page 401.

▶ Obtain *Around the World in Eighty Days* by Jules Verne for TE page 402.

▶ Provide carbonated beverages for SE page 406.

## Skills Development Chart

| Sections | Collect Data | Communicate | Compare | Find Causes | Hypothesize | Observe | Predict | Research |
|---|---|---|---|---|---|---|---|---|
| **17.1** Skills WarmUp | | | | | | ● | | |
| SkillBuilder | | | | | | ● | | |
| Skills WorkOut | | ● | | ● | | | | |
| Activity 17 | | ● | | | ● | ● | | |
| **17.2** Skills WarmUp | ● | | | | | | | |
| **17.3** Skills WarmUp | | | | | ● | | | |
| Skills WorkOut | ● | | | | | | ● | |
| Historical Notebook | | ● | ● | | | | | ● |

## Individual Needs

▶ **Limited English Proficiency Students** Ask students to make a picture dictionary of the boldface terms and any others they do not understand in the chapter. Have them divide several pages of their science portfolios into three columns. In the first column have them copy each term. In the second they should define it in their own words. In the third column have them draw a diagram or paste in a picture that illustrates the term.

▶ **At-Risk Students** Have students work together to plan a campaign to make younger children in their school aware of dangerous changes in the atmosphere. Their campaign should answer such questions as what the atmosphere is, why it is important, how people are damaging it, and what can be done to clean it up. Their campaign should cover smog, the greenhouse effect, and ozone depletion. If possible, they should visit other classes and make an illustrated oral presentation.

▶ **Gifted Students** Invite students to do research about the nitrogen cycle. As they investigate, they should try to answer such questions as what role nitrogen plays in life on the earth, what chemical processes are involved in the cycle, how lightning is involved, and what, if anything, threatens this cycle. Have them present their findings in a diagram with detailed labels and captions.

## Resource Bank

▶ **Bulletin Board** Divide the bulletin board into three sections labeled *Past, Present,* and *Future.* Have students work together to illustrate each section: for *Past* they should create a drawing and captions to illustrate the earth and its atmosphere billions of years ago; for *Present,* have them show conditions as they are today; for *Future* ask them to brainstorm ideas about how the atmosphere will change. They may wish to illustrate what they think will happen if people don't clean up the atmosphere, or they may wish to show an ideal future environment.

| Section | Core | Standard | Enriched | Section | Core | Standard | Enriched |
|---|:---:|:---:|:---:|---|:---:|:---:|:---:|
| **17.1 A Blanket of Air** pp. 393–401 | | | | **Color Transparencies** Transparency 52 | ● | ● | ● |
| **Section Features** Skills WarmUp, p. 393 SkillBuilder, p. 396 Skills WorkOut, p. 398 Skills WorkOut, p. 400 Activity, p. 401 | ● ● ● ● ● | ● ● ● ● ● | ● ● ● ● ● | **17.3 The Changing Atmosphere** pp. 406–410 | | | |
| **Blackline Masters** Review Worksheet 17.1 Reteach Worksheet 17.1 Integrating Worksheet 17.1a Integrating Worksheet 17.1b Integrating Worksheet 17.1c | ● ● ● ● ● | ● ● ● ● ● | ● ● ● ● ● | **Section Features** Skills WarmUp, p. 406 Skills WorkOut, p. 407 Historical Notebook, p. 409 Skills WorkOut, p. 410 | ● ● ● ● | ● ● ● ● | ● ● ● ● |
| **Laboratory Programs** Investigation 26 | | | | **Blackline Masters** Review Worksheet 17.3 Skills Worksheet 17.3 Integrating Worksheet 17.3 Vocabulary Worksheet 17.3 | ● ● ● ● | ● ● ● ● | ● ● ● |
| **Color Transparencies** Transparencies 49a, 49b, 50, 51 | ● | ● | ● | **Overhead Blackline Transparencies** Overhead Blackline Master 17.3 and Student Worksheet | ● | ● | ● |
| **17.2 Structure of the Atmosphere** pp. 402–405 | | | | **Ancillary Options** One-Minute Readings, pp. 52, 92 | | | ● |
| **Section Features** Skills WarmUp, p. 402 | ● | ● | ● | **Laboratory Program** Investigation 27 | ● | ● | |
| **Blackline Masters** Review Worksheet 17.2 Skills Worksheet 17.2 | ● ● | ● ● | ● ● | | | | |

# Bibliography

The following resources can be used for teaching the chapter. See page T–46 for supplier codes.

**Library Resources**

*Farndon, John. How the Earth Works. Pleasantville, NY: The Reader's Digest Association, Inc., 1992.*

*Hann, Judith. How Science Works. Pleasantville, NY: The Reader's Digest Association, Inc., 1991.*

*Schwartz, R. Mathematics and Global Survival, 2d ed. Needham Heights, MA: Ginn Press, 1990.*

**Technology Resources**

*Internet*

**PLANETDIARY** at *http://www.planetdiary.com*

• Learn more about the topics of *Volcano* and *Atmosphere* by clicking on *Phenomena Backgrounders.*

• Review meteorological news and health news in *Current Phenomena.*

*Software*

*Earth Explorer. Mac, Win. LS.*

*The Environment Land and Air. Win. ER.*

*Hothouse Planet. Mac, Win. ESI.*

*CD-ROMs*

*Interactive Earth. SFAW.*

*Laserdiscs*

*Living Textbook. (See barcodes on pages in this chapter.) Optical Data.*

*Videos*

*After the Warming. Two parts, 55 min. each. Ambrose Video.*

*Discovering Our Earth's Atmosphere. 30 min. MMI.*

*Greenhouse Crisis: The American Response. 11 min. Union of Concerned Scientists.*

*Audio-Visual Resources*

*The Atmosphere in Motion. Film. EB.*

### Cooperative Learning

Have students work in cooperative groups of four. They can brainstorm how the earth's atmosphere affects their lives. Have each group share the information on its list with the class. One student can make a master list on the chalkboard that presents the five most common responses.

## Introducing the Chapter

Have students read the description of the photograph. Ask if they agree or disagree with the description. You might want to mention that this effect is also called the northern lights.

### Directed Inquiry

Have students study the photograph. Ask:

▶ What is shown in this photograph? (Students may say colorful lights in a night sky above a forest. They may recognize the lights as an aurora.)

▶ What kind of trees are shown in this photograph? What does this tell you about where auroras take place? (Pines and other evergreens are more common in northern climates. Students may decide that the aurora borealis occurs in the northern latitudes.)

▶ What are the white streaks in the picture? (Students will probably say they are stars or planets. The photograph is a time exposure and the stars changed position while the camera's shutter was open.)

▶ How is the photograph related to the topic of this chapter? (The lights are produced by charged particles that collect in a specific region of the atmosphere.)

## Chapter Vocabulary

air pressure
atmosphere
conduction
greenhouse
  effect
nitrogen cycle

oxygen–carbon
  dioxide cycle
ozone
smog
troposphere

Chapter **17**  The Atmosphere

### Chapter Sections

**17.1**  A Blanket of Air

**17.2**  Structure of the Atmosphere

**17.3**  The Changing Atmosphere

### What do you see?

❝In this picture, I see a large cloud of colors. I think it's called an aurora borealis. I think the best place to see this would be the mountains, forests, or maybe even the North Pole. I mention these places because they do not have very much pollution, and the sky can be seen more clearly.❞

*Leticia Cruz*
*Belvedere Junior High*
*  School*
*Los Angeles, California*

To find out more about the photograph, look on page 412. As you read this chapter, you will learn about the composition and structure of the earth's atmosphere.

## Integrating the Sciences

**Chemistry** Until 1777, scientists thought that a mysterious substance called *phlogiston* was contained in all combustible materials. During burning, phlogiston was given off. In 1777, the French chemist Antoine-Laurent Lavoisier conducted experiments with burning material. He found that there was an increase in the weight of the material after burning. Lavoisier determined that burning was not the result of phlogiston release but the chemical combining of oxygen with a material.

**Section Objectives**
For a list of section objectives, see the Student Edition page.

**Skills Objectives**
Students should be able to:

**Observe** the effects of air pressure.

**Observe** how temperature affects the density of air.

**Find Causes** for how color and temperature are related.

**Communicate** how people protect themselves from the sun.

**Infer** how living things affect the composition of air.

**Observe** air pressure changes.

**Vocabulary**
oxygen–carbon dioxide cycle, nitrogen cycle, air pressure, conduction

## 17.1 A Blanket of Air

### Objectives

▶ **Describe** the ways that heat is transferred in air.

▶ **Explain** what happens to the sun's radiation as it passes to the earth.

▶ **Explain** how the density of air is related to air pressure.

▶ **Infer** how changes in the nitrogen cycle and oxygen–carbon dioxide cycle would affect the composition of air.

▼ **ACTIVITY**

**Observing**

*Potato Physics*

Place a potato on a table. Quickly thrust the end of a plastic drinking straw into the potato. What happens? Hold your thumb over the end of another straw and quickly thrust it into the potato. What happens? Why?

**SKILLS WARMUP**

Take a deep breath. You may not know it, but you will probably breathe about 26 000 times today alone. Your lungs will take in almost 11 000 L of air during a day. Without air, you could only live for several minutes. Almost all organisms need air to survive. Even though you probably don't think about it, air is very important to life on the earth.

### Composition of Air

Look at the composition of air shown in Figure 17.1. Notice that about 78 percent of air is nitrogen. Although most organisms can't use nitrogen directly, nitrogen reacts with other elements to form many compounds that are necessary for life. Oxygen is the next most plentiful gas. Plants and animals use oxygen directly from air to release their food energy during respiration. Plants also produce oxygen during the process of photosynthesis.

Although the amount of carbon dioxide present in air is very small, carbon dioxide is also essential for plant life. During photosynthesis, plants use carbon dioxide, sunlight, water, and materials from air to produce glucose. Glucose is a simple sugar used by plants for energy and growth.

Water vapor, argon, and trace gases, such as neon and helium, make up the rest of the gases contained in air. Water vapor is especially important because it absorbs heat energy from the sun and forms clouds and rain. The amount of water vapor contained in air can vary from 0 to 4 percent.

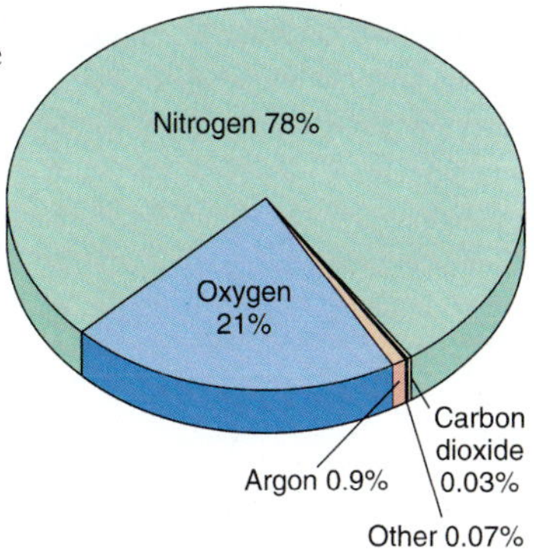

Nitrogen 78%

Oxygen 21%

Argon 0.9%

Carbon dioxide 0.03%

Other 0.07%

**Figure 17.1** ▲
Air is composed of many different chemicals.

## MOTIVATE

### Skills WarmUp

To help students understand that the atmosphere is made of matter, have them do the Skills WarmUp.
**Answer** Students should note that the open-ended straw bends and will not go into the potato; the closed straw pushes into the potato. Air takes up space in the straw. If the air cannot escape, it pushes against the sides of the straw to make the straw stronger. This prevents the straw from bending.

### Misconceptions

Students may think that air is not matter. The Skills WarmUp illustrates how air interacts with other matter physically. Students can observe how air affects other matter chemically by looking at something that has rusted.

## Critical Thinking

**Uncover Assumptions** Ask students to correct the false assumption in the following statement: "There is very little carbon dioxide in the atmosphere, so it must not be an important gas." (The assumption that a small amount is unimportant is incorrect. Plants use carbon dioxide during photosynthesis. Carbon dioxide is essential for plant life.)

### *Explore Visually*

After students have studied Figure 17.2, ask the following questions:

► What are fossil fuels? What part do they play in the oxygen–carbon dioxide cycle? (Remains of plants that don't decompose; they add carbon to the soil and if collected and burned, they release carbon dioxide into the atmosphere.)

► What part(s) do plants play in the oxygen–carbon dioxide cycle? (Living plants convert carbon dioxide to oxygen and carbon; when dead plants decompose, carbon returns to the earth; dead plants that do not decompose may be burned, releasing carbon dioxide.)

► What part(s) do animals play in the oxygen–carbon dioxide cycle? (Breathing animals take in oxygen and release carbon dioxide into the air; as dead animals decay, carbon returns to the earth.)

### *Art Connection*

Have students collect pictures of landscapes from magazines or from prints of paintings. Have them outline the flow of the nitrogen cycle and the oxygen–carbon dioxide cycle in each of the landscapes.

### *Themes in Science*

**Patterns of Change/Cycles** The chemical composition of atmospheric gases continuously changes as they pass through the oxygen–carbon dioxide cycle and the nitrogen cycle. Point out to students the repeating chemical changes that might occur in an individual oxygen and nitrogen molecule as they pass through these two cycles.

## The Oxygen–Carbon Dioxide Cycle

The **oxygen–carbon dioxide cycle** is a closed cycle in which the total amount of carbon and oxygen is kept constant. Look at Figure 17.2. Carbon moves between the atmosphere, inside the earth as fossil fuels, the soil, and the oceans. Carbon dioxide is essential for plants, algae, and some bacteria. Oxygen is released into the air by plants and algae, which absorb carbon dioxide.

**Figure 17.2
Cycles in Nature** ▼

Oxygen

Carbon dioxide

Carbon dioxide is converted to oxygen and carbon by plants through photosynthesis.

Fossil fuels—coal, oil, natural gas—came from dead organisms that did not decompose. When fossil fuels are burned, carbon returns to the air as carbon dioxide.

Carbon dioxide

Carbon dioxide

When a plant or animal dies, the carbon in the organism returns to the earth as decomposers decay the organism.

## Integrating the Sciences

**Life Science** Some of the bacteria that aid in nitrogen fixation live freely in the soil. Other nitrogen-fixing bacteria live on the root nodules of legumes. Beans, peas, clover, and soybeans are examples of legumes. Show students the nodules on the root of a legume plant. Ask them how the nitrogen-fixing bacteria help plants. (Nitrogen forms amino acids that the plants need for proper growth.)

## The Nitrogen Cycle

The **nitrogen cycle** is a closed cycle in which the total amount of nitrogen on the earth is kept constant. Nitrogen helps support life by building proteins and other body chemicals. Nitrogen in the air can't be used directly by most organisms. To be useful, nitrogen is removed from the air and combined with other elements to form nitrogen compounds. This process is called *nitrogen fixation*.

After nitrogen is converted to compounds by lightning, it is washed out of the air by rain and deposited into the soil.

Nitrogen compounds

Nitrogen compounds

When coal or gasoline is burned, nitrogen is released in the form of nitric oxides.

Soil bacteria produce nitrogen compounds from decaying organisms and animal wastes. Denitrifying bacteria break down these compounds to form nitrogen gas.

During nitrogen fixation, bacteria that live on root nodules remove pure nitrogen from the air and release it into the soil.

Nitrogen

Nitrogen compounds

Decomposers

▶ What part of the plant contributes to the nitrogen cycle? Why? (The roots; they provide a home for nitrogen-fixing bacteria.)

▶ What is nitrogen fixation? (Bacteria remove pure nitrogen from the air and release it into the soil.)

▶ What part do decomposers play in the nitrogen cycle? (They break down dead organisms and wastes, and release nitrogen compounds into the soil.)

▶ What two ways form pure nitrogen gas? (By bacteria during nitrogen fixation and by denitrifying bacteria)

**Interpret Data** Ask students to identify at least two events that contribute to both the oxygen–carbon dioxide cycle and the nitrogen cycle. (As an organism decays, carbon returns to the earth and soil bacteria produce nitrogen; when coal or gasoline is burned, carbon dioxide and nitric oxides are released into the air.)

## TEACH ▪ Continued

### Skills Development

**Make a Model** On the chalkboard, draw a seacoast with mountains rising near it. Have students suggest labels for the drawing that show how air density changes as distance from the surface and air temperature decrease or increase.

### SkillBuilder

Help students recognize that temperature affects the density of air in a closed system.

**Answers**

1. Largest after the warm water, smallest after the cold water

2. The circumference increased because the energy of the air molecules increased, and they moved farther apart; it decreased when the air molecules lost energy and moved closer together.

3. They were most dense in the balloon with the smaller circumference, and least dense in the balloon with the larger circumference. The balloon contained the same number (mass) of molecules in each instance. Density is mass/volume. If the mass is constant and the volume increases, density must decrease.

Paragraphs will vary.

### Integrating the Sciences

**Physical Science** Demonstrate the force of air pressure. Fill a deep bowl three-fourths full with water. Tape a paper towel to the inside bottom of a short glass. Ask the students to predict what will happen to the paper towel if the glass is placed upside down into the bowl. Insert the glass into the water and have students observe what takes place. (The force of the air pressure inside the glass prevents the water from filling the glass.)

 ### History Connection

Air pressure was first discovered by Evangelista Torricelli in the early 1600s. Torricelli filled a 1-meter glass tube with mercury. When he held the tube in a bowl of mercury, the mercury in the tube dropped to 76 centimeters. Torricelli concluded that the pressure of the air on the mercury in the bowl prevented the mercury in the tube from emptying completely from the tube.

### Air Density

Recall that density is a measurement of how much matter is packed into a certain volume. Since air is composed of gas molecules, air has density. Gravity affects the density of air. Gravity decreases as you move away from the surface of the earth. Therefore, farther from the surface, the air density decreases as well.

Where would you find more dense air? At a mountaintop, or at sea level? Since a mountaintop is farther from the surface of the earth, it would usually have less dense air than sea level. However, air density is affected by temperature as well as by gravity. In some instances, the temperature offsets the effect of gravity.

Cold air is more dense than warm air. When air is heated, the molecules gain energy and move apart from one another. The air becomes less dense. When air is cooled, the molecules lose energy and move closer together. The density of the air increases.

### SkillBuilder *Observing*

#### Temperature and the Density of Air

Temperature causes the molecules in air to move closer together or farther apart. The distance between the molecules determines the density of the air. Trapped air inside a balloon can show how temperature affects the density of air.

Blow up a round balloon and tie the end. Using a measuring tape, carefully measure the circumference of the balloon as shown. Record the circumference. Place the balloon in hot water for 10 minutes. Remove the balloon, measure the circumference, and record. Now place the balloon in ice water for 10 minutes. Remove the balloon, measure the circumference, and record.

1. Which circumference was the largest? The smallest?

2. What happened to the air molecules to make the circumference increase? To make it decrease?

3. In which balloon were the air molecules the most dense? The least dense? How could you tell?

Write a short report explaining how temperature affects the density of air.

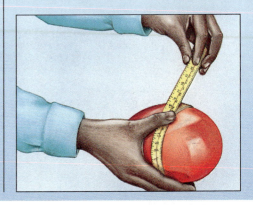

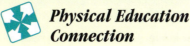
## Air Pressure

Recall that gas is matter. Since all matter has mass, gas also has mass. Gases in the air push against each other and push down on the surface of the earth. When you blow up a balloon or inflate a bicycle tire, you probably notice an increase in pressure as the air pushes against the sides. The force that air exerts in an area is called **air pressure**. The standard used for measuring air pressure is the air pressure at sea level, or atmosphere.

Every day your whole body is being pushed on by many kilograms of gas above you. You don't even notice this tremendous pressure. The air in your body pushes out with a pressure equal to the pressure of the surrounding air.

The density of air and air pressure are directly related. Figure 17.3 shows what happens to air pressure at different heights. At greater heights, the density of the air decreases, so the air pressure decreases as well.

Like density, air pressure is affected by temperature. Air becomes less dense as it is heated and exerts less pressure. If air is cooled, the density and air pressure increase.

The amount of water in air can change the air pressure. Water vapor molecules are smaller and lighter than many gas molecules. When water molecules take the place of larger, heavier molecules, the air pressure decreases.

**Figure 17.3**

How are the density of air and the air pressure related to the height above the surface of the earth? ▶ ①

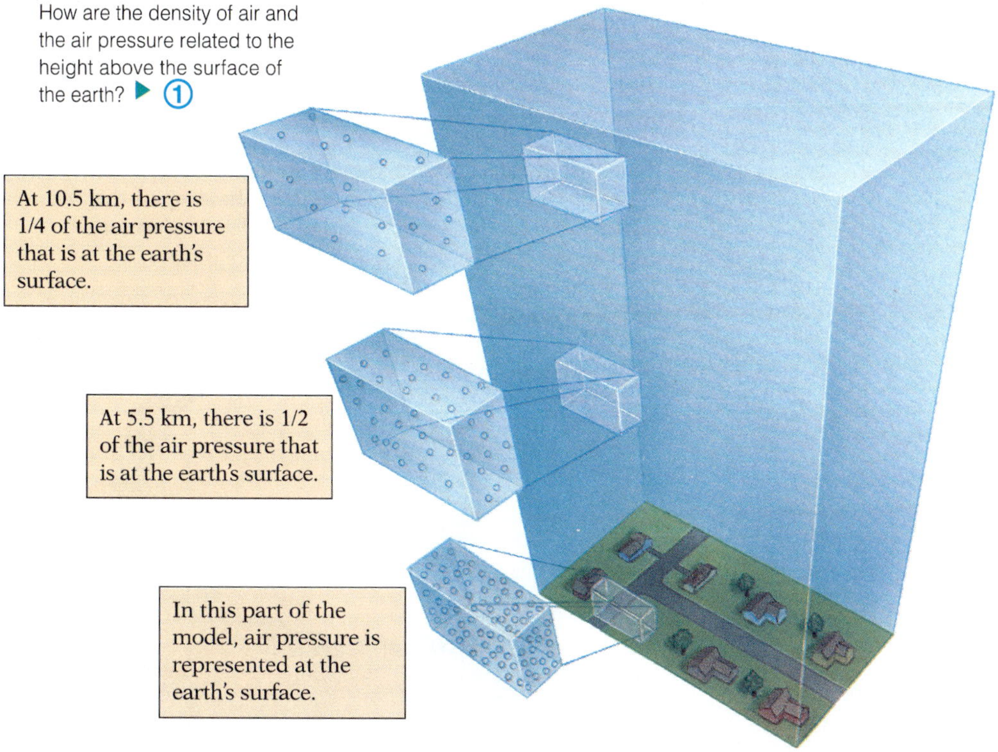

At 10.5 km, there is 1/4 of the air pressure that is at the earth's surface.

At 5.5 km, there is 1/2 of the air pressure that is at the earth's surface.

In this part of the model, air pressure is represented at the earth's surface.

## TEACH ▪ Continued

### Skills WorkOut

To help students understand how color affects heat transfer, have them do the Skills WorkOut.

**Answer** The temperature is likely to be higher in the pan lined with black paper. The black paper absorbed energy from the sunlight, which increased the temperature. Air touching the paper was warmed by conduction; the warmed air could set up small convection cells near the surface of the paper to raise the temperature of the air in the pan.

### Critical Thinking

**Classify** Write phrases describing convection and conduction on the chalkboard. Then have students classify the phrases as conduction or convection. Include phrases such as "Heated air rises then falls" (convection), "Transfers heat from particle to particle" (conduction), "Raises temperature of air touching the earth" (conduction), "Moves heat in the earth's mantle" (convection), and so on.

### Skills Development

**Make a Model** Have students draw pictures that illustrate both conduction and convection. Ideas include a charcoal grill or campfire, the transfer of heat in the air above the earth, and boiling a liquid in a pot. Ask them to label places where conduction and convection take place.

### Answer to In-Text Question

① **Answers will vary, but may include in pots of heated water, hot water heaters, and refrigerators.**

### Answer to Link

Generally, the SPF refers to the number of hours it would take, using the sunscreen, to receive the same amount of sun exposure you would get in an hour without the sunscreen. The SPF number students would require during a typical summer or winter day will vary.

## Integrating the Sciences

**Physical Science** Direct transfer of heat from particle to particle is known as conduction. Some materials are better at conducting heat energy than others. Place a metal, plastic, glass, and wooden spoon or stir stick into a mug of hot water. Ask the students to infer which material will conduct heat energy easily and which will not. (Metal conducts heat easily, the others do not.)

## Themes in Science

**Energy** The energy contained in the gas molecules in air determine the pressure and temperature of air. Energy from the sun in the form of heat, visible light, and radiation travels through the air, eventually reaching the earth.

## Energy in the Air

The movement of gas molecules in air does more than change the air pressure. The energy of the gas molecules also determines the temperature of the air. When air molecules gain energy, they move faster and the air temperature rises. When air molecules lose energy, they slow down and the air temperature drops. The energy of the molecules in air can change through three processes: conduction, convection, and radiation.

**Heat Transfer** Several processes work to reduce the difference between temperatures at the earth's surface and temperatures higher in the atmosphere. One of the processes that moves heat away from the surface is **conduction.** Conduction is the direct transfer of heat from particle to particle. Air touching the surface of the earth is heated by conduction. The movement of heat from the surface to the air transfers heat away from the earth.

Another process that moves heat away from the earth's surface is convection. Convection is the transfer of heat in gas or liquid. Recall that heat in the earth's mantle moves by convection. Convection in the air is similar to convection in the mantle. Heated air rises and cools to form a convection cell. Convection cells move heated air to warm a room, as shown in Figure 17.4. Convection cells are also present in the atmospheric air that surrounds the earth. The uneven heating of the earth between the equator and the poles sets up large convection currents in the earth's atmosphere.

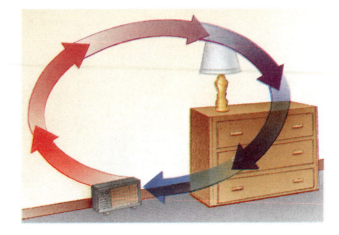

**Figure 17.4 ▶**
Convection cells form in air to warm a room. Where else might you find convection cells in your home? ①

## Integrating the Sciences

**Physical Science** The radiant energy that the earth receives from the sun is only a portion of the types of radiant energy that exist. Obtain a chart of the electromagnetic spectrum. Point out to students that electromagnetic waves travel through empty space. Have student volunteers locate ultraviolet and visible waves. Tell students that ultraviolet waves help create heat on the earth.

**Astronomy** Venus has a very thick cloud layer compared to Earth. Mercury has no atmosphere. Have students infer how the atmospheric conditions on Venus and Mercury affect the amount of solar radiation absorbed or reflected from these two planets. (Given its dense cloud cover, Venus must not absorb much solar radiation, whereas Mercury must absorb significant radiation given its lack of atmospheric protection.)

**Radiation** Energy that can travel through empty space is called radiant energy or radiation. The earth receives energy from the sun by radiation. This radiant energy is in the form of visible light, ultraviolet radiation, and infrared radiation.

Look at Figure 17.5. What happens to the sun's radiation as it passes to the earth? Over 50 percent of the solar radiation is absorbed or reflected by the atmosphere before reaching the surface of the earth. Almost all of the harmful ultraviolet radiation is absorbed. Clouds reflect 25 percent of the visible light that travels toward the earth back into space.

Of the radiation that reaches the surface of the earth, some is absorbed and some is reflected. The solar energy reaching the surface that is reflected varies from as high as 95 percent for fresh white snow to only 5 percent for a black asphalt road. About 70 percent of the solar energy that reaches the earth's surface is absorbed. This high percentage of absorption causes very high temperatures in areas near the equator where the sun shines for many hours.

### Life Science
### L I N K

Research the labels of sunscreen and sunblock products. Draw a graph showing the relationship between sun protection factor (SPF) numbers and the length of time you are protected from the sun.

Which SPF number would you require for an average summer day? Which would you need for a day in winter?

**A C T I V I T Y**

**Figure 17.5**
What might happen to radiant
② energy passing to the earth? ▼

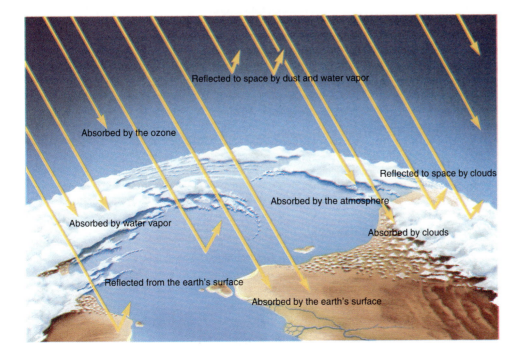

Reflected to space by dust and water vapor

Absorbed by the ozone

Reflected to space by clouds

Absorbed by the atmosphere

Absorbed by water vapor

Absorbed by clouds

Reflected from the earth's surface

Absorbed by the earth's surface

## Class Activity

Have students work in groups to make graphs showing what happens to the sun's radiation as it travels to the earth. Have each group make a graph of radiation passing through the atmosphere: Absorbed or Reflected by Atmosphere (about 50%), Reaches the earth's Surface (about 50%), Reflected by Clouds and Atmosphere (about 25%), Absorbed by Clouds and Atmosphere (about 25%), Reaches the earth's Surface (about 50%). Then have each group make a graph showing what happens to the radiation that reaches the earth: Absorbed by the earth (about 70%) and Reflected by the earth's Surface (about 30%).

## Skills Development

**Infer** Have students infer how the earth would be affected if all of the sun's radiation reached the earth's surface. (Answers may include: temperature would be higher, skin cancer may rise, snow would melt.) Then ask students how the earth would be different if none of the sun's radiation reached the earth's surface. (Answers may include: temperature would be lower, all plants would die, all animals would die.)

## Reteach

Use Reteach Worksheet 17.1.

**Answer to In-Text Question**

② **It might be absorbed or reflected by clouds, the atmosphere, or the earth's surface.**

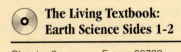

**The Living Textbook:
Earth Science Sides 1-2**

Chapter 2          Frame 00799
Atmosphere and Radiation (1 Frame)
Search:

**399**

## TEACH ▪ Continued

### Skills WorkOut

To help students communicate, have them do the Skills WorkOut **Answer** Answers will vary. Have students check their work either by making a pie graph of the results or adding the percentages

### Enrich

Have students collect articles on the possible damaging effects of too much exposure to the sun. Have them list any preventive measures suggested.

### Integrated Learning

Use Integrating Worksheet 17.1c.

## EVALUATE

### WrapUp

**Reteach** Draw two circles on the chalkboard. Ask volunteers to add to the circles to complete an oxygen–carbon dioxide cycle and a nitrogen cycle.

Use Review Worksheet 17.1.

### Check and Explain

1. In conduction, particles transfer energy during their collisions with each other. During convection, warmed, less-dense air rises, then cools and sets up a circulation pattern that transfers heat from one place to another.

2. Clouds reflect 25 percent of visible light back into space. Once light reaches the earth's surface, it may be reflected or absorbed.

3. Air pressure decreases because density decreases.

4. Without plants there would be less oxygen in the atmosphere and less absorption of carbon dioxide. Without nitrogen-fixing bacteria or denitrifying bacteria, nitrogen would not be released into the soil and the nitrogen cycle would be broken.

**400**

---

## Integrating the Sciences

**Health** Vitamin D is one of the 13 essential vitamins that the human body needs each day to maintain health. Vitamin D is not naturally present in most foods; however, it is routinely added to milk and other dairy products. The body uses sunlight to make the vitamin, and ten minutes of sunlight each day allows for sufficient formation of vitamin D. Most other vitamins can be obtained from foods that are part of a well-balanced diet. Have students do research to find out the dietary sources for the other 12 vitamins.

---

## Science and You
### Protecting Yourself from the Sun

On a sunny, warm day, you may spend the day outdoors at the park, the beach, or in your yard. The sunshine heats your clothes and skin. After staying in the sun for a while, you may notice that your skin becomes darker, or tanned, where it was exposed to the sun. Or maybe your skin becomes red, or burned, from sun exposure.

All skin types are affected by radiation from the sun. Some ultraviolet, or UV, radiation is necessary for the formation of vitamin D. Vitamin D helps your bones develop. However, too much UV radiation is dangerous for anyone. Overexposure to UV radiation can cause sunburn, skin cancer, snow blindness, eye cataracts, and skin aging. UV exposure can lower your body's defenses against diseases that enter through the skin.

To avoid exposing your skin to large amounts of UV radiation, there are several things you can do. Between the hours of 10:00 a.m. and 3:00 p.m., the sun's radiation is strongest, even on cloudy days. During the middle of the day, stay out of the sun, wear protective clothing, or put on a sunscreen.

When buying a sunscreen, look for the sun protection factor, or SPF, on the bottle. This number tells you how well the sunscreen blocks UV radiation. Use a sunscreen with an SPF of 15 or greater. A 15 SPF means that it takes 15 hours to receive the same amount of UV radiation that you would get in 1 hour without the sunscreen.

### ▼ ACTIVITY

**Communicating**

*Melting in the Sun*

Take a survey of ten people to see how they protect themselves from the sun. Questions should be the same as those asked by your classmates. Combine the results of your survey with the rest of the class. What percentage of the people surveyed use sunscreen? Avoid the sun? Wear protective clothing?

**SKILLS WORKOUT**

### Check and Explain

1. Describe the movement of air molecules during the transfer of heat by conduction and convection.

2. Describe what happens to visible light as it travels from the sun to the surface of the earth.

3. **Reason and Conclude** The density of air decreases as you climb a mountain. What happens to the air pressure as you climb higher? Why?

4. **Infer** How would air composition change if there were no plants? No nitrogen-fixing bacteria? No denitrifying bacteria?

### Prelab Discussion

Have students read the entire activity. Discuss the following points before beginning:

▶ Review the causes of atmospheric pressure.

▶ Discuss how the water level in the straw can be higher than the water level in the bottle.

▶ Discuss the effects of temperature on an enclosed gas.

▶ Describe the operation of a barometer and compare it to the apparatus used in this activity.

**Time** 3 days    **Groups** pairs

**Materials**

15 empty 0.5 L plastic soda bottles

15 clear plastic drinking straws

15 droppers

food coloring

15 marking pens

15 metric rulers

clay

15 funnels

## Activity 17 *How can you observe the pressure of air?*

**Skills** Observe; Infer

**Task 1 Prelab Prep**

1. Collect the following items: water, food coloring, empty 0.5 L soda bottle, clear plastic drinking straw, marking pen, metric ruler, dropper, clay, funnel.

2. Add several drops of food coloring to the water.

3. Using the marking pen, draw marks on the drinking straw that are 1 cm apart.

**Task 2 Data Record**

1. On a separate sheet of paper, copy Table 17.1.

2. Record all your observations in the data table.

**Table 17.1 Water Levels**

|  | Day 1 | Day 2 | Day 3 |
|---|---|---|---|
| Weather |  |  |  |
| Height of water |  |  |  |

**Task 3 Procedure**

1. Pour colored water into the empty soda bottle until the bottle is about 1/3 full.

2. Hold the straw in the water until it is just below the surface of the water. Seal the straw securely in place with the clay.

3. Use the dropper to drop water into the straw until it is about halfway up the straw. Your air-pressure bottle should look like the one shown in Figure 17.7.

4. Place your air-pressure bottle in a place where the temperature will remain fairly constant.

5. Measure the height of the water in the straw, starting from the marks at the bottom. Record your measurement in the data table.

6. Measure the height of the water in the drinking straw for several days. Record your measurements in the data table.

**Task 4 Analysis**

1. What happened to the water in the drinking straw?

2. Did the weather affect the height of the water in the drinking straw? How do you know? Explain your observations.

3. If the air pressure outside of the bottle decreases, how will the water level inside the straw change? Why?

**Task 5 Conclusion**

Write a short paragraph explaining how air pressure can be observed.

### Everyday Application

Instruments that measure air pressure are called barometers. Barometers help predict the weather. When the air pressure drops, it often means rainy weather. High air pressure readings mean fair weather. Over the period of several days, use a barometer. Record your observations. Can the barometer predict the weather? Explain your conclusions.

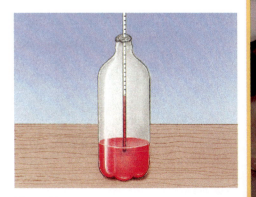

**Figure 17.7** ▲

## Analysis

1. The water in the drinking straw should have risen and/or fallen over the course of observation.

2. Student answers will vary. Make sure answers correspond to recorded data.

3. The pressure on the bottle will decrease, allowing the weight of the water in the straw to push water back into the bottle.

## Conclusion

Changes in air pressure can be observed by measuring the rise and fall of a column of liquid in an otherwise enclosed container of air.

## Everyday Application

An accurate, functioning barometer should respond to changes in atmospheric pressure that accompany changes in the weather.

### Section Objectives
For a list of section objectives, see the Student Edition page.

### Skills Objectives
Students should be able to:

**Collect Data** about the sky.

**Predict** changes in the earth if the atmosphere didn't have layers.

### Vocabulary
atmosphere, ozone, troposphere

### Literature Connection
Have students read *Around the World in Eighty Days* by Jules Verne. Verne wrote this book in 1873. Discuss with students how Verne might change his story if he wrote it based on current knowledge about the atmosphere.

### Themes in Science
**Scale and Structure** The structure of the atmosphere is divided into unique layers. The structure of each layer is defined by its molecules, its height from the surface, and its temperature. Each layer of the atmosphere plays a role in the overall behavior of the atmospheric system.

## MOTIVATE

### Skills WarmUp
To help students understand the characteristics of the different layers of the atmosphere, have them do the Skills WarmUp.

**Answer** Lists will vary. Students might include insects, birds, kites, clouds, aircraft, satellites, meteors, the moon, the sun, stars, and the planets.

### Prior Knowledge
To gauge how much students know about the structure of the atmosphere, ask the following questions:

▶ Why don't airplanes fly in outer space?

▶ Why does a helium balloon float?

▶ Why do mountain climbers sometimes need an oxygen supply?

**The Living Textbook: Earth Science Sides 1-2**

Chapter 2       Frame 00801
Earth's Atmosphere (1 Frame)
Search:

▼ **ACTIVITY**

**Collecting Data**

*In the Sky*

Make a list of everything you have ever seen in the sky. Combine your list with those of your classmates. What objects were most commonly listed?

**SKILLS WARMUP**

# 17.2 Structure of the Atmosphere

## Objectives

▶ **Name** the layers of the atmosphere, from the closest to the farthest layer from the surface of the earth.

▶ **Explain** how the atmosphere affects life on the earth.

▶ **Compare** and **contrast** the magnetosphere and the ionosphere.

▶ **Predict** the changes that would occur on the earth if the atmospheric layers did not exist.

**W**hen you look up at the sky on a sunny day, you may see many fluffy clouds or an airplane moving across the blue sky. It seems like you can see forever. On a clear night, you view the light from the many stars that penetrate the sky. Now you *can* almost see forever.

### Atmospheric Layers

Air that surrounds a planet is called the **atmosphere**. The atmosphere of the earth extends from the surface to about 1,000 km. The earth's atmosphere is composed of several layers of air with different characteristics.

The atmosphere is important to the earth. The layers affect climate, photosynthesis, and even the height of thunderstorms. Meteorites traveling toward the earth burn up from the friction of passing through the atmospheric layers. The atmosphere provides a method for redistributing heat. The layer of atmosphere closest to the surface supports life.

Nineteenth-century meteorologists investigated the first several thousand meters of the atmosphere by using hot-air balloons. Early in this century, scientists made measurements using aircraft and hydrogen-filled balloons. In the last 50 years, sophisticated ways to measure the atmosphere included balloons that radio data back to the earth, rockets, high-flying aircraft, and satellites. This technology helped uncover an atmosphere with distinct layers.

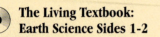

**Figure 17.8** ▲
This weather balloon released in Australia will travel high into the atmosphere.

## STS Connection

Meteors burn up when they pass through the mesosphere. However, spaceships pass through the mesosphere without burning up. Have students research how this is possible. (The cone on a spaceship deflects the heat from the sides of the ship. Also, the tiles on a spaceship are insulated to withstand high temperatures.)

## Language Arts Connection

Have students look up the meanings for the prefixes *tropo-, strato-, meso-, thermo-,* and *exo-.* Ask them why they think each prefix was chosen for each layer of the atmosphere. (*Tropo-* means "a turning," *strato-* means "stratum," *meso-* means "middle," *thermo-* means "heat," and *exo-* means "outer.")

### Explore Visually

After students study Figure 17.9, ask the following questions:

▶ Where is the troposphere? (It extends from the earth's surface to anywhere from 8 to 20 km above the surface.)

▶ In what layer do all organisms live? (Troposphere)

▶ If you were launching a satellite, how high would it have to go in order to orbit the planet? (At least 300 km)

▶ In what part of the atmosphere do auroras occur? How high is this? (In the ionosphere; from about 90 to about 250 km above the earth)

▶ Where is the ozone layer? (Upper stratosphere)

### Skills Development

**Infer** Ask students to determine which level of the atmosphere is the most dense and which is least dense. Have them explain their answers. (Troposphere, exosphere; Troposphere is 20 km thick at most, yet it contains over half the earth's atmosphere; exosphere is so far from the earth that gravity cannot affect air.)

**Interpret Data** Ask students to bring in newspaper weather reports. Have them identify the level(s) of the atmosphere associated with the report. (Almost all weather occurs in the troposphere; weather satellites travel in the exosphere.)

---

**Exosphere** The *exosphere* is the outermost layer of the atmosphere. The exosphere extends to the outer edges of space, several thousand kilometers from the earth. Light gases escape from the exosphere to outer space.

**Thermosphere** Below the exosphere is the *thermosphere*. Thermosphere temperatures increase rapidly with height, reaching 1,200°C. The air in the thermosphere is not very dense. The thermosphere is greatly affected by the sun's radiation.

**Mesosphere** The *mesosphere* extends from the stratosphere to the thermosphere. Mesosphere temperatures decrease with height.

**Stratosphere** The *stratosphere* contains the gas **ozone** (OH zohn). Ozone protects the earth from excessive ultraviolet radiation. Little air exchange occurs between the troposphere and the stratosphere. Gases released during violent volcanic eruptions remain in the stratosphere for years before settling into the troposphere. Very high clouds and large thunderstorms penetrate this layer, but weather generally does not occur here.

**Troposphere** The **troposphere** (TROH puh sfihr) is the layer of air closest to the surface of the earth. It contains over half of all the air in the atmosphere. The height varies from about 20 km at the equator to 8 km at the poles. Temperature in the troposphere decreases with height, which is why mountaintops are much colder than valleys. Almost all weather occurs in the troposphere. Most pollution also remains in the troposphere.

**Figure 17.9**
**Atmospheric Layers** ▶

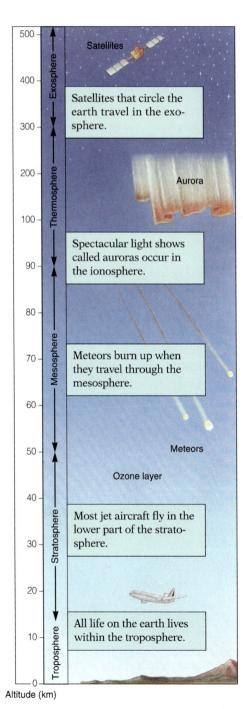

Satellites that circle the earth travel in the exosphere.

Spectacular light shows called auroras occur in the ionosphere.

Meteors burn up when they travel through the mesosphere.

Most jet aircraft fly in the lower part of the stratosphere.

All life on the earth lives within the troposphere.

Altitude (km)

**TEACH ▪ Continued**

### Reteach

Draw on the chalkboard a circle representing the earth. Ask a volunteer to add to the drawing a line that indicates the ionosphere. Have another volunteer draw radio waves or signals sent from a transmitter on the earth. Ask students to explain how the ionosphere allows radio transmissions from one location to be received at a distant point on the globe. (The ionosphere reflects some radio waves back to earth.)

### Skills Development

**Organize Data** Have students make a table that lists the characteristics of the ionosphere and the magnetosphere. Then ask them to indicate how the solar winds affect each. (*Ionosphere:* Solar radiation creates ion layer, ion layer reflects radio waves, solar wind causes ions to emit light. *Magnetosphere:* Solar wind particles trapped by the earth's magnetic field; contains belt of charged particles wider on the side of the earth away from the sun due to the solar wind.)

**Answer to In-Text Question**
① In the magnetosphere

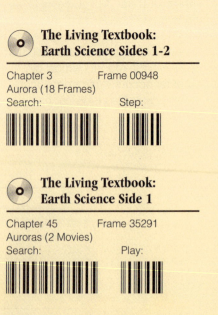

**The Living Textbook: Earth Science Sides 1-2**

Chapter 3          Frame 00948
Aurora (18 Frames)
Search:                    Step:

**The Living Textbook: Earth Science Side 1**

Chapter 45        Frame 35291
Auroras (2 Movies)
Search:                    Play:

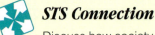 **STS Connection**

Discuss how society today depends on the ionosphere. Have students discuss how the importance of the ionosphere to people has changed over the last 200 years.

### Integrating the Sciences

**Physical Science** Demonstrate a magnetic field using a bar magnet and iron filings. Place the bar magnet on a sheet of paper. Sprinkle the iron filings around the bar magnet. Have students observe and draw the pattern of the iron filings. Ask them how the iron filings model the magnetosphere. (The filings become trapped in the magnet's magnetic field just as charged particles are trapped in the earth's magnetosphere.)

## Ionosphere

The *ionosphere* (eye AHN oh sfihr) is a layer of air within the upper mesosphere and the thermosphere. It is not a distinct atmospheric layer by itself. Solar radiation passing through the ionosphere strips atoms and molecules of their electrons. The atoms and molecules become charged particles called ions. These ions reflect radio waves like a mirror reflects light. The ionosphere allows radio signals to travel by bouncing between the surface of the earth and the ionosphere.

At night, the ionosphere increases in height. Look at Figure 17.10. How does this height change affect radio signals? Notice that radio waves can travel farther at night than during the day. As a result, the signals can travel farther on the earth's surface.

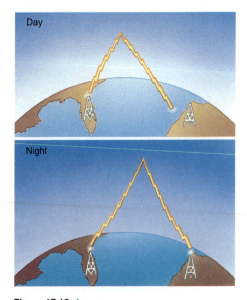

**Figure 17.10 ▲**
The ionosphere reflects radio waves, allowing for worldwide communication.

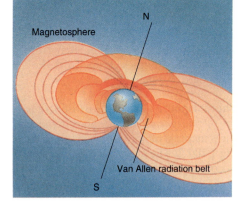

**Figure 17.11 ▲**
Locate the magnetosphere. Where is the Van Allen radiation belt? ①

## Magnetosphere

The outermost region of the atmosphere is called the *magnetosphere*. The magnetosphere is created by the earth's magnetic field and the sun. The sun continuously emits electrically-charged particles called ions. The fast-moving stream of ions, or solar wind, become trapped in the earth's magnetic field. The trapped ions make up the magnetosphere.

Solar wind travels at speeds up to 400 km per second. The solar wind causes the magnetosphere to compress on the side toward the sun and stretch out on the side away from the sun.

The magnetosphere contains a doughnut-shaped belt of charged particles that surrounds the earth. This band is shown in Figure 17.11. It is called the Van Allen radiation belt.

Solar wind also changes the ionosphere. When the solar wind enters the ionosphere, an aurora may occur. An aurora looks like sheets of blue-green light in the sky. The lights occur because the solar wind causes ions to emit energy in the form of light.

## Portfolio

Students can find out how weather affects the transmission of radio signals. For several days, have students record the number and location of the various AM radio stations that they can receive. They should also record the time of day and the weather conditions. Have students keep their records in their portfolios. When the weather conditions change in the area, have them repeat the activity.

### Skills Development

**Communicate** Have students describe the ways in which ions help and hinder radio communication. (*Help:* Ionosphere reflects AM radio transmissions. *Hinder:* Charged particles produce magnetic storms that interrupt transmission; high temperatures produce a blanket of ions around a spacecraft and radio communication is interrupted.)

### WrapUp

**Portfolio** Ask students to draw diagrams of the atmosphere. Remind them to include the five major layers, the ionosphere, and the magnetosphere. Have them label the layers and list several characteristics of each. Encourage them to keep their drawings in their portfolios.

Use Review Worksheet 17.2.

### Check and Explain

1. Troposphere, stratosphere, mesosphere, thermosphere, exosphere

2. Answers will vary. Gases in the troposphere are necessary for life; ozone in the stratosphere protects life from UV radiation; some layers absorb the sun's radiation and redistribute heat.

3. Both contain charged particles and both are affected by solar wind. The ionosphere is formed by solar radiation; the magnetosphere is made up of trapped solar particles; the ionosphere is closer to the earth than the magnetosphere.

4. Troposphere: no life; Stratosphere: increased UV radiation; Mesosphere: more meteors would reach the earth; Thermosphere: no aurorae; Exosphere: some light gases would not escape into space.

## Science and Technology
### *Loud and Clear?*

When you tune in a radio station to listen to your favorite music, you probably don't think about how far the signal has traveled to reach your radio. On AM radio, the signals have probably traveled from the broadcast antenna to the ionosphere and then bounced back to your radio antenna. AM and other shortwave radio signals bounce back and forth between the ionosphere and the earth. They may travel thousands of kilometers. FM radio signals are not reflected by the ionosphere, so they don't travel long distances.

Although the ionosphere allows shortwave signals to travel great distances, it can create noise in the signals. During solar flares the sun releases great amounts of charged particles. The charged particles enter the ionosphere where they produce magnetic storms. These magnetic storms may cause radio fade-outs that can last for several hours, or they may cause noise in the radio signal known as static.

Radio signals are important for communication between astronauts and scientists on the earth. However, when a spacecraft begins to enter the atmosphere, there is a disruption of signals that lasts for 10 to 15 minutes. This area is called the blackout zone. The blackout zone occurs when air friction on the craft reaches such high temperatures that the air molecules ionize. The spacecraft is surrounded by ions that prohibit any radio communication between the earth and the spacecraft.

**Figure 17.12** ▲
Besides music and a clear voice, disc jockeys also need the atmosphere.

### Check and Explain

1. Starting at the surface of the earth, list each layer of the atmosphere by increasing altitude.

2. Why is the atmosphere important to life on the earth? Explain your reasoning.

3. **Compare and Contrast** How are the ionosphere and the magnetosphere the same? How do they differ?

4. **Predict** For each layer of the atmosphere, predict how the earth would change if the layer suddenly disappeared.

## Section Objectives
For a list of section objectives, see the Student Edition page.

## Skills Objectives
Students should be able to:

**Hypothesize** how ocean warming would affect the amount of carbon dioxide in the air.

**Predict** how the atmosphere will change in 100 years.

**Collect Data** about CFC sources.

**Compare** the composition of the early atmosphere with today's atmosphere.

## Vocabulary
smog, greenhouse effect

### Themes in Science
**Evolution** The earth's atmosphere has evolved, or changed over time. The earth's current atmosphere is very different from the ancient atmosphere. This evolution occurs due to changes in the prominent landforms and organisms on the surface of the earth.

### Integrating the Sciences
**Chemistry** Scientists can learn much of the history of the atmosphere by analyzing the chemical composition of air pockets in the ice sheets at the poles. Chemical analysis has provided evidence that the earth's atmosphere has constantly changed throughout time. For example, carbon dioxide in ancient antarctic ice provides evidence that the climate at the South Pole was once much warmer.

## ▼ MOTIVATE

### Skills WarmUp
To help students understand changes in the atmosphere, have them do the Skills WarmUp.

**Answer** Students may choose either hypothesis. In working with carbonated beverages, students should find that the warmer the carbonated liquid, the more gas is released.

### Prior Knowledge
To gauge how much students know about climate change, ask the following questions:

► What is an ice age?

► What is global warming?

► What would it take to change the climate of the area where you live?

### ▼ ACTIVITY

**Hypothesizing**

*Rising Bubbles*

Much of the carbon dioxide in the early atmosphere was absorbed by the oceans. If the oceans warmed, would they release or absorb carbon dioxide? Gather data to form a hypothesis. Test your hypothesis by comparing the amount of carbon dioxide released from carbonated beverages at different temperatures.

**SKILLS WARMUP**

**Figure 17.13**
The early atmosphere was probably created by volcanic eruptions. ▼

# 17.3 The Changing Atmosphere

## Objectives

► **Describe** the early atmosphere of the earth.

► **Explain** how the atmosphere has changed through time.

► **Compare** the early atmosphere and the current atmosphere.

► **Predict** the effects of pollution on the atmosphere.

The atmosphere around you constantly changes. As you read this book, oxygen converts to carbon dioxide each time you breathe. Oxygen is also changed into various different chemicals by cars, trucks, and factories burning fuel. If the atmosphere constantly changes, what was it like a thousand years ago? A million years ago?

## Origin of the Atmosphere

The atmosphere 4.6 billion years ago was probably made of hydrogen and helium gases. Most of the ancient atmosphere escaped the gravity of the earth.

Volcanic activity probably formed the early atmosphere. Volcanoes spew large amounts of carbon dioxide, water vapor, and nitrogen. Because carbon dioxide warms the atmosphere by absorbing outgoing heat, it was probably very warm then, compared to today.

As the earth's inner core cooled, volcanic activity subsided. Water vapor condensed to form clouds, rivers, and lakes. As primitive marine plants photosynthesized, they produced oxygen. The conversion of carbon dioxide to oxygen decreased the carbon dioxide level, allowing the earth to cool.

## The Current Atmosphere

Today the atmosphere is very different from that of the ancient earth. Look at Table 17.2. How does the early atmosphere compare to the atmosphere now? ① Currently, nitrogen and oxygen make up 99 percent of the atmosphere. But there are small amounts of many other gases. Despite their low concentrations, several of these gases are very important.

▶ Plants need carbon dioxide to carry on life processes. Carbon dioxide also absorbs outgoing radiation from the earth's surface, making the air temperature comfortable. Without carbon dioxide, the temperature on the earth would be about −10°C.

▶ Ozone is an essential gas for organisms. It protects organisms from harmful ultraviolet radiation by absorbing the radiation before it reaches the earth's surface.

▶ Water vapor is also necessary for life. All plants and animals rely on water to sustain life. Water vapor also forms clouds. Clouds help control air temperature.

**Table 17.2   Gases in the Early and Present Atmosphere**

| Type of Gas | Early Atmosphere | Present Atmosphere |
|---|---|---|
| Carbon dioxide | 92.2% | 0.03% |
| Nitrogen | 5.1 | 78.1 |
| Sulfur dioxide | 2.3 | Trace |
| Hydrogen sulfide | 0.2 | Trace |
| Ammonia | 0.1 | Trace |
| Methane | 0.1 | Trace |
| Oxygen | 0.0 | 20.9 |
| Argon | 0.0 | 0.9 |

▼ **ACTIVITY**

**Predicting**

**Atmospheric Conditions**

The atmosphere is always changing. Predict how the atmosphere will be different 100 years from now. What might cause the changes?

**SKILLS WORKOUT**

**TEACH**

### Skills WorkOut

To help students understand atmospheric changes, have them do the Skills WorkOut.

**Answer** Answers will vary, but students should be able to support their predictions. For example, the atmosphere may be warmer because the amount of carbon dioxide is increasing.

### Enrich

Tell students that sulfur dioxide, which was 2.3 percent of the early atmosphere, is produced by volcanoes and the decay of organic matter. Today, it is also produced by burning coal and is a component of acid rain. Argon, almost 1 percent of the present atmosphere, is a noble gas released by the decay of radioactive potassium in the earth's crust.

**Answer to In-Text Question**

① Today's atmosphere has much less carbon dioxide and much more nitrogen, oxygen, and argon.

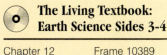

## Skills Development

**Infer** Using a map of North America, ask students which type of smog is most typical in Los Angeles (brown); Denver (brown); Portland (gray); Halifax, N.S. (gray); and Winnipeg, Man. (brown).

### *Portfolio*

Have students collect articles that describe the enhanced greenhouse effect, its causes, and possible remedies. Have them design posters that would draw attention to the enhanced greenhouse effect. Have the class choose three or four posters to place on the school bulletin board.

## Critical Thinking

**Find Causes** Have students use references to determine how the industrial revolution and the enhanced greenhouse effect may be related. Suggest that they compare the onset and rate of industrial activity with the increase in atmospheric carbon dioxide.

## Decision Making

If you have classroom sets of *One-Minute Readings*, have students read Issue 55, "Absorption of Radiation: Greenhouse Effect," on page 92. Discuss the questions.

**Answer to In-Text Question**

① **Gray smog**

**The Living Textbook:**
**Earth Science Sides 3-4**

Chapter 12       Frame 10397
Greenhouse Effect (1 Frame)
Search:

### *Portfolio*

Have students collect newspaper and magazine articles related to smog and global warming. For each article, have them write a brief summary of the information. They can keep the articles and the summaries in their portfolios. Have students add to their portfolios after they read about ozone depletion.
**Use Integrating Worksheet 17.3.**

**Smog** What do you notice about the atmosphere over the city shown in Figure 17.14? The haze over the city is the result of human activity. It is a type of air pollution, called **smog**, that forms from the burning of fossil fuels, such as gasoline and coal. Depending on the climate and the type of air pollution in an area, two different types of smog can form: gray air and brown air.

Gray air occurs in colder, moist climates. Here the pollution combines with moisture in the air to form a grayish haze.

Brown air is typical in warm, dry, sunny climates. The pollution in the air reacts with sunlight to form brown smog. Brown air is referred to as photochemical smog, since it requires photo, or light, to form.

Both smog and photochemical smog have negative effects on human health. They cause burning eyes, headaches, and respiratory problems.

**Figure 17.14 ▲**
Industry and automobiles create smog over Frankfurt, Germany. From the color, determine the type of smog you see over Frankfurt. ①

**Greenhouse Effect** Several gases in the atmosphere help control Earth's temperature. Carbon dioxide and some other gases absorb infrared radiation that reflects from the earth's surface. This traps some of the sunlight's energy that would be lost back to space. So, carbon dioxide and other gases help to keep the atmosphere warm. When heat is trapped by gases in the atmosphere, the result is called the **greenhouse effect.** Without the greenhouse effect, Earth's surface would freeze.

However, the amount of carbon dioxide in the atmosphere has been increasing for the last two centuries. With more carbon dioxide in the air, the atmosphere absorbs more heat and the temperature rises. This rise in the temperature of the atmosphere is called *global warming*. People are concerned that global warming may change the climate of the world. Some scientists predict that the air temperature might rise 2° to 4°C in the next 50 years. Many scientists are trying to analyze how these changes could affect life on Earth.

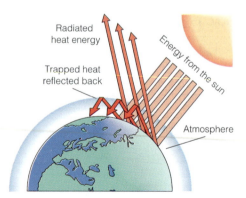

**Figure 17.15 ▲**
The greenhouse effect traps energy from the sun to warm the atmosphere. The greenhouse effect could lead to worldwide global warming.

| Section | Core | Standard | Enriched |
|---|:---:|:---:|:---:|
| **18.1 Humidity** pp. 415–421 | | | |
| **Section Features** | | | |
| Skills WarmUp, p. 415 | ● | ● | ● |
| SkillBuilder, p. 418 | | ● | ● |
| Skills WorkOut, p. 420 | ● | ● | ● |
| Activity, p. 421 | ● | ● | ● |
| **Blackline Masters** | | | |
| Review Worksheet 18.1 | ● | ● | ● |
| Skills Worksheet 18.1 | ● | ● | ● |
| Integrating Worksheet 18.1 | ● | ● | |
| **Color Transparencies** | | | |
| Transparencies 53, 54 | ● | ● | ● |
| **18.2 Clouds** pp. 422–427 | | | |
| **Section Features** | | | |
| Skills WarmUp, p. 422 | ● | ● | ● |
| Skills WorkOut, p. 426 | ● | ● | |
| **Blackline Masters** | | | |
| Review Worksheet 18.2 | ● | ● | |
| Enrich Worksheet 18.2 | | ● | ● |
| Skills Worksheet 18.2 | ● | ● | ● |
| Integrating Worksheet 18.2 | ● | ● | |

| Section | Core | Standard | Enriched |
|---|:---:|:---:|:---:|
| **Laboratory Program** Investigation 28 | | ● | ● |
| **18.3 Precipitation** pp. 428–434 | | | |
| **Section Features** | | | |
| Skills WarmUp, p. 428 | ● | ● | ● |
| Skills WorkOut, p. 429 | ● | ● | ● |
| Consider This, p. 431 | ● | ● | ● |
| Skills WorkOut, p. 433 | ● | ● | |
| **Blackline Masters** | | | |
| Review Worksheet 18.3 | ● | ● | |
| Skills Worksheet 18.3 | ● | ● | ● |
| Integrating Worksheet 18.3 | ● | ● | ● |
| Vocabulary Worksheet 18.3 | ● | ● | |
| **Overhead Blackline Transparencies** | | | |
| Overhead Blackline Master 18.3 and Student Worksheet | ● | ● | |
| **Ancillary Options** *One-Minute Readings,* pp. 60–61, 68–69 | | ● | ● |

# Bibliography

The following resources can be used for teaching the chapter. See page T–46 for supplier codes.

**Library Resources**

*Farndon, John. How the Earth Works. Pleasantville, NY: The Reader's Digest Association, Inc., 1992.*

*MacEachern, D. Save Our Planet: 750 Everyday Ways You Can Help Clean Up the Earth. New York: Dell Publishing Co., 1990.*

*U.S. Office of Environmental Processes and Effects Research. Acid Rain: A Student's First Sourcebook. Washington, DC: U.S. Environmental Protection Agency, 1990.*

**Technology Resources**

*Internet*

**PLANETDIARY** at *http://www.planetdiary.com*
- Find out more about the atmosphere and severe storms; first, click on *Phenomena Backgrounders*.
- Discover meteorological news in *Current Phenomena*.

**Software**

*Earth Science. Mac, Win. ER.*
*The Environment Land and Air. Win. ER.*
*Learning About Weather and Climate. Mac, Dos. LS.*
*Operation: Weather Disaster. Mac, Win. ER.*

*CD-ROMs*

*Interactive Earth. SFAW.*

*Laserdiscs*

*Living Textbook. (See barcodes on pages in this chapter.) Optical Data.*

*Videos*

*Acid Rain. 57 min. 1985. T-L.*

**Audio-Visual Resources**

*Clouds and Precipitation. Still frame. 37 min. FM.*
*Formation of Raindrops. Film. Universal Education & Visual Arts.*
*Snow. Film. BFA.*
*Water in the Air. Still frame. 81 min. FM.*

## *Writing Connection*

Have students write short poems about frost. If students are familiar with the effects of frost, they may choose to write about frost on windows, on grass, or on other objects. If students are not familiar with the effects of frost, have them describe the frost shown on the berries and leaves in the photograph. Student volunteers may want to share their poems with the class.

## Introducing the Chapter

Have students read the description of the photograph. Ask if they agree or disagree with the description. (The frost on the berries formed when water vapor, a gas, turned directly to solid ice crystals.)

### Directed Inquiry

Have students study the photograph. Ask:

- ▶ What is the crystal-like substance on the objects in the photograph? What are the red and yellow objects? (Students will probably accurately identify the frost and the berries and leaves.)

- ▶ Where did the ice or frost come from? (Students should say that it came from water vapor in the air.)

- ▶ How do you think this frost is like the drops of water that form on the inside of a window when you have hot water running in a sink? (Students may recognize that frost and water drops are formed when warmer air comes into contact with a cooler object.)

- ▶ What are some other examples of water in the air changing form? (Students might think of clouds, rain, dew, and frost on other surfaces, such as car or airplane windows.)

## Chapter Vocabulary

| | |
|---|---|
| cirrus | humidity |
| cumulonimbus | precipitation |
| cumulus | psychrometer |
| dew point | stratus |
| fog | |

---

## Chapter **18** Water in the Atmosphere

### Chapter Sections

**18.1** Humidity

**18.2** Clouds

**18.3** Precipitation

### *What do you see?*

**❝**I see berries on a frosty morning with cold dew on them. The berries are just budding. The white stuff is dew that was frozen in little icicles on the berries. Dew forms during the night while it is cold, and in the morning you can see it while the sun rises, before it melts. For this to occur during the night, the temperature has to go below freezing for a period of time.**❞**

*David Rich
Burney Harris Lyons
Middle School
Athens, Georgia*

To find out more about the photograph, look on page 436. As you read this chapter, you will learn about the effects of water in the earth's atmosphere.

## Language Arts Connection

Discuss different uses of the word *relative*, such as relative distance, relative cost, and relative difference. Have students determine the word's meaning as a modifier for a noun. Then have students apply how relative humidity describes the measurement of the moisture content of air.

## Themes in Science

**Energy** The process of evaporation requires energy. For a substance to evaporate, energy must be extracted from the system. For evaporation to take place from the cloth over the wet bulb thermometer, energy is absorbed from the air. This loss of energy is reflected in the thermometer's lower temperature.

## Skills Development

**Interpret Data** Be sure students understand that the numbers in Table 18.1 represent percentages of relative humidity in air. Have students study the text and Table 18.1. Then ask:

▶ Which is cooler, the dry-bulb temperature or the wet-bulb temperature? (Wet-bulb)

▶ For a single dry-bulb temperature, what happens to relative humidity as wet-bulb temperature decreases? (It decreases.)

▶ What is the relative humidity if the temperature difference is 7°C and the dry-bulb temperature is 10°C? (24 percent)

## Research

Ask students to work in cooperative groups to find out what the recommended indoor humidity should be. Have groups report on the health effects of low or high indoor humidity.

**Answer to In-Text Question**

② **51 percent**

**Table 18.1   Relative Humidity in Air**

| Dry-bulb temperature (C°) | Difference between dry-bulb and wet-bulb temperature (C°) | | | | | | | | | | | | | | | |
|---|---|---|---|---|---|---|---|---|---|---|---|---|---|---|---|---|
| | 1 | 2 | 3 | 4 | 5 | 6 | 7 | 8 | 9 | 10 | 11 | 12 | 13 | 14 | 15 | 16 |
| 0 | 81 | 64 | 46 | 29 | 13 | | | | | | | | | | | |
| 2 | 84 | 68 | 52 | 37 | 22 | 7 | | | | | | | | | | |
| 4 | 85 | 71 | 57 | 43 | 29 | 16 | | | | | | | | | | |
| 6 | 86 | 73 | 60 | 48 | 35 | 24 | 11 | | | | | | | | | |
| 8 | 87 | 75 | 63 | 51 | 40 | 29 | 19 | 8 | | | | | | | | |
| 10 | 88 | 77 | 66 | 55 | 44 | 34 | 24 | 15 | 6 | | | | | | | |
| 12 | 89 | 78 | 68 | 58 | 48 | 39 | 29 | 21 | 12 | | | | | | | |
| 14 | 90 | 79 | 70 | 60 | 51 | 42 | 34 | 26 | 18 | 10 | | | | | | |
| 16 | 90 | 81 | 71 | 63 | 54 | 46 | 38 | 30 | 23 | 15 | 8 | | | | | |
| 18 | 91 | 82 | 73 | 65 | 57 | 49 | 41 | 34 | 27 | 20 | 14 | 7 | | | | |
| 20 | 91 | 83 | 74 | 66 | 59 | 51 | 44 | 37 | 31 | 24 | 18 | 12 | 6 | | | |
| 22 | 92 | 83 | 76 | 68 | 61 | 54 | 47 | 40 | 34 | 28 | 22 | 17 | 11 | 6 | | |
| 24 | 92 | 84 | 77 | 69 | 62 | 56 | 49 | 43 | 37 | 31 | 26 | 20 | 15 | 10 | 5 | |
| 26 | 92 | 85 | 78 | 71 | 64 | 58 | 51 | 46 | 40 | 34 | 29 | 24 | 19 | 14 | 10 | 5 |

One thermometer has a cloth attached over the bulb, while the other is uncovered. The cloth on the covered thermometer bulb is dipped in water. The two thermometers are then twirled. As the air passes over both thermometers, the thermometer with the wet cloth cools to the wet-bulb temperature. The dry thermometer measures the air temperature, or the dry-bulb temperature.

Relative humidity is determined by using a relative humidity table, like the one in Table 18.1. To determine relative humidity, you calculate the difference between the dry-bulb temperature and wet-bulb temperature. Using this difference and the dry-bulb temperature, the relative humidity can be located in the table. For example, if the difference between the two temperatures is 4°C and the dry-bulb temperature is 14°C, the relative humidity is 60 percent. What is the relative humidity if the temperature difference is 6°C and the dry-bulb temperature is 20°C? ②

## *Skills WorkOut*

To help students observe, have them do the Skills WorkOut.

**Answer** Most students should find that the area rubbed with alcohol feels cooler. This is because alcohol evaporates faster than water.

## EVALUATE

## WrapUp

**Reteach** Have students draw a concept web using the terms *humidity, relative humidity, water vapor,* and *dew point.*
    Use Review Worksheet 18.1.

## Check and Explain

1. The concentration of water vapor in air compared to the total amount of water vapor air at that temperature can hold; using a hygrometer or a psychrometer and a relative humidity table

2. Answers will vary. Examples from dry areas include gerbils and cacti that conserve water. Examples from humid areas include orchids, miniature frogs, and bromeliads that collect water from the air.

3. Dew forms when air, saturated with water, is cooled. Frost forms if the dew point is below freezing.

4. Students must extrapolate from information in table. Accept any answers less than 5 percent.

### *Integrating the Sciences*

**Life Science** Human skin has two main layers, called the *dermis* and the *epidermis.* In the dermis are sweat glands. Sweat glands are coiled tubes that lead to pores on the skin's surface. Water, salt, and body wastes, or sweat, are released through the pores. Show a diagram of the structure of skin to students. Point out the sweat glands and the pores.

**Health** Discuss with students the importance of keeping skin clean. During adolescence, a person's skin tends to produce more oil and sweat than during any other stage of life. While perspiration is odorless, bacteria present in skin can produce an unpleasant odor. Regular cleaning helps remove the bacteria. The application of deodorants, baking powder, or zinc oxide can also help minimize odor.

▼ **ACTIVITY**

**Observing**

**Cooled Down**

Obtain two cotton balls, rubbing alcohol, and water.
**1.** Soak one cotton ball in rubbing alcohol and another cotton ball in water.
**2.** Wipe each cotton ball along the inside of your arm.
**3.** Blow on the wet area of your arm.
    Which area gets cooler faster? Why?

**SKILLS WORKOUT**

### Science and You
*It's Not the Heat; It's the Humidity*

When water evaporates, heat is absorbed. Maybe you've noticed that when you get out of a swimming pool or a lake on a hot summer day, you sometimes feel chilled. If the humidity is low, the air is dry. Dry air allows evaporation. When the water evaporates from your skin, it removes heat and makes you feel cool. But what happens if it is hot outside and the humidity is high? Very little evaporation occurs. You don't feel chilled even though you are wet.

Your body regulates your skin temperature in a similar manner. When the weather is warm, your body produces perspiration, or sweat. Perspiration covers your body with a thin layer of water. As the perspiration evaporates, your skin is cooled.

In a hot, tropical climate, you would sweat more than in a hot, desert climate. If the weather is dry and hot, your body can keep its temperature steady by producing a small amount of perspiration. Since the air is dry, the perspiration quickly evaporates into the air, and your skin is cooled.

When the humidity is high and it is hot, your body still produces perspiration. However, very little evaporation occurs because the air is already nearly saturated with water vapor. Your skin does not cool significantly. So your body reacts by producing more perspiration.

### Check and Explain

1. What is relative humidity? How do you determine the relative humidity in an area?

2. Describe an organism that has adapted to living in an area with low humidity and one that has adapted to an area with high humidity. Explain how each organism has adapted differently.

3. **Find Causes** What conditions cause dew to form? What conditions cause frost to form?

4. **Interpret Data** Using Table 18.1, determine the relative humidity if the air inside your house is heated to 25°C with a wet-bulb showing 10°C.

### Prelab Discussion

Have students read the entire activity. Discuss a few points before beginning:

▶ Ask students where condensation on windows and cold drink glasses comes from.

▶ Have students predict the relationship between dew point and temperature. Ask: Will a higher air temperature give a higher dew point?

**Time** 20 minutes   **Group** pairs

**Materials**

15 small metal cans

15 thermometers

15 spoons

1 bag of crushed ice

## Analysis

1. Class results will vary, depending on temperature and time of year, but students should have approximately the same values for indoor dew point.

2. Outdoor dew point values should be similar.

3. Answer will depend on time of year and indoor and outdoor temperatures. If the outdoor temperature is lower, the dew point is likely to be lower than the classroom dew point, given the same humidity indoors and outdoors.

4. Variables include: air temperature (indoor and outdoor), dew point (indoor and outdoor), temperature of the water, volume of water.

5. Accept any reasonable explanation.

## Conclusion

Dew point is the temperature of the ice water at which condensation begins to form on the outside of the metal can.

## Everyday Application

Answers will vary depending on time of year and temperature. When the temperature reaches the dew point, water vapor in the air will condense, forming droplets on cold surfaces.

## Extension

Students should find that the dew point varies with the relative humidity.

---

## Activity 18   *How can you determine the dew point?*

**Skills**   Measure; Observe; Compare

### Task 1   Prelab Prep

Collect the following items: small or medium-sized metal can, warm water, crushed ice, spoon, thermometer.

### Task 2   Data Record

1. On a separate sheet of paper, copy Table 18.2.
2. Record your observations from each location in the table.

**Table 18.2   Dew Points**

| Location | Dew Point |
|----------|-----------|
| Classroom | |
| Outdoors | |

### Task 3   Procedure

1. Fill the can about half full with warm water.
2. Place the thermometer in the water. Position the thermometer so it doesn't touch the sides or bottom of the can, as shown in Figure 18.5.
3. Add a spoonful of ice. Watch the sides of the can for condensation as you stir the water. **CAUTION! Stir with the spoon, not the thermometer.**
4. Continue adding spoonfuls of ice, and continue stirring until condensation, or dew, forms on the outside of the can. Record this temperature as the dew point in the data table.
5. Remove the contents from the can.
6. Repeat steps 1 to 4 outdoors.

### Task 4   Analysis

1. What is the dew point of the air in your classroom?
2. What is the dew point outdoors?
3. Compare the dew point of the air in your classroom to the dew point of the air outdoors.
4. List the variables in this activity.

5. List one reason why your dew point may not be the same as the dew point for other groups in your classroom.

### Task 5   Conclusion

Write a short paragraph defining dew point, based on the activity you just completed.

### Everyday Application

Find out the predicted low temperatures for your area over the next seven days. Will the temperature reach the dew point on each day? What will happen if it does? Make a line graph that plots the dew points for each day.

### Extension

Set up a station outdoors on the school grounds to measure relative humidity and dew point. For measuring relative humidity, use wet and dry bulb thermometers. For dew point testing, set out a metal container. Check the container each morning to see if the dew point was reached the night before. Then test to find the relative humidity.

**Figure 18.5** ▼

### Section Objectives
For a list of section objectives, see the Student Edition page.

### Skills Objectives
Students should be able to:

**Infer** causes of cloudiness and cloudlessness.

**Generalize** why fog is used in story settings.

**Classify** clouds.

### Vocabulary
fog, stratus, cumulus, cirrus, cumulonimbus

## MOTIVATE

### Skills WarmUp
To help students understand cloud formation, have them do the Skills WarmUp.

**Answer** Observations depend on the weather. Students may observe that cloudless days are relatively cool and less windy, leading to an inference that clouds may form as a result of warmth and air currents.

### Misconceptions
Students may think that clouds come from somewhere above the sky. Explain that cloud formation is part of the water cycle, which requires water from the ground to evaporate and move upward. Point out that cloud formation is difficult to observe because clouds often form from existing cloud layers.

### Integrating the Sciences

**Physical Science** A cloud appears white in the sky. This is due to the scattering of light frequencies that pass through the water molecules in a cloud. A cloud is made of a variety of different sized clumps of water molecules. The water clusters scatter light into different frequencies, from low to high. These frequencies combine to form what we perceive as the color white. Have students infer why a cloud often becomes very dark right before it rains or snows. (The high concentration of water molecules blocks the passage of light through the cloud.)

### ▼ ACTIVITY

#### Inferring

*Not a Cloud to Speak Of*

Over a period of a few days, observe if there are any clouds in the sky. Record your observations. Were there any days with no clouds? If so, infer reasons why no clouds appeared.

**SKILLS WARMUP**

## 18.2 Clouds

### Objectives

▶ **Explain** two ways that clouds can form.

▶ **Describe** the three types of clouds.

▶ **Predict** the type of fog that forms in different conditions.

▶ **Classify** clouds by altitude.

**Y**ou probably know a lot about clouds without even realizing it. If you notice that it's a gray, cloudy morning, you may bring an umbrella to school. If you see a large, dark cloud, you may cancel the picnic or ball game you planned. You may have admired the puffy clouds floating across a blue sky on a warm summer day. How did these puffy clouds form? Why are there so many different types of clouds?

### Cloud Formation

Clouds can form at any altitude in the troposphere. One way that clouds form, by surface heating and convection, is shown in Figure 18.6. It begins when the sun heats an area of the ground rapidly. The ground heats the air above it, reducing the air density. The warm air rises in a column. As the air column rises, it cools until it reaches its dew point. At dew point, the water vapor condenses and forms a cloud.

**Figure 18.6**
Convection clouds form when moist air rises high enough to cool and condense. ▼

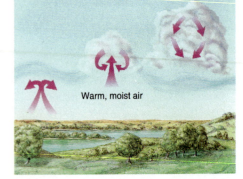

Warm, moist air

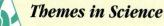

## *Themes in Science*

**Scale and Structure** When microscopic molecules of water vapor meet microscopic particles in air, the water condenses. As more water vapor molecules condense, tiny droplets become visible as clouds. When a great number of droplets collide and collect, they fall as visible rain or snow.

As air rises in the air column, it cools and becomes saturated. At the saturation point, the relative humidity of the air is 100 percent. When the relative humidity reaches 100 percent, water in the atmosphere condenses around small particles called *condensation nuclei*. Condensation nuclei are tiny particles that float in the atmosphere. These small particles enter the atmosphere from windblown dust, volcanoes, factory smoke, forest fires, and even salt from ocean spray. Because so many condensation nuclei are present in the lower atmosphere, the relative humidity is rarely more than 100 percent before condensation begins.

Water vapor molecules stick to the condensation nuclei. As more water molecules attach to the nuclei, a water droplet forms. These droplets are so small that they float in the air. Even a slight air current will keep the droplets suspended. However, when a large number of droplets collect, they form clouds.

You may have noticed that mountains are often covered by clouds, like those in Figure 18.7. Mountain clouds typically are formed by a second cloud-forming process. The process depends on air being affected by the elevation of the land. Clouds can form when warm, moist air is lifted and cools as it passes over higher areas of land. In many regions of the world, the wind carries warm, moist air toward mountains. As the air rises up the sides of the mountains, it cools. When the air reaches its dew point, the water vapor in the air condenses to form clouds.

### Life Science LINK

Collect the following items: two empty plant pots of equal size, potting soil, water, two large clear plastic bags, two wire hangers, and a small potted plant.

**1.** Fill each pot with soil. Transplant your small plant to one of the pots.

**2.** Add an equal amount of water to each pot. Cover each pot with a clear bag, using the wire hanger for support

**3.** Place each pot in the same sunny location for a few days. Determine which bag has the most moisture inside.

Based on your results, could you say that plants could influence the formation of clouds? Explain.

**ACTIVITY**

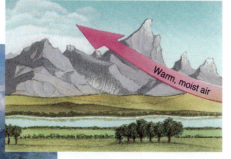

◀ **Figure 18.7**
Some mountains are usually covered by clouds due to the continuous upwelling of warm, moist air.

## TEACH

### Critical Thinking

**Sequence** Write the following phrases in any order on the chalkboard. Ask students to arrange them in the correct sequence:

▶ ground heats air (1)

▶ air density decreases (2)

▶ warm air rises (3)

▶ air temperature decreases (4)

▶ air temperature reaches dew point (5)

▶ water vapor condenses (6)

▶ cloud forms (7)

**Compare and Contrast** Ask students to compare convection currents to the process of cloud formation. (In a convection current, a warm fluid such as water or air rises and cools. This is part of the cloud formation process.)

**If . . . Then Arguments** Have students use an If . . . then argument to explain how air pollution can affect cloud formation. (If pollution increases dust and smoke particles that can act as condensation nuclei, then cloud formation may increase.)

**Reason and Conclude** Have students notice that the top of the mountain in Figure 18.7 appears to break through the clouds. Ask what they think the temperature above the clouds is like. (Lower than dew point)

### Answer to Link

Results may differ, based on method and type of plant used. In general, however, a plant should add more moisture to the bag than the soil does over time, due to transpiration. Transpiration will maintain the transport of moisture to the air, whereas, the moisture in the bare soil will be lost to initial evaporation, or sink down into the soil, where it does not readily supply moisture to the air.

### Explore Visually

After students study the text and illustrations, ask the following questions:

▶ What do stratus clouds look like? (They spread in dull gray sheets across the sky.)

▶ Which clouds can signal fair weather? How? (Cumulus; they may grow larger or evaporate entirely during the day.)

▶ Which clouds are the most vertical? (Cumulus)

▶ How would you classify a cloud that is flat, dark, and produces steady rain? Why? (Nimbostratus; nimbus indicates rain and stratus indicates flatness.)

## Enrich

Use Enrich Worksheet 18.2.

**The Living Textbook:
Earth Science Sides 1-2**

Chapter 2          Frame 00840
Stratus (1 Frame)
Search:

424

### Portfolio

Have students keep a cloud diary. They can record the date, time of day, weather conditions, types of clouds, their description, and a drawing for each diary entry. After several weeks, have students tally the number of the different types of clouds they observed. Ask students if the time of day and the weather conditions affected the types of clouds that formed in the sky. They can keep their diaries in their portfolios.

**Use Integrating Worksheet 18.2.**

### Types of Clouds

Clouds are classified by their appearance. Three of the main types of clouds are **stratus** (STRA tuhs), **cumulus** (KYOO myuh luhs), and **cirrus** (SYR ruhs).

**Stratus**
◀ "Stratus" comes from the Latin word meaning "to spread out." Stratus clouds are flat and dull gray in appearance and cover the entire sky in widespread sheets. Stratus clouds often produce rain or drizzle. In this photograph, you can see stratus clouds above the New York City skyline.

**Cumulus** ▶
"Cumulus" comes from the Latin word for "heap." These clouds are the type often drawn in pictures. Cumulus clouds are puffy in appearance. On a warm summer day, you may see cumulus clouds become larger or evaporate entirely throughout the day.

**Cirrus**
◀ "Cirrus" is the Latin word for curl. Cirrus clouds appear thin and wispy and are located at high altitudes. Cirrus clouds are made of ice crystals. Long streaks of cirrus clouds high in the sky often indicate change in weather.

**Math and Art Connection**
Have students collect cloud photographs and drawings from magazines. Have them tally the number of clouds of each type depicted. They can use the information to make bar graphs for each cloud type listed. Then they can use the cloud pictures to create cloud collages.

**Language Arts Connection**
Review the cloud types and the prefixes that indicate cloud height. Have students infer how these roots might be combined to create the two words for cloud formations not mentioned in the text. Tell students that they do not necessarily have to use a cloud-height prefix, as in *cumulonimbus*. Ask: If you use one of the cloud types as a prefix, how must it change? (Cirrocumulus, nimbostratus; the *-us* must change to an *-o*.)

### Class Activity
Draw a vertical line on the chalkboard. Label the lower end 2 km and the upper end 6 km. Have volunteers place the following clouds at the appropriate altitudes. Ask students to give a short description of each cloud and the type of weather likely to accompany it.

Stratocumulus (below 2 km, soft gray, light rain or snow); nimbostratus (below 2 km, steady precipitation); cirrocumulus (above 6 km, fair weather); cumulonimbus (from 1 km to more than 6 km, dark, lightning and strong winds, heavy rain); altocumulus (2 to 6 km, light gray, fair or rain)

Clouds are also classified by their height or altitude. The prefixes *cirro-*, *alto-*, and *strato-* help identify a cloud's altitude. *Cirro-* refers to high, *alto-* to middle, and *strato-* to low-altitude clouds.

**High-Altitude Clouds** ▲
These are clouds above 6 km that have very low temperatures. The high clouds seen at these altitudes are thin, curling cirrus clouds. High, puffy clouds are called cirrocumulus. Extensive flat, high clouds, called cirrostratus, occur when cirrus clouds spread into thin sheets. Cirrostratus clouds sometimes create halos around the sun or the moon.

**Low-Altitude Clouds** ▶
These clouds have bottoms below 2 km, and they form at warm temperatures. All low-altitude clouds forecast rain or snow. Stratus is a thick, gray cloud that extends over a wide area. Stratocumulus are small, puffy summer clouds. Some clouds start near the ground and extend to very high altitudes. The term *nimbus* is used to identify some rain-bearing clouds. A tall, dark rain cloud is called a **cumulonimbus**. It can produce lightning and strong winds. Cumulonimbus clouds can begin 1,000 m above the ground and extend up to 18,000 m.

**Middle-Altitude Clouds**
◀ These are clouds with bottoms in the altitude range of 2 to 6 km. The temperatures generally vary between –25°C and 0°C. Altostratus, or broad, gray clouds, occur frequently. A thin veil of altostratus clouds means light rain will soon arrive. Altocumulus clouds are white to gray and may have dark, shadowed sides that can mean rain or snow. However, these types of clouds most often occur in the summer.

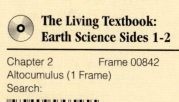

**The Living Textbook:
Earth Science Sides 1-2**

| Chapter 2 | Frame 00842 |
|---|---|

Altocumulus (1 Frame)
Search:

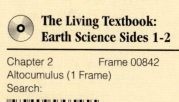

**The Living Textbook:
Earth Science Sides 1-2**

| Chapter 2 | Frame 00839 |
|---|---|

Cirrus (1 Frame)
Search:

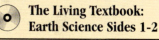

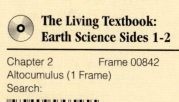

**The Living Textbook:
Earth Science Sides 1-2**

| Chapter 2 | Frame 00818 |
|---|---|

Cumulonimbus (3 Frames)
Search:                   Step:

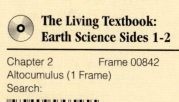

**The Living Textbook:
Earth Science Sides 1-2**

| Chapter 2 | Frame 00837 |
|---|---|

Stratocumulus (1 Frame)
Search:

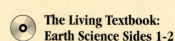

**TEACH** ▪ *Continued*

### Skills WorkOut

To help students generalize, have them do the Skills WorkOut.
**Answer** Answers will vary, but students may indicate that fog adds mystery, danger, or gloom to stories and movies because it makes things hard to see.

### Skills Development

**Observe** Place 4 or 5 cm of warm water in a transparent bottle. (Be sure the water is not hot.) Place an ice cube on the top of the bottle. Ask students to describe what they observe and explain why it occurred. (Fog; air warmed by the water in the bottle rises. Air is cooled as it reaches the top of the bottle. If it is cooled to its dew point, fog forms.)

**Define Operationally** Ask students to describe the following kinds of fog in their own words: steam fog (fog over water); advection fog (fog along coasts); radiation fog (fog above ground when air is cool).

### Writing Connection

Have students write a short story in which the setting is blanketed in fog. Student volunteers may want to share their stories with the class. Ask the students how the foggy setting affected the plot of the story.

### Integrating the Sciences

**Environmental Science** The term *smog* is used to describe the grayish or brownish haze that forms from air pollutants. This term first appeared in 1905 in England to describe the grayish haze that formed over industrial cities. The gray smog was caused by the burning of coal.

▼ **ACTIVITY**

**Generalizing**

*In a Fog*

Fog is part of the settings of many stories and movies. Make a list of examples. Determine why fog was chosen for each movie or story scene on your list. Based on how fog is used in stories and movies, how do you think most people feel about fog? Explain.

**SKILLS WORKOUT**

### Fog

Look at Figure 18.8. What would you call this type of cloud? The photograph shows a landscape covered in **fog**. Actually, fog is a cloud that forms on the earth's surface. But fog develops differently from the way in which clouds form. Fog can form in several ways. The type of fog that forms depends on the location, temperature, and the movement of the air.

Radiation fog forms when warm air cools. At night when the earth's surface cools, the dew point is reached quickly. This process produces millions of tiny water droplets that stay in the air and form fog. You may have seen radiation fog early in the morning before the temperature rises enough to evaporate the water droplets.

Fog also forms where water and land meet. Land cools more quickly than water. The warm air over the water is more moist than the cool air over the land. If the warm, moist air from the water moves across the cooler land, fog forms. This type of fog, called advection fog, is common in the San Francisco Bay Area. You can see advection fog in Figure 18.8.

The reverse process may form a different type of fog. Steam fog occurs when cold air moves over warm water. In this case, the relative humidity of the cold air is very low. As water evaporates from the surface, the cold air becomes saturated. As more water vapor meets the cooler air, it condenses and forms fog. You may have seen this type of fog form over rivers and lakes.

**Figure 18.8** ▶
The Golden Gate Bridge in San Francisco is often blanketed in advection fog.

**The Living Textbook:
Earth Science Sides 1-2**

Chapter 2          Frame 00877
Fog (5 Frames)
Search:              Step:

## Integrating the Sciences

**Life Science** Certain animals use several different techniques for navigation. Bats and dolphins use echolocation. A dolphin makes a clicking noise that creates an echo as it bounces off objects. The echoes help the dolphin navigate through water. A bat uses echolocation to hear in the dark. The bat sends out high-pitched squeaks through its mouth. The sound waves bounce off objects and return to the bat's ears as echoes. The bat's brain computes a "sound picture" from the pattern of the echoes. Migrating birds navigate using a different method. The brains of migratory birds contain small amounts of magnetite, a compound of iron and oxygen. Magnetite acts like a compass that keeps the birds on course.

### Science and Technology
### *Flight Navigation and Clouds*

If you have ever been flying in an airplane on a cloudy day, you may have wondered how the pilot knew where to find the airport runway. Most of the time, pilots can see the countryside they fly over. This type of weather condition is called VFR (visual flight rules). However, when low-altitude clouds form or the weather at the airport makes seeing the runway difficult, the weather conditions are called IFR (instrument flight rules).

Pilots used to navigate during IFR by using sensors that pointed to commercial radio station towers. Now they use transmitters located all over the country called VHF OmniRange (VOR) radio beacons. This system of beacons tells pilots the direction and distance of a station on the ground. In the cockpit, the pilot has a display of this information. At the destination airport, another special radio beacon leads the airplane to the beginning of the runway. If the runway is not visible at that point, it is too dangerous to land. The pilot will then land at another airport.

On-board computers can also use VORs to plot a route anywhere in the United States. This system is used, for example, if a cumulonimbus cloud is spotted that could cause heavy rain, turbulence, or hail.

In the next few years, most aircraft will use satellites for navigation. These satellites are so accurate that a pilot can tell if the airplane is on the left side, the right side, or the middle of the runway.

**Figure 18.9** ▲
On-board computers display cloud patterns in the flight path of an airplane.

### Check and Explain

1. What are the two ways that clouds can form?

2. Describe a stratus cloud, a cumulus cloud, and a nimbus cloud.

3. **Predict** What type of fog would form on a cool night after rain? Over a lake during the fall? During a cold winter night?

4. **Classify** Make a table to classify each cloud according to whether it is a high-, middle-, or low-altitude cloud: cirrostratus, cumulonimbus, altocumulus, stratocumulus, cirrocumulus, altostratus.

### Themes in Science

**Energy** The amount of heat energy in air determines temperature. This heat energy influences the type of precipitation that falls to the ground, as the temperature of the air below a cloud determines the type of precipitation.

### Literature Connection

Have students recall and recite children's rhymes and songs about precipitation. For example, "It's raining, it's pouring . . ." or "Rain, rain go away. . . ." Have students infer why many of the rhymes for young children are about precipitation.

### Section Objectives
For a list of section objectives, see the Student Edition page.

### Skills Objectives
Students should be able to:

**Make a Graph** to document precipitation.

**Make a Model** of raindrops forming.

**Collect Data** about rainfall in different cities.

**Vocabulary**
precipitation

## MOTIVATE

### Skills WarmUp

To help students understand precipitation, have them do the Skills WarmUp.

**Answer** Graphs depend on rainfall. The graphs are unlikely to have even slopes, unless the rainfall is very steady. If students choose their own scales, line graphs will have different shapes and lengths, but should all show similar high and low points.

### Prior Knowledge

To gauge how much students know about precipitation, ask the following questions:

▶ What are some different kinds of precipitation?

▶ How are clouds related to rain and snow?

▶ How do meteorologists measure rainfall?

▶ When and where have you seen hail?

## ▼ ACTIVITY

### Making a Graph

*Waiting for the Rain*

The total amount of rain and the rate at which rain falls are both important. On a rainy day, conduct the following activity:

**1.** Use a container to measure the rainfall every 30 minutes.

**2.** Use a line graph to plot both the rain increase for each 30 minute period and the total rainfall.

**3.** Compare your graph to a classmate's. How do they compare?

### SKILLS WARMUP

# 18.3 Precipitation

## Objectives

▶ **Explain** how raindrops and snowflakes form.

▶ **Describe** how hail increases in size.

▶ **Classify** instruments used for measuring precipitation.

▶ **Compare** and **contrast** sleet and freezing rain.

---

I f you live in an area that receives a lot of snow in the winter, you probably know that the amount of precipitation that falls influences the outcome. What would be the effect on your community if 20 cm of snow fell in 3 hours? Many activities would probably be cancelled.

Precipitation affects people and the earth in many ways. It can be hazardous, such as freezing rain on busy highways. Precipitation is also very beneficial, such as rain for watering crops.

## Causes of Precipitation

Any form of moisture that falls from a cloud to the ground is called **precipitation**. The most common forms of precipitation are rain and snow. Table 18.3 shows that the cloud type and the temperature of the air below the cloud determine the form of precipitation.

**Table 18.3  Precipitation, Cloud Type, and Temperature**

| Cloud Type | Temperature | Precipitation |
|---|---|---|
| Altocumulus | Above freezing | Rain |
| Altostratus | Above freezing | Rain |
| Stratocumulus | Above freezing | Rain |
| Cumulonimbus | Above freezing | Rain |
| Nimbostratus | Above freezing | Rain |
| Altostratus | Below freezing | Snow |
| Stratocumulus | Below freezing | Snow |
| Nimbostratus | Below freezing | Snow |

### Literature Connection

Umbrellas were used in ancient Egypt to symbolize power. This belief was based on the Egyptian myth in which the sky was thought to be the underbelly of a god covering the earth like an umbrella. Priests and pharaohs were often placed in the shade of an umbrella to symbolize their power.

### Integrating the Sciences

**Chemistry** Water molecules attract one another as the negative side of one molecule attracts the positive side of another molecule. Have students observe the attraction of water molecules by using a dropper to deposit separate drops of water onto the underside of a plastic lid. Then have them turn the lid over and move the drops together with a pencil. (The drops will join to form large drops that fall off the lid.)

### TEACH

**Discuss**

Have students discuss how precipitation has affected their lives. Remind them to include examples of too much and too little precipitation.

### Skills WorkOut

Help students make a model by doing the Skills WorkOut.
**Answer** Students should observe that small droplets grow larger as water is added, eventually becoming large enough to fall.

### Discuss

Ask students to explain how ice crystals form in the air. (Water around supercooled droplets evaporates and deposits as ice crystals.) Then have them explain how snowflakes are formed. (Ice crystals cluster together.)

### Critical Thinking

**Uncover Assumptions** Have students find the inaccurate assumption in the following statement, then correct the statement. "Precipitation that reaches the earth as rain is melted snow or ice." (Assumption: Air above the earth is always cold enough to produce snow or ice; only some rain is melted snow or ice. Some is the result of water vapor condensing on condensation nuclei.)

### Integrated Learning

Use Integrating Worksheet 18.3

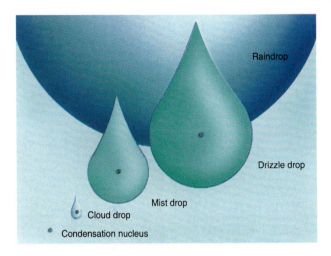

◄ **Figure 18.10**
Compare the relative sizes of different water drops that form in a cloud.

Recall that when water vapor in a cloud condenses onto condensation nuclei, a cloud droplet forms. Air currents move the tiny droplet. The droplet lifts higher in the atmosphere where the temperature is below freezing. As the droplet travels, it collects water and grows larger.

A few droplets, with their nuclei of ice, freeze. Water surrounding the supercooled droplets evaporates and deposits on the frozen droplets as ice crystals. Eventually, the ice crystals become a small snowflake. As the snowflake falls through the cloud, it may collide with other ice crystals and become larger. If the air below the cloud is cold, the snowflake will fall to the ground as snow.

If ice crystals fall into air that is warmer than freezing, they melt and become raindrops. As raindrops fall, they sometimes collide with other raindrops. The raindrops combine to form bigger drops. The bigger raindrops fall faster and collide with more drops. Compare the relative sizes of raindrops in Figure 18.10.

In warm climates, clouds are rarely high enough to reach temperatures below freezing. So a different process forms precipitation. After water vapor condenses on condensation nuclei, the liquid droplets begin to fall very slowly. If one droplet collides with another, they either bounce off each other, or they merge. Droplets that merge get bigger and begin to fall faster. Eventually, the drops reach the ground as large raindrops.

▼ **ACTIVITY**

**Making a Model**

*Rainmaker*

Spray a fine mist of water from a spray bottle onto a window or mirror. Observe the droplets. Spray more water onto the surface. What happens to the drops? How is this similar to the formation of raindrops?

**SKILLS WORKOUT**

**The Living Textbook:**
**Earth Science Side 1**

Chapter 40      Frame 04066
Cloud Droplets (Movie)
Search:              Play:

## TEACH ▪ *Continued*

### Directed Inquiry

Have students look at the pictures on this page. Ask:

▶ What phase of water can you find in all of the pictures? (Liquid; some may also say gas in the air.)

▶ What does this suggest about how precipitation is related to temperature? (Answers will vary; students may point out that precipitation can change phase as temperature changes, and that different phases of water can coexist at some temperatures.)

### Skills Development

**Design an Experiment** Have students design an experiment to determine equivalent amounts of snow and rain. (Answers will vary, but should include collection and measurement of snow, melting snow, and measurement of water from melted snow.)

### Enrich

Tell students that the longest continuous rain occurred during 1918 in Bahia Feliz, Chile. It rained all but 18 days of that year. During the 18 days of relief, it drizzled. Volunteers may wish to research other interesting precipitation occurrences and share them.

**The Living Textbook:
Earth Science Sides 1-2**

Chapter 2         Frame 00873
Rain (1 Frame)
Search:

**The Living Textbook:
Earth Science Sides 1-2**

Chapter 2         Frame 00875
Snowfall (1 Frame)
Search:

430

## Geography Connection

Have the students use an atlas to compare the average precipitation of an area located in the northern latitudes with that of an area in the southern latitudes. You may want to have students work in pairs. One student can record precipitation for areas north of the equator, while the other student can record precipitation for areas south of the equator.

**Rain** ▲

In the United States, rain can fall at a rate from almost 0 cm/h to 4 cm/h. Extremely high rainfall rates approaching 10 cm/h can occur in thunderstorms or other severe weather. Such heavy rain, however, rarely lasts for long. As shown above in Calcutta, India, heavy rains can cause severe flooding.

**Snow** ▶

When the temperature above the ground is near freezing, precipitation may fall as snow. About 10 cm of snow equals 1 cm of rain. Snow is common in areas at middle to high latitudes and at high altitudes.

Snowflakes usually fall more slowly than large raindrops. As snow hits the ground, it accumulates loosely with a great deal of air trapped between flakes. Snowflakes vary greatly in diameter, from several millimeters to several centimeters.

### Forms of Precipitation

When precipitation hits the ground, it can be in many different forms. The most common forms, rain and snow, both begin as ice crystals or water droplets in clouds. Other forms of precipitation are freezing rain, sleet, and hail.

**Freezing Rain** ▶

Besides snow, freezing rain occurs during winter. When the air temperature is between 0°C and 3°C, precipitation falls as rain. But the raindrops freeze into ice as they hit the ground or other objects. The rain forms a thick layer of sheet ice, or glaze ice. Glaze ice occurs during ice storms.

Freezing rain produces beautiful effects, but it is also dangerous. Roads become slippery, and branches or power lines can fall from the weight of the ice.

**Sleet**

Partially melted grains of ice are called *sleet*. Sleet forms when raindrops or snowflakes fall through air layers of different temperatures. A mixture of rain and snow hit the ground. If the temperature near the surface is below –3°C, sleet forms as frozen raindrops.

▼

## Themes in Science

**Diversity and Unity** All of the precipitation that falls from clouds is composed of water. However, the forms that precipitation can take vary greatly.

## Art Connection

The making of candles is similar to the formation of hailstones. You may wish to demonstrate how candles are made by repeatedly dipping string into melted crayon wax or have students research how candles are made. Ask students how candle making is similar to the formation of hailstones. (The layering effect is similar.)

## Discuss

Using the chalkboard, have the class tell you or a student volunteer how to diagram the formation of a hailstone. To assist students, ask about the motion of air in a thunderstorm, how a snow pellet or frozen raindrop forms, and how heavy a hailstone might have to be to finally fall out of the storm.

**Hail** Balls of ice that form in thunderstorms with upward-rising air are known as hail. Hailstones begin as small snow pellets or frozen raindrops. As they fall, they collide with supercooled water droplets in the cloud. The droplets freeze onto the hailstone, making it grow. As strong winds toss the ice crystals up and down in the cloud, more droplets of water freeze around the ice crystals. This process makes the hailstone layered, a little like the layers of an onion. Look at the hailstones in Figure 18.11. What evidence shows the effects of the up and down motion of the ice crystals within the cloud? ①

Most hailstones are the size of a pea, but they can get as large as a golf ball. The largest hailstone ever collected was at Coffeyville, Kansas, in 1970. It weighed 758 g and had a diameter of 14 cm. Hailstorms can be very damaging to crops and buildings. A hailstorm in Denver, Colorado, in July 1990, caused damage to cars and houses that totaled nearly $600 million.

**Figure 18.11** ▲
Hail can fall during any season. What do you think was the season during this hailstorm? ②

## *Consider This*

Ask students to find out if they live in an area where cloud seeding is practiced.

**Think About It** Answers will vary. Students should evaluate benefits to farming and air travel, as well as possible harmful effects. Seeding can shift rainfall within a region, so one community's gain could be another's loss.

**Debate It** Discussions will vary, but all students should support their opinions with facts.

## Decision Making

If you have classroom sets of *One-Minute Reading*, have students read Issue 41, "Cloud Seeding," on page 68. Discuss the questions.

**Answers to In-Text Questions**

① The hailstones appear to be layered.

② Spring or summer

## *Consider This*

### *Is Cloud Seeding Helpful or Harmful?*

In regions that receive little rainfall, a method called cloud seeding is sometimes used to increase the rainfall. In one method, cloud-seeding planes inject crystals of silver iodide into certain clouds. The crystals create huge numbers of ice crystals, increasing the amount of cloud formation and the chance of precipitation.

Cloud seeding can increase rainfall in dry areas by as much as 30 percent. The process is very helpful to farm communities when water reservoirs are low. It can also disperse fog at airports, allowing planes to land. Cloud seeding can also reduce the size of large hailstones that damage crops and structures.

Cloud seeding is also controversial. It often shifts the location of rainfall from one place to another. This means that one region's water increase causes water loss in another region. Some people think that cloud seeding has not proven to be effective. Other people think that the use of silver iodide may have a harmful effect on the environment.

**Think About It** What are the benefits of cloud seeding? What are some of the problems? How might cloud seeding create conflicts between communities in a region?

**Debate It** Imagine that you are on a state water resources board and your state is in a severe drought. A group of citizens comes to your board asking for money to fund a cloud-seeding program. Write which way you would vote on the issue. Include reasons for your decision. With several classmates, have a mock board meeting in which two sides with opposing views debate the issue of cloud seeding.

**The Living Textbook: Earth Science Sides 1-2**

Chapter 2          Frame 00888
Snowflake Crystals (5 Frames)
Search:                    Step:

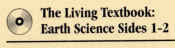

## Skills Development

**Collect Data** Allow students to collect rainfall data in two or three locations. Have them compare data from gauges located at different sites.

**Hypothesize** Have students write a hypothesis that explains their rainfall data. Remind them to say how the hypothesis could be tested. (Hypotheses will vary; test should involve using rain gauges again.)

### Answer to In-Text Question

① **Accept answers between 1.8 and 2.0.**

### *Cooperative Learning*

Have students work in pairs to make a rain gauge. Tell the students that a standard rain gauge uses a funnel with a mouth that is ten times larger than the cylinder into which it falls. Have them construct their rain gauges by choosing from various items that could serve as the container or the funnel, such as plastic soda bottles, film canisters, and plastic cups.

Once the rain gauge is constructed, have students devise a way to measure the amount of rain that falls. Set the rain gauges outside where they will not be disturbed. After a rainfall, have students check their rain gauges. Discuss why the amount of rain measured for different groups varied. (Because the methods of measurement may differ)

## Measuring Rainfall

Rainfall is usually measured with a simple rain gauge like the one shown in Figure 18.12. The rain gauge contains a funnel that collects and directs rain into a small cylinder. The area of the funnel is ten times larger than the area of the cylinder. So 1 cm of rain will appear as 10 cm of water in the cylinder.

Other methods provide rainfall rates, as well as total rainfall. For example, the tipping-bucket gauge has a small bucket at each end of a lever. When one bucket fills to about 1 mm, it tips over and the other bucket begins to fill. The tipping-bucket rain gauge counts the number of tips over a certain time, which tells the rate of rainfall.

Sophisticated radar devices can also measure rainfall. They measure rainfall over a large area without even making a measurement on the ground.

**Figure 18.12** ▲
Estimate the amount of rain collected by this rain gauge. ①

## Measuring Snowfall

Snowfall is difficult to measure because wind blows the snow around unevenly. At most weather stations, such as the one in Figure 18.13, snow accumulates in the funnel of a rain gauge. It is then melted to determine the amount of water. Snowfall rates can also be measured with the tipping-bucket gauge. The gauge is modified so the funnel that collects the snow also heats and melts it. The melted snow drains into the gauge, which then measures it like rain.

Snowpack, or the amount of snow that will melt and flow into rivers, is measured by a different device. This device extracts a vertical column of snow. The snow in the column is weighed to indicate the water content.

**Figure 18.13** ▲
Snowfall is measured in this automated radio-reporting snow gauge in California.

## STS Connection

Have students compare a map of the average annual rainfall in the United States to a map of U.S. population density. Explain that in early U.S. history, people settled where fresh water was most available. Ask students why the population density is not directly related to the amount of rainfall for the United States. (Water moves as groundwater, rivers, and streams, and is transported in canals, so dry areas may have large populations.)

## STS Connection

In the Western United States, the Colorado River brings life to over three million acres of irrigated desert and supports growing populations of people in cities along the sunbelt. Many people are concerned that the demand for water from the Colorado River will one day exceed its supply. Discuss with students why water conservation is particularly important in the arid regions of the United States.

## Precipitation and People

People must get water from some source. Since people need water for many purposes, its availability often determines where they live. Look at the maps in Figure 18.14. The map on the left shows average amounts of rainfall in South America. The map on the right shows population density. How has the availability of water ② affected where people have settled in South America?

Around the world, populations have grown large where water is abundant. Populations are usually fairly small where water is scarce. However, technology has changed population distribution in some countries. In the United States, construction of massive water projects, such as dams and irrigation canals, has enabled people to settle in areas where water resources are very limited.

Southern California is a location where the population has grown dramatically despite limited water resources. Southern California is a desert region. Water is brought into the region from the Colorado River and the Sierra Nevada Mountains. The imported water has enabled farmers to grow a variety of crops. The availability of water made industry growth possible. It has also provided many recreational opportunities on reservoirs.

### ▼ ACTIVITY

#### Collecting Data

*City of Rain*

Select five cities that represent a variety of climates. Using data from a newspaper, keep a record of the daily precipitation in each city for five days. Which city received the most precipitation? The least?

**SKILLS WORKOUT**

**Figure 18.14**

How is the amount of rainfall in an area related to the area's population? ▼ ③

## Skills WorkOut

To help students collect data, have them do the Skills WorkOut.

**Answers** Answers will vary. Have students check one another's work for accuracy.

## Critical Thinking

**Find Causes** Ask students how water availability determined exploration and settlement of the United States. (It affected travel and agriculture.) Then have them describe how a map showing the U.S. population in 1850 might differ from a map showing it in 1990. Have them offer explanations for the differences. (The 1990 map would show more people living away from natural water sources because technology made water available.)

## Enrich

Have students research the pros and cons of diverting water from the Colorado River to the desert regions of southern California. Ask them to find articles supporting each point of view. Hold a class debate on the issue.

### Answers to In-Text Questions

② The population of South America is most dense near rivers, along seacoasts, and in areas of moderate rainfall.

③ Population is sparse in wettest and driest regions.

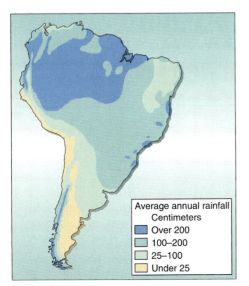

Average annual rainfall
Centimeters
- Over 200
- 100–200
- 25–100
- Under 25

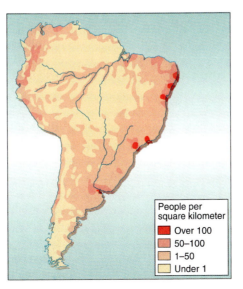

People per square kilometer
- Over 100
- 50–100
- 1–50
- Under 1

## TEACH ▪ Continued

### Directed Inquiry

After students have read about acid rain, ask the following questions:

▶ How does acid rain differ from other acidic rain? (It contains strong acids instead of weak acids.)

▶ What kind of soil can neutralize acid rain? (Soils with natural buffers)

▶ Can lakes neutralize acid rain? Why or why not? (Answers will vary; students should infer that some lakes contain natural buffers.)

### EVALUATE

### WrapUp

**Review** Have each student draw a diagram that shows how rain and snow form. Have students indicate what conditions produce hail, freezing rain, and sleet.

Use Review Worksheet 18.3.

### Check and Explain

1. Cloud droplets collect water and grow larger. Some droplets freeze and evaporated water collects around them in snowflakes. Depending on cloud type and temperature, rain, snow, sleet, or hail forms.

2. By being repeatedly swept upward into a region of freezing temperature

3. Both, both, snow

4. Both are precipitation; sleet is partially melted ice that falls to earth; freezing rain is rain that freezes as it reaches the earth's surface.

### Decision Making

If you have classroom sets of *One-Minute Readings*, have students read Issue 36, "Acid Rain," on page 60. Discuss the questions.

### Cooperative Learning

Have students work in cooperative groups. Have the groups research some of the effects of acid rain in various industrialized areas of the world, such as Canada, the United States, and Europe. Each group should focus on a specific location and find out the causes and effects of acid rain and current efforts to reduce it. The groups should then present their findings to the class.

### Science and Society   *Acid Rain*

As raindrops fall through the air, gases dissolve into the droplets. Some gases, such as carbon dioxide, cause rain to become a weak acid. Over a long period of time, weak acids from rain can cause rocks to weather, and can change the acidity of lakes.

In some areas, however, the acidity of the rain is much higher than normal. This increase in acidity is caused by pollutants from industrial factories, power plants, and cars. Raindrops that dissolve these pollutants cause much stronger acids to fall to the ground. This type of precipitation is called acid rain.

Acid rain can damage a forest ecosystem. Acid rain falling in a forest can kill trees. If acid rain drains into a lake or pond, water animals die. Sometimes these animals are not affected directly by acid rain, but their breeding cycle may be interrupted. This interruption can cause an entire population to die off. Food webs may be disrupted, which in turn affects land animals.

The amount of damage in a forest depends a lot on the type of soil. Some lakes don't contain natural chemicals that counteract acids. Therefore, many lakes are very acidic, and they have lost their fish population. Other areas have soil with natural buffers that neutralize the acid rain.

The best way to reduce acid rain is by reducing the air pollutants that cause acid rain. However, reducing air pollution is a complex task. Finding acceptable ways to do it will involve politics, technology, and economics.

**Figure 18.15** ▲
Acid rain killed many of the trees in Mount Mitchell, North Carolina.

### Check and Explain

1. How does precipitation form before it falls to the surface of the earth?

2. How can a hailstone form several layers of ice?

3. **Classify** State whether each of the following instruments is used to measure rain, snow, or both: rain gauge, tipping-bucket rain gauge, snowpack device.

4. **Compare and Contrast** How are sleet and freezing rain alike? How are they different?

## Air Pressure and Movement

Air exerts pressure on everything at the earth's surface. Air pressure at sea level is about equal to the pressure exerted by a column of air 10 m high and 1 cm square. Because pressure inside your body pushes out with an equal force, you do not feel normal air pressure.

Air pressure is measured with a barometer (buh RAHM uh tur). A barometer is like a tall drinking glass upside down in a sink filled with water. With the rim of the glass under the water, the column of water inside the glass acts like a barometer. As air pressure on the sinkful of water changes, the water column moves up or down.

### Physical Science LINK

Observe and compare the flow of smoke rising from a blown out candle when held next to a closed window and then next to an open window. Should the smoke behave differently at different times of the day? Explain.

**ACTIVITY**

A mercury barometer is ▶ a glass tube 1 m long. It is sealed at one end and filled with mercury. The open end sits in a container of mercury. As the air pressure on the mercury in the container changes, the mercury in the tube moves up or down. At sea level and 0°C, normal barometric pressure is 760 mm of mercury. Barometric pressure is also expressed in millibars, the actual weight of air pressing on a 1 cm² area.

▼ An aneroid (AN ur oyd) barometer contains a sealed, flexible cylinder of air. The cylinder expands when the atmospheric pressure is decreasing. The cylinder gets smaller when the atmospheric pressure is increasing. A mechanism measures changes in the size of the cylinder.

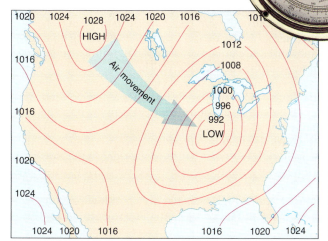

◀ Barometer readings taken in different places at the same time can be shown on a map. Lines called **isobars** connect places with the same barometric pressure. Notice the isobars on the map at left. Isobars forming closed circles show areas of low pressure and high pressure. Air moves from high-pressure areas to low-pressure areas.

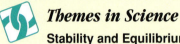
## TEACH ▪ Continued

### Skills Development

**Measure** Have students model how the sun heats the earth unevenly. Have students use a large inflatable ball, such as a beach ball, to represent the curved surface of the earth. Have them tape a strip of lightweight cardboard 10-cm wide from the "North Pole" of the ball to the "South Pole." Have them draw lines on the cardboard to represent the equator, 45°N, and 90°N. Have them place the ball in the sun so that the most direct rays of the sun hit the equator. (Have them tape the base of the ball to the floor or another flat surface to keep it stationary.) Have them use a thermometer to take temperature readings at each of the three lines.

### Critical Thinking

**Reason and Conclude** Explain to students that in coastal areas, the winds often blow in off the water during the day and off the land during the evening. Ask them to suggest why this might be. (During the day, the land heats up more rapidly than the water. The hot air above the land rises and cool air from above the sea rushes in. During the evening, the land cools off more rapidly than the water. The warm air above the sea rises, and the cool air above the land blows out to sea.)

### Enrich

Explain to students that along the equator is a nearly windless zone known to sailors as the doldrums, where the surface air in the trade winds come together. Ships could become trapped for days, unable to catch the slightest breeze.

### Answer to In-Text Question

① **The winds move in different directions at different latitudes because of the Coriolis force caused by the earth's rotation.**

---

### Themes in Science

**Stability and Equilibrium** The world's winds are part of a global system of air circulation. Warm air is circulated from the equator to the poles and cold air is circulated in the opposite direction. This circulation keeps the world temperatures in balance.

### Multicultural Perspectives

A chinook (shih NOOK) is a warm, dry wind that blows down the eastern slopes of the Rocky Mountains. It occurs mostly in winter or early spring. The chinook was named by European settlers for the country of the Chinook Native Americans along the Columbia River. The Chinooks are people of the Pacific Northwest who live mainly in Washington and Oregon.

---

**Figure 19.6 ▶**
Study the earth's wind patterns. Why do they move in different directions at different latitudes? ①

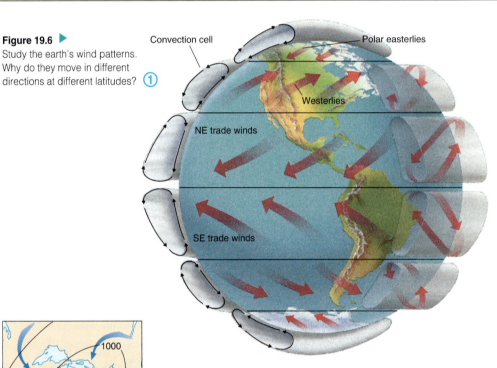

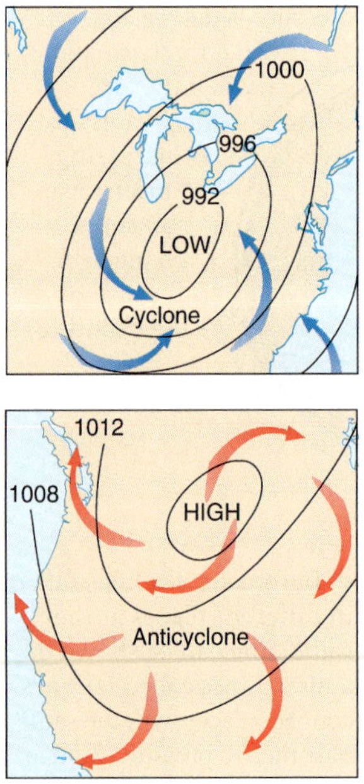

**Figure 19.7 ▲**
Cyclonic winds move in a counterclockwise direction (top). Anticyclonic winds move in a clockwise direction(bottom).

### Winds

Differences in air pressure produce winds. The pressure difference between a high-pressure area and a low-pressure area determines the strength of the wind. Larger pressure differences produce stronger winds.

Differences in air temperature also lead to pressure differences that cause winds. Temperature differences occur because the sun heats the earth unevenly. The warmer air is less dense, so it rises. The rising air creates a low-pressure area. For example, the sun's heat is most intense at the earth's equator. The air there heats up and rises. Air rushes in along the earth's surface to replace the hot air. The moving air becomes a surface wind.

The Coriolis effect influences Earth's wind patterns. Study the global wind map in Figure 19.6. Recall that the Coriolis effect is caused by the earth's rotation. The Coriolis effect pushes winds to the right in the Northern Hemisphere and to the left in the Southern Hemisphere.

Two kinds of smaller wind patterns can form as air moves from a high-pressure area to a low-pressure area. Look at Figure 19.7. At a low-pressure area, the air moves in toward the low-pressure center.

### Portfolio

Most newspaper and television weather reports give the high and low daily temperatures for various cities in the United States. Have each student choose one city in each of the following locations: near the coast, in the central United States, in the northern United States, and in the southern United States. Have students record over several weeks the high and low temperatures for each chosen city, as well as the temperatures for their own city or town. Have students keep the data in their portfolios. After completing this chapter, have students compare the temperatures in the different chosen locations and infer what factors contribute to the temperature variations.

**Section Objectives**
For a list of section objectives, see the Student Edition page.

**Skills Objectives**
Students should be able to:

**Infer** how to change the climate of a small area.

**Find Causes** of worldwide city temperatures.

**Infer** how various factors influence local climate.

**Vocabulary**
climate, altitude, prevailing winds, topography, rain shadow

## 20.1  Causes of Climate

### Objectives

▶ **Distinguish** between weather and climate.

▶ **Describe** two ways that the ocean affects climate.

▶ **Compare** the temperatures of two different regions in the United States.

▶ **Infer** about the factors that influence local climate.

▼ **ACTIVITY**

**Inferring**

*Desert Garden*

What could you do to change a dry plot of ground into a cool, lush garden? Make a list of ways you could change the temperature and moisture of an area.

**SKILLS WARMUP**

I magine it is January 1, the first day of the new year. Under clear blue skies in one part of North America, a group of friends shovel snow from the local pond so they can go ice skating. At the same time, in a different part of North America, another group of friends play volleyball on a warm, sandy beach. Why is the weather so different?

Although both groups might describe their weather as "fair," at least one condition—temperature—is quite different at the two locations. The temperatures are different because each location has a different **climate**. Climate is the characteristic weather for a region over a long period of time. The two major conditions that determine climate are temperature and precipitation.

### Temperature

The temperature of a region depends on a number of factors, including latitude, altitude, and distance from an ocean. These factors are dependent on the heat that the earth receives from the sun. Recall that radiant energy from the sun strikes the earth's surface, where some absorbed energy converts to heat. Some energy isn't absorbed. It is reflected from the earth's surface back into space.

**Latitude**  A measure of distance in degrees, north and south of the equator, is called *latitude*. Latitude and the tilt of the earth's axis determine the angle at which the sun's rays strike different regions of the earth.

**Figure 20.1** ▲
How do the climates in these two locations differ? ①

### MOTIVATE

#### Skills WarmUp
To help students understand what determines climate, have them do the Skills WarmUp.
**Answer**  Students might suggest providing shade, shelter from the wind, and water. Lists could include tree planting, irrigating, and landscaping.

#### Misconceptions
Students may think that climate is determined only by an area's latitude. Remind students that mountainous places in relatively warm latitudes may be snowy. Then use a globe to point out the seaside cities of Halifax, Canada, and Bordeaux, France, which are at the same latitude. Tell students that winter in Halifax is twice as cold as in Bordeaux. Explain that a warm ocean current in the Atlantic gives Western Europe fairly mild winters.

#### Answer to In-Text Question
① **They differ in temperature and precipitation.**

## Integrating the Sciences

**Physical Science** Light travels in a straight line. When light strikes an object at an angle, the amount of energy that reaches the object's surface is decreased. Have students observe the effect of light striking a surface at an angle. Have them shine a flashlight on a sheet of white paper at a 90°, 45°, and 30° angle. Ask students how the angle affects the amount of light that reaches the paper. (The greater the angle, the less concentrated is the light.) Ask students how this activity corresponds to the sun's rays striking the earth. (Because the earth has a curved surface, the sun's rays strike the poles at a greater angle than they strike the equator.)

## Critical Thinking

**Compare and Contrast** Have students think about places on the earth that are in high latitudes, such as Sweden, as compared to places in low latitudes, such as Colombia or Peru. Ask: What is the climate like where the latitude is high? What is the climate like where the latitude is low? (The climate is generally colder at high latitudes and warmer at low latitudes.)

**Generalize** Ask students if the two photographs on this page could exist at the same latitude. (Yes; even at the same latitude, high mountains are much colder than locations a few meters above sea level.)

### Answers to In-Text Questions

① **The sun's rays strike the earth at the poles at a greater angle than at lower latitudes.**

② **At low altitude the temperature is higher than at high altitudes, where the air is less dense and cannot hold as much heat.**

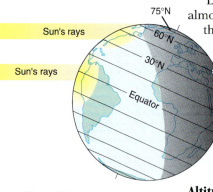

**Figure 20.2** ▲
The sun's rays strike more directly at low latitudes than at high latitudes. Notice how the rays seem to spread out at higher latitudes.

Look at Figure 20.2. Sun rays that strike the earth at almost no slant heat the earth's surface better than rays that strike at a slant. Direct rays provide more radiant energy. Notice that the most direct rays strike the areas near the equator, which is 0° latitude. Temperatures are highest in these regions. So areas near the equator have steady high temperatures, resulting in a warm climate. As latitude increases, the sun's rays strike at more of an angle and over a wider area. Why do you think the coldest places on the earth are at the poles? ①

**Altitude** Look at Figure 20.3. Both locations are at the same latitude near the equator. Notice that one location has lush, tropical vegetation. The other location, however, has little vegetation and snow on the ground all year long. How is this possible? The **altitude** of the two places is different. Altitude is a location's distance above sea level. In Figure 20.3, the location shown at left is a few meters above sea level. The location shown at right is several thousand meters above sea level.

The photographs show that air temperature decreases as altitude increases. The decrease in air temperature occurs because air pressure decreases with altitude. As altitude increases, less air presses down on the earth's surface. Therefore, the particles of air are spread farther apart, and the air is less dense. Less dense air cannot hold as much heat, so air temperature decreases.

**Figure 20.3**
How is climate affected by altitude in each location? ▼ ②

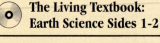

**The Living Textbook:
Earth Science Sides 1-2**

Chapter 13      Frame 02380
Antarctica (7 Frames)
Search:        Step:

## Geography Connection

Refer students to a map of the United States. Have them make a list that identifies the states affected by each of the currents shown in Figure 20.4.

## Integrating the Sciences

**Chemistry** The amount of heat energy required to raise 1 kilogram of a substance 1°C is called *specific heat.* Demonstrate to students how the specific heat of water compares with that of alcohol. Fill a glass half full with water; fill a glass half full with rubbing alcohol. Record the temperature of each. Place both liquids under a lamp. Record the temperature every ten minutes for an hour. (The alcohol should heat faster.)

## Skills Development

**Infer** Have students look at the map of the world ocean currents on page 347. Have students infer how ocean currents affect the temperature of the land that they border. (Warm-water currents increase the temperature of the land they border. For example, the latitude of northern Europe is higher than areas of similar temperatures in the United States. Northern Europe is warmed by the Gulf Stream current.)

## Enrich

Tell students that large lakes can also influence the temperature of surrounding land. For example, compare the daytime temperature of a lakeside city, such as Milwaukee, Duluth, or Buffalo, to the temperature of any inland city, such as Madison, Minneapolis, or Albany.

### Answers to In-Text Questions

③ **San Francisco is coastal; Springfield is inland.**

④ **They moderate temperatures.**

---

**Distance from an Ocean** Oceans have a noticeable effect on the temperature of nearby landmasses. Water heats up and cools down more slowly than land does. This property tends to make the temperatures of coastal areas more moderate. In summer, coastal waters warm slowly, keeping temperatures cool over the water and nearby land. In winter, coastal waters cool very slowly and air temperatures stay relatively mild. By contrast, land far from oceans heats up and cools down quickly. So inland areas usually have hot summers and cold winters. Study Table 20.1. Which city is in a coastal area? Which city is inland? Compare the temperature ③ ranges of the two cities.

Surface ocean currents also affect the temperature of coastal areas. Surface ocean currents are broad bands of water that flow in a definite path over the surface of the ocean. Warm currents carry warm water from the equator toward the poles. Cold currents carry cold water away from the poles toward the equator. Surface currents warm or cool the air above them. Therefore, the presence of an ocean current can affect the air temperature of nearby coastal regions.

Figure 20.4 shows surface ocean currents around the United States during the summer. The Florida Current brings warm temperatures to the southern and middle states. The Labrador Current brings cool temperatures to the Northeast. The California Current brings cool temperatures to much of the West Coast.

**Table 20.1  Average Temperatures**

|  | Springfield, MO (about 37°N) | San Francisco, CA (about 38°N) |
|---|---|---|
| Jan. | −2°C | 10°C |
| Jul. | 26°C | 15°C |
| Year | 13°C | 13°C |

**Figure 20.4**

The map shows ocean currents near the eastern and western coasts of the United States during the summer. How do the currents affect the climates in these two regions? ▼ ④

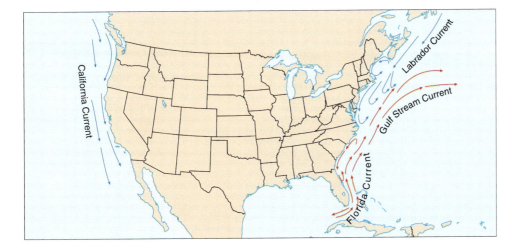

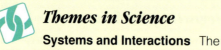

## Skills Development

**Define Operationally** Have students picture the movement of prevailing winds and weather across the United States. Ask: If the weather generally moves from west to east, from which direction do the prevailing winds come? (West)

**Calculate** Have students use the data in Table 20.1 to calculate the differences between average summer and winter temperatures in the two cities. (11°C, 12°C) Ask: How can the average yearly temperature be the same? (Mean temperature can be calculated from various extremes.)

## *SkillBuilder*

### Answers

1. Bangkok, on a river near the coast at a low latitude

2. Moscow, inland at a high latitude

3. Latitude

4. Inland location

Paragraphs will vary, but students should suggest that latitude, altitude, and distance from an ocean are inversely proportional to temperature.

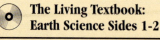

**The Living Textbook:
Earth Science Sides 1-2**

Chapter 30          Frame 06585
Namib Desert and Atlantic Fog (1 Frame)
Search:

### *Themes in Science*

**Systems and Interactions** The topography and prevailing winds interact to dictate a region's climate. The amount of precipitation that falls over an area is the result of an interaction between the moisture in the air and cloud formation. The greater the cloud formation, the greater the chance that the weather system in an area will produce a humid climate.

### *STS Connection*

In homes with forced hot air heating systems, people sometimes use humidifiers to add moisture to the air. Humidifiers blow air over water to create moisture-laden air. The moist air is then released into the room. Demonstrate the effects of a humidifier by blowing a fan over a pan of water. Have students compare how the air blown over the water feels compared to the air blown over a dry surface. (The moist air feels cooler.)

## Precipitation

Does it seem to rain whenever you have plans for an outdoor activity? If so, you probably think you live in a wet climate. Precipitation, along with temperature, determines climate. Prevailing winds and topography are two factors that affect the amount of precipitation a place receives.

**Prevailing Winds** Winds that blow from one direction more often than any other are called **prevailing winds**. Prevailing winds blowing from the water generally carry moisture because the air over oceans and large lakes contains a lot of water vapor. So nearby land receives a great deal of precipitation.

Places where the prevailing winds blow from the land toward the water receive little precipitation. For example, the Sahara Desert is one of the driest places in the world, even though the Atlantic Ocean lies just

## *SkillBuilder* *Finding Causes*

### *Worldwide City Temperatures*

The temperature in an area depends on the latitude, the altitude, and the distance from an ocean. Most newspapers list the daily high and low temperatures for various cities in the world. Study the table on the right, which lists the actual temperatures for some cities on a day in March.

On a world map, locate the two warmest and coldest cities listed in the table. Determine the cause of the regional temperature for each city. Record your findings. Then answer the following questions.

1. What city had the warmest temperatures? Where is this city located?

2. What city had the coldest temperatures? Where is this city located?

3. What factor was the most common for causing warm temperatures?

4. What factor was the most common for causing cold temperatures?

Write a paragraph explaining how latitude, altitude, and distance from an ocean affect an area's temperature.

| City | Temperature (°C) | |
| --- | --- | --- |
| | High | Low |
| Amsterdam | 6 | 2 |
| Bangkok | 34 | 24 |
| Cairo | 17 | 11 |
| London | 9 | 3 |
| Montreal | 1 | −10 |
| Moscow | −6 | −13 |
| Nairobi | 26 | 14 |
| Rio de Janeiro | 29 | 19 |
| Vienna | −1 | −6 |

**Language Arts Connection**

Have students discuss whether the term *rain shadow* accurately describes the dry, leeward side of a mountain. Have students infer how this term came into use.

 **Social Studies Connection**

Have students use a topographic map to trace the Oregon Trail that settlers followed to cross the United States from the 1840s to 1870s. Based on what students know about topography and precipitation patterns, have them determine where the settlers would have encountered very dry regions. (In desert areas and regions on the leeward sides of mountains)

**Directed Inquiry**

Have students study this page and Figure 20.5. Then ask:

▶ How do mountains affect moist air moving east from the Pacific Ocean? (Force it to rise)

▶ What occurs on the side of the mountain facing the wind? (Clouds form and rain falls.)

▶ What is the side of the mountain facing the wind called? (Windward side)

▶ What is the side of the mountain facing away from the wind called? (Leeward side)

▶ What happens to the air that passes over the mountain to the leeward side? (It becomes warmer and drier as it moves down.)

▶ What climate is typical on the leeward side of a mountain? (Dry conditions)

▶ What is the dry region on the leeward side of a mountain called? (Rain shadow)

▶ Why doesn't the air over the plains and prairies usually carry much moisture? (Oceans are far away.)

▶ How is your local climate influenced by topography? (Answers will depend on locale. Have students list regional surface features.)

to the west. The Sahara's prevailing winds blow over dry land from the east, where there is little moisture.

**Topography**  The surface features of an area make up its **topography**. One topographical feature that affects precipitation patterns in an area is a mountain range. In California, the Sierra Nevada Mountains force moist air moving east from the Pacific Ocean to rise. As a result, clouds form, and rain falls on the windward side of the mountains, the side facing the wind. The air continues to move over the mountains and down the leeward side, the side facing away from the wind. This air becomes warmer and drier as it moves down, producing the very dry conditions of the Nevada desert areas. The dry region on the leeward side of a mountain is known as the **rain shadow** of the mountain. Study Figure 20.5 to see how a rain shadow is created.

In contrast to the mountainous regions, plains and prairies generally have little precipitation. There are no mountains in these locations to "catch" any moisture carried by prevailing winds. In addition, the prevailing winds over plains and prairies do not carry very much moisture because the oceans are far away.

**Figure 20.5**

Warm, moist air rises as it hits the windward side of mountains. Rain falls, and dry air moves down the leeward side of the mountains, forming a rain shadow. ▼

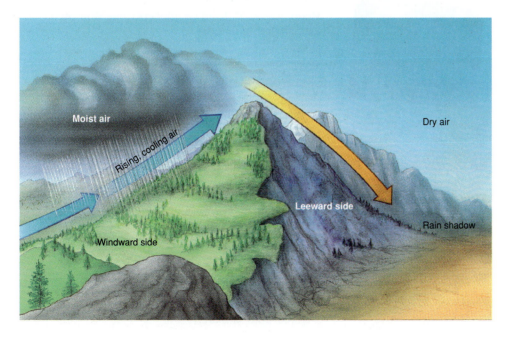

Moist air

Rising, cooling air

Dry air

Leeward side

Rain shadow

Windward side

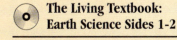 **The Living Textbook: Earth Science Sides 1-2**

Chapter 23          Frame 02832
Sierra Nevada (1 Frame)
Search:

## WrapUp

**Reinforce** Have students work in pairs. Furnish each pair with a list of cities. Have them use references to find out the altitude, latitude, and distance from the ocean for each city. Then have students predict the climate for each city. Have them use references to find out if their predictions are correct.

Use Review Worksheet 20.1.

## Check and Explain

1. Weather changes from hour to hour, day to day, and season to season. Climate is the characteristic weather for a location over a long period of time.

2. Oceans moderate the temperatures of coastal areas. In summer, coastal waters warm slowly, keeping temperatures cool over the water and nearby land. In winter, coastal waters cool slowly and air temperatures stay mild. Ocean currents also warm or cool the air above them.

3. The average temperatures of a southeastern coastal city are moderated by the ocean. A city in the central part of the country is not affected by the ocean, so temperatures may be more extreme.

4. Answers will vary, but students should address latitude, altitude, distance from an ocean, prevailing winds, and topography.

### *Multicultural Perspectives*

Have students research the types of clothing worn by people in different regions of the world. You could suggest such societies as the Pacific Islanders, the Inuit of northern Canada and Greenland, the Lapps or Laplanders of northern Europe, the Tuareg of the Sahara Desert, Malaysians, the Masai of eastern Africa, the Greeks from near the Mediterranean coast, and the Peruvians of the Andes Mountains. Have students present oral reports that include visual aids. After the student presentations, discuss how climate affects the type of clothing that people wear.

**Figure 20.6** ▲
Although both of these people are dressed for cold climates, their type of warm clothing varies greatly.

### Science and You    *Dressing for the Climate*

Imagine you are going on a two-week vacation. One week you'll be in Minneapolis, Minnesota, a northern city in the middle of the United States. The second week you'll be in Miami, Florida, a southeastern city near the ocean. What kinds of clothes should you pack? That depends on what time of year you are traveling. In July, the temperatures for Minneapolis and Miami are about the same. You will probably be most comfortable in shorts and short-sleeved shirts.

If your vacation is in January, you'll find an entirely different situation. The average January temperature in Minneapolis is −12°C. If you're going to spend any time outdoors, you'll need warm clothing and boots. Also, you can probably expect snow. In Miami, the average January temperature is 19°C. While it might be a little chilly for swimming, you'll be comfortable in lightweight clothing. At night or on cloudy days, you might need a sweater. You should also pack some rainwear because winter is the rainy season.

Keep in mind that conditions on any given day can be far different from the average for the month. For example, the lowest temperature ever recorded in Miami was −1°C. Even vacationers from Minneapolis were shivering that day!

### Check and Explain

1. How does the climate of a location differ from its weather?

2. Describe two ways in which oceans affect the climate of coastal areas.

3. **Compare**  How do you think the average temperatures for January and July in a coastal city in the southeastern United States compare with the average temperatures in the central part of the country? Explain your reasoning.

4. **Infer**  Describe the climate where you live. Indicate whether it is wet or dry, hot or cold, and whether it has seasonal changes in precipitation and temperature. Infer how the factors discussed in this section affect your climate.

**Art Connection**

Have students make travel brochures by cutting photographs from magazines. Each brochure should also contain information about the location and the climate of the area shown in the brochure. Encourage students to provide information that really "sells" each region.

 **Themes in Science**

**Stability and Equilibrium** The climate of an area is determined by the predominant weather patterns. The stability of climates has allowed scientists to classify the regions of the world into climate zones. Each climate zone has a relatively consistent temperature range and amount of precipitation.

**Section Objectives**
For a list of section objectives, see the Student Edition page.

**Skills Objectives**
Students should be able to:

**Observe** how climate affects living things.

**Research** state climates.

**Classify** cities by climate zone and climate type.

**Make a Model** of a climate.

**Vocabulary**
climate zone, microclimate

# 20.2 Climate Classification

## Objectives

▶ **Name** and **describe** the three main climate zones.

▶ **Compare** climate types in the United States to other parts of the world.

▶ **Compare** and **contrast** some plants and animals that live in various types of climates.

▶ **Classify** climates based on climate data.

**ACTIVITY**

**Observing**

*Climate and Life*

What kinds of plants and animals live in your area? List as many as you can. Now write what kind of climate your area has. Is it sunny a lot? Rainy? Cold? How do you think the climate affects the living things in your area?

**SKILLS WARMUP**

**MOTIVATE**

**Skills WarmUp**
To help students observe how climate affects living things, have them do the Skills WarmUp.
**Answer** Answers will depend on locale. Students should recognize that living things are adapted to climate.

## Misconceptions

Students may think that climates are based only on temperature ranges. To point out the role precipitation plays in climate, ask students to use their knowledge of geography to give examples of each of the following: dry climate (Sahara, southwestern United States); wet climate (Amazon, Congo Basin); snowy climate (northern Canada, Siberia).

**Answer to In-Text Question**
① **Dry, hot**

S uppose your family is moving from Chicago, Illinois, to Los Angeles, California. It's late December, and it's windy and –3°C in Chicago. The ground is covered with snow as you set out to drive to California.

On your trip, you'll pass through several types of climate. The Great Plains states will have a climate similar to Chicago's. From central Colorado through Utah, you will find a drier, warmer climate and a cold, mountainous climate. In Nevada and southern California, you will cross a desert. When you reach Los Angeles, the temperature will be pleasantly warm, about 15°C, and rain may be falling.

You can see from this example that the climate of the United States is varied. What are the different climate types? What factors cause them?

## Climate Zones

A region that has a characteristic temperature range is called a **climate zone**. Because temperature is influenced primarily by latitude, the climate zones are based on latitude.

The main climate zones are the tropical, temperate, and polar zones. The tropical zone is the warmest of the three zones. It is located between latitudes 30°N and 30°S. The temperate zone lies on both sides of the tropical zone, extending to about 60° north and south latitude. The polar zone, as you might guess, has the coldest temperatures of the three zones. It is located between 60° north and south latitude and the poles.

**Figure 20.7**
What type of climate zone is shown in this photograph?  ①

# TEACH

## Explore Visually

Have students study Figure 20.8 thoroughly. Then ask the following questions:

▶ What type of climate is found in central and eastern North America, and what are the climate's characteristics? (Temperate; warm, humid summers and cold winters)

▶ What type of climate is found in most areas near the equator, and what are the climate's characteristics? (Tropical rainy; areas are hot and can receive over 200 cm of rain a year.)

▶ Where do dry climates occur in North America, and what are the characteristics of these climates? (In western North America between 35° and 50° north latitude; cold winters and warm to very hot summers)

▶ What are the characteristics of polar climates? (Cold and dry, with short, cool summers and very long winters)

▶ How many climate types occur in South America? (Four)

▶ What is Greenland's climate type? (Polar)

▶ Where are dry climates found? (On both sides of the equator between 15° and 30° north and south latitudes)

▶ Where are humid, cold climates found, and what are their characteristics? (In the northern temperate zone; summers are short, warm, and rainy and winters are very cold.)

## Math Connection

Have students make one bar graph for the temperature ranges and one for the average amount of precipitation in the climate types shown in Table 20.2. Have students compare the two graphs. Ask if there is a relationship between the amount of precipitation and the temperature in a region. (The areas with the least amount of rainfall have the most extreme temperatures.)

## Themes in Science

**Diversity and Unity** The climate types of the world are widely diverse and hold a great variety of plant and animal life. However, many similar climate types can be found across the earth as well. Also, even when these similar climate types are separated by great geographical distance, their plant and animal life share similar characteristics.

**Table 20.2   Climate Types**

| Climate Type | Temperature Ranges (°C) | Precipitation (annual average) |
|---|---|---|
| | –20 to 30 | 25–150 cm |
| | 5 to 60 | under 25 cm |
| | –3 to 18 | 200–500 cm |
| | –30 to 30 | 40–125 cm |
| | –40 to 10 | under 30 cm |

## Climate Types

Both the wettest place and the driest place on the earth are located in the tropical climate zone. How is it possible for two very different climates to be located in the same climate zone? The answer is that many factors other than latitude affect the climate of a particular place. Each climate zone is divided into specific climate types that share certain conditions. The most useful

**Figure 20.8   World Climate Types** ▼

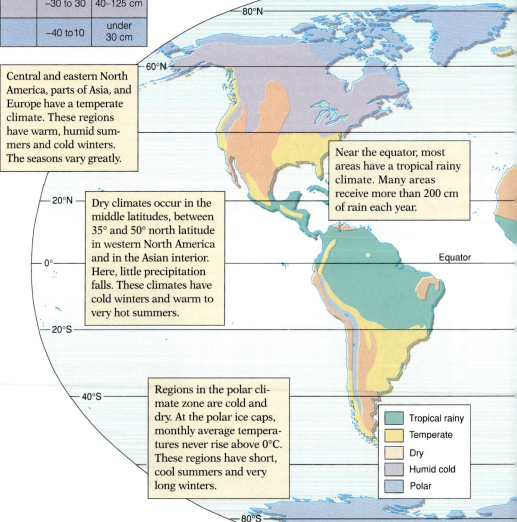

Central and eastern North America, parts of Asia, and Europe have a temperate climate. These regions have warm, humid summers and cold winters. The seasons vary greatly.

Near the equator, most areas have a tropical rainy climate. Many areas receive more than 200 cm of rain each year.

Dry climates occur in the middle latitudes, between 35° and 50° north latitude in western North America and in the Asian interior. Here, little precipitation falls. These climates have cold winters and warm to very hot summers.

Regions in the polar climate zone are cold and dry. At the polar ice caps, monthly average temperatures never rise above 0°C. These regions have short, cool summers and very long winters.

Legend:
- Tropical rainy
- Temperate
- Dry
- Humid cold
- Polar

470

### Cooperative Learning

Have students work in groups of three to design a trip that covers different regions of the United States. Tell the students that they must visit at least three different climate types and that they will travel during the month of December. Each group must include the names of the states and the climates that they will visit, a list of what clothing they will bring, and the type of transportation that they will use.

condition for classifying climate types is the amount of precipitation an area receives. Major plant types, altitude, and seasonal variations in winds and precipitation are also considered when classifying climates.

One version of world climate types is shown in Figure 20.8. They are based on the classification system of Wladimir Köppen, a German meteorologist. This climate map is a simplified version of the one used by climatologists. Notice that the map and Table 20.2 are color-keyed.

▼ **ACTIVITY**

**Researching**

*Extremes*

Find out the wettest, driest, hottest, and coldest locations in your state. What type of climate does each place have?

**SKILLS WORKOUT**

Humid cold climates are found in the northern temperate zone. Summers are fairly short and warm with much precipitation. The main season, winter, has very cold temperatures.

Dry climates are located on both sides of the equator, between 15° and 30° north and south latitude. This region includes some of the earth's driest deserts, such as the Sahara in north Africa.

### Skills WorkOut

To help students research the state's climates, have them do the Skills WorkOut.

**Answers** Answers will vary, but most students will find several different climates within the state.

### Integrated Learning

Use Integrating Worksheet 20.2.

### Skills Development

**Classify** Ask students: What are the two driest climates, and what are the differences between them? (Hot, dry climates occur in the middle latitudes and some occur near the equator. Polar climates are also dry but very cold.)

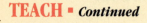

### TEACH ▪ *Continued*

## Directed Inquiry

Have students study the paragraphs and pictures on pages 472 and 473. Then ask:

▶ What kinds of organisms have adapted to the drier parts of the tropical zone? (Grasses and drought-resistant trees, grazing animals, such as buffalo, and burrowing animals, such as gophers)

▶ How have organisms in temperate desert climates adapted? (Cactus plants have tough, thick surfaces and spiny leaves that reduce water loss from evaporation. Many animals conserve water by staying underground during the day.)

**Answers to In-Text Questions**

① **Penguins, polar bears, seals; also certain birds, reindeer, wolves, and summer insects**

② **A variety of trees, vines, ferns, and mosses**

## *Integrating the Sciences*

**Environmental Science** Tropical, rainy climates have the largest diversity of species. Most of these species have yet to be identified. It is estimated that only 10 percent of tropical insects have been discovered. Currently, these regions are being cleared at a rate of 38,400 hectares per day. Discuss with students how rain forest destruction could alter the climate and affect the organisms on earth.

**Life Science** Animals and plants have adapted to the climatic conditions in which they live. Discuss with the students how each organism pictured on pages 472 and 473 is adapted to live in its particular climate.

## Life in the Climate Zones

Each climate zone is home to a variety of living things. In order to survive, animals and plants must adapt to conditions within their climate zone. Conditions include temperature, precipitation, and the amount of sunlight, food, water, and living space. What animals have adapted to conditions in the polar climate zone? ① What plants have adapted to conditions in the tropical climate zone? ②

Grasses and drought-resistant trees are common in drier parts of the tropical zone. Many burrowing animals, such as gophers, and grazing animals, such as buffalo, live in this region. Few plants and animals live in the drier regions of this zone. ▼

▲ The heavy precipitation in tropical rainy climates ensures plentiful plant life. The vegetation of tropical climates includes a variety of trees, vines, ferns, and mosses. The animal life includes many kinds of birds, amphibians, reptiles, insects, and mammals.

▲ Plants and animals of temperate desert climates are suited for survival in arid conditions. Cactus plants have tough, thick surfaces and thin, spiny leaves that reduce water loss from evaporation. Most animals, such as this gecko lizard, conserve moisture by living underground during the day and coming out at night.

## Themes in Science

**Evolution** Over time the animals and plants that live in a certain region evolve to survive successfully in that climate. Organisms may evolve specific features, such as thick fur. Organisms may also evolve certain behaviors, such as hibernation, which help them survive.

## Integrating the Sciences

**Life Science** Share with students the fact that, in polar regions, the snow may appear pink. This coloring is due to the presence of algae that live in the snow. They photosynthesize sunlight and obtain the small amount of nutrients dissolved in the snow. Scientists think that the red color may help the algae filter out the sun's harmful ultraviolet rays.

► What is typical of trees in the temperate zone? (They are deciduous.)

► How do many birds and mammals in the temperate zone respond to cold winter temperatures? (Birds often migrate and many mammals hibernate.)

► In what climate zones do humans rarely live permanently? (Driest deserts or coldest polar regions)

► What vegetation thrives in tundra areas? (Lichens, mosses, and, in warmer areas, shrublike trees)

► What vegetation grows in the ice cap region of the polar zone? Why? (None, because of year-round snow, ice, and cold)

► What do polar bears and seals use for food in the polar zone? (Fishes and other marine animals)

## Generalize

In general, what climates support the most different kinds of life? Why? (Warmer, wetter climates; they have the steadiest supply of energy and nutrients.)

The different climate zones and types also affect humans. Unlike many plants and animals, however, humans have adapted to live in just about every climate type. Though humans don't live permanently in the driest deserts or the coldest polar regions, they are able to survive in those areas for limited amounts of time.

A forest of deciduous trees, trees that lose their leaves annually, is typical of the climate in the temperate zone. Animals include a variety of birds, small mammals, and many insects. Birds often migrate from this climate during winter. Many mammals hibernate during part of the year. ▼

No vegetation grows in the ice cap region of the polar zone. Year-round snow, ice, and cold temperatures prevent plants from growing. Penguins live year-round in the southern polar zone. Polar bears and seals may be found in some seasons. These animals feed on fishes and other marine animals. ▼

▲ The tundra is located in the northern and southern polar zones. As shown above, vegetation in tundra regions is limited to lichens and mosses. In warmer tundra areas, shrublike trees may grow. Animals include birds, reindeer, wolves, and many mosquitoes and flies in the summer.

## Apply

Have students reread the Skills WarmUp on page 463. Ask them to describe how the activity relates to microclimates. (Changing the temperature and moisture of a small area changes its microclimate.)

## Enrich

Use Enrich Worksheet 20.2.

## EVALUATE

## WrapUp

**Reteach** Have students take turns describing each climate. Then have students vote to choose a single ideal climate. Ask them to find out what location in the United States best exhibits this climate.

Use Review Worksheet 20.2.

## Check and Explain

1.  The tropical zone is warmest and is located between latitudes 30°N and 30°S. The temperate zone extends from the tropical zone to about 60° north and south latitudes. The polar zone has the coldest temperatures; it is located between 60° north and south and the poles.

2.  The climate types in the United States are temperate, dry, humid cold, polar (Alaska), and tropical rainy (Hawaii and South Florida).

3.  The warmer and wetter the climate, the more plants and animals live there. Both tropical rainy climates and the humid cold climates have many kinds of life, but tropical rainy climates have more amphibians and reptiles.

4.  Moscow—temperate, humid cold; Lima—tropical, dry; Reykjavik—temperate, temperate; Manila—tropical, tropical rainy

### Cooperative Learning

Have students work in groups of four or five, using an atlas that includes maps of the agricultural resources of each continent. Have students list the main types of crops grown on each continent. From the list, have students infer what types of foods are eaten in different regions of the world. If your atlas lists agricultural resources by country, assign students in each group to list crops grown in the countries of a specific continent.

**Figure 20.9** ▲
Rice paddies growing in Indonesia require flat surfaces and large amounts of water.

### Science and Society
*Microclimates and Farming*

Have you ever heard the saying, "Everybody complains about the weather, but nobody does anything about it"? Though people have never truly controlled the weather, they have changed the climate in very small areas. The climate of a small area is called a **microclimate**.

Farming has done more to create microclimates than any other human factor. To raise crops, farmers often change conditions on their farms. Through the use of irrigation, farmers brought water to dry regions of the world, such as Israel and parts of California. This water changed barren land into rich, fertile farmland.

Farmers in rice-growing countries, such as China, also alter conditions on their land. Much of the farmland lies on steep slopes. Farmers carve out flat surfaces on these slopes to plant rice. Once planted, rice plants require much water. To keep the plants irrigated, farmers create ways of transporting large amounts of water up to the rice paddies.

Farmers sometimes try to control temperatures. In Florida, for example, a sudden frost can destroy much of the citrus crop. To prevent this, farmers use smoke or large fans to keep air temperatures in their citrus groves from falling below freezing, thus saving the fruit.

### Check and Explain

1.  Name and describe the three main climate zones.

2.  Refer to Figure 20.8. List the climate types in the United States. Which one do you live in? What parts of the world have the same climate type as yours?

3.  **Compare and Contrast** How does climate influence the types of plants and animals that live in an area? Compare the types of plants and animals in a tropical rainy climate with those in a humid cold climate.

4.  **Classify** Using a world map, Figure 20.8, and the Data Bank on page 617, classify the following cities by climate zone (polar, temperate, or tropical) and climate type (tropical rainy, dry, temperate, humid cold, or polar): Moscow, Lima, Reykjavik, and Manila.

## Prelab Discussion

Have students read the entire activity. Discuss the following points before beginning:

► What is the difference between the soil types in the two cans?

► Why would a sealed jar provide a better model than an open jar?

► How might conditions other than climate affect plant growth?

**Time** 1 week    **Group** 5

**Materials**

12 small cans

12 large jars with lids

gravel

soil

sand

6 spoons

6 hammers

6 nails

40–50 small plants

# Activity 20  How can you model climates?

**Skills**  Model; Observe

### Task 1  Prelab Prep

1. Collect the following items: 2 small cans (such as tuna fish cans), nail, hammer, 2 jars with lids, gravel, soil, sand, spoon, several plants, water.
2. Make sure each can fits inside a jar by placing a can inside a jar lid. Place the jar upside down on the lid, and screw it closed. If the can doesn't fit, try another can or another jar.
3. Use the hammer and nail to poke three or four holes in the bottom of each can. **Caution! Be careful when using a nail and hammer.**

### Task 2  Data Record

1. Copy Table 20.3 on a separate piece of paper.
2. Record your observations in the data table for several days.

**Table 20.3  Observations of Bottle Climates**

| Bottle Climate | Elapsed Time (Days) | | | |
|---|---|---|---|---|
| | Day 1 | Day 2 | Day 5 | Day 7 |
| Tropical | | | | |
| Desert | | | | |

### Task 3  Procedure

1. Label one jar *Desert* and one jar *Tropical.*
2. For the *Desert* jar, cover the bottom of the can with gravel. Fill the rest of the can with sand.
3. Moisten the sand by sprinkling it with water. Transplant several plants by poking a hole into the sand with your finger and inserting the plant roots into the sand.
4. Place the can on the inside of the jar lid. Lift the lid and can into the *Desert* jar and screw the lid closed.

5. Place the *Desert* jar in a sunny, warm place. Observe for several days, and record your observations.
6. For the *Tropical* jar, cover the bottom of the can with gravel. Fill the rest of the can with soil.
7. Moisten the soil by sprinkling it with water. Transplant several plants by poking a hole into the soil with your finger and inserting the plant roots into the soil.
8. Place the can on the inside of the jar lid. Lift the lid and can into the *Tropical* jar and screw the lid closed.
9. Place the *Tropical* jar in a sunny, warm place. Sprinkle water on the plants every day. Observe for several days, and record your observations.

### Task 4  Analysis

1. Which climate had the most moisture? How could you tell?
2. In which climate did the plants survive the best? Why?
3. How does an actual desert climate differ from your *Desert* jar?
4. How does an actual tropical climate differ from your *Tropical* jar?
5. List the variables in this activity.

### Task 5  Conclusion

Write a paragraph explaining how your models show the similarities and differences between desert and tropical climates.

### Extension

Make climate jars for a tundra and a temperate climate. Follow the same procedure outlined in the activity. Place the tundra jar in the refrigerator and vary the location of the temperate jar. How are tundra and temperate climate types similar? How are they different?

## Analysis

1. The Tropical climate had the most moisture because water was added to the jar every day.
2. Student results will vary.
3. Accept all reasonable answers. An actual desert climate will have wind and more extreme temperature variations. There may also be animals that feed on a particular type of plant.
4. Accept all reasonable answers. An actual tropical climate may have greater humidity than was simulated because of frequent rains. Also, there are many animals in a tropical climate.
5. Soil type, amount of water, temperature, types of plants, health of plants

## Conclusion

The main similarity is that both have warm temperatures. The main difference is the amount of moisture.

## Extension

Varied seasons are more pronounced in a temperate climate, as opposed to the generally cold temperatures of the tundra climate. Both climates have freezing temperatures.

# 20.3

## Section Objectives
For a list of section objectives, see the Student Edition page.

## Skills Objectives
Students should be able to:

**Infer** causes of major climate changes over time.

**Find Causes** for worldwide climate changes.

**Predict** how an ice age would affect a location.

---

## MOTIVATE

### Skills WarmUp
To help students infer what causes climates to change, have them do the Skills WarmUp.
**Answer** The climate must have been much warmer.

### Prior Knowledge
To gauge how much students know about climate change, ask the following questions:

▶ What is an ice age?

▶ What is global warming?

▶ What would it take to change the climate of the area where you live?

## Themes in Science

**Energy** The changing distribution of energy from the sun is related to changes in the climate on the earth. According to some theories, varying heat energy from the sun due to volcanic action has produced major climate changes on the earth.

▼ **ACTIVITY**

### Inferring

*Forest Through the Ice*

Fossils indicate that forests once grew around the Arctic Circle. Today this area is covered year-round with ice and snow. What conditions must have been different for plants to have grown in this area?

**SKILLS WARMUP**

## 20.3 Climate Change

### Objectives

▶ **Explain** the effect of El Niño on climates.

▶ **Describe** the possible effects of major climate changes.

▶ **Name** three possible causes of climate change.

▶ **Predict** how a future ice age could affect an area.

---

Imagine you could travel back 15,000 years to what is now Illinois. You'd expect the winters to be cold and snowy, just as they are today. But you might be surprised to see the landscape in the summer. The land would be covered with ice and snow. The air temperature would be frigid. About 15,000 years ago, the climate in the midwestern United States was very different from the climate today. What could cause such a change to occur? Have other such climate changes occurred?

Scientists have accumulated evidence indicating that the world's climate has changed gradually but dramatically over time. Though they do not know the exact causes, scientists have a number of theories.

### Climate Change Over Time

Major climate changes produce long-lasting shifts in temperature and precipitation patterns worldwide. Long-term changes in climate can have major effects on all living things. About 65 million years ago, many species of plants and animals, including the dinosaurs, died out. Many scientists hypothesize that these mass extinctions were caused by climate changes brought about by natural occurrences.

Although some climate changes can occur quickly, most happen slowly. For example, recall that the earth's continents were once one great landmass called Pangaea. As the landmass broke up and drifted, the distribution of land and water on the earth's surface slowly changed. Because land and water absorb heat differently, the heating of the earth's surface was affected. These changes, in turn, may have produced changes in the world's climates.

**Ice Ages and Climate** Glaciers covered much of the earth's surface in the past. Recall that a period when glaciers grow and advance over the land is referred to as an ice age. Scientists infer from evidence that many ice ages occurred in the past 2 million years. During these ice ages, the average temperature on the earth was about 6°C cooler than it is today, and sea levels were lower.

Each ice age was separated by a period of warming, called an *interglacial*, when the ice sheets melted and retreated. The last ice age ended about 10,000 years ago. Figure 20.10 shows how much of North America was covered by glaciers during the last ice age.

Today large land surfaces, such as Antarctica and Greenland, are still covered by sheets of ice. Some scientists hypothesize that we are now in an interglacial and that the ice sheet may advance again in the future. How would the advance affect the earth's climate? ①

**Figure 20.10** ▲
The last ice age in North America extended into the United States.

Though scientists don't know for certain the cause of the ice ages, they do know that the moving ice sheets changed the earth's surface. For example, the Great Lakes were shaped by the last glacier. Long Island, New York, is made of materials left behind by glaciers.

**Figure 20.11** ▲
The kettle lakes in Wisconsin were formed by the last ice age. Kettle lakes are also common in New York and Minnesota.

**Figure 20.12** ▲
Scientists in South Dakota uncover fossilized mammoth bones from the ice ages. The bones help them learn more about the ice ages.

# TEACH ▪ Continued

## Research

Have students use references to find out how many times El Niño has occurred in the Pacific Ocean in the last 20 years. How did each El Niño affect world climates?

## Skills Development

**Organize Data** Ask students to use their research on El Niño to make a graph of the frequency of their occurrences over the last 20 years. Have them note if there is a pattern to the frequency.

## Class Activity

Provide students with a large bowl or aquarium containing water. Have volunteers pour some warm water in and establish a current. Then have them reverse the current. Allow students to feel the direction and temperature of the water. Ask students for ideas about how changing the direction of the current could affect organisms living in the water.

## Integrated Learning

Use Integrating Worksheet 20.3.

### Themes in Science

**Scale and Structure** A change in the direction and magnitude of the flow of an ocean current can cause climatic changes on a global scale. Have students study a detailed map of world ocean currents. Ask them to identify the direction of flow for various currents, such as the Canary Current (north-to-south); the South Equatorial Current (east-to-west); and the Southwest Monsoon Current (southwest-to-northwest-to southeast).

### Multicultural Perspectives

In Peru, El Niño is also referred to as El Pintor de Callao (The Painter of Calleo). Callao is the name of a port city in Peru that is affected by El Niño. El Niño got this nickname because its warm current is responsible for massive fish kills around Callao. The dead fish pile up on the beaches and produce hydrogen sulfide. This foul-smelling gas blackens the surfaces of ships and produces other discoloring effects.

**El Niño and Climate** Recall that ocean currents affect climate. Air over the ocean is heated or cooled by the water beneath. Warm currents heat the air; cold currents cool it. This uneven heating generates winds. Winds influence climate. Therefore, changes in ocean currents may affect climate.

A warm current flowing across the Pacific Ocean near the equator generally moves from east to west. About every three to eight years, this current changes direction, producing *El Niño*. Recall that El Niño is a warm ocean current that flows from west to east across the Pacific Ocean. When El Niño reaches South America, it moves down the west coast, where a cold current usually flows. El Niño eventually warms the water off the coast.

The warm water affects many living things. For example, it is a hazard to certain fishing industries in these regions. Here, fishes are adapted to a cold water environment. Coral reefs die off. Island nesting birds migrate to cool waters. Marine animals move to escape the warming.

**Figure 20.14** ▲
In Ecuador, El Niño caused massive floods. Bridges, buildings, and homes washed away.

El Niño does more than raise the water temperature off the coast of South America. It disrupts other ocean currents, worldwide precipitation, and temperature patterns. In the early 1980s, the strongest El Niño in history caused dramatic climate changes throughout the world. Parts of Africa and Australia suffered severe drought. Other regions of the world, such as Peru and Ecuador, had heavy rains and flooding. Figures 20.13 and 20.14 show some of the damage caused by El Niño.

When El Niño occurs, scientists can only observe its effects. Currently, computer models developed from past El Niño patterns may help predict how El Niño develops. For example, a computer model at the Lamont-Doherty Geological Observatory in New York forecasted in 1990 that an El Niño warming trend would occur in the central Pacific Ocean in 1992. Scientists were pleased that the model proved to be correct. Although such forecasts cannot prevent El Niño, they can possibly help save lives and property.

**Figure 20.13** ▲
El Niño caused severe droughts in parts of Africa. Crops, livestock, and people suffered.

### Portfolio

Have students collect newspaper or magazine articles about the effects humans have on climate. Some subjects may include deforestation, desertification, global warming, and cloud seeding. Post the articles on a bulletin board. Have students write short summaries of at least three of the articles. They can keep the summaries in their portfolios. Refer students to their summaries when you study Humans and the Environment in Chapter 22.

## Human Causes of Climate Change

Human activities also influence climate. As human populations increase, people need new places to live. They need land to grow food. All over the world, land has been cleared for farming and construction. In many areas, the removal of trees has caused a decrease in the amount of precipitation the area receives. The result is a drier climate.

The building of a city alters the climate in an area. The paved surfaces absorb sunlight and heat up. This heat slightly raises the average temperature of a city compared to the surrounding countryside.

People affect climate through farming, industry, and driving automobiles. Smoke and dust created by farming and industry reduce the amount of radiant energy reaching the earth's surface. Industry and automobiles release carbon dioxide into the air through the burning of fossil fuels.

### Ecology
### L I N K

Collect the following items: a spray bottle, water, a fan, and two plates.

**1.** Spray a fine mist of water onto two plates.

**2.** Use a small fan to blow air over one of the plates.

**3.** Determine which plate dries faster.

Imagine the increase of open space in a dense rain-forest due to deforestation. How might the process you modeled affect vegetation that requires a moist climate?

**A C T I V I T Y**

## Consider This

### What Can Be Done About Global Warming?

Recall that global warming is a worldwide increase in average temperature. Many scientists hypothesize that people contribute to global warming by adding certain gases to the atmosphere.

One major cause of global warming, some scientists say, is the burning of fossil fuels in cars and factories. These activities add large amounts of carbon dioxide to the air. In the atmosphere, carbon dioxide traps heat and prevents it from escaping into space. The result may be higher temperatures on the surface of the earth.

The effects of global warming are difficult to predict. Some scientists say the results will mean human and economic disaster. Others say that global warming may be balanced by a cooling trend, or that its effects will not be great. There may even be benefits, if global warming increases the growth of crops.

**Think About It** Should people and countries reduce their use of fossil fuels in an attempt to prevent global warming?

**Write About It** Pretend you are the editor of a newspaper.

Write an editorial about what kinds of actions, if any, people or countries should take to reduce the use of fossil fuels.

## Skills Development

**Infer** Ask students: Would you say that human activities greatly influence climate, moderately influence climate, or influence climate very little? Why? (Explain that there is no "correct answer." Students might say that human activities greatly influence climate because people clear land, build cities, and increase the amount of dust, smoke, and carbon dioxide released into the air.)

### Consider This

**Think About It** Answers will vary. Students should evaluate the risks, such as an increase in sea level, and the benefits, such as reduced environmental damage. Students may cite global cooperative efforts, such as helping developing countries reduce reliance on fossil fuels.

**Write About It** Answers will vary, but students should support their recommendations with examples or evidence.

### Portfolio

Have students make a list of specific ways in which people change the climate, such as creating lakes, releasing gases that destroy ozone, and cutting down rain forests. Have them compare lists, then have them place the lists in their portfolios.

**Answer to Link**

The increase in open space enables wind to blow over vegetation surfaces that were not previously exposed. Wind increases the rate of evaporation over these surfaces, causing them to dry out much faster than usual and decreasing the amount of needed moisture available. As a result, the moisture-dependent vegetation may undergo stress and die.

## Critical Thinking

**Uncover Assumptions** Ask students to identify the assumption underlying the theory that changes in the tilt of the earth's axis cause ice ages. (The amount of solar radiation is the main cause of climate conditions.)

# EVALUATE

## WrapUp

**Review** Have students make a list of ways that climate can change, the causes for each type of climate change, and the possible effects of each type of change. (For example, a climate could cool due to an ice age. This cooling would affect the type of plants and animals that could survive.)

Use Review Worksheet 20.3.

## Check and Explain

1. El Niño is a warm-water current in the Pacific Ocean that has reversed direction. It disrupts other ocean currents, worldwide precipitation, and temperature patterns.

2. Major climate changes produce long-lasting shifts in temperature and precipitation patterns.

3. Drifting continents, ice ages, and changing ocean currents

4. Answers will vary depending on locale, although temperatures would probably drop almost everywhere.

### *Social Studies Connection*

Have students reread the Science and Society feature about Alfred Wegener and continental drift on page 95 in Chapter 5. Discuss how the research at Devil's Hole is similar to what happened in 1923.

### Science and Technology
*Tracking Climate Change*

For years, some scientists theorized that one of the major causes of the ice ages was changes in the tilt of the earth's axis. The theory states that, as the axis slowly changes, the amount of sunlight hitting part of the earth changes. This, in turn, causes the advance and retreat of glaciers.

Recent studies in an unlikely place are making some scientists rethink this theory. Researchers studied ancient mineral deposits in Devil's Hole, Nevada, for clues to changes in the earth's temperature. Devil's Hole is a water-filled fissure, or crack, in Nevada's desert floor. The hole is more than 120 m deep but only about 210 cm wide. Over thousands of years, the water that seeped into Devil's Hole left layers of the mineral calcite on the walls. Divers used special drills to take out samples.

Study of the calcite suggested to scientists that the warming of the second-to-last ice age began about 140,000 years ago. At this time, the earth was not tilted so that maximum solar radiation reached polar regions any time during the year. However, other research sets the end of the second-to-last ice age at about 128,000 years ago. At that time, the earth's axis was tilted so that the maximum solar radiation reached the polar regions. If the Devil's Hole finding holds true, perhaps the tilt of the earth's axis was not the main reason for the end of this ice age.

The scientists who conducted the Devil's Hole studies think that ice ages come and go for a number of reasons. In addition to the changes in the tilt of the earth's axis, they hypothesize that ice ages are due to changes in the oceans, glaciers, and atmosphere.

**Figure 20.15 ▲**
A core sample from Devil's Hole may hold some answers to the cause of ice ages.

### Check and Explain

1. What is El Niño? How does it change climates?

2. Describe possible effects of major climate changes.

3. **Find Causes** Name three possible natural causes of worldwide climate change.

4. **Predict** How would the place where you live be affected by a new ice age? Explain.

## Check Your Vocabulary

**1.** climate zones

**2.** rain shadow

**3.** prevailing winds

**4.** climate

**5.** altitude

**6.** microclimate

**7.** topography

## Write Your Vocabulary

Students' sentences should show
that they know the meaning of
each word as well as how to use it
in a sentence.

Use Vocabulary Worksheet for
Chapter 20.

# Chapter 20 Review

## Concept Summary

### 20.1 Causes of Climate

▶ Climate is the weather of a region over a long period of time. It is determined mainly by temperature and precipitation.

▶ Generally, temperature decreases as latitude increases.

▶ Air temperature tends to decrease as altitude increases. Altitude is distance above sea level.

▶ Oceans have a moderating effect on temperatures of nearby landmasses.

▶ The amount of precipitation a place receives depends on prevailing winds and topography.

▶ A rain shadow is created when moist air deposits precipitation on a mountain range's windward side.

### 20.2 Climate Classification

▶ The three main climate zones are the tropical, temperate, and polar zones.

▶ Within the climate zones are different climate types, which are classified by the amount of precipitation.

▶ The plants and animals in each climate zone are adapted to the conditions in that zone.

▶ A microclimate is the particular climate of a small area.

### 20.3 Climate Change

▶ Global climate changes can have far-reaching and dramatic effects.

▶ Ice ages are periods of worldwide climate change. Periods when the ice sheets retreated are called interglacials.

▶ El Niño is a change in the normal ocean currents off the coast of South America.

▶ Past climate changes may have been caused by continental drift, changes in the tilt of the earth's axis, and changes in the radiation given off by the sun.

▶ Human activity causes change in microclimates and may produce worldwide global warming.

## Chapter Vocabulary

| | | |
|---|---|---|
| climate (20.1) | topography (20.1) | climate zone (20.2) |
| altitude (20.1) | rain shadow (20.1) | microclimate (20.2) |
| prevailing winds (20.1) | | |

## Check Your Vocabulary

Use the vocabulary words above to complete the following sentences correctly.

1. Many climate types are found in each of the three ____ .

2. On the leeward side of a mountain, a ____ is often located.

3. Winds that blow most often from one direction are called ____ .

4. The weather for a region that occurs over a long period of time is its ____ .

5. One influence on temperature is ____ , which is height above sea level.

6. The climate of a small area is called a(n) ____ .

7. The surface features of an area make up its ____ .

## Write Your Vocabulary

Write sentences using the vocabulary words above. Show that you know what each word means.

## Check Your Knowledge

1. Weather is the set of atmospheric conditions present at any given time. Climate is the pattern of weather in an area over a long period of time.

2. The higher the latitude, the cooler the climate.

3. The ocean keeps coastal temperatures more moderate.

4. Prevailing winds and topography are the main influences on precipitation.

5. The three main climate zones are polar (above 60° north and south), tropical (between 30° north and 30° south), and temperate (between 30° and 60° north and south).

6. The five climate types are tropical rainy, temperate, dry, humid cold, and polar. See Figure 20.8 for possible correct answers for the locations of each type.

7. A microclimate is the climate of a very small area. Changing the physical characteristics of an area, as farming does, creates a microclimate.

8. El Niño can cause changes in precipitation, including the extremes of drought and heavy rain.

9. Student answers may vary. Possible answers include: ice ages, El Niño, volcanic eruptions, and human-made factors like pollution.

10. an interglacial
11. windward
12. equator
13. polar

## Check Your Understanding

1. Air temperature decreases with increasing altitude. Mountain locations can have precipitation patterns that are affected by nearby lowland regions.

2. This region should have very little precipitation, because the winds do not blow moisture-containing clouds over the land.

3. At higher latitudes, the sun strikes the land less directly than at lower latitudes.

4. Heat from the sun is responsible for the prevailing winds, which are a major factor influencing climate.

5. A tropical rain forest is warm and humid, and does not change very much through the year. The green trees would be present during the winter.

6. The volcanic ash can be thick enough to block the sun, causing a microclimate. The ash in the air also increases cloud formation that can increase precipitation.

7. El Niño occurs every four to seven years and can cause relatively rapid climate changes. Ice ages occur thousands of years apart and lead to much slower changes.

8. Conifers are adapted to survive cold temperatures. For example, they stay green all year so they can continue photosynthesis.

## Chapter 20 Review

### Check Your Knowledge

Answer the following in complete sentences.

1. Explain the difference between climate and weather.

2. Describe how latitude is related to temperature.

3. Explain how oceans can affect the temperature of nearby landmasses.

4. List the two main influences on precipitation.

5. What are the three main climate zones, and what are their boundaries?

6. List five climate types and one location where each can be found.

7. What is a microclimate? How is one formed?

8. What are the kinds of climate change that El Niño can cause?

9. List factors that may have caused past climate changes.

Choose the answer that best completes each sentence.

10. A time when ice sheets are retreating is called (an interglacial, an ice age, El Niño, summer).

11. The (leeward, north, windward, south) side of a mountain often receives the most precipitation.

12. The sun's rays strike the earth most directly at the (poles, equator, temperate zone, oceans).

13. Few plants grow in the (temperate, tropical, polar) climate zone.

### Check Your Understanding

Apply the concepts you have learned to answer each question.

1. Explain how two locations at the same latitude but different altitudes can have a very different climate.

2. Would you expect a coastal area where the prevailing winds blow from the land to the ocean to receive much or little precipitation? Explain your thinking.

3. Why are areas at greater latitudes generally cooler than areas at lower latitudes?

4. Explain how variations in the amount of radiation given off by the sun could cause climate change.

5. **Mystery Photo** The photograph on page 462 was taken from an airplane. It shows waterfalls streaming down the hills of a tropical rain forest. What is the typical climate in a tropical rain forest? Would you expect to see these green trees in the winter?

6. **Extension** Some scientists think that great amounts of volcanic dust in the atmosphere could lead to cooler average temperatures over the entire globe. Explain how this cooling might occur.

7. **Compare and Contrast** El Niño and the ice ages are two types of climate change. How are they similar? How are they different?

8. **Infer** Most trees in a humid cold climate are conifers. Why?

## Develop Your Skills

1. a. July; February
   b. April: about –20°C; November: about –20°C
   c. Polar; temperature ranges from about –40°C to about 10°C
2. This type of animal probably lives in a dry climate.
3. a. Moscow, Russia or Reykjavik, Iceland
   b. Manila, Philippines
4. Student posters will vary. Make sure the information presented is accurate.

## Make Connections

1. Concept maps will vary. The map below shows a possible organization of the concepts listed.

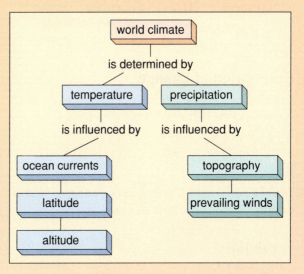

2. In both climates, houses must be well insulated and will need to have a way to humidify the air. In a desert climate, the house must have both air conditioning and heating to handle warm days and cool nights. In the polar climate, heating is the most important consideration.
3. Student reports will vary. Crops are sensitive to temperature, moisture, and length of growing season. Farmers can grow crops not suited to the area in several ways, including: using irrigation, greenhouses, hydroponics, or genetically-engineered plants.
4. Student reports may vary. People in arid climates adapt by wearing different clothing, by avoiding the hottest times of the day and being active during cooler times, and by conserving water.

---

## Develop Your Skills

Use the skills you have developed in this chapter to complete each activity.

1. **Interpret Data**  The graph below shows average temperature ranges in an area over a year. Study the graph, then answer the following questions.

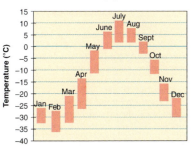

   a. Which month is the warmest? The coldest?
   b. What is the average temperature in April? In November?
   c. What kind of climate is indicated by the graph: polar, temperate, or tropical? How do you know?

2. **Infer**  Some animals excrete wastes that contain almost no water. In which type of climate might such an animal live?

3. **Data Bank**  Use the information on page 617 to answer the following questions.
   a. Which city has the lowest average temperature?
   b. Which city has the highest average rainfall?

4. **Communicate**  Make a poster that shows the five major climate types. List the temperature and precipitation characteristics of each type. Also list plants and animals in each zone.

## Make Connections

1. **Link the Concepts**  Draw a concept map showing how the concepts below link together. Add terms to connect, or link, the concepts.

   world climate
   temperature
   precipitation
   ocean currents
   topography
   prevailing winds
   latitude
   altitude

2. **Science and Technology**  Houses are built differently in different climates. What features would you expect a house built in a desert to have? What features would you expect in a house built in a polar or near-polar climate?

3. **Science and Social Studies**  Climate affects the plants that grow in a region. Use the library to find out how climate affects which types of crops are grown. Also find out about ways that farmers are able to grow a crop in an environment to which that crop is not suited.

4. **Science and Society**  Groups of people called Bedouins live in the deserts of the Middle East. Do some research to find out how these people survive in the extreme heat and aridity of the desert.

## About the Literary Work

"Going Home" was adapted from the novel *Going Home* by Nicholasa Mohr, copyright 1986 by Nicholasa Mohr. Reprinted by permission of Dial Books for Young Readers, a division of Penguin Books USA, Inc.

## Description of Change

This passage from the novel includes a conversation among the narrator's family members. Deletions are indicated by ellipses.

## Rationale

The selection highlights contrasting climates. Some deletions were made for the sake of space.

## Vocabulary

mangos, Puerto Rico

## Teaching Strategies

### Directed Inquiry

After students finish reading, discuss the story. Be sure to relate the story to the science lessons in this unit. Ask the following questions:

▶ What was the important news that Felita's parents wanted to discuss? (That the family would be going to Puerto Rico)

▶ How did everyone feel about the news? Why? (Happy; Reasons stated can vary. They will see other family members and friends of their parents; it is a long-anticipated trip; the climate is warm.)

▶ Why does Puerto Rico's warm climate seem particularly appealing to the characters right now? (It's very cold where the family lives right now.)

▶ Besides the warmth, what else about Puerto Rico's climate appeals to the family? (Breezes, bright sunshine, green plants all year, tropical fruit, low humidity)

▶ According to Papi, what is wrong with the weather where the family lives? (Students may quote Papi: ". . . like here where you freeze in the winter and the humidity makes your bones ache.")

## Critical Thinking

**Infer**  Ask students to discuss the narrator's personality and reasons for wanting to go to Puerto Rico. Suggest that Felita's reasons for wanting to go to Puerto Rico may be different from her father's reasons. Ask: What clues in this selection tell you that Felita is excited by something besides the new climate she will experience? (She wants to go out in the cold to find her friends after hearing the news. Though she notices the cold, it doesn't bother her. Friends and family seem to be more important than the weather to her.)

**Reason and Conclude**  Ask students to point out passages that refer to heat transfer. Ask which process is illustrated in each case—conduction, convection, or radiation. (Examples: the bright sunshine transfers heat by radiation; the wind is caused by convection; the narrator feels the coldness of the stone steps by conduction.)

## Science and Literature Connection

### Going Home

*The following excerpts are from the novel* Going Home *by Nicholasa Mohr.*

When my parents asked me and my brothers to come into the living room to discuss something important, I tried not to act too nervous. I couldn't think of anything I'd done that was bad. Maybe one of my brothers had gotten into trouble.

Papi spoke first. "Kids, we want to tell you all something—something that should make you all feel happy. You know how we've always talked about taking a trip to Puerto Rico? The whole family going there together? Well, now we are going to do it! That's right. This summer we are all gonna spend two weeks in Puerto Rico."

"That's fantastic, Papi!" said Tito. Not only was I relieved, I felt just as happy as Tito. . . .

"Okay, now wait,"—Papi paused—"there's something more. You know how we told you kids that Tio Jorge is retiring and has plans to live permanently in Puerto Rico? Well, the time has come; Tio will be staying in Puerto Rico and he's going to build a house in our village in the countryside. So—"

"That's right!" Tio Jorge interrupted Papi. "A house big enough for all of you to spend time with me."

"Correct," said Papi, "and since Tio Jorge is staying, we have decided that—" Papi turned toward me— "you, Felita, will stay the whole summer in Puerto Rico and keep Tio Jorge company." When I heard those words, I could hardly believe my own ears!

"Papi, you mean I'm going away for the whole summer? Wow!" I hugged Papi, Mami, and Tio Jorge. "Thank you, everybody!"

"The most important thing," Mami said, "is that you children will finally get to meet all of your family. You have your grandfather, Abuelo Juan; your Aunt Julia and Uncle Tomas; and many cousins that you have never met. . . ."

"Listen, children," Papi said, "you are going to eat the most delicious fruits. Mangos right off the trees—so sweet and juicy. You'll see lots of flowers and green everywhere. And the weather is great. Even in the summer you always have a breeze. And, of course, it's never cold like here where you freeze in the winter and the humidity makes your bones ache."

The first thing I did was head for the phone and call my best friend, Gigi, but there was no answer. Maybe my second best friend, Consuela, would be hanging out. Anyway, I wanted to check out my block so I could share the good news with somebody. I asked Mami if I could go out to play.

"It's cold out, Felita. What kind of games are you going to play? And besides, there's probably nobody outside now."

"Come on, Mami, you know we can play tag, hide-and-go-seek, lots of games. Or I can just hang out and talk to my friends." She always gives me a hard time about going out alone just to hang out. "Mami, please, I'd like to tell my friends about our trip. Look, if there's nobody outside, I'll come back up. I promise. Please say yes!"

"All right, but you are not to leave this

# Skills in Science

## Reading Skills in Science

1. Puerto Rico's climate as implied by the narrative is sunny, warm, and less humid than where the narrator lives. Students may refer to the climate as tropical because of the lack of freezing temperatures.

2. Answers depend on students' inferences about the personalities of the brothers. For example, the climate difference might be much more important to the brothers than it is to Felita. They might be jealous that she is staying longer.

## Writing Skills in Science

1. Paragraphs will vary. Students who live in more temperate areas will probably write about how the difference in seasons would affect them. Students might describe year-round outdoor activities, lighter clothing, foods from tropical plants, lighter-framed houses, and outdoor markets.

## Activities

**Collect Data** Aside from the many historical sites, Puerto Rico offers visitors a natural site called El Yunque, a rain forest on a mountainside. Students' travel brochures might also highlight Puerto Rico's beaches for water sports, and the mountains, desert areas, and forests for exploring.

**Communicate** The average monthly temperature for San Juan, Puerto Rico, falls between 21°C and 27°C all year. Graphs will vary. Students may find the information they need in atlases, almanacs, or newspaper listings of temperatures for world cities.

---

block. Understand?"

I put on my warm jacket, hat, and gloves so that I wouldn't freeze when I went outdoors. My street was pretty empty. Except for a passerby now and then, no one was about. Thick dark clouds covered the sky, making everything look gray and gloomy. It wasn't very windy, but it felt cold and humid. I sat down on my stoop and exhaled, watching my hot breath turn into white puffs of smoke as it hit cold air, and I thought about Puerto Rico. All that bright sunshine every day. I shivered, feeling the cold of the stone steps going right through me, and I wondered what it must be like to live in a place where it didn't ever snow and the leaves never left the trees. I stood up, leaning against the railing, and checked my street, hoping to see somebody I could talk to about my trip.

### Skills in Science

#### Reading Skills in Science

1. **Find Context Clues** Use context clues contained in the passage to describe the climate of Puerto Rico.

2. **Predict** The selection is told from the point of view of Felita, who is going to spend the summer in Puerto Rico. Suppose one of her brothers was narrating the story. How might the selection differ? (Remember, her brothers will stay in Puerto Rico for only two weeks.)

#### Writing Skills in Science

1. **If . . . Then Arguments** The climate of the town in which you live impacts many areas of your lifestyle, such as your manner of dress and your leisure activities. Think how the climate of Puerto Rico differs from that of your home town. Write a paragraph describing how your lifestyle might be different if you lived on this island.

#### Activities

**Collect Data** One of Puerto Rico's most valuable natural resources is its climate. In a library, research the weather of this island. Use your findings to create a travel brochure that would encourage tourists to visit Puerto Rico.

**Communicate** Use reference tools to determine the average monthly temperature in San Juan, Puerto Rico. Make a graph to illustrate your findings.

#### Where to Read More

*Puerto Rico in Pictures* prepared by the Geography Department of Lerner Publications. Minneapolis: Lerner Publication Company, 1987. Through the use of photographs and drawings, the reader is introduced to the topography, history, society, economics, and government structure of Puerto Rico.

U nit 7 examines the way people's lifestyles change the earth. Chapter 21 describes the mining and use of natural resources, emphasizing the difference between resources that are renewable and those that cannot be replaced. The last section discusses alternative ways of generating energy. Chapter 22 examines how human societies change the environment. The chapter begins by outlining types of societies and discussing the rise of industrial societies. The last two sections look at industry's impact on the environment and solutions to some of the problems that result. The costs and benefits of environmental solutions are presented.

## Introducing the Unit

### Directed Inquiry

Have students study the photograph and read the caption. Ask:

▶ What does this solar mirror in the picture do? (It captures and focuses solar energy on the pipe that runs along the front.)

▶ How is it like a conventional power plant? How is it different? (The facility produces usable energy—probably by making steam to drive turbines that generate electricity. It does not require a fossil fuel.)

▶ Does this structure hurt the environment? (Students will probably say that it doesn't. The plant is in a fairly barren location, and doesn't require fuel.)

▶ Do you think this structure was expensive to make? How does it contribute to solving environmental problems? (This technology is expensive, and right now the output may not offset the cost of developing the plant. Yet such alternative energy sources can reduce the amount of fossil fuels people consume.)

### Writing About the Photograph

Suggest that students write a poem or story that focuses on this solar energy power plant or the energy that we get from the sun.

Unit **7**
# Energy and Environment

*Chapters*

**21** Mineral and Energy Resources
**22** Humans and the Environment

# Data Bank

Use the information on pages 612 to 625 to answer the following questions about topics explored in this unit.

## Reading a Graph

What percentage of the land in the United States is used for parks and wildlife? What percentage is used for cities?

## Comparing

Which area of the world has more natural gas reserves, North America or Eastern Europe and Russia?

## Predicting

What do you think the graph on land uses will look like in the year 2020? Predict the percentages of land use in 2020. Explain your predictions.

The photograph to the left is of solar mirrors at a power-generating facility in Mohave, California. How can solar mirrors help generate energy?

Have students search the Data Bank on pages 612 to 625 for the answers to the questions on this page.

**Reading a Graph**  3.6 percent of land in the United States is used for parks and wildlife areas; 2.7 percent is used for cities. The answer is found in the graph Land Use in the United States on page 613.

**Extension**  Have students do research to find out how many national parks are in the United States. Have them name a few of the largest parks.

**Comparing**  Eastern Europe and Russia have more gas reserves than North America. The answer is in the graph World Natural Gas Reserves, 1990, on page 623.

**Extension**  Have students research where some of the crude oil reserves are located in the Middle East. Have them find out where some of the natural gas reserves are located in Eastern Europe and Russia.

**Predicting**  Answers will vary. Students may predict that more land will be used for cities by the year 2020. They might also predict that more land may be set aside for parks and wildlife but that cropland area may shrink.

**Answer to In-Text Question**

Mirrors can be precisely shaped to focus sunlight, producing extremely high temperatures. This plant probably operates by heating water to produce steam that runs electricity-generating turbines.

## Overview

Chapter 21 describes the mining and use of natural resources, emphasizing the difference between resources that are renewable and those that cannot be replaced. The second section explains what fossil fuels are, how we use them, and their effect on the environment. The last section discusses alternative ways of generating energy.

## Advance Planner

▶ Provide examples of jingles for TE page 488.

▶ Provide a U.S. mineral resources map for TE pages 492 and 494.

▶ Provide salt, water, tablespoons, beakers, drinking glasses, plastic wrap, rubber bands, and marbles for TE page 502.

▶ Collect pie tins, plastic sheets, thermometers, graph paper, and colored pencils for Activity 21, SE page 504.

## Skills Development Chart

| Sections | Classify | Communicate | Compare/Contrast | Decision-Making | Infer | Make a Graph | Measure | Predict |
|---|---|---|---|---|---|---|---|---|
| 21.1 Skills WarmUp | ● | | | | | | | |
| 21.2 Skills WarmUp  Skills WorkOut | | | ● | | ● | | | |
| 21.3 Skills WarmUp  Consider This  Activity 21 | | ● | ●  ● | ● | ● | ● | ● | ● |

## Individual Needs

▶ **Limited English Proficiency Students** Invite students to write a summary of each section of the chapter in their own words using the headings in the sections as a guide. They should include the boldface chapter vocabulary in their summaries. Encourage them to illustrate their summaries with pictures cut from magazines.

▶ **At-Risk Students** Encourage students to think of a future time when new forms of energy will be used. Then have them do some research and choose a technology or device that interests them. Ask them to create "now and future" illustrations of their technology or device. For example, someone might choose railroads and present contrasting illustrations of today's diesel trains and the maglev trains of tomorrow. Students should add captions to each illustration that tell the kind of energy used and what its advantages and disadvantages are. Make a display of the illustrations.

▶ **Gifted Students** Invite students to investigate the question of who owns the resources under the earth. Have them consider the following questions: What are mineral rights? Can a landowner sell mineral rights to his or her land. Can someone take gas, oil, or water from under a neighbor's property? How should the U.S. government handle the mineral rights to the land it owns? Have the students present what they learn briefly to the rest of the class and then lead a discussion about the problems that arise from these issues.

## Resource Bank

▶ **Bulletin Board** Have students work in groups to create a series of drawings for coal, petroleum, and natural gas showing how each was formed, how it is extracted from the earth, and its various uses. Students may also want to include such information as how much the United States or the world consumes and how long the reserves might last.

| Section | Core | Standard | Enriched | Section | Core | Standard | Enriched |
|---|---|---|---|---|---|---|---|
| **21.1 Mineral Resources** pp. 489–491 | | | | **Color Transparencies** Transparencies 64, 65 | ● | ● | ● |
| **Section Features** Skills WarmUp, p. 489 | ● | ● | ● | **21.3 Alternative Energy Resources** pp. 498–504 | | | |
| **Blackline Masters** Review Worksheet 21.1 Skills Worksheet 21.1 | ● ● | ● ● | | **Section Features** Skills WarmUp, p. 498 Skills WorkOut, p. 501 Consider This, p. 501 | ● ● ● | ● ● ● | ● ● ● |
| **Laboratory Program** Investigation 32 | ● | ● | | **Blackline Masters** Review Worksheet 21.3 Vocabulary Worksheet 21.3 | ● ● | ● ● | ● |
| **21.2 Fossil-Fuel Resources** pp. 492–497 | | | | **Overhead Blackline Transparencies** Overhead Blackline Master 21.3 and Student Worksheet | ● | ● | |
| **Section Features** Skills WarmUp, p. 492 Skills WorkOut, p. 496 Career Corner, p. 496 | ● ● ● | ● ● ● | ● ● ● | **Ancillary Options** *One-Minute Readings,* pp. 59, 97–98 | | ● | ● |
| **Blackline Masters** Review Worksheet 21.2 Reteach Worksheet 21.2 Skills Worksheet 21.2 Integrating Worksheet 21.2 | ● ● ● ● | ● ● ● ● | ● ● | **Color Transparencies** Transparencies 66, 67 | ● | ● | ● |
| **Ancillary Options** *One-Minute Readings,* pp. 65, 99 | | ● | ● | | | | |

# Bibliography

The following resources can be used for teaching the chapter. See page T–46 for supplier codes.

### Library Resources

*Bates, R. L. The Challenge of Mineral Resources. Hillside, NJ: Enslow Publishers, Inc., 1991.*

*Bates, R. L. Industrial Minerals: How They Are Found and Used. Hillside, NJ: Enslow Publishers, Inc.,1988.*

*Energy 90s: Learning about Science, Technology, and Society. Santa Monica, CA: Enterprise for Education, 1991.*

*Lambert, Mark. Spotlight on Iron and Steel. Lye, Keith. Spotlight on Gold. Vero Beach, FL: Rourke Enterprises, Inc., 1988.*

### Technology Resources

#### Internet

**PLANETDIARY** at *http://www.planetdiary.com*
- Find out more about nuclear energy in *Radioactivity* by clicking on *Phenomena Backgrounders.*
- Learn more about oil spills in *Oil Spill*; first, click on *Phenomena Backgrounders.*

### Software

*All About Science I. Mac, Dos. ER.*
*Earth Science. Mac, Win. ER.*
*Earth's Natural Resources. Mac, Win. ER.*

### CD-ROMs

*Interactive Earth. SFAW.*
*An Odyssey of Discovery for Science Insights:* Encourage students to try the activity *Recycler* on the Earth and Space Disk, and the activity *Aquarium* on the Living Science Disk. *SFAW.*

### Laserdiscs

*Living Textbook. (See barcodes on pages in this chapter.) Optical Data.*
*Earth's Natural Resources. SVE.*

### Videos

*Anatomy of an Oil Spill. PBS Video.*
*Greenhouse Crisis: The American Response. 11 min. Union of Concerned Scientists.*
*More for Less. The Annenberg/CPB Project. 1990.*

### Audio-Visual Resources

*Running Out of Steam. 26 min. 1988. Bullfrog Films.*

### Writing and Art Connection

Explain to students that jingles are short, catchy songs or verses. Provide them with examples of jingles. Have students write jingles that promote recycling. They can then use the verses to create pro-recycling posters. Hang the posters in the hallways or in display cases around the school.

## Introducing the Chapter

Have students read the description of the photograph. Ask if they agree or disagree with the description.

### Directed Inquiry

Have students study the photograph. Ask:

► What are the objects shown in this picture? (Students should recognize that they are beverage cans.)

► What has been done to these cans? How can you tell? (They have been crushed together in rectangular chunks, or bales. Faint vertical lines are probably wires that help hold individual bales together.)

► Why have these cans been crushed into bales? (Students will probably say that they have been prepared for recycling, and that more cans can be processed at once if they are crushed.)

► Why do you think this picture is appropriate to a chapter about mineral and energy resources? (Students will probably say that reusing aluminum helps conserve our resources of ore and preserve the land where it is found. They may also know that recycling aluminum takes less energy than producing it from ore.)

## Chapter Vocabulary

| | |
|---|---|
| fossil fuel | petrochemicals |
| hydroelectric energy | petroleum |
| natural gas | reclamation |
| nonrenewable | renewable |
|   resource |   resource |
| nuclear fission | solar energy |
| ore | |

**Chapter 21** **Mineral and Energy Resources**

### Chapter Sections

**21.1** Mineral Resources

**21.2** Fossil-Fuel Resources

**21.3** Alternative Energy Resources

### What do you see?

❝In this picture, crushed aluminum cans are getting ready to be recycled at a recycling center. People are getting it together by recycling aluminum cans to be reused in other aluminum products. This process is very important for the future because it does not waste valuable resources. Please recycle!❞

*Jill Partridge*
*Rockwood South Junior*
*  High School*
*Fenton, Missouri*

To find out more about the photograph, look on page 506. As you read this chapter, you will learn about the mineral and energy resources of the earth.

## Social Studies Connection

Six thousand years ago, people discovered how to use heat to separate the copper ore from rock for making tools and ornaments. This period was known as the Copper Age. Later, around 3000 B.C., metalworkers combined tin with copper to produce bronze. Bronze was stronger than copper. Axes, knives, chisels, and hammers made of bronze were more durable. This period became known as the Bronze Age.

## Social Studies Connection

Tell students that we are currently living in the Iron Age, which began around 1300 B.C. Hammered iron was used in Egypt before 1350 B.C. The Hittites from Asia Minor developed tools and weapons out of iron. It was so much stronger than bronze that it proved to be a superior material in the weapons they used for their raid on Babylonia in 1600 B.C. Iron technology spread throughout Europe, and later to the Americas.

# 21.1 Mineral Resources

## Objectives

▶ **Distinguish** between renewable and nonrenewable resources.

▶ **Describe** the problems associated with mining and processing ores.

▶ **Compare** and **contrast** different views on reclamation.

▶ **Make a table** showing information about three types of mining.

**D**id you know that most things you use each day come from natural resources? *Natural resources* are materials from the environment that people use to carry on their lives. For example, the beverage can you drink from is made from aluminum.

Aluminum, most other minerals, coal, and oil are examples of **nonrenewable resources.** Many nonrenewable resources are removed in great amounts. Once they are removed, they cannot be replaced. Other natural resources include air, water, and plants. They can be replaced as they are used. For this reason, they are called **renewable resources.**

## Formation of Ores

Aluminum belongs to a group of nonrenewable resources called minerals. Recall that a mineral is an element or a compound that forms naturally in the earth. Some elements chemically combine with other elements, forming minerals. Other minerals, such as copper, are in the earth's crust in elemental form. Minerals are commonly found in deposits called ores. An **ore** is a mineral-rich rock deposit that can be removed from the earth and used to make products.

Ores may form as sedimentary, igneous, or metamorphic rocks change during the rock cycle. For example, ores containing iron may form in igneous rock when magma cools. Some ores form in metamorphic rock when minerals dissolve in hot, underground water. The minerals settle and harden, producing pure mineral veins.

▼ **ACTIVITY**

**Classifying**

*Keep It or Toss It?*

Think of an object you use every day. What materials make up this object? For example, what materials were needed to make a pencil? Which of these materials can be replaced after they are used? Which can only be used once?

**SKILLS WARMUP**

**Figure 21.1** ▲
Copper ore (top) is mined and made into copper wire. Copper wire is used in many different types of electrical equipment.

**Section Objectives**
For a list of section objectives, see the Student Edition page.

**Skills Objectives**
Students should be able to:

**Classify** resources as renewable and nonrenewable.

**Collect Data** about mining and its effects.

**Vocabulary**
nonrenewable resource, renewable resource, ore, reclamation

## MOTIVATE

### Skills WarmUp

To help students understand how mineral resources are classified as renewable or nonrenewable, have them do the Skills WarmUp.
**Answer** In a pencil, the wood is renewable, while the graphite, paint, and metal are nonrenewable. The rubber is also nonrenewable if it is synthetic.

### Prior Knowledge

To gauge how much students know about mineral resources, ask the following questions:

▶ What does it mean to renew something?

▶ What are some ways to get minerals out of the earth?

▶ Who decides where to dig mines?

## Directed Inquiry

After students read the text and study the illustrations, ask the following questions:

▶ How are open-pit mining and strip mining alike? How are they different? (Each removes ores near the earth's surface. Open-pit mines produce large open areas on the earth's surface. Strip mines produce strips of rubble filled trenches.)

▶ What kinds of minerals are removed during underground mining? (Salt, uranium, lead, limestone, and potash)

▶ What kinds of materials are quarried? (Stones are removed from the earth by open-pit mines called quarries.)

▶ What happens to ore after it is mined? (Desired minerals are removed from the rest of the ore.)

### The Living Textbook: Earth Science Sides 1-2

Chapter 21          Frame 02745
Strip/Open-Pit/Quarry Mining (32 Frames)
Search:          Step:

### The Living Textbook: Earth Science Sides 1-2

Chapter 21          Frame 02744
Reclamation (1 Frame)
Search:

## *Integrating the Sciences*

**Environmental Science**  Mineral companies are allowed to mine in some U.S. national parks. Two parks with proposed mining projects are Bryce Canyon and Kaiparowits Plateau, Utah. Have students discuss the various uses of national parks and how mining could affect them. Then have a class debate on whether mining should be allowed in national parks.

## Mining of Ores

Once an ore is located, it is mined, or removed from the ground. The type of mining depends on how close the ore is to the earth's surface. Surface mining and open-pit mining remove ores that are close to the earth's surface. Underground mining removes ores that are deep under the earth's surface. Once an ore is removed from the ground, workers and machines separate the desired substance from the rest of the ore.

### Open-Pit Mining

Some ores near the earth's surface are removed by giant earthmoving equipment. This process is called open-pit mining. When open-pit mining removes rocks, it is called quarrying. Rocks, such as granite and marble, are collected from the earth by quarrying. The photograph below shows limestone being quarried. ▼

### Surface Mining

◀ Surface mining removes ores that are very close to the earth's surface. One type of surface mining is strip mining. During strip mining, a trench is cut and the ore is removed. A second trench is dug next to the first one. The material dug up from the second trench is pushed into the first trench. This process continues over an entire site.

### Underground Mining

In underground mining, shafts or tunnels are dug down to ore deposits deep within the earth. The ore is dug or blasted out of the ore-containing rock. It is then transported to the surface. Salt, uranium, lead, limestone, and potash are sometimes mined in this way. ▼

## Integrating the Sciences

**Health** Arsenic is a poisonous metal. In humans, arsenic poisoning can cause vomiting; degeneration of the liver and kidneys; and lung, liver, lymph, and skin cancers. The wastes from uranium mining increase the risk of developing respiratory cancers.

## STS Connection

Have students find out what ores are mined in their home state or the most important ores mined in the United States. Then have them research the following:

▶ The kind of mining used to remove the ores

▶ Changes the mining has caused in the environment

▶ Current reclamation projects

## Science and Society *Effects of Mining*

People benefit from the materials obtained from mining. However, mining can harm the environment. For example, open-pit and surface mining can leave the land scarred and barren. Underground mining can cause collapse or sinking of the surface above. By-products of mining and ore processing can pollute the air, land, and water. For example, uranium mining creates waste materials that give off harmful radiation. Surface mining produces the very poisonous chemical, arsenic (AR suh NIHK).

Surface mining also produces many sources of water pollution. When an area is surface-mined, rain may absorb lead, copper, or arsenic from piles of mining wastes. The polluted water then sinks into the groundwater. Mining can also pollute surface water when silt and pollutants run off into lakes and rivers.

For years, mining companies often abandoned mined areas. Recently, however, laws require operators of mines to return a mined area to a clean, useful condition. Returning a mining site to its former condition is called **reclamation**. In some reclaimed areas, no evidence of mining remains. But often, so much topsoil was lost in mining that a reclaimed area will never be the same.

**Figure 21.2** ▲
The land in the foreground is the result of surface mining for coal. The land in the background was reclaimed after coal mining.

## Check and Explain

1. What are the differences between renewable and nonrenewable resources?

2. What are some problems associated with mining and processing ores?

3. **Compare and Contrast** Compare and contrast the advantages and disadvantages of reclamation. Include two points of view: a resident in a mined area, and a mining company executive.

4. **Collect Data** Make a table that includes three types of mining. For each type list ores obtained, sources of pollution, and the type of area mined.

### Section Objectives
For a list of section objectives, see the Student Edition page.

### Skills Objectives
Students should be able to:

**Compare and Contrast** sources of energy.

**Infer** the impact of fossil fuels.

**Research** which fuels produce electricity for the area.

**Make a Graph** comparing types of fossil fuel consumption in the United States.

### Vocabulary
fossil fuel, petroleum, natural gas, petrochemicals

### Skills WarmUp
To help students compare fossil fuels to another energy source, have them do the Skills WarmUp.
**Answer** Foods and fossil fuels are both processed from raw materials and provide energy through chemical reactions. Food sources are renewable; fossil fuels are non-renewable.

### Misconceptions
Students may think that all coal is used for burning. Ask students if they are familiar with the following non-fuel coal products: creosote (wood preservative); pitch (roofing material); aniline (main ingredient in ink); mauve (synthetic dye); and naphtha (solvent). Have students research coal products.

### Geography Connection
Obtain a map of the locations of coal deposits in the United States. Students can make a list of the states that have coal deposits. Ask them to infer what the climate of these coal areas must have been like millions of years ago. (The areas were swampy and may have been warmer than they are today.)

### Themes in Science
**Energy** Burning fossil fuels produces energy for running machines and power plants. Fossil fuels are sometimes referred to as bottled sunlight. This is because energy from the sun produced the organic compounds in the once-living organisms from whose remains we now obtain concentrated chemical energy.

▼ **ACTIVITY**

**Comparing**

*Running on Empty*
How is the food you eat similar to the gasoline that powers an automobile? How is it different? Explain.

**SKILLS WARMUP**

## 21.2 Fossil-Fuel Resources

### Objectives

▶ **Name** the four stages of coal formation.

▶ **Describe** how petroleum and natural gas form.

▶ **Identify** the uses of fossil fuels and some problems associated with burning fossil fuels.

▶ **Make a graph** showing numerical data about energy sources.

C oal, oil, and natural gas are formed from the preserved remains of plants and animals. The preserved remains of once-living things are called fossils. Therefore, coal, oil, and natural gas are known as **fossil fuels.**

The energy stored in fossil fuels can be traced to the sun. Plants use energy in sunlight to produce a sugar called glucose. Animals eat plants for the energy provided by glucose. Some of the energy is stored in the bodies of animals. When animals and plants die, this energy remains stored. If conditions are right, the remains may become fossil fuels. Thus, the energy stored in fossil fuels originally came from the sun.

**Figure 21.3**
A teenager who lives in Ireland unloads peat. Peat serves as a fuel for fires in many countries.
▼

### Coal

Millions of years ago, swamps covered much of the land. Plant life was plentiful. After plants and other organic materials died in swamp waters, they slowly decayed. They eventually lost most of their oxygen and hydrodgen. However, most of their carbon remained. As the sediment aged and compacted, it changed into coal. Coal is an organic sedimentary rock. Different types of coal form in stages, as shown on page 493.

Coal deposits are located all over the world. In areas with coal deposits near the earth's surface, surface mining removes the coal from the ground. An example of this type of coal is peat, shown in Figure 21.3. Some coal deposits deep under the surface are mined using underground methods.

### STS Connection

On March 24, 1989, the Exxon *Valdez* oil tanker ran aground and spilled 10.9 million gallons of crude oil into the waters of Prince William Sound near Alaska. This was the largest oil spill in U.S. history. It took 11,000 people and 1 billion dollars to clean up the spill.

### Integrating the Sciences

**Life Science** Oil spills kill many marine organisms directly and indirectly. In otters, the oil damages organs such as the kidneys, liver, and lungs. Birds with oil-coated feathers are unable to fly and are vulnerable to cold. The oil also poisons fish and marine plants, which disrupts the food chain. It can take between two and ten years for organisms to recover after an oil spill.

### Research

Have students collect information about the effects of a major oil spill, such as the Exxon *Valdez* disaster in Alaska in 1989. Have them find out about clean up efforts and current conditions in the areas they research. Volunteers can present their findings to the class.

### WrapUp

**Portfolio** Have students review the lists they made in the previous lesson. Ask them to identify which items are made from petrochemicals and which used coal or petrochemicals in the manufacturing process. Have students pool their results and list the items that were the most and the least dependent on coal or petrochemicals.

Use Review Worksheet 21.2.

### Science and Society
*Pumping Oil from the Sea*

Some of the richest oil deposits in the world are beneath the ocean floor near continental coasts. To drill down to these offshore deposits, oil companies often use portable drilling platforms. These platforms support the derrick, drilling equipment, and living quarters for up to 50 workers. The platforms are built on the shore and then towed to the drilling site. At the drilling site, legs are lowered until they rest on the ocean floor. Once the offshore rig is set up, the methods for drilling and removing oil and gas are similar to those used on land.

Offshore oil drilling presents a few problems that do not exist on land. The drill must be lowered through many meters of water. Also, weather conditions can affect offshore drilling operations. For example, when Hurricane Andrew struck the Gulf of Mexico in 1992, several thousand oil workers had to return to shore until the storm passed.

One of the biggest disadvantages of offshore drilling is the possibility of oil spills. Sometimes, the pressure of the oil or gas can cause blowouts. During a blowout, large amounts of oil spill into the sea. Oil spills also result from leaks in pipelines and tankers. Oil spills cause very serious pollution problems that can kill many marine organisms. When oil spills wash onshore, coastal plants and animals are killed or injured, and the land is polluted.

**Figure 21.9** ▲
An accident at an oil platform (above) could cause major environmental damage (below).

### Check and Explain

### Check and Explain

1. Name and describe the four stages of coal formation in the order in which they occur.

2. What is petroleum, and how did it form? What is natural gas, and how did it form?

3. **Reason and Conclude** How would your life be different without fossil fuels? Explain.

4. **Make a Graph** Make a circle graph using the percentage of energy in the United States supplied by each of the following types of fossil fuels: petroleum, 43 percent; natural gas, 24 percent; coal, 22 percent; other, 11 percent.

1. Peat—formed by decaying twigs, leaves and branches with a high water content; lignite—formed as peat ages and compresses into soft brown coal with a carbon content of about 40 percent; bituminous coal—formed as heat and pressure compress lignite into coal with a carbon content of about 85 percent; anthracite—formed as great pressure and heat change bituminous coal into hard coal that is about 90 percent carbon.

2. Petroleum is a liquid mixture of hydrocarbons; natural gas is a gaseous mixture of hydrocarbons. Both were formed as the remains of ancient ocean-dwelling plants and animals were compressed over millions of years.

3. Answers will vary, but should center on the use of electricity, gasoline, and other petrochemicals.

4. Check students' graphs.

## Section Objectives

For a list of section objectives, see the Student Edition page.

## Skills Objectives

Students should be able to:

**Predict** how the availability of a fuel affects its use.

**Predict** the application of a perfect energy source.

**Make a Graph** of colors used in solar heating.

## Vocabulary

hydroelectric energy, nuclear fission, solar energy

---

## MOTIVATE

### Skills WarmUp

To help students understand how alternative energy resources have become important, have them do the Skills WarmUp.

**Answer** Students may think of wood for burning, because it was so available. Other answers include energy resources that are considered "alternative" resources today, such as water power (waterwheels), solar energy (to dry things), or geothermal energy (hot springs for cooking and washing).

### Prior Knowledge

To gauge how much students know about alternative energy resources, ask the following questions:

▶ What is the difference between the way steam was used one hundred years ago, and the way it is used today?

▶ If the wind and the sun cost nothing, why are wind energy and solar energy so expensive?

▶ What happens at a nuclear power plant?

498

### Integrating the Sciences

**Physical Science** When a magnet is moved through a coil, electricity is generated. As long as the magnet is moving, the electric current will continue to flow. An electric current is also generated when a coil of wire moves through a magnetic field. In an electric generator, mechanical energy is applied to a crank, or turbine, that rotates a coil through a magnetic field to produce a current. Fossil fuels generate electricity by heating water to create steam that will turn the crank. Discuss with students how electricity is produced. You may want to show them a diagram of an electric generator from a physical science textbook or other reference. Point out that the primary goal of conventional and alternative energy resources is to turn the turbine that rotates the coil in a magnetic field.

---

▼ **ACTIVITY**

**Predicting**

*In the Stone Ages*

Fossil fuels became widely used only during the last century. What energy resources do you think people used before coal and oil were easily available? Explain.

**SKILLS WARMUP**

---

## 21.3 Alternative Energy Resources

### Objectives

▶ **List** reasons for the increased demand for energy.

▶ **Identify** alternative ways of generating energy.

▶ **Compare** and **contrast** direct and indirect solar power.

▶ **Predict** which factors determine the possibility of using alternative ways of generating energy.

---

How much oil do you use every year? You may not believe it, but you use about ten barrels of oil a year. And every year, the amount increases. In fact, the demand for energy has almost doubled every 20 years since 1900. Some reasons for higher energy demand include an increase in world population, an increased use of electricity, and the invention of energy-using devices.

As the demand for energy rises, the use of fossil fuels increases. The result is that reserves of fossil fuels are being used up. Therefore, scientists and engineers are working to develop alternative ways of generating energy that do not require the use of fossil fuels. Most alternative energy comes from renewable resources.

### Wind Energy

In recent years, windmills, such as those shown in Figure 21.10, have been used to generate electricity. The blades of the windmills serve as turbines that turn the shaft of a generator to produce electricity. The amount of electricity produced by one windmill is small. However, hundreds of windmills together produce enough energy for commercial use.

Wind may seem to be the perfect energy source because it is clean and free. But at most locations the wind doesn't blow constantly. Power companies need a constant, reliable source of energy. Only a few locations can provide enough wind to meet their needs. Also, snow and freezing rain can interfere with the operation of windmills.

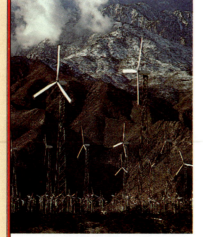

**Figure 21.10** ▲
Windmills in California generate electricity.

## Themes in Science
### Systems and Interactions

Geothermal and hydroelectric power systems both use water that interacts with turbines to generate electricity.

## Multicultural Perspectives

Much of the power in Iceland is generated by geothermal energy. In China, hydroelectric power will soon account for 35 percent of the country's energy sources. Have students use references to find out the principal energy sources for different countries.

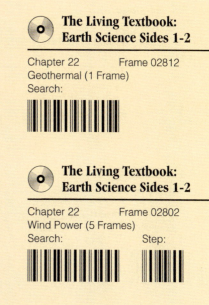
## Geothermal Energy

Geothermal energy is heat energy from within the earth. In some parts of the world, magma heats surrounding igneous rock. Hot igneous rock near the earth's surface heats underground water and changes it to steam. Geothermal reservoirs form when rock traps the hot water and steam underground.

Steam and hot water from geothermal wells are used to heat homes and buildings. Some electric power plants use geothermal steam to turn turbines in generators. Look at Figure 21.11. Water is pumped into wells dug into an area with very hot underground rock. As the water boils, it creates steam. The steam is brought to the surface to run a generator. The electricity produced powers homes and businesses.

Geothermal energy isn't a practical source in areas without present or past volcanic activity. But some scientists are studying how to use the ordinary heat trapped in underground rocks.

**Figure 21.11** ▲
A geothermal power plant in Iceland uses steam escaping from within the earth to produce electricity.

## Energy from Water

The production of electricity from water power is called **hydroelectric energy**. Look at Figure 21.12. Water moving through huge dams built across rivers turns turbines and generators that produce electricity. In the United States about 10 percent of the electricity used is produced at hydroelectric plants. Hydroelectric energy is energy efficient, and it doesn't create pollution. But the construction of dams is costly and requires the use of much energy. Also, the lake formed by damming a river changes the river and surrounding area's ecosystem.

Another form of hydroelectric energy is tidal energy. Tidal energy comes from the movement of ocean water during tidal changes. In some coastal areas, the water of an incoming tide rushes into narrow rivers or bays. When the tide changes, the water rushes with great force back to the ocean. Hydroelectric plants built in such areas use moving water to generate electricity. This type of power plant is currently used in France and eastern Canada. However, because tidal energy needs special conditions, it will never be widely used.

**Figure 21.12** ▲
The Bonneville Dam, on the Columbia River at the Washington–Oregon border, generates hydroelectric energy.

## Skills Development

**Interpret Data** Have students use the information in Figure 21.14 to draw a second and third step in the nuclear chain reaction. (Drawings will vary, but should show that a neutron from the first reaction hits a second uranium nucleus and releases energy, lighter elements, and more neutrons. The process is repeated in the third step.)

**Compare and Contrast** Have students explain what nuclear, geothermal, and hydroelectric power have in common with fossil fuels, and how they compare to wind power. (Except for wind power, all these energy resources heat water to generate steam to turn turbines that generate electricity. Wind power turns turbines directly.)

**Classify** Have students make a chart to classify the advantages and disadvantages of nuclear energy. (Advantages—clean, efficient, reduces dependence on fossil fuels; disadvantages—harmful radiation accompanies uranium ore mining, accidents at reactors, and waste from reactors.)

## Decision Making

If you have classroom sets of *One-Minute Readings*, have students read Issue 35, "Radioactive Waste Disposal," on page 59 and Issue 57, "Nuclear Power: Risk Assessment," on page 97. Discuss the questions.

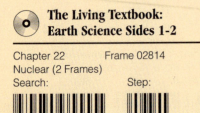

**The Living Textbook: Earth Science Sides 1-2**

Chapter 22     Frame 02814
Nuclear (2 Frames)
Search:          Step:

**500**

 **STS Connection**

On April 26, 1986, an explosion occurred at the Chernobyl nuclear power plant in the Ukraine. It was the worst nuclear disaster in history. About 100,000 people living within a 30-kilometer radius of the reactor were evacuated as were children within 160 kilometers. Hundreds of people died as a result of radiation exposure. It is estimated that over the next 20 years, thousands who were exposed to lesser levels of radiation will die from cancers that will develop as a result of the accident.

## Nuclear Energy

Nuclear energy is produced when the nucleus of an atom splits into smaller particles. This splitting is known as **nuclear fission** (FIHSH uhn). Study the fission reaction shown in Figure 21.14.

**Figure 21.13** ▲
This nuclear power station in England has several nuclear reactors.

The element uranium is used as the fuel for nuclear energy. A certain type of uranium nucleus splits easily into lighter particles. This type of uranium is collected and put in long, metal pipes at a nuclear power plant. The pipes are lowered into a pool of water contained in a large structure, called a nuclear reactor. The reactor bombards uranium nuclei with fast-moving neutrons. When hit, the nuclei split and release particles. The released particles cause other nuclei to split. As each nucleus splits, it releases a large amount of energy in the form of heat. The heat is used to produce steam, which turns a turbine, producing electricity. A nuclear power plant is shown in Figure 21.13.

The use of nuclear energy helps save the world's oil and natural gas reserves. However, the materials for producing nuclear energy give off radiation that can harm living things. Even the mining and processing of uranium ores can be very dangerous. Also, the waste products left behind in fission reactors are radioactive and extremely dangerous. These materials release radiation for a very long time.

**Figure 21.14**
**Nuclear Fission Reaction** ▼

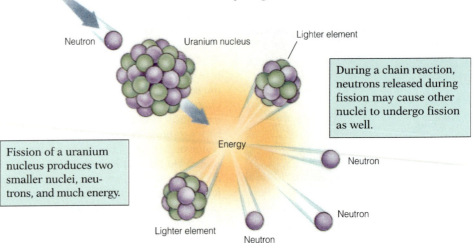

During a chain reaction, neutrons released during fission may cause other nuclei to undergo fission as well.

Fission of a uranium nucleus produces two smaller nuclei, neutrons, and much energy.

### STS Connection

Tell students about some of the alternative energy resources, such as tidal power, gasohol, biomass, oil shale, ocean currents, and nuclear fusion. Ask students to infer how each resource provides energy based on its name. Use references to validate the primary energy source for each resource. Student volunteers may want to present short reports to the class on each potential energy resource.

Today, about 16 percent of the electricity in the United States is produced by nuclear energy. Other countries, such as France, rely more on nuclear energy. About 60 percent of the electricity in France is generated by nuclear power plants.

When the first nuclear power plant in the United States began operation in 1957, many people believed that one day nuclear energy would generate all the electricity in this country. Since then many people have questioned the safety of nuclear energy. In the 1980s, people became concerned about the dangers of radiation on living things. They also worried about the possibility of an accident at a nuclear power plant. As a result of these concerns, the construction of nuclear power plants stopped in the United States in 1989. Researchers all over the world are trying to solve the problems with nuclear energy and the disposal of radioactive wastes.

## ▼ ACTIVITY

### Predicting

*Future Fuels*

Describe the characteristics of the perfect energy source. How would it be different from the energy sources we use now? Do you think we will ever find the perfect energy source? Why or why not?

**SKILLS WORKOUT**

### Skills WorkOut

To help the students predict, have them do the Skills WorkOut.
**Answer** Answers will vary, but should reflect students' awareness of the need for renewable, clean, affordable energy. Accept any reasonable answer the students can justify.

### Research

Have students consult newspapers and periodicals to determine the current state of nuclear power plant construction. Ask students to find out if all construction was stopped in 1989, and if plants under construction were allowed to be completed. Also ask students to find out if any plants have been licensed to produce power since 1989.

### Consider This

Many people subscribe to the "not in my back yard" theory of locating radioactive storage. Yet wastes must be stored somewhere. Encourage students to address the large question rather than expressing a personal view of radioactive storage.
**Think About It** Answers will vary, but should show students' awareness of the need to bury wastes in nonporous rock. Students may mention cost, appearance, and potential radiation danger as factors affecting the area near a storage site.
**Write About It** Answers will vary, but students should give reasons supporting their positions.

## *Consider This*

### *Should Radioactive Wastes Be Stored?*

Radioactive wastes give off harmful radiation for thousands of years. Currently, wastes are stored at nuclear power plants and in steel tanks buried in shallow trenches. Neither method is safe from natural disasters. Leakage could release radiation into the air and water. Wastes buried near the surface could be dug up during mining or construction operations.

A deep underground repository, or pit, could provide a permanent storage area. It would keep dangerous wastes far away from living things and the environment.

A deep repository would protect nuclear wastes from natural disasters. The wastes would be far away from air and groundwater. Deeply buried wastes are not likely to be accidentally uncovered.

On the other hand, locating a site and building the repository would be costly. Many organisms in the chosen area would be greatly disturbed by the construction.

**Think About It** What type of rock would be best for a repository? How could the choice of a storage site affect you?

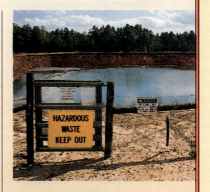

**Write About It** Your area is being considered for the building of a nuclear waste repository. Write a letter stating your position for or against the proposal.

## TEACH ▪ Continued

### Explore Visually

After students read the text and study figure 21.15, ask the following questions:

▶ What is the purpose of the black metal sheet in a solar collector? Why is it black? (The plate absorbs energy from the sunlight, heats, and then transfers the heat to the liquid in the collector's pipes. It is black because black absorbs more energy than any other color.)

▶ What happens to the heat absorbed by the liquid in the solar collector? (It is transferred to water in the heat exchanger where it is stored.)

▶ What is the difference between passive and active solar heating? (Passive solar heating uses the warmth of direct sunlight to heat the air and objects in a room; active solar heating uses heated liquid to warm water, which is then pumped throughout a home as hot water and heat.)

## Apply

Have students indicate places on Figure 21.15 where conduction, radiation, and convection of energy occur. (Radiation—to and from the black plate in the collector, to and from the south-facing windows; Conduction—in the liquid in the collector pipes, in the heat exchanger, near the hot water heating pipes in rooms; Convection—in the south-facing room, in the air around the hot water heating pumps)

**The Living Textbook:
Earth Science Sides 1-2**

Chapter 22          Frame 02793
Solar (9 Frames)
Search:              Step:

### Cooperative Learning

Have students work in cooperative groups of three to build a solar freshwater still. Provide the following for each group: salt, water, a tablespoon, a large beaker, a small drinking glass that will fit into the beaker, plastic wrap, a rubber band, and a marble. Tell each group to follow these directions: Fill the beaker one-fourth full with water. Dissolve two tablespoons of salt into the water. Place the drinking glass into the center of the beaker. Cover the beaker loosely with plastic wrap and secure the plastic wrap with the rubber band. Place the marble in the center of the plastic wrap and place the solar still in direct sun. Leave undisturbed for several hours. Then remove the glass from the beaker and taste the water. Have students describe what they taste. (The water in the glass should be fresh.)

**Figure 21.15** ▲
Both passive and active solar heating is used in this home. ▼

## Solar Energy

Energy from the sun is called **solar energy**. Direct solar power produces heat directly from the sun's energy and is used to heat buildings and homes. Although the sun's energy is free and nonpolluting, it cannot yet be collected and used on a large scale.

Look at Figure 21.15. In active solar heating, a solar collector absorbs energy from sunlight to heat a liquid. The hot liquid heats a tank of water. A pump forces the heated water to flow through a system of pipes. The piped water delivers home heating and hot water.

Passive solar heating uses conduction to transfer heat. Windows and skylights trap sunlight and heat energy. The heat raises the temperature in the room.

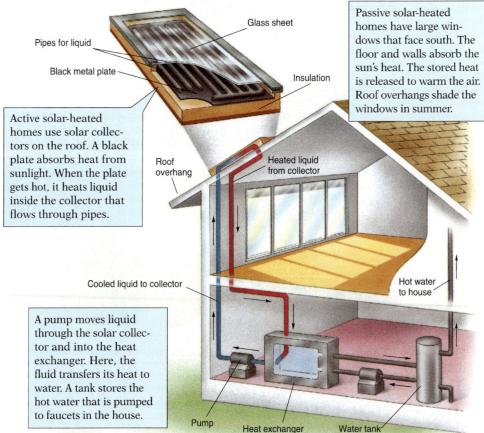

Passive solar-heated homes have large windows that face south. The floor and walls absorb the sun's heat. The stored heat is released to warm the air. Roof overhangs shade the windows in summer.

Glass sheet

Pipes for liquid

Black metal plate

Insulation

Active solar-heated homes use solar collectors on the roof. A black plate absorbs heat from sunlight. When the plate gets hot, it heats liquid inside the collector that flows through pipes.

Roof overhang

Heated liquid from collector

Cooled liquid to collector

Hot water to house

A pump moves liquid through the solar collector and into the heat exchanger. Here, the fluid transfers its heat to water. A tank stores the hot water that is pumped to faucets in the house.

Pump          Heat exchanger          Water tank

# Skills in Science

## Reading Skills in Science

1. The women are part of a hunting-and-gathering society. Their people have settled near a plentiful undomesticated food source. Their technology is simple, and their activities rely on the changing of the seasons.

2. The women know precisely when it is time to harvest, which grains to collect, and when the harvest is done. The deliberate burning will enrich the soil for the next cycle of growth and harvest. Students might point out that the women know their way around quite well, and seem to be prepared for what they will find—including rattlesnakes.

3. *Renewable:* grain, materials for clothing, fiber for tools, abalone shells, bundles of straw for torches, water for bathing; *nonrenewable:* No examples are cited. It isn't clear how the torches were ignited, but flint could be considered nonrenewable.

## Writing Skills in Science

1. The grain harvest prevents the grasses from propagating further. This is sustainable because there are enough seeds in the ground to ensure next spring's harvest. The burning destroys many plants. This action enriches the soil with carbon, which helps to nourish the seedlings. On the other hand, students might argue that the burning needlessly releases carbon dioxide into the atmosphere.

## Activities

**Communicate** To get students started, have them consult the chamber of commerce, or a geographic map of Native Americans from an encyclopedia or a social studies textbook.

**Science and Art** Students' art will vary. Drawings might show the harvest and fire, the burnt field in summer, then germinating seedlings in the rain.

---

as the women wade through them. Also, the baskets feel heavier now; the walk along the path seems longer. The mother grows impatient with her daughter, and they occasionally snap at each other and quarrel. "The harvest is over," declares the mother one day. "There is enough food. We deserve a rest."

But before they desert the meadow for the year, there is something else that has to be done.

The two women are holding torches made out of bundled grass. They touch the torches to the meadow. The grass crackles and sputters around them as the flames creep along the ground, heading toward the oak-bay forest. The heat becomes more intense. The women now drop their torches and hurry along the path, up alongside the creek bed, and over the ridge to the crest of hills to rejoin their people. They feel happy once again. The harvest is in, and it has been a good year.

As for the meadow, it will lie blackened and desolate throughout the summer. Then, when the first rains come in October, seeds in the ground will germinate again; by the following spring the meadow will once more be a rich source of flowers and grasses.

### Skills in Science

#### Reading Skills in Science

1. **Find Context Clues** To what type of society do the women belong? Give reasons for your answer. Who are the Ohlones?

2. **Infer** In what ways do the women demonstrate knowledge about their environment and natural cycles? Explain.

3. **Classify** What are three natural resources used by the women? Are the resources renewable or nonrenewable? Explain.

#### Writing Skills in Science

1. **Identify** What are two things the women do that significantly affect the environment? What is the impact of their actions on their ecosystem? Write whether you think their way of life is or is not sustainable. Explain your reasoning.

#### Activities

**Communicate** Research the traditional lifestyle of Native Americans who lived near where you live. Write a short report describing (1) how their way of life was related to the earth's natural cycles and (2) how their way of life affected their ecosystem.

**Science and Art** Make a series of drawings showing the meadow at four different times from when the women begin gathering seeds to the following spring.

#### Where to Read More

*The Talking Earth* by Jean Craighead George. New York: Harper & Row, 1983. Billie Wind ventures into the Florida Everglades to test the legends of her Seminole ancestors and deepens her understanding of nature and her relationship with it.

nit 8 covers astronomy. Chapter 23 presents a study of the movements and interactions of Earth and the moon. The first section discusses astronomical causes of the cycles of day and night, the seasons, and of measured hours. The next two sections examine the moon and the Earth-moon system. Theories of the moon's origins are presented, as well as information about the Apollo missions. The chapter concludes by explaining the phases of the moon, the tides, and eclipses. Chapter 24 explores the sun and the solar system. Students learn about the sun's structure and the source of the sun's energy. The chapter includes a look at the nine planets, as well as other non-planetary objects of the solar system: asteroids, meteoroids, and comets. Chapter 25 discusses the characteristics, life cycles, and groupings of stars.

## Introducing the Unit

### Directed Inquiry

Have students study the photograph and read the caption. Explain that this point of view is looking toward the center of the Milky Way galaxy. Ask:

▶ What is a constellation? Which stars in the picture form part of a constellation? (A constellation is a pattern of stars as seen from Earth. The four brightest stars form the upper part of Sagittarius.)

▶ What makes some stars brighter than others? (Answers include: distance from Earth, temperature, age, mass, and viewing conditions.)

▶ What other celestial objects can you see in this picture? (Nebulae, star clusters, clouds of stellar dust)

▶ Where is this cluster of stars in relation to our solar system? In relation to our galaxy? (It is far outside of our solar system, but within our galaxy, the Milky Way.)

### Writing About the Photograph

Have students write a humorous itinerary for a family vacation trip from Earth to the constellation Sagittarius. Suggest that students include plenty of interesting stops for their travelers.

Unit **8**
## Astronomy

### Chapters

23 Earth and the Moon
24 The Solar System
25 Stars and Galaxies

# Data Bank

Use the information on pages 612 to 625 to answer the following questions about topics explored in this unit.

## Calculating

How much longer does it take Saturn to revolve around the sun than Mars?

## Interpreting a Diagram

If you live in the Northern Hemisphere, where would you look in the night sky to see the Little Dipper in the spring?

## Inferring

Why is Earth so much more dense than Saturn?

## Collecting Data

Of the winter constellations shown, which ones contain bright stars? Make a list of these stars and their constellations.

The photograph to the left is of a group of stars in the constellation Sagittarius. Have you seen constellations in the night sky? If so, can you name any of them?

535

## Data Bank Answers

Have students search the Data Bank on pages 612 to 625 for the answers to the questions on this page.

**Calculating** It takes Saturn almost 28 years longer to revolve around the sun than Mars. The answer is found in the table Planetary Statistics on page 612.

**Extension** Have students list the diameters of the planets in order, from largest to smallest.

**Interpreting a Diagram** You would look toward the north to try to find the Little Dipper in the spring. The answer is found in the Star Charts for the Northern Hemisphere on pages 614 and 615.

**Inferring** Earth is so much more dense than Saturn because Saturn is primarily made up of gases. The answer is found in the table Planetary Statistics on page 612.

**Extension** Have students find out the major gases contained in the atmospheres of all nine planets.

**Collecting Data** The star Regulus is in the constellation Leo; Polaris is in the Little Dipper; Deneb is in Cygnus; Rigel and Betelgeuse are in Orion; Sirius is in Canis Major; Castor and Pollux are in Gemini; Capella is in Auriga. The answer is found in the Star Charts for the Northern Hemisphere on pages 614 and 615.

**Answer to In-Text Question**

Answers depend on students' own experiences. Some constellations of the autumn sky are pictured on pages 603 and 615.

535

## Overview

Chapter 23 presents a study of the movements and interactions of the earth and the moon. The first section discusses the cycles of day and night and the seasons. The next two sections examine the moon and the earth-moon system. Theories of the moon's origins are presented, as well as information about the *Apollo* missions. The chapter concludes by explaining the phases of the moon, the tides, and eclipses.

## Advance Planner

▶ Obtain a toy top for TE page 537, and a magnet and an iron rod for TE page 538.

▶ Collect materials for Activity 23, SE page 544.

▶ Obtain aerial photographs of the earth for TE page 546 (top) and a lunar map for TE page 546 (side).

▶ Provide plastic foam balls for TE page 551.

▶ Obtain photographs of Stonehenge for TE page 552 (top), and of solar eclipses for TE page 552 (side).

▶ Obtain a flashlight and props for SE page 553.

## Skills Development Chart

| Sections | Communicate | Infer | Interpret Data | Measure | Make a Model | Predict | Research |
|---|---|---|---|---|---|---|---|
| **23.1** Skills WarmUp | | ● | | | | | |
| Skills WorkOut | | | ● | | | | |
| Activity 23 | | ● | | ● | ● | | |
| **23.2** Skills WarmUp | | ● | | | | | |
| Skills WorkOut | | | | | ● | | |
| Historical Notebook | ● | | | | | | ● |
| **23.3** Skills WarmUp | | | | | | ● | |
| Skills WorkOut | | | ● | | | | |
| SkillBuilder | | | | | ● | | |
| Skills WorkOut | ● | | | | | | |

## Individual Needs

▶ **Limited English Proficiency Students** Encourage students to make a poster-sized chart comparing and contrasting the earth and the moon. Suggest that they label three columns *Features, Earth,* and *Moon* and fill in the chart with information from the chapter. Features could include everything from size and shape to rotation and atmosphere. Have them use complete sentences in describing the features of each body.

▶ **At-Risk Students** Invite students to work in small groups to model the motions of the earth and the moon. Allow them to act out the motions if they wish to. Let students choose props. For example, a student playing the role of the earth as it orbits the sun might want to hold a meter stick at the same angle as the earth's axis. Encourage groups to demonstrate their models for the class.

▶ **Gifted Students** Invite students to design a ten-year eclipse calendar with geographic data for interested observers. Have them use questions such as the following to guide their research: Why don't eclipses occur more often than they do? How do astronomers predict when an eclipse will occur? Why do people go to specific geographic locations to observe eclipses? What can astronomers learn from studying eclipses?

## Resource Bank

▶ **Bulletin Board** Create an exhibit about different calendars throughout the ancient and modern world. Encourage students from different ethnic backgrounds to contribute materials about their calendar systems. Include some problems for students to work, such as finding their birthdays in a different calendar system or figuring out how old they are using the Maya sacred calendar of 260 days in a year. Have students share their answers to the problems and discuss the advantages and disadvantages of the calendar systems on the board and how they relate to the sun and moon.

| Section | Core | Standard | Enriched | Section | Core | Standard | Enriched |
|---|---|---|---|---|---|---|---|
| **23.1 Earth in Space** pp. 537–544 | | | | **Blackline Masters** Review Worksheet 23.2 Skills Worksheet 23.2 | ● ● | ● ● | ● ● |
| **Section Features** Skills WarmUp, p. 537 Skills WorkOut, p. 542 Activity, p. 544 | ● ● | ● ● ● | ● ● ● | **Laboratory Program** Investigation 35 | ● | ● | ● |
| **Blackline Masters** Review Worksheet 23.1 Reteach Worksheet 23.1 Skills Worksheet 23.1 Integrating Worksheet 23.1 | ● ● ● ● | ● ● ● ● | ● ● ● ● | **23.3 Earth–Moon System** pp. 550–554 | | | |
| **Overhead Blackline Transparencies** Overhead Blackline Master 23.1 and Student Worksheet | ● | ● | | **Section Features** Skills WarmUp, p. 550 SkillBuilder, p. 553 Skills WorkOut, p. 553 Skills WorkOut, p. 554 | ● ● | ● ● ● ● | ● ● ● ● |
| **Color Transparencies** Transparencies 69, 70, 71, 72 | ● | ● | ● | **Blackline Masters** Review Worksheet 23.3 Skills Worksheet 23.3a Skills Worksheet 23.3b Vocabulary Worksheet 23.3 Integrating Worksheet 23.3 | ● ● ● ● ● | ● ● ● ● ● | ● ● ● ● ● |
| **23.2 Earth's Moon** pp. 545–549 | | | | **Ancillary Options** *Multiculturalism in Mathematics, Science, and Technology,* pp. 29–30 | | ● | ● |
| **Section Features** Skills WarmUp, p. 545 Skills WorkOut, p. 547 Historical Notebook, p. 548 | ● ● ● | ● ● ● | ● ● ● | **Laboratory Program** Investigation 36 | ● | ● | ● |
| | | | | **Color Transparencies** Transparencies 73a, 73b, 74 | ● | ● | ● |

# Bibliography

The following resources can be used for teaching the chapter. See page T–46 for supplier codes.

## Library Resources

*Berliner, Don. Our Future in Space.* New York: Lerner, 1991.

*Farndon, John. How the Earth Works.* Pleasantville, NY: The Reader's Digest Association, Inc., 1992.

*Lauber, Patricia. Seeing Earth from Space.* New York: Orchard, 1990.

*Schatz, Dennis. Astronomy Activity Book.* New York: Simon and Schuster, 1991.

## Technology Resources

### Internet

**PLANETDIARY** at *http://www.planetdiary.com*
• *Find out more about astronomy and recent events by exploring Astronomy/Space* (click on *Phenomena Backgrounders* and *Current Phenomena*). Also, see *Calendar.*

## Software

*Planetary Taxi. Mac, Win. ER.*
*RedShift 2. Mac, Win. ER.*

## CD-ROMs

*Interactive Earth. SFAW.*

*An Odyssey of Discovery for Science Insights:* Encourage students to try the activities *Data From Space* and *Shadow Watch* on the Earth and Space Disk. *SFAW.*

## Videos

*Discovering Our Universe. 30 min. MMI.*

## Audio-Visual Resources

*The Earth in Motion. Film. EB.*
*How We Know the Earth Moves. Film. BFA.*

## Writing Connection

Have students study the earthrise in the photograph and make a list of adjectives to describe Earth. Then have students use their lists to write a poem that describes Earth from space. Volunteers may want to share their poems with the class.

## Themes in Science

**Scale and Structure** The study of Earth is carried out at many different scales. Physicists and chemists study the composition of Earth at a microscopic scale. Geologists study the surface of Earth at a visible scale. Astronomers study Earth by comparing it to other large bodies in the solar system.

## ► Introducing the Chapter

Have students read the description of the photograph, which shows an "earthrise" from the moon. Ask if they agree or disagree with the description.

### Directed Inquiry

Have students study the photograph. Ask:

► What does this photograph show? What would you name this photograph? (Answers will probably be similar to the student's description given. Their names for the picture will vary.)

► What are the blue and white areas visible on Earth? (Students should identify the white areas as clouds in the atmosphere and the blue areas as oceans.)

► Why can't you see more of Earth over the horizon? (The sun is shining only on the top half of the visible part of the sphere.)

► How is this view like our view of the moon from Earth? (This perspective produces an "earthrise" the same way our perspective on Earth allows us to see a moonrise. Earth has phases as seen from the moon, just as the moon has phases as seen from Earth.)

## ► Chapter Vocabulary

| | |
|---|---|
| axis | revolution |
| crater | rotation |
| eclipse | solstice |
| equinox | umbra |
| orbit | zenith |
| penumbra | |

Chapter **23** **Earth and the Moon**

### Chapter Sections

### What do you see?

❝I see the Earth and it seems to be rising from another planet. It looks like the photograph was taken from another planet or maybe the moon. The photograph makes me curious about what other planets and the moon are like.❞

*Eddie White
Mabelvale Junior High
    School
Mabelvale, Arkansas*

To find out more about the photograph, look on page 556. As you read this chapter, you will learn about Earth and its moon.

## Cooperative Learning

Ask volunteers to work in a cooperative group to model the movement of Earth for the class. Have one student represent the sun, while the other student has the role of Earth. Have other students from the class tell Earth how to move. Students might say, "Rotate in a counterclockwise direction," or "Revolve around the sun."

**Skills Objectives**
Students should be able to:

**Infer** Earth's unique features as a planet.

**Interpret Data** based on time zones.

**Make a Model** of Earth's orbit.

**Infer** from a model why Earth bulges at the equator.

**Vocabulary**
axis, rotation, revolution, orbit, zenith, solstice, equinox

## 23.1 Earth in Space

### Objectives

▶ **Describe** the rotation and revolution of planet Earth.

▶ **Explain** how time is measured on Earth.

▶ **Explain** how the tilt of Earth's axis affects life on the planet.

▶ **Make a model** of Earth's orbit.

▼ **ACTIVITY**

| Inferring |
| --- |

*One of a Kind?*

   What features on Earth make it a unique planet? List at least five features. Exchange your list with a classmate's. Are your lists the same? If not, how do they differ?

**SKILLS WARMUP**

Y ou are a passenger on a gigantic spaceship called planet Earth. This spaceship spins like a top as it hurtles through space. But you don't sense the motion because everything on Earth moves and spins at the same speed.

Although you aren't directly aware of Earth's motions, you can probably point out some clues to its movements. For example, the sun appears to cross the sky every day. Summer changes to autumn. All these changes are caused by Earth's motions.

### Earth's Rotation

Earth has a spherical, or ball-like, shape that is slightly more than 40 000 km in circumference, with a diameter of about 12 760 km. Look at Table 23.1. What is the surface area of Earth? ①

Earth moves in two ways. It travels, or revolves, around the sun. At the same time, it spins, or rotates, like a top. If you observe a spinning top, you can see that it turns around a line running through the center. This line is called an **axis**. Earth's axis is an imaginary line that extends from the North Pole through Earth to the South Pole. The spinning of Earth on its axis is called **rotation**. Earth makes one complete rotation in 23 hours and 56 minutes.

Have you ever observed a sunrise or a sunset? If so, you may know that the earth rotates from west to east. On Earth you see the sun come into view over the eastern horizon, move across the sky from east to west, and disappear below the western horizon. Earth's rotation is responsible for the changing of day and night.

**Table 23.1   Facts about the Earth**

| | |
| --- | --- |
| Average distance from the sun | 149 700 000 km |
| Surface area | 512 175 090 km² |
| Circumference at equator | 40 074 km |
| Circumference at poles | 40 007 km |
| Diameter at equator | 12 760 km |
| Diameter at poles | 12 714 km |
| Period of rotation | 23 h, 56 mn |
| Period of revolution around the sun | 365.26 days |

**MOTIVATE**

### Skills WarmUp

To help students infer, have them do the Skills WarmUp.
**Answer**   Lists will vary and may include Earth's atmosphere, oceans, living things, weather patterns, and sea-floor spreading.

### Misconceptions

Students may think that Earth's geologic and planetary features are unique. Point out that several planets have volcanic activity, mountains, and atmospheres. Mars has ice caps at its poles; Jupiter, Saturn, Uranus, and Neptune have moons.

**TEACH**

### Skills Development

**Observe**   Bring a top to class and have a volunteer spin it. Ask students to compare its motion to Earth's rotation in terms of direction, speed, and position of the axis.

**Answer to In-Text Question**
① **512 175 090 km²**

### Explore Visually

Have students examine Figure 23.1, then ask:

▶ Where is the sun in relation to this diagram? (To the left)

▶ How does the solar wind affect Earth's magnetosphere? (It appears to keep the magnetosphere relatively compact on the side facing the sun and extends the magnetosphere on the opposite side.)

▶ What evidence in both pictures shows that lines of force are most concentrated near the magnetic poles? (In the photograph, lines of iron filings are closer together at the magnet's poles; lines in the diagram come together at the poles.)

▶ How does Earth's magnetic field differ from the forces around a bar magnet? (Its shape is influenced by the solar wind.)

## Class Activity

Give groups a compass and a magnet, and have groups prepare brief reports on how the compass needles move near the magnet and away from it.

## Reteach

Use Reteach Worksheet 23.1.

## Integrating the Sciences

**Physical Science** Scientists think that Earth's magnetic field is caused by the moving molten metals of Earth's core. Explain that magnetism occurs when atoms in a material line up, and their spinning electrons produce a magnetic field. In certain materials, such as iron, cobalt, and nickel, the atoms can be lined up relatively easily to make the metal magnetic. The material is then magnetized.

Demonstrate how to magnetize a metal. Obtain an iron rod and line it up with a compass to point north. Test to see if the rod is magnetic by pouring iron filings near the rod. Using a hammer, strike one end of the rod firmly and squarely. See if the rod is now magnetized by pouring iron filings near the rod.

Earth is not a perfect sphere. Forces created by rotation displace some material, causing the planet to bulge slightly at the equator. So Earth's shape is actually a slightly flattened sphere. The distance around Earth at the equator is about 67 km greater than around the poles. However, this difference is so small in relation to the planet's size that the flattening isn't detected from space.

### Earth as a Magnet

A compass can be used to find direction. One end of a compass needle always points north because Earth behaves like a giant bar magnet. Earth's magnetism is caused by its rotation. Recall that the core is composed mainly of iron. Rotation causes the iron in the core to become magnetized.

Look at the photograph in Figure 23.1. What happens when iron filings are sprinkled over a bar magnet? The filings form a pattern around the magnet. This pattern shows the lines of force surrounding the magnet. Earth is surrounded by similar lines of force. Notice in Figure 23.1 that the lines of force are most concentrated near the magnetic poles. The magnetic poles attract a compass needle. From the poles, the lines of force spread out to form a magnetic field, called the magnetosphere.

**Figure 23.1**
Compare the magnetic field around Earth to the forces around a bar magnet. ▼

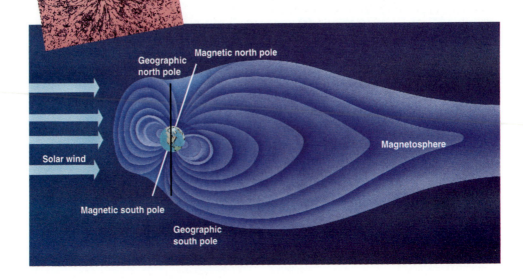

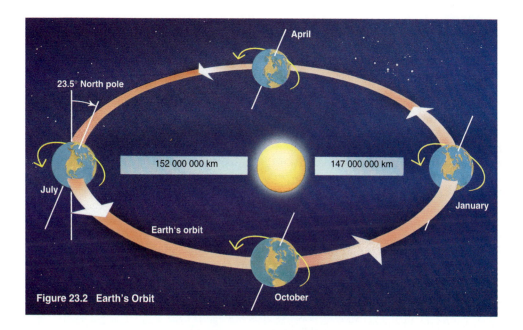

Figure 23.2 Earth's Orbit

## Earth's Revolution

As Earth rotates on its axis, it also travels around the sun. The movement of a body in space around another body is called **revolution**. It takes Earth about 365 days, or one Earth year, to complete one revolution around the sun. During that time, Earth travels about 958 million km. To cover that distance, Earth and its passengers travel at a speed of about 109 000 km/hr!

The path a body follows as it revolves around another body is called its **orbit**. As shown in Figure 23.2, Earth's orbit is elliptical. So the distance between Earth and the sun changes throughout the year. The closest point of Earth's orbit to the sun is called *perihelion* (pur uh HEEL yuhn). Find the distance at perihelion in Figure 23.2. Earth reaches this point about January 3. Six months later, Earth reaches the farthest point from the sun, called *aphelion* (a FEEL yuhn).

## Seasons

How do you know what season it is? How does winter compare with summer? Most people experience several seasons during a year. Notice in Figure 23.2 that Earth's axis is tilted at an angle of 23.5°. Also notice that as Earth revolves around the sun, its axis always points in the same direction. The tilt of the axis is important for the changing of seasons on Earth.

Because of the tilt of Earth's axis, the amount of sunlight falling on the different regions of the earth changes throughout the year. For example, when the Northern Hemisphere is tilted toward the sun, the sun's rays strike this area more directly. There are also more hours of sunlight. The combination of increased daylight and more direct rays cause higher temperatures. Look at Figure 23.2. Although Earth is at aphelion, the position of greatest distance, it is summer in the Northern Hemisphere.

## Research

Have half of the class use resources to learn about people's lifestyles in the Tropic of Cancer, and have the other half study lifestyles in the Tropic of Capricorn. Ask each group to make a poster that illustrates what they have learned.

## Critical Thinking

**If . . . Then Arguments**  Using what they have learned about solstices, have students write an *If . . . then* statement about summer in the Southern Hemisphere. (For example, if the sun is over 23°S at the winter solstice, then it must be the beginning of summer in the Southern Hemisphere.)

## Reteach

Tell students that in the Northern Hemisphere, solstices and equinoxes occur on June 20 or 21, September 22 or 23, December 21 or 22, and March 20 or 21. Have them match each date to the correct event and describe the appropriate lengths of night and day.

### *Language Arts Connection*

Have students use a dictionary to find the origins of the words *solstice* and *equinox*. Ask students how the original meanings relate to these two solar conditions. (*Equinox* is Latin for "equal night." *Solstice* is Latin for "sun stop.")

### *Multicultural Perspectives*

During the solstice in high latitudes, the sun does not set; there is a 24-hour period of daylight. In many Scandinavian countries, the summer solstice is celebrated by a Midsummer Festival. During the festival, people dance around a decorated pole to celebrate the return of the sun.

When the Northern Hemisphere points toward the sun, the Southern Hemisphere tilts away from the sun. The sun's rays reach the Southern Hemisphere at a greater slant. Slanted rays spread out the heat. The number of daylight hours is short. It is winter.

**Solstices and Equinoxes**  During the day, the most direct sunlight rays arrive when the sun reaches its highest elevation in the sky, at noon. The most slanted sunlight rays arrive when the sun is on the *horizon*, the line where the earth seems to meet the sky. The sun is on the horizon at sunrise and sunset.

The highest point of the sky is the **zenith.** When you stand outside, the zenith is directly overhead. Look at Figure 23.3. Due to the tilt of Earth, the noon sun appears directly overhead in various places between the latitudes 23°N and 23°S throughout the year. When the noon sun is directly overhead at either of these exact latitudes, it is called a **solstice.** The first day of summer is the summer solstice.

Between the two solstices are two equinoxes. An **equinox** (EE kwuh nahks) is when the noon sun is directly over the equator. During an equinox the hours of daylight and darkness are equal everywhere on Earth.

**Figure 23.3  Solstices and Equinoxes on Earth** ▼

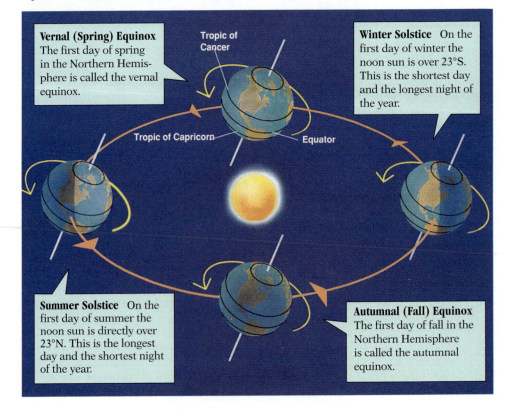

**Vernal (Spring) Equinox**  The first day of spring in the Northern Hemisphere is called the vernal equinox.

Tropic of Cancer

Tropic of Capricorn

Equator

**Winter Solstice**  On the first day of winter the noon sun is over 23°S. This is the shortest day and the longest night of the year.

**Summer Solstice**  On the first day of summer the noon sun is directly over 23°N. This is the longest day and the shortest night of the year.

**Autumnal (Fall) Equinox**  The first day of fall in the Northern Hemisphere is called the autumnal equinox.

## Themes in Science

### Patterns of Change/Cycles

The cycle of Earth orbiting the sun corresponds to life-cycle changes in organisms.

## Integrating the Sciences

**Chemistry** Scientists have located a pigment that is responsible for plant responses to light. The pigment is called phytochrome. Its structure changes in the presence of different colors of light. Scientists do not completely understand how phytochrome functions in plants. However, they do know that phytochrome plays a part in flowering, seed germination, and seasonal dormancy.

## Discuss

Remind students that organisms must adapt to their environments. Then ask the following questions.

▶ In which of the kingdoms of living things is it easiest to observe seasonal changes? Why? (For example: Plants, because of blooms, color changes, change of foliage; Animals, because of migrations and nesting behavior; Fungi, because of blooms, color changes, spore cases)

▶ How do butterflies change with the seasons? (They usually emerge from chrysalises and lay eggs in spring. Adults cannot tolerate cold weather. Some, such as monarchs, migrate and others hibernate.)

▶ How do people change with the seasons? (Answers will vary and can relate to outdoor activities, travel, nutrition, and clothing.)

## Skills Development

**Define Operationally** Have students describe how a tree or perennial plant near the school adapts to seasonal changes.

## Integrated Learning

Use Integrating Worksheet 23.1.

## Life Cycles and Seasons

How does your life and your daily routine change with the seasons? You probably dress differently at different times of the year. Your outdoor activities may be affected by the temperature and the number of hours of daylight. The activities of most living things change with the seasons. Animals and plants go through cycles of activity. These cycles are regulated by the availability of food and the number of daylight hours.

Some animals, especially birds, migrate with the changing seasons. Many birds follow the sun's movement in the sky north and south throughout the year. Migrating birds travel toward the equator in winter and away from the equator in summer. Other migrating animals include some types of fishes and whales. ▶

Some plants always flower during summer, while other plants flower only in fall. Plants have a light-sensitive chemical that measures the length of time between light and dark. Some plants need long daylight hours to trigger blooming; others need short daylight hours. ▼

▲ In areas with both mild and cold or dry seasons, deciduous trees grow. Sap flows freely through deciduous trees. In some trees, this sap is collected to make maple syrup. When fall arrives, leaves turn color and fall from deciduous trees. The plants enter a period of dormancy, ready to begin the cycle again the following spring.

▲ In places where winter temperatures are low and food is scarce, some animals go through a period of dormancy. Chipmunks and bears hibernate. During dry seasons, amphibians may estivate (EHS tuh vayt), or burrow underground and remain dormant until wet weather arrives.

## Class Activity

Have students use resources to design a sundial for use outside the school. If materials are available, have the class build the sundial.

## Critical Thinking

**Find Causes** Ask students to compare Figure 23.4 to a map of the actual time-zone boundaries in the United States. Ask them why the actual boundaries do not follow lines of longitude. (The irregular boundaries allow neighboring communities to have the same time.)

## *Skills WorkOut*

To help students interpret data, have them do the Skills WorkOut.
**Answer** 8 p.m.

## Answers to In-Text Questions

① 6

② Answer depends on location.

## *Geography Connection*

Have students use a world map to list a country in each of the 24 time zones. Then have students imagine that they can travel in a plane that takes one hour to travel from one time zone to another. Ask students to determine what time they would arrive at every country on their list if they started a flight from their home town at 10:00 a.m.

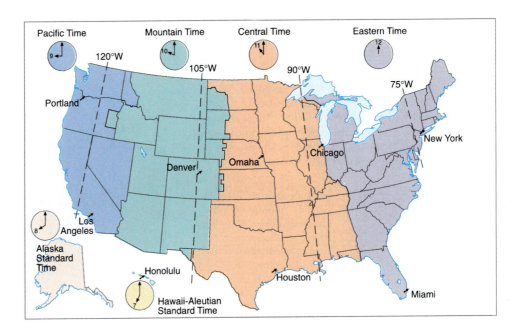

**Figure 23.4 ▲**
How many time zones are
① located in the United States?
② Which time zone do you live in?

## Time Zones

People have always been interested in measuring time. About 2,500 years ago, shadow clocks, or sundials, kept track of time using the motion of the sun in the sky. Since the length of a day varies with Earth's revolution, these clocks weren't very accurate.

In 1883, an international system was established to standardize time measurement worldwide. This system divides Earth into 24 time zones. A time zone is the distance Earth rotates in one hour. Since Earth rotates 360° in 24 hours, each time zone is 15° wide. The map in Figure 23.4 shows the time zones in the United States.

The starting point of the world's time zones is at 0°, or the prime meridian. The prime meridian passes through Greenwich, England. Halfway around the world is the 180° meridian, or the international date line. At midnight, in Greenwich, it is noon at the international date line.

When you move across a time zone, the time changes by one hour. If you travel east, the time is one hour later; if you travel west, it is one hour earlier. When you cross the international date line, you change days! If you travel east across the meridian, you gain one day. If you travel west, you lose one day.

### Science and Society
*Telling Time Through Time*

Every day, you are probably reminded of the date. You know the date of your birth and the dates of holidays. To keep track of these kinds of important events, calendars were developed hundreds of years ago.

Most ancient calendars were based on the changing shape and position of the moon. A lunar year has 354 days divided into 12 months. A month in the lunar calendar begins on the new moon and lasts 29 or 30 days. This type of dating system was used by the Babylonians and the Chinese. A type of lunar calendar is still used by the Moslems today.

About 4,000 B.C., the Egyptians developed a solar calendar. It was based on the apparent motion of the sun and the seasons. This calendar had 12 months. Each month had 30 days, with five days added at the end of the year.

The Jewish calendar is a combination of a lunar and solar calendar, or a lunisolar calendar. It is over 5,000 years old. In the Jewish calendar, each month is based on the orbit of the moon, as in the lunar calendar. However, a lunar year is 11 days shorter than a solar year. To correct this, a 19-year period was developed. Each 19-year period consists of 12 years of 12 months and 7 years of 13 months.

In the first century A.D., the Maya from Central America used several calendars. The calendar they used for agriculture had 365 days, with every fourth year containing an extra day.

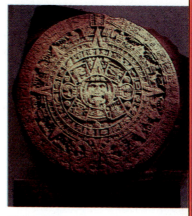

**Figure 23.5** ▲
The Aztecs, who lived in the central valley of Mexico, created this stone calendar during the 1480s. It weighs almost 20 tons and is called the Sun Stone.

### Check and Explain

1. What are two important motions of Earth? Describe each motion.

2. If you take off from New York at noon in a jet plane, how is it possible to arrive in California at 11 a.m.? Explain.

3. **Infer** How would life on Earth be different if Earth's axis were not tilted?

4. **Make a Model** Using two thumbtacks, a piece of string, paper, cardboard, and a pencil, draw a figure that is similar in shape to that of Earth's orbit. Label the sun, perihelion, and aphelion.

**Time** 30 minutes    **Group** one

**Materials**

30 long, sharpened pencils

30 sheets of construction paper

metric rulers

scissors

tape

hole punch

## Analysis

1. The sphere represents Earth.

2. Rolling or twirling the pencil represents the rotation of Earth about its axis.

3. The center bulges out.

4. The paper near the ends of the pencil slide toward the center.

5. Student answers may vary. The model is not solid, and has far less mass than Earth. The material making up the model is uniform compared to Earth.

## Conclusion

The activity models Earth's rotation. Paper strips form a sphere around a pencil. When the pencil is twirled, the poles of the sphere come closer together, and the equator bulges outward, suggesting that Earth bulges around the equator due to its rotation.

## Extension

Accept workable designs. A possible design is to put markings on the pencil to measure how far the paper strips slide.

### Prelab Discussion

Have students read the entire activity. Before beginning, discuss reasons for using models in science. Remind students that a model will always differ from the actual phenomenon in some way. Discuss the way this model differs in mass, size, materials, and spin velocity from the rotating Earth.

## *Activity 23*   Why does Earth bulge at the equator?

**Skills**   Model; Infer; Measure

### Task 1   Prelab Prep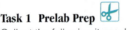

Collect the following items: long, sharpened pencil, construction paper, metric ruler, scissors, tape, hole punch, sheet of paper.

### Task 2   Data Record

On a sheet of paper, copy Table 23.2. Record your observations in the table.

**Table 23.2**   **Earth Rotation Observations**

| Location on Earth | Observation 1 | Observation 2 |
|---|---|---|
| Equator | | |
| Poles | | |

### Task 3   Procedure

1. From the construction paper, cut 2 separate strips that each measure 3 cm by 40 cm.
2. Mark an X at the center of each strip.
3. Cross the strips at their centers, and tape them together.
4. Bring the four loose ends together. Overlap the ends, and secure together with tape.
5. Using a hole punch make a hole in the center of each end where the strips overlap.
6. Push the pencil through the holes in each end. The completed setup should look like Figure 23.6.
7. Hold each end of the pencil, and roll the pencil in your fingers. Observe what happens to the equator and the poles.
8. Record your observations of the equator and the poles in the data table under Observation 1.
9. Re-form a sphere with the strips of paper.
10. Place a sheet of paper on a flat surface.

11. Place the tip of the pencil on the paper. Twirl the pencil. Observe the equator and the poles. Record your observations in the data table under Observation 2.

### Task 4   Analysis

1. What does the sphere represent?
2. What does rolling or twirling the pencil represent? Explain.
3. Describe what happens at the equator when the pencil is rolled or twirled.
4. Describe what happens at the poles when the pencil is rolled or twirled.
5. How is this model different from Earth? Explain.

### Task 5   Conclusion

Write a short paragraph describing how your model is similar to what happens as Earth rotates.

### *Extension*

How can you find out how much the sphere in your model flattened? Design an experiment to figure out how much your sphere flattens from its original shape when it is rotated.

**Figure 23.6** ▼

### Art Connection

Have students cut out pictures of the moon from magazines. Then have students draw or paint pictures to incorporate the moon photographs. Create a bulletin board display with some of the pictures.

### Language Arts Connection

Ask students what the word *satellite* means to them. Most will probably refer to the satellites that the United States and other countries put into orbit for telecommunications and other purposes. Have students look up the word *satellite* in a dictionary. Point out that *satellite* also refers to smaller planets and moons that revolve around larger planets. Explain that the moon is Earth's natural satellite and that human-made satellites are artificial.

**Section Objectives**
For a list of section objectives, see the Student Edition page.

**Skills Objectives**
Students should be able to:

**Infer** characteristics of the moon.

**Make a Model** of a lunar eclipse.

**Vocabulary**
crater

## 23.2 Earth's Moon

### Objectives

▶ **Identify** four features of the moon's surface.

▶ **List** some major events in the exploration of the moon.

▶ **Explain** how the motion of the moon affects the view of the moon from Earth.

▶ **Infer** which theory about the formation of the moon is the most logical.

▼ **ACTIVITY**

**Inferring**

*Moonscapes*

Based on your direct observations and on photographs of the moon, describe its shape, color, and composition in a paragraph.

**SKILLS WARMUP**

**MOTIVATE**

### Skills WarmUp

To help students infer, have them do the Skills WarmUp.
**Answer** Paragraphs will vary. Size can be relative; color may be white, gray, or yellow; composition could be rocky or dusty.

### Prior Knowledge

Gauge how much students know about Earth's moon by asking the following questions:

▶ What shape is the moon?

▶ Is there gravity on the moon?

▶ How did the moon form?

**Answer to In-Text Question**
① **Students should give one-sixth of their Earth weights.**

Imagine you are given a photograph of some object on Earth's surface taken from an altitude of 1,000 km. How would you try to identify the object? You would study the specimen and its surroundings very carefully. Then you would use your observations to compare the object with some familiar object. Finally, you would make inferences based on your observations.

For hundreds of years, scientists have used similar techniques to study an object almost 400 000 km from Earth. That object is Earth's moon.

### The Lunar Satellite

Dozens of artificial satellites circle the planet. But the moon is Earth's only natural satellite. The largest artificial satellite is dwarfed by the moon, which has a diameter of 3,476 km.

At its surface, the moon's gravity is about one-sixth that of Earth. Since weight measures the pull of gravity, a person's weight on the moon would be one-sixth of that on Earth. What is your moon weight? ①

During the 1970s, astronauts left many scientific instruments on the lunar surface. Data from these instruments reveals that the moon doesn't have a magnetic field, because it doesn't spin as fast on its axis as Earth does. Seismic instruments record moonquakes and provide data about the moon's interior. This information shows that the moon's interior is probably similar to that of Earth, except with a smaller iron core.

**Figure 23.7** ▲
You can see the moon's surface very clearly in this moonrise over New York City.

The Living Textbook:
Earth Science Sides 1-2

Chapter 31        Frame 06931
Moonscapes (4 Frames)
Search:                Step:

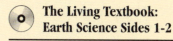

## Directed Inquiry

Have students examine the photographs and descriptions on this page. Then ask:

▶ How do maria differ from craters? (Maria are broad, flat planes while craters are more indented and have round edges.)

▶ Where are the craters in the top photograph? (Students should find three large craters and many smaller ones.)

▶ Can there be craters in maria? (Yes) How? (Meteorites could have struck them.)

▶ Can there be craters in the lunar highlands? (Yes) How? (Volcanoes may have caused some. Meteorites probably caused most of them.)

## Research

Have each student use a map of the moon's surface to pick out the names of five features. Ask students to use resources to find the origins of at least two of the names they have chosen.

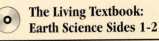

**The Living Textbook: Earth Science Sides 1-2**

Chapter 35      Frame 06935
Moon Surface Images (78 Frames)
Search:         Step:

## Writing Connection

Have students write several paragraphs that compare the features on the lunar surface to features on the surface of Earth. Students may want to observe aerial photographs and landscapes of both the moon and Earth before writing their paragraphs.

### The Lunar Surface

Exploration of the moon's surface has shown it to be barren and lifeless. Temperatures may range from 130°C at lunar noon to –175°C at night. Evidence indicates there is no water on the lunar surface. There is almost no atmosphere. Consequently, there is no weather. The absence of water and an atmosphere means that no weathering of the lunar surface occurs. Therefore, the rocks and rock formations have remained almost unchanged for much of the moon's history.

◀ When Galileo first turned his telescope on the lunar surface almost 400 years ago, he clearly saw regions of bright and dark that are vaguely visible with the unaided eye. Galileo thought the dark regions resembled seas here on Earth. So he called them *maria* (MAR ee uh), the Latin word for seas. Today, these dark regions are known to be broad, flat plains. Cutting across the maria are features called *rilles* (RIHLS). Rilles are long, narrow valleys.

The most obvious features on the moon's surface are circular indentations called **craters**. Most of the moon's craters were created by meteorites striking the lunar surface. But some of the smaller ones may be volcanic in origin. Copernicus, one of the largest craters, is more than 90 km in diameter. ▼

▲ The bright areas that Galileo saw on the moon are called *highlands*. Highlands consist of mountainous terrain on the surface of the moon.

## Integrating the Sciences

**Physical Science** Many satellites orbit Earth, whereas other spacecraft float through the solar system. To lift any rocket off of the surface of Earth, the gravitational force must be overcome. In order for any object to escape Earth's gravity and achieve an Earth orbit, it must reach a velocity of 11.2 km/s vertically. If a spacecraft is given more speed than 11.2 km/s, it will escape from Earth completely. Once the craft is above the atmosphere, another thrust of 8 km/s tips it from its vertical course. Like the moon, the spacecraft gets caught in the gravitational pull of Earth and continues to orbit.

## Moon's Movements

The moon has an elliptical orbit around Earth. The moon remains in its orbit because the gravity of Earth and the gravity of the moon pull on each other. The moon's closest point to Earth is called *perigee.* (PEHR uh JEE) The farthest point in its orbit is called *apogee* (AP uh JEE).

The moon's period of revolution is the same as its period of rotation. The moon completes one revolution in 27.3 days. During this period, it also rotates once on its axis. Because these two periods are equal, the same side of the moon always faces Earth, as shown in Figure 23.8.

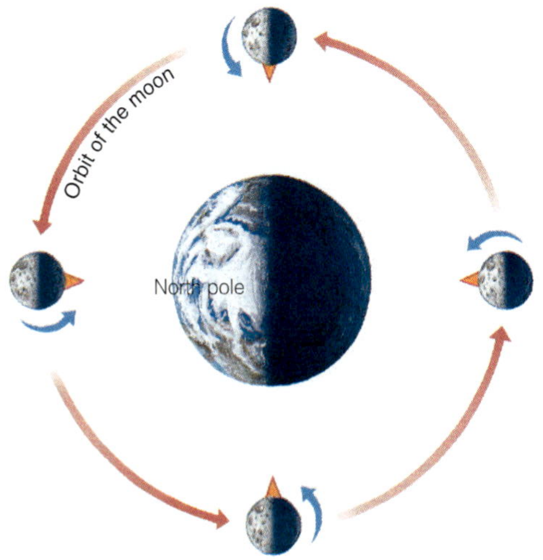

## Origin of the Moon

For centuries, people have wondered about the origin of the moon. Although several theories have been developed, most have flaws.

▶ The *daughter theory* suggests that a piece of Earth split off to form the moon. However, the daughter theory doesn't explain why the moon is not solely composed of Earth's crust material. Also, there is no evidence that Earth ever spun fast enough to eject such a large mass.

▶ The *sister theory* states that Earth and the moon formed from gas and dust during the formation of the solar system. This theory can't account for the differences in the rock composition between the two bodies.

▶ The *capture theory* proposes that the moon formed elsewhere and was captured by Earth's gravity as it passed. It is argued that the moon couldn't have attained a stable orbit without assistance from a third body. No evidence of such a body has ever been found.

▶ The most accepted theory today is that an impact knocked a large quantity of material from Earth. Earth's gravity captured and collected material from the impacting body and Earth to form the moon.

**Figure 23.8** ▲
As the moon orbits Earth, the same side of the moon always faces toward Earth.

Orbit of the moon

North pole

## ▼ ACTIVITY

### Making a Model

*A Fickle Moon*

Draw an ellipse. Locate the center of the ellipse. Draw Earth in the center. Locate the point when the moon's position is farthest from (apogee) and closest to (perigee) Earth. Label these two points. What does your model represent?

**SKILLS WORKOUT**

## Enrich

Explain that the side of the moon facing away from Earth is called the far side. It has fewer maria and more craters than the visible side.

## Critical Thinking

**Uncover Assumptions** Have students review the theories of the moon's origins. Then ask:

▶ Which theory or theories do not account for the differences in the compositions of Earth and the moon? (Daughter and sister theories)

▶ Which theory or theories suggest that the moon and Earth have similar compositions? (Today's most accepted theory)

## *Skills WorkOut*

To help students make a model, have them do the Skills WorkOut.
**Answer** It represents the moon's orbit around Earth.

TEACH ▪ Continued

## Class Activity

Divide the class into six groups. Assign each group an Apollo mission from Apollo 12 through Apollo 17. Have groups use resources to find out the scientific reason for the mission and some of its results.

## Historical Notebook

**Define Operationally** When students have read the paragraphs, ask them what the moon's surface must be like to walk on. Have them use evidence from the text to develop a description.

**Answers**

1. Neil Armstrong, Edwin "Buzz" Aldrin, Jr.

2. It felt like soot or flour, resisted downward force, and shifted easily sideways.

3. Study of moon rocks and soil has revealed mostly minerals that occur naturally on Earth. There are two main rock types: basalt and breccia. About half the moon's soil consists of bits of glass. Nothing lives in moon soil. Moon rocks and soil tell scientists that volcanic activity and meteoroid impacts formed the moon's surface.

### History Connection

On January 28, 1986, the space shuttle *Challenger* exploded a little over a minute after take-off. All of the crew were killed in the disaster. One of the crew members was Christa McAuliffe, a teacher from New Hampshire. She was the first teacher and the first ordinary citizen in space. You may wish to discuss the *Challenger* tragedy with students and create a bulletin board that commemorates McAuliffe and the other crew members of the *Challenger*.

## Exploration of the Moon

In 1959, the Soviet spacecraft Luna 3 radioed back the first photographs of the moon's far side. Motivated by the Soviet's success, the United States began the Apollo project. The project's goal was to place an astronaut on the moon before 1970.

On July 16, 1969, Apollo 11 was launched. Neil Armstrong became the first person to set foot on the moon. He was followed by Edwin "Buzz" Aldrin, Jr. The two astronauts collected lunar materials and set up experiments before returning to Earth.

Over the next three years, five more lunar landings were accomplished. Astronauts explored large areas of the lunar surface. The last lunar mission, Apollo 17, was completed in December 1972. Since then, no people have returned to the moon. However, much information has been gained from instruments left on the moon by the astronauts.

## Historical Notebook

### Moon Landing

"One small step for man, one giant leap for mankind." These were the first words spoken by Neil Armstrong as he took the very first step on the moon. The results of this first step were uncertain. Would he sink into the dust? Would the ground be slippery? But when Armstrong stepped onto the moon's surface, he found it to be like walking on soot or flour.

Aldrin (shown at right) and Armstrong found that moving across the moon's surface was easiest when they floated across it with their feet in the air. They moved about 2 to 4 meters at a time.

These first astronauts discovered something strange about the lunar surface. When they planted the American flag into the ground, they had to press hard to force the flagstaff down. Once in the ground, the staff would easily fall over. The lunar soil resisted downward force, but shifted easily sideways.

1. Who were the first two people to walk on the moon?

2. What did the astronauts find out about the surface of the moon?

3. **Research** Find out how moon rocks helped scientists learn about the composition and history of the moon.

### Science and Technology  *Moon Machines*

Before 1969, the lunar surface was barren of any technology. Since then, machines have landed, traveled, and been left behind on the moon.

The machine that carried the astronauts to the lunar surface is called the lunar module, or LM. The lunar module is a small spacecraft that separates from the larger command module. The LM has a separate fuel system that allows it to land and take off. The LM serves as the headquarters for astronauts while they are on the moon. When the mission is completed, the lunar module leaves the moon to reconnect with the command module. The LM is later discarded into space.

Even though the LM doesn't remain on the moon, other machines brought to the moon are still on its surface. The Lunar Rover, or moon buggy, is a battery-powered vehicle similar to a dune buggy. It was first used during Apollo 15. The Lunar Rover allowed astronauts on Apollo missions 15, 16, and 17 to explore large areas of the lunar surface. It was left on the surface for possible use in the future.

Instruments were also left on the moon to conduct scientific experiments. The passive seismic experiment records moonquakes and meteorite impacts. The lunar surface gravimeter detects changes in the gravitational field. The lunar atmospheric composition instrument analyzes lunar gases. The solar wind spectrometer measures the number of electrons and protons streaming in solar wind. The data from these scientific devices is sent back to Earth for analysis.

**Figure 23.9** ▲
Astronaut Eugene Cernan drives the Lunar Rover during the Apollo 17 mission.

### Check and Explain

1. Describe four features of the moon's surface.

2. List two major events in the exploration of the moon. Explain why you chose these two events.

3. **Reason and Conclude**  How would the view of the moon from Earth be different if the moon rotated around its axis more slowly than it now does?

4. **Infer**  Decide which theory about the origin of the moon is the most logical. Explain why you chose this theory, and why you rejected the other theories.

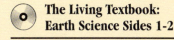

### Themes in Science

**Systems and Interactions** The regular interaction between Earth and the moon is due to gravitational pull. This consistent interaction produced the relatively stable Earth-Moon system.

**Section Objectives**
For a list of section objectives, see the Student Edition page.

**Skills Objectives**
Students should be able to:

**Predict** phases of the moon.

**Make a Model** of an eclipse.

**Interpret Data** about moon phases and tides.

**Communicate** a legend about the moon.

**Compare and Contrast** lunar and solar eclipses.

**Vocabulary**
eclipse, umbra, penumbra

## ◢ MOTIVATE

### Skills WarmUp

To help students predict, have them do the Skills WarmUp.
**Answer** Predictions and actual dates will depend on the time of year. A full cycle takes 27.3 days.

### Misconceptions

Students may think that the moon produces its own light energy, like the sun, and that phases of the moon are caused by Earth's shadow. Explain that moonlight is reflected light from the sun. Remind students that the moon, sun, and Earth do not always travel on the same plane. When Earth's shadow covers the moon, a lunar eclipse occurs.

## ▼ ACTIVITY

### Predicting

*The Phase is Familiar . . .*

Using a calendar, list the dates of the new moon, quarter moon, and full moon for six months. Observe the rhythm of the moon cycles. Predict the date of the next full moon, new moon, and quarter moon. Check the calendar to see if your prediction was correct.

**SKILLS WARMUP**

**Figure 23.10**
**Phases of the Moon** ▼

## 23.3 Earth–Moon System

### Objectives

▶ **Relate** the phases of the moon to its revolution.

▶ **Describe** a waxing moon and a waning moon.

▶ **Predict** how the distance of the moon affects tides.

▶ **Compare** and **contrast** a lunar eclipse and a solar eclipse.

I f you look at the sky at night, what do you see? You see stars, of course, and the moon. If you look at the sky during the day, what do you see? Do you ever see the moon? Sometimes you can see the moon even during the day.

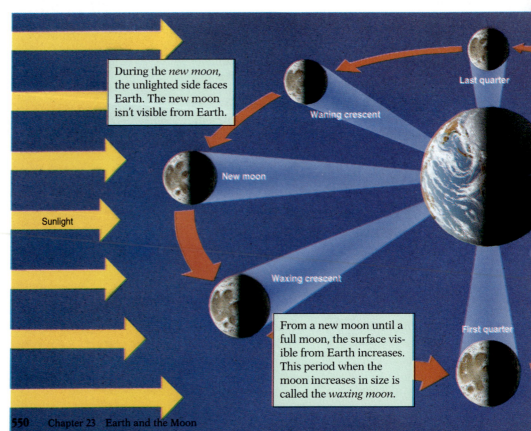

During the *new moon,* the unlighted side faces Earth. The new moon isn't visible from Earth.

Last quarter

Waning crescent

New moon

Sunlight

Waxing crescent

First quarter

From a new moon until a full moon, the surface visible from Earth increases. This period when the moon increases in size is called the *waxing moon.*

## Language Arts Connection

Have students use a dictionary to look up the meanings of *chromo-*, *photo-*, and *sphere*. Then have students look up the origin of the word *corona*. Ask students how these meanings help to describe the layers of the sun. (*Chromo-* means "color," *photo-* means "light," *sphere* means "circle." *Corona* comes from the Latin word for crown or garland.)

## Integrating the Sciences

**Physical Science** Mention the nursery rhyme "Twinkle, Twinkle Little Star." Ask students to describe a twinkling star and infer why stars twinkle in the sky. Tell students that physics helps explain a star's twinkling. Light from distant suns passes through Earth's atmosphere. The different layers of atmosphere vary in temperature and density. This causes the light to bend slightly. The interference makes the light appear to shimmer or twinkle.

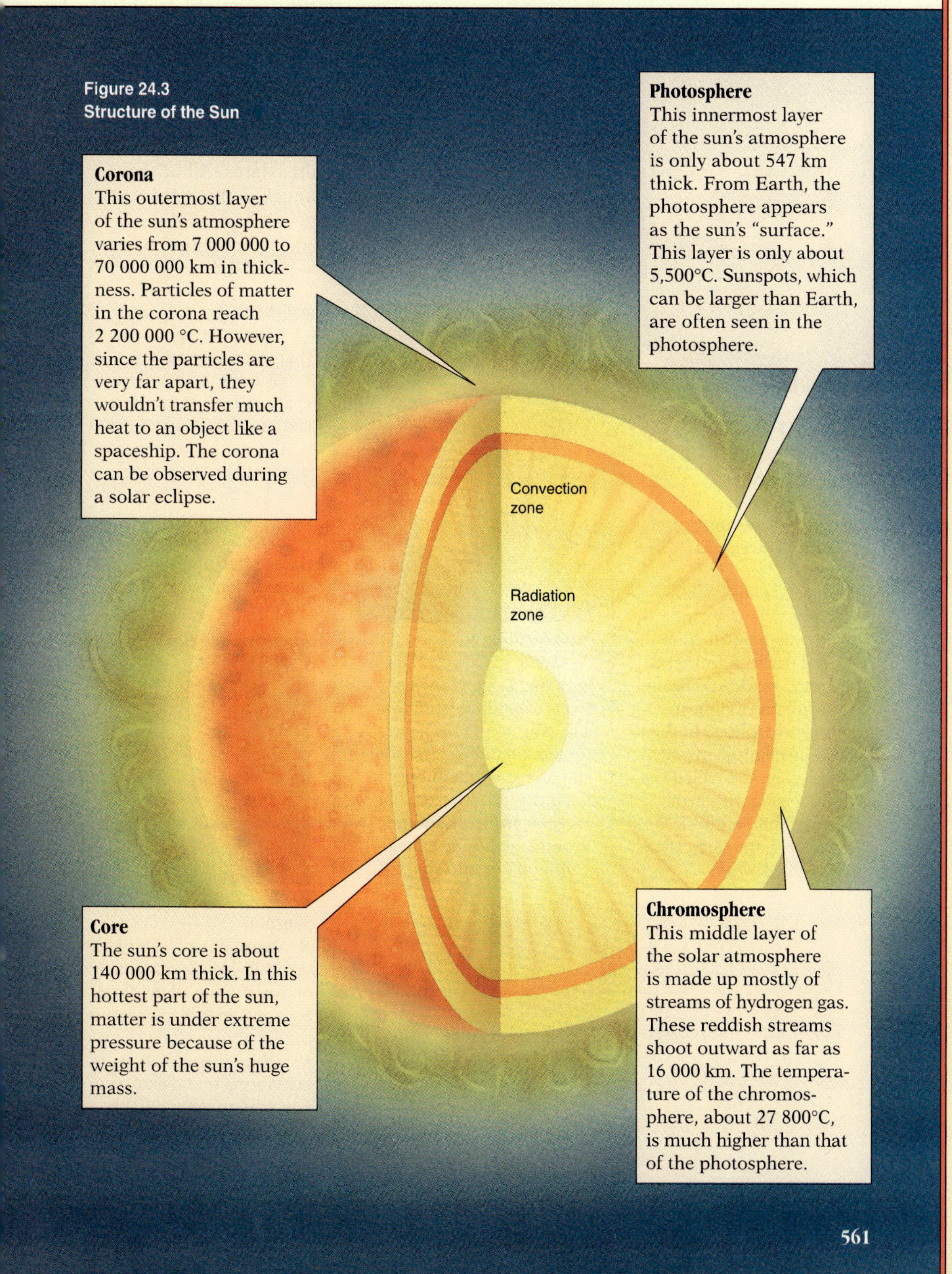

## Explore Visually

Have students study Figure 24.3. Then ask:

► Which three layers make up the sun's atmosphere? (Photosphere, chromosphere, and corona)

► Why is the core under extreme pressure? (The contraction of the sun's huge mass causes the greatest pressure at the center.)

► When people see sunspots, where are the spots? (Photosphere)

► What makes up most of the chromosphere? (Streams of hydrogen gas.)

► When can we observe the outermost layer of the sun's atmosphere? (During a solar eclipse)

► Which layer of the sun's atmosphere do people usually see? (Photosphere)

► **Infer** Have students think about sunspots. Ask: Since sunspots are dark, what would you infer about their temperature? Why? (They are cooler than nearby areas because they appear darker.)

**Figure 24.3**
**Structure of the Sun**

**Corona**
This outermost layer of the sun's atmosphere varies from 7 000 000 to 70 000 000 km in thickness. Particles of matter in the corona reach 2 200 000 °C. However, since the particles are very far apart, they wouldn't transfer much heat to an object like a spaceship. The corona can be observed during a solar eclipse.

**Photosphere**
This innermost layer of the sun's atmosphere is only about 547 km thick. From Earth, the photosphere appears as the sun's "surface." This layer is only about 5,500°C. Sunspots, which can be larger than Earth, are often seen in the photosphere.

Convection zone

Radiation zone

**Core**
The sun's core is about 140 000 km thick. In this hottest part of the sun, matter is under extreme pressure because of the weight of the sun's huge mass.

**Chromosphere**
This middle layer of the solar atmosphere is made up mostly of streams of hydrogen gas. These reddish streams shoot outward as far as 16 000 km. The temperature of the chromosphere, about 27 800°C, is much higher than that of the photosphere.

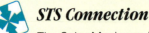

**TEACH ▪ Continued**

- How does the solar wind affect Earth? (It interacts with Earth's magnetic field to form the magnetosphere. It may also cause auroras.)

- What supports prominences? (Magnetic fields that stretch from one sunspot group to another)

- What are sunspots? (Storms that occur where powerful magnetic fields break through the photosphere and prevent interior light and heat from escaping)

- What do prominences and sunspots have in common? (They involve magnetic fields.)

- What are solar flares? (Intense spurts of electromagnetic radiation even more powerful than prominences)

- Why do solar flares affect radio communications on Earth? (They produce cosmic rays that affect the electromagnetic spectrum, of which radio waves are a part.)

### STS Connection

The Solar Maximum Mission satellite, or Solar Max, has been measuring the sun's energy output since February 1980. Information from Solar Max indicates that the energy output of the sun is not constant. The satellite's instruments detected a decrease in the energy output of the sun from 1980 to 1985. This trend seemed to then reverse itself.

### Integrating the Sciences

**Health** Explain to students that they should never look directly at the sun. The light from the sun is so intense that it can damage the retina of the eye. The retina lines the eye and is the immediate instrument of vision. Light that enters the eye is focused by the lens onto the retina and forms an image. Light from the sun can burn the retina, possibly causing blindness.

## Activity on the Sun

The surface of the sun is very active. In fact, three kinds of storms occur in the upper layers of the sun: sunspots, prominences, and solar flares. All of these solar storms are caused by changes in the magnetic field of the sun. Like Earth, the sun has a magnetic field that acts as if a huge bar magnet lies within it.

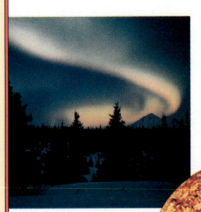

**Solar Wind ▲**

The corona sends a steady stream of high-energy particles into space. This stream is called the *solar wind*. It interacts with Earth's magnetic field to form Earth's magnetosphere. Charged particles from the solar wind may cause beautiful displays of light in the magnetosphere. In the Northern Hemisphere, these light displays are called the *aurora borealis*, or northern lights. In the Southern Hemisphere, they are called the *aurora australis*.

**Prominences ▲**

These spectacular storms look like huge arches or loops extending from the sun's surface. *Prominences* (prahm uh nuhn suhz) are supported by magnetic fields that stretch from one sunspot group to another. Prominences may extend 1 million km into space.

**Solar Flares**

Even more powerful than prominences are solar flares. A *solar flare* is a very intense spurt of radiation. In some flares, matter reaches a temperature of 20 million °C. A flare may last from 10 minutes to 1 hour. Cosmic rays produced by large solar flares interrupt radio communications on Earth. ▼

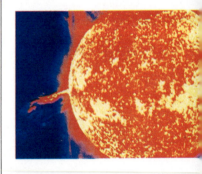

**Sunspots**

◄ Astronomers have observed spots like black blemishes on the sun for a long time. Sunspots look black because they are cooler than the surrounding matter. *Sunspots* are storms that occur where powerful magnetic fields break through the photosphere and prevent interior light and heat from escaping.

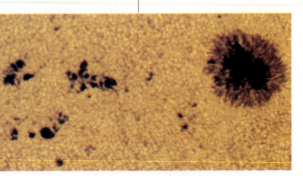

## Cooperative Learning

Have students safely observe the sun as a class. Obtain a telescope or binoculars and a square of white cardboard. Have one student hold the cardboard. Have a second student hold the telescope or the binoculars in a reversed viewing position, and capture the image of the sun onto the cardboard. Warn students that they should not look directly into the sun. Instead they should adjust the board and the scope until the sun's image is on the board. Have students focus the scope until the sun's image is sharp. Ask them to try to identify sunspots or prominences.

## Enrich

Tell students that in food chains and food webs, plants are the producers. Animals are consumers because they rely on plants, directly or indirectly, for their energy. Some consumers use plants for energy, some consumers use animals for energy, and some use both for energy. Ask students which group they fit into.

## Explore Visually

Have students study Figure 24.5, then ask the following questions:

► Where does all the chemical energy in the figure come from? (Plants)

► Where does the electrical energy produced by a power plant come from? (Burning fossil fuels)

► How can solar energy from the sun be used in a home? (Solar cells on a roof can generate electricity or warm the home.)

## Energy Source for Life

All organisms need a constant supply of energy to fuel the chemical reactions in their cells. You get your energy from the food you eat. But where did the energy in the food come from? Its original source was the sun. Plants are the link in this flow of energy between the sun and you.

Plants use light energy from the sun to power a chemical reaction that produces glucose from water and carbon dioxide in the air. Recall that this process is called photosynthesis. Through photosynthesis, the sun's light energy is converted to chemical energy stored in the chemical bonds of glucose. Plants use the glucose and its stored energy to grow and produce new plant material.

When an animal eats a plant, the solar energy stored in the plant's cells transfers to the animal's body. The animal's body uses the energy to live and grow. When an animal eats another animal, solar energy originally captured by a plant enters its body, too.

Sunlight is also the source of the oil and coal that people burn for energy. Oil and coal formed millions of years ago from fossil plants. The energy in oil and coal, therefore, all came originally from the sun.

**Figure 24.4** ▲
Photosynthesis occurs in the cells of leaves.

**Figure 24.5**
The sun is the original source of most energy used on Earth. ▼

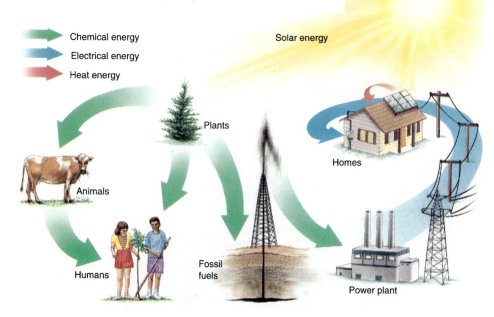

Chemical energy
Electrical energy
Heat energy

Solar energy

Plants

Animals

Humans

Fossil fuels

Homes

Power plant

## TEACH ▪ Continued

### Skills WorkOut

To help students infer, have them do the Skills WorkOut.

**Answer** Answers will vary, but most students would say their body rhythms and sleep-wake cycles would change because they would not know when it was night or day.

## EVALUATE

### WrapUp

**Portfolio** Ask each student to draw and label the sun's layers. Also have them draw and label a sunspot, a prominence, and a solar flare. Have students place their drawings in their portfolios.

Use Review Worksheet 24.1.

### Check and Explain

1. In nuclear fusion, hydrogen nuclei fuse to create helium nuclei.

2. The photosphere is a thin layer that has sunspots. The chromosphere is made up of reddish streams of hydrogen gas. The corona varies in thickness from 7 000 000 to 70 000 000 km.

3. These phenomena all involve powerful magnetic fields. Thus, one kind of change in the sun may produce all three types of activity at the same time.

4. Models will vary, but students should use Table 24.1 and page 560 to focus on the core, radiation zone, and convection zone.

### Writing Connection

Have students write stories about what would happen if the sun were to disappear. Student volunteers may want to share their stories with the class.

### Integrating the Sciences

**Life Science** Many behaviors in birds, such as mating, nest-building, and migration, are triggered by variations in the duration of sunlight. Longer periods of sunlight in spring cause the onset of mating behaviors. The shorter duration of sunlight in fall cause migratory birds to become restless. Ask students how other organisms change as a result of variations in the duration of sunlight. (An example is tree leaves changing color.)

## ▼ ACTIVITY

### Inferring

#### Deep Sleep

What do you think would happen to your daily cycle if you lived for a week deep in a cave or under the ocean in a submarine? Would you be able to tell day from night? Would you want to go to bed at the same time as usual? Explain.

**SKILLS WORKOUT**

### Science and You
#### Sunlight and Body Rhythms

How does light affect the way plants grow? If you watch flowers, you may notice that some of them open when the sunlight has a certain brightness and close when the light begins to fade. Many animals also respond to light. They are active at dawn and rest at night. But did you know that sunlight also affects *your* body?

Your body has an internal clock that keeps your systems working according to a certain rhythm. Your body is used to a cycle of 8 hours of sleep and 16 hours of being awake. Sunlight helps your body set its clock to keep you in step with its cycle.

People who travel often experience jet lag if they cross time zones when flying. Jet lag causes them to feel tired, yet unable to sleep well. Jet lag especially affects people when they travel eastward. The reason is that the journey subtracts hours of daylight and upsets their biological clock.

Do you notice a difference between the way you usually feel in the winter and the way you usually feel in the summer? If so, it may be due to winter's shorter days. About 6 percent of the adults who live where winter days are very short are especially affected by shorter days. They suffer from an illness known as seasonal affective disorder, or SAD. In winter, these people are often depressed and tired because they receive too little daylight. Physicians treat the disorder by exposing their patients to bright lights. They quickly feel normal in spite of the shorter winter days.

### Check and Explain

1. How does the sun produce energy?

2. Name the three layers of the sun's atmosphere and one distinguishing characteristic of each layer.

3. **Reason and Conclude** Why might astronomers find sunspots, solar flares, and prominences at the same time on the sun?

4. **Make a Model** Use different materials to make a model of the sun's interior and the processes occurring in the interior.

### Prelab Discussion

Have students read the entire activity. Discuss a few points before beginning:

▶ Discuss the importance of the direction the sundial points.

▶ Discuss the importance of calibrating scientific instruments. You might use the balance scale as an example.

**Time** 40 minutes

**Group** individuals

**Materials**

cardboard, 4 m²

tape

scissors

30 protractors

30 directional compasses

## Activity 24 *How can you use the sun to tell time?*

**Skills** Measure; Observe; Infer; Interpret Data

**Task 1 Prelab Prep**

1. Collect the following items: cardboard, tape, scissors, protractor, directional compass.
2. Look up the latitude of where you live.

**Task 2 Data Record**

1. Copy Table 24.2 on a separate sheet of paper, leaving more space than is shown.
2. Use the table to record the times you check your sundial and your observations.

**Table 24.2 Sundial Observations**

| Date | Time | Observations |
| --- | --- | --- |
|  |  |  |
|  |  |  |
|  |  |  |
|  |  |  |
|  |  |  |

North

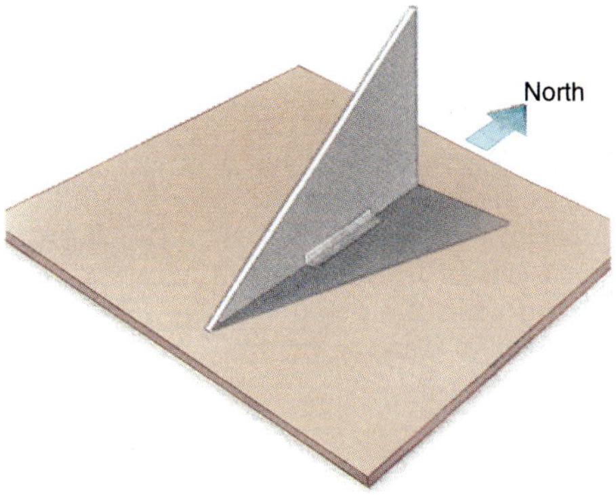

**Figure 24.6** ▲

5. Check the shadow on the sundial at various times during the day. If possible, do it every hour on the hour. Each time you check the shadow, use a pencil to mark the leading edge of the shadow with a line, and label the line with the time.
6. Repeat this procedure for a few days.

**Task 4 Analysis**

1. **Observe** Did the shadow fall at the same place at the same time each day?
2. Once you have labeled your sundial with all the hours, how accurate would it be for telling time?
3. Why do you have to make certain that the gnomon is always pointing north when you make your readings?
4. What does your sundial tell you about how Earth moves?

**Task 5 Conclusion**

Write a short paragraph explaining how your sundial works.

### Everyday Application

If you take your sundial with you on vacation to another part of the country, will you have to make any adjustments? Explain.

**Task 3 Procedure**

1. Cut out a square piece of cardboard about 30 cm on each side.
2. Make a cardboard triangle with a base 15.25 cm long. The angle at one end of the base should be 90°. The angle at the other end should be the same number of degrees as the latitude of the place where you live. The triangle is the *gnomon* (NOH mahn) of your sundial—the part that will cast a shadow.
3. Mount the gnomon on the cardboard with two strips of tape, as shown in Figure 24.6. Make sure the gnomon is vertical.
4. Take the sundial outdoors. Find a place where it won't be disturbed. Use a compass to find north. Position the sundial so the gnomon points north.

## Analysis

1. The shadow should fall at the same point each day.
2. Student answers may vary. The sundial would be as accurate as the marks made. The sharpness of the shadow also affects accuracy.
3. The gnomon needs to point in the same direction it as it did when the sundial was first marked (calibrated). North is convenient because at noon, the sun will be straight overhead, and the shadow will probably be easiest to read over more of the day.
4. It indicates that Earth rotates at a constant rate in an easterly direction (counterclockwise when viewed from above the north pole).

## Conclusion

Accept all logical conclusions. The sundial takes advantage of the fact that Earth rotates at a constant rate. This means that shadows cast by the sun will point the same direction at the same time each day. By marking the hours on the cardboard, one can tell the time by the position of the shadow of the gnomon.

## Everyday Application

The sundial will need to be calibrated again because the relative position of geographic north will have changed. The sundial will also need to agree with the local time zone.

## Integrating the Sciences

**Physical Science**  The formation of the gases that make up the solar system is part of what is called the "big bang theory" for the origin of the universe. This theory states that all the matter in the universe was condensed into one clump. The mass reached tremendous temperatures and exploded to release all of the gases that later formed the stars and the planets. Tell students they will read more about the universe's origins in Chapter 25.

## Themes in Science

**Diversity and Unity**  Each of the structures in the solar system has unique features. However, each of the structures also has common characteristics. All of the solar system bodies have a similar shape. Also, all of the bodies in the solar system and the features on each of the structures were created from the original gas and dust that produced the sun.

### Section Objectives
For a list of section objectives, see the Student Edition page.

### Skills Objectives
Students should be able to:

**Communicate** plans to explore Mars.

**Make a Model** showing the scale of the solar system.

**Make a Model** of planetary rotation and revolution.

---

## MOTIVATE

### Skills WarmUp

To help students understand planets within the solar system, have them do the Skills WarmUp.

**Answer**  Plans should take into account not only conditions on Mars, but also the duration of the trip and the need to record data.

### Misconceptions

Students who have had planets pointed out to them in the night sky may think that planets are luminous like the sun. Explain the difference between an object that is visible because it makes its own light (such as the sun) and an object that you can see only because it reflects light (such as a planet). Brainstorm a list of objects that are luminous and a list of objects that are reflective.

### Answer to In-Text Question
① **Saturn**

---

▼ **ACTIVITY**

**Communicating**

*Travel Arrangements*

What would you need to take along if you were going to explore the surface of Mars? Write a description of your spaceship and equipment, based on what you know about Mars.

**SKILLS WARMUP**

---

# 24.2 Planets in the Solar System
## Objectives

▶ **Describe** the theory of the formation of the solar system.

▶ **Explain** how the planets move around the sun.

▶ **Compare** and **contrast** the inner and the outer planets.

▶ **Hypothesize** which of the planets besides Earth could possibly have living things.

---

Imagine you are selected as part of the first team of astronauts to explore the entire solar system. How long will it take? How far will you go? You realize that the trip is not a pleasure cruise. For most of the trip, you will be stuck in your cramped spacecraft. But you will see things that no other human being has ever experienced directly.

## Formation of the Solar System

Before you leave on your journey, you may want to learn more about how the solar system came into being. This knowledge will help you better understand your observations. According to the theory most widely accepted today, the solar system began as a large swirling sphere of gas and dust. This gas and dust cloud was similar to distant nebulae (NEHB yuh LEE) that can be observed from Earth today. The particles making up the cloud slowly pulled themselves together because of gravitational attraction. The smaller and denser the cloud became, the faster it rotated. The matter gradually flattened out, forming a disk. Ninety-five percent of the matter accumulated at the center of the disk. This large mass of matter grew denser and became a primitive sun, or protosun. Some matter became concentrated in various parts of the disk, away from the protosun. Each of these clumps of matter grew by pulling neighboring matter into itself. In time, each spinning mass gave rise to a protoplanet.

**Figure 24.7** ▲
This object may be the most recognizable planet in the solar system. Do you know its name? ①

**Evolution** The universe has changed throughout its history. Gases clumped together to form stars and planets. The stars and planets evolved to form solar systems. The stars and the planets have continued to evolve. Over time, living things evolved on Earth. Students may be curious about the geologic history of the other planets and their satellites. You might want to mention that at one time, Mars probably had active volcanoes, for example.

### Research

Tell students that only one theory about the origin of the solar system is presented. Have them use references to find out about other theories. Have students draw diagrams to illustrate different theories. You may wish to put some of these drawings on the bulletin board.

### Critical Thinking

**Generalize** Have students think about the entire universe. Ask: If scientists observe stars that die and the possible beginnings of new stars, what can be said about the universe as a whole? (It is constantly changing.)

### Skills Development

**Infer** Tell students that nine planets are known, but that evidence suggests there might be a tenth. Ask: Is there any reason to believe there were only ten protoplanets? Why or why not? (No; perhaps some protoplanets joined together or perhaps some broke up.)

The young sun continued to shrink and grow warmer. About 5 billion years ago, the sun became hot enough for nuclear fusion to begin inside it. It then started radiating great amounts of heat and light. This energy heated the protoplanets and swept away all the matter between them.

As each protoplanet rotated, it changed from a sphere to a disk. The center of each disk grew denser and then spherical. Just as the protosun became a star, each protoplanet became a planet. Matter circling the protoplanets became moons.

Astronomers recently observed how the stage may have been set for the collapse of the cloud of dust and gas that began the formation of the solar system. They observed a huge, faraway bubble of extremely hot gas, produced by the kind of explosion that occurs when a very large star dies. The shock wave from the explosion seems to have triggered the collapse of various clouds of dust and gas in the area. One star dies, and new ones are born. Astronomers hypothesize that the solar system began in this way. Think of it: The matter in your body may once have been part of a star.

◀ **Figure 24.8**
The solar system began as a contracting cloud of dust and gas (top). As the cloud rotated, matter collected in the center and in outlying clumps (middle). The protosun gradually changed into the sun (bottom).

TEACH ▪ Continued

## Explore Visually

Have students study
Figure 24.9 and read the material
on each planet. Ask:

▶ What planets are in the solar
system? (Mercury, Venus, Earth,
Mars, Jupiter, Saturn, Uranus,
Neptune, and Pluto)

▶ Where is the planet Mercury,
and what is it like? (Mercury is
closest to the sun. It looks like
Earth's moon and has no atmosphere.)

▶ How is Venus like Earth, and
how is it different? (It has similar
size, mass, and density, but its
dense, carbon dioxide atmosphere keeps the surface temperature near 480°C.)

▶ How does Earth differ from all
the other planets? (It is the only
planet that supports life, as far
as scientists know.)

▶ How is Mars different from
Earth? (It is much colder and
has two moons instead of one.)

## Integrated Learning

Use Integrating Worksheet 24.2a.

**The Living Textbook:
Earth Science Sides 3-4**

Chapter 13        Frame 10473
Mercury Data (17 Frames)
Search:              Step:

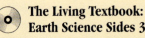

**The Living Textbook:
Earth Science Sides 3-4**

Chapter 14        Frame 10762
Venus Data (10 Frames)
Search:              Step:

## Integrating the Sciences

**Chemistry** Have students use references to find out the ten principle elements that make up humans, rocks, and
stars. Have them infer from the information what elements are responsible for
making humans, rocks, and stars different
and why most of the elements are
the same.

## Planets

The solar system includes nine planets. On your
journey, you will visit each one and observe its size, and
unique features. Each planet in Figure 24.9 is drawn to
scale. The relative sizes of the planets and sun are accurate, but the distances between them are not.

**Figure 24.9
The Solar System**

**Venus**
Venus could be Earth's
twin in size, mass, and
density. But in other ways,
Venus is very different
from Earth. Its dense
atmosphere of carbon
dioxide keeps the surface
temperature around 480°C
both day and night.

**Mercury**
The rocky surface of
Mercury is heavily
cratered, and looks much
like Earth's moon. This
planet lacks an atmos-
phere. The surface facing
the sun gets hot enough
to melt lead.

**Earth**
As far as scientists know,
Earth is the only planet
that supports living things.
It is a living planet because
it has liquid water, oxygen
in the atmosphere, and
moderate air temperatures
and pressure.

**Mars**
The fourth planet from the
sun is much colder than
Earth. But at the Martian
equator in summer, it can
reach 20°C. At one time,
Mars probably had water
on its surface. The planet
has two moons, Phobos
and Deimos.

### Math Connection

Have students make a model to scale for each planet and the sun. Have them draw circles based on the diameter for each body in the solar system. First have students convert the diameter measurement to thousands of kilometers or $10^3$ km. The equatorial diameters are Mercury—4,880 km, Venus—12,106 km, Earth—12,755 km, Mars—6,790 km, Jupiter—142,800 km, Saturn—120,020 km, Uranus—50,900 km, Neptune—48,600 km, Pluto—2,400 km, and the sun—1,392,000 km. Ask students: How many Earths could fit across the middle of Jupiter? (11) How many Jupiters could fit across the middle of the sun? (About 10) Interested students may wish to calculate volume for the planets and the sun. The formula for the volume of a sphere is: $Volume = (4 \times \pi \times r^3) \div 3$.

▶ How much more mass does Jupiter have than the earth? (300 times)

▶ What does Jupiter look like? (It has clouds in bands, a ring, and many moons.)

▶ How does Saturn compare to Jupiter? (Saturn has only one-third the mass. Both planets are mostly hydrogen and helium gas. Saturn has more rings and moons.)

▶ Why does Uranus look green? (Because of methane gas in its atmosphere)

▶ What forms the atmosphere of Neptune? (Hydrogen, helium, and methane)

▶ How is Pluto different from all other planets? (Its orbit is very elongated and tilted. Its moon is half the size of the planet.)

▶ **Observe** What do the four largest planets have in common? (Rings)

**Saturn**
Saturn is nearly as large as Jupiter but has only one third Jupiter's mass. Like Jupiter, it is made up mostly of hydrogen and helium gas. Saturn has a spectacular ring system and 23 or more moons.

**Neptune**
The eighth planet from the sun, Neptune, is similar to Uranus. It is a ball of water, ammonia, and molten rock, surrounded by hydrogen, helium, and methane. It has 8 moons and a number of rings.

**Pluto**
The ninth planet is not like the other outer planets. It is even smaller than Mercury in size. Its orbit is very elongated and tilted. Pluto has one moon, Charon, that is nearly half the size of the planet itself.

**Jupiter**
Jupiter is a giant, with 300 times more mass than Earth. It is mostly a ball of hydrogen and helium gas. Clouds in Jupiter's atmosphere form colored bands around the planet. Jupiter has at least 16 moons.

**Uranus**
Beyond Saturn is Uranus, the third-largest planet. It appears greenish because of methane gas in its atmosphere. Uranus is unusual because its axis of rotation is nearly parallel to the plane of its orbit. Uranus has 15 moons and a system of rings.

570

## TEACH ▪ *Continued*

### Critical Thinking

**Compare and Contrast**  Have students compare the inner and outer planets. Ask: Besides size, rings, and the number of moons, how do these groups differ? (The outer planets are mostly gas and the inner planets have a liquid core, a rocky mantle, and a crust.)

### Enrich

In 1989, the *Voyager 2* spacecraft verified what astronomers suspected: Neptune has a ring. Rings have now been discovered and verified for each of the gaseous planets.

### Ancillary Options

If you are using the blackline masters from *Multiculturalism in Mathematics, Science, and Technology,* have students read about Benjamin Banneker and complete pages 26 to 30.

### Answer to In-Text Question

① **Mars is smaller than Earth, but has the tallest mountain and the deepest canyon in the solar system. It is colder and does not have oxygen in its atmosphere.**

---

### *Social Studies Connection*

When viewed through a telescope from Earth, Mars appears to have a network of canals. In the early 1900s, Percival Lowell proposed a hypothesis that the canals were constructed by a race of intelligent beings, or Martians. Martians became the subject of many books, comics, movies, and television and radio shows. In 1938, actor/director Orson Wells presented a radio show that staged a Martian invasion of Earth. Many listeners tuned in and thought they were hearing a news broadcast, and panicked. Obtain an audiotape of the program for students.

---

## Inner Planets

As you have seen, the four innermost planets have many common features and all are very different from the next four planets. For this reason, they are often grouped together and called the inner planets.

As the inner planets formed, the heat of the sun boiled off the lighter elements that surrounded them. Each inner planet was left with a liquid core made of nickel and iron and a rocky mantle and crust. Another common feature of these planets is that they have few or no moons.

But each inner planet is also unique. The surface of Mercury is extremely hot during the day and frozen at night. Venus rotates on its axis in the opposite direction of the other planets. Earth is the only planet with oxygen in its atmosphere because many organisms, such as plants, produce oxygen as a waste product. Mars has the solar system's tallest mountain and its deepest canyon.

**Figure 24.10** ▲
How does Mars differ from Earth? ①

**Figure 24.11** ▲
Gaseous Jupiter is a typical outer planet.

## Outer Planets

The five planets farthest from the sun—Jupiter, Saturn, Uranus, Neptune, and Pluto—are called the outer planets. The first four are also known as Jovian planets because they share so many characteristics with Jupiter.

The Jovian planets are all mostly gas, with relatively small solid or liquid centers. When these planets formed, they were too far from the sun for its heat to drive off lighter elements. As a result, they remain large and mostly gaseous.

All the Jovian planets have numerous moons. And, unlike the inner planets, the Jovian planets have rings. Scientists think the rings were created when asteroids or meteors slammed into moons of these planets and smashed them to bits.

Pluto is very different from any of the Jovian planets. It is, however, similar to the large moons of these planets. Scientists hypothesize that Pluto may once have been a moon of Neptune. The gravity from a passing object may have pulled it far enough away from Neptune to form its own orbit around the sun.

## Math Connection

Light travels at a speed of 300 thousand km/s. Have students calculate how long it takes sunlight to reach each planet. Have them round their answers to the nearest minute. The mean distance for each planet from the sun in millions of kilometers is Mercury—57.9, Venus—108.2, Earth—149.7, Mars—228.1, Jupiter—778.7, Saturn—1,427.7, Uranus—2,897.5, Neptune—4,498.8, and Pluto—5,902.8. (Mercury—3 min; Venus—6 min; Earth—8 min; Mars—13 min; Jupiter—43 min; Saturn—1 h 19 min; Uranus—2 h 40 min; Neptune—4 h 10 min; Pluto—5 h 28 min)

## Moons of the Outer Planets

Orbiting the Jovian planets are more than 40 moons, or satellites. Unlike the planets they orbit, these moons are solid. Some are made of rock, some of ice, and others a combination of rock and ice. Six of these moons are about as large as, or larger than, Earth's moon. Each could be a planet on its own.

Jupiter has four large moons: Ganymede, Callisto, Io, and Europa. Ganymede is the largest moon in the solar system. It is even larger than Mercury. Io has active volcanoes. The large moons of Jupiter are good landing sites for your spacecraft, since Jupiter itself has no solid surface.

Saturn has the most moons of any planet, but only one—Titan—is larger than Earth's moon. Titan has its own atmosphere. The solar system's sixth large moon is Triton, in orbit around Neptune.

**Figure 24.12** ▲
The colorful materials on Io's surface are sulfur-containing compounds spewed out by volcanoes.

## SkillBuilder  *Making a Model*

### A Solar System Model

How big is the solar system? Figure 24.9 shows the relative sizes of the planets but not their relative distances from the sun.

Look at the table at the right. It shows the distance between each planet and the sun in astronomical units, or A.U. One A.U. is the average distance from Earth to the sun. Copy the table on a separate sheet of paper. Fill in the blank column of the table by simply rounding off the A.U. measurement for each planet.

Now draw a line 39.5 cm long. This line represents the distance between the sun and Pluto. Place the other planets on this line according to this scale. Draw each planet as a dot and label it.

1. Why do you think each planet is shown only as a dot?
2. What happens to the distance between planets as they get farther from the sun?

Write a paragraph on what you learned about the solar system by making this model.

| Planet | Distance from Sun (AU) | Distance in Your Model (cm) |
|---|---|---|
| Mercury | 0.39 | |
| Venus | 0.72 | |
| Earth | 1.0 | |
| Mars | 1.5 | |
| Jupiter | 5.2 | |
| Saturn | 9.5 | |
| Uranus | 19.2 | |
| Neptune | 30.0 | |
| Pluto | 39.5 | |

## Class Activity

Have students compare the sizes of large moons and Mercury by having them use compasses to draw circles 15.5 cm in diameter. This circle represents Ganymede, the largest moon. Have students use the same center point to draw a circle 14.5 cm in diameter. This circle represents Mercury. Then have students draw circles with diameters of 14 cm for Callisto and Titan, 12 cm for Triton, 11 cm for Earth's moon, 10 cm for Io, and 9 cm for Europa.

## SkillBuilder

### Answers

1. The scale is much too small to show size differences. The inner planets are very close together on this scale: Mercury and Venus are only 0.3 cm apart.

2. It increases.

Paragraphs should mention that the outer planets are very far apart.

## Integrated Learning

Use Integrating Worksheet 24.2b.

## Skills WorkOut

To help students make a model, have them do the Skills WorkOut. **Answer** Be sure students try to rotate and revolve smoothly.

## Discuss

Remind students that an ellipse is a regular oval shape, and that some ellipses are close to being circles but others are very elongated. Ask students to compare a planet's orbit to the moon's orbit around Earth. Ask: How might gravity keep a moon or planet in orbit?

## Research

Have students use references to find out more about Kepler's works. Ask them to find out what Kepler discovered about the orbit of the inner compared to the outer planets. (Planets closer to the sun take less time to orbit it.)

## Enrich

Use Enrich Worksheet 24.2.

### Themes in Science

**Stability and Equilibrium** The planets follow regular elliptical orbits around the sun. These orbits are stable and predictable. The movement of the planets around the sun occurs in a state of equilibrium due to the gravitational attraction between the sun and each planet.

### History Connection

In the 1800s, astronomers noticed that the orbit of Uranus had perturbations. John Couch Adams and Urbain Leverrier determined independently from each other that the fluctuations in Uranus' course were due to the gravitational attraction of another planet. Both astronomers calculated the location of Neptune. In 1846, Leverrier sent his calculations to the Berlin Observatory and on September 23, Neptune was observed by telescope.

### ▼ ACTIVITY

#### Making a Model

*Planet Motions*

Use two balls of different sizes to represent the sun and a planet. Demonstrate the rotation of the planet in combination with its revolution.

#### SKILLS WORKOUT

**Figure 24.13**
Each planet follows an elliptical path in its orbit around the sun. Except for Pluto, all the planets have orbits that lie in roughly the same plane. ▼

## Movement of the Planets

Like Earth, all the planets have two kinds of motion: revolution and rotation. Recall that a planet revolves in an orbit around the sun. A model of the solar system based on the planets orbiting the sun is called a *heliocentric*, or sun-centered, model.

Five-hundred years ago, scientists were convinced that Earth, not the sun, was the center of the solar system. Then, in 1543, Nicolaus Copernicus shocked the world by proposing that Earth and the other planets revolve around the sun.

When scientists finally accepted Copernicus's theory, they assumed the planets orbited in perfect circles around the sun. Then, in the early 1600s, Johannes Kepler discovered that the planets have *elliptical* orbits. Kepler also showed that the sun is not in the center of a planet's elliptical orbit, but off to one side at one of the focal points of the ellipse.

**Gravity and Inertia** Although Kepler described how the planets move, he did not explain why they move as they do. Isaac Newton showed that the planets do not fly off into space because of the gravitational attraction between the sun and each planet. This attracting force exists between objects because of their mass. The greater the mass, the greater the attraction of gravity.

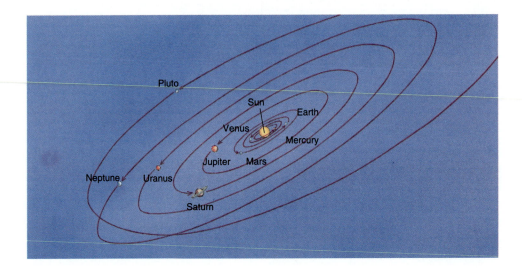

## Integrating the Sciences

Newton also explained why planets keep moving in orbit around the sun. He found that an object's motion will not change in speed or direction unless it is acted on by an outside force. This law explains the property known as *inertia*. The dust cloud that became the solar system had inertia of motion because of its rotation. That inertia has kept the planets moving in orbit around the sun ever since. Look at Figure 24.14. You can see that a planet's orbit is the result of the combined forces of gravity and inertia.

The amount of time it takes for a planet to complete one revolution is called its *period of revolution*. A planet's period of revolution is equal to one year on that planet. Look at Table 24.3, which lists the periods of all the planets. You know that Earth has a period of revolution, or year, of just over 365 days. How long is a year on Pluto? ① Notice how the periods of revolution vary. What pattern do you detect in their variation? ②

**Rotation**  The planets' speeds of rotation vary, too. One rotation around a planet's axis is equal to one day on that planet. Look again at Table 24.3. How long is a day ③ on Venus? Which planet has a day about the same ④ length as an Earth day? Notice that the planets' periods of rotation do not have any noticeable pattern.

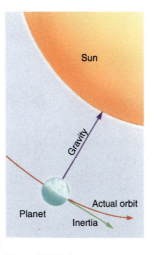

**Figure 24.14** ▲
What would happen to the orbit of a planet without the force of the sun's gravitational attraction? What would happen to it ⑤ without the force of inertia? ⑥

**Table 24.3   Periods of Revolution and Rotation**

| Planet | Period of Rotation (Earth time) | Period of Revolution (Earth time) |
|---|---|---|
| Mercury | 59 days | 88 days |
| Venus | 243 days | 224.7 days |
| Earth | 24 hours | 365 days |
| Mars | 24.5 hours | 687 days |
| Jupiter | 9.9 hours | 11.9 years |
| Saturn | 10.2 hours | 29.5 years |
| Uranus | 17 hours | 84 years |
| Neptune | 16 hours | 164.8 years |
| Pluto | 6.4 days | 247.7 years |

**TEACH** ▪ *Continued*

## Skills Development

**Collect Data** Have half the class collect articles about how the Magellan space probe sends images of Venus to Earth. Have the other half collect articles about how the Mars Observer was meant to send images. Ask each group to organize its data into a report.

## EVALUATE

### WrapUp

**Reteach** As students think about the solar system, ask:

▶ Why are the inner planets less gaseous than the outer planets? (The heat of the sun boiled off the lighter elements.)

▶ How does a planet's revolution differ from its rotation? (Revolution is the planet's orbit around the sun, and rotation is the planet's turn on its axis.)

Use Review Worksheet 24.2.

### Check and Explain

1. As a contracting, rotating cloud of gas and dust

2. The sun's gravity and the planets' inertia

3. The inner planets are small and have liquid cores, rocky mantles and crusts, and few or no moons. The outer planets are large, mostly gas, and have rings and many moons.

4. Mars has the best chance because the Martian equator can reach 20°C.

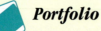

### Portfolio

Have each student make a drawing of a landing probe for exploring Venus or Mars. Tell students to include an exterior and an interior view of the probe. Each student should also include the various scientific instruments the probe would carry and how it would communicate information back to Earth. Student volunteers may want to make actual models and share their probes with the class. Students can keep their designs in their portfolios.

**Figure 24.15** ▲
The terrain of Mars is rough and rocky, as shown in this photograph from Viking 1 (top). The experimental rover has six wheels and two camera "eyes."

### Science and Technology
*Exploring Mars and Venus*

Even though people have yet to set foot on Mars or Venus, scientists know a great deal about our nearest neighbors in the solar system. In 1962, the space probe Mariner 2 flew by Venus, sending back data to Earth. Mariner 4 completed a flyby of Mars in 1964. In 1971, the Soviet Union's Mars 3 landed on Mars, sending back the first images of the planet's surface. In 1976, two orbiter-landers from the United States—Viking 1 and 2 —landed on Mars and carried out experiments.

Scientists are now designing rovers that will explore the surface of Mars. The rovers will be controlled by on-board computers. Rovers on the moon can be controlled by engineers on Earth because signals travel back and forth between the moon and Earth in only 2.6 seconds. However, signals would take up to 40 minutes to make the round trip between Earth and Mars. Imagine what could happen if a Mars rover were left without guidance for 40 minutes!

The computer on the rover has to be programmed to keep the rover from driving off a cliff. And the rover itself must be able to move over boulders. One design for a rover is a wheelwalker that can step up and down, as well as roll forward and backward. The wheelwalker changes its shape and motion to adapt to the terrain.

A different method of exploration is already being used to study Venus. Since September 1990, the Magellan space probe has imaged the surface of our closest neighbor with radar. Global maps of Venus are created from these images. The maps show a rugged surface marked by volcanoes, some craters, and winding channels.

### Check and Explain

1. How did the solar system probably begin?

2. What forces control the movement of the planets around the sun?

3. **Compare and Contrast** Explain the main differences between the inner planets and the outer planets.

4. **Hypothesize** State a hypothesis that explains what planet besides Earth could best support life.

574

## Integrating the Sciences

**Environmental Science** Many different types of satellites have been launched into space. Some of the objects in solar orbit are not natural. For example, when satellites no longer function, they are often simply left floating in space. Some people refer to this defunct space equipment as space garbage. Discuss with students how space garbage could affect the rest of the solar system and how space garbage could be recovered or avoided altogether.

# 24.3 Asteroids, Meteoroids, and Comets

## Objectives

▶ **Locate** the asteroid belt.

▶ **Compare** meteoroids, meteors, and meteorites.

▶ **Describe** the orbits of the comets.

▶ **Predict** how a comet will change over time.

---

▼ **ACTIVITY**

**Communicating**

*Meteors*

With your classmates, share descriptions of shooting stars that you have seen. What do your observations have in common?

**SKILLS WARMUP**

The solar system is full of objects orbiting the sun that are neither planets nor moons. You couldn't travel through the solar system without observing some of them. In fact, you would have to be very careful not to let one of the larger ones crash into your spacecraft. These objects range in size from microscopic bits of ice to moon-sized masses of rock.

## Asteroids

The larger objects you might see on a trip through the solar system are like small planets. As many as 100,000 of these small, irregularly shaped, solid bodies, called **asteroids** (AS tuh ROYDZ), revolve around the sun. All the asteroids move around the sun in the same direction as the planets do. The brightest asteroid, Vesta, is seen without a telescope.

**Asteroid Belt** Most asteroids exist between the orbits of Mars and Jupiter in an area known as the *asteroid belt*. Some scientists hypothesize that the asteroid belt formed when a planet was prevented from forming by the gravitational force of Jupiter. Scientists also think that some of the larger asteroids may have been ejected from the asteroid belt and are currently scattered throughout the solar system.

**Other Asteroids** Some asteroids have orbits that cross the orbit of Mars. Others, called the Apollo asteroids, cross Earth's orbit. The largest Apollo asteroid, called Icarus, has passed within 1 million km of Earth—about twice the distance to the moon.

**Figure 24.16**
Unlike planets, asteroids have irregular shapes. This is the asteroid Gaspra. ▼

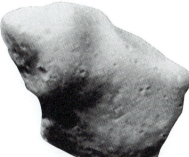

**Section Objectives**
For a list of section objectives, see the Student Edition page.

**Skills Objectives**
Students should be able to:

**Communicate** observations of meteors.

**Infer** whether a comet could collide with the earth.

**Vocabulary**
asteroid, comet, meteor, meteorite, meteoroid

## MOTIVATE

### Skills WarmUp

To help students understand objects in the solar system besides the sun and planets, have them do the Skills WarmUp.

**Answer** Students describing meteor sightings will probably tell of sudden, bright, brief, soundless, relatively minute trails of light against a dark night sky.

### Misconceptions

Students may think that planets are the only bodies in the solar system that revolve around the sun, and that moons are the only objects that orbit planets. Explain that all the mass in the solar system was created at about the same time, so the motion of asteroids, comets, and meteoroids is related to the motion of the sun and planets.

## TEACH

### Research

Have students find out how Ceres, the largest asteroid, was discovered and where it is in the solar system. (By accident; between Mars and Jupiter)

## Career Corner

**Reason and Conclude** Ask students: When a spacecraft is to be built, who are the first aerospace workers to be involved? Why? (Aerospace scientists and engineers design a new spacecraft based on what they want it to do.) How might the quality of a spacecraft be improved if it malfunctions? (Answers will vary; if it cannot be recovered for study, sensors on board the spacecraft might tell engineers what devices are not working properly. Prelaunch testing and inspecting could correct malfunctions.)

**Answer to In-Text Question**

① **Between Mars and Jupiter**

### Themes in Science

**Scale and Structure** Rock pieces that orbit the sun may have come from asteroids that collided. Although the scale of the asteroids obviously changed after they collided, the general rock structure remains the same. Also the smaller rocks follow the same laws of motion that the larger asteroids did.

### Language Arts Connection

Have students look up the Greek origin of the prefixes *astr-* and *astro-*. Have them apply the meaning of the prefixes to explain words such as astronomy, astronaut, and asteroid. (Both prefixes mean "star.")

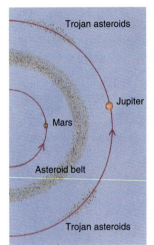

**Figure 24.17** ▲
Where are most asteroids? ①

Two groups of asteroids follow the same orbit as Jupiter. They are called the Trojan asteroids. One group of Trojan asteroids travels ahead of Jupiter, the other trails behind. Still other asteroids are outside the orbit of Jupiter. Over time, the orbits of some asteroids change because of the gravitational pull of Jupiter and the other large planets.

Over 2,000 asteroids measuring at least 1 km in diameter, cross Earth's orbit at times. Every million years or so, an asteroid collides with Earth. Many scientists hypothesize that an asteroid collision 65 million years ago sent up a cloud of dust into the atmosphere that cut off sunlight for a long time. Many plant and animal species on the planet died at that time, including dinosaurs. A small asteroid coming close to Earth would just burn up in the atmosphere. A large asteroid more than 1 km in diameter, however, could have disastrous effects if it struck Earth.

## Career Corner *Aerospace Worker*

### Who Builds Spacecraft?

Space shuttles, satellites, and space probes gather valuable information about the solar system and the universe. Aerospace workers design, assemble, and repair these craft and the rocket boosters that launch them into space.

Aerospace employees may work on production lines, in machine shops, with engineering firms, or at space centers. Aerospace engineers design new spacecraft and the many machines that make them up. Inspectors check the quality of the crafts to make sure each machine is complete and safe. The aerospace industry also employs clerical workers, computer technicians, managers, and accountants.

The aerospace industry uses the latest technologies. Workers often specialize in a particular kind of machine. Most aerospace scientists and engineers have advanced college degrees in science or engineering. Aerospace machinists may train as apprentices or learn skills at trade schools. Mechanical drawing and blueprint reading are important skills for aerospace machinists. Almost every aerospace job requires some knowledge of computers.

If you are interested in astronomy and space exploration, consider a career in the aerospace industry. Courses in science, mathematics, and shop will help you prepare for an aerospace career.

## Integrating the Sciences

**Life Science** Geologic evidence suggests that a large meteor may have caused the extinction of the dinosaurs. Scientists hypothesize that a large meteor struck Earth and caused enormous volumes of dust to collect in the atmosphere. The dust would have blocked the sun and a worldwide cooling would have occurred as a result. The cool temperatures and the lack of sunlight for plant growth resulted in the dying off of dinosaurs. Scientists think they may have located the site of the meteor impact on the Atlantic Ocean floor in the Gulf of Mexico.

## Meteoroids

Have you seen a shooting star? This streak of light in the night sky is caused by an object entering Earth's atmosphere and burning up. The object is called a meteoroid (MEE tee uh ROYD). A **meteoroid** is a chunk of rock or metal, smaller than an asteroid, in orbit around the sun.

**Meteors** The light that results from the entry of a large meteoroid into the atmosphere is called a **meteor**, or shooting star. Its glow may last for several seconds. The light is caused by friction between the fast-moving meteor and the atmosphere. A meteor is the luminous gas heated by the meteoroid passing through the atmosphere.

Most meteoroids are so small that they leave no visible trace when they burn up in the atmosphere. But each one leaves a small amount of dust that falls to Earth. So many tiny meteoroids burn up in the atmosphere that thousands of tonnes of meteoroid dust fall to the ground each year.

As Earth moves in its orbit, it periodically crosses the orbit of a stream of meteoroids. The result is a meteor shower. The major meteor showers occur at regular times during the year. The most spectacular ones happen in August and October.

**Figure 24.18** ▲
This iron meteoroid survived its plunge through Earth's atmosphere to become a meteorite. It was sliced in two to show the inside.

### Physical Science
**L I N K**

Review the section on meteors. What physical property causes the meteoroid and the area around it to heat up as it enters Earth's atmosphere?

Design an activity that demonstrates how this property produces heat. Can you connect this property to the presence of extensive cratering on the moon? Explain.

**A C T I V I T Y**

◀ **Figure 24.19**
These meteors were photographed during the Leonid meteor shower, which happens every year in November.

## Critical Thinking

**If . . . Then Arguments** Have students create an If . . . then statement that explains why meteoroids sometimes leave their orbits and enter Earth's atmosphere. (Answers will vary. For example, if a meteoroid crosses Earth's orbit, then Earth's gravity attracts it.)

## Research

Have students use references to find out the names of the meteor showers that occur in August (Perseid) and October (Orionid) and why they are named that way. Also have them find out why these meteor showers occur regularly.

## Enrich

Tell students that most rocky meteoroids consist of silicate minerals, and most metallic meteoroids are of nickel-iron alloy. Some meteorides are both rocky and metallic. Refer students to Chapter 9 for a description of silicate minerals.

### Answer to Link

Friction is the property that generates heat. Student-designed activities should demonstrate how matter heats up when it rubs against other matter. The lack of an atmosphere on the moon means there is no matter to rub against moon-bound meteors, hence no friction. Without friction there is no heat generated to burn up incoming objects, enabling objects to impact without obstruction.

578

## TEACH ▪ *Continued*

### Enrich

Tell students that the meteorite that made the Barringer Crater is estimated to have had a diameter of over 60 m and to have weighed at least 1 million metric tons. When a meteorite this size strikes the ground, heat causes gases to expand explosively. The explosion forms a crater and scatters pieces of the meteorite all over the surrounding area.

### Reteach

Have students return to the solar system model from the SkillBuilder on page 571, or have them trace Figure 24.13. Ask them to add asteroids, meteors, and comets to the model. (Asteroids between Mars and Jupiter; meteoroid placement may vary; comets beyond Pluto)

#### Answers to In-Text Questions

① **Answers will vary, but most students will probably say they'd see a ball of fire and feel the ground tremble.**

② **Gases forced from the comet by solar radiation and solar wind**

## *Multicultural Perspectives*

As early as 4000 B.C., the Chinese were studying astronomy. Chinese astronomers determined the length of the year to be 365 1/4 days, predicted solar and lunar eclipses, recorded constellations that were used in navigation, and determined that the moon takes about 28 days to revolve around Earth. The Chinese also recorded the first known appearance of Halley's comet in 239 B.C.

**Meteorites**  When a meteoroid does not completely burn up in its passage through the atmosphere, it is called a **meteorite** (MEE tee uh RYT). Meteorites, like the one in Figure 24.18, have been found all over Earth's surface. The most common type of meteorite is made up of iron and nickel. Others are stone or a combination of stone and metal. The huge crater in Figure 24.20 was caused by the impact of a large meteorite. The crater is 174 m deep and 1,219 m across. Like other craters, it is a bowl-shaped depression. At least 150 meteorite craters have been found on Earth. What do you think you would see and feel if you watched a large meteorite strike the ground? ①

**Figure 24.20** ▲
The meteorite impact that made the Barringer crater in Arizona probably occurred within the last 20,000 years.

### Comets

An icy object that travels around the sun, usually in a huge elliptical orbit, is called a **comet**. Scientists estimate that there are about 100,000 comets in the solar system. Most comets are far beyond the orbit of Pluto.

When a comet comes close to the sun, heat vaporizes some of its frozen matter. Solar radiation and solar wind force gases from the comet, causing a streaming tail to form. Notice the tail of the comet in Figure 24.21. With each pass close to the sun, a comet loses matter.

Comets may have formed in a ring close to the edge of the flattened disk of the early solar system. One by one, due to the gravitational force of the outer planets, comets changed their orbits. Their new orbits bring them close to the sun.

**Figure 24.21**
What causes the streaming tail of a comet? ▼ ②

**Orbits of Comets** Edmond Halley, an English astronomer, was the first to recognize that comets travel in a fixed orbit around the sun. When he observed a comet in 1682, he found that a similar comet had been seen in 1531 and again in 1607. Halley hypothesized that these sightings were all of the same comet. The comet seemed to reappear every 76 years. This led him to theorize that comets orbit around the sun.

Look at Figure 24.22. It shows the orbits of several comets. Notice how their shapes differ from that of planets. Some comets have orbits that bring them close to the sun a few times in a decade. Others approach the sun only once in thousands of years. In 1973, Comet Kohoutek rounded the sun after a very long time away. Its period of revolution is 75,000 years. Comet West, seen in 1976, has a period of 500,000 years. Some comets are jolted out of orbit by a planet's gravity and sent out of the solar system, never to return.

**Halley's Comet** Halley predicted that the comet he observed in 1682 would reappear in 1758. Although Halley died before that happened, the comet was named after him because of his findings. Halley's Comet last approached the sun in 1986. If you missed that appearance, you'll have to wait until 2061 to see it.

▼ **ACTIVITY**

| Inferring |
| --- |

*Impact*

Is it possible for a comet to collide with Earth? Explain your reasoning.

**SKILLS WORKOUT**

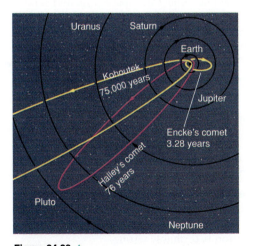

**Figure 24.22** ▲
Comets have very elliptical orbits. Their periods of revolution vary greatly.

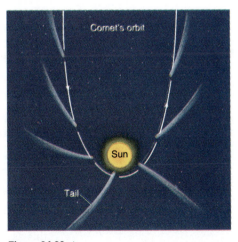

**Figure 24.23** ▲
Why does a comet's tail always point away from the sun? ③

580

## TEACH ▪ Continued

### Critical Thinking

**Predict** Ask students to predict what would happen to the matter from space junk that is burned up in Earth's atmosphere. (Answers will vary; students may say it will become part of or pollute the atmosphere.)

## EVALUATE

### WrapUp

**Reinforce** Have students discuss the similarities and differences among asteroids, meteoroids, and comets. (Similarities include orbits and size relative to planets; differences include composition and appearance from Earth.)

Use Review Worksheet 24.3.

### Check and Explain

1. Between Mars and Jupiter; others cross the orbits of Mars or Earth, follow Jupiter's orbit, or are outside Jupiter's orbit.

2. Meteoroids are chunks of rock or metal that orbit the sun; meteors are the lights that result from the entry of large meteoroids into the atmosphere; meteorites are meteoroids that do not completely burn up in passing through the atmosphere.

3. Most comets are too far away to affect Earth.

4. It will eventually break up or disappear, because some of its frozen matter vaporizes each time it nears the sun.

### Decision Making

If you have classroom sets of *One-Minute Readings*, have students read Issue 63, "Outer Space: Infinite Dump," on page 106. Discuss the questions.

### *Portfolio*

Have students collect newspaper and magazine articles on the solar system and space exploration. For each article, have students write a short summary. You may want to display articles on a bulletin board. Have students keep their summaries in their portfolios.

## Science and Society *Dodging Space Junk*

Whoever said that space is empty? If you examined a spacecraft after it returned from space, you would find craterlike scars on the exterior. These pits are caused by collisions with objects in orbit around Earth, many of them left there by humans.

A fleck of paint the size of a grain of sand would be harmless if it struck your car. But a speck in orbit is flying at orbital speed—about 8,000 m/s, or over 28 000 km/hr. Such speed changes harmless specks into dangerous hurling objects.

More than just flecks of paint orbit Earth. Some of the items are slivers, bolts, screws, and clamps from exploded satellites and rocket bodies. There is even a lost camera from a Gemini flight still in orbit. The Long Duration Exposure Facility (LDEF), recovered by a space-shuttle mission after six years in orbit, was struck at least 5,000 times by small, high-speed objects. The hits caused craters, all of which were very small. However, if an instrument had been struck, it might have been put out of order.

To avoid damage to space shuttles, satellites, and, later, to a space station, experts work on ways to get rid of the debris in space. One plan is to have space garbage-collectors. They would collect the space junk and send it plunging into Earth's atmosphere, where it would burn up. In the meantime, designers plan to "harden" the planned space station against possible collisions.

**Figure 24.24** ▲
This scanning electron micrograph shows a hole in a satellite that was returned to Earth. The hole was caused by impacts with paint flakes.

### Check and Explain

1. Where is the asteroid belt? Where are other asteroids in the solar system located?

2. Explain how meteoroids, meteors, and meteorites are different.

3. **Uncover Assumptions** The appearance of comets has been blamed for many kinds of events on Earth, such as hot weather and lost battles. Explain why this assumption is probably wrong.

4. **Predict** What will eventually happen to a comet after it has made many trips around the sun? Explain.

## Chapter 24 Review

### Concept Summary

**24.1 The Sun**
▶ Nuclear fusion in the sun releases enormous amounts of energy.
▶ The sun is made up of many layers, including the core, the radiation zone, and the convection zone. Its atmosphere consists of three layers: the photosphere, chromosphere, and corona.
▶ Sunspots, prominences, and solar flares occur in the sun's outer layers.
▶ The sun is the original source of energy for nearly all living things on Earth.

**24.2 Planets in the Solar System**
▶ The solar system formed from a swirling cloud of dust and gas.
▶ The four inner planets are rocky planets with metal cores.

▶ Except for Pluto, the five outer planets are large balls of gas with solid or liquid cores and many moons.
▶ The planets revolve around the sun in elliptical orbits, the result of a balance between inertia and gravity.

**24.3 Asteroids, Meteoroids, and Comets**
▶ Asteroids are bodies of rock, too small to be planets, that orbit the sun.
▶ Meteoroids are chunks of rock or metal smaller than asteroids. They become meteors if they enter Earth's atmosphere, and meteorites if they reach the surface.
▶ Comets are icy objects with very huge elliptical orbits that periodically come close to the sun.

### Chapter Vocabulary

| | | |
|---|---|---|
| solar system (24.1) | corona (24.1) | meteor (24.3) |
| photosphere (24.1) | asteroid (24.3) | meteorite (24.3) |
| chromosphere (24.1) | meteoroid (24.3) | comet (24.3) |

### Check Your Vocabulary

Use the vocabulary words above to complete the following sentences correctly.

1. During a solar eclipse, the sun's ____ is visible.
2. Meteor showers occur when Earth passes through the orbit of a swarm of ____.
3. The sun's coolest layer is the ____.
4. Another name for a ____ is a shooting star.
5. Streams of hydrogen gas make up the layer of the sun called the ____.
6. Bodies of rock resembling small planets are called ____.
7. An icy object that develops a tail when it nears the sun is a ____.
8. If a meteor doesn't completely burn up in the atmosphere, it becomes a ____
9. Earth, eight other planets and many smaller objects make up the ____

Explain the difference between the words in each pair.

10. asteroid, satellite
11. photosphere, sunspot
12. comet, meteor

### Write Your Vocabulary

Write sentences using the vocabulary words above. Show that you know what each word means.

### Check Your Vocabulary

1. corona
2. meteoroids
3. photosphere
4. meteor
5. chromosphere
6. asteroids
7. comet
8. meteorite
9. solar system
10. Asteroids are small, irregularly shaped objects that orbit the sun. Satellites are objects that orbit planets.
11. The photosphere is the innermost layer of the sun's atmosphere. A sunspot is a storm that occurs where magnetic fields break through the photosphere and prevent light and heat from escaping.
12. A meteor is a meteoroid that enters the earth's atmosphere and burns up. A comet is an icy object that orbits the sun.

### Write Your Vocabulary

Students' sentences should show that they know the meaning of each word as well as how to use it in a sentence.
   Use Vocabulary Worksheet for Chapter 24.

## Check Your Knowledge

1. Mercury, Venus, Earth, Mars

2. The planets follow elliptical orbits around the sun.

3. Pluto is not like the other outer planets.

4. Prominences look like huge arches and are supported by magnetic fields on the sun. Solar flares are very intense spurts of cosmic rays. Sunspots are magnetic field storms in the photosphere.

5. Plants and some protists are organisms that can convert the sun's energy into chemical energy.

6. The moons of the Jovian planets are made up of rock and/or ice, while the planets themselves are mostly gaseous.

7. Both are a result of magnetic field activity in the sun's outer layers.

8. Planets, asteroids, meteoroids, comets, satellites, the sun

9. core

10. year

11. third

12. Earth

13. Jupiter

## Check Your Understanding

1. The nuclear fusion in the sun releases far more energy than any chemical reaction; it changes elements into different elements, whereas chemical reactions change only the chemical bonds between atoms.

2. All the planets and sun formed from the same rotating cloud of gas and dust.

3. Pluto's orbit crosses that of Neptune.

4. Both the sun and Earth are made up of layers, with the hottest layer in the center.

5. Because Mars is much colder than Earth, any liquid water on Mars probably turned to ice.

6. Venus has a year nearest in length to an Earth year. The length of a day on Mars is very close to a day on Earth.

7. Solar energy travels from the sun to Earth where it is absorbed by plants and turned into chemical energy. The plants die and are buried by sediment. Over millions of years, the buried remains turn into coal. The coal is mined and burned at a power plant, where the chemical energy is turned into heat to change water into steam. The kinetic energy of the steam turns the blades of turbines which turn generators which convert the kinetic energy into electrical energy. The electrical energy travels to the lightbulb filament, where it is converted to light and heat energy.

8. If the spot is not visible, it may be on the side of Jupiter pointing away from Earth.

9. Accept any reasonable answer. It is possible for a comet to collide with Earth, provided the comet's orbit intersects Earth's orbit, and the comet and Earth pass near enough to each other.

10. Jupiter is mostly gaseous, with no solid surface.

---

## Chapter 24 Review

### Check Your Knowledge

Answer the following in complete sentences.

1. List the four inner planets by increasing distance from the sun.

2. What is the shape of a planet's orbit around the sun?

3. Which of the outer planets is not like the others?

4. Name and describe the three kinds of storm activity that occur on the sun.

5. Which organisms on Earth can capture the sun's energy and convert it into chemical energy?

6. How are the moons of the Jovian planets different from the planets themselves?

7. How are sunspots and prominences related?

8. Name five different kinds of objects found in the solar system.

Choose the answer that best completes each sentence.

9. Nuclear fusion occurs in the sun's (core, radiation zone, convection zone, corona).

10. The time it takes a planet to complete a revolution around the sun is equal to a (day, month, season, year) on that planet.

11. Earth is the (first, third, fifth, seventh) planet from the sun.

12. The two planets most similar in size, mass, and density are Venus and (Mercury, Earth, Mars, Neptune).

13. The Trojan asteroids are in the same orbit as (Mars, Jupiter, Uranus, Saturn).

### Check Your Understanding

Apply the concepts you have learned to answer each question.

1. How is the nuclear fusion that takes place in the sun different from a chemical reaction?

2. Why do all the planets revolve around the sun in the same direction?

3. **Infer** Until 1999, Pluto is closer to the sun than Neptune. Explain how this is possible.

4. **Compare and Contrast** How is the structure of the sun similar to the structure of Earth?

5. **Infer** If Mars once had liquid water on its surface, where is that water now?

6. Which planet has a year closest in length to that of an Earth year? On which planet is a day about as long as an Earth day?

7. **Application** Trace the path of energy from the sun's core to the light bulb in your room. How does the energy travel each step of the way? What different forms does the energy take on?

8. **Mystery Photo** The photograph on page 558 shows the great red spot of Jupiter. The photograph was taken by Voyager 1. The great red spot can easily be seen from Earth with a powerful telescope. If you looked at Jupiter with such a telescope and couldn't find the great red spot, what would you conclude?

9. Is it possible for a comet to collide with Earth? Explain the reasons for your answer.

10. Why is it not possible for a spacecraft to land on Jupiter?

## Develop Your Skills

1. a. 80 percent
   b. Mercury
   c. Mars is the least dense (it has the smallest mass/volume ratio).
2. a. 6794 km
   b. 19.191 AU
3. Approximately two-and-one-quarter Earths could fit across Jupiter's Great Red Spot.

## Make Connections

1.

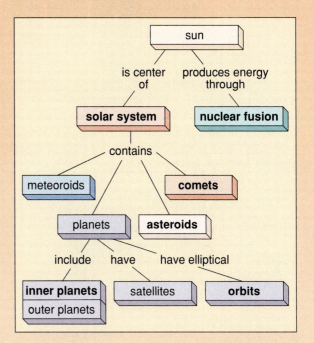

2. Data may show a correspondence between day length and sleep time. Students will need to recognize other factors that are likely to have an effect on sleep time (such as the school year) before hypothesizing a cause-and-effect relationship between seasons and sleep.

3. Students will need to interpret what they find. Here are some ideas: Mercury—fast messenger god/planet is difficult to spot; Venus—goddess of love and beauty/interpretations will vary; Mars—god of war/reddish color associated with blood; Jupiter—ruling god/consistently brightest planet; Saturn—father of Jupiter/interpretations will vary; Uranus—father of Greek titans/interpretations will vary; Neptune—god of the sea/planet may look watery from Earth; Pluto—god of the underworld/interpretations will vary.

4. Discussion of these astronomers' lives should include important discoveries and contributions to space science.

---

## Develop Your Skills

Use the skills you have developed in this chapter to complete each activity.

1. **Interpret Data** The graph below shows the mass and volume of each inner planet as a proportion of Earth's mass and volume.

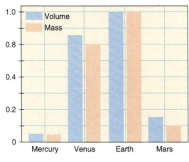

   a. What is the mass of Venus compared to the mass of Earth? Express your answer as a percentage.
   b. Which planet has the same mass-to-volume ratio as Earth?
   c. Which of the four planets is the least dense?

2. **Data Bank** Use the information on page 612 to answer the following questions.

   a. What is the diameter of Mars?
   b. How far from the sun is Uranus?

3. **Estimate** The great red spot of Jupiter is about 29 000 km wide. Earth is about 12 760 km in diameter. About how many Earths could fit across the great red spot's width?

## Make Connections

1. **Link the Concepts** Below is a concept map showing how some of the main concepts in this chapter link together. Only parts of the map are filled in. Complete the map, using words and ideas from the chapter.

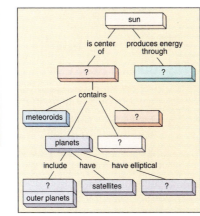

2. **Science and You** Record the number of hours you sleep each night for at least six months. Then analyze the data to determine if seasonal changes in day length might have had an effect on your sleep time.

3. **Science and Literature** The planets are all named after gods or goddesses from Roman and Greek mythology. Find out how each planet was named.

4. **Science and History** Learn more about the lives of important early astronomers such as Nicolaus Copernicus, Galileo Galilei, Tycho Brahe, and Johannes Kepler.

## Overview

Chapter 25 discusses the characteristics, life cycles, and groupings of stars. The first section introduces the equipment used by astronomers through history. The second section explains how stars are classified, and the third section explores the life cycles of stars. The final section discusses galaxies, star clusters, and constellations.

## Advance Planner

▶ Obtain a prism and a box for TE page 588.

▶ Collect metric rulers, pencils, chalk, and masking tape for Activity 25, SE page 595.

▶ Provide thick rubber bands for SE page 602.

▶ Gather black construction paper, cardboard, pins, and glow-in-the-dark paint for TE page 603.

▶ Provide a box, black construction paper, and a flashlight for TE page 606.

## Skills Development Chart

| Sections | Communicate | Compare/Contrast | Decison-Making | Infer | Interpret Data | Make a Model | Observe | Predict |
|---|---|---|---|---|---|---|---|---|
| **25.1** Skills WarmUp | | | | | | | ● | |
| **25.2** Skills WarmUp | | | | ● | | | | |
| SkillBuilder | | | | | ● | | ● | ● |
| Activity 25 | ● | | | | ● | | ● | ● |
| **25.3** Skills WarmUp | | ● | | | | | | |
| Skills WorkOut | ● | | | | | | | |
| **25.4** Skills WarmUp | | | | | | | ● | |
| Skills WorkOut | | | | | | ● | | |
| Consider This | ● | | ● | | | | | |

## Individual Needs

▶ **Limited English Proficiency Students** Ask students to copy each concept in the Chapter 25 Concept Summary in their science portfolios. Have them leave space after each concept and explain it in two or three sentences. Where appropriate, students may also give examples and draw diagrams. Encourage them to use their summary when they review the chapter.

▶ **At-Risk Students** Have students work in small groups to make a constellation map. Arrange to meet on a night when the sky is clear. Have them face North and pick out a few easy-to-recognize constellations such as the Big Dipper, Cassiopeia, and the Pleiades. Have them sketch the constellations they see on a circular piece of paper starting with those right above them (in the center of the paper) and working toward the northern horizon (toward the top edge of the circle). Have them add stars they see that are not in the constellations. They should continue until they have filled in the circle. Inside the edges have them draw any obstructions such as trees and houses that kept them from seeing all the way to the horizons. Encourage them to transfer their sketches to blue or black construction paper using light ink for the stars.

▶ **Gifted Students** Invite students to learn about the objects in space that astronomers call *quasars* and *pulsars*. Students should find out what they are, how they are related to other space objects, and how astronomers learned about them. Ask students to write an illustrated report detailing their findings.

## Resource Bank

▶ **Bulletin Board** Title the bulletin board *Distances in the Universe*. Attach photographs and pictures of various objects and entities in the universe, including the earth, moon, sun, solar system, as well as stars and galaxies. Add labels to identify each. Then invite students to find out the distances from the earth to these objects and entities and their sizes. Have students make labels showing this information and add them to the bulletin board. You might want to also display a scale that correlates distances in light-seconds, -minutes, and -hours with kilometers.

| Section | Core | Standard | Enriched | Section | Core | Standard | Enriched |
|---|:---:|:---:|:---:|---|:---:|:---:|:---:|
| **25.1 The Study of Stars** pp. 585–589 | | | | **25.3 Life Cycles of Stars** pp. 596–600 | | | |
| **Section Features** Skills WarmUp, p. 585 | ● | ● | ● | **Section Features** Skills WarmUp, p. 596 Skills WorkOut, p. 597 | ● | ● | ● |
| **Blackline Masters** Review Worksheet 25.1 Skills Worksheet 25.1 Integrating Worksheet 25.1 | ● ● ● | ● ● ● | ● ● ● | **Blackline Masters** Review Worksheet 25.3 Reteach Worksheet 25.3 Skills Worksheet 25.3 | ● ● ● | ● ● ● | ● ● ● |
| **Ancillary Options** *One-Minute Readings,* p. 108 | ● | ● | ● | **Laboratory Program** Investigation 38 | ● | ● | ● |
| **Color Transparencies** Transparencies 77, 78 | ● | ● | ● | **Color Transparencies** Transparencies 81a, 81b | ● | ● | ● |
| **25.2 Characteristics of Stars** pp. 590–595 | | | | **25.4 Galaxies and Star Groups** pp. 601–606 | | | |
| **Section Features** Skills WarmUp, p. 590 SkillBuilder, p. 592 Activity, p. 595 | ● ● | ● ● | ● ● | **Section Features** Skills WarmUp, p. 601 Skills WorkOut, p. 604 Consider This, p. 605 | ● ● ● | ● ● ● | ● ● ● |
| **Blackline Masters** Review Worksheet 25.2 Skills Worksheet 25.2 | ● ● | ● ● | ● ● | **Blackline Masters** Review Worksheet 25.4 Integrating Worksheet 25.4 Vocabulary Worksheet 25.4 | ● ● ● | ● ● ● | ● ● ● |
| **Color Transparencies** Transparencies 79, 80 | ● | ● | ● | **Overhead Blackline Transparencies** Overhead Blackline Master 25.4 and Student Worksheet | ● | ● | ● |

# Bibliography

The following resources can be used for teaching the chapter. See page T–46 for supplier codes.

## Library Resources

Dickinson, Terence. *Exploring the Night Sky: The Equinox Astronomy Guide for Beginners.* Camden East, Ont.: Camden East, 1987.

Schatz, Dennis. *Astronomy Activity Book.* New York: Simon and Schuster, 1991.

Sneider, Cary I. *Earth, Moon and Stars.* Berkeley, CA: Laurence Hall of Science, 1986.

## Technology Resources

### Internet

**PLANETDIARY** at *http://www.planetdiary.com*
- Explore astronomy and recent events in *Astronomy/Space* (click on *Phenomena Backgrounders*) and *Current Phenomena.*

### Software

*Discover Astronomy.* Win. LS.
*Encyclopedia of Space and the Universe.* Win. LS.
*Universe.* Mac, Dos, Win. LS.

### CD-ROMs

*Interactive Earth.* SFAW.
*An Odyssey of Discovery for Science Insights:* Have students try the activity *Shadow Watch* on the Earth and Space Disk. SFAW.

### Videos

*Discovering Our Universe.* 30 min. MMI.
*Universe.* 60 min. CABISCO.

 *Writing Connection*

After students closely observe the photograph, tell them to imagine that they can travel in a special space shuttle to other galaxies. Have them write at least one entry in a journal in which they describe the purpose of their mission and what they observe from the shuttle. Have them write another journal entry in which they discover a new galaxy. Have volunteers read their entries to the class.

## ◄ Introducing the Chapter

Have students read the description of the photograph. Ask if they agree or disagree with the description. (This is not a picture of the Milky Way, but of another galaxy, named M33.)

### Directed Inquiry

Have students study the photograph. Ask:

▶ How would you describe the image in the photograph? (Students should mention the spiral shape, the dense center, the dots scattered around it, and the various colors.)

▶ What do you think the photograph shows? (Students may say it shows a galaxy composed of stars and clouds of dust and gases.)

▶ Do you think this galaxy is close to Earth? Why or why not? (Students will recognize that it is far away because it is not part of the solar system, whose bodies are closest to Earth.)

▶ How would you describe the motion of this galaxy? (Students may say that it is rotating like a pinwheel.)

▶ What do you think the different colors indicate? (Answers will vary. Visible colors of stars and nebulae differ according to their chemical makeup and temperature.)

## ◄ Chapter Vocabulary

| | |
|---|---|
| constellation | light-year |
| Doppler effect | magnitude |
| electromagnetic | nebula |
|   spectrum | parallax |
| galaxy | supernova |

Chapter **25** **Stars and Galaxies**

### Chapter Sections

**25.1** The Study of Stars

**25.2** Characteristics of Stars

**25.3** Life Cycles of Stars

**25.4** Galaxies and Star Groups

### What do you see?

❝It looks like a picture of the Milky Way. This is our galaxy in space. The galaxy is large, but in the picture it is small compared to the space around it. The objects in it are vaguely roundish. There seems to be a spiral swirl of stars grouped together. The heat from the gases in the stars causes the blue-green color. Some of the other stars are red, pink, white, and orange, depending on how hot they are.❞

*Annemarie Hanrahan*
*St. Mary of the*
  *Annunciation School*
*Danvers, Massachusetts*

To find out more about the photograph, look on page 608. As you read this chapter, you will learn about stars and galaxies.

## Themes in Science

**Energy** The transfer of energy in a star occurs through the processes of conduction, convection, and radiation. In most stars, energy flows outward by electromagnetic radiation. Heat transfer through conduction occurs mainly during the early stages of a star's life cycle. Convection occurs only in certain layers, where the gas temperatures increase at a faster rate than the pressures do.

# 25.1 The Study of Stars

## Objectives

▶ **Describe** the electromagnetic spectrum.

▶ **Explain** how reflecting and refracting telescopes work.

▶ **Compare** and **contrast** optical telescopes and spectroscopes.

▶ **Infer** the relationship between the frequency of electromagnetic waves and their wavelength.

▼ **ACTIVITY**

### Observing

*Star Words*

Take a pencil and some paper outside on a clear night. Look up at the stars. Write as many words as you can to describe the stars. Then write something you can't know about stars just by looking at them. Bring your notes to class to compare your observations with those of your classmates.

**SKILLS WARMUP**

There are more than 200,000,000,000 billion stars in the universe. You may have looked up on a clear night and wished upon one of these stars. The star most important to Earth is the sun. The sun gives energy to all living things. Like all stars, it is a swirling, glowing ball of gas. In the past, the sun was so important to many cultures, such as the Zuni of New Mexico, that they looked upon it as a god and worshipped it.

And yet, in the universe, the sun is just an ordinary star. There are many stars much, much bigger and brighter than the sun. But these stars are so far away that they look like tiny dots of light from Earth.

## Starlight Observation

What do you do when you're served a new kind of food? If you want to know more about the food before you eat it, you probably look at it and smell it. You might poke it with a fork to see what its texture is like. Finally, you might take a tiny bite and taste it. In other words, you use your five senses to make observations of the new food.

How do astronomers make observations of the stars? Stars can't be touched, smelled, or tasted, but they can be looked at in many ways. Stars send out many forms of energy. Light you see with your eyes is only one of these many forms of energy. The other forms of energy can be "seen," or detected, using a variety of special tools developed for space observation.

**Figure 25.1** ▲
How do scientists observe the stars that fill the night sky? ①

## Section Objectives
For a list of section objectives, see the Student Edition page.

## Skills Objectives
Students should be able to:

**Observe** stars and distinguish between what can and can't be learned from direct observation of stars.

**Infer** The relationship between frequency and wavelength of electromagnetic wave energy.

## Vocabulary
electromagnetic spectrum

### Skills WarmUp
To help students understand the study of stars, have them do the Skills WarmUp.
**Answer** Answers will vary. Students may list words such as *twinkling, sparkling, white, tiny dots of light,* and *distant.* They may say they can't tell the size, shape, composition, temperature, or distance from Earth of the stars.

## Misconceptions
Students may think that stars give off only visible light and that all observations of the stars rely on the sense of sight. Explain that visible light waves are just one form of energy given off by stars. In addition to visible light, stars produce other forms of electromagnetic waves invisible to the human eye, such as radio waves and X-rays. Explain that scientists make important observations of the stars using scientific tools that allow them to "see" the other forms of energy.

**Answer to In-Text Question**
① **They use special tools that allow them to "see" the many forms of energy the stars produce.**

► TEACH

## Directed Inquiry

Have students study Figure 25.2. Ask:

► Which type of wave energy has a higher frequency, X-rays or microwaves? (X-rays)

► Which type of wave energy has longer wavelengths, infrared or ultraviolet? (Infrared)

► Describe gamma rays in terms of frequency and wavelength. (High frequency, short wavelength)

► Which type of energy has longer wavelengths, visible light or radio waves? (Radio waves)

► In general, what is the proportional relationship between wavelength and frequency? (As wavelength decreases, frequency increases.)

## Integrated Learning

Use Integrating Worksheet 25.1.

### Answer to Link

Designs will differ, but may include variations on a demonstration showing how red and blue light are more prominent on the white paper than they are on the green leaf. The green leaf, of course, absorbs more of the red and blue light than the paper does.

## Integrating the Sciences

**Physical Science** Electromagnetic waves are different from sound waves. Electromagnetic waves can travel through a vacuum and do not require a medium, as sound waves do. Electromagnetic waves vary in their energy, wavelength, and frequency.

**Life Science** Ask students what they know about infrared rays, X-rays, ultraviolet rays, and gamma rays. Point out that when they feel heat on their skin, they are detecting infrared rays. X-rays can travel through matter and are used to photograph bones. Most students will know that the sun is the main source for ultraviolet rays. Gamma rays can harm living cells. They are used in cancer treatment to destroy cancer cells.

### Life Science
### L I N K

Collect a large plant leaf, a prism, and white paper.

**1.** Using these materials and sunlight, design an activity that demonstrates which wavelengths of visible light a plant uses to produce its food.

**2.** Explain how your activity works. Are your results what you expected?

### A C T I V I T Y

**Figure 25.2**
Stars and other objects in the universe produce many kinds of electromagnetic wave energy. All these forms of energy are part of the electromagnetic spectrum. ▼

## Electromagnetic Spectrum

Stars produce visible light, radio waves, heat, X-rays, and other types of radiant energy. All these kinds of energy are in the form of *electromagnetic waves*. Each type of electromagnetic wave energy has a characteristic wavelength and frequency, or number of waves per second. All types of electromagnetic wave energy, from very low to very high frequency, make up the **electromagnetic spectrum.** You can see the different parts of the electromagnetic spectrum in Figure 25.2.

Visible light occupies only a small part of the middle of the electromagnetic spectrum. This part of the spectrum's visible light is made up of red, orange, yellow, green, blue, indigo, and violet light. These colors combine to make "white" light.

The first astronomers had to observe the sky with only their eyes, observing pinpoints of visible light. Astronomers today have many important tools to help them observe stars. These tools not only let them see much more with the visible light that reaches Earth, but also much more of the electromagnetic spectrum.

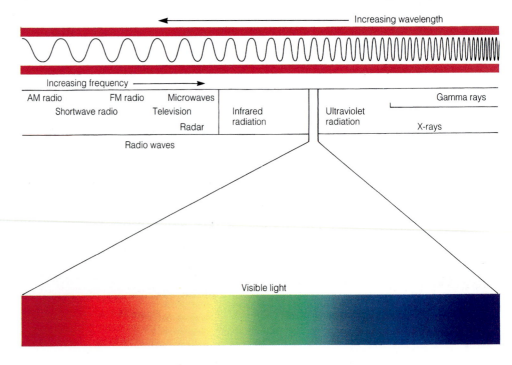

## History Connection

One of the most famous optical telescopes ever built is the Hale reflecting telescope, located at Hale Observatories in Palomar, California. The Hale telescope is considered one of the technological wonders of this century. American astronomer George Ellery Hale planned the telescope's construction in 1928. The objective mirror is 508 cm in diameter, 61 cm in thickness at the edge, and about 13,000 km in weight. Many technical problems plagued the construction of the telescope, and it was not completed until 1949. Have students find out some details about the construction of this telescope and report their findings to the class. Encourage them to include photographs in their discussion.

## Optical Telescopes

How do you see more detail in a very small object? You may use a hand lens or a microscope. In these tools, lenses collect visible light from the object and produce an image that appears much larger than the object. An optical telescope works in much the same way. It also uses lenses to collect visible light. The main difference is that the light comes from a very large but distant object instead of a very small one. An optical telescope makes the distant object, such as a star, look larger and closer to the viewer.

A Dutch eyeglass maker named Hans Lippershey is thought to have made the first simple telescope in 1608. Just one year later, Galileo used a telescope to observe craters on the moon and to discover moons orbiting Jupiter. Modern telescopes are much more powerful than the one Galileo used.

A refracting telescope uses lenses to collect and focus visible light. A reflecting telescope, in contrast, uses mirrors. The way each of the telescopes works is shown in Figure 25.3.

The larger a telescope's mirror or lenses, the larger the image it can produce. Both mirrors and lenses, however, are limited in size. If they get too big, they bend from their own weight. The telescope with the largest single mirror, 5 m in diameter, is at the Hale Observatory in California.

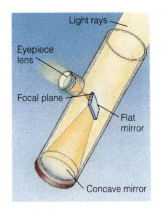

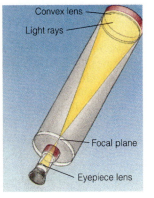

**Figure 25.3** ▲
Which of these is a reflecting telescope? Which is a refracting telescope? How do you know? ①

◀ **Figure 25.4**
This building at Lick Observatory in California houses a large reflecting telescope.

## TEACH ▪ Continued

### Apply

Ask students how scientists could use a spectroscope or a spectrograph to determine the chemical makeup of other substances. (A sample of the substance is burned, and the light given off is examined through a spectroscope. Stars may be observed directly through a spectroscope.)

### Critical Thinking

**Compare and Contrast**  Have students compare and contrast the kinds of information provided by optical telescopes and radio telescopes. (Optical telescopes collect visible light to provide information about nearby objects. Radio telescopes collect radio waves to provide information about more distant objects.) Ask students:

▶ Why can't scientists use optical telescopes to study some distant objects in space? (Gas and dust block the visible light waves.)

▶ Why are radio telescopes useful? (Radio waves aren't blocked by gas and dust; some objects emit only radio waves.)

### Decision Making

If you have classroom sets of *One-Minute Readings*, have students read Issue 64, "Extraterrestrial Intelligence," on page 108. Discuss the questions.

### Answer to In-Text Question

① The star's chemical makeup

---

## Integrating the Sciences

**Physical Science**  To help students understand how a spectroscope works, show them that light bends when it enters a prism at an angle. Cut out a semicircle about 3 cm high on a shoe box. Tape a comb across this opening. Place a flashlight on a desk and turn it on. Place the box over it. Slip paper under the opening and adjust the flashlight until rays can be clearly seen on the paper. Then place a prism about 5 cm in front of the opening. Darken the room and place the prism at various positions in front of the box. Have students observe how the light bends.

---

## Spectroscopes

The visible light given off by a star can be collected to make a larger image of the star. It also contains valuable information about the star's composition. A star's visible light has a characteristic spectrum, or array of light with different wavelengths. A star produces a spectrum because each chemical element in the star blocks particular wavelengths of light given off by the star. By observing a star's spectrum, scientists can determine the star's chemical makeup.

Scientists use certain tools to break up a star's visible light into its spectrum. A *spectroscope* contains a prism that separates the light. The spectrum is then viewed with a small optical telescope. A *spectrograph* separates light through a prism or a device called a diffraction grating. The spectrum is recorded with a camera or electronic detector.

With data from these tools, scientists have determined that most stars contain about 75 percent hydrogen and 22 percent helium. There are also smaller amounts of other elements.

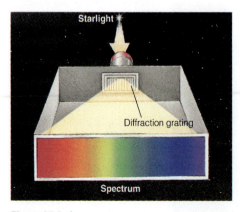

**Figure 25.5** ▲
What does a star's spectrum tell you? ①

**Figure 25.6** ▲
This radio telescope at Arecibo, Puerto Rico, has a dish 300 m wide.

## Radio Telescopes

Optical telescopes and spectroscopes have some limits in their usefulness. Gas and dust may block the faint visible light from very distant objects. But many distant objects produce radiant energy in other parts of the electromagnetic spectrum that isn't as easily blocked.

Radio waves are especially valuable to space scientists. As you saw in Figure 25.2, radio waves have wavelengths much longer than those of visible light. Radio waves from distant objects in space are not affected by visible light, Earth's atmosphere, or space dust.

Scientists collect radio waves from space with radio telescopes like the one in Figure 25.6. The reflecting dish collects weak radio waves that are reflected to the antenna, and then amplified. Computers record and interpret the data.

Radio telescopes are important tools for studying quasars and pulsars, objects in space that emit radio waves as well as visible light. Radio telescopes have also helped scientists learn about the materials in the center of our own galaxy.

## STS Connection

The Keck telescope in Mauna Kea, Hawaii, is considered one of the most sophisticated telescopes in use today. However, telescope technology is advancing rapidly. The major advances are in mirror technology. The Keck telescope and others like it are considered ground-based optical infrared telescopes. There are a number of telescope projects around the world that are in various stages of implementing mirror technology. Examples include the Very Large Telescope (or VLT) project, sponsored by the European Southern Observatory; the Japanese Subaru Telescope, sponsored by the National Astronomy Observatory of Japan; and the Columbus Project, sponsored by Italy and the University of Arizona.

## Science and Technology
### *The Keck Telescope*

For many years, the reflecting telescope at the Hale Observatory was thought to be the biggest telescope that could be built. A telescope with a mirror larger than the Hale's 5-m mirror could not be built because it would bend from its own weight. Then scientists thought of making telescopes with many separate mirrors, called multiple-mirror telescopes.

The largest multiple-mirror telescope now in use is the Keck telescope. It is located on top of Mauna Kea, an extinct volcano in Hawaii. Together, its 36 six-sided mirrors equal a single mirror 10 m across.

The small mirrors of the Keck telescope adjust to changing temperatures more quickly than a big mirror. And the lightness of the mirrors makes them easy to support. If one massive mirror was used, it would crush the mount holding it up.

The use of so many small mirrors does have some drawbacks. It is difficult to keep each one aligned so that all the mirrors work together. To solve this problem, the mirrors on the Keck telescope have computer-controlled pistons that adjust twice a second. This adjustment keeps the mirrors perfectly aligned.

With the Keck telescope, astronomers see more objects in the universe. They form clearer images of distant objects. Scientists using the telescope hope to learn more about how the first stars formed. Other powerful multiple-mirror telescopes are now being built.

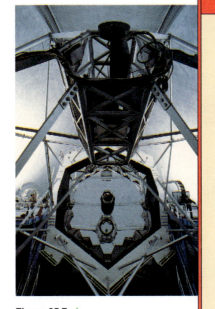

**Figure 25.7** ▲
If you look closely you can see the separate six-sided mirrors of the Keck telescope.

## Check and Explain

1. What types of radiant energy make up the electromagnetic spectrum?

2. Trace the path of light from a star through the parts of a reflecting telescope to the eye of an observer. What happens to the light at each part?

3. **Compare and Contrast** How are optical telescopes and spectroscopes similar? How do they differ?

4. **Infer** Study Figure 25.2. What can you infer about the relationship between the frequency and wavelength of electromagnetic wave energy?

## MOTIVATE

### Skills WarmUp

To help students identify some of
the characteristics of stars, have
them do the Skills WarmUp.
**Answer** Possible answers: Sun's
characteristics—big; gives off heat,
light; yellowish color; very bright;
generates energy by nuclear
fusion. Characteristics shared by
all stars—give off heat, light; generate energy by nuclear fusion.
Characteristics that vary—color,
brightness, size.

### Prior Knowledge

To gauge how much students know
about characteristics of stars, ask
the following questions:

▶ Why do stars have different
colors?

▶ What is a light-year?

▶ What is a red giant?

**Answer to In-Text Question**
① **Yellow; 5,800°C**

---

## INTEGRATED LEARNING

### *Math Connection*

Students will notice that star temperatures in this book are given in
degrees Celsius. Explain that scientists
often use the Kelvin temperature scale to
identify star temperatures. The Kelvin
(symbol K) scale is also an SI temperature
scale. Temperatures are measured from
absolute zero, which is defined as the
lowest temperature that matter can have.
Explain that one Kelvin equals one degree
Celsius, but the two temperatures differ by
273.15 degrees. On the Celsius scale,
absolute zero is –273.15°. Give students
the following formula for converting
Celsius to Kelvin: $K = C + 273.15$. Have
students convert at least three of the star
temperatures in Table 25.1 to Kelvin temperatures. (For example, the temperature
of Betelgeuse would be 3,073.15 K.)

▼ **ACTIVITY**

**Inferring**

*Stars in the Sky*

Make a list of the sun's
characteristics. Which of
these characteristics do you
think are shared by all other
stars? Which characteristics
of the sun are different from
other stars?

**SKILLS WARMUP**

## 25.2 Characteristics of Stars

### Objectives

▶ **Relate** the temperature of a star to its color.

▶ **Explain** how measurements of parallax are used to measure a
star's distance from Earth.

▶ **Contrast** absolute magnitude and apparent magnitude.

▶ **Interpret data** from the H-R diagram.

**H**ow do stars vary? When you look at the night
sky, you can tell some stars are brighter than
others. You may also notice that stars have
slightly different colors. Some are bluish, and others are
reddish or yellowish. Besides these visible characteristics, scientists know that stars vary greatly in size and
mass. All these characteristics are used to describe
and classify stars.

### Color and Temperature

The color of a star is related to its temperature. The
coolest stars are 2,800°C and appear red. The hottest stars
are 28 000°C or higher and look blue. The sun, a yellowish
star, has a temperature of 5,500°C at its surface. Stars a little cooler than the sun appear orange. Stars a little hotter
than the sun are white. Look at Table 25.1. What is the
color and temperature of Polaris? ①

**Table 25.1**
**Color and Temperature of Some Stars**

| Name | Color | Temperature (°C) | Name | Color | Temperature (°C) |
|------|-------|------------------|------|-------|------------------|
| Betelgeuse | Red | 2,800 | Polaris | Yellow | 5,800 |
| Antares | Red | 2,900 | Altair | White | 7,800 |
| Castor C | Red | 3,300 | Vega | White | 9,700 |
| Aldebaran | Orange | 3,600 | Algol | Blue | 11,700 |
| Arcturus | Orange | 4,100 | Spica | Blue | 22,700 |
| Sun | Yellow | 5,500 | Beta | Blue | 28,000 |

## Distance of Stars

Hold a finger in front of your face. Look at it with your left eye closed. Then look at it with your right eye closed. What do you observe? Your finger seems to move, or change position, relative to the background. This apparent change in the position of an object caused by a change in the position of the observer is called **parallax** (PAIR uh laks).

Scientist use parallax to determine how far away a star is from Earth. Look at Figure 25.8. Because of Earth's movement around the sun, nearer stars appear to change position relative to the more distant stars behind them. The closer a star is to Earth, the greater its apparent change of position. Measurements of this change in position can be converted into measurements of distance. Very distant stars don't seem to shift position at all. Scientists must use other methods to determine their distance from Earth.

Distances between stars are so great that scientists cannot use any of the units of measurement for distances on Earth for measuring distances in the universe. For this reason, scientists express distances to the stars in light-years. A **light-year** is the distance that light, traveling at a speed of 310 000 km per second, will cover in one year. Since light travels fast enough to circle Earth seven times each second, it can travel very far in a year. A light-year is about 9.5 *trillion* km.

Only a few stars are within 10 light-years. The closest star, Proxima Centauri, is 4.2 light-years from Earth. Many of the stars you see in the sky are hundreds of light-years away.

**Figure 25.8 Parallax** ▼

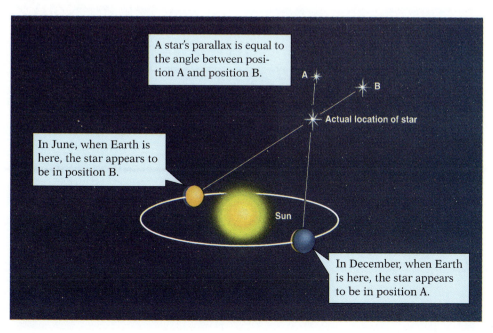

A star's parallax is equal to the angle between position A and position B.

A ✦     ✦ B

✦ Actual location of star

In June, when Earth is here, the star appears to be in position B.

Sun

In December, when Earth is here, the star appears to be in position A.

## Discuss

Ask students what factors affect apparent magnitude. (Actual brightness of the star and its distance from Earth) On a scale of apparent magnitude, which star would be the brightest? (The sun) What does apparent magnitude tell you about absolute magnitude? (There's no relation because apparent magnitude is not a measure of how much light a star actually gives off.)

## *SkillBuilder*

**Interpret Data**  Ask students if the sun is a relatively bright star in terms of absolute magnitude. (No; it is less bright than all the other stars listed in the chart.)

**Answers**

1. Its mass is 14 times greater.

2. In general, as mass increases, so does absolute magnitude.

3. No relation

4. Mass

5. Spica, Rigel; by comparing mass to diameter; Arcturus, Polaris

6. No, because stars of the same magnitude (Rigel and Deneb) have very different densities.

In general, stars with greater mass have greater absolute magnitudes. Diameter and density do not directly correlate with a star's absolute magnitude.

### *History Connection*

Hipparchus, a Greek astronomer, constructed the first known system for identifying stars according to their apparent brightness. He did this in the second century B.C. The list included more than a thousand stars. Each star was assigned a number from 1 to 6 to indicate apparent brightness. The smaller the number on the magnitude scale, the brighter the star. The present magnitude system was proposed by Norman Pogson in 1856.

## Magnitude of Stars

When you look at the night sky, some stars appear brighter than others. Astronomers compare the brightness of stars by using a number called the star's **magnitude** (MAG nih tood). The brighter the star is, the smaller the number that describes its magnitude. The brightest stars have negative magnitudes. A star with a magnitude of –2 is brighter than one with a magnitude of 2.

A star's brightness, as it appears from Earth, is called its *apparent magnitude*. However, the way stars appear to you does not tell you how much light they actually give off. There are very bright stars so far away that they don't look very bright from Earth. To describe the actual brightness of a star, scientists use *absolute magnitude*. A star's absolute magnitude is the brightness a star would appear to have if it were a standard distance, or 32.6 light-years, from Earth.

## *SkillBuilder*  *Interpreting Data*

### *Factors Affecting Magnitude*

Why are some stars brighter than others? By studying data on the mass and size of stars, you can infer relationships between these characteristics and a star's magnitude. Study the table at the right, then answer the following questions.

1. How much larger than the sun is Polaris?

2. Explain how mass and absolute magnitude are related.

3. Explain how diameter and absolute magnitude are related.

4. Which is most closely related to magnitude, mass or diameter?

5. Which stars in the table have a *density* much greater than that of the sun? How do you know? Which stars are much less dense than the sun?

6. Is there a relationship between density and magnitude? Explain.

Write a paragraph about the relationships you see between a star's magnitude and its mass, diameter, and density.

| Star | Absolute Magnitude | Mass* | Diameter* |
|------|--------------------|-------|-----------|
| Sun | 5 | 1 | 1 |
| Sirius | 1 | 3 | 2 |
| Arcturus | 0 | 4 | 18 |
| Spica | –3 | 14 | 7 |
| Polaris | –5 | 14 | 90 |
| Rigel | –7 | 43 | 22 |
| Deneb | –7 | 42 | 44 |

*In relation to the sun.

## Integrating the Sciences

**Physical Science** Explain to students that most of a star's life cycle is spent on the main-sequence line. Have students recall what they learned about the sun and nuclear fusion in Chapter 24 (pages 559 and 560). Explain that a main-sequence star is stable because it generates its energy in its core at the same rate as its surface radiates energy into space. Ask: Why do you think a brighter and more massive star leaves the main sequence earlier than a star that is less massive and dimmer? (The more massive, brighter star converts hydrogen into helium at a much higher rate.)

## The Hertzsprung-Russell Diagram

In your study of planet Earth, you have learned how to classify many things. These include rocks, elements, faults, volcanoes, clouds, and soils. Stars can also be classified according to their characteristics.

In the early 1900s, Ejnar Hertzsprung and Henry Norris Russell found an interesting pattern in the characteristics of stars. Each of them graphed a large number of stars according to magnitude and temperature. The resulting diagram is shown in Figure 25.9. It is called the Hertzsprung-Russell diagram, or H-R diagram, for short.

Look closely at Figure 25.9. A star's position on the graph is determined by its temperature and absolute magnitude. Most stars are grouped in a diagonal band from the hot, bright area to the dim, cool corner. These are the main-sequence stars. As you can see in Figure 25.9, other stars are classified in one of three other types depending on their location in the H-R diagram. What kind of star is the sun? ①

**Figure 25.9**
**The H-R Diagram** ▼

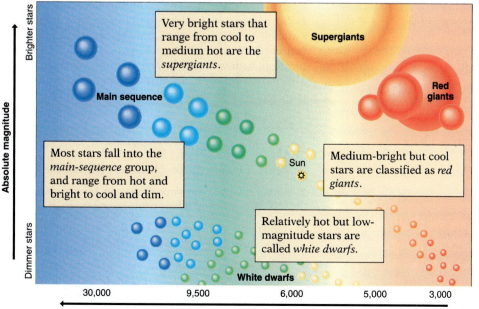

Very bright stars that range from cool to medium hot are the *supergiants*.

**Supergiants**

**Red giants**

**Main sequence**

Most stars fall into the *main-sequence* group, and range from hot and bright to cool and dim.

**Sun**

Medium-bright but cool stars are classified as *red giants*.

Relatively hot but low-magnitude stars are called *white dwarfs*.

**White dwarfs**

Brighter stars — Dimmer stars (Absolute magnitude)

Average surface temperature (°C): 30,000   9,500   6,000   5,000   3,000

## Explore Visually

After students study page 591 and Figure 25.9, ask the following questions:

▶ What determines a star's position on the H-R diagram? (Average surface temperature and absolute magnitude)

▶ Into what group do most stars fall? (Main-sequence group)

▶ In main-sequence stars, what is the relationship between magnitude and temperature? (Hotter stars are brighter.)

▶ What are the characteristics of supergiants? (Bright, cool to medium hot)

▶ Which stars are relatively hot but dim? (White dwarfs)

▶ What is the approximate temperature range for red giants? (3,000–5,000°C)

▶ How would you compare a red giant to the sun in terms of magnitude and temperature? (A red giant is brighter and cooler than the sun.)

## Skills Development

**Generalize** Ask students: How are size, magnitude, and temperature related in stars outside the main-sequence group? (If stars are bright but have low temperatures, they are generally large in size. If stars are dim, but hot, they are generally small in size.)

**Answer to In-Text Question**
① **A main-sequence star**

## TEACH ▪ Continued

### Discuss

Ask students if they have ever looked at the stars through a telescope. Have them share their observations. Ask them what role amateur astronomers have in astronomy. (They can collect important data, make discoveries, study variable stars, monitor the surfaces of planets, search for comets.)

### EVALUATE

### WrapUp

**Review** Have students compare and contrast the magnitude, temperature, and color of main-sequence stars, white dwarfs, supergiants, and red giants.

Use Review Worksheet 25.2.

### Check and Explain

1. Red, blue

2. Only the apparent position of the star changes, because Earth moves around the sun.

3. You can't tell much about a star from the way it appears from Earth because that is only an indication of its apparent brightness. The star could be relatively dim but close to Earth, or it could be relatively bright but distant from Earth.

4. Answers will vary, but should reflect an understanding of Figure 25.9.

**The Living Textbook:
Earth Science Sides 3-4**

Chapter 11          Frame 10044
Amateur Astrophotography (44 Frames)
Search:                    Step:

### Portfolio

If your classroom or individual students have access to telescopes, have them start their own amateur astronomy club. If you don't have access to telescopes, you may wish to have students map constellations after they read about them in Section 25.4. Have students write about their observations in their portfolios.

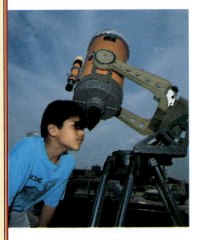

**Figure 25.10** ▲
Have you looked at objects in the sky through a telescope?

### Science and You    *Discoveries by Amateurs*

Astronomy is one of the only branches of science in which amateurs play a serious part. Thousands of devoted star-gazers spend hours every year observing the night sky and collecting important data. Sometimes they make new discoveries.

In 1885, there was a giant explosion in the Andromeda galaxy. This bright spot in the sky was discovered by several amateur observers. One such observer was a Hungarian baroness who had dinner guests at the time. For fun, she set up a telescope on the lawn in front of her castle. She and her party were among the first to view this extraordinary event.

There are certain kinds of astronomical studies that professionals rarely take on, but amateurs do. For example, amateurs often make a serious study of variable stars. They spend many hours recording the changing brightness of these stars. Amateurs also monitor the surfaces of planets and search for comets. They produce data that professionals often find valuable.

One amateur astronomer, John Dobson, did much to make astronomy a popular pastime. At first, he lived in a monastery as a monk. But he was asked to leave because he spent too much time behind his handmade telescopes. Dobson then devoted his life to making astronomy available to people on the street. He created an organization called Sidewalk Astronomers. While in the organization, he invented a special mount for his telescope. This mount is now widely used among amateur astronomers. It is both stable and easily transportable.

### Check and Explain

1. What color are the coolest stars? The hottest?

2. Explain why a star you observe in January has changed position when you observe it again in July.

3. **Generalize** What do you know about a star that appears from Earth to be very bright?

4. **Interpret Data** Choose one star, other than the sun, from the H-R diagram in Figure 25.9. Compare this star's absolute magnitude, temperature, and color to that of the sun.

### Prelab Discussion

Have students read the entire activity. Discuss a few points before beginning:

▶ Emphasize the importance of understanding all of the directions before beginning the activity.

▶ Point out the path of light to each eye and discuss how the individual images reach the brain.

▶ Discuss examples of stereoscopic vision, such as "3-D" effects and old stereoscopic viewers.

**Time** 40 minutes    **Group** 3

**Materials**

10 metric rulers

10 long pencils

chalk

masking tape

## Analysis

1. Answers will vary due to varied pupil-to-pupil distances among individuals and due to the placement of the sighting pencil. Check that parallax is calculated accurately from data.

2. The farther away the pencil is from the eyes, the smaller the difference between the two positions.

3. Answers will vary. Check calculations for accuracy.

## Conclusion

The object will appear to move to a position opposite the eye viewing it. For example, if you view the pencil with the left eye and change to the right eye, the pencil will appear to move to the left. The closer to the pencil, the greater the parallax.

## Everyday Application

Accept any reasonable explanations. Parallax allows a perception of depth, which is an advantage in running, hunting, and working with the hands, for example.

## *Activity 25*  *How are star observations affected by location?*

*Skills*  Observe; Measure; Predict; Calculate; Interpret Data

### Task 1  Prelab Prep

1. Collect the following items: metric ruler or tape measure, chalk, paper, masking tape, long pencil.

2. At eye level, draw 11 parallel, vertical lines, 10 cm apart, on the chalkboard. Label the line on the left 0, the next line 10, and so on, until you have a metric ruler on the chalkboard labeled in cm.

3. Measure 4 m straight out from the 50-cm line on the chalkboard, and put a piece of tape on the floor to mark this spot.

4. Also mark with tape the places on the floor that are 3, 2, and 1 m from the chalkboard.

### Task 2  Data Record

On a separate sheet of paper, copy Table 25.2.

### Task 3  Procedure

1. Stand at the 4-m mark, facing the chalkboard.

2. Have a classmate hold the pencil vertically exactly over the 3-m mark, so that the pencil is 1 m away from your face. The pencil should remain as still as possible.

3. Use your left eye to observe the pencil's position against the lines on the chalkboard. Estimate this apparent position in cm. Record this observation in your data table.

4. Without moving your head or the pencil, repeat step 2, this time observing with your right eye. Record the result.

### Task 4  Analysis

1. The apparent change in the position of the pencil, in relation to the lines on the chalkboard, is called parallax. Calculate the parallax for your two observations in cm. Record your answer in your data table.

2. Predict how your data will change when you move the pencil farther away from your face. Discuss and compare your predictions with your classmates.

3. Repeat steps 2 and 3 in Task 3, having your partner hold the pencil 2 m and then 3 m away from your face. Record your data, and calculate the parallax for each pair of left-eye and right-eye observations.

### Task 5  Conclusion

How does the position of an object appear to change when you look at it with only one eye and then with only the other?

What is the relationship between the amount of parallax and your distance from the pencil?

### *Everyday Application*

Most of the time you look at objects using both of your eyes. Why do you think people have two eyes rather than just one?

**Table 25.2  Density Comparisons**

| Distance from pencil (m) | Position viewed with left eye (cm) | Position viewed with right eye (cm) | Difference between positions (cm) |
|---|---|---|---|
| 1. | | | |
| 2. | | | |
| 3. | | | |

### Themes in Science

**Evolution** Although a star's life cycle is not a process that scientists can study in the laboratory, mathematical models have been devised with the help of computers. Even though stellar evolution occurs over millions of years, computers can simulate their life cycles in a matter of minutes. Scientists use the models to hypothesize the life histories of stars. Explain to students that stellar evolution is based on indirect observations, and ideas about the process continue to change.

---

### Section Objectives
For a list of section objectives, see the Student Edition page.

### Skills Objectives
Students should be able to:

**Compare and Contrast** the life cycle of a star with the human life cycle.

**Communicate** the stages of a star's life.

**Predict** what will happen for the rest of the sun's life cycle.

### Vocabulary
nebula, supernova

---

## MOTIVATE

### Skills WarmUp
To introduce students to the concept of a star's life cycle, have them do the Skills WarmUp.
**Answer** Students may list and describe the following stages of human life: birth, childhood, adulthood, middle age, old age, death. The length of the life cycle of a star is much greater than that of a human.

### Misconceptions
Students may think of the stars as unchanging. Explain that the changes may not be apparent because the life cycle of a star is measured in billions of years. Point out that the sun is about halfway through its life cycle of 10 billion years.

---

▼ **ACTIVITY**

### Comparing

*The Life of Stars*

List and describe each stage of the human life cycle. How do you think the human life cycle is different from that of a star?

**SKILLS WARMUP**

---

## 25.3 Life Cycles of Stars

### Objectives

▶ **Explain** how stars come into being.

▶ **Describe** the stages of a star's life cycle.

▶ **Contrast** the different ways in which high-mass and low-mass stars end their life cycles.

▶ **Predict** what will happen for the rest of the sun's life cycle.

---

Think of some of the ways you have changed since you were born. You've grown taller and gained weight. Your voice may have changed. Your muscles have gotten stronger. Eventually, your skin will wrinkle, and your hair may turn gray. These events are a part of the human life cycle. The human life cycle lasts about 75 years.

Stars have life cycles, too. In fact, a star is born, changes, and then dies. In contrast to the human life cycle, the life cycle of a typical star is measured in billions of years.

Every star in the sky is at a different stage in its life cycle. Some stars are relatively young, while others are near the end of their existence. The sun, as you may recall, is about halfway through its 10-billion-year-long life cycle.

### Birth of a Star

If you could travel among the stars, you would notice that the space between them is not entirely empty. In some places, there are great clouds of gas and dust. Each of these clouds is a **nebula** (NEHB yoo luh). A nebula is where stars are born.

The element hydrogen makes up most of a nebula. Helium and a sprinkling of dust are also present. The particles in a nebula are spread very thin. In fact, the particles are a million times less dense than the particles in the air you breathe. However, since nebulae are very large, they contain enormous amounts of matter.

**Figure 25.11**
The Horsehead nebula is one of many nebulae visible from Earth. ▼

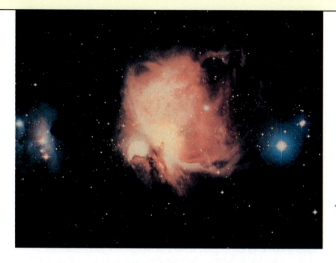

◀ **Figure 25.12**
Scientists observe protostars and young stars within the Orion nebula.

Gravity causes matter to be attracted to other matter. Therefore, as a nebula travels through space, it collects more dust and gas. The cloud becomes packed tighter and tighter, as gravity pulls it all together.

Whenever matter is packed in this way, it heats up. An especially dense part of the nebula may form a hot, spinning ball of matter. Such a ball of hot matter is called a *protostar*.

A protostar doesn't yet shine by ordinary light, but it does give off infrared energy. Scientists identify protostars within nebulae using infrared telescopes. A protostar eventually becomes hot enough for nuclear fusion to take place in its core. When nuclear fusion produces great amounts of energy, a star comes to life.

Look at Figure 25.12. It shows the Orion nebula, which is 1,600 light-years away from Earth. It contains several "newborn" stars, less than a million years old.

## Life of a Low-Mass Star

Stars begin their life cycles with different masses. A star's mass determines how long its life cycle will last and how it will die. Stars with a mass less than five times that of the sun are called low-mass stars. Most stars are in this group.

A low-mass star begins its life cycle as a main-sequence star. Over a period of billions of years, its supply of hydrogen is slowly changed by nuclear fusion into helium. During this time, the star undergoes few major changes.

▼ **ACTIVITY**

**Communicating**

*Fred the Star*

Make up a name for a star. Write its life story, from birth until death. Describe each stage of its life cycle.

**TEACH ▪ Continued**

### Explore Visually

After students study pages 596–599 and Figure 25.13, ask the following questions:

▶ How are the life cycles of high-mass and low-mass stars alike? (Both begin as main-sequence stars. Both go through several different stages and end up in a form that gives off no visible light.)

▶ Which of the two types of stars ages more quickly? (High-mass stars)

▶ Which type of star is older, a supergiant or a red giant? (Red giant)

▶ How long does it take a low-mass star to become a red giant? (About 10 billion years)

▶ Which type of star is the sun? (A low-mass star) If the sun is about halfway through its life cycle, where would you expect to find it on the diagram? (Halfway from a main-sequence star on its way to becoming a red giant) How will the sun end its life cycle? (As a black dwarf)

## Integrating the Sciences

**Physical Science** Point out to students that red giants are very different from main-sequence stars. The density, temperature, and pressure in a main-sequence star changes fairly smoothly and gradually from the core to the surface. The cores of low-mass red giants are extremely hot and compressed because their hydrogen was used up in the previous stage. Although the core contains one-fourth to one-half of the star's mass, it packs into it only the inner 1 percent of the star's radius. Point out that at this stage, the density of the star is less than that of the air in the earth's lower atmosphere.

**Red Giant Stage** As the hydrogen in the core of a low-mass star is used up, the core starts to collapse. The core of the star becomes denser and hotter. The increased temperature causes another kind of nuclear reaction. Helium is converted to carbon. This nuclear reaction gives off great amounts of energy, causing the star to expand. It becomes a red giant.

The red giant stage in a star's life is relatively short. The sun will be a main-sequence star for a total of 10 billion years. But the sun will be a red giant for only about 500 million years.

**Dwarf Stage** Eventually, most of the helium in a red giant's core is changed into carbon. Nuclear fusion slows. The star cools, and gravity makes it collapse inward. The matter making up the star is squeezed together very tightly, and the star becomes a white dwarf, as shown in Figure 25.13.

A typical white dwarf is about the size of Earth. But its matter is far denser than any matter on Earth. Eventually, the star becomes a burned-out black chunk of very dense matter that gives off no visible light. Then it is called a black dwarf.

**Figure 25.13
Stellar Evolution** ▼

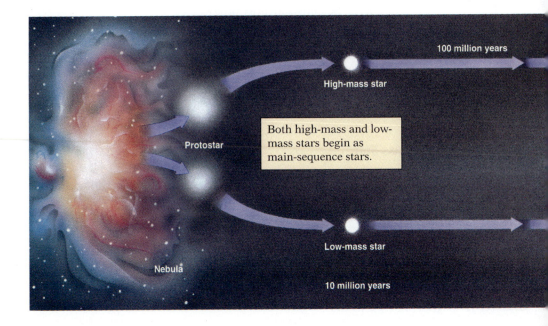

Both high-mass and low-mass stars begin as main-sequence stars.

100 million years

High-mass star

Protostar

Low-mass star

Nebula

10 million years

### Multicultural Perspectives

In the year 1054, Chinese astrologers of the Sung Dynasty observed the sudden appearance of an extremely bright star. The star was so bright that people could even see it during the day over a period of about 23 days. The star was regarded as a promising omen.

Today, scientists think that people were observing the supernova explosion that created the Crab Nebula. Have volunteers find out more about the Sung Dynasty, a time when some of China's finest cultural treasures were created.

### Life of a High-Mass Star

Stars more than six times as massive as the sun have a very different life cycle than low-mass stars. A high-mass star uses up its hydrogen at a much faster rate. After only about 50 to 100 million years, a high-mass star has no hydrogen left. At this time, the core collapses, and the outer layers expand greatly. The star becomes a supergiant, as shown in Figure 25.13.

Eventually, the core of the supergiant can no longer stand the pressure of the outside layers of the star. The outside layers crash inward very suddenly, causing a tremendous explosion that gives off an extraordinary amount of light. Great shells of gases fly off the star. The star becomes a **supernova**. A supernova explosion is the most violent event known to happen in the universe.

After a supernova explodes, only the tiny core of the star remains. This core, made up of neutrons, is called a *neutron star*. Neutron stars are extremely dense. Astronomers hypothesize that after a very massive star undergoes a supernova explosion, it may also become a *black hole*. A black hole is so dense, and its gravity so strong, that nothing can escape from it, not even light.

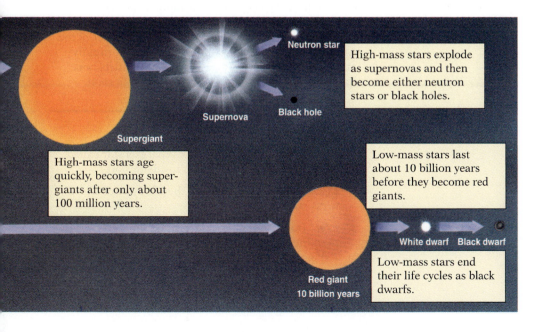

High-mass stars explode as supernovas and then become either neutron stars or black holes.

Neutron star

Black hole

Supernova

Supergiant

High-mass stars age quickly, becoming supergiants after only about 100 million years.

Low-mass stars last about 10 billion years before they become red giants.

White dwarf   Black dwarf

Red giant
10 billion years

Low-mass stars end their life cycles as black dwarfs.

## Critical Thinking

**Predict** Ask students to imagine that the sun were a high-mass star. Where would it be in its life cycle? What effects would this have on Earth? (The sun is about 5 billion years old, so it would have already become a supergiant and possibly even a supernova. In its supergiant stage the sun might burn Earth with its heat. Earth would probably be destroyed as the sun exploded in a supernova.)

## EVALUATE

## WrapUp

**Review** Have students draw a diagram showing the life cycle of the sun.
Use Review Worksheet 25.3

## Check and Explain

1.  A nebula, a protostar

2.  Main-sequence star, red giant, white dwarf, black dwarf

3.  No, only its density changes.

4.  The sun is a low-mass star in its main-sequence stage. When it becomes a red giant, it will give off great amounts of energy. Earth will probably grow warmer as a result. In the white dwarf stage, the sun will cool, so Earth will also be cooler. When the sun becomes a black dwarf, no heat or light will reach Earth.

### STS Connection

On the chalkboard, list the following obstacles astronomers have in studying space. Then have students discuss why a space observatory, such as the Hubble, can overcome these obstacles.

▶ Earth's atmosphere blocks radiation given off by celestial objects. (Astronomers can only observe objects that are in visible light and radio waves. These objects are a limited portion of the electromagnetic spectrum, so astronomers need access to technology that can detect radiation in space.)

▶ Earth's atmosphere blurs the visible images of stars and galaxies. (Only a telescope orbiting above the atmosphere can escape this blurring.)

▶ Earth's atmosphere radiates and reflects light. (A telescope in space isn't affected by the glow.)

### Science and Technology
*New Evidence for Black Holes*

Do black holes really exist? So far, scientists have no real proof. Black holes do not release light, so they can't be observed directly. However, the Hubble Space Telescope enables scientists to collect new evidence for black holes. The light that comes to the telescope from distant objects doesn't have to pass through Earth's atmosphere. The telescope can, therefore, "see" faraway objects more clearly than a telescope based on Earth.

One strong piece of evidence for a black hole has come from Hubble's observations of M87, a galaxy over 50 million light-years away. You can see Galaxy M87 in Figure 25.14. Using Hubble's technology, scientists peered into this galaxy. They made the clearest photograph yet of a bright but fuzzy blob at the galaxy's center.

The photograph shows that the blob is an extremely dense cluster of stars. Scientists hypothesize that a very massive black hole at the center of the blob holds the stars together. The black hole would require a mass about 2.6 billion times that of the sun in order to have the necessary gravitational attraction.

Similar observations of other galaxies provide more good evidence of other black holes. In the center of the Andromeda galaxy, for example, stars orbit rapidly around some object with great mass. Scientists hope to have more direct evidence of a black hole soon.

**Figure 25.14** ▲
Galaxy M87 may contain a black hole at its center.

### Check and Explain

1.  From what does a star form? What is a star called before nuclear fusion begins inside its core?

2.  List, in order, four stages in the life cycle of a low-mass star.

3.  **Infer** Does a red giant star contain any more mass than the main-sequence star from which it formed? Explain.

4.  **Predict** Based on what you know about the lives of stars, predict what will happen to Earth as the sun goes through the rest of its life cycle.

## History Connection

Ptolemy of Alexandria wrote about the Milky Way in A.D. 150. He said that "the Milky Way is not a circle but a zone, which is everywhere as milk and this has given it the name it bears. . . ." Galileo first examined the Milky Way with a telescope in 1609 and 1610. Comparing it to a "cloven grindstone," William Herschel in the late 1700s was the first person to record the approximate shape of the Milky Way. In the 1920s, Harlow Shapley calculated distances to nearby galaxies by measuring fluctuating light from certain "variable" stars. But the size and structure of the Milky Way only became clear when Edward Hubble showed that the Milky Way is a spiral galaxy. The final proof of our galaxy's size came from radio astronomy in the 1940s.

# 25.4 Galaxies and Star Groups

## Objectives

▶ **Describe** the four types of galaxies.

▶ **Explain** what a constellation is and how it differs from a galaxy or a star cluster.

▶ **Explain** how scientists know the universe is expanding.

▶ **Predict** how the constellations will look in the distant future.

### ▼ ACTIVITY

**Observing**

*Lions and Tigers and . . .*

Look at the sky on a clear night. What shapes do the stars make? What do some of the shapes look like to you? Draw what you see.

**SKILLS WARMUP**

**H**ave you looked at the sky on a clear, moonless night and seen the Milky Way? It is a broad band of murky, faint light. If you look at the Milky Way with a telescope or even binoculars, you see incredible numbers of stars. And behind those stars is still more murky light coming from millions of stars so far away you can't see them as separate points of light.

### Galaxies

The stars of the Milky Way make up a very large group of stars called a galaxy. A **galaxy** is a collection of stars, nebulae, gases, dust, and planets. The objects in a galaxy move through space as a unit, held together by gravity. There are at least ten billion galaxies in the universe.

Look at Figure 25.15. The Milky Way galaxy is shaped like a disk. Notice where the sun is. When you see the Milky Way in the sky, you are looking through the diameter of the disk.

Almost every point of light you see in the sky is also in the Milky Way galaxy, except for a few other nearby galaxies. People in the Northern Hemisphere, for example, can see the Andromeda galaxy. It is 2 million light-years away. The light coming from this galaxy has been traveling through space for over 2 million years. People in the Southern Hemisphere can see two other galaxies, the Large and the Small Magellanic Clouds. These galaxies are about 160,000 and 180,000 light-years away. They appear as small smudges of light even though they are close neighbors to the Milky Way.

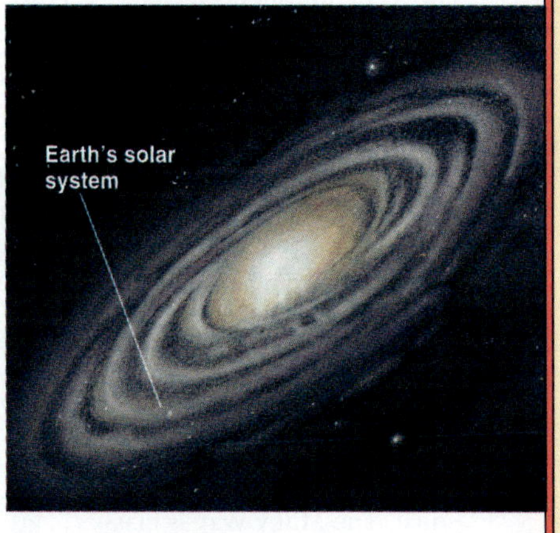

Earth's solar system

**Figure 25.15** ▲
Earth is located in one of the spiral arms of the Milky Way galaxy.

TEACH

## Critical Thinking

**Compare and Contrast** Ask students how elliptical galaxies and spiral galaxies are alike and different. (Similarities: Both are collections of stars, nebulae, gases, dust, and planets. Differences: Elliptical galaxies are shaped like slightly flattened spheres; spiral galaxies are shaped like flat disks with a bulge in the center and arms that swing out around it like a pinwheel. Spiral galaxies rotate; most elliptical galaxies don't. Elliptical galaxies contain less dust and gas than spiral galaxies do.)

## Integrated Learning

Use Integrating Worksheet 25.4.

### STS Connection

Scientists think that quasars, or quasi-stellar radio sources, may be whole galaxies in an early stage of development. Quasars were first discovered in 1960. They looked like stars and emitted radio waves. But quasars are much larger and more massive than any star that has been discovered so far. They appear to be the most luminous objects in the universe and radiate radio and light waves at very high rates. Quasars also appear to be moving at nearly 80 percent of the speed of light. Have students calculate this speed. (300,000 km/s × 0.80 = 240,000 km/s). Have interested students find out more about quasars and share it with the class.

## Types of Galaxies

Through powerful telescopes, scientists observe many different galaxies outside the Milky Way. They classify these galaxies into four types, based on shape. Within each group, galaxies vary in their size. The average galaxy contains billions of stars.

**Elliptical Galaxies** ▲

Some galaxies are shaped something like a football or a slightly flattened sphere. Most of these *elliptical galaxies* do not rotate as spiral galaxies do. Those that rotate do so more slowly than spirals. Elliptical galaxies also contain less dust and gas than spiral galaxies. The largest elliptical galaxies are made up of trillions of stars.

**Irregular Galaxies** ▲

Many galaxies don't have regular shapes. They are called *irregular galaxies*. Irregular galaxies vary greatly in size. The Small Magellanic Cloud, a very small galaxy near the Milky Way, is an irregular galaxy. Irregular galaxies are the least common type of galaxy.

**Spiral Galaxies** ▶

Many galaxies are shaped like a flat disk with a bulge in the center. They have long, spiral arms that swing out from the center of the galaxy and rotate around it like a pinwheel. These *spiral galaxies* usually contain large amounts of gas and dust. The Milky Way is classified as a spiral galaxy. The sun rotates around the center of the galaxy about every 220 million years.

**Barred Spiral Galaxies** ▲

Some galaxies have a spiral shape but differ from spiral galaxies because their arms are attached to a straight bar shape. Usually, the bar is much brighter and denser than the arms. These galaxies are called *barred spiral galaxies*. They are less common than spiral galaxies.

## *History Connection*

Ptolemy listed 48 constellations. All of these constellations are found on astronomical maps today. Ptolemy's constellations were named after mythological figures, living things, and some inanimate objects. The Latin names that he gave the constellations are still used, such as Aries (the Ram). Have students compile the list of 48 constellations named by Ptolemy and display them on a bulletin board.

## *Multicultural Perspectives*

Star gazing extends back to ancient times. The zodiacal map of the Babylonians led to our present 12-month division of a year. The ancient Egyptians and Chinese also drew maps of the sky and named some constellations. Have students research to find out what various zodiacal signs are in different cultures.

## Other Star Groups

Galaxies are not the only groupings of stars in the universe. Galaxies form even larger clusters of galaxies. The Milky Way is part of a cluster of over 20 galaxies called the *local group*.

Other star groups are much smaller than galaxies. Within the Milky Way are large numbers of *star clusters*. Star clusters are areas where many stars are grouped especially close together. If you live in the Northern Hemisphere, you can see a star cluster of seven stars called the Pleiades (PLEE uh deez). If you look at the Pleiades with a telescope, you can see that among the seven bright stars are many, many more stars.

The smallest and most common type of star groups are simple pairs of stars called *binary stars*. They are even more numerous than single stars. Many of the stars you see in the sky are binary stars that appear as one point of light.

## Constellations

For thousands of years, people have looked at the stars and seen patterns shaped like people and animals. These star patterns are called **constellations**. If you've found the Big Dipper in the sky, then you've seen part of the constellation Ursa Major. Astronomers officially recognize a total of 88 constellations.

Constellations are unlike other star groups because the stars that make them up are usually not close together at all. They appear close as viewed from Earth, but they may actually be far apart. Rigel and Betelgeuse (BEET uhl JOOZ), for example, are both in the constellation of Orion. And yet they are separated by the huge distance of 600 light-years.

Constellations are important in the study of space because they help form a map of the sky. Any location in the sky is described in relation to a constellation. Stars are also named according to the constellation in which they are located.

**Figure 25.16**

You can see these constellations during autumn in the Northern Hemisphere. ▼

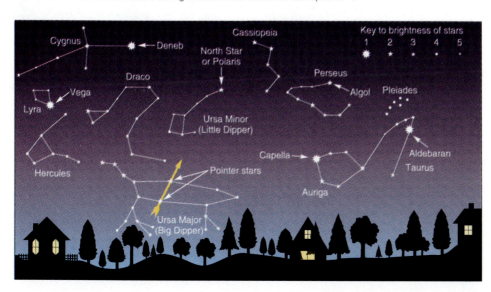

## Skills WorkOut

To help students understand the concept of an expanding universe, have them do the Skills WorkOut.
**Answer** It increases; expansion of the universe

## Skills Development

**Predict** Ask students what they would predict about the nature of the universe if the wavelengths of light from galaxies were shifted toward the blue end of the visible-light spectrum. (The universe is shrinking.)

## Integrating the Sciences

**Physical Science** Explain that the Doppler effect, in general, refers to the change in the frequency of a wave when there is relative motion between its source and observer. Have a student describe the sound of an approaching siren, and how the sound changes as it passes him or her. Explain that the sound waves ahead of the ambulance are close together. The frequency and pitch of the siren increases as it approaches the student. As the ambulance moves away, the frequency and pitch decrease.

### ▼ ACTIVITY

**Making a Model**

**Expansion**

1. Obtain a thick rubber band. Draw four dots on one side.

2. Carefully stretch the rubber band. Be sure not to let go of it.

What happens to the spacing between the dots? What are you modeling with the rubber band?

**SKILLS WORKOUT**

**Figure 25.17**
Because of the Doppler effect, an object moving away from the earth shows a red shift in its spectrum. ▼

## Expansion of the Universe

About 15 to 20 billion years ago, all the matter in the universe was packed into one giant fireball. The fireball exploded, spreading matter and energy outward in every direction. As the matter cooled, the force of gravity pulled together the particles of matter to form stars and galaxies. The universe was born. The theory for the origin of the universe is called the *big bang theory*.

There are several other ideas about how the universe began, but the big bang theory is accepted by most scientists. The main piece of evidence supporting the big bang theory is the observation that the universe is expanding. This observation is expected if the universe began in a huge explosion.

How do scientists know the universe is expanding? Look at Figure 25.17. The light waves from an object moving away from Earth are spaced more widely apart than they would be if the object were standing still. The waves appear to have a longer wavelength than they really have. The waves shifted to the red end of the visible-light spectrum. This apparent change in wavelength due to an object's motion is called the **Doppler effect**. Spectroscopic study of other galaxies shows that all galaxies have a red shift in their spectrums. Therefore, all the other galaxies are moving away from Earth.

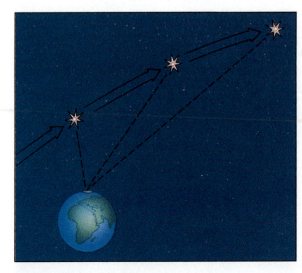

Fixed object

Object moving toward Earth

Object moving away from Earth

### Cooperative Learning

In October of 1991, the United States Congress approved $2.03 billion in funding to continue NASA's effort to build an international space station. Also participating in the effort are Canada, Japan, Russia, and the European Space Agency. The aim of the project is to have a permanent base in low Earth orbit by the year 2000. Astronauts would live and work on the base for a year at a time. The project began in 1984 and has progressed very slowly. The station has been redesigned a number of times. NASA estimates that the space station will cost $30 billion through 1999. Many people oppose the project. Have students organize two cooperative groups. One group should consider and write about positive aspects of such a station. The other group should consider and write about negative aspects. Have a class debate.

### Science and Technology   *Exploring Space*

Will people ever explore beyond the solar system? Some scientists think that reaching other stars may some day be possible. But many obstacles stand in the way. The greatest problem is distance. The closest star is 4.2 light-years away. So a spaceship traveling at the speed of light would take over 8 years to make the round-trip journey to this neighboring star. Another major obstacle is providing for the needs of astronauts for this long trip. Imagine the room needed to store 8 years worth of food and other supplies! In addition, no technology exists for making a spaceship travel anywhere near as fast as the speed of light.

Because it will be so difficult for people to journey beyond the solar system, scientists are focusing on other ways of exploring space. Space probes, for example, can be sent out of the solar system. They can collect data and relay the information back to Earth.

## Consider This

### Is Space Exploration Worth the Cost?

Exploring space is one of the challenges of this age. However, space exploration is costly and sometimes dangerous. People debate whether the cost is worth the results obtained.

Space exploration has many benefits. It helps you better understand your planet. It lets different countries work together peacefully. New discoveries in space give young people an interest in the study of science. In addition, the technologies developed for space exploration often have many uses on Earth. The heat and fire resistant suits worn by the firefighters in the photograph are one such "spinoff" that can help solve world problems.

However, it costs billions of dollars to fund space research. Many people argue that the money would be better spent helping people on Earth.

**Think About It**   How valuable is more knowledge about the universe? What could be done with the money that is currently being used for space exploration?

**Debate It**   Write a paper stating your position for or against

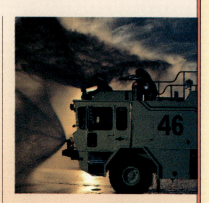

funding space exploration. Include your reasons for your position. Then, have a class debate in which two teams debate their opposing views.

## Critical Thinking

**Decision Making**   Have students imagine they are in charge of the space program in the year 3000. Vehicles can now travel at the speed of light. Have students choose a destination for a space expedition. Have them give reasons in support of their choices.

### Consider This

**Research**   Have students find out how much money is currently spent by the federal government on space research and compare that amount with the amounts spent in other areas, such as education, defense, and health care. Have them use the information to strengthen their positions.

## Discuss

Ask students to identify some ways in which people learn about deep space without leaving Earth. (Space probes; observation technology; celestial events; historical records; composition of the moon, the sun, meteorites, and Earth itself.)

## EVALUATE

### WrapUp

**Portfolio** Have students figure out how to make a star box in which they can display different star groups. Students need a cardboard box, black construction paper, tape, and pins. Have students make star maps with pin holes in the black construction paper and place them over the open box. They can use a flashlight to illuminate the maps through the box's other end.

Use Review Worksheet 25.4.

### Check and Explain

1. Elliptical, spiral, irregular, barred spiral; check against photos on page 602.

2. Galaxies and clusters include stars that are closer together than in constellations.

3. Because Earth moves around the sun, different parts of the sky are visible in different seasons.

4. Earth (as part of the solar system) rotates around the galaxy, so the view from Earth will also change.

---

## STS Connection

The Hubble Space Telescope was launched on April 24, 1990, and was plagued by problems from its first day in orbit. The worst news for NASA came in June, when engineers found that the telescope could not return clear images in visible light. One of the two mirrors on the telescope was flawed. The flaw was in the telescope's 2.4-m primary mirror, which directs light onto scientific instruments. After the successful repair of the telescope in 1993, the Hubble began functioning better than ever. In fact, the images sent back to Earth from the Hubble revealed that the telescope is gathering light four times better than it did before the repairs.

**Figure 25.18** ▲
The Voyager II space probe has been sending data back to Earth since 1979.

The space probe Voyager II is now on its way into deep space. It was launched from Earth in 1979 to explore the outer planets. It flew by Jupiter, Saturn, Uranus, and Neptune, returning detailed photographs of these planets. Voyager II will continue sending information from deep space until the year 2020. However, a space probe such as Voyager won't get close to another star within your lifetime.

Another way of learning more about what lies beyond the solar system is to build better tools of observation. More powerful telescopes are built on Earth, but there is a limit to what they see because of Earth's atmosphere. The atmosphere causes distortion of the light waves from distant objects. This distortion is what makes stars appear to twinkle.

To overcome the problems caused by the atmosphere, scientists built the Hubble Space Telescope. Recall that the Hubble Telescope has been used to collect evidence of black holes. It was launched in 1990.

The Hubble Telescope is the largest astronomical instrument ever placed in orbit. Hubble's main telescope has a mirror 2.5 m in diameter. This telescope is smaller than the largest Earth-based telescopes, but it can form clearer images because it is above the atmosphere. Unfortunately, a flaw in the mirror kept the telescope from working as well as it could until 1993. In December of 1993, a team of astronauts aboard the space shuttle *Endeavour* successfully repaired the telescope.

### Check and Explain

1. Name the four types of galaxies, and draw a simple model of each type.

2. How do constellations differ from galaxies and star clusters?

3. **Reason and Conclude** Why are different constellations visible in the summer and winter? Explain your reasoning.

4. **Predict** A million years from now, will the constellations look the same as they do today? Explain the reasons for your answer.

# Chapter 25 Review

## Concept Summary

### 25.1 The Study of Stars
▶ Stars produce many different types of electromagnetic wave energy, including visible light, radio waves, and X-rays.
▶ Optical telescopes use visible light to form images of distant objects.
▶ Spectroscopes reveal a star's composition by analyzing the makeup of its visible light.
▶ Radio telescopes detect the radio waves from distant objects.

### 25.2 Characteristics of Stars
▶ The color of a star is related to its temperature.
▶ By measuring a star's apparent change of position, or parallax, its distance from Earth can be calculated.
▶ A star's absolute magnitude and distance from Earth determine its apparent magnitude.

▶ Stars are classified into four groups depending on their location on the H-R diagram.

### 25.3 Life Cycles of Stars
▶ Stars come into being in nebulae.
▶ A low-mass star goes through the stages of main-sequence star, red giant, white dwarf, and black dwarf.
▶ A high-mass star goes through the stages of main-sequence star, supergiant, supernova, and neutron star or black hole.

### 25.4 Galaxies and Star Groups
▶ Galaxies are classified into four types based on shape.
▶ Within galaxies, stars form star clusters and exist as binary stars.
▶ To an observer on Earth, stars form patterns called constellations.

### Chapter Vocabulary

electromagnetic spectrum (25.1)
parallax (25.2)
light-year (25.2)

magnitude (25.2)
nebula (25.3)
supernova (25.3)

galaxy (25.4)
constellation (25.4)
Doppler effect (25.4)

## Check Your Vocabulary

Use the vocabulary words above to complete the following sentences correctly.

1. Outside of the Milky Way, there are many other ____ .
2. The brighter the star is, the smaller the number that describes its ____ .
3. All types of electromagnetic wave energy together make up the ____ .
4. A star begins to form when matter in a(n) ____ is drawn together by gravity.
5. Light from other galaxies shows a red shift because of the ____ .

6. A supergiant star will eventually become a(n) ____ .
7. Scientists map the sky using the ____ .
8. Because of ____ , some stars appear to shift position from winter to summer.
9. The star nearest the solar system is 4.2 ____ away.

## Write Your Vocabulary

Write sentences using the vocabulary words above. Show that you know what each word means.

## Check Your Knowledge

1. The mass of the star determines whether it will become a supernova.

2. Apparent magnitude is the brightness of a star as it appears from Earth. Absolute magnitude is the brightness a star would have if it were 32.6 light-years from Earth.

3. Scientists think that the universe began as a giant fireball that exploded.

4. The Milky Way is a spiral galaxy.

5. A constellation is a pattern formed by stars in the sky.

6. A high-mass star may end its life as a black hole.

7. True

8. False; spectroscope

9. False; two

10. False; lower

11. True

12. False; year

13. False; nebulae

5. Iron is denser than the other typical components of stars, so an iron-containing star would probably be relatively dense.

6. To predict the life cycle of a star, scientists need to know its age and mass.

7. As the galaxy spins, the matter tends to move toward the galaxy's "equator."

8. a. Spiral galaxy

   b. Humanlike organisms, or hominids, lived on Earth.

## Check Your Understanding

1. Main sequence stars are younger than the other stars in the H–R chart.

2. If one star is closer to Earth than the other, but both are in the same part of the sky, they will appear close together.

3. Red giant, main sequence, white dwarf, black hole

4. The star that was ten times farther away would appear dimmer. Absolute magnitude is the brightness of a star at a standard distance from Earth. If both stars were the same distance from Earth, they would appear equally bright.

---

# Chapter 25 Review

## Check Your Knowledge

Answer the following in complete sentences.

1. What characteristic of a star determines whether it will explode as a supernova at some time in its life cycle?

2. What is the difference between a star's apparent magnitude and its absolute magnitude?

3. How do scientists think the universe began?

4. What type of galaxy is the Milky Way?

5. What is a constellation? Give an example of a constellation.

6. What type of star ends its life cycle as a black hole?

Determine whether each statement is true or false. Write *true* if it is true. If it is false, change the underlined word(s) to make the statement true.

7. A low-mass star will end its life cycle as a <u>black dwarf</u>.

8. An <u>optical telescope</u> is used to determine the composition of a star.

9. A binary star is made up of <u>three</u> stars together.

10. The higher the frequency of electromagnetic wave energy, the <u>higher</u> the wavelength.

11. A star with a low magnitude and high surface temperature is a <u>white dwarf</u>.

12. A light-year is the distance light travels in a <u>month</u>.

13. Stars come into being in <u>star clusters</u>.

## Check Your Understanding

Apply the concepts you have learned to answer each question.

1. Compared to the three other types of stars in the H-R diagram, how old are main-sequence stars?

2. Draw a diagram showing how two stars may appear close together from Earth even though they are far apart.

3. **Infer** Arrange the following in order of increasing density.

   a. Red giant.

   b. White dwarf.

   c. Black hole.

   d. Main-sequence star.

4. **Application** Suppose two stars have the same absolute magnitude, but one is ten times farther away. Which star will appear brighter from Earth? If both stars were moved to the same distance from Earth, how would their brightness compare? Explain your answers.

5. **Critical Thinking** What type of star would you expect to contain the largest amount of the element iron?

6. To predict the entire life cycle of a "newborn" star, what do scientists need to know about it?

7. **Critical Thinking** Why do you think spiral and barred spiral galaxies are disk-shaped?

8. **Mystery Photo** The photograph on page 584 shows the galaxy M33, which is over 2 million light-years away.

   a. Which type of galaxy is M33?

   b. What was happening on Earth when the light that made this photograph left M33?

## Develop Your Skills

1. a. *A* could be a supergiant.
   b. *C* is a main-sequence star.
   c. C (main-sequence), A (supergiant), B (red giant)
   d. b (main-sequence), a (red giant), c (white dwarf)
2. a. Ursa Major, or "Big Dipper"; students may also say Leo.
   b. Canis Major
   c. You would look to the far north.

## Make Connections

1. Concept maps will vary. The map shown below is a possible organization of the concepts listed.

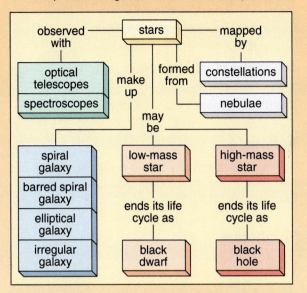

2. Research will vary. Navigators have taken advantage of the fact that stars occupy predictable positions in the sky relative to specific places and times on Earth, and can therefore be used as reference points for navigation.
3. Answers will vary. Students should correctly identify the constellation associated with their sign.
4. Check student art. Make sure the drawings accurately depict the constellation they choose.
5. Research will vary. Two examples: The Very Large Telescope will be made up of four telescopes; the shapes of the mirror surfaces will be computer-controlled. The Columbus Telescope will have two telescopes, each with honeycomb-like mirror arrays. Both telescopes use multiple-mirror arrays, as the Keck does, but the mirrors of all three are made differently.
6. Star charts may be found in astronomy periodicals, in encyclopedias, atlases, field guides, and in every month's issue of *Science and Children*.

---

## Develop Your Skills

Use the skills you have developed in this chapter to complete each activity.

**1. Interpret Data** Each sequence of colored points on the H-R diagram below represents stages in the life cycle of a star.

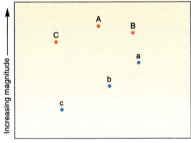

a. What type of star is A?
b. What type of star is C?
c. What is the correct order of stages for the star shown with red dots? Describe each stage.
d. What is the correct order of stages for the star shown with blue dots? Describe each stage.

**2. Data Bank** Use the information on pages 614–615 to answer the following questions.

a. What constellation is nearly overhead in the spring sky, as viewed from the middle latitudes of the Northern Hemisphere?
b. In which constellation is the bright star Sirius?
c. If you live in the Northern Hemisphere, where would look in the night sky to see the Big Dipper in autumn?

## Make Connections

**1. Link the Concepts** Draw a concept map showing how the concepts below link together. Add terms to connect, or link the concepts: stars, optical telescope, constellations, elliptical galaxy, nebulae, high-mass star, black dwarf, spiral galaxy, black hole, low-mass star, spectroscope, barred spiral galaxy, irregular galaxy.

**2. Science and Society** Do research on how stars, star maps, and constellations have been used by sailors throughout history for navigation on the oceans.

**3. Science and You** What is your astrological sign? Most signs are named after constellations. Find out where your constellation is located, and try to see it at night. What are the names of the stars that make it up? What stories are connected with this constellation?

**4. Science and Art** Choose a constellation. Draw the pattern of stars in the constellation as they appear in the sky. Then, around these stars, draw the animal or mythological figure for which the constellation is named.

**5. Science and Technology** Do research on plans for large, multiple-mirror telescopes, such as the Very Large telescope in Europe, the Columbus telescope, and the Magellan telescope. How do these telescopes differ from the Keck telescope?

**6. Science and You** Read about amateur astronomy. Obtain a telescope that you can use, and begin observing the stars at night. If you find you enjoy astronomy, you may want to build your own telescope or form an astronomy club.

## About the Literary Work

"To Space and Back" was adapted from *To Space and Back* by Sally Ride with Susan Okie, copyright 1986 by Lothrop, Lee & Shepard Books. Reprinted by permission of Lothrop, Lee & Shepard.

## Description of Change

The excerpt is a direct pickup from the text and illustrates the book's easy readability.

## Rationale

The excerpt illustrates how the experiences of outer space explorers can be quite different from those of Earth explorers.

## Vocabulary

weightless

## Teaching Strategies

### Directed Inquiry

After students finish reading, discuss the excerpt. Be sure to relate discussion to the science lessons in this unit. Ask the following questions:

▶ What does the selection describe? (How weightlessness in space affects familiar activities like eating and sleeping)

▶ What causes weightlessness? (Lack of gravitational pull)

▶ Why is a person weightless while in space but not while on Earth? (On Earth, gravity is exerted on the person's body. In space, there is no gravity exerted on a person's body, causing weightlessness.)

## Critical Thinking

**Compare and Contrast** Discuss with students the relationship that exists between mass, gravity, and weight. Then ask, If you were traveling in a space shuttle, would your mass be the same as it is on Earth? What about your weight? (The mass of an individual is the same whether on Earth or in space. However, an individual's weight varies according to the gravitational pull being exerted on the body.)

# Science and Literature Connection

## To Space and Back

*The following excerpt is from the book* To Space and Back *by Sally Ride with Susan Okie.*

The best part of being in space is being weightless. It feels wonderful to be able to float without effort; to slither up, down, and around the inside of the shuttle just like a seal; to be upside down as often as I'm right side up and have it make no difference. On Earth being upside down feels different because gravity is pulling the blood toward my head. In space I feel exactly the same whether my head is toward the floor or toward the ceiling.

When I'm weightless, some things don't change. My heart beats at about the same rate as it does on Earth. I can still swallow and digest food. My eyes, ears, nose, and taste buds work fine; I see, hear, smell, and taste things just as I do at home.

Astronauts can't always resist the fun of playing with weightless food. On one of my flights, we set a cookie floating in the middle of the room and then "flew" an astronaut, with his mouth wide open, across the cabin to capture it. We often share bags of peanuts because it gives an excuse to play catch, floating peanuts back and forth into each other's mouths. We race to capture spinning carrots and bananas, and practice catching spoonfuls of food in our mouths while they twirl in mid-air. These tricks are easy in space, but I don't recommend trying them on Earth.

After meals we clean up. We simply wipe off whatever utensils have been used and stow them in our pockets. Since each serving of food comes in its own carton, can, or pouch, "washing the dishes" really means disposing of the trash. We pack our empty food containers into garbage bags and bring all our trash back to Earth with us.

The first time I tried to sleep while weightless, I discovered that my arms and legs moved automatically into a "sleep position." Instead of hanging at my sides, as they would on Earth, my arms drifted out in front of me, motionless, at about shoulder height. It was strange to open my eyes and see my arms dangling in front of my face.

# Skills in Science

## Reading Skills in Science

1. She expresses excitement about her experiences in space. The author most likely wanted to explain to nonprofessionals what everyday life is like aboard the space shuttle.

2. Because the interior of the space shuttle is constantly lit, she has a hard time sleeping. The mask helps her sleep.

## Writing Skills in Science

1. One humorous rhyme might be:
   When up in space, I brush my teeth,
   Unless my toothbrush floats out of reach.

2. Examples of journal-entry descriptions: the effect of weightlessness on everyday tasks, the view of the earth from a different perspective, the excitement of traveling to a place few other people had explored.

# Activities

**Make a Model**  Models should show an orbiter that resembles a bulky-looking airplane. The launch vehicle includes an external tank and two solid rocket boosters.

**Make a Model**  Student inventions will vary. Students might suggest a way to help astronauts brush their teeth or to sleep more comfortably, for example.

---

I also found that I couldn't turn over in space. There was no such thing as lying on my back, on my side, or on my stomach—it was all the same. No matter how much I twisted and turned, my body would go back to exactly the same natural sleep position as soon as I relaxed.

I don't use my pillow because I have discovered that my head will not stay on it unless I strap it there. I don't use the stiff pad, either—just the light bag. When it's time to sleep, I gather my bag, my sleep mask, and my tape player with earphones and float up to the flight deck. Then I crawl into the bag, zip it around me, and float in a sort of sitting position just above a seat, right next to a window. Before I pull the mask down over my eyes, I relax for a while, listening to music and watching the Earth go by beneath me.

When I'm in orbit it seems as though I don't need quite as much sleep as I do on Earth. Maybe that's because when I am weightless I don't use my muscles as much, so I don't feel as tired. Or maybe it's because I'm excited to be in space and don't want to waste time sleeping.

## Skills in Science

### Reading Skills in Science

1. **Detect the Writer's Mood**  How does the author seem to feel about her experiences in space? Give evidence to support your answer. What do you think the author wants to convey to the reader?

2. **Infer**  The author states that before falling asleep she pulls the sleep mask down over her eyes. Why is this necessary?

### Writing Skills in Science

1. **Generalize**  In the selection, the author describes the effect weightlessness had on her actions. Think about how weightlessness might affect your daily actions. Write a limerick or other poem that describes life in a weightless state. Share your poem with the class.

2. **Communicate**  Imagine you are flying in the space shuttle with Sally Ride. Write three or four entries in your daily journal describing the experiences. What was it like to sleep and eat in the shuttle? What views of space did you have from the shuttle?

### Activities

**Make a Model**  Visit the school or local library to find out more about the structure of a space shuttle like the one Sally Ride lived in while in space. Use the information to draw a model of the shuttle. Present your model to the class.

**Make a Model**  Identify an everyday task that would be difficult to do in a weightless state. Design an invention that members of the space shuttle crew could use to complete the task. You may wish to draw the model or make a "prototype" from materials such as cardboard. Examples of tasks to consider may include brushing one's teeth, combing one's hair, writing a letter, and sleeping.

### Where to Read More

*Flying to the Moon and Other Strange Places* by Michael Collins. New York: Farrar, 1976. The space program before the advent of the space shuttle is described through the eyes of Michael Collins, the command pilot of the spacecraft Columbia.

# Data Bank

## Silt Loads of Major Rivers

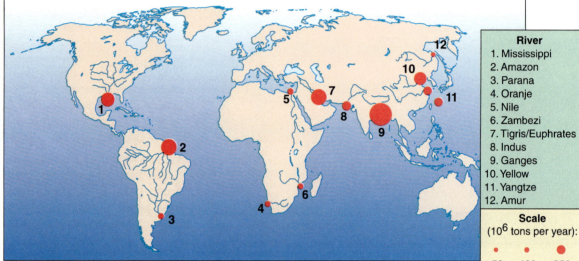

**River**
1. Mississippi
2. Amazon
3. Parana
4. Oranje
5. Nile
6. Zambezi
7. Tigris/Euphrates
8. Indus
9. Ganges
10. Yellow
11. Yangtze
12. Amur

**Scale**
($10^6$ tons per year):

50  100  250
500  1000  2000

## The Cenozoic Era

| Period | | Epoch | Duration in millions of years | Millions of years ago |
|---|---|---|---|---|
| Quaternary | | Pleistocene | 1.6 | 1.6 |
| Tertiary | Neo-gene | Pliocene | 3.7 | 5 |
| Tertiary | Neo-gene | Miocene | 18.4 | 24 |
| Tertiary | Paleogene | Oligocene | 12.9 | 37 |
| Tertiary | Paleogene | Eocene | 21.2 | 58 |
| Tertiary | Paleogene | Paleocene | 8.6 | 66 |

## Planetary Statistics

| Planet | Density (g/cm$^3$) | Diameter (km) | Rotation (Earth time) | Revolution (Earth time) | Average Orbital Speed (km/s) | Average Distance to Sun (AU) |
|---|---|---|---|---|---|---|
| Mercury | 5.42 | 4 878 | 59 days | 88 days | 47.89 | 0.387 |
| Venus | 5.24 | 12 104 | 243 days | 224.7 days | 35.03 | 0.723 |
| Earth | 5.50 | 12 756 | 24 hours | 365 days | 29.79 | 1.000 |
| Mars | 3.94 | 6 794 | 24.5 hours | 687 days | 24.13 | 1.524 |
| Jupiter | 1.31 | 142 796 | 9.9 hours | 11.9 years | 13.06 | 5.203 |
| Saturn | 0.70 | 120 660 | 10.2 hours | 29.5 years | 9.64 | 9.529 |
| Uranus | 1.30 | 51 118 | 17 hours | 84 years | 6.81 | 19.191 |
| Neptune | 1.66 | 49 528 | 16 hours | 164.8 years | 5.43 | 30.061 |
| Pluto | 2.03 | 2 290 | 6.4 days | 247.7 years | 4.74 | 39.529 |

## Climate and Weathering

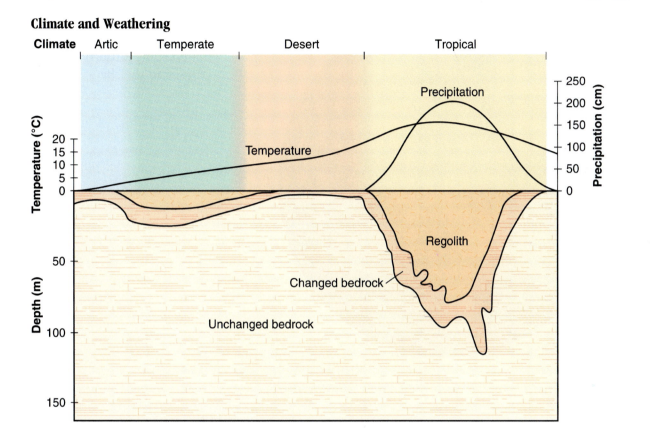

**Climate**   Artic   Temperate   Desert   Tropical

Temperature (°C): 20, 15, 10, 5, 0

Precipitation (cm): 250, 200, 150, 100, 50, 0

Precipitation

Temperature

Depth (m): 50, 100, 150

Regolith

Changed bedrock

Unchanged bedrock

## Earth Depths

Crust

Mantle

Outer Core

Inner Core

0 km

0 km

4 km — Deepest mine

12 km — Deepest well

6,300 km

## Land Use in the United States

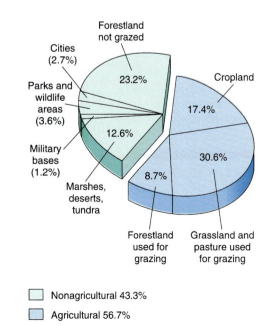

Forestland not grazed

Cities (2.7%)

Parks and wildlife areas (3.6%)

Military bases (1.2%)

23.2%

12.6%

Marshes, deserts, tundra

8.7%

Forestland used for grazing

30.6%

Grassland and pasture used for grazing

Cropland

17.4%

Nonagricultural 43.3%

Agricultural 56.7%

**Star Charts for the Northern Hemisphere**

### SPRING

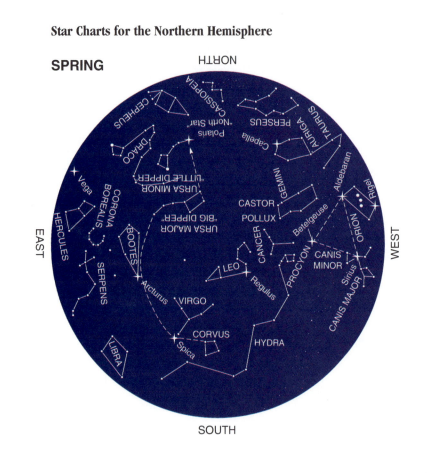

When using a star chart, hold it up toward the sky in the direction you are looking. Rotate it until the star pattern on the map matches the pattern that you see in the sky.

### SUMMER

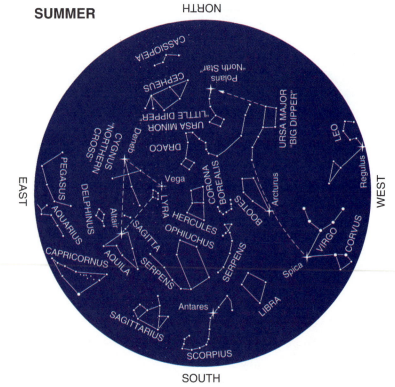

**AUTUMN**

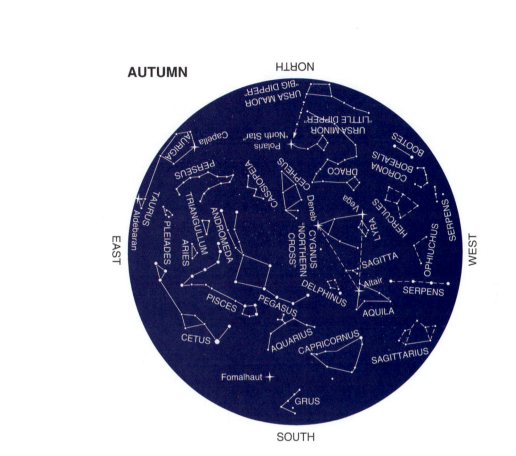

**WINTER**

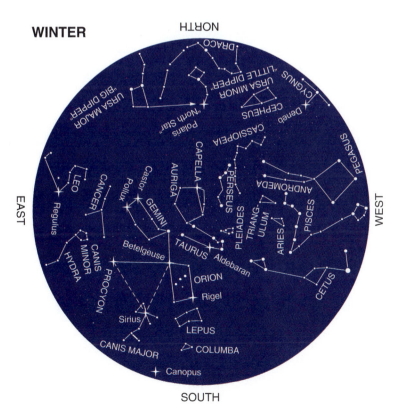

## Synoptic Chart

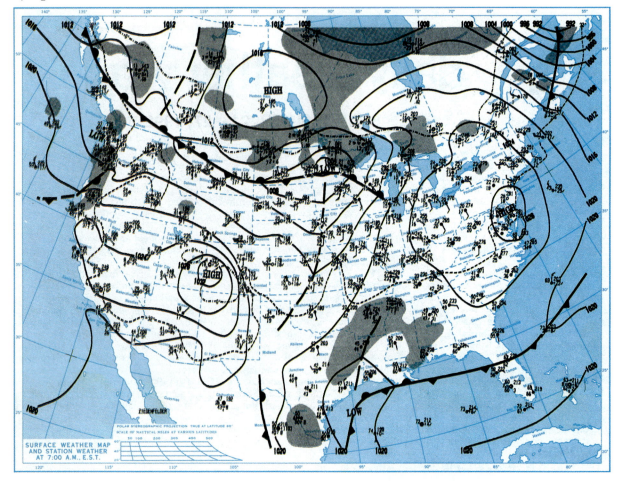

**Tide Table**    **Week of January 24–30**

| Date/Day | A.M. | | | | P.M. | | | |
|---|---|---|---|---|---|---|---|---|
| | Time | Meters | Time | Meters | Time | Meters | Time | Meters |
| 24 Sunday | 1:06 | 1.5 | 6:00 | 0.7 | NOON | 1.7 | 6:25 | 0.0 |
| 25 Monday | 1:31 | 1.5 | 6:39 | 0.7 | 12:35 | 1.6 | 6:54 | 0.1 |
| 26 Tuesday | 1:58 | 1.6 | 7:21 | 0.7 | 1:14 | 1.5 | 7:23 | 0.2 |
| 27 Wednesday | 2:25 | 1.6 | 8:09 | 0.6 | 1:57 | 1.4 | 7:54 | 0.4 |
| 28 Thursday | 2:56 | 1.6 | 8:58 | 0.6 | 2:51 | 1.2 | 8:27 | 0.6 |
| 29 Friday | 3:31 | 1.7 | 10:01 | 0.6 | 4:03 | 1.1 | 9:08 | 0.7 |
| 30 Saturday | 4:12 | 1.7 | 11:07 | 0.5 | 5:45 | 1.1 | 10:01 | 0.9 |

## Average Temperatures and Precipitation for Selected World Cities

| City | Average Daily Temperature (°C) | | | | Average Annual Precipitation |
|---|---|---|---|---|---|
| | Jan. Max. | Jan. Min. | July Max. | July Min. | (cm) |
| Athens, Greece | 12 | 6 | 32 | 22 | 40 |
| Bangkok, Thailand | 31 | 19 | 32 | 24 | 147 |
| Bogotá, Colombia | 19 | 9 | 17 | 10 | 106 |
| Capetown, South Africa | 25 | 15 | 17 | 7 | 51 |
| Denver, Colorado, USA | 6 | –17 | 31 | 15 | 39 |
| Geneva, Switzerland | 4 | –2 | 25 | 14 | 39 |
| Istanbul, Turkey | 7 | 2 | 26 | 18 | 80 |
| Lagos, Nigeria | 30 | 23 | 28 | 23 | 184 |
| Lima, Peru | 28 | 19 | 19 | 13 | 4 |
| Manila, Philippines | 30 | 20 | 31 | 23 | 208 |
| Moscow, Russia | –6 | –13 | 24 | 12 | 63 |
| Reykjavik, Iceland | 2 | –2 | 14 | 9 | 86 |
| Shanghai, China | 8 | 0 | 32 | 23 | 114 |
| Sydney, Australia | 25 | 18 | 15 | 8 | 118 |

## Rocks in North America

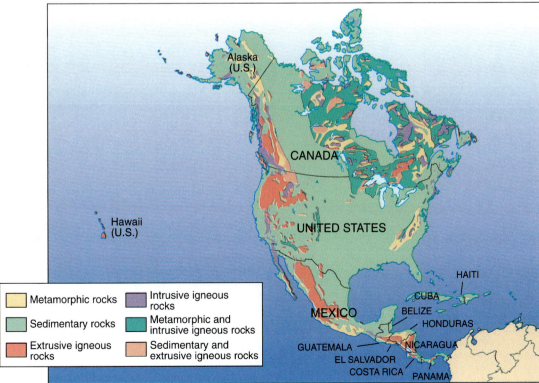

Metamorphic rocks
Sedimentary rocks
Extrusive igneous rocks
Intrusive igneous rocks
Metamorphic and intrusive igneous rocks
Sedimentary and extrusive igneous rocks

Data Bank

## Distance Between the Earth and Moon

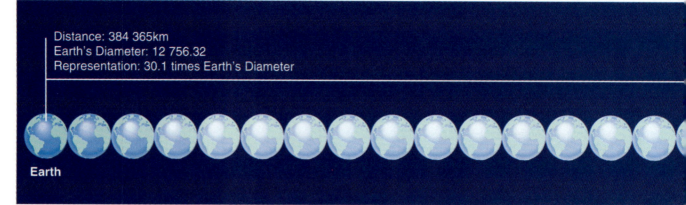

Distance: 384 365km
Earth's Diameter: 12 756.32
Representation: 30.1 times Earth's Diameter

Earth

## The Tallest Mountain on Each Continent

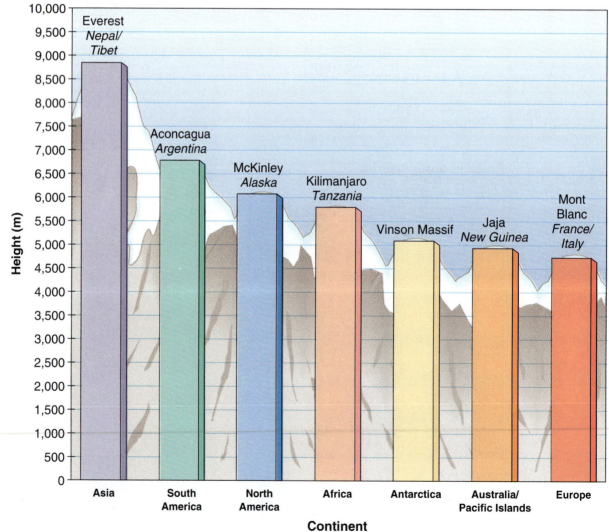

Everest
*Nepal/*
*Tibet*

Aconcagua
*Argentina*

McKinley
*Alaska*

Kilimanjaro
*Tanzania*

Vinson Massif

Jaja
*New Guinea*

Mont
Blanc
*France/*
*Italy*

Height (m)

Asia    South    North    Africa    Antarctica    Australia/    Europe
        America  America                          Pacific Islands

Continent

Data Bank

## Some Major Earthquakes in the Twentieth Century

| Location | Date | Magnitude | Deaths |
|---|---|---|---|
| Japan | Mar. 2, 1933 | 8.9 | 2,990 |
| India, Assam | Aug. 15, 1950 | 8.7 | 1,530 |
| China, Gansu | Dec. 16, 1920 | 8.6 | 100,000 |
| Alaska | Mar. 27, 1964 | 8.4 | 131 |
| Chile, Chillan | Jan. 24, 1939 | 8.3 | 28,000 |
| China, Tangshan | July 28, 1976 | 8.2 | 242,000 |
| NW. Argentina | Nov. 23, 1977 | 8.2 | 100 |
| Mexico City | Sept. 19 & 21, 1985 | 8.1 | 4,200+ |
| Indonesia | Sept. 12, 1979 | 8.1 | 100 |
| Indonesia | Aug. 19, 1977 | 8.0 | 200 |
| Colombia, Ecuador | Dec. 12, 1979 | 7.9 | 800 |
| N. Afghanistan | June 17–19, 1956 | 7.7 | 2,000 |
| N. Peru | May 31, 1970 | 7.7 | 66,794 |
| NW. Iran | June 21, 1990 | 7.7 | 40,000+ |
| Luzon, Philippines | July 16, 1990 | 7.7 | 1,621 |
| Italy, Messina | Dec. 28, 1908 | 7.5 | 83,000 |
| Guatemala | Feb. 4, 1976 | 7.5 | 22,778 |
| Romania | Mar. 4, 1977 | 7.5 | 1,541 |
| New Guinea, Irian Jaya | June 26, 1976 | 7.1 | 433 |
| San Francisco Bay Area | Oct. 17, 1989 | 6.9 | 62 |
| Morocco, Agadir | Feb. 29, 1960 | 5.8 | 12,000 |

## Physical Map of the United States

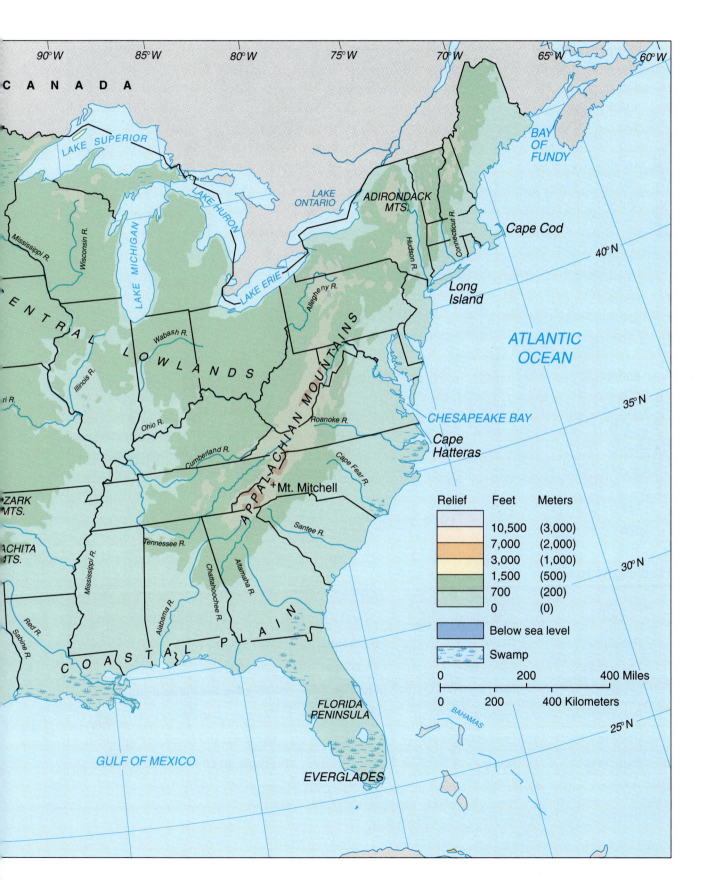

CANADA

LAKE SUPERIOR

Mississippi R.

Wisconsin R.

LAKE HURON

LAKE MICHIGAN

LAKE ERIE

LAKE ONTARIO

ADIRONDACK MTS.

BAY OF FUNDY

Cape Cod

Connecticut R.

Hudson R.

40° N

Long Island

Allegheny R.

Wabash R.

C E N T R A L   L O W L A N D S

Illinois R.

ri R.

Ohio R.

A P P A L A C H I A N   M O U N T A I N S

ATLANTIC OCEAN

Roanoke R.

35° N

CHESAPEAKE BAY

Cumberland R.

Cape Fear R.

Cape Hatteras

OZARK MTS.

+ Mt. Mitchell

Santee R.

ACHITA MTS.

Tennessee R.

Altamaha R.

30° N

Mississippi R.

Chattahoochee R.

Alabama R.

C O A S T A L   P L A I N

Red R.

Sabine R.

| Relief | Feet | Meters |
|---|---|---|
|  | 10,500 | (3,000) |
|  | 7,000 | (2,000) |
|  | 3,000 | (1,000) |
|  | 1,500 | (500) |
|  | 700 | (200) |
|  | 0 | (0) |

Below sea level

Swamp

0        200        400 Miles

0        200        400 Kilometers

FLORIDA PENINSULA

BAHAMAS

25° N

GULF OF MEXICO

EVERGLADES

Data Bank

**621**

## World's Largest Oceans and Seas

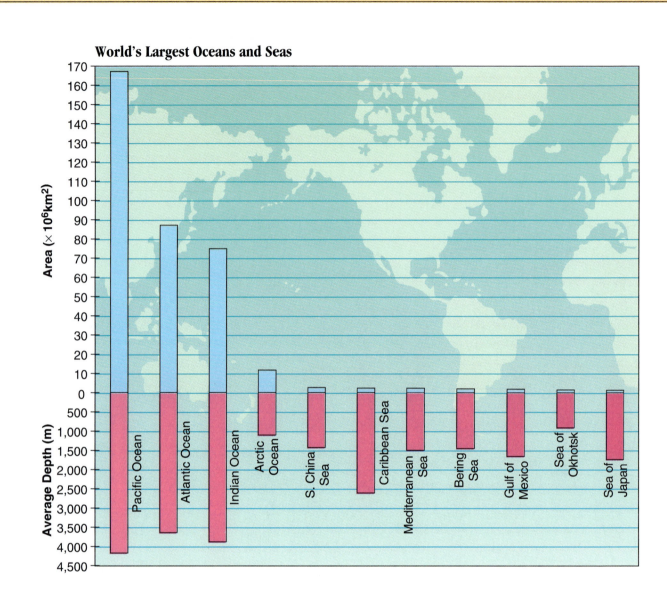

## Radioactive Isotopes

| Isotope | Decay Product | Half-life (years) | Is Used to Date |
|---|---|---|---|
| Rubidium-87 | Strontium-87 | 50 billion | Very old rocks |
| Thorium-232 | Lead-208 | 14 billion | Very old rocks |
| Uranium-238 | Lead-206 | 4.5 billion | Old rocks and fossils in the rocks |
| Potassium-40 | Argon-40 | 1.3 billion | Old rocks and fossils in the rocks |
| Uranium-235 | Lead-207 | 713 million | Old rocks and fossils in the rocks |
| Carbon-14 | Nitrogen-14 | 5,730 | Fossils less than 50,000 years old |

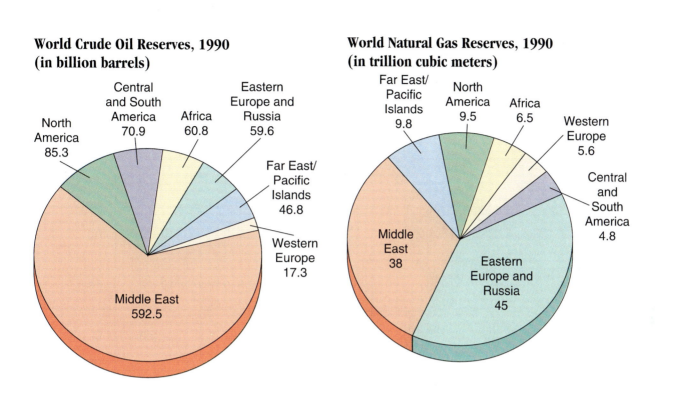

**World Crude Oil Reserves, 1990 (in billion barrels)**

- North America 85.3
- Central and South America 70.9
- Africa 60.8
- Eastern Europe and Russia 59.6
- Far East/Pacific Islands 46.8
- Western Europe 17.3
- Middle East 592.5

**World Natural Gas Reserves, 1990 (in trillion cubic meters)**

- Far East/Pacific Islands 9.8
- North America 9.5
- Africa 6.5
- Western Europe 5.6
- Central and South America 4.8
- Middle East 38
- Eastern Europe and Russia 45

## Human Causes and Health Effects of Major Air Pollutants

| Pollutant | Human Causes | Health Effects |
|---|---|---|
| Carbon monoxide | Transportation; Industry | *Short-term intense exposure:* headache, dizziness, decreased energy, death<br><br>*Long-term exposure:* stress on cardiovascular system, decreased tolerance to exercise, heart attack |
| Sulfur oxides | Home, business and power plant energy use; Industry | *Short-term intense exposure:* inflammation of respiratory tract, aggravation of asthma<br><br>*Long-term exposure:* emphysema, bronchitis |
| Nitrogen oxides | Transportation; Home, business and power plant energy use | *Short-term intense exposure:* irritation of lungs<br><br>*Long-term exposure:* bronchitis |
| Particulates | Home, business, and power plant energy use; Industry | *Long-term exposure:* Irritation of respiratory system, cancer |
| Hydrocarbons | Transportation | Unknown |
| Photochemical oxidants | Transportation; Home, business, and power plant energy use (indirectly, through hydrocarbons and nitrogen oxides) | *Short-term intense exposure:* respiratory irritation, eye irration<br>*Long-term exposure:* emphysema |

## Properties of Selected Common Minerals

| Mineral | Color | Streak | Type of Cleavage | Hardness | Specific Gravity | Symbol |
|---|---|---|---|---|---|---|
| **Metals/Non-metals** | | | | | | |
| gold | rich yellow | yellow | none (fracture) | 2.5–3 | 19.3 | Au |
| silver | white | white | none (fracture) | 2.5–3 | 10–12 | Ag |
| iron | steel-gray | gray | 3 directions | 2.5–3 | 10–12 | Fe |
| graphite | silver-gray to black | grayish-to black | 1 direction | 1–2 | 2.3 | C |
| sulfur | light yellow | white to yellow | indistinct | 1.5–2.5 | 2 | S |
| **Sulfides** | | | | | | |
| galena | bluish lead gray | lead gray | 3 directions | 2.5–2.7 | 7.5 | PbS |
| sphalerite | colorless to yellowish-black | yellowish | 6 directions | 3.5–4 | 4 | ZnS |
| pyrite | rich yellow | greenish-black | none (fracture) | 6–6.5 | 5 | $FeS_2$ |
| **Oxides** | | | | | | |
| bauxite | white to red-brown | white to red-brown | poor | 1–3 | 2.0–2.5 | $Al(OH)_2$ |
| magnetite | black | black | none (fracture) | 6 | 5.2 | $Fe_3O_4$ |
| **Halides** | | | | | | |
| halite | colorless and various colors | colorless | 3 directions | 2.5 | 2.1 | NaCl |
| fluorite | variety of colors | colorless | 4 directions | 4 | 3–3.2 | $CaF_2$ |

| Mineral | Color | Streak | Type of Cleavage | Hardness | Specific Gravity | Symbol |
|---|---|---|---|---|---|---|
| **Carbonates** | | | | | | |
| calcite | variety of colors | colorless | 3 directions; not 90° | 3 | 2.7 | $CaCO_3$ |
| **Sulfates** | | | | | | |
| gypsum | yellowish, reddish | colorless | 2 directions | 2 | 2.3 | $CaSO_4 \cdot 2H_2O$ |
| **Phosphates** | | | | | | |
| apatite | variety of colors | white | indistinct | 5 | 3.2 | $Ca_5(PO_4)_3$ $(Cl,F)$ |
| **Silicates** | | | | | | |
| quartz | variety of colors | colorless | none (fracture) | 7 | 2.6 | $SiO_2$ |
| talc | white, greenish-gray | colorless | 1 direction | 1 | 2.8 | $Mg_3Si_4O_{10}$ $(OH)_2$ |
| olivine | yellowish, greenish | white to light green | none (fracture) | 6.5 | 3.5 | $(MgFe)_2$ $SiO_4$ |
| serpentine | greenish | colorless | none (fracture) | 2–5 | 2.2-2.6 | $Mg_3Si_2O_5$ $(OH)_4$ |
| hornblende | green to black | gray to white | 2 directions | 5–6 | 3.4 | complex structure |
| muscovite (mica) | white to dark | colorless | 1 direction | 2–2.5 | 2.8 | complex structure |
| topaz | variety of colors | colorless | 3 directions | 8 | 3.5 | complex structure |

# Glossary

A simple, phonetic spelling is given for words in this book that may be unfamiliar or hard to pronounce.

Stressed syllables are printed in capital letters. Sometimes a word has two stressed syllables. The syllable with the primary stress is printed in full capitals. The syllable with the secondary stress is printed in small capitals.

***Example:*** *Asteroid* is pronounced AS tuh ROYD.

Most of the time, the phonetic spelling can be interpreted without referring to the key. The key to the right gives the pronunciations for letters that are commonly used for more than one sound.

## *Pronunciation Key*

| | | | |
|---|---|---|---|
| a | c**a**t | ih | p**i**n |
| ah | h**o**t | oh | gr**ow** |
| ai | c**a**re | oo | r**u**le, m**u**sic |
| ah | **a**ll | ow | n**ow** |
| ay | s**ay**, **a**ge | oy | v**oi**ce |
| ee | m**ee**t | u | p**u**t |
| eh | l**e**t | uh | s**u**n, **a**bout |
| eye | **i**ce or b**y** | ur | t**er**m |

**abrasion**  Mechanical weathering process that is the result of gravity, wind, or moving water, causing rocks to rub against each other, wear each other down, or break into smaller pieces. (pp. 241, 282)

**absolute age**  The approximate age in years of particular rocks, determined through radiometric dating. (p. 83)

**absolute magnitude**  The brightness a star would appear if it were a standard distance (32.6 light-years) from Earth. (p. 592)

**abyssal plain**  (uh BIHS uhl) Flat areas, covered with layers of sediment, deep on the ocean floor. (p. 374)

**adapted**  Characteristic of a species that makes it able to survive in its environment. (p. 290)

**air mass**  One of six different types of weather conditions in a given area: continental polar, continental tropical, maritime polar, maritime tropical, equatorial, and arctic. (p. 440)

**air pressure**  The pressure exerted by air in a particular area. (p. 397)

**alluvial fan**  (uh LOO vee uhl) Fan-shaped type of sediment deposit formed when a river flows down a steep mountain slope onto a broad, flat, desert area. (p. 268)

**altitude**  A location's distance above sea level. (p. 464)

**anthracite**  (AN thruh syt) The fourth stage of coal formation, anthracite is about 90 percent carbon, generating a great amount of heat while releasing few pollutants. (p. 493)

**anticline**  (ANT ee klyn) A fold that produces an upward bulge. (p. 115)

**anticyclonic wind pattern**  Air, rushing away from a high-pressure center, creates a clockwise wind pattern, resulting in warm, sunny weather. (p. 445)

**aphelion**  (uh FEEL yuhn) The place in the Earth's orbit where Earth is farthest away from the sun. (p. 539)

**apogee**  (AP uh JEE) Point in the moon's orbit where it is farthest away from the Earth. (p. 547)

**apparent magnitude**  The measure of a star's brightness as it appears from Earth. (p. 592)

**aquifer**  (AH kwih fur) A groundwater-containing layer of rock or sediment. (p. 331)

**archipelago**  A chain or cluster of islands. (p. 35)

**asteroid**  (AS tuh ROYD) A small, irregularly-shaped body that revolves around the sun in the same direction as the planets do. (p. 575)

**asteroid belt**  In the gap between Mars and Jupiter, a large group of asteroids makes up this belt. (p. 575)

**asthenosphere**  (as THEHN uhs FEER) The hot, semi-liquid layer of the earth's mantle below the lithosphere. (p. 57)

**atmosphere**  An envelope of gases surrounding the earth that extends about 1,000 km above the earth's surface. (p. 402)

**atoll**  (A tohl)  The ring of coral left behind when a volcanic island has sunk below the surface of the water. (p. 375)

**atom**  The smallest particle of an element, with all the properties of this element, that can combine with other atoms to form a molecule. (p. 161)

**atomic number**  The number of protons in an element's nucleus that identifies the element. (p. 162)

**aurora australis** In the Southern Hemisphere, the beautiful display of lights in the sky, caused by charged particles carried by solar wind. (p. 562)

**aurora borealis** In the Northern Hemisphere, the display of beautiful lights in the sky that is caused by a steady stream of solar wind from the sun's corona, which carries charged particles. (p. 562)

**axis** An imaginary line extending through the Earth from the North Pole to the South Pole, around which the Earth rotates. (p. 537)

 **barometer** (buh RAHM uh tur) Instrument used to measure air pressure. (p. 443)

**barred spiral galaxy** A galaxy with a spiral shape, with the arms attached to a straight bar shape. (p. 602)

**batholith** A large pluton that has been exposed at the earth's surface by erosion. (p. 124)

**bathymetric map** (BATH uh MEH trihk) Topographic map of the ocean floor. (p. 368)

**bathyscaph** (BATH ih skaf) A small, submarinelike submersible that scientists use to explore the ocean depths. (p. 370)

**beach** Shoreline formed when sand, gravel, or other sediments accumulate over a long period of time. (p. 272)

**bedrock** Layer of solid rock that underlies soil, sand, clay, and gravel layers on the earth's surface. (p. 230)

**benthos** (BEHN thohs) Organisms, such as clams, crabs, seaweeds, and tube worms, that live on the ocean floor. (p. 380)

**big bang theory** Theory stating that the universe was at one time one giant fireball that exploded; as the matter cooled, the force of gravity pulled particles together to form stars and galaxies. (p. 604)

**binary stars** The most common type of star group, this is two stars close to each other, that sometimes appear as one bright star. (p. 603)

**biodiversity** (BY oh dih VURS uh tee) The wide variety of different species in an ecosystem. (p. 517)

**biome** A large community of plants and animals whose makeup is determined by soil and climate. (p. 36)

**biosphere** (BY uhs feer) A life-supporting zone extending from the earth's crust into the atmosphere. (p. 24)

**bituminous coal** (by TOO mihn uhs) Most common type of coal mined and used in the United States; about 85% carbon, it burns cleaner and releases fewer pollutants than lignite. (p. 493)

**black hole** The remains of a supernova explosion, it is a dense object with very strong gravity from which nothing can escape, including light. (p. 599)

**capture theory** Idea proposing that the moon formed elsewhere and was trapped by the Earth's gravity. (p. 547)

**carbonation** Chemical weathering process produced by carbonic acid, where the rock develops small pits or holes; common in rocks like limestone and marble. (p. 243)

**cast** Fossil formed by minerals in water that build up in a mold. (p. 295)

**cementation** Sedimentary process where sediment spaces fill and bind together with minerals. (p. 221)

**Cenozoic Era** (SEE nuh ZOH ihk) The time from the end of the Mesozoic Era (66 million years ago) up to the present. (p. 85)

**chemical bond** The force of attraction that holds atoms or ions together. (p. 163)

**chemical change** Change in the chemical identity of a substance. (p. 168)

**chemical formula** A combination of chemical symbols used to represent compounds. (p. 166)

**chemical rock** Rock formed when minerals come out of solution and crystallize. (p. 223)

**chemical symbol** A one- or two-letter abbreviation for every element, used by scientists worldwide. (p. 166)

**chemical weathering** Type of weathering that changes the chemical composition of rock. (p. 242)

**chromosphere** (KROH muh sfeer) The middle layer of the sun's atmosphere, made up mostly of streams of hydrogen gas. (p. 561)

**cinder cone volcano** A volcano formed from ash, cinder, and other volcanic debris. (p. 147)

**cirque** (SURK) Large, bowl-shaped hole in the side of a mountain where a glacier began. (p. 276)

**clastic rock** Rock that is formed when particles of country rock and mineral grains compact together. (p. 222)

**cleavage** Property of a mineral when it breaks along a flat plane or surface. (p. 194)

**climate** Characteristic weather for a region over a long period of time, determined by latitude, altitude, distance from the ocean, topography, and prevailing winds. (p. 463)

**climate zone** A region with a particular range of temperatures, based on latitude. (p. 469)

**cold front**  Weather boundary characterized by strong gusts of wind and rain where cold, dry air displaces warm, moist air. (p. 441)

**comet**  An object made of ice that travels in an orbit around the sun. (p. 578)

**compaction**  Sedimentary rock process where the water is squeezed out of the spaces, and the particles of sediment pack tightly together. (p. 221)

**composite volcano**  A volcano that contains alternating layers of volcanic debris and lava. (p. 147)

**composting**  Creating a garden area where organic material can break down to be reused in the soil as fertilizer. (p. 527)

**compound**  A substance made of two or more chemically combined elements. (p. 165)

**compression**  Type of stress in the earth's crust where rocks are squeezed together. (p.114)

**conchoidal**  Property of a mineral when it breaks and forms a curving surface. (p. 194)

**condensation**  Phase change that occurs when water vapor rises in the air, then cools, forming liquid droplets which make clouds. (p. 320)

**condensation nuclei**  In the atmosphere, small particles of salt, dust, or smoke around which water condenses when the relative humidity reaches 100 percent. (p. 423)

**conduction**  The transfer of heat energy or electrons between objects in direct contact. (p. 398)

**conservation**  The careful use of our natural resources. (p. 523)

**constellation**  Star pattern seen in the sky in the shape of a person, animal, or object. (p. 603)

**continent**  One of the seven major landmasses of the earth. (p. 32)

**continental drift**  The theory that all the world's landmasses were at one time joined together in a supercontinent called Pangaea. (p. 91)

**continental glacier**  A glacier that covers a large area in a polar region. (p. 274)

**continental margin**  The downward-sloping part of a continent that extends out into the ocean. (p. 372)

**continental rise**  Part of the continental margin; the area from the continental slope to the deep ocean floor. (p. 373)

**continental shelf**  The gently-sloping surface of the continental margin, extending underwater from the shoreline. (p. 373)

**continental slope**  Part of the continental margin, at the edge of the continental shelf, that drops off steeply to the ocean floor, where the boundary between the continental crust and ocean crust occurs. (p. 373)

**contour line**  Line on a topographic map connecting points that have the same elevation. (p. 45)

**control**  A test where all variables are identical to the experiment being performed except the independent variable. (p. 7)

**convection**  (kuhn VEHKT shuhn) Circular flow of matter in currents in a heated material. (p. 59)

**convection zone**  About 400 000 km from the core of the sun, the area where matter expands and rises, then cools, becomes denser, and sinks back. (p. 560)

**convergent boundary**  Boundary where two plates collide. (p. 100)

**core**  The innermost layer of the earth, composed primarily of iron and nickel. Also, the innermost layer of the sun where nuclear fusion occurs. (pp. 56, 560)

**Coriolis effect**  (KOR ee OH lihs) Caused by the earth's rotation, this effect makes the earth's winds and ocean currents bend and curve. (p. 345)

**corona**  (kuh ROH nuh) The outermost layer of the sun. (p. 560)

**crater**  A hollowed-out area at the top of a volcano; or, a circular indentation on the surface of the moon. (pp. 145, 546)

**creep**  Slow, steady movement along an active fault. Also, the gradual downslope movement of soil. (pp. 140, 264)

**crest**  The highest point of a wave. (p. 352)

**crust**  Outermost layer of the earth that covers the mantle. (p. 56)

**cumulonimbus cloud**  (KYOO myuh low NIM buhs) A tall, dark, puffy rain cloud. (p. 425)

**cumulus cloud**  (KYOO myuh luhs) Large, puffy cloud common on a warm summer day. (p. 424)

**current**  The flow and movement of water in the ocean. (p. 345)

**cyclone**  A hurricane that forms over the Indian Ocean. (p. 450)

**cyclonic wind pattern**  (sy CLAH nihk) Counterclockwise wind pattern that surrounds a low-pressure area, creating hurricanes and major winter storms. (p.445)

  **data**  Information from which analyses and conclusions can be made. (p. 3)

**database** A large collection of organized material in a computer. (p. 520)

**daughter theory** Idea that suggests that the moon was formed from a piece of the Earth that split off at some time. (p. 547)

**decay** Process where an atom of a radioactive isotope breaks down and releases matter and energy from its nucleus. (p. 300)

**deflation** Process of wind carrying away loose sediment. (p. 282)

**deforestation** The systematic cutting down of forests. (p. 518)

**deformation** A change in the shape or structure of the earth's crustal material resulting from bending, folding, breaking, sliding, or tilting. (p. 113)

**delta** Triangular-shaped sediment deposit formed at the mouth of a river. (p. 268)

**density** Measure of how much matter exists in a given volume; density = mass/volume. (p. 16)

**dependent variable** The observed variable in an experiment that changes in response to the independent variable. (p. 7)

**deposition** (DEHP uh ZIH shuhn) The buildup of sediments on the bottoms of lakes, valleys, and the ocean floor. (pp. 78, 263)

**desert pavement** Hard, pebbly surface that is left behind after the wind carries away any loose sediment. (p. 282)

**dew point** Certain temperature at which the air becomes saturated with water vapor. (p. 416)

**diatomaceous earth** (DY uh tuh MAY shuhs) Powdery material, made of glasslike skeletons of diatoms. (p. 384)

**diurnal tides** Pattern of tides with one high tide and one low tide per day. (p. 357)

**divergent boundary** Any boundary where plates move away from each other, and where new crust is being created. (p. 100)

**divide** A ridge separating different drainage systems. (p. 325)

**domesticated** Characteristic of plants and animals that are cared for by agricultural societies. (p. 511)

**Doppler effect** A change in wave frequency, and therefore in the pitch of sound, caused by movement of either the source or the receiver of the sound. (p. 604)

**drainage system** A pattern of streams and rivers that flows into the ocean. (p. 325)

**dry climate** Located on both sides of the equator between 15° and 30° north and south latitudes, this climate includes some of the earth's driest deserts. Dry climates also occur in the middle latitudes between 35° and 50° north latitudes in western North America and the Asian interior, and are characterized by little rainfall, cold winters, and warm to very hot summers. (p. 470)

**ductile** Able to change shape without breaking. (p. 113)

**dune** A deposit formed from windblown sand. (p. 283)

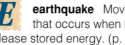 **earthquake** Movement of the earth's crust that occurs when rocks suddenly break and release stored energy. (p. 133)

**eclipse** (ee KLIHPS) The shadow caused when one astronomical body passes between the sun and another body. (p. 552)

**ecosystem** (EEK oh SIHS tuhm) Area in which living things interact with each other and the environment. (p. 381)

**elastic limit** The amount of stress a material can absorb without breaking apart. (p. 134)

**electromagnetic spectrum** The entire range of visible and invisible electromagnetic waves, from radio waves to gamma rays. (p. 586)

**electromagnetic wave** Wave of energy that makes up the electromagnetic spectrum. (p. 586)

**electron** (ee LEHK trahn) A subatomic particle with a negative charge located outside an atom's nucleus. (p. 161)

**elevation** Distance measured above sea level. (p. 34)

**elliptical** Referring to an object's orbit in space, which is not in a perfect circle, but rather in the shape of an ellipse. (p. 572)

**elliptical galaxy** A galaxy shaped like a slightly flattened circle. (p. 602)

**El Niño** A disturbance of ocean winds and currents off the western coast of South America, occurring every three to eight years, that warms coastal waters, killing many organisms and starving many fishes. (pp. 350, 478)

**endangered species** Particular species of plant or animal that is in immediate danger of becoming extinct. (p. 517)

**epicenter** The point on the earth's surface directly above the focus of an earthquake. (p. 134)

**epoch** Subdivision of a geological period on the geologic timescale. (p. 85)

**equator** The imaginary line around the earth's center, equidistant from the poles, and perpendicular to the earth's axis of rotation. (p. 38)

**equinox** (EE kwuh nahks) The first day of spring or fall, when the sun is directly over the equator, called the vernal equinox (spring) or autumnal equinox (fall). (p. 540)

**era** The largest division of the earth's history; the Precambrian, Paleozoic, Mesozoic, and Cenozoic Eras are measured in millions of years. (p. 84)

**erosion** (ee ROH zhuhn) Process by which smaller particles of rock are displaced by moving water, wind, or ice. (pp. 77, 263)

**estivate** (EHS tuh vayt) What amphibians, such as frogs, do when they burrow in the mud and remain dormant for the winter. (p. 541)

**estuary** (EHS choo AIR ee) A bay or inlet of low salinity, where river water mixes with ocean water. (p. 340)

**evaporation** Phase change when liquid water turns to vapor by the heat energy of the sun. (p. 320)

**evaporite** Sedimentary rock formed from the evaporation of ocean or lake waters. (p. 223)

**evolution** A change in a living population over time. (p. 290)

**exfoliation** (EHKS foh lee AY shun) Process where outer layers of granite expand, crack, and flake off; caused by extreme changes in temperature. (p. 239)

**exosphere** Outermost layer of the atmosphere that extends several thousand kilometers above the earth. (p. 403)

**exponential growth** (EHKS poh NEHN shuhl) Growth of a population that doubles its numbers at regular, predictable intervals. (p. 513)

**extinction** The dying out of a species that is unable to adapt to its environment. (p. 290)

**extrusive rock** Igneous rock formed from lava that solidifies on or near the earth's surface. (p. 215)

 **fault** A fracture in the earth's crust where movement has occurred. (p. 117)

**fault plane** The fracture line of a fault. (p. 117)

**fissure** Long crack in soil or rock resulting from an earthquake. (p. 141)

**floodplain** Valley area surrounding the banks of a river that has been built up from sediment left by repeated flooding. (pp. 267, 269)

**fluorescence** (flor EHS uhns) Property of a mineral that glows when exposed to ultraviolet light. (p. 196)

**focus** The point along a fault where rocks first break and move, causing an earthquake. (p.134)

**fog** A cloud that forms on the earth's surface. (p. 426)

**folding** The bending of rock layers resulting from compressional stress. (p. 115)

**foliated rock** Striped-looking, metamorphic rock with grains arranged in parallel bands. (p. 228)

**food chain** Sequence of organisms through which food energy passes. (381)

**footwall** Formed from the rocks below the fault plane. (p. 117)

**fossil** Remains or traces of an organism that lived in the past. (p. 79)

**fossil fuel** An energy source made from the buried remains of decayed plants and animals that lived hundreds of millions of years ago: coal, oil, and natural gas. (p. 492)

**fossil record** Record of life on the earth provided by fossils. (p. 294)

**fracture** Property of a mineral that breaks, leaving an uneven or splintered surface. (p. 194)

**front** The boundary where two different air masses meet, causing sudden weather changes. (p. 441)

**G** **galaxy** A very large collection of stars, nebulae, gases, dust, and planets, that travels through space bound together by gravity. (p. 601)

**gem** Rare, beautiful mineral that is cut and polished; used for jewelry and ornamentation. (p. 203)

**geode** Mineral rock formed when hot, mineral-containing liquid inside the rock evaporates, leaving the rock's interior lined with mineral crystals. (p. 187)

**geologic time** The time scale of the history of the earth and its life. (p. 76)

**geothermal energy** Alternative energy source that comes from heat energy within the earth, such as water that has been heated near igneous rocks by magma. (p. 499)

**geyser** Vent in the ground where superheated water builds up pressure and finally blows out of the small surface opening. (p. 332)

**gibbous moon** Phase of the moon when more than half of the side that faces Earth is lighted. (p. 551)

**glacier** Formed when the amount of snow is so great that all of the snow is unable to melt. (p. 274)

**Gondwanaland** (gahnd WAH nuh LAND) The large southern continent formed when the supercontinent of Pangaea broke apart. (p. 92)

**gravity** The attracting force between the sun and each planet that exists because of their mass, keeping the planets in their orbits. (p. 572)

**greenhouse effect** A process that traps energy from the sun by allowing radiant energy to enter a given space, but preventing heat energy from escaping. (p. 408)

**groundwater** Water beneath the earth's surface that soaked into the ground from rain or melted snow. (p. 329)

**gully** Channel formed from stream erosion when rainwater produces rills, and the rills join together, flowing downhill and removing topsoil. (p. 266)

**guyot** (GEE oh) Volcanic island that has stopped growing and been flattened by wave action. (p. 375)

**gyre** (JY ur) Surface current that flows in a circular pattern: clockwise in the Northern Hemisphere, and counterclockwise in the Southern Hemisphere. (p. 347)

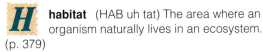 **habitat** (HAB uh tat) The area where an organism naturally lives in an ecosystem. (p. 379)

**hachures** (HASH oorz) Short lines used on a map to indicate slopes, their degree, and direction. (p. 46)

**hail** Type of precipitation that forms when small snow pellets or frozen raindrops collide with supercooled water droplets in a cloud, are caught in upward-rising air, and returned to the thundercloud. (p. 431)

**half-life** Measurement scientists use to describe how long it takes for half of the atoms in a sample to decay. (p. 300)

**hanging wall** Formed from the rocks above the fault plane. (p. 117)

**heft** Property of a mineral that is measured by picking the mineral up and comparing its mass to an equal volume of another mineral. (p. 194)

**heliocentric** Descriptive of something that is centered around the sun, as a model of the solar system. (p. 572)

**hemispheres** The halves of the earth north and south of the equator; also the halves of the earth east and west of the prime meridian. (p. 38)

**highland** Bright, mountainous terrain on the surface of the moon. (p. 546)

**high tide** Highest level the ocean water reaches on the shore. (p. 356)

**hominid** (HAHM uh nihd) First humanlike organism that appeared between 4 and 8 million years ago. (p. 307)

**Homo erectus** First upright-walking ancestor of modern man, whose fossils date back about 1.6 million years. (p. 307)

**Homo sapiens** Species of human that evolved from Homo erectus, and appeared between 500,000 and 130,000 years ago. (p. 307)

**horizon** One of the three boundary layers of mature soils. Also, the line where the Earth seems to meet the sky. (pp. 248, 540)

**horn** Sharp peak formed when several cirques are close together. (p. 276)

**hot spot** An area of frequent volcanic activity on the earth's surface, which develops from an especially hot area of the mantle. (p. 148)

**humid cold climate** Found in the northern temperate zone, climate characterized by short, warm, wet summers, and long, very cold winters. (p. 471)

**humidity** Amount of water vapor that is contained in the air. (p. 415)

**humus** (HYOO muhs) The uppermost, nutrient-rich layer of soil. (p. 248)

**hurricane** A violent, tropical storm with sustained winds of at least 120 km/h that forms over warm oceans near the equator. (p. 450)

**hydroelectric energy** Alternative energy resource that produces electricity from water moving through dams; also uses tidal energy to make electricity, but this process has limited use. (p. 499)

**hygrometer** A device that measures humidity using human hair. (p. 418)

**hypothesis** (hy PAHTH uh sihs) A possible answer or solution to a particular problem, based on current information. (p. 5)

 **igneous rock** (IHG nee uhs) Rocks produced by the cooling and solidifying of magma. (p. 215)

**impermeable** Describes a rock with spaces that do not easily conduct water. (p. 329)

**independent variable** A manipulated variable in an experiment that causes the change in the dependent variable. (p. 7)

**inertia** The tendency of an object to remain at rest or in motion until acted upon by an external force. (p. 573)

**infer** To make a conclusion based on available data. (p. 4)

**inner planets** Mercury, Venus, Earth, and Mars, all of which have a liquid core made of nickel and iron, and a rocky mantle and crust. (p. 570)

**interglacial** Period of warming that separated the ice ages, when glaciers melted and retreated. (p. 477)

**international date line** The imaginary line of longitude where the date changes, directly opposite the prime meridian. (p. 39)

**intrusive rock** Igneous rock formed when magma cools and solidifies beneath the earth's surface. (p. 215)

**invertebrate** Animal without a backbone common during the early Paleozoic Era. (p. 304)

**ion** (EYE ahn) An atom or group of atoms having an electric charge as a result of losing or gaining one or more electrons. (p. 161)

**ionic bond** (eye AHN ihk) A chemical bond between a metal and a nonmetal in which electrons are transferred from one atom to another. (p. 163)

**ionosphere** (eye AHN oh sfihr) An indistinct layer of air within the upper mesosphere and the thermosphere where solar radiation strips atoms and molecules of their electrons, which then become ions. These ions reflect light and radio signals, and bounce them back to earth. (p. 404)

**irregular galaxy** The least common type of galaxy, without a regular shape or form. (p. 602)

**isobar** Line on a weather map that connects points of equal atmospheric pressure. (p. 443)

**isobath** (EYE soh bath) Contour line on a bathymetric map. (p. 368)

**isostasy** (eye SAHS teh see) The balance of gravity and buoyancy in the earth's crust. (p. 127)

**isotherm** (EYE soh thurm) Curving line on a weather map that connects points with the same temperature. (p. 457)

**isotope** (EYE soh tohp) Atoms of the same element having different numbers of neutrons, with resultant different atomic masses. (p. 162)

 **jet stream** A narrow ribbon of winds located 8 000 to 12 000 m above the earth's surface. (p. 445)

 **kettle lake** Lake formed when a block of ice breaks off from a glacier, is buried, and melts. (p. 277)

**kilogram** Basic SI unit of mass; abbreviated kg. (p. 15)

**kingdom** One of the five major divisions into which all living things can be classified. (p. 291)

 **laccolith** A bulge or dome-shaped formation resulting from magma intruding into layers of existing rocks. (p. 217)

**landform** Main feature of the earth's surface. (p. 34)

**landslide** Type of mass movement where large amounts of rock and soil move rapidly downhill. (p. 264)

**lateral fault** A fault characterized by side-to-side movement, caused by shear stress, with little or no up-and-down movement. (p. 117)

**laterite** (LAYT er YT) Rusty, red tropical soil, heavily leached by frequent rains, with a high content of iron oxide. (p. 257)

**latitude** Distance measured in degrees north and south of the equator. (pp. 39, 463)

**Laurasia** (lawr AY zhuh) The large northern continent that was formed when the supercontinent of Pangaea broke apart. (p. 92)

**lava** Hot liquid rock (magma) which reaches the earth's surface. (p. 144)

**layer** A single thickness of a material covering a surface, usually horizontally. (p. 55)

**leaching** Chemical weathering process where rainwater carries dissolved minerals from the surface soil deeper into the ground, resulting in mineral-poor surface soil with a mineral-rich layer below it. (p. 243)

**levee** Sediment that is deposited in a long ridge along a mature or old riverbank during floods. (p. 269)

**light-year** The distance light travels in one year at a speed of 310 000 km per second, about 9.5 trillion km. (p. 591)

**lignite** The second stage of coal development, lignite is a soft brown coal that contains about 40% carbon, and releases harmful pollutants when burned; used in some European countries. (p. 493)

**liter** Metric unit of volume; abbreviated L. (p. 15)

**lithification** Process where sediment is hardened into rock. (p. 221)

**lithosphere** (LITH uhs FEER) The cool, solid, outer layer of the earth extending to a depth of about 100 km. (p. 57)

**littoral zone** (LIHT uh ruhl) Ocean life zone in the shallow water area between the low-tide line and the high-tide line. (p. 380)

**local group** A large cluster of galaxies including the Milky Way galaxy. (p. 603)

**loess** Fine-grained angular particles, formed from rocks during the last ice age, that are deposited by wind erosion to make up prairie soil. (pp. 255, 283)

**scale** A proportion used to determine the distance between two points on a map. (p. 43)

**scarp** Cliff created by sudden earth movements along a fault. (p. 141)

**schist** Coarse-grained metamorphic rock formed from shale or slate. (p. 226)

**scientific method** Involves the systemized testing of hypotheses, predictions, and inferences about the scientific world, where scientists constantly exchange ideas and information. (p. 8)

**sea-floor spreading** The theory claiming that the mid-ocean ridge is a huge crack in the earth's crust where the hot mantle pushes through and spreads the ocean floor apart. (p. 97)

**seamount** Formed near mid-ocean ridges, a volcanic mountain that rises more than 1,000 meters above the ocean floor. (p. 375)

**secondary wave** (or S wave) A seismic wave that travels by up–and–down movement of rock. (pp. 62, 134–135)

**sediment** Particles carried away by erosion. (p. 77)

**sedimentary rock** Rock formed from layered sediments that pile up and squeeze together, providing clues to the earth's past. (pp. 78, 220)

**seismic array** (SYZ mihk) Cluster of interconnected seismographs. (p. 65)

**seismic wave** Shock wave in the earth caused by an earthquake. (pp. 61, 134)

**seismograph** Instrument used to detect earthquake (seismic) waves. (p. 65)

**semidiurnal tides** Pattern of tides where there are two high tides and two low tides each day. (p. 357)

**shadow zone** An area around the earth directly opposite the focus of an earthquake, where no seismic waves can be detected. (p. 63)

**shear** Type of stress where rocks in the earth's crust are pushing in different horizontal directions. (p. 114)

**shield volcano** A volcano with a flat, shieldlike top that produces runny, easily-flowing lava. (p. 147)

**SI** (Système internationale d'unités) The metric system, the most commonly used system of measurement based on the meter. (p. 13)

**silicates** Rocky materials in the crust and mantle, composed of silicon, oxygen, and other elements, such as aluminum, iron, and magnesium. (p. 56)

**sister theory** Theory that proposes that the Earth and moon formed at the same time and from the same material. (p. 547)

**sleet** Type of precipitation formed when raindrops or snowflakes fall through air layers of different temperatures. (p. 430)

**slide** Rapid downslope movement of soil, debris, and rock. (p. 141)

**slope** Steepness of a landform. (p. 47)

**slump** Mass movement caused by weak layers of underlying material moving downslope as a single unit. (p. 264)

**smog** Air pollution caused by using fossil fuels, which results in air that is unhealthy to breathe. (p. 408)

**soil profile** A cross section of the layers of soil, such as a hole that is dug in the ground. (p. 248)

**solar eclipse** When the moon passes between the sun and the Earth, causing the moon's shadow to fall on Earth. (p. 552)

**solar energy** Energy from the sun used to heat buildings and homes. (p. 502)

**solar flare** On the sun's surface, a very intense spurt of radiation, lasting from 10 minutes to 1 hour, which interrupts radio communications on Earth. (p. 562)

**solar system** The Earth and the eight other planets, along with various other bodies that orbit the sun. (p. 559)

**solar winds** A steady stream of charged particles from the corona of the sun that are responsible for the displays of light in the sky called the aurora borealis and the aurora australis. (p. 562)

**solstice** In the northern hemisphere, the first day of summer when the noon sun is directly over 23°N; or, the first day of winter when the noon sun is directly over 23°S. (p. 540)

**sonar** Devices that bounce sound waves off the ocean floor, providing scientists with an accurate image of the ocean-floor topography. (pp. 96, 366)

**species** (SPEE sheez) The basic unit of classification, the division of a genus, made of very similar organisms that are able to mate and reproduce offspring of the same type. (p. 290)

**specific gravity** Ratio of a mineral's density compared to the density of water. (p. 194)

**spectrograph** Tool used to separate light through a prism or diffraction grating. The spectrum is recorded with a camera or electronic detector. (p. 588)

**spectroscope** An instrument used by scientists that disperses a beam of light into a spectrum of its component wavelengths. (p. 588)

**spiral galaxy**  A pinwheel-shaped galaxy like the Milky Way. (p. 602)

**spit**  A deposit of sediment, extending out from a beach across a bay or inlet. (p. 272)

**stalactite**  An icicle-like mineral form that hangs from cavern ceilings. (p. 331)

**stalagmite**  A pillar of minerals that forms on a cavern floor. (p. 331)

**star cluster**  A group of stars close together, but smaller in number than a galaxy. (p. 603)

**stationary front**  Boundary between two nonmoving air masses, generally causing light rain. (p. 442)

**steam fog**  Fog that forms when cold air moves over warm water. (p. 426)

**stratosphere**  Layer of the atmosphere, between the troposphere and the mesosphere, that contains the ozone layer. (p. 403)

**stratus cloud**  (STRA tuhs) Widespread flat, dull gray clouds that frequently produce rain or drizzle. (p. 424)

**streak**  Colored powder that a mineral leaves on a streak plate. (p. 193)

**stress**  Forces that act on the rocks of the earth's crust, causing movement of the crust, or a change in shape or volume. (p. 114)

**stromatolite**  (stroh MAT uh lyt) Oldest known fossil of moneran that lived about 3,500 million years ago. (p. 303)

**subduction**  (suhb DUHK shuhn) The process of one plate moving under another plate. (p.101)

**submarine canyon**  Canyons made from currents, and cut by rivers that carried great amounts of water and sediments to the ocean during the ice ages. (p. 373)

**submersible**  (suhb MUR suh buhl) Underwater research vessels that enable scientists to explore deep in the ocean. (p. 367)

**sunspot**  Cool, black looking storm areas that occur on the sun's surface. (p. 562)

**supergiant**  A very bright star, ranging from cool to medium hot. (p. 593)

**supernova**  The most violent event known to occur in the universe, it is the explosion of a supergiant. (p. 599)

**surface tension**  Property of liquids that makes their molecules tend to stick together in a stretched, cohesive manner like a membrane. (p. 318)

**swell**  Wave energy that forms a series of smooth, rolling hills of water. (p. 352)

**syncline**  (SIHN klyn) Type of folding where a middle area has sunk below the level of its two sides. (p. 115)

**synoptic chart**  A weather map that shows current weather data from many different locations, using symbols for air temperature, type of storm or cloud cover, wind direction and speed, and atmospheric pressure. (p. 457)

**T**  **temperate zone**  Mildest of the three climate zones, lying on both sides of the tropical zone and extending to 60° north and south latitude. (p. 469)

**tension**  Type of stress in the earth's crust where rocks are stretched or pulled apart. (p. 114)

**theory**  A set of facts, based on separate but related hypotheses, explaining the behavior of a particular phenomenon. (p. 9)

**thermocline**  (THUR moh KLYN) Zone of rapid temperature change in ocean water beneath the surface zone. (p. 341)

**thermosphere**  Layer of the atmosphere right below the exosphere. (p. 403)

**thrust fault**  Fault where the hanging wall rides up and over the footwall as a result of compression. (p. 117)

**thunderstorm**  Caused when a cumulonimbus cloud, filled with positive and negative ions, has a great enough difference in charges to cause lightning and thunder. (p. 449)

**tide**  Daily ebb and flow of water levels in the oceans and other large bodies of water. (pp. 356, 553)

**till**  Mixture of different sediment sizes in a moraine. (p. 277)

**topography**  A precise description of the surface features of a particular area, including elevation. (pp. 45, 467)

**tornado**  (tor NAY doh) A whirling, funnel-shaped windstorm, with rotating winds of more than 500 km/h, that moves or skips on a narrow path along the ground. (p. 451)

**toxin**  A chemical with the capacity to damage the health of organisms. (p. 519)

**trace fossils**  Footprints, tracks, trails, and burrows left by animals or early humans. (p. 295)

**transducer**  Device that changes energy from one form to another. (p. 202)

**transform boundary**  Boundary where two plates slide in opposite directions beside each other. (p. 100)

**transpiration** (TRAN spuh RAY shun) Process where water moves up through a plant, eventually exiting through tiny holes in the leaves. (p. 322)

**transverse wave** A wave in which matter moves at a right angle to the direction of the wave. (p. 135)

**trench** A deep valley on the ocean floor. (p. 101)

**tributary** (TRIHB yoo TAIR ee) A small stream that flows into a larger one. (p. 325)

**tropical zone** Warmest of the three climate zones, located between latitudes 30°N and 30°S, characterized by high temperatures and heavy amounts of rain. (p. 469)

**troposphere** (TROH puh sfihr) Life-containing layer of the atmosphere that is closest to the surface of the earth. (pp. 403, 439)

**trough** (TROF) The lowest point of a wave. (p. 352)

**tsunami** (soo NAHM ee) A giant ocean wave that travels at speeds over 700 km/h, caused by underwater earthquakes, landslides, or volcanic eruptions. (pp. 142, 354)

**typhoon** A hurricane that forms over the western Pacific Ocean. (p. 450)

 **umbra** In an eclipse, the blackest part of a shadow cast by the Earth, moon, or other body. (p. 552)

**unconformity** (UHN kuhn FORM uh tee) A definitive line between two rock layers indicating a break in geologic time. (p. 83)

**undertow** Type of current formed when water, carried to the shore in waves, pulls back toward the ocean. (p. 349)

**universal solvent** Another name for water, so-named because it can dissolve more substances than any other liquid. (p. 319)

**uplift** Process by which parts of the earth's crust are raised up higher than other parts, forming mountains and plateaus. (p. 78)

**upwelling** In the ocean, the upward movement of cold, deep water. (p. 348)

**valley glacier** Glacier that forms in a high mountain valley. (p. 274)

 **Van Allen radiation belt** A belt of charged particles that surrounds the earth; a part of the magnetosphere, which is part of the thermosphere. (p. 404)

**vent** An opening in the earth's surface where volcanic material, gas, or steam emerges. (p. 145)

**vertebrate** Animal with a backbone that appeared during the Ordovician period. (p. 304)

**volcano** An opening in the earth's crust that has released molten rock. (p. 144)

**volume** The amount of space that something occupies. (p. 15)

 **watershed** Surrounding land area that supplies runoff to streams in a drainage system. (p. 325)

**warm front** Boundary where a warm, less dense air mass overtakes a cold, dense air mass, producing cloudy skies, rain, or snow. (p. 442)

**water table** The boundary between the zone of aeration and the zone of saturation. (p. 330)

**wave** The periodic up-and-down motion of a body of water. (p. 351)

**wave height** The vertical distance measured between a wave's crest and its trough. (p. 352)

**wavelength** The distance measured from the crest of one wave to the crest of another wave. (p. 352)

**weathering** The process during which rocks are broken up into smaller particles by the action of water, the atmosphere, and organisms. (pp. 77, 239)

**white dwarf** A low-magnitude, relatively hot star. (p. 593)

 **x-axis** The horizontal line on a graph. (p. 20)

 **y-axis** The vertical line on a graph. (p. 20)

**zenith** The highest point in the sky, directly overhead. (p. 540)

# Index

Oceans, *22*, *32-33*, 33-34
  elements of, 179
  tide patterns, 357
Oil, crude. *See* Petroleum
Oil drilling, *494*, 494
  offshore, *497*, 497
Oil spills, 497
Open-pit mining, *490*, 490, 491
Optical telescopes, **25**, *585*, 585
Orbits
  of comets, 578-579, *579*
  of Earth, around sun, **539**, *539*, 539
  of planets, 572
  of moon around Earth, *549*, 549
Ores, **489**
  formation of, 489
  mining of, *490*, 490
Organic matter, **178**
Organic rock, **223**, 223
Organisms, *23*
  in soil, *249*, 249, *250*, 250
  and water, 322
Organizational skills, 5
Origin of earth, 76
Orion Nebula, *597*, 597, *603*
Orthorhombic crystal structure, *189*
Oscillators, *202*
Outwash, **277**
Outwash plains, **277**
Oxbow lakes, 267
Oxidation, **242**, *242*
Oxides, *188*, 188
Oxygen, 56, 58, 77, 178
  altitude and, 128
  in atmosphere, 77, *393*, 407
Oxygen-carbon dioxide cycle, **394**, *394*
Ozone, 180, 403, 407, *409*, 409

**P**  P waves, *63*
  Pacific Ocean, *33*
Paleontologists, 307
Paleozoic Era, 84, 94, *304*, 304
Pangaea, **91**, 92, 304, 305, 476
Parallax, in viewing stars, **591**, *591*
Parent rock, **246**, *246*
Peat, *492*, **493**, 493, 495
Peninsulas, **35**, *35*
Penumbra, **552**
Perigee, **547**
Perihelion, **539**
Period of revolution, **573**, *573*, 573
Periodic table, 175, *176-177*
  organization of, *176-177*
Periods, of ocean waves, **352**
Permafrost, 257
Permeability, **329**
Perspiration, 322, 420
Pest control, organic, *525*
Petrified fossils, 295
Petrochemicals, **495**

Petroleum, *494*, 494
  drilling for, *494*, 494
  locating deposits of, 494
  refining of, *495*, 495
  uses of, *495*, 495
Phase changes of substances, **169**, *169*, 169, *170*, 170
  of water, 318
Phases, of moon, *551*, 551
Phosphorus, 190, 247
Photosphere, *560*, 560, 561
Photosynthesis, **322**, 393, 563
Physical changes in matter, 168
Physical properties, 160
  of ocean water, 341
  of water, 318
Plains, **34**, *34*
Planets, 76, 559, 567, *568-569*, 570-574
  elliptical orbits of, *572*, 572
  inner, 570
  Jovian, 570
  movement of, 572-573
  outer, 570-571
  periods of revolution, *573*, 573
  periods of rotation, *573*, 573
Plankton, *380*
Plant kingdom, *291*, 303
Plant nutrients, *247*, 247
Plant weathering, *240*
Plants
  flowering, first, 305
  and water, 322
Plasma phase, 170
Plastics, biodegradable, *524*
Plate boundaries, 100-101, *102-103*, 377-378
  diverging, 375
  types of, *100*
Plate movement, *102-103*, 102, 103-104
  measuring, 103, 104
  models for, 107
  physics of, 106-108
Plate tectonics theory, 98-104
Plateaus, **34**, *34*
  types of, 126
Plates, 98-104, *102*
  continental, *99*, 99
  interactions at boundaries of, 100-102
  oceanic, *99*, 99
  structure of, *99*, 99
Pleiades, 601
Pluto, 569, 570
Plutonic mountains, 124, 125
Plutons, **124**, 124, 217, 217
Podsols, **254**
Polar climate zone, *470*, 473
Polar molecules, **318**
Polarity
  normal, *97*
  reversed, *97*, 97
Pollution, 410

from burning fossil fuels, 493, 496, 497, 515, 519
  of groundwater, 332, 333
  and human health, 519
  from mining, 491
  from nuclear fission reactors, 500-501
  solutions to, *524-525*
Ponds, *326*
Population growth, *513*, 513
  and precipitation, *433*, 433
Porosity, **329**
Porphyritic rock, *215*, 215
Potassium, 247
Power plants
  nuclear, *500-501*, 500
  tidal, 360
Prairie soils, *255*, 255
Precambrian Era, 84, *303*, 303
Precipitation, **187**, **320**, 321, **428**
  acid rain, 434, 518
  and air temperature, *428*
  causes of, 428-429
  and climate, 463, 466-467
  and cloud type, *428*
  forms of, *430*
  and population growth, *433*, 433
  and prevailing winds, 448, 466-467
  rainfall, 36, 77, 320-321, 428, 429, *430*, 434, 518
  of storms, 448-450
  and topography, *467*, 467
Predictions, 4
Preservation of natural habitats, **522**, *522*
Preserves, 522
Pressure, and ocean depth, 341
Primary (P) waves, 135
Prime meridian, **39**, 542
Prominences, solar, *562*
Protist kingdom, *291*, 303
Protons, **161**, *161*
Protoplanets, 566-567
Protostars, **595**, 595
Protosun, 566, *567*, 567
Proxima Centauri, 589
Psychrometer, **418-419**, *418*, 418-419
Pumice, 215, *216*, 216

**Q**  Quartz, useful properties of, 202
  Quasars, 104

**R**  Radar, in weather forecasting, *454*
Radiant energy, *399*, 399
Radiation fog, 426
Radiation zone, of sun, *560*, 560, 561
Radiant energy, *399*, 399
Radio signals, and atmosphere, 405
Radio telescopes, *26*, 26, *104*, 588

everyday uses of, 251
fertile, 247
forest, 254
grassland, *255*, 255
horizons, *248*, 248, 254
immature, *246*
mature, *246*
of mountains, *256*, 256
particle size and shape, *247*
plant nutrients in, *247*, 247, *250*, 250
prairie, *255*, 255
property of, 247
sources of, 245
tropical, *257*, 257
tundra, *257*, 257
types of, throughout world, *253*, 253-258
Solar eclipses, **552**, *552*, 552
Solar energy, 463, *464*, 502-503, *525*, 559-560, *563*, 563
Solar flares, *562*
Solar heating, *502*, 502
active, *502*, 502
passive, *502*, 502
Solar power
direct, 502
indirect, 503
Solar radiation, 399, 559
Solar storms, *562*, 562
Solar system, 558-580, **559**
formation of, 566-567
orbits, *572*, 572
planets in, *567*, *568-569*
Solar wind, *562*
Solids, 169
Solomon, Susan, 409
Solstices, **540**, *540*, 540
Solubility, **160**
Solutions, 167
precipitation from, 187
Solvent, universal, **319**
Sonar devices, 96
Sonar research methods, 366, 369
South America, *32*, 32, 92
South Pole, *38*, 38
Space exploration, 605-606
Space junk, 580
Space probes, 574, 605-606, *606*
Space science careers, *24*
Species, **290**
Specific gravity, of minerals, 194
Spectroscopes, 588
Spiral galaxies, *600*
Spits, 272
Spring tides, *358*, *358*, **553**
Stalactites, **331**
Stalagmites, **331**
Star clusters, **601**
Stars, 585-603
classification of, 593
colors of, *590*, 590
distance of, 590

distances between, 589
dwarf stage, 596
energy sent out by, 583
evolution of, *596*
life-cycle of, 567, 595-596, *596-597*
low-mass, 595-596
magnitude of, 590
observation of, 583
red giant stage, 596
temperatures of, 590
State fossils, 297
Stationary fronts, **442**, 442
Steam fog, 426
Steel, 200, 204
Storm warnings, 452
Storms, 448-452
characteristics of, 448
major types of, 449-451
regional, 451
Straits, **35**, *35*
Stratosphere, **403**, 403
Stratus clouds, **424**, *424*, 425
Streak, of minerals, **193**
Stream deposition, 268
Stream erosion, 266
Streams, 325
Streptomyces, **249**
Stresses, crustal, 114, *114*
Stromatolites, 303
Subatomic particles, 161
Subduction, **101**
Subduction zones, 101, 107, 137, *376*, 376, 377
Submarine canyons, **373**, 373
Submersibles, *367*, 367
robotic, 370
Subscripts, 166
Subsoil, 248
Sulfates, *188*, 188
Sulfides, *188*, 188
Sulfur, 201, 247
Sulfuric acid, 243, 244
Summer, 539
Summer solstice, *540*, 540
Sun, 59-564
activity on surface of, 562
birth of, 76
and body rhythms, 564
energy from, 463, *464*, 502-503, *525*, 559-560, *563*, 563
gravitational attraction of, 572-573, *573*
layers of, **560**, 560
nuclear fission reactions in, 559-560
nuclear fusion in, 567
and tides, 553
Sunlit zone, of oceanic zone, **381**
Sunspots, *562*
Superconductors, 173
Supergiant stars, 599
Supergiants, *592*
Supernovas, **599**
Superposition, principle of, *298*

Surface (L) waves, 135
Surface mining, *490*, 490, *491*, 491, 492
Surface tension, 319
Surface water, 324-328
Symbols, chemical, 166
Synclines, **115**, *115*, 116
Synoptic charts, **457**
*Système internationale d'unités*, *13*, 13-16, 18

 Technology, **509**
of agricultural societies, 513
and climate changes, 80
cultural differences in, 509-512
of hunting-and-gathering societies, *510*, 510, *513*
of industrial societies, *512*, 512, *513*
and science, 520
Tectonic plates. *See* Plates
Telescopes, 25-26
optical, *587*, 587
radio, *26*, 26, *104*, 588
refracting, 26, *587*, 587
reflecting, **25-26**, 25-26, *26*, *587*, 587, 589
Temperate climate zone, *470*, *472*, *473*
Temperature change, weathering by, *241*
Temperature measurement scales, 17
Temperatures, 36
and climate, 463-465
of earth, 80
of earth's interior, 57, 61
factors influencing, 463-465
Tension, as crustal stress, **114**, *114*, 117
Tetragonal crystal structure, *189*
Theories, scientific, 9
Thermocline, **341**
Thermosphere, **403**, 403
Thrust faults, 117, 122
Thunderstorms, *449*, 449
Tidal energy, 360, 499
Tidal wetlands, 381
Tides, 357, **553**, 553
diurnal, **357**, *357*
as energy source, 360
mixed, **357**
monthly cycles, *358*, 358
moon's influence on, 553
organisms and, 359
semidiurnal, **357**, *357*
tide level differences, *358*, 358
Till, **277**
Time, geologic. *See* Geologic time scale
Time, SI units of, 18
Time zones, *542*, 542
Topographic maps, 45-49, *46*
contour lines, 45-46, *46*
satellite information for, 49
symbols, *48*

# Acknowledgments

## Photographs

**Title page** iTL Dan McCoy/Rainbow; iTLC NASA; iTR Robert Caputo/Stock, Boston; iTRC Joyce Photographics/Photo Researchers; iB Geoffrey Nilsen*

**Contents** iiiB Bjorn Bolstad/Photo Researchers; iiiT Ken Karp*; ivC Kevin Schafer/AllStock; ivLB NASA; ivLT Kevin Schafer & Martha Hill/Tom Stack & Associates; ivR Roger Ressmeyer/Starlight; vBC Geoffrey Nilsen*; vBL Geoffrey Nilsen*; vRC M. Long/Visuals Unlimited; vTL Geoff Tompkinson/SPL/Photo Researchers; vTR Larry Lefever/Grant Heilman Photography; viBL Adam Hart-Davis/SPL/Photo Researchers; viBR Douglas Mazonowicz/Gallery of Prehistoric Art; viC Andrew Leitch/Discover Magazine; viTL David M. Dennis/Tom Stack & Associates; viTR Gregory G. Dimijian/ Photo Researchers; viiBC Dave Fleetham/Tom Stack & Associates; viiBR Jeff Simon/Bruce Coleman Inc.; viiCR Jan Hinsch/SPL/Photo Researchers; viiL Jeff Foott/DRK Photo; viiTR F. Stuart Westmorland/AllStock; viiiBL Runk-Schoenberger/ Grant Heilman Photography; viiiBR Mike Price/Bruce Coleman Inc.; viiiTL Joel W. Rogers/AllStock; viiiTR Gary Withey/Bruce Coleman Inc.; ixBR William McCoy/Rainbow; ixCR Paul Silverman/Fundamental Photographs; ixL Will & Deni McIntyre/AllStock; ixTR K. H. Switak/Photo Researchers; xBL NASA; xR NASA/Jet Propulsion Lab; xTL Jim Ballard/AllStock; xiBCL Ernst Jahn/Bruce Coleman Inc.; xiBL Tom McHugh/ Photo Researchers; xiBR Renee Purse/Photo Researchers; xiBRC George Whiteley/Photo Researchers; xiTR NASA; xiiiL Craig Walker/Rainbow; xiiiR Wetmore/Photo Researchers; xivBR Eric Simmons/Stock, Boston; xivL Michael Fogden/ Bruce Coleman Inc.; xivTR John Elk/Bruce Coleman Inc.; xvBC Randy Brandon/Peter Arnold, Inc.; xvBL Bill Gallery/ Stock, Boston; xvT Geoffrey Nilsen*; xviBC NASA/Peter Arnold, Inc.; xviBL Breck P. Kent/Animals, Animals; xviBR Runk-Schoenberger/Grant Heilman Photography; xviTR Runk-Schoenberger/Grant Heilman Photography.

**Unit 1** xii Stocktrek Photo Agency; 1 Galen Rowell

**Chapter 1** 2 National Center for Atmospheric Research; 3 Runk-Schoenberger/Grant Heilman Photography; 4B Peter B. Kaplan/Photo Researchers; 4T Tom Bean/DRK Photo; 5 Tom Bean/AllStock; 7 Ken Karp*; 10 Ken Karp*; 14 Ken Karp*; 15 Ken Karp*; 16 Ken Karp*; 17 Ken Karp*; 18 National Institute of Standards & Technology; 25 Ken Karp*; 26L Tom Tracy/The Stock Shop; 26R Greg Hadel/Tony Stone Images

**Chapter 2** 30 George Hall/Woodfin Camp & Associates; 31 NASA; 37 Richard Kolar/Earth Scenes; 42 NASA; 44 Ken Karp*; 45 Tom Bean/AllStock; 47 Peeter Vilms*; 49 Andy Sacks/Tony Stone Images

**Chapter 3** 54 Dieter Blum/Peter Arnold, Inc.; 55 Bjorn Bolstad/ Photo Researchers; 60 Randall Hyman/Stock, Boston; 61 Will & Deni McIntyre/Photo Researchers; 64 Ocean Drilling Program, Texas A&M University; 65 Vince Streano/The Stock Market; 70-71 Cesar Rubio Photography;

**Unit 2** 72 Krafft/Photo Researchers; 72-73 Alberto Garcia/Saba

**Chapter 4** 74 Kim Heacox/AllStock; 75 Chip Carroon/AllStock; 76T David Cannon/Allsport; 77L K. & M. Krafft/Explorer/Photo Researchers; 77R Keith Gunnar/Bruce Coleman Inc; 78L Darrell Gulin/AllStock; 78R Laura Dwight/Peter Arnold, Inc.; 79B SPL/Photo Researchers; 79T Kevin Schafer & Martha Hill/Tom Stack & Associates; 82 Spencer Swanger/Tom Stack & Associates; 83 Albert J. Copley/Visuals Unlimited

**Chapter 5** 90 William Waterfall/The Stock Market; 91 NASA; 102BL George Hall/Woodfin Camp & Associates; 102BR F. Gohier/Photo Researchers; 102TL David Falconer; 103L David Madison/ Bruce Coleman Inc.; 103R Keren Su/Stock, Boston; 104 Dan McCoy/Rainbow; 107 Simon Fraser/SPL/Photo Researchers

**Chapter 6** 112 Michael Collier/Stock, Boston; 113 Joyce Photographics/Photo Researchers; 116 Collier-Condit/Stock, Boston; 117 Tom Bean/DRK Photo; 118 Fletcher & Bayles/ Photo Researchers; 121 Tom Bean/DRK Photo; 122B J. Couffer/Bruce Coleman Inc.; 122T NASA/Grant Heilman Photography; 123 Peter French Photography/DRK Photo; 124 Roy Bishop/Stock, Boston; 125 Steve Vidler/Leo de Wys Inc.; 125B Peeter Vilms*; 126B Tibor Bognar/The Stock Market; 126T David Muench; 128 Keren Su/Stock, Boston

**Chapter 7** 132 Dan McCoy/Rainbow; 133 Ted Mahieu/The Stock Market; 135 Tim Davis*; 140 Kevin Schafer/AllStock; 141BR Mike Andrews/Earth Scenes; 141L Yoav Levy/Phototake; 141TR Francois Gohier/Photo Researchers; 142B Steve McCutcheon/AllStock; 142T Hank Morgan /Rainbow; 144 Galen Rowell; 146C Dieter & Mary Plage /Bruce Coleman Inc.; 146L Dan McCoy/Rainbow; 146R Keith Murakami/Tom Stack & Associates; 147B Darrell Gulin /AllStock; 147L Lindsay Hebberd/Woodfin Camp & Associates; 147T Breck P. Kent/Earth Scenes; 149B Stella Snead/Bruce Coleman Inc.; 149T Oddo & Sinibaldi/The Stock Market; 150 Roger Ressmeyer/Starlight; 154-155 J. Lotter/Tom Stack & Associates

**Unit 3** 156 Karl Hartmann/ Sachs/Phototake; 156-157 David Muench

**Chapter 8** 158 Dan McCoy/Rainbow; 159 Art Wolfe/AllStock; 160BC Dennis Purse/Photo Researchers; 160BL M. Long/ Visuals Unlimited; 160BR Ron Watts/Westlight; 160T Kip Peticolas/Fundamental Photographs; 162CL Michael Dalton/ Fundamental Photographs; 162CR Geoffrey Nilsen*; 162T Larry Lefever/Grant Heilman Photography; 163 Omikron/ Science Source/Photo Researchers; 164 Geoffrey Nilsen*; 165BL Paul von Stroheim; 165BR Breck P. Kent; 165CL Michael Dalton/Fundamental Photographs; 165CR Paul Silverman/Fundamental Photographs; 168B Geoffrey Nilsen*; 169 Geoffrey Nilsen*; 170BC Kent Wood/Peter Arnold, Inc.; 170T Chlaus Lotscher/Peter Arnold, Inc.; 171 Erwin & Peggy Bauer/Bruce Coleman Inc.; 172 Geoffrey Nilsen*; 173 Geoff Tompkinson/SPL/Photo Researchers; 175 Geoffrey Nilsen*; 178B John Gerlach/Visuals Unlimited; 178T Kevin Schafer/ Peter Arnold, Inc.; 179 F. Stuart Westmorland/Tom Stack & Associates

**Chapter 9** 184 Martin Land/SPL/Photo Researchers; 185 Geoffrey Nilsen*; 186 Geoffrey Nilsen*; 187 Geoffrey Nilsen*; 188 Geoffrey Nilsen*; 190 Breck P. Kent; 192 Geoffrey Nilsen*; 193 Geoffrey Nilsen*; 194 Geoffrey Nilsen*; 195 M. Courtney-Clarke/Photo Researchers; 196 E. R. Degginger; 198 Geoffrey Nilsen*; 199 E. R. Degginger; 200 Gene Stein/Westlight; 201 Richard Hutchings/Photo Researchers; 202 Geoffrey Nilsen*; 203B George Holton/Photo Researchers; 203T Geoffrey Nilsen*; 204 Jim Larsen/West Stock

**Chapter 10** 208 Richard Steedman/The Stock Market; 209 Geoffrey Nilsen*; 210 Geoffrey Nilsen*; 211 Geoffrey Nilsen*; 212 Geoffrey Nilsen*; 214 Joseph Nettis/Stock, Boston; 215 Geoffrey Nilsen*; 216 Geoffrey Nilsen*; 218 Geoffrey Nilsen*; 219 C. J. Allen/Stock, Boston; 220 S. J. Krasemann/Peter Arnold, Inc.; 221B Breck P. Kent; 221T J. C. Leacock/West Stock; 222B Grant Heilman/Grant Heilman Photography; 222C John Cancalosi/Peter Arnold, Inc.; 222T Runk-Schoenberger/Grant Heilman Photography; 223B Kevin Schafer/Tom Stack & Associates; 223T Barbara Filet/Tony Stone Images; 224 Frank Fisher/West Stock; 226 Geoffrey Nilsen*; 228 Geoffrey Nilsen*; 229B Ernst Jahn/Bruce Coleman Inc.; 229BL Geoffrey Nilsen*; 229BR Geoffrey Nilsen*; 229CL Geoffrey Nilsen*; 229CR Geoffrey Nilsen*; 229TL Geoffrey Nilsen*; 229TR Geoffrey Nilsen*; 230 Steve Leonard/Tony Stone Images; 234-235 Ric Ergenbright/AllStock; 234BL George Whiteley/Photo Researchers; 234BR Renee Purse/Photo Researchers; 234T Geoffrey Nilsen*; 235 Ed Cooper Photo

**Unit 4** 236 Breck P. Kent/Earth Scenes; 236-237 John Shaw/Tom Stack & Associates

**Chapter 11** 238 Richard Weymouth Brooks/Photo Researchers; 239 Craig Walker/Rainbow; 240C Tom Bean/DRK Photo; 240L Copr. Jim Cummins/AllStock; 240R Len Rue Jr./Stock, Boston; 241C Stan Osolinski/The Stock Market; 241L David M. Dennis/Tom Stack & Associates; 241R Andy Levin/Photo Researchers; 242BL GHP Studio*; 242BR GHP Studio*; 242L Charlie Ott/Photo Researchers; 242TR Robert Harding Picture Library; 243C Adam Hart-Davis/SPL/Photo Researchers; 243L Gerald Davis/Phototake; 243R Gregory G. Dimijian/ Photo Researchers; 244B Runk-Schoenberger/Grant Heilman Photography; 244T Carlos V. Causo/Bruce Coleman Inc.; 245 John Coletti/Stock, Boston; 248 Kenneth W. Fink/Photo Researchers; 249C Runk-Schoenberger/Grant Heilman Photography; 249L Jeff Foott/Bruce Coleman Inc.; 249R Kim Taylor/Bruce Coleman Inc.; 251 J. C. Carton/Bruce Coleman Inc.; 254B James B. Sanderson/The Stock Market; 254TL Michael P. Gadomski/Earth Scenes; 255BL David Muench; 255BRC Tom Bean/AllStock; 256BL Manfred Gottschalk/ Westlight; 256TL K. Gunar/Bruce Coleman Inc.; 257L Charlie Ott/Photo Researchers; 257R Randall Hyman/Stock, Boston; 258 Gary R. Zahm/DRK Photo

**Chapter 12** 262 Don Mason/The Stock Market; 263 Robert Caputo/Stock, Boston; 264BL Brian Parker/Tom Stack & Associates; 264BR Owen Franken/Stock, Boston; 264C Dick Canby/Positive Images; 264T Barbara Alper/Stock, Boston; 265 Smolan/Stock, Boston; 267B Steve McCutcheon/Visuals Unlimited; 267C Kim Heacox/DRK Photo; 267T Breck P. Kent; 268B Keith Gunnar/Bruce Coleman Inc.; 268T Bill Ross/AllStock; 269B Thomas G. Rampton/Grant Heilman Photography; 269T Jack

Couffer/Bruce Coleman Inc.; 271B Michael Ventura/Bruce Coleman Inc.; 271C Randy Brandon/ Peter Arnold, Inc.; 271TL Brian Parker/Tom Stack & Associates; 271TR W. Cody/Westlight; 272L Keith Gunnar/ Bruce Coleman Inc.; 272R T. Kitchin/Tom Stack & Associates; 273 Fred Whitehead/Earth Scenes; 274L Breck P. Kent; 274R Dr. E. R. Degginger; 275 Douglas Mazonowicz; 278 Ann Hawthorne/Black Star; 280 Jerry Howard/Stock, Boston; 281 Peter Pickford/DRK Photo; 282B David Epperson/AllStock; 282T Tom Bean/DRK Photo; 283B Stanley Breeden/DRK Photo; 283C Dr. E. R. Degginger; 283T Francois Gohier/Photo Researchers

**Chapter 13** 288 John Cancalosi/Tom Stack & Associates; 289B Ken Lucas/Biological Photo Service; 289T Francois Gohier; 294 Jack Helle/AllStock; 295L Jeff Gnass/West Stock, Inc.; 295R Breck P. Kent; 296 Breck P. Kent; 297 Breck P. Kent; 298 Richard Kolar/Earth Scenes; 301 Andrew Leitch/Discover Magazine; 307B Tom McHugh/Photo Researchers; 307T John Reader/SPL/Photo Researchers; 312-313 Dallas & Jim Heaton/Westlight

**Unit 5** 314 Johnny Johnson/DRK Photo; 314-315 Ed Cooper

**Chapter 14** 316 Stephen Frisch/Photo 20-20; 319 Steve Solum/Bruce Coleman Inc.; 322 Runk-Schoenberger/Grant Heilman Photography; 324 Bill Horsman/Stock, Boston; 325L USGS EROS Data Center; 326B Doug Wilson/Westlight; 326C Milton Rand/Tom Stack & Associates; 326T Rich Buzzelli/Tom Stack & Associates; 328 C. C. Lockwood/Cactus Clyde Productions; 329B Geoffrey Nilsen*; 329T Runk-Schoenberger/Grant Heilman Photography; 332B Holt Confer/Grant Heilman Photography; 332T Prisma/Westlight; 333 Jeff Amberg/Gamma-Liaison

**Chapter 15** 338 Steve Lissau/Rainbow; 339 Tom Van Sant/Geosphere Project, Santa Monica/SPL/Photo Researchers; 342B Jan Hinsch/SPL/Photo Researchers; 342TL F. Stuart Westmorland/AllStock; 342TR Zig Leszczynski/ Animals, Animals; 343 Grant Heilman/Grant Heilman Photography; 357L Breck P. Kent; 357R Breck P. Kent/Earth Scenes; 359B George Post/CA Maritime Academy; 359T Jeff Foott/DRK Photo; 360 Jean Pierre Ducatez

**Chapter 16** 364 Runk-Schoenberger/Grant Heilman Photography; 365 Jeff Simon/Bruce Coleman Inc.; 366C Rona/Bruce Coleman Inc.; 366L Barry L. Runk/Grant Heilman Photography; 366R Dr. Ken C. MacDonald et. al./UCSB; 367B NASA; 367C NASA; 367T Richard Pasley/Stock, Boston; 370 Rona/Bruce Coleman Inc.; 372 Charles Preitner/Visuals Unlimited; 376 Dr. Peter W. Sloss/NOAA/ NGDC; 378 C. C. Lockwood/Animals, Animals; 379 Dave B. Fleetham/Tom Stack & Associates; 382R Dr. E. R. Degginger; 282L Scott Blackman/Tom Stack & Associates; 383L Helen Elizabeth Carr/Biological Photo Service; 383R Tom McHugh/Photo Researchers; 384 Runk-Schoenberger/Grant Heilman Photography; 388-389 David Muench

**Unit 6** Runk-Schoenberger/Grant Heilman Photography; 390-391 Richard Kaylin/AllStock

**Chapter 17** 392 Brett Baunton/AllStock; 402 Joyce Photographics/ Photo Researchers; 405 Will McIntyre/Photo Researchers; 408 Owen Franken/Stock, Boston; 409B Philippe Plailly/SPL/Photo Researchers; 409T NASA/Jet Propulsion Lab

**Chapter 18** 414 John Gerlach/Tom Stack & Associates; 416B Gary Withey/Bruce Coleman Inc.; 416T Don Kelly/Grant Heilman Photography; 417CB M. & R. Borland/Bruce Coleman Inc.; 417CL Michael Fogden/Bruce Coleman Inc.; 417CT Jerry Howard/Positive Images; 417L Bill Everitt/Tom Stack & Associates; 417TL Harry Haralambou/Positive Images; 419 Runk-Schoenberger/Grant Heilman Photography; 422L W. Cody/Westlight; 423L Manfred Gottschalk/Westlight; 424B Milton Rand/Tom Stack & Associates; 424C Larry Lefever/Grant Heilman Photography; 424T Joseph Schuyler/Stock, Boston; 425C E. R. Degginger; 425L Joel W. Rogers/AllStock; 425R Copr. Thomas L. Dietrich/ AllStock; 426 Owen Franken/Stock, Boston; 427 A. Glauberman/ Photo Researchers; 430BR E. R. Degginger; 430CB Charles Feil/Stock, Boston; 430TL David C. Hauston/ Bruce Coleman Inc.; 430TR Mike Price/Bruce Coleman Inc.; 431 Nuridsany & Perennou/Photo Researchers; 432B Link/ Visuals Unlimited; 432T Stephen Frisch*; 434 Judy Canty/ Stock, Boston

**Chapter 19** 438 European Space Agency/SPL/Photo Researchers; 443B Richard Palsey/Stock, Boston; 443T Runk-Schoenberger/Grant Heilman Photography; 445 Peeter Vilms*; 446 USDA/Grant Heilman Photography; 448 Wetmore/Photo Researchers; 450T Dr. Fred Espenak/ SPL/Photo Researchers; 451B E. R. Degginger/Bruce Coleman Inc.; 451T E. R. Degginger; 452 Chris Brown/Stock, Boston; 453 E. R. Degginger; 454B Mark C. Burnett/Photo Researchers; 454L Phil Degginger; 454R David Parker/SPL/Photo Researchers; 454T Bill Gallery/Stock, Boston; 458 NASA

**Chapter 20** 462 Brian Parker/Tom Stack & Associates; 463B David Madison/Bruce Coleman Inc.; 463T Carl Purcell/Photo Researchers; 464L Patti Murray/Earth Scenes; 464R Rob Crandall/Stock, Boston; 468B N. Pecnik/Visuals Unlimited; 468T Ben Blankenburg/Stock, Boston; 469 Manfred Gottschalk/Tom Stack & Associates; 472B Leonard Lee Rue III/Stock, Boston; 472BR K. H. Switak/Photo Researchers; 472C Stephen J. Krasemann/DRK Photo; 472TL Chip & Jill Isenhart/Tom Stack & Associates; 472TLC Michael Fogden/ DRK Photo; 472TR Bruce Forster/AllStock; 473BL John Mitchell/Photo Researchers; 473BR Craig Aurness/ Westlight; 473C Jim Zipp/Photo Researchers; 473CR Johnny Johnson/ Earth Scenes; 473TL E. R. Degginger/Bruce Coleman Inc.; 474 Jon Bertsch/Visuals Unlimited; 477L Tom Bean/DRK Photo; 477R Phil Degginger; 478 Tom Nebbia; 479 T. Kitchin/Tom Stack & Associates; 480 Ray Hoffman/USGS; 484-485 Jim Corwin/AllStock; 484B Christopher Arnesen/ AllStock; 484T Brian Parker/Tom Stack & Associates; 485 W. Bertsch/Bruce Coleman Inc.

**Unit 7** 486 Jim Zuckerman/Westlight; 486-487 Kathleen Campbell/AllStock

**Chapter 21** 488 Robert Winslow/Tom Stack & Associates; 489B John Cancalosa/Tom Stack & Associates; 489T Paul Silverman/Fundamental Photographs; 490B George Hunter/ Tony Stone Images; 490L Lester Lefkowitz/Tony Stone Images; 490T Larry Lefever/Grant Heilman Photography; 492 Nicholas Devore/Bruce Coleman Inc.; 494L Grant Heilman/ Grant Heilman Photography; 494R Ken Graham/ AllStock; 496 Anne Dowie*; 497B Larry Lefever/ Grant Heilman Photography; 497T Kristin Finnegan/ AllStock; 498 Jerry Howard/Positive Images; 499B E. R. Degginger/Bruce

Coleman Inc.; 499T Kevin Schafer/Tom Stack & Associates; 500 Dr. Jeremy Burgess/SPL/Photo Researchers; 501 Will McIntyre/Photo Researchers; 502T Andrew Rakoczy/Bruce Coleman Inc.; 503 William McCoy/Rainbow

**Chapter 22** 508 Barrie Rokeach; 510C John Eastcott-Yva Momatiuk/DRK Photo; 510L David R. Austen/Stock, Boston; 510R Bruce Davidson/Earth Scenes; 511BR Craig Aurness/ Westlight; 511L Nigel Smith/Animals, Animals; 511TR Tom Nebbia; 512B Peter French/Bruce Coleman Inc.; 512R Andy Sacks/Tony Stone Images; 512TL Anne Dowie*; 513 Tom Nebbia; 514T Waugh/Peter Arnold, Inc.; 515 Bob Daemmrich/ Stock, Boston; 517C George H. Harrison/Grant Heilman Photography; 517L Tom Walker/Stock, Boston; 517R Tom McHugh/Photo Researchers; 518R Bernard Wolff/Photo Researchers; 518L Tom Bean/AllStock; 519 Kevin Morris/ AllStock; 520 Alan D. Carey/Photo Researchers; 521 Chip & Jill Isenhart/Tom Stack & Associates; 522 Runk-Schoenberger/ Grant Heilman Photography; 523B Larry Lefever/Grant Heilman Photography; 523T Greg Vaughn/Tom Stack & Associates; 524B Will & Deni McIntyre/AllStock; 524R Anne Dowie*; 524L GHP Studio*; 524TC J. Cancalosi/DRK Photo; 525BR Jerry Howard/Positive Images; 525C Dewitt Jones/ Woodfin Camp & Associates; 525TR Joe Sohm/Chromosohm/ AllStock; 526L Robert E. Daemmrich/Tony Stone Images; 526R Robert E. Daemmrich/Stock, Boston; 532-533 Greg Ryan-Sally Beyer/AllStock

**Unit 8** 534 SPL/Photo Researchers; 534-535 Royal Observatory, Edinburgh

**Chapter 23** 536R NASA/Rainbow; 538T Richard Megna/ Fundamental Photographs; 541BL James P. Rowan/ Tony Stone Images; 541C Breck P. Kent/Animals, Animals; 541CL David Carriere/Tony Stone Images; 541L Carson Baldwin, Jr./Earth Scenes; 541TL Jeff Lepore/ AllStock; 543T George Holton/Photo Researchers; 545 Ed Degginger/Bruce Coleman Inc.; 546BL NASA/Peter Arnold, Inc.; 546R NASA; 548 NASA/Finley Holiday Film; 549 NASA; 551 Lick Observatory; 552B NASA; 552T S. Nielsen/Bruce Coleman Inc.

**Chapter 24** 558 NASA JPL/Starlight; 559B Eric Simmons/ Stock, Boston; 559T John Elk/Bruce Coleman Inc.; 560 National Optical Astronomy Observatories; 562BL National Optical Astronomy Observatories; 562CT NASA; 562R NASA/Science Source/Photo Researchers; 562TL Johnny Johnson/AllStock; 563 Del Mulkey/Photo Researchers; 566 NASA; 570B F. Rossotto/Stocktrek; 570T NASA; 571 NASA/ Jet Propulsion Lab; 574B Bruce H. Frisch/Photo Researchers; 574T NASA/Grant Heilman Photography; 575 NASA; 576 Lockheed; 577B National Optical Astronomy Observatories; 577T Richard Megna/ Fundamental Photographs; 578B Lowell Observatory/ NOAO; 578T Breck P. Kent/Earth Scenes; 580 NASA

**Chapter 25** 584 Dr. Jean Lorre/SPL/Photo Researchers; 585 Jim Ballard/AllStock; 587 John Lawlor/Tony Stone Images; 588T Roger Ressmeyer/Starlight; 589 Roger Ressmeyer/ Starlight; 594 Robert E. Daemmrich/Tony Stone Images; 596 Royal Observatory, Edinburgh; 597 Royal Observatory, Edinburgh; 600 Lick Observatory; 602BC Regents, Univ. Hawaii; 602CR National Optical Astronomy Observatories; 602TL National Optical Astronomy Observatories; 602TR U.S. Naval Observatory; 605 G. Robert Bishop/AllStock; 606 NASA/Jet Propulsion Lab;